Petroleum Engineering Handbook

Petroleum Engineering Handbook

Larry W. Lake, Editor-in-Chief

Petroleum Engineering Handbook

Larry W. Lake, Editor-in-Chief
U. of Texas at Austin

Volume IV

Production Operations Engineering

Joe Dunn Clegg, Editor
Consultant

Society of Petroleum Engineers

ISBN 978-1-55563-118-5 (print)
ISBN 978-1-55563-334-9 (digital)
ISBN 978-1-61399-129-9 (print and digital)
ISBN 978-1-55563-126-0 (Complete 7-Vol. Set, print)
ISBN 978-1-61399-133-6 (Complete 7-Vol. Set, digital)
ISBN 978-1-61399-134-3 (Complete 7-Vol. Set, print and digital)

20 / 9 8 7 6 5 4

Society of Petroleum Engineers
222 Palisades Creek Drive
Richardson, TX 75080-2040 USA

http://www.spe.org/store
service@spe.org
1.972.952.9393

Foreword

This 2006 version of SPE's *Petroleum Engineering Handbook* is the result of several years of effort by technical editors, copy editors, and authors. It is designed as a handbook rather than a basic text. As such, it will be of most benefit to those with some experience in the industry who require additional information and guidance in areas outside their areas of expertise. Authors for each of the more than 100 chapters were chosen carefully for their experience and expertise. The resulting product of their efforts represents the best current thinking on the various technical subjects covered in the *Handbook*.

The rate of growth in hydrocarbon extraction technology is continuing at the high level experienced in the last decades of the 20th century. As a result, any static compilation, such as this *Handbook*, will contain certain information that is out of date at the time of publication. However, many of the concepts and approaches presented will continue to be applicable in your studies, and, by documenting the technology in this way, it provides new professionals an insight into the many factors to be considered in assessing various aspects of a vibrant and dynamic industry.

The *Handbook* is a continuation of SPE's primary mission of technology transfer. Its direct descendents are the "Frick" *Handbook*, published in 1952, and the "Bradley" *Handbook*, published in 1987. This version is different from the previous in the following ways:

- It has multiple volumes in six different technical areas with more than 100 chapters.
- There is expanded coverage in several areas such as health, safety, and environment.
- It contains entirely new coverage on Drilling Engineering and Emerging and Peripheral Technologies.
- Electronic versions are available in addition to the standard bound volumes.

This *Handbook* has been a monumental undertaking that is the result of many people's efforts. I am pleased to single out the contributions of the six volume editors:

General Engineering—John R. Fanchi, Colorado School of Mines
Drilling Engineering—Robert F. Mitchell, Landmark Graphics Corp.
Facilities and Construction Engineering—Kenneth E. Arnold, AMEC Paragon
Production Operations Engineering—Joe D. Clegg, Shell Oil Co., retired
Reservoir Engineering and Petrophysics—Ed Holstein, Exxon Production Co., retired
Emerging and Peripheral Technologies—Hal R. Warner, Arco Oil and Gas, retired

It is to these individuals, along with the authors, the copy editors, and the SPE staff, that accolades for this effort belong. It has been my pleasure to work with and learn from them.

—*Larry W. Lake*

Preface

Production Operations Engineering, Vol. IV of the new *Petroleum Engineering Handbook,* is designed to replace the production engineering chapters found in the 1987 edition of the *Handbook.* There have been significant changes in technology and operating practices in the past 20 years, and these new chapters will bring you up to date in the areas of design, equipment selection, and operation procedures for most oil and gas wells.

The 16 chapters in this volume are divided into three groups: well completions, formation damage and stimulation, and artificial lift. Related subjects may be found in the other volumes of the *Handbook,* and specific data on equipment can be found in the American Petroleum Institute (API) Specifications and Recommended Practices or the International Organization for Standards (ISO) documents. Many of these chapters are interrelated, and references are made to other chapters. For example, tubing movement is not covered in the chapter on tubing but in the chapter on completion design. In general, the necessary tables and figures are included to make the design, but specific manufacturer data may have to be obtained from the vendors. Computer programs for design are not included, but in most cases, example problems in design are covered.

The initial chapters are concerned primarily with well completions. Chapter 1 is "Inflow and Outflow Performance," by M. Wiggins. The first step in design is predicting or measuring the production rate of the well. Thus, predicted flow rates from the reservoir (inflow) and flow to the surface storage tanks (outflow) are needed. The fundamentals of Darcy's law and the correlations used for typical oil- and gas-well multiphase flow are covered. A system analysis is used that allows the petroleum engineer to both analyze production systems and design well completions. "Completion Systems," by D. Ruddock, covers the common equipment used in most well completions and states that the packer forms the basis of the cased-hole completion design. Use of standard equipment purchased from the service companies is common practice, and such equipment is often covered by API and ISO standards. Good selection of this completion equipment is essential to a successful well completion. The next chapter is "Tubing Selection, Design, and Installation," by J. Clegg and E. Klementich. Most oil and gas wells are completed with tubing, and the proper selection is necessary for long-time, trouble-free service. Shallow wells present few problems, but deep, high-pressure, and/or corrosive wells may present significant difficulties. Chapter 4 is "Perforating," by G. King, which covers one of the fundamentals of well completions. Openhole completions are an option, but most operators use the technique of perforating through the casing to establish flow. Understanding and selecting the best types of perforating equipment and methods is mandatory for an efficient completion. The goal of this chapter is to describe methods of creating the best flow path for a particular completion. "Sand Control," by W. Penberthy, covers the various approaches and concentrates on gravel packs. One of the more difficult problems is completing a well that tends to produce sand without significant skin damage, initially and over time.

The next four chapters discuss formation damage problems. Chapter 6, by M. Sharma, is entitled "Formation Damage" and covers problems in drilling, completing, and producing that result in skin damage and reduced production rates. "Matrix Acidizing," by H. McLeod, discusses the various treatments that are commonly used to enhance the formation, mostly by removing plugging material and avoiding further damage. S.A. Holditch reviews "Hydraulic Fracturing," which enhances the well's ability to flow and may bypass any wellbore formation damage. Chapter 9, "Well Production Problems," by R. Jasinski, concerns scale, asphaltenes, and paraffin that are common in many areas and result in reduced production and increased operating costs.

There are seven chapters that deal with artificial lift—a major concern for production engineers. Chapter 10 is "Artificial Lift Systems," by J. Lea, and it presents the common methods used to produce wells when they will no longer flow. The proper selection of the artificial lift method is essential to producing the well economically over its life. The next chapter is "Sucker-Rod Lift," by N. Hein, and it offers a practical approach to designing, selecting, installing, and operating the most commonly used method of artificial lift, rod pumping. In "Gas Lift," J. Blann and H. Winkler discuss in detail both continuous and intermittent gas lift. "Electrical Submersible Pumps," by J. Bearden, reviews the use of these pumps from inception to the present and provides the reader with a general understanding of the ESP artificial lift method. The next chapter, "Hydraulic Pumping in Oil Wells," by J. Fretwell, is a discussion of where power fluid is used to operate downhole hydraulic or jet pumps. Chapter 15, "Progressing Cavity Pumping Systems," by C. Matthews *et al.,* addresses the equipment, design, application, and systems of screw pumps, a now widely used method of artificial lift. Chapter 16, "Plunger Lift," by S. Listiak and D. Phillips, discusses how to use the well's energy to produce oil and gas with a free piston to enhance flow.

I thank all the authors for their time and effort in producing this volume, which should provide excellent guidance to all involved in completing and producing wells. Additional thanks to the Editor-in-Chief, Larry Lake, and to the SPE personnel involved in this work.

—Joe Dunn Clegg

Contents

Chapter 1
Inflow and Outflow Performance
Michael L. Wiggins, U. of Oklahoma

1.1 The Production System

Understanding the principles of fluid flow through the production system is important in estimating the performance of individual wells and optimizing well and reservoir productivity. In the most general sense, the production system is the system that transports reservoir fluids from the subsurface reservoir to the surface, processes and treats the fluids, and prepares the fluids for storage and transfer to a purchaser. **Fig. 1.1** depicts the production system for a single well system. The basic elements of the production system include the reservoir; wellbore; tubular goods and associated equipment; surface wellhead, flowlines, and processing equipment; and artificial lift equipment.

The reservoir is the source of fluids for the production system. It is the porous, permeable media in which the reservoir fluids are stored and through which the fluids will flow to the wellbore. It also furnishes the primary energy for the production system. The wellbore serves as the conduit for access to the reservoir from the surface. It is composed of the drilled wellbore, which normally has been cemented and cased. The cased wellbore houses the tubing and associated subsurface production equipment, such as packers. The tubing serves as the primary conduit for fluid flow from the reservoir to the surface, although fluids also may be transported through the tubing-casing annulus.

The wellhead, flowlines, and processing equipment represent the surface mechanical equipment required to control and process reservoir fluids at the surface and prepare them for transfer to a purchaser. Surface mechanical equipment includes the wellhead equipment and associated valving, chokes, manifolds, flowlines, separators, treatment equipment, metering devices, and storage vessels.

In many cases, the reservoir is unable to furnish sufficient energy to produce fluids to the surface at economic rates throughout the life of the reservoir. When this occurs, artificial lift equipment is used to enhance production rates by adding energy to the production system. This component of the system is composed of both surface and subsurface elements. This additional energy can be furnished directly to the fluid through subsurface pumps, by reducing the backpressure at the reservoir with surface compression equipment to lower wellhead pressure, or by injecting gas into the production string to reduce the flowing gradient of the fluid.

Recognizing the various components of the production system and understanding their interaction generally leads to improved well productivity through analysis of the entire system. As

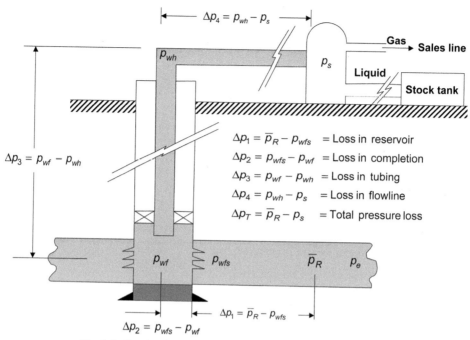

Fig. 1.1—Production system and associated pressure losses.[1]

the fluid flows from the reservoir into and through the production system, it experiences a continuous pressure drop (as Fig. 1.1 shows). The pressure begins at the average reservoir pressure and ends either at the pressure of the transfer line or near atmospheric pressure in the stock tank. In either case, a large pressure drop is experienced as the reservoir fluids are produced to the surface. It is the petroleum engineer's responsibility to use this pressure reduction in an optimal manner. The pressure reduction depends on the production rate and, at the same time, the production rate depends on the pressure change. Understanding the relationship between pressure and production rate is important to predicting the performance of individual oil and gas wells.

To design a well completion or predict the production rate properly, a systematic approach is required to integrate the production system components. Systems analysis, which allows the petroleum engineer to both analyze production systems and design well completions, accomplishes this. This chapter focuses on the flow of reservoir fluids through the production system, particularly inflow performance, which is the reservoir pressure-rate behavior of the individual well, and outflow performance, which is the flow of reservoir fluids through the piping system.

1.2 Reservoir Inflow Performance
Mathematical models describing the flow of fluids through porous and permeable media can be developed by combining physical relationships for the conservation of mass with an equation of motion and an equation of state. This leads to the diffusivity equations, which are used in the petroleum industry to describe the flow of fluids through porous media.

The diffusivity equation can be written for any geometry, but radial flow geometry is the one of most interest to the petroleum engineer dealing with single well issues. The radial diffusivity equation for a slightly compressible liquid with a constant viscosity (an undersaturated oil or water) is

$$\frac{1}{r}\frac{\partial}{\partial r}\left(r\frac{\partial p}{\partial r}\right) = \frac{\phi\mu c_t}{k}\left(\frac{\partial p}{\partial t}\right) . \text{...} (1.1)$$

The solution for a real gas is often presented in two forms: traditional pressure-squared form and general pseudopressure form. The pressure-squared form is

$$\frac{1}{r}\frac{\partial}{\partial r}\left(r\frac{\partial p^2}{\partial r}\right) = \frac{\phi\mu c_t}{k}\left(\frac{\partial p^2}{\partial t}\right), \text{...} (1.2)$$

and the pseudopressure form is

$$\frac{1}{r}\frac{\partial}{\partial r}\left[r\frac{\partial p_p(p)}{\partial r}\right] = \frac{\phi\mu c_t}{k}\left[\frac{\partial p_p(p)}{\partial t}\right], \text{...} (1.3)$$

where the real gas pseudopressure is defined by Al-Hussainy, Ramey, and Crawford[2] as

$$p_p(p) = 2\int\frac{p}{\mu z}dp . \text{..} (1.4)$$

The pseudopressure relationship is suitable for all pressure ranges, but the pressure-squared relationship has a limited range of applicability because of the compressible nature of the fluid. Strictly speaking, the only time the pressure-squared formulation is correct is when the μz product is constant as a function of pressure. This usually occurs only at low pressures (less than approximately 2,000 psia). As a result, it generally is recommended that the pseudopressure solutions be used in the analysis of gas well performance.

1.2.1 Single-Phase Analytical Solutions.
Radial diffusivity equations can be solved for numerous initial and boundary conditions to describe the rate-pressure behavior for single-phase flow. Eqs. 1.1 through 1.3 have similar forms, which lends themselves to similar solutions in terms of pressure, pressure-squared, and pseudopressure. Of primary interest to the petroleum engineer is the constant terminal-rate solution for which the initial condition is an equilibrium reservoir pressure at some fixed time while the well is produced at a constant rate. The steady-state and semisteady-state flow conditions are the most common, though not exclusive, conditions for which solutions are desired in describing well performance.

The steady-state condition is for a well in which the outer boundary pressure remains constant. This implies an open outer boundary such that fluid entry will balance fluid withdrawals exactly. This condition may be appropriate when the pressure is being maintained because of active natural water influx or under active injection of fluid into the reservoir. The steady-state solution for single-phase liquid flow in terms of the average reservoir pressure can be written as

$$q = \frac{kh(\overline{p}_R - p_{wf})}{141.2B\mu\left(\ln\frac{r_e}{r_w} - \frac{1}{2} + s\right)} . \text{...} (1.5)$$

The semisteady-state condition is for a well that has produced long enough that the outer boundary has been felt. The well is considered to be producing with closed boundaries; therefore, there is no flow across the outer boundaries. In this manner, the reservoir pressure will decline with production and, at a constant production rate, pressure decline will be constant for all radii and times. This solution for single-phase liquid flow in terms of the average reservoir pressure is

$$q = \frac{kh\left(\overline{p}_R - p_{wf}\right)}{141.2 B\mu\left(\ln \dfrac{r_e}{r_w} - \dfrac{3}{4} + s\right)} \quad \ldots\ldots\ldots\ldots\ldots\ldots\ldots\ldots\ldots (1.6)$$

The stabilized flow equations also can be developed for a real gas and are presented in pressure-squared and pseudopressure forms. For steady state, the solutions are

$$q = \frac{kh\left(\overline{p}_R^2 - p_{wf}^2\right)}{1422\mu z T\left(\ln \dfrac{r_e}{r_w} - \dfrac{1}{2} + s\right)} \quad \ldots\ldots\ldots\ldots\ldots\ldots\ldots (1.7)$$

and

$$q = \frac{kh\left[p_p\left(\overline{p}_R\right) - p_p\left(p_{wf}\right)\right]}{1422 T\left(\ln \dfrac{r_e}{r_w} - \dfrac{1}{2} + s\right)} \quad \ldots\ldots\ldots\ldots\ldots\ldots (1.8)$$

The semisteady-state solutions for gas are

$$q = \frac{kh\left(\overline{p}_R^2 - p_{wf}^2\right)}{1422\mu z T\left(\ln \dfrac{r_e}{r_w} - \dfrac{3}{4} + s\right)} \quad \ldots\ldots\ldots\ldots\ldots\ldots (1.9)$$

and

$$q = \frac{kh\left[p_p\left(\overline{p}_R\right) - p_p\left(p_{wf}\right)\right]}{1422 T\left(\ln \dfrac{r_e}{r_w} - \dfrac{3}{4} + s\right)} \quad \ldots\ldots\ldots\ldots\ldots\ldots (1.10)$$

Steady-state or semisteady-state conditions may never be achieved in actual operations. However, these stabilized conditions are often approximated in the reservoir and yield an acceptable estimate of well performance for single-phase flow. In addition, these solutions provide a means to compare production rates for various estimates of rock and fluid properties and well completion options. These relationships are useful as they allow the petroleum engineer the opportunity to estimate production rates before any well completion operations or testing.

Little difference is obtained in estimates of production rates or pressure drops when using the steady-state or semisteady-state solutions and, in practice, many engineers use the semisteady-state solutions. While each solution represents a distinctly different physical system, the numerical difference is minor when compared with the quality of the estimates used for rock and fluid properties, drainage area, and skin factor, as well as accounting for the heterogeneous nature of a reservoir. Dake,[3] Craft, Hawkins, and Terry,[4] and Lee and Wattenbarger[5] provide complete details regarding the development of the diffusivity equations and the associated stabilized-flow solutions.

1.2.2 Gas Well Performance. Early estimates of gas well performance were conducted by opening the well to the atmosphere and then measuring the flow rate. Such "open flow" practices were wasteful of gas, sometimes dangerous to personnel and equipment, and possibly damaging to the reservoir. They also provided limited information to estimate productive capacity under varying flow conditions. The idea, however, did leave the industry with the concept of absolute open flow (AOF). AOF is a common indicator of well productivity and refers to the maximum rate at which a well could flow against a theoretical atmospheric backpressure at the reservoir.

The productivity of a gas well is determined with deliverability testing. Deliverability tests provide information that is used to develop reservoir rate-pressure behavior for the well and generate an inflow performance curve or gas-backpressure curve. There are two basic relations currently in use to analyze deliverability test data. An empirical relationship was proposed by Rawlins and Schellhardt[6] in 1935 and is still frequently used today. Houpeurt[7] presented a theoretical deliverability relationship derived from the generalized radial diffusivity equation accounting for non-Darcy flow effects.

Rawlins and Schellhardt[6] developed the empirical backpressure method of testing gas wells based on the analysis of tests on more than 500 wells. They noted that when the difference between the squares of the average reservoir pressure and flowing bottomhole pressures were plotted against the corresponding flow rates on logarithmic coordinates, they obtained a straight line. This led them to propose the backpressure equation:

$$q_g = C\left(\overline{p}_R^2 - p_{wf}^2\right)^n, \quad\dotfill \quad (1.11)$$

where C is the flow coefficient and n is the deliverability exponent. The deliverability exponent is the inverse of the slope of the curve. Once n is determined, C can be obtained by substituting pressure and rate data read directly from the straight-line plot into Eq. 1.11 and solving the resulting relation.

As discussed previously, solutions for gas well performance in terms of pressure-squared are appropriate only at low reservoir pressures. As a result, Rawlins and Schellhardt's deliverability equation can be rewritten in terms of pseudopressure as

$$q_g = C\left[p_p\left(\overline{p}_R\right) - p_p\left(p_{wf}\right)\right]^n, \quad\dotfill \quad (1.12)$$

where C and n are determined in the same manner as for Eq. 1.11. The values of n range from 0.5 to 1.0, depending on flow characteristics. Flow characterized by Darcy's equation will have a flow exponent of 1.0, while flow that exhibits non-Darcy flow behavior will have a flow exponent ranging from 0.5 to 1.0. While the Rawlins and Schellhardt deliverability equation is not rigorous, it is still widely used in deliverability analysis and has provided reasonable results for high-permeability gas wells over the years.

Eqs. 1.11 and 1.12 can be rewritten to facilitate the development of the inflow performance curve. In terms of pressure-squared, the relationship is

$$\frac{q_g}{q_{g,\,max}} = \left[1 - \left(\frac{p_{wf}}{\overline{p}_R}\right)^2\right]^n, \quad\dotfill \quad (1.13)$$

$$\text{and} \quad \frac{q_g}{q_{g,\,max}} = \left[1 - \frac{p_p(p_{wf})}{p_p(\overline{p}_R)} \right]^n \quad \dots\dots\dots\dots\dots\dots\dots\dots (1.14)$$

in terms of pseudopressure. Once the deliverability exponent is determined from a multirate test and the AOF estimated, Eqs. 1.13 and 1.14 can be applied readily to estimate the rate for a given flowing bottomhole pressure.

Houpeurt developed a theoretical deliverability relationship for stabilized flow with a Forchheimer[8] velocity term to account for non-Darcy flow effects in high-velocity gas production. The resulting relationship can be written in terms of pressure-squared or pseudopressure as

$$q_g = \frac{kh\left(\overline{p}_R^2 - p_{wf}^2\right)}{1422\mu z T\left(\ln \dfrac{r_e}{r_w} - \dfrac{3}{4} + s + Dq_g \right)} \quad \dots\dots\dots\dots\dots\dots\dots\dots (1.15)$$

$$\text{or} \quad q_g = \frac{kh\left[p_p(\overline{p}_R) - p_p(p_{wf})\right]}{1422T\left(\ln \dfrac{r_e}{r_w} - \dfrac{3}{4} + s + Dq_g \right)} \quad \cdot \dots\dots\dots\dots\dots\dots\dots (1.16)$$

Eqs. 1.15 and 1.16 are quadratic in terms of the flow rate, and the solutions can be written for convenience as shown in Eqs. 1.17 and 1.18.

$$\overline{p}_R^2 - p_{wf}^2 = aq_g + bq_g^2 \cdot \quad \dots\dots\dots\dots\dots\dots\dots\dots (1.17)$$

$$p_p(\overline{p}_R) - p_p(p_{wf}) = aq_g + bq_g^2 \cdot \quad \dots\dots\dots\dots\dots\dots (1.18)$$

Jones, Blount, and Glaze[9] suggested Houpeurt's relationship be rewritten as shown in Eqs. 1.19 and 1.20 to allow the analysis of well-test data to predict deliverability.

$$\frac{\overline{p}_R^2 - p_{wf}^2}{q_g} = a + bq_g \cdot \quad \dots\dots\dots\dots\dots\dots\dots\dots (1.19)$$

$$\frac{p_p(\overline{p}_R) - p_p(p_{wf})}{q_g} = a + bq_g \cdot \quad \dots\dots\dots\dots\dots\dots (1.20)$$

A plot of the difference in pressures squared divided by the flow rate or the difference in pseudopressure divided by the flow rate vs. the flow rate yields a straight line on a coordinate graph. The intercept of the plot is the laminar flow coefficient a, while turbulence coefficient b is obtained from the slope of the curve. Once these two coefficients have been determined, deliverability can be estimated from the following relationships in terms of pressure-squared or pseudopressure.

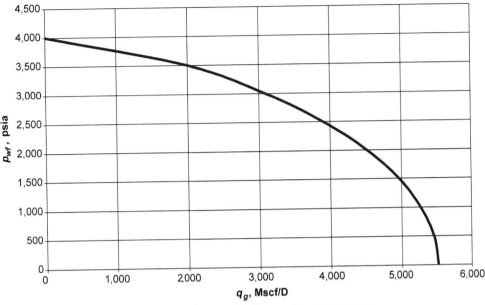

Fig. 1.2—Typical gas well inflow performance curve.

$$q_g = \frac{-a + \sqrt{a^2 + 4b\left(\overline{p}_R^2 - p_{wf}^2\right)}}{2b} \quad \text{.. (1.21)}$$

$$\text{and } q_g = \frac{-a + \sqrt{a^2 + 4b\left[p_p(\overline{p}_R) - p_p(p_{wf})\right]}}{2b} \quad \text{.................................... (1.22)}$$

After the coefficients of the deliverability equations have been determined, the relationships can be used to estimate production rates for various bottomhole flowing pressures. This determination of rate vs. pressure is often referred to as the reservoir inflow performance, which is a measure of the ability of the reservoir to produce gas to the wellbore. The inflow performance curve is a plot of bottomhole pressure vs. production rate for a particular well determined from the gas well deliverability equations. **Fig. 1.2** depicts a typical gas well inflow performance curve. This curve allows one to estimate the production rate for different flowing bottomhole pressures readily.

Deliverability Test Methods. Several different deliverability test methods have been developed to collect the data for use with the basic deliverability models. These tests can be grouped into three basic categories: tests that use all stabilized data, tests that use a combination of stabilized and transient data, and tests that use all transient data. The basic deliverability test method that uses all stabilized data is the flow-after-flow test. Deliverability test methods that use both transient and stabilized test data include the isochronal and modified isochronal tests. The multiple modified isochronal test consists of all transient test data and eliminates the need for stabilized flow or pressure data.

Flow-After-Flow Tests. Rawlins and Schellhardt[6] presented the basic deliverability test method that uses all stabilized data. The test consists of a series of flow rates. The test is often referred to as a four-point test because many tests are composed of four rates, as required by various regulatory bodies. This test is performed by producing the well at a series of stabilized

TABLE 1.1—FLOW-AFTER-FLOW TEST DATA

Average reservoir pressure, psia	3,360
Reservoir temperature, °F	210
Gas specific gravity	0.734
Pseudocritical pressure, psia	658.7
Pseudocritical temperature, °R	385.9

Flow Period	Flow Rate (Mscf/D)	Pressure (psia)
1	1,012	3,317
2	2,248	3,215
3	3,832	3,020
4	5,480	2,724

TABLE 1.2—RAWLINS AND SCHELLHARDT ANALYSIS OF FLOW-AFTER-FLOW TEST DATA

Flow Period	q_g (Mscf/D)	p (psia)	Δp^2 (psia^2)	p_p (psia^2/cp)	Δp_p (psia^2/cp)
Shut-In	0	3,360	—	759,800,000	—
1	1,012	3,317	287,111	744,010,000	15,790,000
2	2,248	3,215	953,375	706,790,000	53,010,000
3	3,832	3,020	2,169,200	636,750,000	123,050,000
4	5,480	2,724	3,869,424	533,730,000	226,070,000

$p_p(14.65) = 14,066$ psia^2/cp

flow rates and obtaining the corresponding stabilized flowing bottomhole pressures. In addition, a stabilized shut-in bottomhole pressure is required for the analysis. A major limitation of this test method is the length of time required to obtain stabilized data for low-permeability gas reservoirs.

Example 1.1 Table 1.1 provides example flow-after-flow test data, which are analyzed with the Rawlins and Schellhardt and Houpeurt deliverability equations. The traditional Rawlins and Schellhardt analysis requires that the difference in the pressures squared be plotted vs. the flow rate on logarithmic graph paper and a best-fit straight line constructed through the data points. The data should provide a straight-line plot, which serves as the deliverability curve. From this plot, the deliverability exponent, n, is the inverse of the slope of the constructed straight line. Once the deliverability exponent is determined, the flow coefficient, C, can be determined from Eq. 1.11 with a point taken from the straight-line plot. The same approach is used when pseudopressures are used to analyze the data, except that the differences in the pseudopressures are plotted vs. the flow rate and Eq. 1.12 is used to determine C.

Table 1.2 shows the data to be plotted for the Rawlins and Schellhardt analysis, while Figs. 1.3 and 1.4 show the logarithmic plots for the pressure-squared and the pseudopressure analyses, respectively.

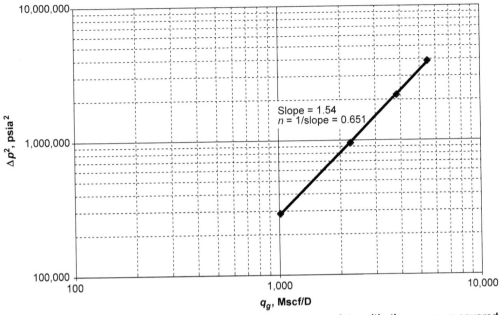

Fig. 1.3—Rawlins and Schellhardt analysis of flow-after-flow test data with the pressure-squared approach.

Solution. Working with the traditional pressure-squared data, draw a straight line through the four data points to yield a slope of 1.54. The deliverability exponent, n, is the inverse of the slope, or 0.651. The flow coefficient, C, can be determined from a point on the straight line. Since the third test point lies on the line, it can be used to determine C using Eq. 1.23 to yield 0.2874 Mscf/D/psia^{2n}.

$$C = \frac{q_g}{\left(\bar{p}_R^2 - p_{wf}^2\right)^n} = \frac{3,832}{(2,169,200)^{0.651}} = 0.2874. \quad\text{...............................} \quad (1.23)$$

Once n and C are determined, the deliverability equation can be written and used to determine the AOF and the production rate for any given flowing bottomhole pressure. Eq. 1.24 is the deliverability equation for this particular example well.

$$q_g = 0.2874\left(\bar{p}_R^2 - p_{wf}^2\right)^{0.651}. \quad\text{....................................} \quad (1.24)$$

The AOF is determined by allowing the flowing bottomhole pressure to be equal to the atmospheric pressure for the current average reservoir pressure of 3,360 psia. In this example, when the atmospheric pressure is assumed to be 14.65 psia, the AOF is 11,200 Mscf/D.

The same approach is used to analyze the data when pseudopressures are used in the analysis. Using Fig. 1.4, the slope of the straight line through the data points is 1.57, yielding an n of 0.637. The flow coefficient, C, is determined to be 0.0269 Mscf/D/(psia^2/cp)^n from Eq. 1.25 using the third test point.

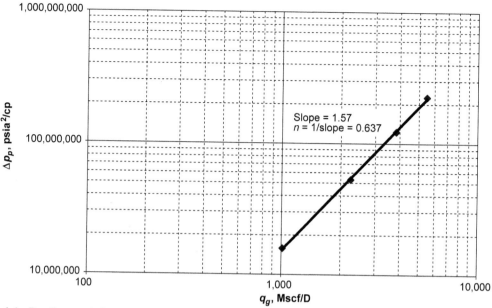

Fig. 1.4—Rawlins and Schellhardt analysis of flow-after-flow test data with the pseudopressure approach.

$$C = \frac{q_g}{\left[p_p(\bar{p}_R) - p_p(p_{wf}) \right]^n} = \frac{3{,}832}{(123{,}050{,}000)^{0.637}} = 0.0269 \ . \quad \text{................} \ (1.25)$$

The resulting deliverability equation is

$$q_g = 0.0269 \left[p_p(\bar{p}_R) - p_p(p_{wf}) \right]^{0.637}, \quad \text{................................} \ (1.26)$$

and the AOF is calculated to be 12,200 Mscf/D using the appropriate pseudopressure values at the current reservoir pressure of 3,360 psia and atmospheric pressure of 14.65 psia.

The difference in the calculated AOF using the pressure-squared approach and the pseudopressure method is noticeable. This variation results from the inclusion of the pressure dependence of the gas viscosity and gas deviation factor in the pseudopressure term. As noted earlier, the pressure-squared approach is only suitable at low pressures, while the pseudopressure method is good for all pressure ranges. Also, the Rawlins and Schellhardt method is not theoretically rigorous, although it is widely used.

The test data can also be analyzed with the Houpeurt approach using both the pressure-squared and pseudopressure approaches. **Table 1.3** provides the data to be plotted in the Houpeurt analysis. **Fig. 1.5** presents the Houpeurt plot of the pressure squared data, while **Fig. 1.6** shows the pseuodpressure data. From Fig. 1.5, one can construct a best-fit line through the data points and determine the slope and the intercept of the line. The slope, b, is 0.0936 psia^2/ (Mscf/D)^2, while the intercept, a, is determined to be 200 psia^2/Mscf/D. These deliverability coefficients can be use to develop a deliverability equation after the form of Eq. 1.21 as shown in Eq. 1.27:

TABLE 1.3—HOUPEURT ANALYSIS OF FLOW-AFTER-FLOW TEST DATA					
Flow Period	q_g (Mscf/D)	p (psia)	$\Delta p^2/q$ (psia^2/Mscf/D)	p_g (psia^2/cp)	$\Delta p_p/q$ (psia^2/cp/Mscf/D)
Shut-In	0	3,360	—	759,800,000	—
1	1,012	3,317	283.7	744,010,000	15,603
2	2,248	3,215	424.1	706,790,000	23,581
3	3,832	3,020	566.1	636,750,000	32,111
4	5,480	2,724	706.1	533,730,000	41,254

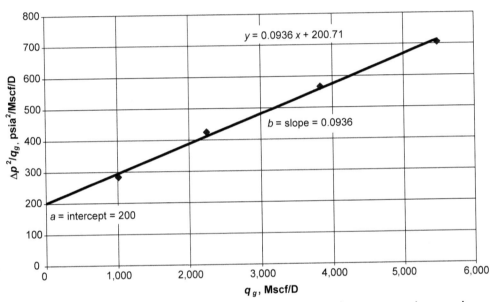

Fig. 1.5—Houpeurt analysis of flow-after-flow test data with the pressure-squared approach.

$$q_g = \frac{-200 + \sqrt{200^2 + 4(0.0936)\left(\overline{p}_R^2 - p_{wf}^2\right)}}{2(0.0936)} \quad \text{...............................} \quad (1.27)$$

The AOF can be estimated for the reservoir pressure of 3,360 psia to be 9,970 Mscf/D.

A similar analysis can be undertaken for the pseudopressure data shown in Fig. 1.6. From this plot, the intercept of the constructed best-fit line is determined to be 10,252 psia^2/cp/Mscf/D, while the slope is 5.69 psia^2/cp/(Mscf/D)^2. These coefficients are used to write the deliverability equation as

$$q_g = \frac{-10,252 + \sqrt{10,252^2 + 4(5.69)\left[p_p(\overline{p}_R) - p_p(p_{wf})\right]}}{2(5.69)} \quad \text{.........................} \quad (1.28)$$

From this equation for the current reservoir pressure, the AOF is estimated to be 10,700 Mscf/D. As with the Rawlins and Schellhardt analysis, the AOFs determined by the pressure-

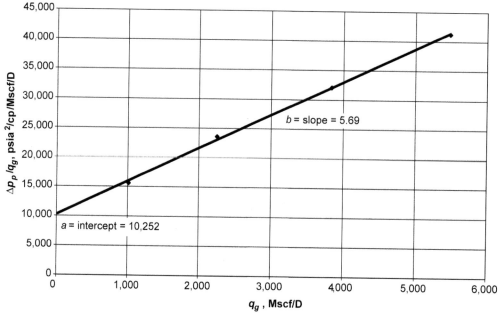

Fig. 1.6—Houpeurt analysis of flow-after-flow test data with the pseudopressure approach.

squared method and the pseudopressure approach are different because of the pressure dependence of the μz product.

Isochronal Test. Cullendar[10] proposed the isochronal test to overcome the need to obtain a series of stabilized flow rates required for the flow-after-flow test for the slow-to-stabilize well. This test consists of producing the well at several different flow rates with flowing periods of equal duration. Each flow period is separated by a shut-in period in which the shut-in bottomhole pressure is allowed to stabilize at essentially the average reservoir pressure. The test also requires that an extended stabilized flow point be obtained. The test method is based on the principle that the radius of investigation is a function of the flow period and not the flow rate. Thus, for equal flow periods, the same drainage radius is investigated in spite of the actual flow rates.

To analyze the data from an isochronal test, the flow data from the equal flow periods is plotted according to the Rawlins and Schellhardt[6] or Houpeurt[7] methods. These data points are used to determine the slope of the deliverability curve. The stabilized flow point is then used to estimate the flow coefficient, C, for the Rawlins and Schellhardt method or the intercept, a, for the Houpert method by extending the slope of the multirate data to the stabilized flow point.

Example 1.2 **Table 1.4** details isochronal test data for a particular well in which the flow periods are one hour in duration. The Rawlins and Schellhardt approach with pressures and the Houpeurt approach with pseudopressures are used to demonstrate the analysis of isochronal test data. **Table 1.5** presents the plotting data for both methods. **Fig. 1.7** shows the logarithmic plot of the pressure data for the Rawlins and Schellhardt analysis.

Solution. A straight line can be constructed through the three transient points to yield a slope of 1.076. The inverse of the slope defines the deliverability exponent, n, which is 0.9294 for this example. The slope through the transient points is extended to the stabilized flow point

TABLE 1.4—ISOCHRONAL TEST DATA

Period	Mode	Time (hrs)	p (psia)	q_g (Mscf/D)	p_p (psia²/cp)
Initial	Shut-in	24.0	1,798		284,360,000
1	Flow	1.0	1,768	1,800	275,660,000
	Shut-in	1.0	1,798		284,360,000
2	Flow	1.0	1,747	3,000	269,630,000
	Shut-in	1.5	1,798		284,360,000
3	Flow	1.0	1,682	6,200	251,270,000
Stabilize	Flow	10.0	1,600	6,300	228,830,000
Final	Shut-in	14.0	1,798		284,360,000

TABLE 1.5—PLOTTING DATA FOR ISOCHRONAL TEST

Period	q_g (Mscf/D)	p (psia)	Δp^2 (psia²)	p_p (psia²/cp)	$\Delta p_p/q$ (psia²/cp/Mscf/D)
1	1,800	1,768	106,980	275,660,000	4,833
2	3,000	1,747	180,795	269,630,000	4,910
3	6,200	1,682	403,680	251,270,000	5,337
Stabilized	6,300	1,600	672,804	228,830,000	8,814

to depict the deliverability curve. The flow coefficient, C, is calculated from the stabilized flow point,

$$C = \frac{q_g}{\left(\overline{p}_R^2 - p_{wf}^2\right)^n} = \frac{6,300}{(672,804)^{0.9294}} = 0.0242, \quad\quad\quad\quad\quad (1.29)$$

to be 0.0242 Mscf/D/psia²ⁿ. The flow exponent and flow coefficient are used to define the Rawlins and Schellhardt deliverability equation for this well,

$$q_g = 0.0242\left(\overline{p}_R^2 - p_{wf}^2\right)^{0.9294}, \quad\quad\quad\quad\quad (1.30)$$

which is used to determine the AOF. For an atmospheric pressure of 14.65 psia, the AOF is estimated to be 27,100 Mscf/D. A similar analysis can be undertaken with pseudopressures following the same method described for the pressures squared.

Applying the Houpeurt approach, the transient flow points are used to determine the slope of the best-fit straight line constructed through the data points. This slope is used to determine the intercept from the stabilized flow point. **Fig. 1.8** shows the plot of the pseudopressure data for the Houpeurt analysis. From the plot, the slope is determined to be 0.1184 psia²/cp/(Mscf/D)², which is used to calculate an intercept from the stabilized flow point of 8,814 psia²/cp/Mscf/D as shown in Eq. 1.31.

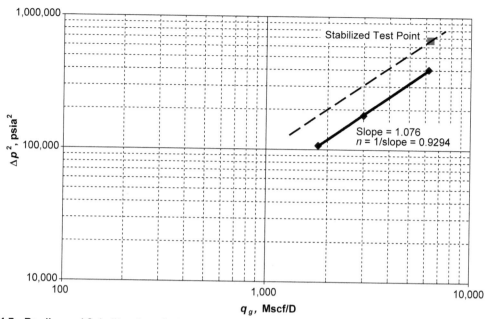

Fig. 1.7—Rawlins and Schellhardt analysis of isochronal test data with the pressure-squared approach.

$$a = \frac{p_p(\bar{p}_R) - p_p(p)}{q_g} - bq_g = \frac{284{,}360{,}000 - 228{,}830{,}000}{6{,}300} - 0.1184(6{,}300) = 8{,}065. \quad \text{...... (1.31)}$$

The deliverability equation can be written in a form similar to Eq. 1.22 to yield Eq. 1.32.

$$q_g = \frac{-8065 + \sqrt{(8065)^2 + 4(0.1184)\left[p_p(\bar{p}_R) - p_p(p_{wf})\right]}}{2(0.1184)} \quad \text{........................ (1.32)}$$

This equation can be used to estimate the AOF of 25,600 Mscf/D for the well or estimate the production rate at any other flowing bottomhole pressure. As the analysis of the flow-after-flow test data showed, the Rawlins and Schellhardt and Houpeurt methods yield different estimates of deliverability.

Modified Isochronal Test. For some low-permeability wells, the time required to obtain stabilized shut-in pressures may be impractical. To overcome this limitation, Katz *et al.*[11] proposed a modification to the isochronal test by requiring equal shut-in periods. The modified isochronal test is essentially the same as the isochronal test, except the shut-in periods separating the flow periods are equal to or longer than the flow periods. The method also requires the extended stabilized flow point and a stabilized shut-in bottomhole pressure. The modified isochronal test method is less accurate than the isochronal method because the shut-in pressure is not allowed to return to the average reservoir pressure. In the analysis of the collected data, the measured bottomhole pressure obtained just before the beginning of the flow period is used in Eqs. 1.11 and 1.12 or Eqs. 1.19 and 1.20 instead of the average reservoir pressure.

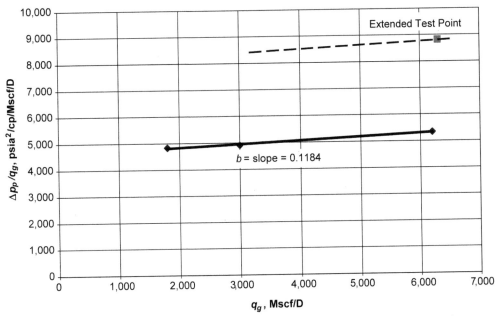

Fig. 1.8—Houpeurt analysis of isochronal test data with the pseudopressure approach.

The analysis of the data is exactly the same as that used to analyze the isochronal test data. With the Rawlins and Schellhardt data, the transient flow points are used to construct a best-fit straight line through the data points. The inverse of the slope of this line yields the deliverability exponent, n. The deliverability exponent is then used with the data of the stabilized flow point to estimate the flow coefficient, C, with Eqs. 1.11 or 1.12 depending on whether pressure or pseudopressure data is used. In the Houpeurt analysis, a best-fit straight line is constructed through the transient flow points to yield the slope, b. Once the slope is determined, it is used with the stabilized flow point in the appropriate equation for pressure or pseudopressure (Eqs. 1.19 and 1.20) to determine the intercept, a. Once the flow coefficients are determined by either analysis method, the deliverability equation can be written and used to estimate the AOF and production rates for the well.

Transient Test Methods. The multiple modified isochronal test consists of all transient test data and eliminates the need for stabilized flow or pressure data. The analysis method requires estimates of drainage area and shape along with additional reservoir and fluid property data that are not required with the previous deliverability test methods. As a result, the analysis techniques are more complex than for flow-after-flow, isochronal, or modified isochronal test data. However, the method provides a means to estimate deliverability of slow-in-stabilizing wells and consists of running a minimum of three modified isochronal tests with each test composed of a minimum of three flow rates. To analyze the test data, modifications to the Rawlins and Schellhardt analysis have been proposed by Hinchman, Kazemi, and Poettmann[12] while modifications to the Houpeurt pressure-squared technique have proposed by Brar and Aziz,[13] Poettmann,[14] and Brar and Mattar.[15] These modifications have been extended to the pseudopressure analysis technique by Poe.[16] See Refs. 12 through 16 for complete details on estimating deliverability from transient test data.

Future Performance Methods. The petroleum engineer is required to forecast or predict gas well performance as the reservoir pressure depletes. There are several methods to assist in making these future performance estimates, including the direct application of the appropriate analytical solution to provide estimates of rate vs. pressure for different average reservoir pressures. However, the use of Eqs. 1.7 through 1.10 requires that one estimate rock and fluid properties for the well of interest.

Another technique also requires knowledge of rock and fluid properties by estimating the flow coefficients, a and b, in Houpeurt's relationships (Eqs. 1.17 and 1.18). When Houpeurt's method is used in terms of pressure-squared, a and b are

$$a = \frac{1422\mu zT\left(\ln \dfrac{r_e}{r_w} - \dfrac{3}{4} + s\right)}{kh} \dotfill (1.33)$$

$$\text{and } b = \frac{1422\mu zT}{kh}D, \dotfill (1.34)$$

where the non-Darcy flow coefficient

$$D = \frac{2.715 \times 10^{-15}\beta k M p_{sc}}{h\mu_g r_w T_{sc}}. \dotfill (1.35)$$

The value of β, the turbulence factor,[17] can be estimated from

$$\beta = 1.88 \times 10^{10}k^{-1.47}\phi^{-0.53}. \dotfill (1.36)$$

When Houpeurt's relationship is used in terms of pseudopressure, a and b are estimated from

$$a = \frac{1422T\left(\ln \dfrac{r_e}{r_w} - \dfrac{3}{4} + s\right)}{kh} \dotfill (1.37)$$

$$\text{and } b = \frac{1422T}{kh}D. \dotfill (1.38)$$

The variables D and β are estimated with Eqs. 1.35 and 1.36. Once the flow coefficients, a and b, are determined at new average reservoir pressures, Eqs. 1.21 and 1.22 can be used to estimate rates for different pressures to generate the inflow performance curve.

Russell et al.[18] studied the depletion performance of gas wells and proposed a technique to estimate gas well performance that was dependent on gas compressibility and viscosity. From this study, Greene[19] presented a relationship to describe the well performance.

$$q = \frac{C_1}{\mu(\bar{p})z(\bar{p})}\left(\bar{p}_R^2 - p_{wf}^2\right). \dotfill (1.39)$$

In this equation, C_1 is a constant that is a function of permeability, reservoir thickness, and drainage area, which can be estimated from a single-point flow test with knowledge of gas compressibility and viscosity. This value is not the same as the flow coefficient C in Eqs. 1.11 and 1.12. C_1 will remain constant during the life of the well, assuming no changes in permeability. Once C_1 is determined, one can estimate future performance from Eq. 1.39 with the gas compressibility and viscosity estimated at the average bottomhole pressure defined as

$$\overline{p} = \frac{\left(\overline{p}_R + p_{wf}\right)}{2} . \dots\dots\dots\dots\dots\dots\dots\dots\dots\dots\dots\dots\dots\dots\dots\dots (1.40)$$

A technique that does not require the use of rock and fluid properties assumes that the deliverability exponent, n, remains essentially constant during the life of the well.[20] While this assumption may not be accurate, many gas wells have exhibited behavior such that the deliverability exponent has varied slowly over the life of the well. Under this assumption, future performance can be predicted with the following relationships in terms of pressure-squared and pseudopressure, respectively.

$$q_{g,max,f} = q_{g,max,p}\left(\frac{\overline{p}_{R,f}}{\overline{p}_{R,p}}\right)^{2n} . \dots\dots\dots\dots\dots\dots\dots\dots\dots\dots\dots\dots (1.41)$$

$$q_{g,max,f} = q_{g,max,p}\left[\frac{p_p(\overline{p}_{R,f})}{p_p(\overline{p}_{R,p})}\right]^{2n} . \dots\dots\dots\dots\dots\dots\dots\dots\dots\dots\dots (1.42)$$

Once the new AOF at the future reservoir pressure has been determined, the inflow performance curve can be constructed with a modified version of the deliverability equation as shown in Eqs. 1.13 and 1.14.

1.2.3 Oilwell Performance. When considering the performance of oil wells, it is often assumed that a well's performance can be estimated by the productivity index. However, Evinger and Muskat[21] pointed out that, for multiphase flow, a curved relationship existed between flow rate and pressure and that the straight-line productivity index did not apply to multiphase flow. The constant productivity index concept is only appropriate for oil wells producing under single-phase flow conditions, pressures above the reservoir fluid's bubblepoint pressure. For reservoir pressures less than the bubblepoint pressure, the reservoir fluid exists as two phases, vapor and liquid, and techniques other than the productivity index must be applied to predict oilwell performance.

Inflow Performance. There have been numerous empirical relationships proposed to predict oilwell performance under two-phase flow conditions. Vogel[22] was the first to present an easy-to-use method for predicting the performance of oil wells. His empirical inflow performance relationship (IPR) is based on computer simulation results and is given by

$$\frac{q_o}{q_{o,max}} = 1 - 0.2\left(\frac{p_{wf}}{\overline{p}_R}\right) - 0.8\left(\frac{p_{wf}}{\overline{p}_R}\right)^2 . \dots\dots\dots\dots\dots\dots\dots\dots (1.43)$$

To use this relationship, the engineer needs to determine the oil production rate and flowing bottomhole pressure from a production test and obtain an estimate of the average reservoir pressure at the time of the test. With this information, the maximum oil production rate can be estimated and used to estimate the production rates for other flowing bottomhole pressures at the current average reservoir pressure.

Fetkovich[23] proposed the isochronal testing of oil wells to estimate productivity. His deliverability equation is based on the empirical gas-well deliverability equation proposed by Rawlins and Schellhardt.[6]

$$q_o = C\left(\overline{p}_R^2 - p_{wf}^2\right)^n \dots (1.44)$$

and requires a multiple rate test to obtain values of C and n. A log-log plot of the pressure-squared difference vs. flow rate is expected to plot as a straight line. The inverse of the slope yields an estimate of n, the flow exponent. The flow coefficient can be estimated by selecting a flow rate and pressure on the log-log plot and using the information in Eq. 1.44 to calculate C. An IPR can be developed by rearranging Fetkovich's deliverability equation to obtain Eq. 1.45.

$$\frac{q_o}{q_{o,\,max}} = \left[1 - \left(\frac{p_{wf}}{\overline{p}_R}\right)^2\right]^n . \dots (1.45)$$

Jones, Blount, and Glaze[9] also proposed a multirate test method in which they attempted to incorporate non-Darcy flow effects. The basic equation to describe the flow of oil is

$$\frac{\overline{p}_R - p_{wf}}{q_o} = a + bq_o, \dots (1.46)$$

where a represents the laminar flow coefficient and b is the turbulence coefficient. To use the method, one must obtain multiple rate test information similar to Fetkovich's method. A plot of the ratio of the pressure difference to flow rate vs. the flow rate on coordinate paper is expected to yield a straight line. The laminar flow coefficient a is the intercept of the plot, while the slope of the curve yields the turbulence coefficient b. Once a and b have been determined, the flow rate at any other flowing wellbore pressure can be obtained by solving

$$q_o = \frac{-a + \sqrt{a^2 + 4b\left(\overline{p}_R - p_{wf}\right)}}{2b} . \dots (1.47)$$

The maximum flow rate can be estimated from Eq. 1.47 by allowing the flowing bottomhole pressure to equal zero.

There are several other two-phase IPR methods available in the literature. Gallice and Wiggins[24] provide details on the application of several of these methods and compare and discuss their use in estimating oilwell performance with advantages and disadvantages.

In certain circumstances, both single-phase and two-phase flow may be occurring in the reservoir. This results when the average reservoir pressure is above the bubblepoint pressure of the reservoir oil while the flowing bottomhole pressure is less than the bubblepoint pressure. To handle this situation, Neely[25] developed a composite IPR that Brown[26] demonstrates. The composite IPR couples Vogel's IPR for two-phase flow with the single-phase productivity index. The relationship that yields the maximum oil production rate is

$$q_{o,\,max} = J\left(\overline{p}_R - p_b + \frac{p_b}{1.8}\right) . \dots (1.48)$$

The relationships to determine the oil production rate at various flowing bottomhole pressures are

$$q_o = J(\overline{p}_R - p_{wf}), \qquad p_{wf} \geq p_b . \qquad (1.49)$$

when the flowing bottomhole pressure is greater than the bubblepoint pressure, and

$$q_o = (q_{o,\,max} - q_b)\left[1.0 - 0.2\frac{p_{wf}}{p_b} - 0.8\left(\frac{p_{wf}}{p_b}\right)^2\right] + q_b, \qquad p_{wf} \leq p_b . \qquad (1.50)$$

when the flowing bottomhole pressure is less than the bubblepoint pressure. The flow rate at the bubblepoint pressure, q_b, used in Eq. 1.50 is determined with Eq. 1.49 where p_{wf} equals p_b.

The appropriate J to use in Eqs. 1.48 and 1.49 depends on the flowing bottomhole pressure of the test point. If the flowing bottomhole pressure is greater than the bubblepoint pressure, then the well is experiencing single-phase flow conditions and J is determined by

$$J = \frac{q_o}{\overline{p}_R - p_{wf}}, \qquad \overline{p}_R \geq p_{wf} \geq p_b . \qquad (1.51)$$

When the flowing bottomhole pressure is less than the bubblepoint pressure, J is determined from

$$J = \frac{q_o}{\overline{p}_R - p_b + \dfrac{p_b}{1.8}\left[1.0 - 0.2\dfrac{p_{wf}}{p_b} - 0.8\left(\dfrac{p_{wf}}{p_b}\right)^2\right]}, \qquad \overline{p}_R \geq p_b \geq p_{wf} . \qquad (1.52)$$

Once J is determined for the test conditions, it is used to calculate the complete inflow performance curve both above and below the bubblepoint pressure with Eqs. 1.49 and 1.50. The composite IPR is only applicable when the average reservoir pressure is greater than the bubblepoint pressure.

Wiggins[27] presented an easy-to-use IPR for three-phase flow, which is similar in form to Vogel's IPR. It was based on a series of simulation studies. It yields results similar to two other three-phase flow models[26,28] and is easier to implement. Eqs. 1.53 and 1.54 give the generalized three-phase IPRs for oil and water, respectively.

$$\frac{q_o}{q_{o,\,max}} = 1 - 0.52\frac{p_{wf}}{\overline{p}_R} - 0.48\left(\frac{p_{wf}}{\overline{p}_R}\right)^2 . \qquad (1.53)$$

$$\frac{q_w}{q_{w,\,max}} = 1 - 0.72\frac{p_{wf}}{\overline{p}_R} - 0.28\left(\frac{p_{wf}}{\overline{p}_R}\right)^2 . \qquad (1.54)$$

Example 1.3 Table 1.6 presents data for a multipoint test on a producing oil well used to demonstrate the two-phase IPR methods. The average reservoir pressure for this example is 1,734 psia.

TABLE 1.6—OILWELL TEST DATA FOR EXAMPLE 1.1*

Test Rate	p_{wf} (psia)	q_o (STB/D)
1	1,653	252
2	1,507	516
3	1,335	768

* $\bar{p}_R$ = 1,734 psia

Solution. To apply the IPR methods, obtain test information, which includes production rates, flowing bottomhole pressures, and an estimate of the average reservoir pressure. Vogel's IPR is a single-rate relationship, and the highest test rate is used to demonstrate this IPR. The data obtained at the largest pressure drawdown can be used with Eq. 1.43 to solve for the maximum oil-production rate.

$$q_{o,\,max} = \frac{q_o}{1.0 - 0.2\dfrac{p_{wf}}{\bar{p}_R} - 0.8\left(\dfrac{p_{wf}}{\bar{p}_R}\right)^2}$$

$$= \frac{768}{1.0 - 0.2\left(\dfrac{1,335}{1,734}\right) - 0.8\left(\dfrac{1,335}{1,734}\right)^2} = 2,065 \ \text{STB}/\text{D}. \quad \dotfill (1.55)$$

The estimated maximum oil production is 2,065 STB/D. This value is then used to estimate the production rate at other values of flowing bottomhole pressures to develop a complete inflow performance curve. Once again, Eq. 1.43 will be rearranged to calculate the production rate for a flowing bottomhole pressure of 800 psia.

$$q_o = q_{o,\,max}\left[1 - 0.2\left(\frac{p_{wf}}{\bar{p}_R}\right) - 0.8\left(\frac{p_{wf}}{\bar{p}_R}\right)^2\right]$$

$$= 2,065\left[1.0 - 0.2\left(\frac{800}{1,734}\right) - 0.8\left(\frac{800}{1,734}\right)^2\right] = 1,523 \ \text{STB}/\text{D}. \quad \dotfill (1.56)$$

Fetkovich's IPR requires multiple test points to determine the deliverability exponent n. **Table 1.7** shows the test data prepared for plotting. The data are plotted on a logarithmic graph, which is used to estimate the slope of the best-fit straight line through the data. The deliverability exponent n is the inverse of the slope. Once n is determined, Eq. 1.45 can be used to estimate the maximum oil production rate. **Fig. 1.9** is the plot of the data that shows the best-fit straight line has a slope of 1.347 yielding an n value of 0.743. The estimated maximum oil production rate is 1,497 STB/D, as Eq. 1.57 shows.

$$q_{o,\,max} = \frac{q_o}{\left[1.0 - \left(\frac{p_{wf}}{\bar{p}_R}\right)^2\right]^n} = \frac{768}{\left[1.0 - \left(\frac{1,335}{1,734}\right)^2\right]^{0.743}} = 1,497 \ \text{STB}/\text{D}. \quad \dotfill (1.57)$$

TABLE 1.7—PLOTTING DATA FOR FETKOVICH IPR			
Test Rate	q_o (STB/D)	p_{wf} (psia)	Δp^2 (psia^2)
1	252	1,653	274,300
2	516	1,507	735,700
3	768	1,335	1,225,000

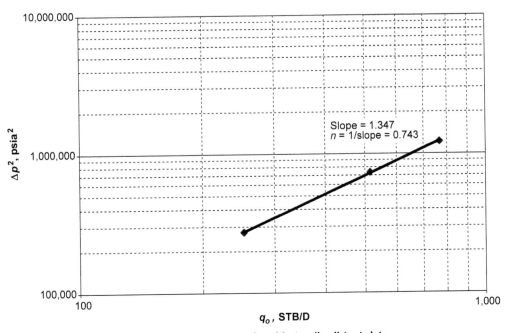

Fig. 1.9—Fetkovich analysis of multirate oilwell test data.

Once the maximum rate is estimated, it is used with Eq. 1.45 to estimate production rates at other flowing bottomhole pressures to develop the inflow performance curve in a manner similar to that demonstrated with Vogel's IPR. For Fetkovich's method, the production rate is estimated to be 1,253 STB/D at a flowing bottomhole pressure of 800 psia.

To apply the method of Jones, Blount, and Glaze to this data set, **Table 1.8** was prepared and the data plotted on a coordinate graph as shown in **Fig. 1.10**. The best-fit straight line yielded a slope of 0.0004 psia/(STB/D)^2, which is the turbulence coefficient b. The intercept is the laminar flow coefficient and is determined to be 0.23 psia/STB/D. These values are used in Eq. 1.47 to determine the maximum oil production rate of 1,814 STB/D when the flowing bottomhole pressure is 0 psig.

$$q_{o,\,max} = \frac{-0.23 + \sqrt{0.23^2 + 4(0.0004)(1,734 - 0)}}{2(0.0004)} = 1,814 \ \text{STB}/\text{D} . \ .... \ (1.58)$$

TABLE 1.8—PLOTTING DATA FOR JONES, BLOUNT, AND GLAZE IPR			
Test Rate	q_o (STB/D)	p_{wf} (psia)	$\Delta p/q_o$ (psia/STB/D)
1	252	1,653	0.321
2	516	1,507	0.440
3	768	1,335	0.520

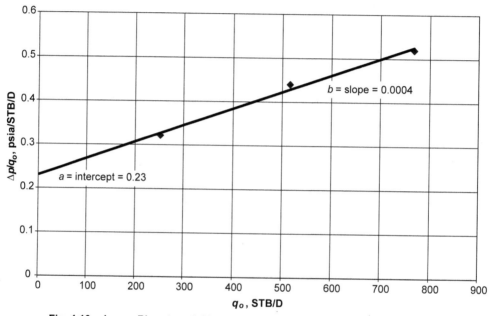

Fig. 1.10—Jones, Blount, and Glaze analysis of multirate oilwell test data.

This same relationship is used to estimate the production rate at other flowing bottomhole pressures to generate the inflow performance curve. For a flowing bottomhole pressure of 800 psia, the production rate is estimated to be 1,267 STB/D.

From this example, each of the three methods yielded different values for the maximum oil production rate as well as the production rate at a flowing bottomhole pressure of 800 psia. As a result, production estimates will be dependent on the IPR used in the analysis, and the petroleum engineer should be aware of this concern in any analysis undertaken.

The application of the composite IPR and Wiggins' IPR is straight-forward and similar to applying Vogel's IPR. In applying the composite IPR, the appropriate relationship must be used to estimate J because it depends on the flowing bottomhole pressure of the test point. With Wiggins' IPR, estimates of both oil and water production rates are generated. The inflow performance curve will be developed by adding the estimated oil rates to the water rates to create a total liquid rate.

Future Performance Methods. Once the petroleum engineer has estimated the current productive capacity of a well, it is often desired to predict future performance for planning purposes. Standing[29] was one of the first to address the prediction of future well performance from IPRs. He used Vogel's IPR with a modified multiphase productivity index to relate current well performance to future performance. Unfortunately, his relationship requires knowledge of fluid properties and relative permeability behavior. This makes Standing's method difficult to use because one must estimate saturations, relative permeabilities, and fluid properties at a future reservoir pressure.

Fetkovich[23] suggested that Standing's modified multiphase productivity index ratios could be approximated by the ratio of the pressures. He proposed that the future maximum oil production rate could be estimated from the current maximum production rate with

$$\frac{q_{o,\max,f}}{q_{o,\max,p}} = \frac{\overline{p}_{r,f}}{\overline{p}_{r,p}}\left(\frac{\overline{p}_{r,f}}{\overline{p}_{r,p}}\right)^{2n} = \left(\frac{\overline{p}_{r,f}}{\overline{p}_{r,p}}\right)^{2n+1} . \quad\ldots\ldots\ldots\ldots\ldots\ldots\ldots (1.59)$$

Fetkovich applied this idea to the use of his IPR. The exponent n in Eq. 1.59 is the deliverability exponent from his IPR; however, Fetkovich's future performance method has been applied to other IPR methods by allowing the exponent to be one, which provides good results in many cases. This method requires no more information to apply than that obtained for applying the various IPRs. It is important to note that Fetkovich's method assumes the deliverability exponent does not change between the present and future conditions. Uhri and Blount[30] and Kelkar and Cox[31] have also proposed future performance methods for two-phase flow that require rate and pressure data at two average reservoir pressures.

At the time Wiggins[27] proposed his three-phase IPRs, he also presented future performance relationships for the oil and water phases. These relationships are presented in Eqs. 1.60 and 1.61.

$$\frac{q_{o,\max,f}}{q_{o,\max,p}} = 0.15\frac{\overline{p}_{r,f}}{\overline{p}_{r,p}} + 0.84\left(\frac{\overline{p}_{r,f}}{\overline{p}_{r,p}}\right)^2 . \quad\ldots\ldots\ldots\ldots\ldots\ldots\ldots (1.60)$$

$$\frac{q_{w,\max,f}}{q_{w,\max,p}} = 0.59\frac{\overline{p}_{r,f}}{\overline{p}_{r,p}} + 0.36\left(\frac{\overline{p}_{r,f}}{\overline{p}_{r,p}}\right)^2 . \quad\ldots\ldots\ldots\ldots\ldots\ldots\ldots (1.61)$$

In all cases, once the future maximum production rate is estimated from the current data, inflow performance curves at the future average reservoir pressure of interest can be developed with the IPR of one's choosing.

1.3 Wellbore Flow Performance

The pressure drop experienced in lifting reservoir fluids to the surface is one of the main factors affecting well deliverability. As much as 80% of the total pressure loss in a flowing well may occur in lifting the reservoir fluid to the surface. Wellbore flow performance relates to estimating the pressure-rate relationship in the wellbore as the reservoir fluids move to the surface through the tubulars. This flow path may include flow through perforations, a screen and liner, and packers before entering the tubing for flow to the surface. The tubing may contain completion equipment that acts as flow restrictions such as profile nipples, sliding sleeves, or subsurface flow-control devices. In addition, the tubing string may be composed of multiple tubing diameters or allow for tubing/annulus flow to the surface. At the surface, the fluid must pass through wellhead valves, surface chokes, and through the flowline consisting of surface piping, valves, and fittings to the surface-processing equipment. The pressure drop experienced as the fluid moves from the reservoir sandface to the surface is a function of the mechanical configuration of the wellbore, the properties of the fluids, and the producing rate.

Relationships to estimate this pressure drop in the wellbore are based on the mechanical energy equation for flow between two points in a system as written in Eq. 1.62.

$$\frac{p_1}{\rho} + \frac{g}{g_c} Z_1 + \alpha \frac{v_1^2}{2g_c} = \frac{p_2}{\rho} + \frac{g}{g_c} Z_2 + \alpha \frac{v_2^2}{2g_c} + W + E_l . \qquad (1.62)$$

In this relationship, α is the kinetic energy correction factor for the velocity distribution, W is the work done by the flowing fluid, and E_l is the irreversible energy losses in the system including the viscous or friction losses. For most practical applications, there is no work done by or on the fluid and the kinetic energy correction factor is assumed to be one. Under these conditions, Eq. 1.62 can be rewritten in terms of the pressure change as

$$\frac{\Delta p}{\rho} = \frac{g}{g_c} \Delta Z + \frac{\Delta(v^2)}{2g_c} + E_l . \qquad (1.63)$$

This relationship states that the total pressure drop is equal to the sum of the change in potential energy (elevation), the change in kinetic energy (acceleration), and the energy losses in the system. This relationship can be written in the differential form for any fluid at any pipe inclination as

$$\frac{dp}{dL} = \frac{g}{g_c} \rho \sin \theta + \frac{\rho v}{g_c} \frac{dv}{dL} + \frac{f \rho v^2}{2 g_c d} . \qquad (1.64)$$

Methods to estimate the pressure drop in tubulars for single-phase liquid, single-phase vapor, and multiphase flow are based on this fundamental relationship.

With Eq. 1.64, the pressure drop for a particular flow rate can be estimated and plotted as a function of rate. In the typical application, the wellhead pressure is fixed and the bottomhole flowing pressure, p_{wf}, is calculated by determining the pressure drop. This approach will yield a wellbore flow performance curve when the pressure is plotted as a function of rate as shown in **Fig. 1.11.** In this example, the wellhead pressure is held constant, and the flowing bottomhole pressure is calculated as a function of rate. This curve is often called a tubing-performance curve because it captures the required flowing bottomhole pressure needed for various rates.

The following paragraphs summarize the basic approaches for estimating the pressure loss in the tubulars. Complete details of making these calculations are outside the scope of this section.

1.3.1 Single-Phase Liquid Flow. Single-phase liquid flow is generally of minor interest to the petroleum engineer, except for the cases of water supply or injection wells. In these cases, Eq. 1.64 is applicable where the friction factor, f, is a function of the Reynolds number and pipe roughness. The friction factor is most commonly estimated from the Moody friction factor diagram. The friction factor is an empirically determined value that is subject to error because of its dependence on pipe roughness, which is affected by pipe erosion, corrosion, or deposition.

1.3.2 Single-Phase Vapor Flow. There are several methods to estimate the pressure drop for single-phase gas flow under static and flowing conditions. These methods include the average temperature and compressibility method[32] and the original and modified Cullendar and Smith methods.[33,34] They require a trial-and-error or iterative approach to calculate the pressure drop for a given rate because of the compressible nature of the gas. These techniques are calculation

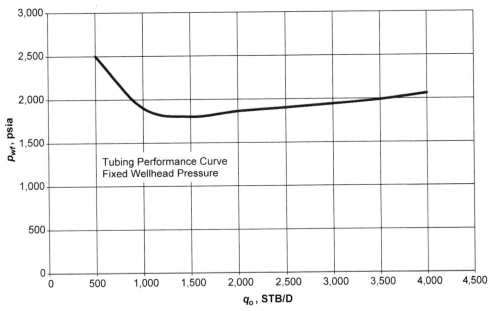

Fig. 1.11—Typical tubing performance curve for constant wellhead pressure.

intensive but can be implemented easily in a computer program. Lee and Wattenbarger[5] provide a detailed discussion of several methods used for estimating pressure drops in gas wells.

A simplified method for calculating the pressure drop in gas wells assuming an average temperature and average compressibility over the flow length was presented by Katz et al.[11]

$$q_g = 200 \left[\frac{Sd^5 \left(p_{wf}^2 - e^S p_{wh}^2\right)}{\gamma_g TzL f_M \left(e^S - 1\right)} \right], \quad \text{.. (1.65)}$$

where

$$f_M = \{2 \log \left[3.71 / (\varepsilon / d)\right]\}^{-2} \quad \text{.. (1.66)}$$

$$\text{and } S = \frac{0.0375 \gamma_g L}{Tz} . \quad \text{.. (1.67)}$$

This relationship can be solved directly if the wellhead and bottomhole pressures are known; however, in most applications, one pressure will be assumed and the other calculated. Thus, this method will be an iterative method as the compressibility factor is determined at the average pressure. Eq. 1.65 can be used to calculate the pressure drop for either flowing or static conditions.

1.3.3 Multiphase Flow. Much has been written in the literature regarding the multiphase flow of fluids in pipe. This problem is much more complex than the single-phase flow problem because there is the simultaneous flow of both liquid (oil or condensate and water) and vapor (gas). The mechanical energy equation (Eq. 1.64) is the basis for methods to estimate the pressure drop under multiphase flow; however, the problem is in determining the appropriate velocity, friction factor, and density to be used for the multiphase mixture in the calculation. In addition, the problem is further complicated as the velocities, fluid properties, and the fraction of vapor to liquid change as the fluid flows to the surface due to pressure changes.

Many researchers have proposed methods to estimate pressure drops in multiphase flow. Each method is based on a combination of theoretical, experimental, and field observations, which has led some researchers to relate the pressure-drop calculations to flow patterns. Flow patterns or flow regimes relate to the distribution of each fluid phase inside the pipe. This implies that a pressure calculation is dependent on the predicted flow pattern. There are four flow patterns in the simplest classification of flow regimes:[35] bubble flow, slug flow, transition flow, and mist flow, with a continually increasing fraction of vapor to liquid from bubble to mist flow. Bubble flow is experienced when the liquid phase is continuous with the gas phase existing as small bubbles randomly distributed within the liquid. In slug flow, the gas phase exists as large bubbles separating liquid slugs in the flow stream. As the flow enters transition flow, the liquid slugs essentially disappear between the gas bubbles, and the gas phase becomes the continuous fluid phase. The liquid phase is entrained as small droplets in the gas phase in the mist-flow pattern.

Poettman and Carpenter[36] were some of the earliest researchers to address developing a multiphase-flow correlation for oil wells, while Gray[37] presented an early multiphase correlation for gas wells. A large number of studies have been conducted related to multiphase flow in pipes. Brill and Mukerjee[38] and Brown and Beggs[39] include a review of many of these correlations. Application of the multiphase-flow correlations requires an iterative, trial-and-error solution to account for changes in flow parameters as a function of pressure. This is calculation intensive and is best accomplished with computer programs. Pressure calculations are often presented as pressure-traverse curves, like the one shown in **Fig. 1.12**, for a particular tubing diameter, production rate, and fluid properties. Pressure-traverse curves are developed for a series of gas-liquid ratios and provide estimates of pressure as a function of depth. These curves can be used for quick hand calculations.

1.4 Flow Through Chokes

A wellhead choke controls the surface pressure and production rate from a well. Chokes usually are selected so that fluctuations in the line pressure downstream of the choke have no effect on the production rate. This requires that flow through the choke be at critical flow conditions. Under critical flow conditions, the flow rate is a function of the upstream or tubing pressure only. For this condition to occur, the downstream pressure must be approximately 0.55 or less of the tubing pressure.

For single-phase gas flow, Beggs[40] presents Eq. 1.68, which relates the gas production rate through a choke to the wellhead pressure.

$$q_g = \frac{27.611 C_d p_{wh} d^2 T_{sc}}{p_{sc}\sqrt{\gamma_g T_{wh} z}} \left[\left(\frac{k}{k-1} \right) \left(y^{2/k} - y^{k+1/k} \right) \right] . \quad \text{................................} (1.68)$$

The pressure ratio, y, is the ratio of the downstream pressure to the wellhead pressure. Under critical flow conditions, the pressure ratio is replaced by the critical pressure ratio, y_c. The critical pressure ratio is the pressure ratio at which flow becomes critical. This ratio depends on the ratio of the specific heats of the produced gas, as Eq. 1.69 shows.

$$y_c = \left(\frac{2}{k+1} \right)^{k/k-1} . \quad \text{................................} (1.69)$$

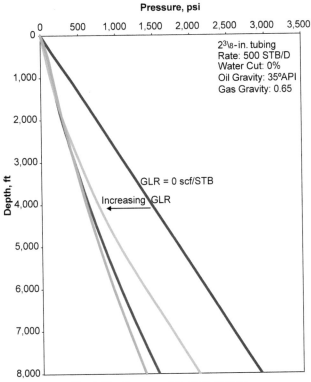

Fig. 1.12—Pressure traverse curves.

TABLE 1.9—MULTIPHASE CHOKE COEFFICIENTS			
Researcher	A_1	A_2	A_3
Gilbert	3.86×10^{-3}	0.546	1.89
Ros	4.26×10^{-3}	0.500	2.00
Baxendell	3.12×10^{-3}	0.546	1.93
Achong	1.54×10^{-3}	0.650	1.88

Empirical equations have been developed to estimate the relationship between production rate and wellhead pressure for two-phase critical flow. These correlations can be presented in a form similar to Eq. 1.70.

$$p_{wh} = \frac{A_1 q_L R^{A_2}}{d^{A_3}} \text{ .} \quad\dots\dots\dots\dots\dots\dots\dots\dots\dots\dots\dots\dots (1.70)$$

Gilbert[41] was the first to present such a relationship based on field data collected from the Ten Section field of California. Ros[42] and Beggs[40] have also presented relationships that are often used. **Table 1.9** summarizes the parameters for each equation.

Example 1.4 This example illustrates the use of the multiphase choke equation (Eq. 1.70) to estimate the flowing wellhead pressure for a given set of well conditions. However, this equation can be used to estimate flow rate or choke diameter. The example well is producing 400 STB/D of oil with a gas-liquid ratio of 800 Scf/STB. Estimate the flowing wellhead pressure for a choke size of 12/64 in. with Gilbert's choke equation.

Solution. Use Eq. 1.70 and the proper variable from Table 1.9 to calculate

$$p_{wh} = \frac{3.86 \times 10^{-3}(400)(800)^{0.546}}{(12/64)^{1.89}} = 1,405 \text{ psia} . \quad \text{.............................} \quad (1.71)$$

For these conditions, the estimated flowing wellhead pressure is 1,405 psia. If the Ros choke equation is used, an estimated flowing wellhead pressure of 1,371 psia is calculated. Each of the relationships provides slightly different estimates of the calculated value.

1.5 Systems Analysis

Systems analysis has been used for many years to analyze the performance of systems composed of multiple interacting components. Gilbert[41] was perhaps the first to introduce the approach to oil and gas wells but Mach, Proano, and Brown[1] and Brown[26] popularized the concept, which is often referred to as Nodal Analysis™ within the oil and gas industry. The objective of systems analysis is to combine the various components of the production system for an individual well to estimate production rates and optimize the components of the production system.

The flow of reservoir fluids from the subsurface reservoir to the stock tank or sales line requires an understanding of the principles of fluid flow through porous media and well tubulars. As the fluid moves through the production system, there will be an associated pressure drop to accompany the fluid flow. This pressure drop will be the sum of the pressure drops through the various components in the production system. Because of the compressible nature of the fluids produced in oil and gas operations, the pressure drop is dependent on the interaction between the various components in the system. This occurs because the pressure drop in a particular component is not only dependent on the flow rate through the component, but also on the average pressure that exists in the component.

As a result, the final design of a production system requires an integrated approach, since the system cannot be separated into a reservoir component or a piping component and handled independently. The amount of oil and gas produced from the reservoir to the surface depends on the total pressure drop in the production system, and the pressure drop in the system depends on the amount of fluid flowing through the system. Consequently, the entire production system must be analyzed as a unit or system.

Depending on the terminal end of the production system, there is a total pressure drop from the reservoir pressure to the surface, as depicted in Fig. 1.1. If the separator represents the end of the production system, the total pressure drop in the system is the difference between the average reservoir pressure and the separator pressure:

$$\Delta p_T = \bar{p}_R - p_s . \quad \text{...} \quad (1.72)$$

This total pressure drop is then composed of individual pressure drops as the reservoir fluid flows to the surface. These pressure drops occur as the fluid flows through the reservoir and well completion, up the tubing, through the wellhead equipment and choke, and through the surface flowlines to the separator. Thus, the total pressure drop of Eq. 1.72 can be represented by Eq. 1.73.

$$\Delta p_T = \Delta p_1 + \Delta p_2 + \Delta p_3 + \Delta p_4 . \quad\text{(1.73)}$$

These individual pressure drops can be divided into yet additional pressure drops to account for restrictions, subsurface safety valves, tubing accessories, etc.

Systems analysis is based on the concept of continuity. At any given point in the production system, there is a particular pressure and production rate associated with that point for a set of conditions. If there is any change in the system, then there will be an associated change in pressure and/or production rate at that same point. This concept allows the production system to be divided at a point of interest for evaluation of the two portions of the system. This evaluation determines the conditions of continuity of pressure and production rate at the division point, which is the estimated producing condition for the system being evaluated.

The approach provides the flexibility to divide the production system at any point of interest within the system to evaluate a particular component of the system. The most common division points are at the wellhead or at the perforations, either at the reservoir sandface or inside the wellbore. The terminal ends of the system will be the reservoir on the upstream end of the system and the separator at the downstream end of the system or the wellhead if a wellhead choke controls the well.

The components upstream of the division point or node comprise the inflow section of the system, while the components downstream of the node represent the outflow section. Once the system is divided into inflow and outflow sections, relationships are written to describe the rate-pressure relationship within each section. The flow rate through the system is determined once the conditions of continuity are satisfied: flow into the division point equals flow out of the division point, and the pressure at the division point is the same in both inflow and outflow sections of the system.

After the division point is selected, pressure relationships are developed for the inflow and outflow sections of the system to estimate the node pressure. The pressure in the inflow section of the system is determined from Eq. 1.74, while the outflow section pressure drop is determined from Eq. 1.75.

$$\bar{p}_R - \Delta p_u = p_n . \quad\text{(1.74)}$$

$$p_s + \Delta p_d = p_n . \quad\text{(1.75)}$$

The pressure drop in any component, and thus in either the inflow or outflow section of the system, varies as a function of flow rate. As a result, a series of flow rates is used to calculate node pressures for each section of the system. Then, plots of node pressure vs. production rate for the inflow section and the outflow section are made. The curve representing the inflow section is called the inflow curve, while the curve representing the outflow section is the outflow curve. The intersection of the two curves provides the point of continuity required by the systems analysis approach and indicates the anticipated production rate and pressure for the system being analyzed.

Fig. 1.13 depicts a systems graph for a sensitivity study of three different combinations for outflow components labeled A, B, and C. For outflow curve A, there is no intersection with the inflow performance curve. Because there is no intersection, there is no continuity in the system and the well will not be expected to flow with System A. The inflow and outflow performance curves do intersect for System B. Thus this system satisfies continuity, and the well will be expected to produce at a rate and pressure indicated by the intersection of the inflow

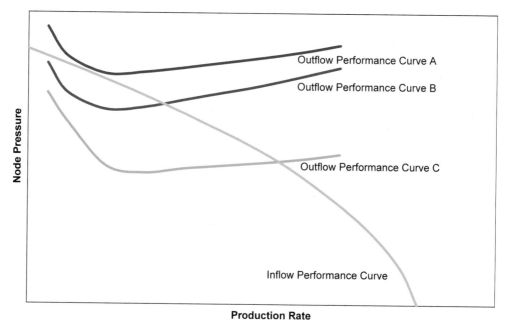

Production Rate
Fig. 1.13—Inflow and outflow performance curves for systems analysis.

and outflow curves. System C also has an intersection and would be expected to produce at a higher rate and lower pressure than System B, as indicated by the graph.

The outflow curve for System C has a rapidly decreasing pressure at low flow rates, reaches a minimum, and then begins to slowly increase with increasing rate. This is typical for many outflow curves, which, in some cases, will yield two intersection points with the inflow curve; however, the intersection at the lower rate is not a stable solution and is meaningless. The proper intersection of the inflow and outflow curves should be the intersection to the right of and several pressure units higher than the minimum pressure on the outflow curve.

The effect of changing any component of the system can be evaluated by recalculating the node pressure for the new characteristics of the system. If a change is made in an upstream component of the system, then the inflow curve will change and the outflow curve will remain unchanged. On the other hand, if a change in a downstream component is made, then the inflow curve will remain the same and the outflow curve will change. Both the inflow and outflow curves will be shifted if either of the fixed pressures in the system is changed, which can occur when evaluating the effects of reservoir depletion or considering different separator conditions or wellhead pressures.

Systems analysis may be used for many purposes in analyzing and designing producing oil and gas wells. The approach is suited for evaluating both flowing wells and artificial lift applications. The technique provides powerful insight in the design of an initial completion. Even with limited data, various completion scenarios can be evaluated to yield a qualitative estimate of expected well behavior. This process is very useful in analyzing current producing wells by identifying flow restrictions or opportunities to enhance performance.

Typical applications include estimation of flow rates, selection of tubing size, selection of flowline size, selection of wellhead pressures and surface choke sizing, estimation of the effects of reservoir pressure depletion, and identification of flow restrictions. Other typical applications are sizing subsurface safety valves, evaluating perforation density, gravel pack design, artificial lift design, optimizing injection gas-liquid ratio for gas lift, evaluating the effects of lower wellhead pressures or installation of compression, and evaluating well stimulation treat-

TABLE 1.10—INFLOW PERFORMANCE DATA FOR EXAMPLE 1.5	
Flowing Bottomhole Pressure (psia)	Production Rate (Mscf/D)
4,000	0
3,500	1,999
3,000	3,094
2,500	3,902
2,000	4,512
1,500	4,963
1,000	5,275
500	5,458
14.65	5,519

TABLE 1.11—OUTFLOW PERFORMANCE DATA FOR EXAMPLE 1.5			
Production Rate (Mscf/D)	1.90-in. Tubing p_{wf} (psia)	2.375-in. Tubing p_{wf} (psia)	2.875-in. Tubing p_{wf} (psia)
1,000	1,334	1,298	1,286
1,500	1,400	1,320	1,294
2,000	1,487	1,351	1,305
2,500	1,592	1,390	1,319
3,000	1,712	1,435	1,336
3,500	1,843	1,487	1,356
4,000	1,984	1,545	1,378
4,500	2,132	1,609	1,403
5,000	2,287	1,677	1,431
5,500	2,446	1,749	1,461
6,000	2,609	1,824	1,493

p_{wh} = 1,000 psia

ments. In addition, systems analysis can be used to evaluate multiwell producing systems. Systems analysis is a very robust and flexible method that can be used to design a well completion or improve the performance of a producing well.

1.5.1 Systems Analysis Examples. Examples 1.5 and 1.6 demonstrate the systems analysis approach. Example 1.5 considers the effects of tubing size on gas well performance. Example 1.6 demonstrates the effects of reservoir depletion on the performance of an oil well. Greene,[19] Brown and Lea,[43] and Chap. 4 of Lee and Wattenbarger[5] and Brown[26] provide a series of detailed applications that further exemplify the use of systems analysis for gas and oil wells.

Example 1.5 Analyze a gas well to select an appropriate tubing size. The gas well under consideration is at 9,000 ft with a reservoir pressure of 4,000 psia.

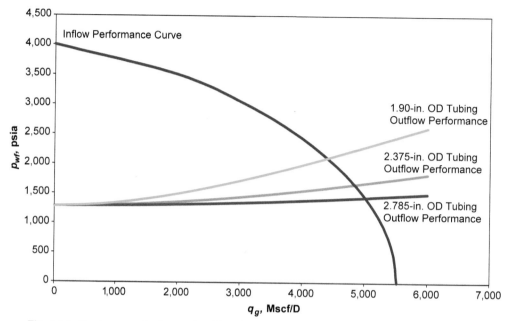

Fig. 1.14—Systems analysis graph with a bottomhole pressure node for Example 1.5.

Production Rate (Mscf/D)	Inflow Performance			Outflow Performance
	1.90 in. Tubing p_{wh} (psia)	2.375 in. Tubing p_{wh} (psia)	2.875 in. Tubing p_{wh} (psia)	p_{wh} (psia)
1,000	3,487	3,524	3,536	1,000
1,500	3,276	3,356	3,382	1,000
2,000	3,012	3,149	3,195	1,000
2,500	2,700	2,903	2,973	1,000
3,000	2,338	2,615	2,714	1,000
3,500	1,923	2,279	2,410	1,000
4,000	1,445	1,883	2,050	1,000
4,500	879	1,403	1,608	1,000
5,000	164	774	1,020	1,000

TABLE 1.12—INFLOW AND OUTFLOW PERFORMANCE FOR EXAMPLE 1.5

Solution. The first step in applying systems analysis is to select a node to divide the system. Initially, the node is selected to be at the perforations to isolate the inflow performance (reservoir behavior) from the flow behavior in the tubing. For this particular case, the well is flowing at critical flow conditions, and, consequently, the wellhead choke serves as a discontinuity in the system, which allows the use of the wellhead pressure as the terminal point for the outflow curve. Once the node point is selected, the pressure relations for the inflow and outflow sections of the system are determined. For this example, Eqs. 1.76 and 1.77 represent the inflow and outflow pressure relationships, respectively.

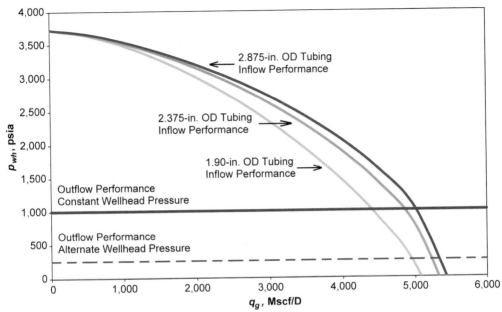

Fig. 1.15—Systems analysis graph with a wellhead pressure node for Example 1.5.

$$\bar{p}_R - \Delta p_1 - \Delta p_2 = p_{wf} . \qquad (1.76)$$

$$p_{wh} + \Delta p_3 = p_{wf} . \qquad (1.77)$$

With these basic relationships, the flowing bottomhole pressure is calculated for different production rates for both the inflow and outflow sections. **Table 1.10** presents the inflow performance data while **Table 1.11** presents the calculated pressures for three different tubing sizes using a constant wellhead pressure of 1,000 psia. These data are used to construct the inflow and outflow curves in **Fig. 1.14** to estimate the production rates and pressures for each tubing size. The intersection of the outflow curves with the inflow curve dictates the estimated point of continuity and the anticipated producing conditions for the analyzed system. For this example, the production rate increases with increasing tubing size, yielding 4,400 Mscf/D for 1.90-in. tubing, 4,850 Mscf/D for 2⅜-in. tubing, and 5,000 Mscf/D for 2⅞-in. tubing.

The same well could be analyzed with the wellhead as the system node. This allows the effect of changes in wellhead pressure on well performance to be determined. The new inflow and outflow pressure relationships are

$$\bar{p}_R - \Delta p_1 - \Delta p_2 - \Delta p_3 = p_{wh} \qquad (1.78)$$

for the inflow curve, and

$$p_{wh} = p_{wh} \qquad (1.79)$$

for the outflow curve. **Table 1.12** shows the pressure-rate relationship for both the inflow and outflow curves. Because the wellhead is the node in this analysis, the outflow curve will be constant and equal to the anticipated flowing wellhead pressure.

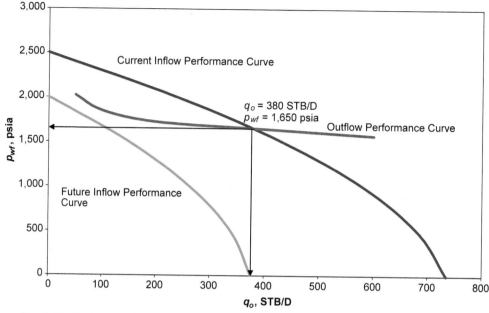

Fig. 1.16—Systems analysis graph with a bottomhole pressure node for Example 1.6.

The data are plotted in **Fig. 1.15** and yield the same producing rates and flowing bottomhole pressures that were determined when the flowing bottomhole pressure was used as the node. This is as expected because the choice of a division point or node does not affect the results for a given system. If the wellhead pressure is decreased to 250 psia, the producing rate will change also. This effect is readily determined by constructing a constant wellhead pressure line of 250 psia on the graph and selecting the points of intersection for each tubing size. As observed from the graph, the anticipated production rates increase to 4,950 Mscf/D, 5,200 Mscf/D, and 5,300 Mscf/D for the three tubing sizes by lowering the wellhead pressure.

Example 1.6 Investigate the effects of reservoir depletion of an oil well to estimate producing conditions and consider the need for artificial lift. The well under consideration is producing with a constant wellhead pressure of 250 psia and is controlled by the choke.

Solution. Isolate the reservoir performance to visualize the effect of changing reservoir pressure. The flowing bottomhole pressure at mid-perforations is selected as the node and, as the well is producing under critical flow conditions, the wellhead will serve as the terminal end of the system.

The inflow and outflow rate-pressure data is generated with Eqs. 1.76 and 1.77. **Table 1.13** provides the inflow performance data for average reservoir pressures of 2,500 psia and 2,000 psia. **Table 1.14** shows the tubing-intake data or outflow performance data for a flowing wellhead pressure of 250 psia with 2⅞-in. tubing. **Fig. 1.16** plots this information, which is used to determine the producing conditions at the two reservoir pressures. At an average reservoir pressure of 2,500 psia, the curves intersect at an oil production rate of 380 STB/D and a flowing bottomhole pressure of 1,650 psia. However, there is no intersection or point of continuity between the inflow and outflow performance curves when the reservoir pressure declines to 2,000 psia. This indicates that the well will not flow under these reservoir conditions. On the basis of this analysis, the effects of lowering the wellhead pressure, reducing the tubing size, or in-

TABLE 1.13—INFLOW PERFORMANCE DATA FOR EXAMPLE 1.6		
Well depth, ft	7,000	
Tubing size, in.	2⅞	
Test Data:		
p_R , psia	2,500	
p_{wf}, psia	1,600	
q_o, STB/D	400	
GOR, Scf/STB	800	
Flowing Bottomhole Pressure (psia)	Production Rate* (STB/D)	Production Rate** (STB/D)
2,500	0	
2,000	241	0
1,500	435	150
1,000	582	263
500	682	339
0	735	376

* At reservoir pressure of 2,500 psia. **At reservoir pressure of 2,000 psia.

TABLE 1.14—OUTFLOW PERFORMANCE DATA FOR EXAMPLE 1.6	
Well depth, ft	7,000
Tubing size, in.	2⅞
Tubing pressure, psia	250
Production Rate (STB/D)	Flowing Bottomhole Pressure (psia)
50	2,025
100	1,850
200	1,725
400	1,650
600	1,575

stalling artificial lift early in the life of the well to enhance its deliverability should be investigated.

1.6 Summary

This chapter describes the flow of reservoir fluids through the production system and provides methods to estimate oil and gas well deliverability. Analytical and empirical methods that describe fluid flow through the reservoir to the wellbore are presented to assist in predicting the inflow performance of an individual well. A brief overview of flow through circular conduits is used to assist in describing the pressure drop in the production system. Finally, an integrated approach called systems analysis is described to provide the tools needed to estimate well deliverability by integrating the reservoir performance with the tubing performance. These two aspects of the production system must be integrated to determine actual producing conditions.

Systems analysis is an excellent engineering tool for optimizing the design of a new well completion or analyzing the behavior of a current production system. The application of systems analysis requires a thorough understanding of the relationship between flow of reservoir fluids in the subsurface reservoir and fluid flow through the well completion and tubulars to the surface stock tank. Unfortunately, this understanding is often lacking in practice. Inefficient operations may occur because the petroleum engineer does not have a complete understanding of the fluid-flow process or fails to take a comprehensive look at the production system. The proper application of systems analysis provides a basis for determining the interaction of the various components in the production system to optimize the desired production rates for both oil and gas wells.

Nomenclature

a = laminar flow coefficient, m^2/L^5t^3, psia^2/Mscf/D or m/L^4t^2, psia^2/cp/Mscf/D or mL^4/t, psia/STB/D

A_{1-3} = coefficient in Eq. 1.70

b = turbulence coefficient, m^2/L^8t^2, psia^2/(Mscf/D)^2 or m/L^7t, psia^2/cp/(Mscf/D)^2 or mL^7, psia/(STB/D)^2

B = formation volume factor, dimensionless, RB/STB

c_t = total compressibility, Lt^2/m, psia^{-1}

C = flow coefficient, $L^{3+2n}t^{4n-1}/m^{2n}$, Mscf/D/psia^{2n} or $L^{3+n}t^{3n-1}/m^n$, Mscf/D/(psia^2/cp)^n or $L^{3+2n}t^{4n-1}/m^{2n}$, STB/D/psia^{2n}

C_1 = flow coefficient in Eq. 1.39, $L^{3+2n}t^{4n-2}/m^{2n-1}$, cp-Mscf/D/psia^{2n}

C_d = discharge coefficient, dimensionless

C_p = specific heat capacity at constant pressure, L^2/t^2T

C_v = specific heat capacity at constant volume, L^2/t^2T

d = pipe diameter, L, in.

D = non-Darcy flow coefficient, t/L^3, D/Mscf

E_l = energy loss per unit mass, L^2/t^2, ft-lbf/lbm

f = friction factor, dimensionless

f_M = Moody friction factor in Eq. 1.66, dimensionless

g = gravitational acceleration, L/t^2, ft/sec^2

g_c = conversion factor, dimensionless, 32.2 ft-lbm/lbf-sec^2

h = formation thickness, L, ft

J = productivity index, L^4t/m, STB/D/psia

k = permeability, L^2, md

k = specific heat capacity ratio, C_p/C_v in Eqs. 1.68 and 1.69, dimensionless

L = length, L, ft

M – molecular weight, m, lbm/lbm-mole

n = deliverability exponent, dimensionless

p = pressure, m/Lt^2, psia

$\bar{p}$ = average bottomhole pressure, m/Lt^2, psia

p_b = bubblepoint pressure, m/Lt^2, psia

p_e = external boundary pressure, m/Lt^2, psia

p_n = node pressure, m/Lt^2, psia

P_p = gas pseudopressure, m/Lt^3, psia^2/cp

$p_p(\bar{p}_R)$ = average reservoir pseudopressure, m/Lt^3, psia^2/cp

$p_p(p_{wf})$ = flowing bottomhole pseudopressure, m/Lt^3, psia^2/cp

$\bar{p}_R$ = average reservoir pressure, m/Lt^2, psia

p_s = separator pressure, m/Lt^2, psia

p_{sc} = standard pressure, m/Lt^2, psia

p_{wf} = bottomhole pressure, m/Lt^2, psia

p_{wfs} = sandface bottomhole pressure, m/Lt^2, psia

p_{wh} = wellhead pressure, m/Lt^2, psia

q = flow rate, L^3/t, STB/D or Mscf/D

q_b = oil flow rate at the bubblepoint pressure, L^3/t, STB/D

q_g = gas flow rate, L^3/t, Mscf/D

$q_{g,max}$ = AOF, maximum gas flow rate, L^3/t, Mscf/D

q_L = liquid flow rate, L^3/t, STB/D

q_o = oil flow rate, L^3/t, STB/D

$q_{o,max}$ = maximum oil flow rate, L^3/t, STB/D

q_w = water flow rate, L^3/t, STB/D

$q_{w,max}$ = maximum water flow rate, L^3/t, STB/D

r = radius, L, ft

r_e = external drainage radius, L, ft

r_w = wellbore radius, L, ft

R = producing gas/liquid ratio, dimensionless, scf/STB

s = skin factor, dimensionless

S = defined by Eq. 1.67, m/L^2t

t = time, t

T = temperature, T, °R

T_{sc} = standard temperature, T, °R

T_{wh} = wellhead temperature, T, °R

v = velocity, L/t, ft/sec

W = work per unit mass, L^2/t^2, ft-lbf/lbm

y = ratio of downstream pressure to upstream pressure, p_1/p_2, dimensionless

y_c = critical pressure ratio defined by Eq. 1.69, dimensionless

z = gas compressibility factor, dimensionless

Z = elevation, L, ft

α = kinetic energy correction factor, dimensionless

β = turbulence factor, L^{-1}, ft^{-1}

γ_g = gas specific gravity, dimensionless

Δp = pressure loss, m/Lt^2, psia

Δp_1 = pressure loss in reservoir, m/Lt^2, psia

Δp_2 = pressure loss across completion, m/Lt^2, psia

Δp_3 = pressure loss in tubing, m/Lt^2, psia

Δp_4 = pressure loss in flowline, m/Lt^2, psia

Δp_d = change in downstream pressure, m/Lt^2, psia

Δp_p = difference in pseudopressures, m/Lt^3, psia²/cp

Δp_T = total pressure loss, m/Lt^2, psia

Δp_u = change in upstream pressure, m/Lt^2, psia

Δp^2 = difference in pressures squared, m^2/L^2t^4, psia

ε = absolute pipe roughness, L, in.

μ = viscosity, m/Lt, cp

ρ = fluid density, m/L^3, lbm/ft³

ϕ = porosity, fraction

Subscripts

$$f = \text{future time}$$
$$g = \text{gas}$$
$$o = \text{oil}$$
$$p = \text{present time}$$
$$w = \text{water}$$

References

1. Mach, J., Proano, E., and Brown, K.E.: "A Nodal Approach for Applying Systems Analysis to the Flowing and Artificial Lift Oil or Gas Well," paper SPE 8025 available from SPE, Richardson, Texas (1979).
2. Al-Hussainy, R., Ramey, H.J. Jr., and Crawford, P.B.: "The Flow of Real Gases Through Porous Media," *JPT* (May 1966) 624; *Trans.*, AIME, **237.**
3. Dake, L.P.: *Fundamentals of Reservoir Engineering*, Elsevier Science Publishers, Amsterdam (1978).
4. Craft, B.C., Hawkins, M.F., and Terry, R.E.: *Applied Petroleum Reservoir Engineering*, second edition, Prentice-Hall Inc., Englewood Cliffs, New Jersey (1991).
5. Lee, W.J. and Wattenbarger, R.A.: *Gas Reservoir Engineering*, Textbook Series, SPE, Richardson, Texas (1996) **5.**
6. Rawlins, E.L. and Schellhardt, M.A.: *Backpressure Data on Natural Gas Wells and Their Application to Production Practices*, Monograph Series, U.S. Bureau of Mines (1935) **7.**
7. Houpeurt, A.: "On the Flow of Gases in Porous Media," *Revue de L'Institut Francais du Petrole* (1959) **XIV (11)** 1468–1684.
8. Forchheimer, P.: "Wasserbewegung durch Boden," *Zeitz ver deutsch Ing.* (1901) **45**, 2145.
9. Jones, L.G., Blount, E.M., and Glaze, O.H.: "Use of Short Term Multiple Rate Flow Tests To Predict Performance of Wells Having Turbulence," paper SPE 6133 presented at the 1976 SPE Annual Technical Conference and Exhibition, New Orleans, 3–6 October.
10. Cullendar, M.H.: "The Isochronal Performance Method of Determining the Flow Characteristics of Gas Wells," *Trans.*, AIME (1955) **204**, 137–142.
11. Katz, D.L. *et al.*: *Handbook of Natural Gas Engineering*, McGraw-Hill Publishing Co., New York City (1959).
12. Hinchman, S.B., Kazemi, H., and Poettmann, F.H.: "Further Discussion of The Analysis of Modified Isochronal Tests To Predict the Stabilized Deliverability of Gas Wells Without Using Stabilized Flow Data," *JPT* (January 1987) 93.
13. Brar, G.S. and Aziz, K.: "Analysis of Modified Isochronal Tests To Predict the Stabilized Deliverability Potential of Gas Wells Without Using Stabilized Flow Data," *JPT* (February 1978) 297; *Trans.*, AIME, **265.**
14. Poettmann, F.H.: "Discussion of Analysis of Modified Isochronal Tests To Predict the Stabilized Deliverability Potential of Gas Wells Without Using Stabilized Flow Data," *JPT* (October 1986) 1122.
15. Brar, G.S. and Mattar, L.: "Authors' Reply to Discussion of The Analysis of Modified Isochronal Tests To Predict the Stabilized Deliverability Potential of Gas Wells Without Using Stabilized Flow Data," *JPT* (January 1987) 89.
16. Poe, B.D. Jr.: "Gas Well Deliverability," ME thesis, Texas A&M U., College Station, Texas (1987).
17. Jones, S.C.: "Using the Inertial Coefficient, β, To Characterize Heterogeneity in Reservoir Rock," paper SPE 16949 presented at the 1987 SPE Annual Technical Conference and Exhibition, Dallas, 27–30 September.
18. Russell, D.G. *et al.*: "Methods for Predicting Gas Well Performance," *JPT* (January 1966) 99.
19. Greene, W.R.: "Analyzing the Performance of Gas Wells," *JPT* (July 1983) 1378.
20. Golan, M. and Whitson, C.H.: *Well Performance*, second edition, Prentice-Hall Inc., Englewood Cliffs, New Jersey (1991).

21. Evinger, H.H. and Muskat, M.: "Calculation of Theoretical Productivity Factor," *Trans.*, AIME (1942) **146,** 126.
22. Vogel, J.V.: "Inflow Performance Relationships for Solution-Gas Drive Wells," *JPT* (January 1968) 83; *Trans.*, AIME, **243.**
23. Fetkovich, M.J.: "The Isochronal Testing of Oil Wells," paper SPE 4529 presented at the 1973 SPE Annual Meeting, Las Vegas, Nevada, 30 September–3 October.
24. Gallice, F. and Wiggins, M.L.: "A Comparison of Two-Phase Inflow Performance Relationships," *SPEPF* (May 2004) 100–104.
25. Neely, A.B.: "Use of IPR Curves," Shell Oil Co., Houston (July 1967).
26. Brown, K.E.: *The Technology of Artificial Lift Methods,* PennWell Publishing Co., Tulsa (1984) **4.**
27. Wiggins, M.L.: "Generalized Inflow Performance Relationships for Three-Phase Flow," *SPERE* (August 1994) 181; *Trans.*, AIME, **297.**
28. Sukarno, P.: "Inflow Performance Relationship Curves in Two-Phase and Three-Phase Flow Conditions," PhD dissertation, U. of Tulsa, Tulsa (1986).
29. Standing, M.B.: "Concerning the Calculation of Inflow Performance of Wells Producing from Solution Gas Drive Reservoirs," *JPT* (September 1971) 1141.
30. Uhri, D.C. and Blount, E.M.: "Pivot Point Method Quickly Predicts Well Performance," *World Oil* (May 1982) 153–164.
31. Kelkar, B.G. and Cox, R.: "Unified Relationship To Predict Future IPR Curves for Solution Gas-Drive Reservoirs," paper SPE 14239 presented at the 1985 SPE Annual Technical Conference and Exhibition, Las Vegas, Nevada, 22–25 September.
32. Smith, R.V.: "Determining Friction Factors for Measuring Productivity of Gas Wells," *Trans.*, AIME (1950) **189,** 73.
33. Cullender, M.H. and Smith, R.V.: "Practical Solution of Gas-Flow Equations for Wells and Pipelines with Large Temperature Gradients," *Trans.*, AIME (1956) **207,** 281.
34. Oden, R.D. and Jennings, J.W.: "Modification of the Cullender and Smith Equation for More Accurate Bottomhole Pressure Calculations in Gas Wells," paper SPE 17306 presented at the 1988 SPE Permian Basin Oil and Gas Recovery Conference, Midland, Texas, 10–11 March.
35. Orkiszewski, J.: "Predicting Two-Phase Pressure Drops in Vertical Pipe," *JPT* (June 1967) 829; *Trans.*, AIME (1967) **240.**
36. Poettman, F.H. and Carpenter, P.G.: "The Multiphase Flow of Gas, Oil and Water Through Vertical Flow Strings with Application to the Design of Gas-Lift Installations," *Drill. & Prod. Prac.*, API, Dallas (1952) 257–317.
37. Gray, H.E.: "Vertical Flow Correlation in Gas Wells," *User's Manual for API 14B*, API, Dallas (June 1974) Appendix B.
38. Brill, J.P. and Mukherjee, H.: *Multiphase Flow in Wells*, Monograph Series, SPE, Richardson, Texas (1999) **17.**
39. Brown, K.E. and Beggs, H.D.: *The Technology of Artificial Lift Methods*, PennWell Publishing Co., Tulsa (1977) **1.**
40. Beggs, H.D.: *Production Optimization Using Nodal Analysis*, OGCI Publications, Tulsa (1991) 123–127.
41. Gilbert, W.E.: "Flowing and Gas-Lift Well Performance," *Drill. & Prod. Prac.*, API, Dallas (1954) 126–57.
42. Ros, N.C.J.: "An Analysis of Critical Simultaneous Gas/Liquid Flow Through a Restriction and Its Application to Flowmetering," *Applied Scientific Research* (1960) **9,** Series A, 374.
43. Brown, K.E. and Lea, J.F.: "Nodal Systems Analysis of Oil and Gas Wells," *JPT* (October 1985) 1751.

SI Metric Conversion Factors

bbl	×	1.589 873	E–01	= m^3
cp	×	1.0*	E–03	= Pa·s
ft	×	3.048*	E–01	= m
ft^3	×	2.831 685	E–02	= m^3
in	×	2.54*	E+00	= cm

lbf ×	4.448 222	E+00	= N
lbm ×	4.535 924	E–01	= kg
md ×	9.869 233	E–04	= μm^2
psi ×	6.894 757	E+00	= kPa
psi^2 ×	4.753 8	E+01	= kPa^2
°R ×	5/9		= K

*Conversion factor is exact.

Chapter 2
Completion Systems
David Ruddock, SPE, Baker Oil Tools (a division of Baker Hughes Inc.)

2.1 Introduction
There are many completion options available to oil and gas producers today. Today's cased-hole completion systems vary from relatively simple single-zone low-pressure/low-temperature (LP/LT) designs to complex high-pressure/high-temperature (HP/HT) applications that were unthinkable with the technology available 50 years ago. Many of the basic components appear similar to those used in the past, yet they have been vastly improved, and their performance has been optimized to suit numerous environments.

There are several keys to designing a successful completion system and selecting components that are fit for purpose for both the downhole environment and application. Consideration must be given to the various modes under which the completion must operate and the effects any changes in temperature or differential pressure will have on the tubing string and packer. Ultimately, the system must be both efficient and cost-effective to achieve production and financial goals. A key factor in the completion design is the production rate; see other chapters in this section of the Handbook for additional information on this topic. The intention of this chapter is to familiarize the reader with the common components that make up the completion system and to understand their applications and constraints.

2.2 Packers
The packer forms the basis of the cased-hole completion design. The packer is a sealing device that isolates and contains produced fluids and pressures within the wellbore to protect the casing and other formations above or below the producing zone. This is essential to the basic functioning of most wells.

In addition to providing a seal between the tubing and casing, other benefits of a packer are as follows:
- Prevent downhole movement of the tubing string.
- Support some of the weight of the tubing.
- Often improve well flow and production rate.
- Protect the annular casing from corrosion from produced fluids and high pressures.
- Provide a means of separation of multiple producing zones.
- Limit well control to the tubing at the surface for safety purposes.
- Hold well-servicing fluid (kill fluids, packer fluids) in the casing annulus.

Packers have four key features: slip, cone, packing-element system, and body or mandrel. The slip is a wedge-shaped device with wickers (or teeth) on its face, which penetrate and grip the casing wall when the packer is set. The cone is beveled to match the back of the slip and forms a ramp that drives the slip outward and into the casing wall when setting force is applied to the packer. Once the slips have anchored into the casing wall, additional applied setting force energizes the packing-element system and creates a seal between the packer body and the inside diameter of the casing.

Production packers can be classified into two groups: retrievable and permanent. Permanent packers can be removed from the wellbore only by milling. The retrievable packer may or may not be resettable; however, removal from the wellbore normally does not require milling. Retrieval is usually accomplished by some form of tubing manipulation. This may necessitate rotation or require pulling tension on the tubing string.

The permanent packer is fairly simple and generally offers higher performance in both temperature and pressure ratings than does the retrievable packer. In most instances, it has a smaller outside diameter (OD), offering greater running clearance inside the casing string than do retrievable packers. The smaller OD and the compact design of the permanent packer help the tool negotiate through tight spots and deviations in the wellbore. The permanent packer also offers the largest inside diameter (ID) to make it compatible with larger-diameter tubing strings and monobore completions.

The retrievable packer can be very basic for LP/LT applications or very complex in HP/HT applications. Because of this design complexity in high-end tools, a retrievable packer offering performance levels similar to those of a permanent packer will invariably cost more. However, the ease of removing the packer from the wellbore and features such as resettability and being able to reuse the packer often may outweigh the added cost.

Before selecting either tool, it is important to consider the performance and features of each design, as well as the application in which it will be used. Perhaps in some instances, the permanent packer is the only option, as may be the case in some HP/HT applications. However, in those instances in which either will suffice, the operator must decide which features offer the best return over the life of the well.

When selecting a packer for a cased-hole completion, the differential pressure and temperature requirements of the application must be considered. The well depth, deployment and setting method desired, and final tubing landing conditions are also factors that come into play. The various operational modes (flowing, shut-in, injection, and stimulation) that are anticipated over the life of the well are critical and must be considered carefully in the design phase. The changes in the operational modes that influence changes in temperature, differential pressure, and axial loads all have a direct impact on the packer. Understanding the uses and constraints of the different types of packers will help clarify the factors to consider when making a selection.

2.2.1 Retrievable Tension Packer. The tension packer (**Fig. 2.1**) is typically used in medium- to shallow-depth (LP/LT) production or injection applications. The tension packer has a single set of unidirectional slips that grip only the casing when the tubing is pulled in tension. Constant tubing tension must be maintained to keep the packer set and the packing element energized. Tension packers typically are set mechanically and are released by means of tubing rotation. Most models also have an emergency shear-release feature should the primary release method fail.

The tension packer does not have an equalizing (or bypass) valve to aid in pressure equalization between the tubing and annulus to facilitate the retrieval of the packer. This seldom presents a problem with the tension packer because the packer is run at relatively shallow depths, and differential pressures across the packer during retrieval should be low. The use of packers without bypass valves should be avoided in deeper applications for which hydrostatic and differential pressures can be greater. High differential pressures can make packers difficult

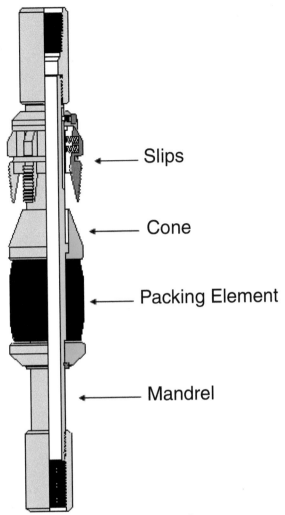

Slips

Cone

Packing Element

Mandrel

Fig. 2.1—Tension packer.

or impossible to release because of the forces created by the pressure acting on the cross-sectional area of the packer. In packers with no bypass feature, the pressures must be equalized at the surface by adding fluid or pressure to the tubing or annulus and, in some extreme cases, swabbing the tubing string.

The tension packer is suited for applications in which pressure below the packer is always greater than the annulus pressure at the tool. Pressure from below the tool boosts the packing element into the slip assembly, which is designed to hold in tension and capture this force. Conversely, when annular pressure is higher than tubing pressure at the tool, the element is boosted downward away from the slips, and packoff force is lost. Therefore, care must be taken to ensure that sufficient tension is applied to keep the element energized to contain differentials in favor of the annulus.

Consideration should be given to the type of wellhead and Christmas tree that will be employed when using tension packers in extremely shallow operations. After the packer is set and tubing is pulled in tension, it is difficult or impossible for the tubing to stretch enough to facilitate installation of some types of wellheads.

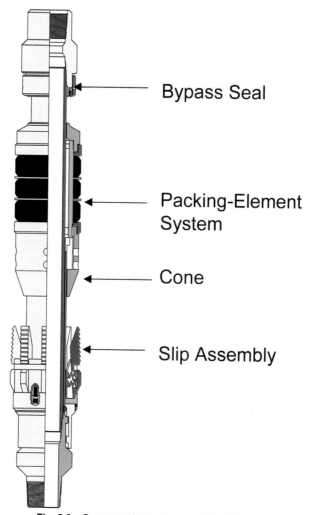

Bypass Seal

Packing-Element
System

Cone

Slip Assembly

Fig. 2.2—Compression packer with fluid bypass.

2.2.2 Retrievable Compression Packer With Bypass. The retrievable compression packer with fluid-bypass valve (**Fig. 2.2**) is recommended for low- to medium-pressure/medium-temperature oil- or gas-production applications. The retrievable compression packer is prevented from setting by means of a mechanical interlock while it is being run in the hole. Once the packer has been run to the desired depth, the tubing string is rotated to initiate the setting sequence. As the tubing is being rotated, the drag blocks on the packer are used to hold the packer in place and provide the resistance to set it. Once the interlock system is released, the tubing string is lowered to close the bypass seal and set the slips. The continued application of slackoff force energizes the packing-element system and creates a seal. The packer is released by simply picking up on the tubing string—a desirable feature.

The packing-element system is enhanced over that of the tension packer to make it suitable for moderately higher pressures and temperatures. The addition of the integral bypass valve assists equalization of pressures in the tubing and annulus and aids in releasing the packer. The valve can be opened by picking up on the tubing string without releasing the packer. Constant compression or tubing weight must be maintained to sustain the packoff and keep the bypass valve closed. Because of this design constraint, compression packers generally are not suitable

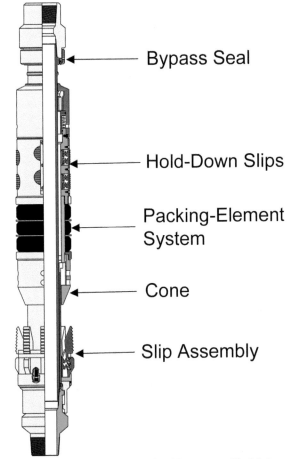

Fig. 2.3—Compression packer with fluid bypass and hold-down anchor.

for injection wells or low-volume pressure-treating operations. The bypass valve could open or the packer may fail if pressure limitations are exceeded from below, or a decrease in temperature because of operational changes may result in a reduction of tubing length and a loss of packoff force on the packer.

More common models of the compression packer with bypass have an additional set of hold-down slips, or an anchor system above the packing-element system (**Fig 2.3**). This packer sets and releases in much the same manner as the compression packer discussed previously. In this model, however, the addition of the hold-down slip helps to keep the packoff force and bypass valve locked in place when pressure below the tool is greater than the pressure in the annulus. This variation can be used in limited treating operations, in gas lift applications, or in production applications in which tubing pressures are greater than annular pressures. However, there are limitations to the ability of the anchor to keep the bypass closed, and any operational modes that will result in loss of set-down weight must be planned carefully.

2.2.3 Wireline Set—Tubing Retrievable. There are several retrievable packers designed to be installed in the wellbore on electric wireline and retrieved on the tubing string (**Fig 2.4**). On the top of the packer is located a special nipple. The nipple has a polished seal surface on its OD and has j-lugs that are used to anchor a seal housing or washover shoe in place. The pol-

Bypass Seal

Hold-Down Slips

Packing-Element System

Cone

Slip Assembly

Fig. 2.4—Wireline-set tubing retrievable packer. Shown set with plug in place (first view) and with tubing connected and plug retrieved (second view).

ished nipple also has a landing nipple profile in its ID. This allows the installation of a slickline retrievable blanking plug if desired.

The packer is first run and set on electric wireline. The electric wireline setting tool provides the force necessary to anchor the slips in the casing wall and energize the packing element. Once the packer is installed and the wireline is retrieved, a seal housing (similar to an overshot) is run in the hole on the bottom of the production tubing. The housing has internal seals that, when landed on the polished nipple, create a seal between the tubing and the annulus. The housing also has an internal j-profile that engages the lugs of the nipple and anchors the tubing string to the packer.

The tubing can be retrieved from the wellbore at any time without disturbing the packer by unjaying the seal housing from the polished nipple, or (if desired) the packer can be released and retrieved mechanically with the tubing.

The main advantage of this system is that it can be run and set under pressure on electric wireline (with a blanking plug preinstalled in the nipple profile) in a live oil or gas well. Once the packer is set, the electric line is removed, and the pressure above the packer can be bled off. With the plug in place, the packer will act as a temporary bridge plug for well control while the tubing string and seal housing are run and landed. Because the plug is located near the top of the packer assembly, it can be circulated free of any debris before landing the tubing. Once the tree has been installed, the plug is removed with slickline, and the well is placed on production.

Common applications are for completion of the well after a high-rate fracture is performed down the casing or after underbalanced perforating with a casing gun. This underbalanced completion method is especially useful in applications in which formation damage may occur if kill-weight fluid is introduced into the wellbore.

2.2.4 Retrievable Tension/Compression Set—Versatile Landing. Tension- or compression-set packers that allow the tubing to be landed in tension, compression, or neutral are the most common types of mechanical-set retrievable packers run today. This group of mechanical-set retrievable packers (**Fig. 2.5**) will vary greatly in design and performance and may require tension, compression, or a combination of both to set and pack off the element. The exact setting method depends on the design of the tool. Various packing-element systems and differential ratings are available, making this type of packer suitable for a large number of applications— up to and including some HP/HT completions.

The one common feature found in this style of packer is that once the element is sealed off and the packoff force is mechanically locked in place, the tubing string may be landed in compression, tension, or neutral. Slips located above and below the packing element (or a single set of bidirectional slips) are designed to hold axial tubing loads from either direction to keep the packer anchored in place. An internal lock system mechanically traps the packoff force and keeps the elements energized until the packer is released. A bypass valve is present to aid in equalization and the release of the packer. It is locked from accidentally opening until the packer-releasing sequence has been initiated.

Because the packer does not rely on constant tubing forces to maintain its packoff, this tool is much more versatile in application. It can be used in production or injection applications, as well as in completions for which well stimulation is planned, and it is almost universal in application. The only constraint is in deep deviated wells, where tubing manipulation or getting packoff force to the tool may present a problem. Extreme shallow depth setting is achievable in models that allow the elements to be energized with tension.

Care must be taken to ensure that tubing movement during production or injection operations does not exceed the tensile or compression limitations of either the packer or the tubing string.

2.2.5 Retrievable Hydraulic-Set Single-String Packer. The hydraulic-set packer (**Fig. 2.6**) has a bidirectional slip system that is actuated by a predetermined amount of hydraulic pressure applied to the tubing string. To achieve a pressure differential at the packer and set it, a temporary plugging device must be run in the tailpipe below the packer. The applied hydraulic pressure acts against a piston chamber in the packer. The force created by this action sets the slips and packs the element off. Some models have an atmospheric setting chamber and use the hydrostatic pressure of the well to boost the packoff force. Regardless of design, all of the

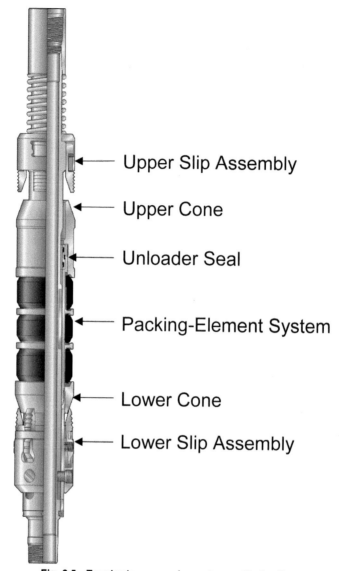

Fig. 2.5—Tension/compression-set versatile landing.

force generated during the setting process is mechanically locked in place until the packer is later released. Once the packer is set, the tubing may be landed in tension (limited by the shear-release value of the packer), compression, or neutral.

Because no tubing manipulation is required to set a hydraulic packer, it can be set easily after the wellhead has been flanged up and the tubing has been displaced. This promotes safety and allows better control of the well while displacing tubing and annulus fluids. The hydraulic-set packer can be run in a single-packer installation, and because no packer body movement occurs during the setting process, it can be run in tandem as an isolation packer in single-string multiple-zone production wells. The hydraulic-set single-string packer is ideal for highly deviat-ed wells in which conditions are not suitable for mechanical-set packers.

Special considerations include the following:

• Well stimulation must be planned carefully to avoid premature shear release of the packer.

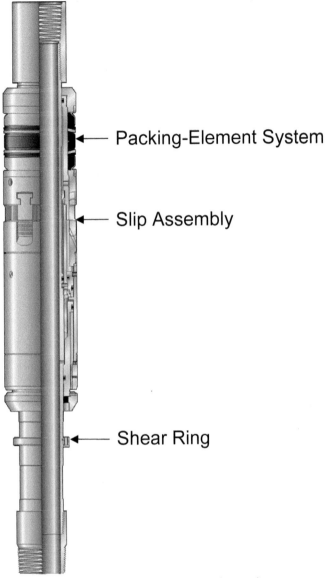

Fig. 2.6—Hydraulic-set single-string packer.

• Maximum tensile capabilities of the tubing string when selecting the shear-release value of the packer are required.

• A temporary plugging device must always be incorporated below the lowermost hydraulic-set packer to facilitate hydraulic setting of the packer.

Retrieval of the hydraulic-set single-string packer is accomplished by pulling tension with the tubing string to shear a shear ring, or shear pins, located within the packer. Most models also have a built-in bypass system that allows the pressures in the tubing and annulus to equalize, or balance, as the packer is released. The tension load required to release the packer must be considered carefully in the initial completion design and in the selection of the shear-ring value. The shear-release value must not be set too high so that it will not be beyond the tensile capabilities of the tubing string, yet it must be high enough so that the packer will not release prematurely during any of the planned operational modes over the life of the completion.

A variation of the hydraulic-set single-string retrievable packer, which can be furnished without the shear-release feature, is available for the larger-size casing and tubing combinations commonly used in big monobore completions. This design is better described as a "removable" packer because it is not retrieved by conventional means. The running and the hydraulic setting procedure remain the same, but to remove the packer from the wellbore, the inner mandrel of the packer must be cut. This is done either with a chemical cutter on electric wireline or by a mechanical cutter on drillpipe or coiled tubing. Once the mandrel is cut, retrieval is accomplished by picking up on the tubing string or the top of the packer. The packer is also designed to be millable should the cut-to-release feature fail. The elimination of the shear ring enables the packer to achieve higher tensile and differential-pressure ratings. This permits well-treating and well-injection operations to occur that were not possible with the conventional shear-release hydraulic-set packer.

2.2.6 Dual-String Packers.
This is basically a "mid-string" isolation packer that is designed to seal off approximately two strings of tubing (**Fig. 2.7**). The dual packer allows the simultaneous production of two zones while keeping them isolated. Most multiple-string packers are retrievable; however, some permanent models exist for use in HP/HT applications. Standard configurations have bidirectional slips to prevent movement and maintain packoff with the tubing landed in the neutral condition.

For the most part, multiple-string retrievable packers are set hydraulically because the tubing manipulation required to set a mechanical packer is not desirable or (often) not feasible in a dual-string application. However, mechanical-set models do exist, and in applications in which the tubing strings are run independently, the mechanical-set dual packer can be set with applied slackoff force by the upper tubing string.

The dual-string hydraulic-set packer is set much the same as the hydraulic-set single-string packer. The setting pressure typically is applied to the upper tubing (short string); however, some models are designed to be set with pressure applied to the lower tubing (long string). A temporary plugging device is required to be run below the dual packer on the appropriate string to allow the actuating pressure to be applied.

The hydraulic-set dual packers are released by applying tubing tension to shear an internal shear ring. The same considerations in shear-value selection that apply to the single-string hydraulic-set packer also apply to the dual packer. Too high of a value can overstress the tubing during retrieval, and too low a value can lead to a premature packer release during one of the various operational modes to which the packer will be exposed.

Other uses for multiple-string packers include electrical submersible pump applications in which both the electrical cable and the production tubing must pass through the packer. Multiple-string packers are also used in tandem to isolate damaged casing.

2.2.7 Permanent and Retrievable Sealbore Packers.
The permanent (**Fig. 2.8**) and retrievable (**Fig. 2.9**) sealbore packers are designed to be set on electric wireline or hydraulically on the tubing string. Wireline setting affords speed and accuracy; however, the one-trip hydraulic-set versions offer the advantage of single-trip installations and allow the packer to be set with the wellhead flanged up.

Sealbore packers have a honed and polished internal sealbore. A tubing seal assembly with elastomeric packing forms the seal between the production tubing and the packer bore. Well isolation is accomplished by the fit of the elastomeric seals in the polished packer bore. To accommodate longer seal lengths, a sealbore extension may be added to the packer.

In the case of the one-trip hydraulic-set sealbore packer system, the production tubing, tubing seal assembly, and packer are made up together and run as a unit. However, if the packer

Fig. 2.7—Hydraulic-set dual-string packer.

is to be installed on electric wireline or set on a work string, the seal assembly is run on the production tubing after the packer is installed and stabbed into the packer bore downhole.

The seal assembly may be a locator type (**Fig. 2.10**), which allows seal movement during production and treating operations, or an anchor type (**Fig. 2.11**), which secures the seals in the packer bore and restricts tubing movement. The decision about the best seal assembly to run depends on tubing movement and hydraulic calculations based on initial landing, flowing, or shut-in conditions, as well as any stimulation or treatment that may be planned for the well.

Fig. 2.8—Permanent sealbore packer.

The removable seal assembly allows tubing to be retrieved for workover without the need of pulling and replacing the packer.

Generally, the permanent sealbore packers, both wireline and hydraulic set, afford much higher performance in both temperature and pressure ratings than do any of the retrievable packers. The one disadvantage is that the permanent packer must be milled over to remove the packer from the wellbore. For the most part, milling is not prohibitive and, in many cases, may never be required. However, removal may be necessary if subsequent workover operations require full-bore access to the casing below the packer or if a packer failure should occur.

Because of the complexity of their design, retrievable sealbore packers usually have a higher cost associated with them (as well as lower pressure and temperature ratings) than do the permanent versions. However, they are in most cases easily removable from the wellbore with-

Fig. 2.9—Retrievable sealbore packer (left) and releasing tool (right).

out milling. Normally, removal is accomplished in two trips: the first to retrieve the seal assembly, and the second with a releasing tool to retrieve the packer. Like the permanent sealbore packer, the retrievable models are available in both wireline and one-trip hydraulic-set versions.

When making the determination of which type of packer to use, careful consideration must be given to the completion design, wellbore geometry, and packer-performance requirements. The contingency plans for packer removal must be developed and reviewed. While many technical advances in milling techniques have been achieved, it ultimately may prove more cost-

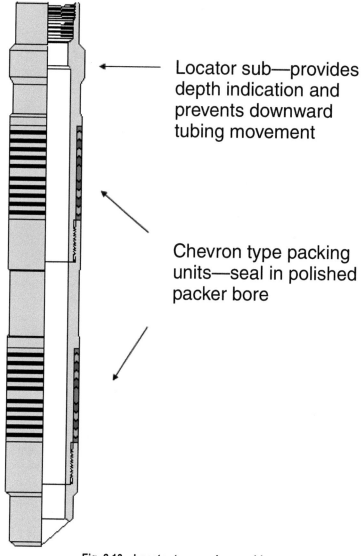

Locator sub—provides depth indication and prevents downward tubing movement

Chevron type packing units—seal in polished packer bore

Fig. 2.10—Locator type seal assembly.

effective to use a retrievable sealbore packer in horizontal applications in which packer milling is not desirable, or in low-fluid wells in which circulating cuttings to the surface is not possible. In applications in which it is known that the packer must be removed at some point in the life of the well and packer milling may be prohibitive, the retrievable sealbore may be recommended.

2.3 Methods of Conveyance
For the most part, both permanent and retrievable packers can be run and set on the production tubing string, requiring no additional trips for installation. This one-trip system is both cost-effective and efficient. However, at times it may be necessary or desirable to install the packer in the wellbore first and then run the production tubing. In these instances, a packer is selected that can be run and set either on a workstring or on electric wireline. Once the packer is in-

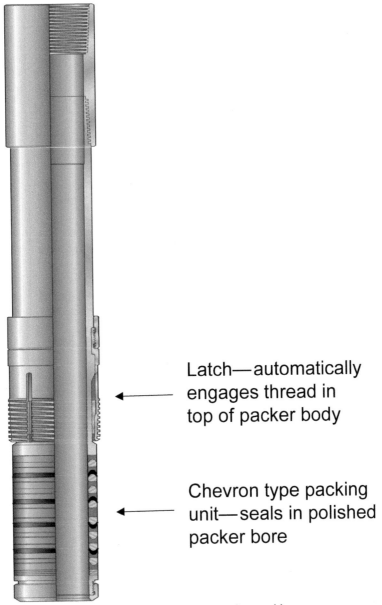

Latch—automatically engages thread in top of packer body

Chevron type packing unit—seals in polished packer bore

Fig. 2.11—Anchor type seal assembly.

stalled, a sealing device is attached to the end of the production tubing and connected to the packer downhole to form a seal.

Electric wireline setting of the packer affords several benefits. First, it offers fast installation and accurate placement of the packer. This is important in instances in which the packer must be set in a very short interval (perhaps because of damaged casing) or in cases in which the zones are very close together. Electric wireline deployment also can allow the packer to be installed and set under pressure in a live well without the need for a snubbing unit. In this case, a temporary plugging device is used in conjunction with the packer to allow the well pressure above the packer to be bled off once it is installed.

Running and setting the packer on a work string may be necessary in highly deviated wells in which the hole angle is too high to run the packer in on electric wireline. Although this method requires the most time for packer installation, it does afford the benefit of being able to hydraulically pressure test the packer and ensure that it is properly set before picking up and running the production tubing.

Consideration should be given to the run-in speed of the packer, whether run on tubing or electric line. Too fast of a run-in speed in fluid can cause the rubber element to begin to pack off or swab. This will inflict damage to the element and lead to packer failure. Slower speeds also afford the operator a chance to prevent damage to the packer should an obstruction in the wellbore be encountered.

2.3.1 Landing Conditions. The tubing string is attached to the packer by two methods:
- It is latched or fixed to the packer by means of an anchor seal assembly (in the case of a sealbore packer) or tubing thread (most retrievable packers).
- The tubing is landed with a seal assembly and locator sub in the polished bore of a permanent or retrievable sealbore packer. In this case, the upward tubing movement at the packer is limited only by the length of the seal assembly. Any downward movement is restricted by the locator sub.

There are basically three tubing landing conditions associated with completion packers. The term "landing condition" refers to the amount of slackoff weight or tension that is left on the packer when the tree is landed and the wellhead is flanged up. In these three cases, the tubing can be landed in either tension or compression, or it can be left in neutral with no axial loads on the packer.

Packer design, operational modes, and hydraulics dictate the optimum landing condition. Many types of retrievable packers, for example, often require either constant tension or compression to maintain their seal because of design. Other models of retrievable packers mechanically lock the packoff force in place and allow the tubing to be landed in tension, compression, or neutral. The permanent or retrievable sealbore packer is extremely versatile and can accommodate any of the three landing conditions.

2.3.2 Through-Tubing Operations. Consideration should be given to future through-tubing operations such as coiled-tubing operations, swabbing, slickline, or electric wireline work to ensure that the internal diameter of the completion equipment is adequate to allow passage of the tools. Operational modes and tubing landing conditions can cause helical buckling of the tubing string, which also may interfere with running longer lengths of tools through the tubing string.

Ideally, the inside diameter of the packer should be equal to that of the tubing string to facilitate through-tubing operations. This is especially critical in monobore well designs, in which any restriction will limit access to the lower wellbore. In some high-pressure completion designs, obtaining a large packer ID is not always possible because of packer-design limitations required to achieve the higher pressures.

Excessive tubing buckling can severely limit the length and diameter of through-tubing tools that can be run through the tubing string. Tubing buckling is caused by (1) tubing landing conditions that require compression on the packer; (2) an overall increase in tubing temperature, which will cause the tubing to elongate; (3) an increase in internal tubing pressure; and (4) the piston effect on locator type seal assemblies. These conditions can be minimized if the completion is designed properly. Care should be taken when planning the completion to thoroughly review the various operating conditions to which the well will be subjected and to select a packer to fit the operation.[1]

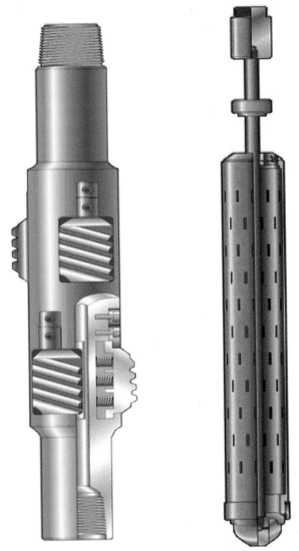

Fig. 2.12—Casing scraper (left); wireline junk basket and gauge ring (right).

2.3.3 Casing Cleanup Operations. Any debris or obstruction that is present in the wellbore can cause most packers to malfunction. Any cement that may have been left on the casing wall from previous cementing operations, as well as scale buildup in the case of old wells, can also lead to poor packer performance. To properly grip the casing and form a leakproof seal, the packer slip and element system must make 100% contact with the casing wall. It is advisable to run a casing scraper or other suitable casing cleanout tool and circulate the well clean before installing the production packer. A casing scraper should *always* be run in instances in which a packer is to be conveyed through new perforations (**Fig 2.12**).

Before running any packer on electric wireline, it is advisable to run a wireline junk basket and gauge ring (Fig 2.12). The gauge ring has a slightly larger OD than the packer and "gauges" the hole to ensure that there are no tight spots that might cause the packer to become stuck, or accidentally set in the hole. The junk basket is also designed to collect any debris that is suspended in the completion fluid that otherwise might interfere with running the packer.

2.3.4 Other Casing Considerations. Before installing the packer, a cement bond log should be considered to verify the integrity of the primary cementing job on the casing string. If a poor cement bond exists in the interval in which the packer is to be set, the packer's ability to serve as a barrier may be compromised should a leak in the casing string occur. Such a leak could allow the formation below to communicate to the annulus above the packer. If such a channel is created, the annulus could be exposed to high formation pressures, or the formation itself may be damaged. Either case could lead to a costly workover.

There are special applications in which the packer is intentionally set in unsupported or uncemented casing. Care should be taken in these instances to ensure that the design of the packer is such that radial loads and stresses created by setting the packer, and those anticipated to be encountered during various operating conditions, do not exceed the stress limitations of the casing.

2.4 Metallurgy

Ideally, the packer should be built out of materials that will last the life of the well. Also, in the case of retrievable packers that may be reconditioned and used elsewhere, the advantage of being able to reuse the packer may be lost if the well environment corrodes or damages the tool beyond repair. In potentially corrosive environments, material failure can lead to a packer leak or difficulty in removing a retrievable packer from the wellbore. In these cases, corrosion-resistant alloy materials must be properly selected that are best suited to the downhole well environment. The Natl. Assn. of Corrosion Engineers (NACE) Standard MR-01-75 establishes guidelines and acceptance criteria for material selection for sour service in H_2S environments.[2]

Metallurgical requirements are dictated both by the downhole well environment and the design and performance requirements of the packer. Consideration must be given to both when selecting and specifying materials for corrosive environments. Many types of materials that are applicable for tubing and casing in corrosive environments are not always suitable (or practical) for packer manufacture.

Some commonly used materials for manufacture of downhole equipment are as follows:[3]

• Low-alloy steels with minimum yield strengths of 110 ksi are used for standard service in noncorrosive environments. These materials are similar in property to P110 tubing and do not meet NACE MR-01-75 requirements for sour service.[4]

• Low-alloy steels with a maximum hardness of Rockwell 22C, which meet NACE MR-01-75 requirements, are intended for use in both standard service and service in sour H_2S environments. Materials that fall into this range would be similar in properties to J-55 to L-80 grades of tubing.

• Martensitic steels such as 9% chromium, 1% molybdenum, and 13% chromium alloy steels are used in some wet CO_2 environments. Certain grades of these steels meet NACE MR-01-75 requirements and can be used in limited H_2S applications.[5]

• 22% chromium and 25% chromium duplex stainless steel are commonly used in some wet CO_2 and mild H_2S environments.

• Austenitic stainless steels, cold worked 3% Mo high-nickel alloy steels, and precipitation-hardening nickel-based alloys are suitable for some environments containing high levels of H_2S, CO_2, and chlorides at moderately high temperatures.

The successful application of any of these materials depends strongly on the specific downhole well environment. Many factors such as temperature, pH, chlorides, water, H_2S, and CO_2 concentrations can have adverse effects on the material performance and can lead to failures associated with pitting, corrosion, chloride stress cracking, or hydrogen embrittlement. Because of this and the vast number and variations of packer designs and tensile requirements of their components, the consumer cannot know which materials are appropriate for each particular design. Ultimately, the user must rely on the packer manufacturer to help make the determination as to which materials will meet the downhole requirements without sacrificing packer performance and reliability.

2.5 Elastomers

There are many suitable elastomers on today's market to match almost any downhole condition. Care must be taken to ensure that the elastomer selected for the packer and seal assembly meets all the downhole conditions to which it will be subjected. Things that must be considered are the downhole operating temperature; exposure to produced or injected fluids and gases; exposure to completion fluids such as oil-based mud, brine, bromides, high pH completion fluids, and amine base inhibitors; and exposure to solvents such as xylene, toluene, and methanol. There is no single best elastomer that will perform under all conditions combined, and selection must be tailored to suit individual well requirements and application.

By far, the most common elastomer used in downhole completion packers is nitrile. Nitrile is used in low- to medium-temperature applications for packers and packer-to-tubing seal assemblies in one form or another. It shows good chemical resistance to oils, brines, and CO_2 exposure. However, its use is limited in wells that contain even small amounts of H_2S, amine inhibitors, or high-pH completion fluids. Exposure to high concentrations of H_2S and bromides generally is not recommended.[3,6]

Hydrogenated nitrile or HNBR (chemical name: hydrogenated acrylonitrile butadiene) has a somewhat higher temperature rating and shows slightly better chemical resistance to H_2S and corrosion inhibitors than standard nitrile. HNBR is more prone to extrusion than standard nitrile and, as a result, requires a more sophisticated mechanical backup system similar to that found on most permanent and higher-end retrievable packers.

Two fluoroelastomers that are commonly used in the oil and gas industry are hexafluoropropylene (vinylidene fluoride, commonly known by the trade name Viton[*] and tetrafluoroethylene (propylene, trade name Aflas[**]). These compounds are used in medium- to high-temperature applications. Both compounds show excellent resistance to H_2S exposure in varying limits, CO_2, brines, and bromides. However, the use of Viton should be questioned when amine inhibitors are present in packer fluids and in the case of high-pH completion fluids.

Aflas will swell when exposed to oil-based fluids and solvents. Swelling because of exposure of Aflas to hydrocarbons is generally only a concern when running the tool in the well. Element swell may cause the packer to become stuck on the trip in the hole, and swelling of the seals can result in seal damage during stab-in. After the packer is set and seals are in place, the swelling generally is no longer a concern.

The use of Kalrez[†] and Chemraz[‡] in the packer industry is by and large limited to chevron-type "vee" seals and o-rings. On the cost scale, they are by far some of the most expensive materials used in these designs. Kalrez and Chemraz show good resistance to most chemicals found in oilwell and gas-well environments. Because of their ability to maintain stability at extreme temperatures, they are normally recommended for use in HP/HT applications and in most environments in which high levels of H_2S are encountered.

Ethylene propylene (EPDM) is an elastomer commonly used in steam-injection operations. EPDM exhibits poor resistance to swelling when exposed to oil and solvents; however, EPDM can operate in pure steam environments to temperatures of 550°F.

---

* Viton is a registered trademark of Dupont Dow Elastomers.

** Aflas is a registered trademark of Ashai Glass Co. Ltd.

† Kalrez is a registered trademark of Dupont Dow Elastomers.

‡ Chemraz is a registered trademark of Green, Tweed and Co.

2.5.1 Packing Element. The term "packing element" is used to describe the elastomeric sealing system that creates the seal between the OD of the packer and the ID of the casing. The ability of the packing element to hold differential pressure is a function of the elastomer pressure, or stress across the seal. To form a seal, the elastomer pressure must be greater than the differential pressure across the packer. The elastomer pressure is generated by the packoff or setting force applied to the packer.

The packing-element system consists of the seal or packing element and a packing-element backup system. When energized, the packing element expands to conform to the ID of the casing wall. The packing-element backup system contains the energized packing element and restricts the element from extruding or losing its elastomer pressure.

There are many different packing-element-system designs. Each element-system design is suited to a specific application and covers a myriad of well environments. The most basic packing-element system consists of a single packing element with fixed metal backup rings located above and below the element. More sophisticated designs may consist of multidurometer elastomers using a lower durometer element between two elements of a higher durometer. In this design, the lower durometer, or softer-center element, creates the working seal while the higher durometer, or harder-end, elements expand to the casing ID to restrict extrusion. Fixed metal backup rings also may be replaced with flexible or expandable backup rings to further restrict the extrusion of the elastomer.

2.5.2 Packer-to-Tubing Seal Stacks. Permanent and retrievable sealbore packers contain a honed sealbore to accept packer-to-tubing seals or seal assembly to connect the tubing string to the packer. This seal assembly, or stinger, consists of a seal sub with multiple packing units or seal stacks fixed on its OD. The packing units come in a variety of configurations and elastomeric compounds to suit a wide range of downhole conditions. There are two basic types of packing units: bonded and chevron.

The bonded packing unit is composed of one or more metal rings, with a specific elastomer compound bonded or molded to the ring. The bonded seal by design is slightly larger than the ID of the sealbore, and a predetermined amount of stress on the elastomer is created when the seals are inserted into the honed packer bore. The elastomer pressure generated by this stress in turn creates a seal between the seal assembly and the honed packer bore.

Because the bonded seals are self-energized, they are particularly useful in LP/LT gas-injection operations such as CO_2 flood projects. The bonded seals are also less susceptible to dynamic unloading damage and should be selected any time that the seals must leave the honed bore under pressure.

Only a few elastomer compounds are suitable for use in bonded seal designs. The three most common compounds found on bonded seal stacks are Nitrile, Viton, and Aflas. Also, because the bonding tends to fail at higher temperatures, most bonded seals are generally not recommended for service above 300°F.

Chevron seal stacks come in a wide variety of designs and elastomeric compounds. They consist of a number of "vee"-shaped chevron seal rings supported by metal (or a combination of metal and nonelastomeric) backup rings such as Ryton[*] or Teflon.[**] Each individual chevron seal ring holds pressure in one direction only, so each seal stack must contain a number of seal rings facing in either direction.

The chevron seal stacks are the most versatile and widely used. They are available with various elastomers and designs. Common materials used for the vee-type seal rings include nitrile (the most common), Viton, Aflas, and Kalrez. Some specialized premium seal stacks can

---

[*] Ryton is a registered trademark of Chevron Phillips Chemical.

[**] Teflon is a registered trademark of E.I. DuPont Co.

handle pressures up to 15,000 psi (and beyond) at temperatures approaching 550°F. Each has its own environmental application, as well as temperature and pressure rating. Matching the proper elastomer to the environment is a key to long-term sealing success.

The chevron seal stacks do not lend themselves well to differential unloading conditions that might be experienced during fracturing or treating operations in which locator-type seal assemblies are used in sealbore packers. The temperature and piston effects will cause the tubing to shorten, and the seal assembly will move upward out of the packer bore. Any chevron seal that is allowed to leave the polished sealbore will be subject to severe damage because of the sudden change in differential pressure. Because of this, locator-type seal-assembly designs should be such that the working seals are never allowed to leave the polished packer bore under differential pressure.[7]

To reduce the possibility of seal failure and greatly extend the life of the seal assembly, it is recommended that seal movement be restricted whenever possible. While both chevron and bonded seals are designed to hold pressure under dynamic conditions, completion designs that allow continuous seal movement over the life of the well can significantly shorten the life of the seal. Seal movement should be eliminated altogether if possible by anchoring the seals in the packer bore. Locator seal assemblies should be landed so that the locator sub will be in constant compression when the well is producing, thus limiting movement to those cases in which the well is either treated or killed.

2.6 ISO and API Standards

The Intl. Organization for Standardization (ISO) and the American Petroleum Inst. (API) have created a standard [reference ISO 14310:2001(E) and API Specification 11D1][8,9] intended to establish guidelines for both manufacturers and end users in the selection, manufacture, design, and laboratory testing of the many types of packers available on today's market. Perhaps more importantly, the standards also establish a minimum set of parameters with which the manufacturer must comply to claim conformity. The International Standard is structured with the requirements for both quality control and design verification in tiered rankings. There are three grades, or levels, established for quality control and six grades (plus one special grade) for design verification.

The quality standards range from grade Q3 to Q1, with grade Q3 carrying the minimum requirements and Q1 outlining the highest level of inspection and manufacturing verification procedures. Provisions are also established to allow the end user to modify the quality plans to meet his specific application by including additional needs as "supplement requirements."

The six standard design-validation grades range from V6 to V1. V6 is the lowest grade, and V1 represents the highest level of testing. A special V0 grade was included to meet special acceptance criteria requirements. The following is a brief summary outlining the basic requirements of the various levels of test-acceptance criteria.

2.6.1 Grade V6 Supplier/Manufacturer Defined. This is the lowest grade established. The performance level in this instance is defined by the manufacturer for products that do not meet the testing criteria found in grades V0 through V5.

2.6.2 Grade V5 Liquid Test. In this grade, the packer must be set in the maximum ID casing it is rated for at the maximum recommended operating temperature. The testing parameters require that it be set with the minimum packoff force or pressure as specified by the manufacturer. The pressure test is performed with water or hydraulic oil to the maximum differential-pressure rating of the packer. Two pressure reversals across the tool are required, meaning it must be proved that the packer will hold pressure from both above and below. The hold periods for each test are required to be a minimum of 15 minutes long. At the end of the test, retrievable packers must be able to be removed from the test fixture by using the procedures of its intended design.

2.6.3 Grade V4 Liquid Test + Axial Loads. In this grade, all parameters covered in Grade V5 apply; however, in addition to passing V5 criteria, it also must be proved that the packer will hold differential pressure in combination with compression and tensile loads, as advertised in the manufacturer's performance envelope.

2.6.4 Grade V3 Liquid Test + Axial Loads + Temperature Cycling. All test criteria mandated in Grade V4 apply to V3; however, to achieve V3 certification, the packer also must pass a temperature cycle test. In the temperature cycle test, the packer must hold the maximum specified pressure at the upper and lower temperature limits in which the packer is designed to work. The test is started at maximum temperature, as in V4 and V5; however, after passing this segment of the test, the temperature is allowed to cool to the minimum, and another pressure test is applied. After successfully passing the low-temperature test, the packer also must pass a differential-pressure hold after the test-cell temperature is raised back to the maximum temperature.

2.6.5 Grade V2 Gas Test + Axial Loads. The same test parameters used in V4 apply to Grade V2, but in this instance, the test medium is replaced with air or nitrogen. A leak rate of 20 cm^3 of gas over the hold period is acceptable; however, the rate may not increase during the hold period.

2.6.6 Grade V1 Gas Test + Axial Loads + Temperature Cycling. The same test parameters used in V3 apply to Grade V1, but again in this instance, the test medium is replaced with air or nitrogen. Similar to the V2 test, a leak rate of 20 cm^3 of gas over the hold period is acceptable, and the rate may not increase during the hold period.

2.6.7 Special Grade V0 Gas Test + Axial Loads + Temperature Cycling + Bubble Tight Gas Seal. This is a special validation grade that is added to meet customer specifications in which a tight-gas seal is required. The test parameters are the same as those for V1; however, a gas-leak rate is not allowed during the hold period.

If a packer is qualified for use in a higher grade, it may be deemed suitable for use in any of the lower validation grades. For example, if tested to grade V4, it is accepted that the packer meets or exceeds the service requirements of V4, V5, and V6 applications.

2.7 Packer Rating Envelopes
Packers are not only designed and required to hold differential pressure at various downhole temperatures, but they also must be able to maintain pressure integrity when subjected to various tensile and compression loads created by hydraulic and temperature effects on the tubing string. The rating envelope is a graphical representation of the safe operating limits of the packer in combination with both differential pressure and axial loads.[10,11]

A packer may hold (for example) 10,000 psi differential from below with no axial loads, or it may hold 100,000 lbf tension at 0 psi, but when the forces are combined, the stresses on the components and the element system may become too great and cause the packer to fail. The combination of axial loading and differential pressure affects various packer models differently. Obviously, it is important to know what the various safe operating parameters of the packer are so that downhole failure can be avoided.

The envelope is a graph consisting of two axis lines. On the "X" axis, negative values represent tension, and positive values equal compression (**Fig. 2.13**). The values of the "Y" axis depict differential pressure from above the packer as negative and below the packer as

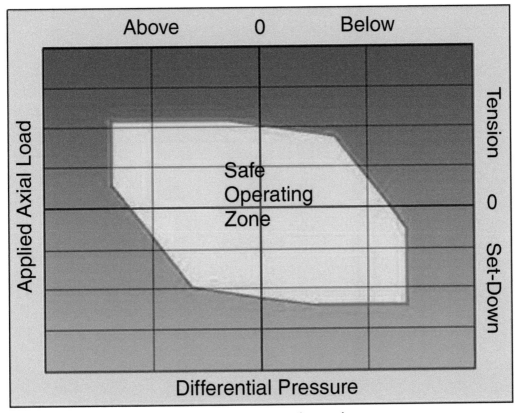

Fig. 2.13—Typical packer-rating envelope.

positive. The maximum tested packer ratings under the all-combined load conditions are plotted on the graph and connected by boundary lines that more or less take the shape of a box. Any combinations of pressure and axial loads that fall within the box are considered safe and within the tested limits of the packer.

To use the rating envelope effectively, tubing-movement calculations must be done to determine the packer tubing loads and differential pressures to be encountered in any of the production, shut-in, injection, or treating modes to which the completion will be subjected. These points are then plotted on the rating envelope to see if the applications fall within the safe operating limits of the packer. If they do not, an alternate packer must be selected, or the operation must be tailored to suit the limits of the packer.

2.8 Flow-Control Accessories
Flow-control accessories add to the flexibility of the cased-hole completion design and perform a multitude of tasks, from temporarily plugging off the tubing string to establishing temporary communication between the tubing and the annulus. Profile seating nipples and sliding sleeves have a special locking groove and a honed sealbore to allow a flow-control device to lock in the nipple and seal off when installed. By design, the sleeves and nipples will have a smaller ID than that of the tubing string. For this reason, careful consideration must be given to the overall application and completion design when selecting and sizing the various models of profile seating nipples and sleeves. This is especially true in any case in which through-tubing operations or perforating are planned.

Fig. 2.14—Wireline re-entry guide.

Correct application of flow-control accessories can greatly reduce the time and money spent on diagnosing well problems (such as tubing or leaks) should they occur. Strategically placed profile seating nipples above and below the packer aid in isolating the leak to the packer or the tubing string. Once the source of the failure is known, a plan can be formulated to resolve the problem. Not much can be done to fix a packer leak without well intervention; however, special flow-control devices are available to straddle across sections of leaking tubing and deter workovers. In either case, the knowledge gained by being able to use flow-control accessories and devices to perform downhole diagnostics is extremely valuable in planning corrective action to be addressed in the subsequent workover.

2.8.1 Wireline Re-Entry Guides. In some operations, it is necessary to run electric wireline, slickline tools, or coiled-tubing assemblies past the end of the tubing string and into the casing below (**Fig. 2.14**). Upon retrieving these tools, there may be problems pulling them back into the tubing string if the tubing is run open-ended and unprotected. Sharp edges and square shoulders of pin threads, couplings, or muleshoes can cause the tools to snag or hang up on re-entry. The wireline re-entry guide is run on the end of the tubing string (or the tailpipe below the packer) and is designed to facilitate re-entry into the tubing string of those electric-line or slickline assemblies. It has an internally beveled, bell-shaped ID that eliminates any sharp edges or square shoulders and helps align the tools as they are pulled back up into the tubing string.

2.8.2 Profile Seating Nipples. Profile seating nipples are often referred to as "top no-go," "bottom no-go," and "selective" types. As the names indicate, each has a unique machined profile with a locking groove to accept a flow-control device that is run and installed on slickline or coiled tubing. The profile seating nipple also has a honed and polished sealbore to allow the slickline device to not only land and lock into the nipple, but also to seal off, assuming the accessory item to be installed also has a packing stack.

Profile seating nipples are positioned at strategic locations within the tubing string to allow the accurate placement of slickline plugs, check valves, bottomhole chokes, downhole flow regulators, and bottomhole pressure recorders. At least one profile seating nipple is recommended near the bottom.

Top No-Go Profile Seating Nipple. The "top no-go" nipple accepts a lock assembly with a no-go shoulder located on the lock itself (**Fig. 2.15**). When the lock assembly is run in the hole, the no-go shoulder on the lock engages or locates on top of the nipple. Once located, the locks are engaged into the locking groove, and the installation process is complete. Care must be taken when designing the completion to ensure that there are no ID restrictions above the nipple to prevent passage of the lock assembly. The "top no-go" nipple is generally run when a single nipple is required in the hole and the largest ID possible is required through the nipple profile. However, more than one "top no-go" may be run if the IDs of the profiles are reduced sufficiently as the nipples progress in the hole to allow passage of the appropriate locking assembly through the nipple located immediately above the intended target nipple.

Bottom No-Go Profile Seating Nipple. The "bottom no-go" nipple has a no-go shoulder located in the bottom of the nipple (**Fig 2.16**). The lock assembly or slickline device landed in this type of nipple locates the nipple by landing on the bottom no-go. Once landed and located in the nipple, the locks can be engaged and the installation completed. Because its ID will not allow passage of any flow-control device through the nipple, the bottom no-go nipple is always run as the lowermost nipple in the completion. Another benefit of having a no-go nipple in the completion is that any other slickline tools or tubing swabs that are lost in the tubing string should not fall to the bottom. The lost equipment usually can be fished out of the tubing string or, in cases when it cannot, the tubing can be pulled to recover the tools.

Selective Profile Seating Nipple. "Selective" type profile nipples are perhaps the most versatile of the three (**Fig 2.17**). In such a design, an unlimited number of the same size and type profile seating nipples may be run in the hole because the locking assembly or flow-control device is able to find and selectively land in any of them. In most systems, either the packing stack or a collett indicator is used to help the slickline operator locate the nipple, and alternately picking up and slacking off through the nipple actuates the locks and sets the flow-control device. The benefit of this type system is a larger ID through the completion and fewer slickline accessory items that must be inventoried. Generally, it is still advised that a no-go nipple be run on the bottom of the tubing string to prevent any lost tools from falling into the cased hole below the completion.

2.8.3 Sliding Sleeves. In oil- and gas-well completions, the sliding sleeve provides a means of establishing communication between the tubing and annulus for fluid circulation, selective zone production, or injection purposes (**Fig 2.18**). The sliding sleeve is ported from ID to OD and has an internal closing sleeve that can be cycled multiple times using slickline or coiled-tubing shifting tools. When in the open position, the sleeve allows communication from tubing to annulus, and when closed, pressures are once again isolated.

The sliding sleeve also incorporates a nipple profile and polished sealbore above and below the ports to allow the landing of various flow-control devices or an isolation tool should the sleeve fail to close. The isolation tool locks into the profile in the upper end of the sleeve, and seal stacks on the tool straddle the ports to achieve isolation. The success of sliding sleeves depends on well conditions. High temperature, sour gas, scale, and sand may cause operational problems in the opening and closing of sliding sleeves.

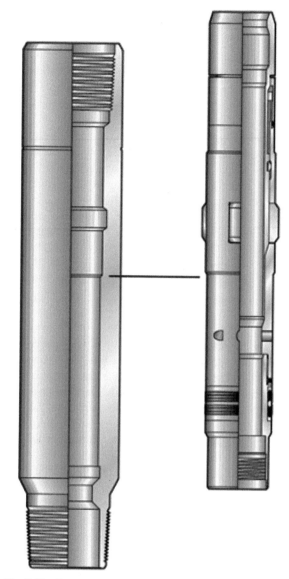

Fig. 2.15—Top no-go profile nipple and lock assembly.

2.8.4 Blast Joints. The blast joint is used in multiple-zone wells in which the tubing extends past a producing zone to deter the erosional velocity of the produced fluids and formation sand from cutting through the tubing string. In most cases, the blast joint is simply a thick, heavy wall joint of steel pipe; however, there are also more sophisticated designs that use materials such as Carbide® for severe service applications. Care must be taken when running and spacing out the tubing string to position the blast joint evenly across the open perforations. It is wise to run enough length of blast joint to provide 5 to 10 ft of overlap across the perforations to allow for errors in tubing measurements.

2.8.5 Flow Couplings. Flow couplings are usually the same OD as the tubing couplings and have the same ID as the tubing string with which they are run. They are run above and below

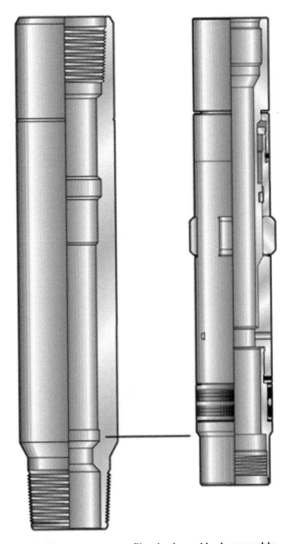

Fig. 2.16—Bottom no-go profile nipple and lock assembly.

any profile seating nipple and sliding sleeve in which it is anticipated that the turbulence created by the flow through the nipple restriction can reach erosional velocity and damage the tubing string. The flow coupling does not stop the erosion; however, because of its thick cross section, it can and will extend the life of the completion because more material must be lost to erosion before failure occurs than in the case of the tubing string alone. Flow couplings are recommended when a flow-control device is to be installed on a permanent basis (i.e., safety valve or bottomhole choke).

2.8.6 Blanking Plugs. Blanking plugs may be landed in profile seating nipples or sliding sleeves to temporarily plug the tubing string, allowing pressure to be applied to the tubing string to test tubing or set a hydraulic packer, or to isolate and shut off the flow from the formation. The basic blanking plug consists of a lock subassembly, a packing stack, and a plug bottom. Each size and type of blanking plug is designed to fit a specific size and type of profile seating nipple or sleeve. Slickline blanking plugs always have an equalizing device

Fig. 2.17—Selective profile nipple.

incorporated into the design to allow pressure above and below the plug to equalize before releasing the lock from the nipple to prevent the toolstring from being blown up the hole.

2.8.7 Bottomhole Choke. Bottomhole chokes are flow-control devices that are landed in profile seating nipples. The bottomhole choke restricts flow in the tubing string and allows control of production from different zones. It can be used to prevent freezing of surface controls. The choke assembly consists of a set of locks, packing mandrel, packing assembly, and choke bean. The choke bean is available with orifices of varying sizes. The orifice size must be predetermined and sized specifically for the intended application.

2.9 Subsurface Safety Systems
If a catastrophic failure of the wellhead should occur, the subsurface safety valve provides a means to automatically shut off the flow of the well to avoid disaster. There are basically two types of downhole safety valves—subsurface-controlled safety valves and surface-controlled subsurface safety valves (SCSSV).[12]

Fig. 2.18—Sliding sleeve (shown in closed position).

2.9.1 Subsurface-Controlled Safety Valves. The subsurface-controlled safety valves (often called velocity valves or Storm® chokes) are wireline retrievable and are installed in standard profile seating nipples in the tubing string below the surface tubing hanger (**Fig 2.19**). A subsurface safety valve requires a change in the operating conditions at the valve to activate the closure mechanism. There are two models of subsurface controlled safety valves. The velocity valve contains an internal orifice; the orifice is specifically sized to the flow characteristics of the well. The valve is normally open and is closed by an increase in flow rate across the orifice. This creates a pressure drop, or differential pressure, across the valve that causes it to close. The velocity valve reopens when the pressure is equalized across the valve.

Another type of subsurface-controlled valve is the gas-charged or low-pressure valve. This valve is normally closed, and the bottomhole pressure must be higher than the preset pressure

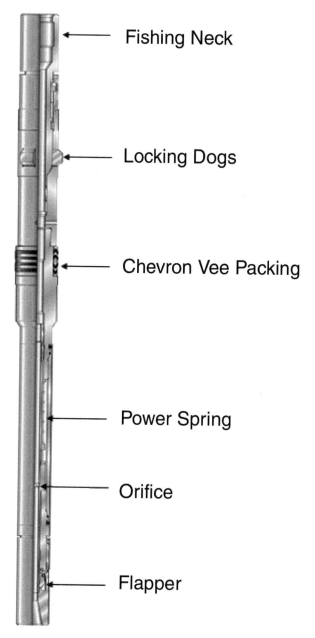

Fishing Neck

Locking Dogs

Chevron Vee Packing

Power Spring

Orifice

Flapper

Fig. 2.19—Subsurface-controlled safety valve—velocity type.

valve for the valve to remain open. If the flow rate of the well becomes too great and the bottomhole pressure falls below the preset value of the valve, the valve will automatically close. It is reopened by applying pressure to the tubing string to raise the pressure above the preset pressure value of the valve.

For either valve to work properly, the well must be capable of flowing at sufficient rates to close the valve, and the catastrophe must be severe enough to create the conditions necessary to actuate the closing system. The settings of the valves are critical to success, and they must be checked periodically.

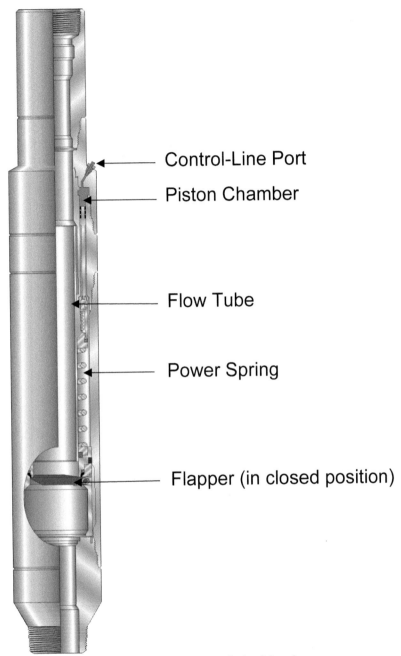

Control-Line Port

Piston Chamber

Flow Tube

Power Spring

Flapper (in closed position)

Fig. 2.20—Surface-controlled safety valve.

2.9.2 SCSSVs. The SCSSVs are also installed in the tubing string below the surface tubing hanger; however, they are controlled by hydraulic pressure through a capillary (control) line that connects to a surface control panel (**Fig 2.20**). Most SCSSV designs today use a flapper to form a seal. Both elastomeric and metal-to-metal seal designs are available.

The SCSSV is a normally closed (failsafe) valve and requires continuous hydraulic pressure on the control line to keep it open. The pressure acts upon an internal piston in the valve, which pushes against a spring. When the hydraulic pressure is relieved, the internal spring moves a flow tube upward and uncovers the flapper. The flapper then swings closed, shutting the well in. Ball valves work similarly. The surface control panel, because of a change in flowing characteristics that exceed predetermined operating limits, generally initiates the closing sequence. However, any failure of the system that results in loss of control-line pressure should result in the valve shutting in the well.

To open the SCSSV, the pressure above it must be equalized (usually by pressuring up on the tubing string), and hydraulic pressure must be reapplied to the control line. Some models have a self-equalizing feature and can be reopened without the aid of pressuring up on the tubing. Whether the valve is working or not, most models have a pump-through kill feature that allow fluids to be pumped down the tubing to regain control of the well.

The SCSSV is available in a tubing-retrievable model and a wireline-retrievable type. The wireline-retrievable SCSSV is installed in a special ported safety-valve nipple. The capillary line is connected from the surface control panel to the ported nipple. The hydraulic pressure applied at the surface communicates to the valve through the ported nipple. The wireline-retrievable SCSSV can be pulled and serviced without pulling the tubing string out of the hole. However, because of the design and the use of elastomeric seals, they are somewhat less reliable than the tubing-retrievable version. Because of its smaller ID, the wireline-retrievable valve has a reduced flow area for production to pass through. The reduction in ID can create a pressure drop across the valve and turbulence in the tubing above it. In high-flow-rate wells, the turbulence can lead to erosion of the valve or tubing string. Access to the tubing string below the valve is restricted when the wireline-retrievable SCSSV is installed. The valve must be removed before performing any through-tubing workover or wireline operations below the valve.

The tubing-retrievable model is more robust and offers a larger internal flow diameter. This helps eliminate turbulence and increases production capabilities. It also allows full-bore access to the tubing string below the valve. One disadvantage, in some instances, is its large OD. This may limit the size of tubing that can be run into certain sizes of casing. To service the tubing-retrievable SCSSV, the tubing string must be retrieved. However, to avoid this and extend the life of the completion, it is possible to disable the valve permanently by locking it open. A new wireline-retrievable SCSSV can then be inserted into the sealbore of the retrievable valve, enabling the well to continue production without interruption.

2.10 Cased-Hole Applications
Matching the correct equipment to the application is critical to the success of the completion. The equipment must meet or exceed the temperature, pressure, and axial-load conditions created by the various operating modes anticipated over the life of the well, and material selection should match the well environment. Most of all, the completion design should be fit for purpose and meet the production objectives in an efficient and cost-effective manner.[13]

2.10.1 Single-String LP/LT Wells. Single-string low-pressure (less than 3,000 psi) flowing or injection wells completed at relatively shallow depths (less than 3,000 ft) generally use a retrievable tension packer (**Fig 2.21**). This is largely out of necessity because the tubing weight is not sufficient to energize the element of a compression set packer, but it is also driven by the economics of the lower cost and simplistic design of the tension set packer. Another consideration in injection applications is that the tubing will contract as cold fluid or gases are pumped into the tubing. This contraction can remove any available set-down weight on a packer that requires constant compressive loads to maintain its packoff and cause the packer to fail.

A wireline entry guide below the packer but above the perforations should be used to facilitate any through-tubing operations that are planned. It is advisable, but not mandatory, to run a profile seating nipple either above or below the packer. The addition of the seating nipple

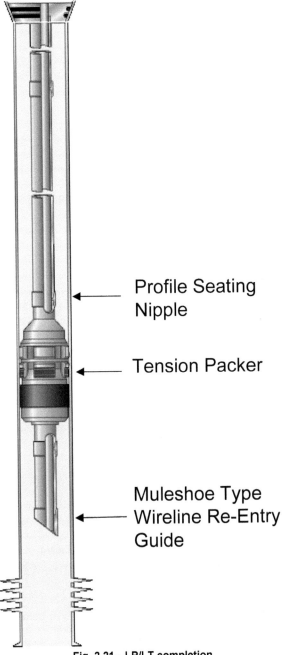

Profile Seating
Nipple

Tension Packer

Muleshoe Type
Wireline Re-Entry
Guide

Fig. 2.21—LP/LT completion.

allows a blanking plug to be run to test tubing if a leak occurs, and the nipple will act as a stop should tools be lost in the hole.

2.10.2 Single-String Medium-Pressure/Medium-Temperature Wells. In median pressure and temperature applications, a retrievable compression/tension set versatile landing-condition packer may be used. In these applications, pressures typically will range from 3,000 to 10,000 psi, and bottomhole temperatures (BHTs) may be anywhere between 100 and 300°F (**Fig 2.22**).

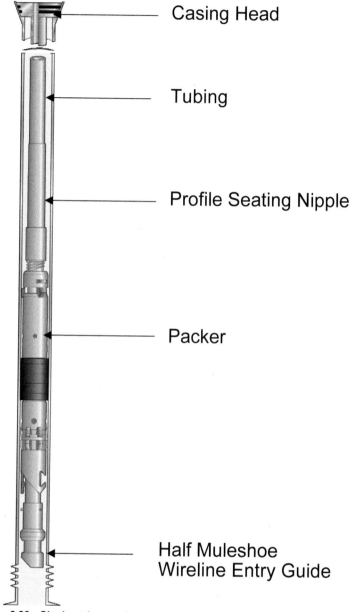

Casing Head

Tubing

Profile Seating Nipple

Packer

Half Muleshoe
Wireline Entry Guide

Fig. 2.22—Single-string medium-pressure/medium-temperature completion.

These types of tools are generally suited for the higher pressures and temperatures that will be encountered because of the more sophisticated packing-element systems they have. Also, in deeper installations, the addition of a bypass system aids in equalizing the tubing and annular fluids to facilitate retrieval of the packer. In these applications, the longer tubing length presents a different challenge from that in the shallow applications, in which a tension packer would have been used. In flowing wells, the tubing will heat up and elongate and add weight to the packer if landed with compression on the packer, or it will lose tension if landed in tension. In injection wells, the opposite will be true. Careful consideration should be given to these conditions and to future planned pumping or stimulation operations and their effects on tubing movement when making a packer selection.

As for most wells equipped with packers, a wireline entry guide on the bottom of the packer will aid in guiding electric-line and coiled-tubing tools back into the tubing string when performing through-tubing operations. A profile seating nipple is run below the packer to facilitate the running of bottomhole-pressure recorders or to allow a blanking plug to be installed for temporary well control. A second profile seating nipple may be run above the packer to test and verify tubing integrity or to land a bottomhole choke. The addition of a sliding sleeve or gas-lift mandrel with a dummy to the tubing string allows the tubing to be displaced with lighter fluid to bring the well in or circulate kill-weight fluid into the tubing string during subsequent workover operations while the wellhead is flanged up.

2.10.3 Single-String HP/HT Wells. In HP/HT applications, where the pressure can exceed 10,000 psi and temperatures are above 300°F, a permanent sealbore packer is generally used (**Fig. 2.23**). However, there are some specialized retrievable packers that can work in these applications under limited conditions.

The permanent sealbore packers are very versatile and are designed to accommodate the extreme tubing movement and high axial packer-to-tubing forces encountered in HP/HT completions. Tubing-movement calculations should be performed to determine the length changes and stresses on the tubing string in the production, shut-in and treating, or injection modes. Depending on the length changes and stress created on the tubing, a permanent packer with a located (floating) or fixed (anchored) seal assembly may be required.

As before, a wireline-entry guide on the bottom of the packer will aid in guiding electric-line and coiled-tubing tools back into the tubing string when performing through-tubing operations. One, and in some instances two, profile seating nipples are run in the tailpipe below the sealbore packer for landing bottomhole-pressure recorders and facilitating well control during completion and workover operations. The seal assembly may be anchored into the packer or a locator type with additional seal length to accommodate tubing movement. A profile seating nipple is run above the seal assembly for tubing-test purposes or for landing a bottomhole choke.

2.10.4 Multiple-Zone Single-String Selective Completion. Multizone single-string completions with median temperatures and differential pressures will likely use hydraulic-set single-string retrievable packers (**Fig 2.24**). This style of completion allows all the available zones in the well to be completed at once and produced individually or commingled. Sliding sleeves are positioned between each isolation packer. There is no limit to the number of packers and sliding sleeves that may be run; however, each addition should be justified. When one zone depletes, the workover is accomplished with slickline by landing a blanking plug in the lowermost profile nipple or opening and closing one or more of the sliding sleeves. It should be noted that complex completion designs with multiple packers and accessories cost more and often increase major workover costs significantly. The designer should have a feasible plan for pulling the well's tubing string(s).

The hydraulic-set retrievable packers can be run in on one trip and set simultaneously by applying pressure to the tubing against a plug set below the lowermost packer. After setting the packers, the plug may be retrieved and the lowermost zone may be produced or, alternately, one of the sliding sleeves may be opened to produce one of the corresponding upper zones.

A profile seating nipple is run below the lowermost packer to accept a blanking plug (or check valve) to set the hydraulic-set packers and to provide well control for the lower zone. Sliding sleeves are positioned between each packer for zonal isolation. Blast joints should be positioned across the perforations between the isolation packers to reduce the risk of erosion damage to the tubing string from well fluids and produced sand. A sliding sleeve or gas-lift mandrel with dummy may be positioned above the uppermost hydraulic-set packer to aid in circulating kill fluid in the hole or circulating lighter fluid or gas in the tubing to bring the well on production.

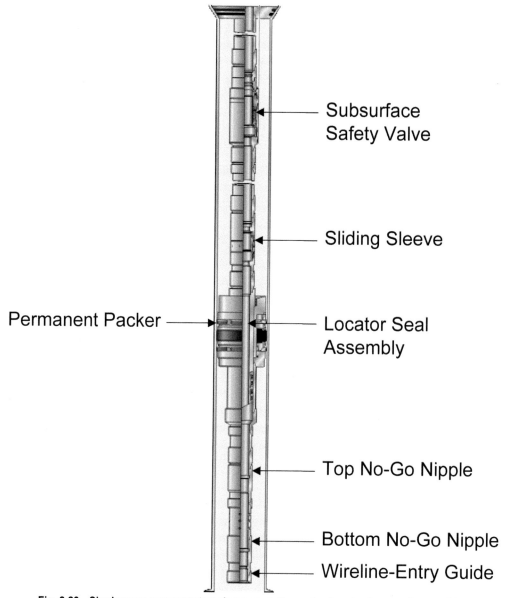

Fig. 2.23—Single-zone permanent packer completion using locator type seal assembly.

2.10.5 Dual-Zone Completion Using Parallel Tubing Strings. The dual-zone completion method generally is used in applications in which it is desirable to produce two zones simultaneously while keeping them isolated from each other (**Fig 2.25**). In this completion, two strings of tubing are run from the surface to the dual packer. One string terminates at the dual packer, and the other string of tubing extends from the dual packer to the lower single-string packer. The tubing string that produces the upper zone is referred to as the "short string" (or upper tubing), and the tubing string that produces the lower zone is called the "long string" (or lower tubing).

In cases in which the zones are of equal pressure and crossflow is not an issue during the completion stage, a single-string hydraulic-set packer may be used as the lower packer. This

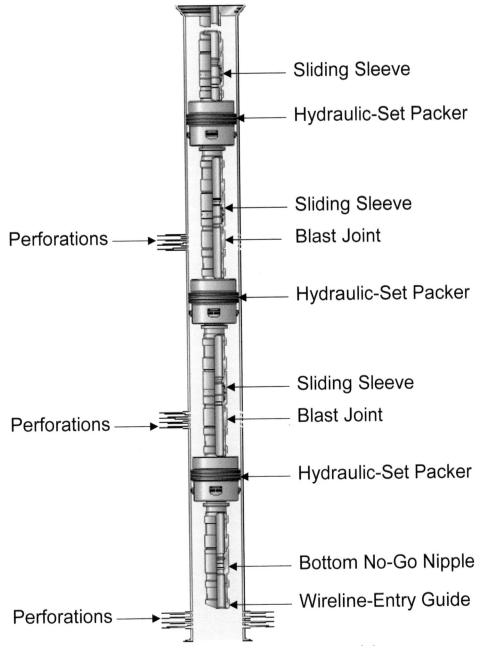

Fig. 2.24—Multiple-zone single-string selective completion.

allows the entire completion to be run in a single trip and both packers to be set after the wellhead is flanged up.

In parallel string completions in which the zones are subject to crossflow because of unequal pressures, the lowermost single-string packer is generally a sealbore packer. The sealbore packer is set with a temporary plug in place for well control before perforating and running the upper completion. The plug keeps the two zones separated until the upper completion is installed and the wellhead is flanged up.

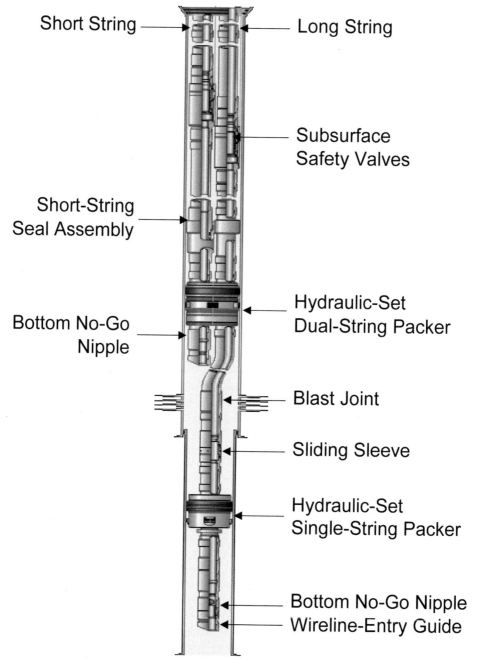

Short String —— Long String

—— Subsurface
Safety Valves

Short-String
Seal Assembly

Hydraulic-Set
Dual-String Packer

Bottom No-Go
Nipple

—— Blast Joint

—— Sliding Sleeve

Hydraulic-Set
Single-String Packer

Bottom No-Go Nipple
Wireline-Entry Guide

Fig. 2.25—Parallel-string dual-zone completion.

The upper packer in this example is a hydraulic-set dual-string retrievable packer. Models exist that can be set by applying pressure to the long string, but the more common models require the short string to be pressurized to accomplish packer setting. The decision about which type depends on the various operations that are planned.

A profile seating nipple is run below the lowermost packer and below the dual packer on the short string to accept a blanking plug (or check valve) to set the packer and to provide well control. A sliding sleeve is positioned between the packers for aid in circulating kill-weight fluid in the hole or circulating lighter fluid or gas in the tubing strings to bring the well on production. A blast joint should be positioned across the perforations of the zone between the packers to reduce the risk of erosion damage to the long string from well fluids and produced sand. Profile seating nipples should be run above the dual packer on both strings for well control or testing tubing for well-diagnostic purposes.

2.10.6 Big-Bore/Monobore Completions. In highly prolific reservoirs, tubing of 6⅝ in. and larger diameters is required to meet cost-effective production and injection objectives. The use of big monobore-completion techniques can increase production rates significantly while decreasing both capital and operating expenses. The advantages of the big monobore completion systems include the elimination of gas-turbulence areas and restrictions on production while providing access for well-intervention purposes. This can translate to fewer wells required for optimized reservoir production, resulting in a faster return on initial investments and lower long-term operating expense.[14]

Big monobore completions are basically liner-top completion systems. The key is the large ID tubing that allows increased production rates and provides full-bore access to the production liner. This full-bore access gives the operator the ability to run conventional tools through the tubing to perform remedial work in the production liner without disturbing the completion or pulling the production tubing. There are many styles of monobore completions from which to choose. The selection of the type system that is used depends largely on the pressure integrity, and the pressure capability, of the liner top and intermediate casing string.

In the most basic monobore-completion design (**Fig 2.26**), the production liner is run and cemented in the hole. At the top of the liner hanger is a polished bore receptacle (PBR) to accept a seal assembly. The production tubing that is used has basically the same ID as the liner. When the completion is run, a seal assembly is run on the bottom of the production tubing and landed in the PBR. The seal assembly and liner top provide the annular barrier for the tubing string. The constraints of this system are that the ID of the polished bore receptacle can become damaged during liner cleanout trips and fail to seal, and the ability of the liner top to hold pressure is totally dependent on the quality of the cement job. Remedial work to the liner may be required before running the completion.

A more reliable monobore system (**Fig 2.27**) will use a packer above the liner top. In this system, the liner is run and cemented as before; however, when the completion is run, a large-bore hydraulic-set permanent packer is installed. The packer will have a PBR located above it, with the tubing seals run in place. There is also a seal assembly on the tailpipe below the packer, which is stabbed into the liner top. The packer provides a more positive annular barrier, and a new PBR has been installed.

2.11 Multilateral Completions

Multilateral completion systems allow the drilling and completion of multiple wells within a single wellbore. In addition to the main wellbore, there are one or more lateral wells extending from the main wellbore. This allows for alternative well-construction strategies for vertical, inclined, horizontal, and extended-reach wells. Multilaterals can be constructed in both new and existing oil and gas wells. A typical installation includes two laterals; the number of laterals would be determined by the number of targets, depths/pressures, risk analysis, and well-construction parameters.

Multilateral systems combine the advantages of horizontal-drilling techniques with the ability to achieve multiple target zones. The advantages of horizontal drilling include higher production indices, the possibility of draining relatively thin formation layers, decreased water and gas coning, increased exposure to natural fracture systems in the formation, and better sweep efficiencies. Depending on the type of multilateral design used, the target zones can be

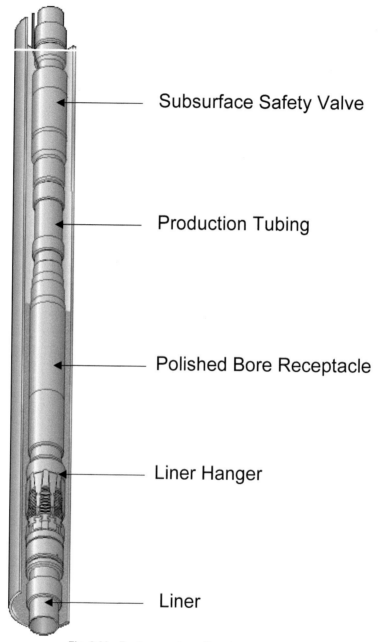

Subsurface Safety Valve

Production Tubing

Polished Bore Receptacle

Liner Hanger

Liner

Fig. 2.26—Basic monobore liner-top completion.

isolated and produced independently—or produced simultaneously, if commingled production is allowed or if a parallel string completion is used.

The various degrees of multilateral systems have been categorized by the Technology Advancement of MultiLaterals (TAML), a group of operators and suppliers with experience in developing multilateral technology. The TAML system for multilateral-well classification is based on the amount and type (or absence) of support provided at the lateral junction. There are six industry levels defined by TAML; this categorization system makes it easier for opera-

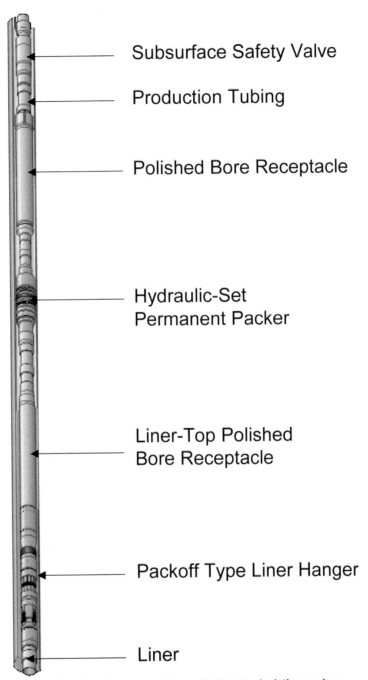

Subsurface Safety Valve

Production Tubing

Polished Bore Receptacle

Hydraulic-Set
Permanent Packer

Liner-Top Polished
Bore Receptacle

Packoff Type Liner Hanger

Liner

Fig. 2.27—Monobore completion with liner-top isolation packers.

tors to recognize and compare the functionality and risk-to-reward evaluations of one multilateral completion design to another. As the TAML level increases, so does the complexity and cost of the system.[15]

2.11.1 TAML Level 1. The most fundamental multilateral system consists of an openhole main bore with multiple drainage legs (or laterals) exiting from it (**Fig 2.28**). The junction in

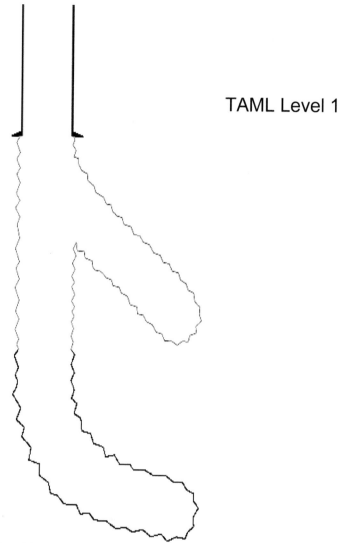

Fig. 2.28—TAML Level 1: openhole main bore and lateral; unsupported slotted liner or screen may be set in lateral or main bore.

this design is left with no mechanical support or hydraulic isolation. The integrity of the junction is dependent on natural borehole stability; however, it is possible to land a slotted liner in the lateral or the main bore to help keep the hole open during production. The production from a Level 1 system must be commingled, and zonal isolation or selective control of production is not possible. Re-entry into either the main bore or the lateral may be difficult or impossible should well intervention be required in the future.

2.11.2 TAML Level 2. This system is similar to Level 1, with the exception that the laterals are drilled off of a cased and cemented main bore (**Fig 2.29**). The cased main bore minimizes the chances of borehole collapse and provides a means of hydraulic isolation between zones. As with Level 1, there is no actual mechanical support of the lateral junction; however, it is possible to run a slotted liner into the lateral to maintain borehole stability.

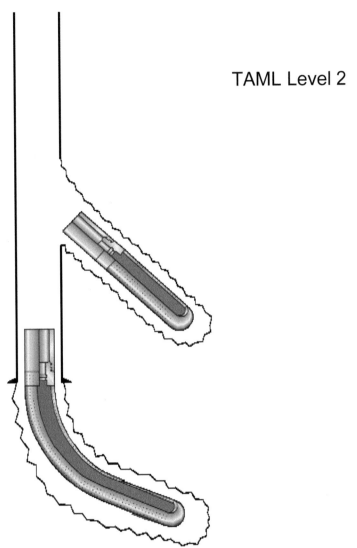

TAML Level 2

Fig. 2.29—TAML Level 2: cased and cemented main bore with an openhole lateral; an unsupported slotted liner or screen may be installed in the lateral.

2.11.3 TAML Level 3. The Level 3 system again uses a cased and cemented main bore with an openhole lateral (**Fig 2.30**). However, in this design, a slotted liner or screen is set in the lateral and anchored back into the main bore. This system offers mechanical support of the lateral junction, but the advantage of hydraulic isolation is lost, and the zones must be commingled to be produced. The production from the zone below the junction must flow through the whipstock assembly and past the slotted liner to reach the main bore. This system provides easy access into the lateral for coiled-tubing assemblies, but re-entry into the main bore below the junction is not possible.

2.11.4 TAML Level 4. This system offers both a cased and a cemented main bore and lateral (**Fig 2.31**). This gives the lateral excellent mechanical support, but the cement itself does not offer pressure integrity at the junction. While the cement does protect the junction from sand

TAML Level 3

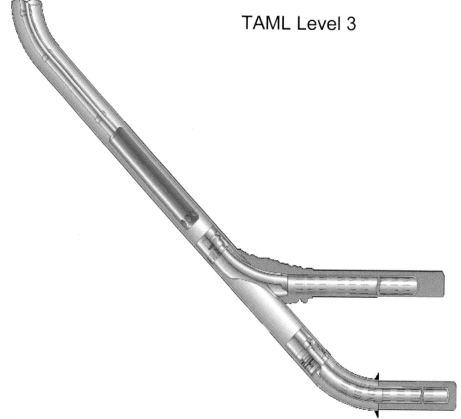

Fig. 2.30—TAML Level 3: cased and cemented main bore with an openhole lateral; slotted liner or screen is set in the lateral and anchored in the main bore, offering mechanical support of the junction.

infiltration and potential collapse, it is not capable of withstanding more than a few hundred psi of differential. There is a potential for failure if the junction is subjected to a pressure draw-down, as might be experienced in an electrical submersible pump (ESP) application. Zonal isolation and selectivity is possible by installing packers above and below the junction in the main bore. Systems are available that also offer coiled-tubing intervention, both into the lateral and into the main bore below the junction.

2.11.5 TAML Level 5. The Level 5 multilateral is similar in construction to the Level 4 in that it has both a cased and a cemented main bore and lateral, which offers the same level of mechanical integrity (**Fig 2.32**). The difference is that pressure integrity has now been achieved by using tubing strings and packers to isolate the junction. Single-string packers are placed in both the main bore and lateral below the junction and connected by tubing strings to a dual-string isolation packer located above the junction in the main bore. This system offers full access to both the main bore and the lateral. The zones can be produced independent of one another, or the completion can be designed to allow them to be commingled.

2.11.6 TAML Level 6. In the Level 6 multilateral system, both mechanical and pressure in-tegrity are achieved by using the casing to seal the junction (**Fig 2.33**). Cementing the junction, as was done in the Level 4 system, is not acceptable. The Level 6 system uses a premanufactured junction. In one type of system, the junction is reformed downhole. In yet

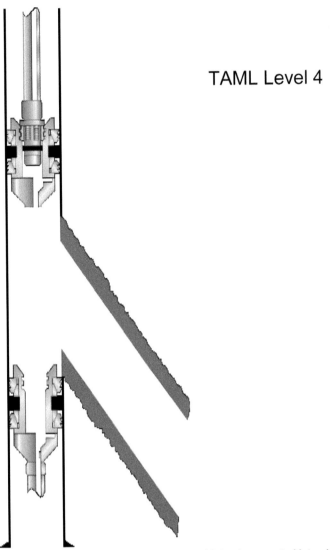

Fig. 2.31—TAML Level 4: cased and cemented main bore and lateral; cemented lateral provides mechanical support, but the cement does not provide pressure integrity for the junction.

another, two separate wells are drilled out of a single main bore, and the premanufactured junction is assembled downhole.

2.12 Operational Well Modes

There are four modes of operation that any given well might experience: shut-in; producing (liquid, gas, or a combination); injecting (hot or cold liquids, or gases); or treating (high, low, or intermediate pressures and volumes). It is important that all planned operations be considered when designing the completion and selecting a packer. While the primary application may be oil or gas production, any subsequent operations (such as acidizing or fracturing the well) and their associated pressure and temperature changes are extremely important to packer utilization success.[16,17]

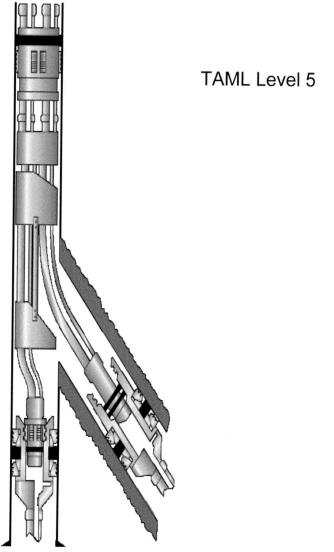

TAML Level 5

Fig. 2.32—TAML Level 5: cased and cemented main bore and lateral; pressure integrity across the junction is achieved through use of tubing and isolation packers.

Typical temperature vs. depth profiles are illustrated in **Figs 2.34 through 2.37**. These profiles are similar to those measures in wells operating in the shut-in, producing, injecting, or treating modes.

Fig. 2.34 depicts a typical geothermal gradient, with the temperature increasing with depth to that of the BHT. Every time a well is shut in, the operating temperature will begin to move toward the shape of the natural geothermal profile.

Producing-well-temperature profiles for both oil and gas wells are shown in Fig. 2.35. The wellhead temperature of an oil well will be somewhat less than the BHT. The amount of cooling as crude flows to the surface will depend on several factors: the relative amounts of oil and water, the specific heats of oil and water, the flow rate, the gas/liquid ratio, the vertical-flow pressure drop that controls the gas liberated and the attendant cooling effect, and the thermal heat transfer rate from the wellbore.

TAML Level 6

Fig. 2.33—TAML Level 6: mechanical and pressure integrity at the junction is achieved by using casing to seal the junction.

The temperature profile of a gas well may have a wellhead temperature lower than ambient. In any case, the wellhead temperature of a gas well will depend on the BHT, the flow rate, the pressure drop in the tubing, the specific heat of the gas, and other factors.

Injection-temperature profiles can be quite varied (Fig 2.36). The profile will depend on such factors as the nature of the injection fluid (liquid or gas), the rate of injection, and the injected-fluid temperature (cold or hot liquids or gas, or even steam). Initial temperatures of injected fluids are also subject to seasonal changes. These changes can become more severe depending on the local geography and climate in which the operation is being performed. Injected liquids will tend to have little heat gain or loss as they are pumped down the tubing string, while injected gases will tend to pick up or lose heat to approach the BHT.

While treating is simply a special case of the injection mode and is temporary in nature, it is considered important enough to be discussed separately. As with the liquid-injection profile

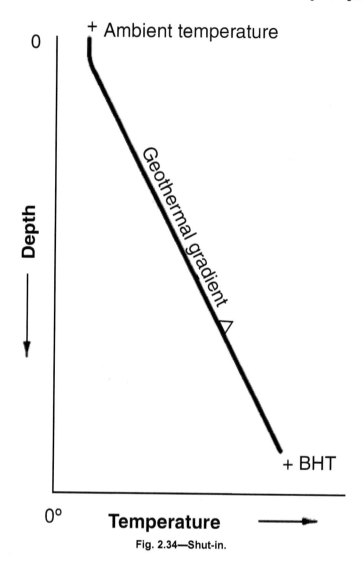

Fig. 2.34—Shut-in.

[for rates above 1 barrel per minute (BPM)], the treating liquid will not pick up any appreciable amount of heat as it moves down the tubing, and the treating temperature is essentially vertical (Fig 2.37).

As illustrated in some examples later, the important thing about these profiles is not their shape but how much the shape and temperature change from one operation mode to another, and how those temperature changes affect the tubing and packer system. It is strongly recommended that anticipated temperature profiles for each operational mode be drawn accurately when planning the various steps of any completion or major workover.

Figs. 2.38 through 2.41 show the pressure profiles of the four modes of well operation. Fig. 2.38 illustrates a typical shut-in well with well-servicing fluid in the wellbore. The slope of the profile and the height to which the fluid level rises on the depth scale (and in the wellbore) will depend on the average reservoir pressure, p_R, and the gradient of the well-servicing fluid. Fig. 2.39 shows the profiles of typical producing oil and gas wells. A liquid-injection profile (Fig. 2.40) is similar to the shut-in profile, the difference being that the bottomhole

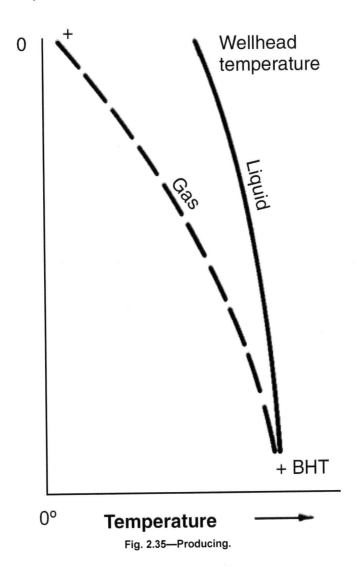

Fig. 2.35—Producing.

injection pressure, $(p_i)_{bh}$, is greater than the average reservoir pressure, p_R. The wellhead pressure, p_{wh}, can have any value, from a vacuum to several thousand psi. The gas-injection profile may have a reverse slope on it, or it may have a normal but steep slope, depending on the rate, tubing size, and bottomhole injection pressure.

The treating pressure (Fig. 2.41) is a special temporary case of the injection profile. The bottomhole treating pressure, $(p_t)_{bh}$, often will be greater than the injection pressure, especially in a fracturing job. The surface pressure will be constrained by the burst strength of the tubing and casing and the safety considerations. The slope of the pressure profile will depend on the tubing size, the treating rates, and the treating pressure downhole, $(p_t)_{bh}$.

It is recommended that pressure profiles for each operational mode be drawn for each step of the completion or major workover. As the examples will point out, the importance of pressure changes from one well mode to another and their effects on the tubing and packer system cannot be overemphasized.

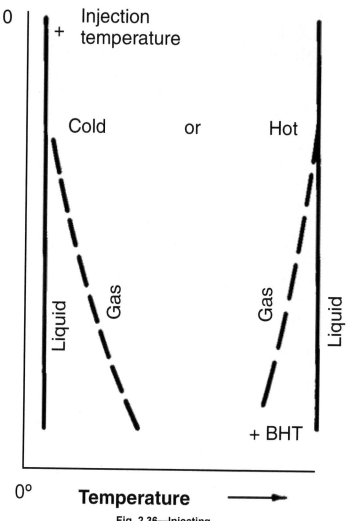

Fig. 2.36—Injecting.

2.13 Impact of Length and Force Changes to the Tubing String

Changing the mode of a well (producer, injector, shut-in, or treating) causes changes in temperature and pressure inside and outside the tubing. After the packer is installed and the tubing landed, any operational mode change will cause a change in length or force in the tubing string. The resultant impact on the packer and tubing string is dependent on (1) how the tubing is connected to the packer, (2) the type of packer, (3) how the packer is set, and (4) tubing compression or tension left on the packer.

The length and force changes can be considerable and can cause tremendous stresses on the tubing string, as well as on the packer under certain conditions. The net result could reduce the effectiveness of the downhole tools and/or damage the tubing, casing, or even the formations open to the well. Failure to consider length and force changes may result in costly failures of such operations as squeeze cementing, acidizing, fracturing, and other remedial operations.

Potential tubing-length changes must be understood to determine the length of seal necessary to remain packed off in a polished sealbore packer, or to prevent tubing and packer

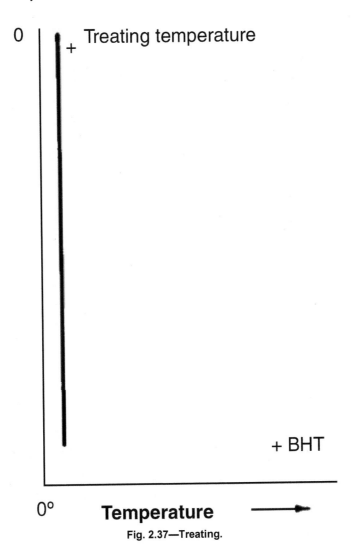

Fig. 2.37—Treating.

damage when seals are anchored in the packer bore. Potential induced forces need to be calculated to prevent tubing and packer damage, unseating packers, or opening equalizing valves.

There are four factors that tend to cause a change in the length or force in the tubing
string[1,18]: the temperature effect, which is directly influenced by a change in the *average* temperature of the string; the piston effect, caused by a change in the pressure in the tubing or
annulus above the packer acting on a specific affected area; the ballooning effect, caused by a
change in *average* pressure inside or outside the tubing string; and the buckling effect, which
occurs when internal tubing pressure is higher than the annulus pressure.

Buckling will shorten the tubing string; however, the others may tend to lengthen or short-
en the string depending on the application of the factors. As long as the tubing is allowed to
move in the packer bore, the temperature and ballooning effects will only have an impact on
tubing-length changes, but if movement is prevented (or restrained) at the packer, these two
factors would then create a force.

It is important to remember that a string of tubing landed in any packer is initially in a
neutral condition, except for any subsequent mechanical strain or compression loads applied by

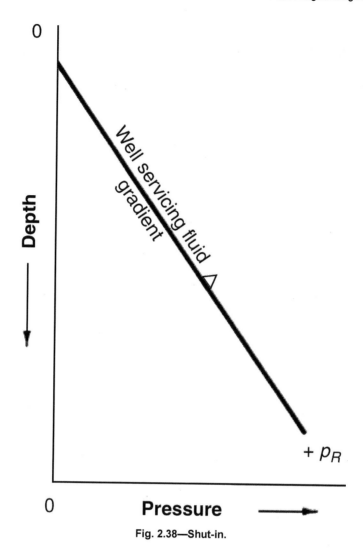

Fig. 2.38—Shut-in.

the rig operator. After the tubing is landed, the factors that cause changes in length or force are always the result of a change in temperature and pressure.

2.13.1 Piston Effect. The length change or force induced by the piston effect is caused by pressure changes inside the annulus and tubing at the packer, acting on different areas (**Fig. 2.42**). The length and force changes can be calculated as follows:

$$\Delta L_1 = \frac{-L}{E A_s}\left[\left(A_p - A_i\right)\Delta p_i - \left(A_p - A_o\right)\Delta p_o\right] \dots\dots\dots\dots\dots\dots (2.1)$$

and $F_1 = \left(A_p - A_i\right)\Delta p_i - \left(A_p - A_o\right)\Delta p_o,$ ....(2.2)

where ΔL_1 = length change because of the piston effect, F_1 = force change because of the piston effect, L = tubing length, E = modulus of elasticity (30,000,000 for steel), A_s = cross-

Wellhead pressure

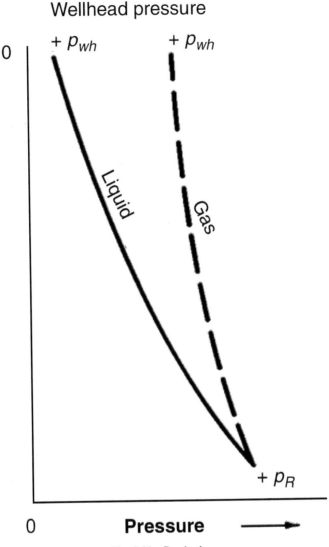

Fig. 2.39—Producing.

sectional area of the tubing wall, A_p = area of the packer bore (values for common sizes can be found in **Table 2.1**), A_i = area of the tubing ID, A_o = area of the tubing OD, Δp_i = change in tubing pressure at the packer, and Δp_o = change in annulus pressure at the packer.

Note that the length change ΔL_1 is a product of L/EA_s and the piston force (F_1). The piston force is the sum of two pressures acting on two areas—one for the tubing and one for the annulus. The area acted upon by changes in pressure in the tubing is the cross-sectional area between the area of the packer bore and the area of the tubing ID in square inches (A_p–A_i). The area acted upon by changes in pressure in the annulus is the cross-sectional area between the area of the packer bore and the area of the tubing OD in square inches (A_p–A_o).

Fig. 2.42a shows a large-bore packer with a tubing string that has both a smaller OD and ID than the packer bore. In this instance, annulus pressure causes downward force, while tubing pressure causes an upward force. For a small-bore packer, this situation is reversed (Fig.

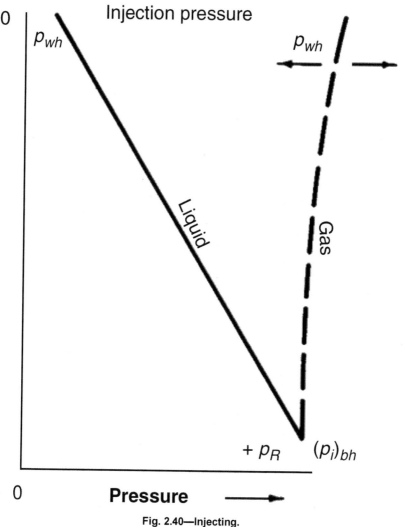

Fig. 2.40—Injecting.

2.42b). The force greatest in magnitude will determine the resulting direction of action. An accurate schematic of the tubing and packer bore for each case should be made for proper determination of areas, forces, and the resulting direction of action.

It is possible to eliminate the forces generated on the tubing string by the piston effect by anchoring the seals in the packer bore. In a string that is restrained at the packer from movement in either direction, the piston effect on the tubing string is zero. All the forces are now being absorbed or contained completely within the packer.

2.13.2 Buckling Effects. Tubing strings tend to buckle only when the internal tubing pressure (p_i) is greater than the annulus pressure (p_o). The result is always a shortening of the tubing string, but the actual force exerted is negligible. The decrease in length occurs because of the tubing string being in a spiral shape rather than straight. The tubing-length change is calculated with the following:

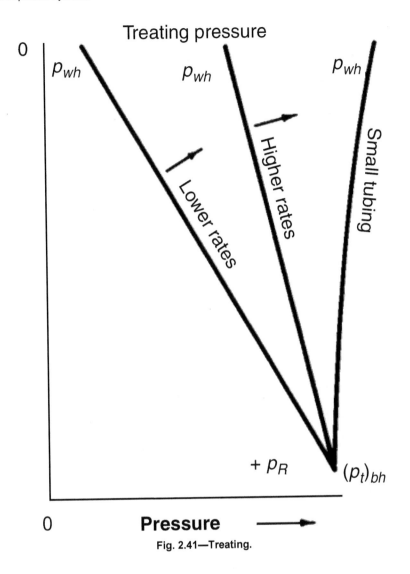

Fig. 2.41—Treating.

$$\Delta L_2 = \frac{-r^2 A_p^2 (\Delta p_i - \Delta p_o)^2}{8EI(W_s + W_i - W_o)}, \quad\text{..} (2.3)$$

where ΔL_2 = length change because of the buckling effect; r = radial clearance between tubing OD and casing ID, $[(ID_C - OD_t)/2]$; A_p = area of the packer bore; A_i = area of the tubing ID; A_o = area of the tubing OD; Δp_i = change in tubing pressure at the packer; Δp_o = change in annulus pressure at the packer; E = modulus of elasticity (30,000,000 for steel); I = moment of inertia of tubing about its diameter $[I = \pi/64\ (D^4 - d^4$, where D is the tubing OD and d is the tubing ID*]; W_s = weight of tubing per inch*; W_i = weight of fluid in tubing per inch*; and W_o = weight of displaced fluid per inch.* (* = values for common tubing sizes can be found in **Tables 2.2 and 2.3**).

TABLE 2.1—AREA OF PACKER BORES			
Bore (in.)	Area (in.^{2})	Bore (in.)	Area (in.^{2})
6.00	28.26	2.50	4.91
5.24	21.55	2.42	4.60
4.75	17.71	2.28	4.08
4.40	15.20	2.06	3.33
4.00	12.56	1.96	3.00
3.87	11.76	1.87	2.75
3.62	10.29	1.68	2.22
3.25	8.30	1.53	1.84
3.00	7.07	1.43	1.61
2.68	5.67	1.25	1.23

2.13.3 Ballooning and Reverse Ballooning. The ballooning effect is caused by the change in average pressure inside or outside the tubing string. Internal pressure swells or "balloons" the tubing and causes it to shorten. Likewise, pressure in the annulus squeezes the tubing, causing it to elongate. This effect is called "reverse ballooning." The ballooning and reverse ballooning length change and force are given by

$$\Delta L_3 = \frac{-2L\gamma}{E}\frac{\Delta p_{ia} - R^2 \Delta p_{oa}}{\left(R^2 - 1\right)} \quad\text{...} (2.4)$$

and $F_3 = -0.6\left(\Delta p_{ia}A_i - \Delta p_{oa}A_o\right),$ .... (2.5)

where ΔL_3 = length change because of ballooning/reverse ballooning, F_3 = force change because of ballooning/reverse ballooning, L = tubing length, γ = Poisson's ratio (0.3 for steel), E = modulus of elasticity (30,000,000 for steel), Δp_{ia} = change in average tubing pressure, Δp_{oa} = change in average annulus pressure, A_i = area of the tubing ID, A_o = area of the tubing OD, and R = ratio of tubing OD to ID (given in Table 2.2) for common tubing sizes and weights.

The ballooning effect will always result in tubing-length changes, but it does not become a force unless the tubing movement is restrained at the packer.

2.13.4 Temperature Effect. Thermal expansion or contraction causes the major length change in the tubing. Heated metal expands, and cooled metal contracts. In a long string of tubing with a temperature change over its entire length, this contraction or elongation can be considerable. The three operational modes that influence temperature effect are producing, injecting (water, gas, or steam), and treating.

The change in tubing length because of temperature effect is calculated as follows:

$$\Delta L_4 = L\beta\Delta t, \quad\text{...} (2.6)$$

where ΔL_4 = change in tubing length, L = tubing length, β = coefficient of thermal expansion (0.0000069 for steel), and Δt = change in average temperature.

Length changes are calculated readily if the average temperature of the tubing can be determined for the initial condition and then again for future operations. The average string

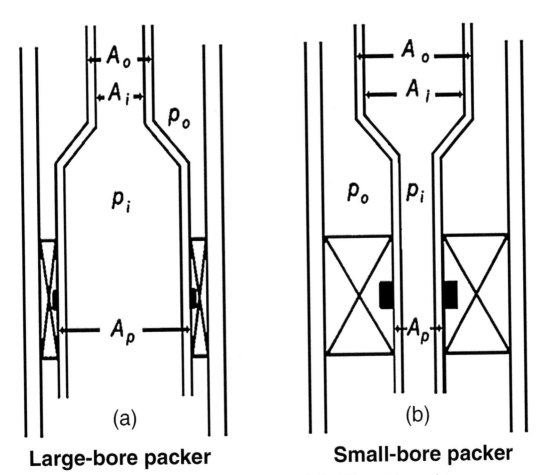

(a)
(b)

Large-bore packer
Small-bore packer

Fig. 2.42—Areas acted upon by pressure in the tubing and the annulus.

temperature in any given operating mode is approximately one-half the sum of the temperatures at the top and the bottom of the tubing. Thus, in the initial condition, the average temperature would be based upon the mean yearly temperature and the BHT. The mean yearly temperature is generally considered to be the temperature 30 ft below ground level; Δt is the difference between the average temperatures of any two subsequent operating modes.

If tubing movement is constrained, forces will be introduced as a result of the temperature change. The temperature-induced force is

$$F_4 = 207 A_S \Delta t, \quad \text{...} \quad (2.7)$$

where F_4 = pounds force (tensile or compression, depending on the direction of Δt), A_S = cross-sectional area of the tubing wall, and Δt = change in average tubing temperature.

2.13.5 Net Results of Piston, Buckling, Ballooning, and Temperature Effects. The net or overall length change (or force) is the sum of the length changes (or forces) caused by the temperature, piston, and ballooning effects. The direction of the length change for each effect (or action of the force) must be considered when summing them. It follows that for a change

TABLE 2.2—WEIGHT PER INCH OF TUBING AND FLUID

$W_s+W_i-W_o$

Tubing OD (in.)	Weight (lbm/in.)	W_i and W_o (lbm/in.)	7.0 52.3	8.0 59.8	9.0 67.3	10.0 74.8	11.0 82.3	12.0 89.8	13.0 97.2	14.0 104.7	15.0 112.2	16.0 119.7	17.0 127.2	18.0 lbm/gal 134.6 lbm/ft³
1.660	W_s = .200	W_i	.045	.052	.058	.065	.071	.078	.064	.091	.097	.104	.110	.116
		W_o	.065	.075	.084	.094	.103	.112	.122	.131	.140	.150	.159	.169
1.900	W_s = .242	W_i	.062	.070	.079	.088	.097	.106	.115	.123	.132	.141	.150	.159
		W_o	.086	.098	.110	.123	.135	.147	.159	.172	.184	.196	.209	.221
2.000	W_s = .283	W_i	.066	.076	.085	.095	.104	.114	.123	.133	.142	.152	.161	.171
		W_o	.095	.109	.122	.136	.150	.163	.177	.190	.204	.218	.231	.245
$2^1/_{16}$	W_s = .283	W_i	.073	.083	.094	.104	.114	.125	.135	.146	.156	.167	.177	.187
		W_o	.101	.116	.130	.145	.159	.174	.188	.202	.217	.231	.246	.260
$2^3/_8$	W_s = .392	W_i	.095	.108	.122	.135	.149	.162	.176	.189	.203	.217	.230	.243
		W_o	.134	.153	.172	.192	.211	.230	.249	.268	.288	.307	.326	.345
$2^7/_8$	W_s = .542	W_i	.142	.162	.182	.203	.223	.243	.263	.284	.304	.324	.344	.364
		W_o	.196	.225	.253	.281	.309	.337	.365	.393	.421	.450	.478	.506
3½	W_s = .767	W_i	.213	.243	.274	.304	.335	.365	.395	.426	.456	.487	.517	.548
		W_o	.291	.333	.365	.416	.458	.500	.541	.583	.625	.666	.708	.749

Formula for W_s, W_i, and W_o:

Weight of steel: W_s = Pipe weight (lbm/ft)/12

Weight of fluid in tubing: W_i = Mud weight (lbm/gal) x A_i/231

Weight of displaced fluid: W_o = Mud weight (lbm/gal) x A_o/231

in conditions, the motion (or force) created by one effect can be offset, or enhanced, by the motion (or force) developed by some other effect.

Mosely[19] presented a method for graphically determining the length and force changes as a result of buckling and ballooning (L_2, L_3, and F_3). This method is particularly useful on a field-wide basis, where wells have the same-size tubing, casing, and packers.

When planning the sequential steps of a completion or workover, care should be taken to consider the temperatures and pressures in each step once the tubing and packer systems become involved. By careful selection of the packer bore and use of annulus pressures, one pressure effect (or a combination of pressure effects) could be used to offset the adverse length or force change of another effect.

2.14 Combination Tubing/Packer Systems

Uniform completions have been discussed previously (i.e., a single tubing and casing size). Hammerlindl[20] presented a method for solving problems with combination completions. A combination completion consists of (1) more than one size of tubing, (2) more than one size of casing, (3) two or more fluids in the tubing and/or annulus, or (4) one or more of these. His paper in particular covered two items not previously addressed by Lubinski et al.[18] He includes a direct mathematical method for calculating forces in uniform completions in which tubing movement is not permitted and a method of handling hydraulic packers is set with the wellhead in place.

There are several computer programs available today, modeled after Hammerlindl's methods, that can easily calculate the length changes and forces generated by changes in temperature and pressure within the wellbore. These programs not only determine critical length

TABLE 2.3—TUBING DIMENSIONAL DATA

OD (in.)	Nominal Weight (lbm/ft)	ID (in.)	Wall Thickness (in.)	Inside Area (in.^{2})	Outside Area (in.^{2})	Cross-Sectional Area (in.^{2})	Moment of Inertia (in.^{4})	OD/ID Ratio R^2
1.050	1.20	.824	.113	.533	.866	.333	.037	1.624
	1.50	.742	.154	.432		.434	.045	2.002
1.315	1.80	1.049	.133	.864	1.358	.494	0.87	1.779
	2.25	.957	.179	.719		.639	.105	1.868
1.650	2.10	1.410	.125	1.561	2.164	.603	.179	1.385
	2.40	1.380	.140	1.496		.668	.195	1.447
	3.02	1.278	.191	1.283		.881	.242	1.687
1.900	2.40	1.650	.125	2.138	2.835	.697	.276	1.326
	2.90	1.610	.145	2.006		.799	.310	1.393
	3.64	1.500	.200	1.767		1.068	.391	1.604
2.000	3.40	1.670	.165	2.191	3.142	.951	.404	1.434
2.063	3.25	1.751	.156	2.408	3.343	.935	.428	1.388
2.375	4.00	2.041	.167	3.272	4.430	1.158	.710	1.354
	4.70	1.995	.190	3.126		1.304	.754	1.417
	5.30	1.939	.218	2.953		1.477	.868	1.500
	5.95	1.867	.254	2.738		1.692	.965	1.618
	6.20	1.853	.261	2.697		1.733	.983	1.643
	7.70	1.703	.336	2.278		2.152	1.149	1.945
2.875	6.50	2.441	.217	4.630	6.492	1.812	1.611	1.387
	7.90	2.323	.276	4.238		2.254	1.924	1.532
	8.70	2.259	.308	4.008		2.484	2.075	1.620
	9.50	2.195	.340	3.784		2.708	2.214	1.716
	10.70	2.091	.392	3.434		3.058	2.415	1.890
	11.00	2.065	.405	3.349		3.143	2.461	1.938
	11.65	1.995	.440	3.126		3.366	2.576	2.077
3.500	7.70	3.058	.216	7.393	9.621	2.228	3.017	1.301
	9.30	2.992	.254	7.031		2.590	3.432	1.368
	10.30	2.922	.289	3.706		2.915	3.788	1.435
	12.80	2.764	.368	6.000		3.621	4.501	1.503
	12.96	2.750	.375	5.939		3.682	4.569	1.620
	15.80	2.548	.476	5.103		4.518	5.297	1.887
	16.70	2.480	.510	4.830		4.791	5.509	1.992
4.000	9.50	3.548	.226	9.887	12.566	2.679	4.788	1.271
	11.00	3.476	.262	9.459		3.077	5.400	1.324
	11.60	3.428	.286	9.229		3.337	5.788	1.362
	13.40	3.340	.330	8.761		3.805	6.458	1.434
4.500	12.75	3.958	.271	12.304	15.904	3.600	8.082	1.293
	13.50	3.920	.290	12.069		3.835	8.538	1.318
	15.50	3.825	.337	11.497		4.437	9.610	1.383
	19.20	3.640	.430	10.406		5.498	11.512	1.528

changes but also the stresses generated on the tubing string and packer. The use of such programs is recommended.

2.14.1 Tubing/Packer Forces on Intermediate Packers. Intermediate packers are an integral part of the tubing string. Examples are dual packers and single-string selective-completion packers. The packer-to-tubing force on the intermediate packer is needed so that wells can be treated through the tubing string. Without proper design, it is possible to shear the release mechanism in the intermediate packer(s) or permanently corkscrew the tubing between the intermediate packer and lower packer, either of which would result in an expensive failure of the completion or workover.

Hammerlindl[21] wrote an extension of his[20] and Lubinski et al.'s[18] earlier works that developed a theory required to solve for the intermediate packer-to-tubing forces. The calculation procedure regarding pressure effects requires working the problem from the lowest packer to the surface in sections. The first section is the tubing between the bottom and second packers. The second section is the tubing between the second and third packers (or the surface if there are only two packers). The procedures are the standard ones for uniform completions. The only changes are those to determine the changes in length as a result of applied forces on the intermediate packers; in addition, the actual and fictitious force-calculation procedures are modified. After the results of each section have been resolved, the sections must be looked at as a whole to determine the net results on the packer(s). Interested readers are referred to Hammerlindl's 1980 paper[22] for additional information on the nebulous fictitious force of Lubinski et al.[18]

Nomenclature

A_i = area of the tubing ID (in.^{2})

A_o = area of the tubing OD (in.^{2})

A_p = area of the packer bore (in.^{2})

A_S = cross-sectional area of the tubing wall (in.^{2})

E = modulus of elasticity (psi) (30,000,000 for steel)

F_1 = force change (pounds) because of the piston effect

F_3 = force change (pounds) because of ballooning/reverse ballooning

F_4 = pounds force (tensile or compression, depending on the direction of Δt)

I = moment of inertia of tubing about its diameter; $I = \pi/64 \, (D^4 - d^4)$ (in.^{4}), where D is the tubing OD and d is the tubing ID

L = tubing length (in.)

p_i = internal tubing pressure

p_o = annulus pressure

$(p_i)_{bh}$ = bottomhole injection pressure

$(p_t)_{bh}$ = bottomhole treating pressure

p_R = reservoir pressure

p_{wh} = wellhead pressure

r = radial clearance between tubing OD and casing ID, $[(ID_C - OD_t)/2]$ (in.)

R = ratio of tubing OD to ID

W_i = weight of fluid in tubing per inch (lb/in.)

W_o = weight of displaced fluid per inch (lb/in.)

W_s = weight of tubing per inch (lb/in.)

β = coefficient of thermal expansion (in./in./°F) (0.0000069 for steel)

ΔL_1 = length change (in.) because of the piston effect

ΔL_2 = length change (in.) because of the buckling effect

ΔL_3 = length change (in.) because of ballooning/reverse ballooning

ΔL_4 = change in tubing length (in.)

Δp_i = change in tubing pressure at the packer (psi)

Δp_o = change in annulus pressure at the packer (psi)

Δp_{ia} = change in average tubing pressure (psi)

Δp_{oa} = change in average annulus pressure (psi)
Δt = change in average temperature (°F)
γ = Poisson's ratio (0.3 for steel)

References

1. *Packer Calculations Handbook*, Baker Oil Tools Div. (1992).
2. Intl. Std., NACE MR-01-75/ISO 15156-1, "Petroleum and Natural Gas Industries—Materials for Use in H_2S Containing Environments in Oil and Gas Production—Part 1: General Principles for Selection of Cracking Resistant Materials," Ref. NACE MR-01-75/ISO 15156-1:2001 (E).
3. *Packer Systems Catalog,* Baker Oil Tools, Baker Hughes Inc. (2000) Publication No. 20002663-30M-09/00.
4. Intl. Std., NACE MR0175/ISO 15156-2, "Petroleum and Natural Gas Industries—Materials for Use in H_2S Containing Environments in Oil and Gas Production—Part 2: Cracking-Resistant Carbon and Low Alloy Steels, and the Use of Cast Irons," Ref. NACE MR0175/ISO 15156-2:2003 (E).
5. Intl. Std., NACE MR0175/ISO 15156-1, "Petroleum and Natural Gas Industries—Materials for use in H_2S Containing Environments in Oil and Gas Production—Part 3: Cracking-Resistant CRA's (corrosion resistant alloys) and Other Alloys," Ref. NACE MR 175/ISO 15156-3:2003 (E).
6. "Considerations in the Design and Selection of Dynamic Tubing to Packer Seals," Baker Oil Tools —Engineering Tech Data Paper Number CS003 (1986).
7. Rubbio, R.: "What to Consider When Designing Downhole Seals," *World Oil.*
8. Intl. Std., ISO 14310, "Petroleum and Natural Gas Industries—Downhole Equipment—Packers and Bridge Plugs," Ref. ISO 14310:2001 (E), first edition (2001-12-01).
9. API Specification 11D1, "Petroleum and Natural Gas Industries—Downhole Equipment— Packers and Bridge Plugs," API Specification 11D1, first edition (July 2002) ISO 14310:2001.
10. Hopmann, M. and Walker, T.: "Predicting Permanent Packer Performance," *Petroleum Engineering Intl.,* Hart Publications Inc.
11. Fothergill, J.: "Ratings Standardization for Production Packers," paper SPE 80945 presented at the 2003 SPE Production Operations Symposium, Oklahoma City, Oklahoma, 22–25 March.
12. *Subsurface Safety Systems Catalog,* Baker Hughes Inc. (1995) BSS-2-10M-95118 Rev.9/95.
13. *Cased Hole Applications Catalog,* Baker Hughes Inc. (2001) Publication No. BOT-01-1485 15M-09/01.
14. Almond, K. *et al.:* "Improving Production Results in Monobore, Deepwater and Extended Reach Wells," paper SPE 77519 presented at the 2002 SPE Annual Technical Conference and Exhibition, San Antonio, Texas, 29 September–2 October.
15. Hogg, C.: "Comparison of Multilateral Completion Scenarios and Their Application," paper SPE 38493 presented at the 1997 SPE Offshore Europe Conference, Aberdeen, 9–10 September.
16. Eichmier, J.R., Ersoy, D., and Ramey, H.J. Jr.: "Wellbore Temperatures and Heat Losses During Production Operations," paper CIM 7016 presented at the 1976 CIM Soc. Meeting, Calgary, 6–7 May.
17. Arnold, R.B., Sandmeyer, D.J., and Eichmier, J.R.: "Production Problems of a High-Pressure, High-Temperature Reservoir," paper CIM 7232.
18. Lubinski, A., Althouse, W.H., and Logan, J.L.: "Helical Buckling or Tubing Sealed in Packers," *JPT* (June 1962) 655; *Trans.,* AIME, **225.**
19. Moseley, N.F.: "Graphic Solutions to Tubing Movement in Deep Wells," *Petroleum Engineering Intl.* (March 1973) 59.
20. Hammerlindl, D.J.: "Movement, Forces, and Stresses Associated With Combination Tubing Strings Sealed in Packers," *JPT* (February 1977) 195.
21. Hammerlindl, D.J.: "Packer-to-Tubing Forces for Intermediate Packers," *JPT* (March 1980) 515.
22. Hammerlindl, D.J.: "Basic Fluid and Pressure Forces on Oilwell Tubulars," *JPT* (January 1980) 153.

23. Langenkamp, R.: "The Illustrated Petroleum Reference Dictionary," fourth edition, PennWell Publishing Co., Tulsa (1994).

General References

Allen, T. and Roberts, A.P.: *Production Operations,* fourth edition (1993) **I and II.**

"Factors and Conditions Which Cause Seal Assemblies Used in Downhole Enviornments to Get Stuck," Baker Oil Tools—Engineering Tech Data paper Number CS007.

Patton, L.D. and Abbott, W.A.: "Well Completions and Workovers: The Systems Approach," second edition, Energy Publications, Dallas (1985) 57–67.

Glossary[23]

Annulus. In a completion, the space between the ID of the casing and the OD of the tubing string.

Borehole. The uncased hole in the earth made by the drill.

Bypass Valve. An internal unloaded packer valve that aids in equalization of the tubing and annulus pressures when the packer is released.

Casing. Normally, steel pipe used to seal off fluids from the borehole and prevent the hole from sloughing off or caving in.

Christmas Tree. The assembly of valves at the wellhead through which the well is produced. The valves provide a means of surface control for the well.

Coiled Tubing. A reel of continuous steel tubing mounted on a powered unit that may be run into the wellbore to perform various downhole tasks, such as milling, washing, circulating, and perforating.

Commingled Well. A well producing hydrocarbons or gas from two or more formations through a common string of tubing.

Durometer. The relative hardness of an elastomer.

Elastomer. Any number of various elastic compounds resembling rubber that are used in the construction of packing elements and tubing-seal stacks.

Electric Wireline. A stranded cable with an internal electrical conduit that is used for conveying logging tools, perforating, and setting packers or bridge plugs in a well.

HP/HT. High-pressure/high-temperature well environments, generally considered as being above 300°F and 10,000 psi differential pressure.

Liner. A length of casing used downhole to shut off a water or gas formation so that drilling can proceed. Several liners may be run into a well over the course of the drilling operation. The liner at the bottom of the hole may be referred to as the production liner because it generally sits in the pay zone.

Packer. A sealing device that isolates and contains produced fluids and pressures within the wellbore to protect the casing and other formations above or below the producing zone.

Packer-Rating Envelope. A graphical representation of the safe operating limits of a packer combining both differential pressure and axial loads.

Packing Element. The elastomeric seal found on the OD of a packer that, when energized, forms a pressure-containing barrier between the ID of the casing and the packer body.

Scraper. A mechanical device with scraping blades used to clean the inside of the casing string of scale and cement before installing a packer.

Slickline. A nonelectric wireline used for through-tubing work such as deploying and actuating flow-control devices.

Slip. In a packer, a wedge-shaped piece of metal with wicker teeth that grip the ID of the casing and anchor the packer in place.

Swabbing. The removal of fluid from the tubing string with a special tool on wireline (cable) to reduce the hydrostatic pressure sufficiently and allow the formation to flow into the wellbore.

Tubing. Normally, steel pipe that goes inside the well's casing and reaches from the surface to the top of the pay zone. Produced or injected fluids and gases are contained inside the tubing string.

Tubing Buckling. The helical corkscrewing of the tubing string caused by internal tubing pressure or excessive compressive loads. If the yield strength of the tubing is exceeded, the buckling can become permanent.

Wellhead. The top of the casing and the attached control and flow valves.

Wireline Junk Basket. A device that is run into the well on electric line, or slickline, to clear the hole of any debris. It is usually run in conjunction with a "gauge ring" that gauges the hole ID to ensure passage of subsequent tools.

Workover. The operations performed on a well to restore or increase production; typically requires pulling the tubing using a workover or drilling rig.

Work String. A string of either drillpipe or tubing used to perform specific maintenance operations downhole (e.g., fishing, milling, squeeze cementing).

SI Metric Conversion Factors

ft	$\times$ 3.048*	E – 01	= m
ft^3	$\times$ 2.831 685	E – 02	= m^3
°F	(°F – 32)/1.8		= °C
gal	$\times$ 3.785 412	E – 03	= m^3
in.	$\times$ 2.54*	E + 00	= cm
in.^{2}	$\times$ 6.451 6*	E + 00	= cm^2
in.^{3}	$\times$ 1.638 706	E + 01	= cm^3
lbf	$\times$ 4.448 222	E + 00	= N
lbm	$\times$ 4.535 924	E – 01	= kg
psi	$\times$ 6.894 757	E + 00	= kPa

*Conversion factor is exact.

Chapter 3
Tubing Selection, Design, and Installation
Joe Dunn Clegg, Consultant and **Erich F. Klementich,** Consultant

3.1 Introduction
Tubing is the normal flow conduit used to transport produced fluids to the surface or fluids to the formation. Its use in wells is normally considered a good operating practice. The use of tubing permits better well control because circulating fluids can kill the well; thus, workovers are simplified and their results enhanced. Flow efficiency typically is improved with the use of tubing. Furthermore, tubing is required for most artificial lift installations. Tubing with the use of a packer allows isolation of the casing from well fluids and deters corrosion damage of the casing. Multicompletions require tubing to permit individual zone production and operation. Governmental rules and regulations often require tubing in every well. Permission may be obtained for omission of tubing in special cases (tubingless completions). These special completions typically are flowing wells with relatively small casing. Tubing strings are generally in outside diameter (OD) sizes of 2⅜ to 4½ in. but may be as large as 20 in. or as small as 1.050 in.

The proper selection, design, and installation of tubing string are critical parts of any well completion. See the chapter on inflow and outflow in this section of the handbook for more information. Tubing strings must be sized correctly to enable the fluids to flow efficiently or to permit installation of effective artificial lift equipment. A tubing string that is too small causes large friction losses and limits production. It also may severely restrict the type and size of artificial lift equipment. A tubing string that is too large may cause heading and unstable flow, which results in loading up of the well and can complicate workovers. The planned tubing must easily fit inside the installed casing. When selecting the material, environmental conditions, the projected corrosivity of the well fluids, the minimum and maximum pressures and temperature, safety aspects, and cost-effectiveness must be considered.

The tubing must be designed to meet all stresses and conditions that occur during routine operation of the well and should have an adequate margin for unusual load conditions. It must withstand the stresses caused by tension, burst, and collapse, and it must resist the corrosive action of well fluids throughout the well life. In addition, the tubing must be handled and installed so that the tubing produces the well without failure or without causing undue operating problems.

3.2 Oilfield Tubing

The American Petroleum Institute (API) developed Specifications, Recommended Practices, and Bulletins for steel tubing that meet the major needs of the oil and gas industry.[1-13] API documents are reviewed and updated every 5 years. This effort continues, and many of these documents (with modifications) have become International Organization for Standardization (ISO) documents. Currently, API and ISO are the international standards for products intended for worldwide use in the petroleum and natural gas industry. The information in API and ISO documents is covered here in some detail. API tubing sizes range from ODs of 1.050 to 4.500 in. For high-rate wells, tubing larger than 4½ in. may be beneficial. API and ISO specifications contain provisions when casing is used as tubing.

In addition to API steel tubing, there are hostile well conditions that may be better served by other materials. There are proprietary steel grades that do not conform to all aspects of the API specifications but are used in the petroleum-producing industry for resistance to weight-loss corrosion, higher strengths, less susceptibility to sulfide stress corrosion cracking (SSC), and wear resistance. Corrosion-resistant alloy (CRA) is a special material that is sometimes used in hostile environments. These special materials are usually expensive but may prove worthwhile over the life of the well; however, CRA tubing does not always eliminate corrosion and may be incompatible with some completion fluids. See ISO 13680 for information on CRA seamless tubes.[14]

Thermoplastic (fiberglass) tubing has been used successfully in corrosive wells. Most thermoplastic tubing has good tension properties and burst resistance, but has relatively small collapse-pressure resistance and poorer wear resistance properties than steel tubing. If temperatures exceed 150°F, a derating service factor may be required. Other metals and materials have been used as tubing but rarely are used in current oil and gas completions either because of their cost or because of limited applicability.

3.3 API/ISO Tubing Requirements

API has numerous manufacturing requirements for tubing. The tubing purchaser and designer should be aware of these requirements and of API testing procedures (see API *Spec. 5CT*).[10] All tubing should meet API minimum requirements. In critical wells, the purchaser may want to receive and review the manufacturer's test results. For tubing used in sour wells (wells with H_2S content greater than 0.05 psi partial pressure), the specific sour service requirements should be reviewed.

When placing orders for tubing to be manufactured in accordance with API *Spec. 5CT*, the purchaser should consult API *Spec. 5CT* Sec. 4. At a minimum, the following requirements should be specified on the purchase order: the specification (API/ISO), quantity, size designation (OD, normally in inches), weight designation, grade and type, end finish (type of connection), range length, seamless or electric weld, delivery date, and shipping instructions.

API tubing specifications contain several provisions that are optional for the purchaser and other stipulations that are by agreement between the purchaser and the manufacturer. Some of these added provisions may be critical to a particular application; therefore, familiarity with API/ISO tubing specifications is needed.

3.3.1 Tubing Connectors/Tubing Joints. API developed specifications for three different connectors for use as tubing joints: external-upset tubing and coupling, non-upset tubing and couplings, and integral-joint tubing. **Fig. 3.1** shows API tubing joint connections. All three connections have tapered and round thread forms with either 8 or 10 threads/in., depending on the size. When casing is used as tubing, long-thread coupling/short-thread coupling and buttress-thread coupling connections can be specified.

The API external-upset-end (EUE) tubing connection is widely used because it is a good, serviceable connection in most wells. The EUE joint has a designed joint strength in tension

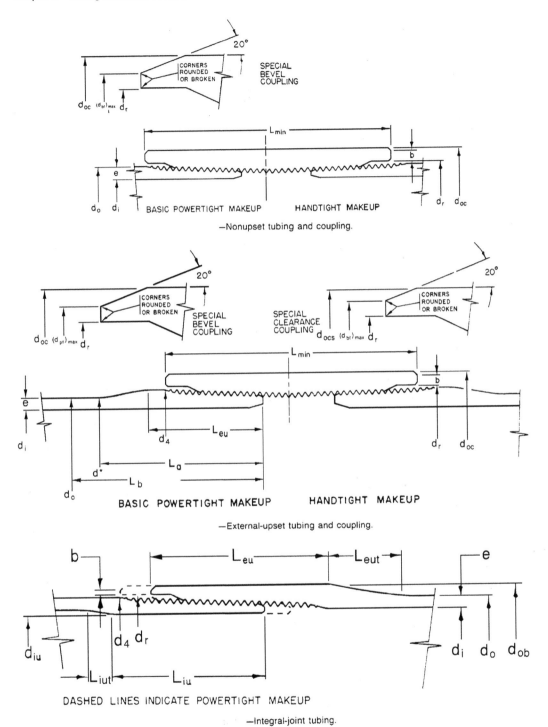

Fig. 3.1—API tubing joint and connections. (Reproduced courtesy of the American Petroleum Institute from API *Spec. 5CT.*[10])

and pressure strength greater than that of the pipe body and, therefore, is considered a 100% joint efficient connection. For proper lubrication and sealing, the joint requires a good thread compound as outlined in API *RP 5A3*.[1] To improve the seal performance of API EUE tubing in high-pressure service, a grooved coupling, which accepts nonmetallic seal rings, is sometimes used in the coupling (see API *Spec. 5CT SR 13*). To provide more clearance, API special clearance EUE couplings are available. API EUE joints come in OD sizes of 1.050 to 4.500 in.

API nonupset (NUE) tubing is used much less than EUE tubing. The cost of NUE is only slightly less than EUE, and the joint strength is substantially less. The coupling joint diameter of NUE is less than EUE, which offers some advantages when clearance is small. API NUE joints are available in sizes of 1.050 to 4.500 in.

API integral-joint tubing is available in OD sizes of 1.315 to 2.063 in. API integral-joint tubing has a 10-round form with a joint strength that is less than the body minimum yield, which restricts its use. The small OD of integral-joint tubing permits its use inside larger tubing strings or in wells as unloading or vent strings. **Table 3.1** lists API tubing size, designations, ODs, wall thickness, grade, and applicable end finish.

Tables 3.2 and 3.3 list the coupling dimensions, weights, and tolerances for NUE and EUE tubing couplings. The couplings should meet all the minimum requirements outlined in API *Spec. 5CT*.[10] API *Spec. 5B*[3] and API *RP 5B1*[4] cover threading, gauging, and thread inspection. **Table 3.4** shows EUE tubing thread gage, NUE tubing thread gage, and integral-joint-tubing thread gage dimensions.

Several proprietary (non-API) connections are available. These joints are useful when greater leak resistance or more clearance is needed than that provided by the standard API joints. These specialty joints obtain their improved properties through unique thread profiles, a torque shoulder, metal-to-metal seals, seal rings, internal upsets, external upsets, integral joints, etc. Tubing reference tables, which summarize the available non-API tubing joints and tubing, are published yearly in trade magazines such as *World Oil*. Many operators commonly use these proprietary connections in critical wells. Before ordering or using a specific proprietary tubing connection in a critical well, the suitability of such a connection for a particular application must be assessed by either a review of service history or a comprehensive connection test program such as ISO 13679.[15] Sec. 3.7 discusses the use of coiled tubing in some well completions. See API *RP 5C7*[9] for guidelines on its use. For information on workovers with coiled tubing, review the chapter on workover design and procedures in the Drilling Engineering section of this *Handbook*.

3.3.2 Process of Manufacture. Tubing made to API specifications uses seamless or electric-weld processes. Seamless pipe is defined as a wrought steel tubular product made without a welded seam. It is manufactured by hot-working steel or, if necessary, by subsequently cold-finishing the hot-worked product to produce the desired shape, dimensions, and properties. Because of the nature of the manufacturing, the cross section of the tubing wall area may be slightly eccentric and the tubing slightly oval and not perfectly straight.

Electric-welded pipe has one longitudinal seam formed by electric-resistance or electric-induction welding without the addition of filler metal. The edges to be welded are pressed together mechanically, and the heat for welding is generated by the resistance to flow of electric current. The weld seam of electric welded pipe is heat-treated after welding to a minimum temperature of 1,000°F or processed so that no untempered martensite remains. See API *Spec. 5CT* for exceptions.[10]

Both seamless and electric-weld processes are acceptable for most oil and gas services, but some prefer seamless tubulars for sour service because the electric-weld process may result in a slightly different grain structure near the weld. Such differences are usually eliminated if the electric-weld tubing is heat-treated by the quenched-and-tempered process, which is mandatory for API grades L80, C90, T95, and P110. Couplings usually are made of seamless tubular product of the same grade and type as the pipe.

TABLE 3.1—API TUBING LIST (Reproduced courtesy of the American Petroleum Institute from API *Spec. 5CT*[10])

Size Designation	Weight Designation*,** Non-upset T&C	External Upset T&C	Integral Joint	OD (in.)	Wall Thickness (in.)	Type of End Finish†,‡ H-40	J-55	L-80	N-80	C-90§	T-95§	P-110
1.050	1.14	1.20	—	1.050	0.113	PNU	PNU	PNU	PNU	PNU	PNU	—
1.050	1.48	1.54	—	1.050	0.154	PU	PU	PU	PU	PU	PU	PU
1.315	1.70	1.80	1.72	1.315	0.133	PNUI	PNUI	PNUI	PNUI	PNUI	PNUI	—
1.315	2.19	2.24	—	1.315	0.179	PU	PU	PU	PU	PU	PU	PU
1.660	—	—	2.10	1.660	0.125	PI	PI	—	—	—	—	—
1.660	2.30	2.40	2.33	1.660	0.140	PNUI	PNUI	PNUI	PNUI	PNUI	PNUI	
1.660	3.03	3.07	—	1.660	0.191	PU	PU	PU	PU	PU	PU	PU
1.900	—	—	2.40	1.900	0.125	PI	PI	—	—	—	—	—
1.900	2.75	2.90	2.76	1.900	0.145	PNUI	PNUI	PNUI	PNUI	PNUI	PNUI	—
1.900	3.65	3.73	—	1.900	0.200	PU	PU	PU	PU	PU	PU	PU
1.900	4.42	—	—	1.900	0.250	—	—	P	—	P	P	—
1.900	5.15	—	—	1.900	0.300	—	—	P	—	P	P	—
2.063	—	—	3.25	2.063	0.156	PI	PI	PI	PI	PI	PI	—
2.063	4.50	—	—	2.063	0.225	P	P	P	P	P	P	P
2⅜	4.00	—	—	2.375	0.167	PN	PN	PN	PN	PN	PN	—
2⅜	4.60	4.70	—	2.375	0.190	PNU	PNU	PNU	PNU	PNU	PNU	PNU
2⅜	5.80	5.95	—	2.375	0.254	—	—	PNU	PNU	PNU	PNU	PNU
2⅜	6.60	—	—	2.375	0.295	—	—	P	—	P	P	—
2⅜	7.35	7.45	—	2.375	0.336	—	—	PU	—	PU	PU	—
2⅞	6.40	6.50	—	2.875	0.217	PNU	PNU	PNU	PNU	PNU	PNU	PNU
2⅞	7.80	7.90	—	2.875	0.276	—	—	PNU	PNU	PNU	PNU	PNU
2⅞	8.60	8.70	—	2.875	0.308	—	—	PNU	PNU	PNU	PNU	PNU
2⅞	9.35	9.45	—	2.875	0.340	—	—	PU	—	PU	PU	—
2⅞	10.50	—	—	2.875	0.392	—	—	P	—	P	P	—
2⅞	11.50	—	—	2.875	0.440	—	—	P	—	P	P	—
3½	7.70	—	—	3.500	0.216	PN	PN	PN	PN	PN	PN	—
3½	9.20	9.30	—	3.500	0.254	PNU	PNU	PNU	PNU	PNU	PNU	PNU
3½	10.20	—	—	3.500	0.289	PN	PN	PN	PN	PN	PN	—
3½	12.70	12.95	—	3.500	0.375	—	—	PNU	PNU	PNU	PNU	PNU
3½	14.30	—	—	3.500	0.430	—	—	P	—	P	P	—
3½	15.50	—	—	3.500	0.476	—	—	P	—	P	P	—
3½	17.00	—	—	3.500	0.530	—	—	P	—	P	P	—
4	9.50	—	—	4.000	0.226	PN	PN	PN	PN	PN	PN	
4	—	11.00	—	4.000	0.262	PU	PU	PU	PU	PU	PU	
4	13.20	—	—	4.000	0.330	—	—	P	—	P	P	—
4	16.10	—	—	4.000	0.415	—	—	P	—	P	P	—
4	18.90	—	—	4.000	0.500	—	—	P	—	P	P	—
4	22.20	—	—	4.000	0.610	—	—	P	—	P	P	—
4½	12.60	12.75	—	4.500	0.271	PNU	PNU	PNU	PNU	PNU	PNU	—
4½	15.20	—	—	4.500	0.337	—	—	P	—	P	P	—
4½	17.00	—	—	4.500	0.380	—	—	P	—	P	P	—
4½	18.90	—	—	4.500	0.430	—	—	P	—	P	P	—
4½	21.50	—	—	4.500	0.500	—	—	P	—	P	P	—
4½	23.70	—	—	4.500	0.560	—	—	P	—	P	P	—
4½	26.10	—	—	4.500	0.630	—	—	P	—	P	P	—

*Designations are shown for the purpose of identification in ordering. **The densities of martensitic chromium steels (L-80 types 9Cr and 13Cr) are different from carbon steels. The weights shown are therefore not accurate for martensitic chromium steels. A weight correction factor of 0.989 may be used. † P= plain end, N= nonupset threaded and coupled (T&C), U = external upset T&C, I = integral joint. ‡Items designated plain end (P) only have been added as standard to provide the industry with a list of standardized heavy wall thicknesses. Although API has not standardized on a thread for this thickness, a nominal T&C weight designation is listed for identification. See Pars. 10.3.a.5 and b.5 and Appendix D Pars. D.3.a.5 and b.5 of API *Spec. 5CT*. §Grade C-90 and T-95 tubing shall be furnished in sizes, weights, and wall thicknesses as listed here or as shown on the purchase order.

TABLE 3.2—NONUPSET TUBING COUPLING DIMENSIONS, WEIGHTS, AND TOLERANCES (Reproduced courtesy of the American Petroleum Institute from API *Spec. 5CT*[10])*

Group	Size Designation**	W†	N_L	Q	b	Special Bevel B_f	Weight (lbm)
1,2	1.050‡	1.313	$3^3/_{16}$	1.113	$1/_{16}$	1.181	0.51
1,2	1.315	1.660	$3^1/_4$	1.378	$3/_{32}$	1.488	0.84
1,2	1.660	2.054	$3^1/_2$	1.723	$1/_8$	1.857	1.29
1,2	1.900	2.200	$3^3/_4$	1.963	$1/_{16}$	2.050	1.23
1,2,3	$2^3/_8$	2.875	$4^1/_4$	2.438	$3/_{16}$	2.625	2.82
1,2,3	$2^7/_8$	3.500	$5^1/_8$	2.938	$3/_{16}$	3.188	5.15
1,2,3	$3^1/_2$	4.250	$5^5/_8$	3.563	$3/_{16}$	3.875	8.17
1,2	4	4.750	$5^3/_4$	4.063	$3/_{16}$	4.375	9.57
1,2	$4^1/_2$	5.200	$6^1/_8$	4.563	$3/_{16}$	4.850	10.76

Note: See API *Spec. 5CT* for nomenclature. *All dimensions in inches. **Size designation of the coupling is the same as the corresponding pipe size designation. †Tolerance on outside diameter, W, ±1%. ‡For information only; marking with the *Spec. 5CT* designation or the API monogram is not permitted.

TABLE 3.3—EXTERNAL-UPSET TUBING COUPLING DIMENSIONS, WEIGHTS, AND TOLERANCES (Reproduced courtesy of the American Petroleum Institute from API *Spec. 5CT*[10])*

Group	Size Designation**	Regular and Special Bevel, W†	W_c‡	N_L	Q	b	Special Bevel	Special Clearance	Regular	Special Clearance
1,2	1.050	1.660	....	$3^1/_4$	1.378	$3/_{32}$	1.488	....	0.84	....
1,2	1.315	1.900	....	$3^1/_2$	1.531	$3/_{32}$	1.684	....	1.26	....
1,2	1.660	2.200	....	$3^3/_4$	1.875	$1/_8$	2.006	....	1.49	....
1,2	1.900	2.500	....	$3^7/_8$	2.156	$1/_8$	2.297	....	1.85	....
1,2,3	$2^3/_8$	3.063	2.910	$4^7/_8$	2.656	$5/_{32}$	2.828	2.752	3.42	2.29
1,2,3	$2^7/_8$	3.668	3.460	$5^1/_4$	3.156	$7/_{32}$	3.381	3.277	5.29	3.33
1,2,3	$3^1/_2$	4.500	4.180	$5^3/_4$	3.813	$1/_4$	4.125	3.965	9.02	5.08
1,2	4	5.000	....	6	4.313	$1/_4$	4.625	....	10.62	....
1,2	$4^1/_2$	5.563	....	$6^1/_4$	4.813	$1/_4$	5.156	....	13.31	....

(Headers: Outside Diameter; Maximum Bearing Face Diameter, B_f (Special Bevel, Special Clearance); Weight (lbm) (Regular, Special Clearance))

Note: See API *Spec. 5CT* for nomenclature. *All dimensions in inches.
**Size designation of the coupling is the same as the corresponding pipe size designation.
†Tolerance on outside diameter, W, ±1%. ‡Tolerance on outside diameter, W_c, ±0.015 in.

3.3.3 API Grades. API standardized several grades of steel that have different chemical content, manufacture processes, and heat treatments and, therefore, different mechanical properties. API organized these tubing grades into three groups. Group 1 is for all tubing in grades H40, J55, and N80. Group 2 is for restricted-yield tubing grades L80, C90, and T95. Group 3 is for high-strength tubing in seamless grade P110. The API grade letter designation was selected arbitrarily to provide a unique name for various steels. Numbers in the grade designation indicate the minimum yield strength of the steel in thousand psi. API defines the yield strength as the tensile stress required to produce a specific total elongation per unit length on a standard test specimen. **Table 3.5** lists the manufacture process and heat treatment of API tubing, **Table**

TABLE 3.4—TUBING THREAD GAGE DIMENSIONS
(Reproduced courtesy of the American Petroleum Institute from API *Spec. 5B*[3])*

External-Upset Tubing

OD of Pipe	D_4	D_u	Q	q	Threads Per Inch	E_1	E_7	g	L_1	L_4	U	S
1.050	1.315	1.1438	1.378	0.200	10	1.25328	1.26240	0.500	0.479	1.1250	0.200	0.300
1.315	1.469	1.2976	1.531	0.200	10	1.40706	1.41615	0.500	0.604	1.2500	0.200	0.300
1.660	1.812	1.6413	1.875	0.200	10	1.75079	1.75990	0.500	0.729	1.3750	0.200	0.300
1.900	2.094	1.9226	2.156	0.200	10	2.03206	2.04115	0.500	0.792	1.4375	0.200	0.300
2.375	2.594	2.3912	2.656	0.125	8	2.50775	2.52550	0.500	1.154	1.9375	0.250	0.375
2.875	3.094	2.8912	3.156	0.125	8	3.00775	3.02550	0.500	1.341	2.1250	0.250	0.375
3.500	3.750	3.5475	3.813	0.125	8	3.66395	3.68175	0.500	1.591	2.3750	0.250	0.375
4.000	4.250	4.0475	4.313	0.125	8	4.16395	4.18175	0.500	1.716	2.5000	0.250	0.375
4.500	4.750	4.5475	4.813	0.125	8	4.66395	4.68175	0.500	1.841	2.6250	0.250	0.375

Nonupset Tubing

OD of Pipe	D_4	D_u	Q	q	Threads Per Inch	E_1	E_7	g	L_1	L_4	U	S
1.050	1.050	0.8788	1.113	0.200	10	0.98826	0.99740	0.500	0.448	1.0938	0.200	0.300
1.315	1.315	1.1438	1.378	0.200	10	1.25328	1.26240	0.500	0.479	1.1250	0.200	0.300
1.660	1.660	1.4888	1.723	0.200	10	1.59826	1.60740	0.500	0.604	1.2500	0.200	0.300
1.900	1.900	1.7288	1.963	0.200	10	1.83826	1.84740	0.500	0.729	1.3750	0.200	0.300
2.375	2.375	2.2038	2.438	0.200	10	2.31326	2.32240	0.500	0.979	1.6250	0.200	0.300
2.875	2.875	2.7038	2.938	0.200	10	2.81326	2.82240	0.500	1.417	2.0625	0.200	0.300
3.500	3.500	3.3288	3.563	0.200	10	3.43826	3.44740	0.500	1.667	2.3125	0.200	0.300
4.000	4.000	3.7975	4.063	0.125	8	3.91395	3.93175	0.500	1.591	2.3750	0.250	0.375
4.500	4.500	4.2975	4.563	0.125	8	4.41395	4.43175	0.500	1.779	2.5625	0.250	0.375

Integral-Joint Tubing

OD of Pipe	D_4	D_u	Q	q	Threads Per Inch	E_1	E_7	g	L_1	L_4	U	S
1.315	1.315	1.1438	1.378	0.200	10	1.25328	1.26240	0.500	0.479	1.1250	0.200	0.300
1.660	1.660	1.4888	1.723	0.200	10	1.59826	1.60740	0.500	0.604	1.2500	0.200	0.300
1.900	1.900	1.7288	1.963	0.200	10	1.83826	1.84740	0.500	0.729	1.3750	0.200	0.300
2.063	2.094	1.9226	2.156	0.200	10	2.03206	2.04115	0.500	0.792	1.4375	0.200	0.300

*Included taper on diameter, all sizes, 0.0625 in. per inch.
Note: The 1.315, 1.660, and 1.900 integral-joint tubing gages are identical to nonupset tubing gages of the same size and may be used interchangeably. The 2.063 integral-joint tubing gages are identical to 1.900 external-upset tubing gages and may be used interchangeably. The 1.050 external-upset tubing gages, the 1.315 nonupset tubing gages, and the 1.315 integral-joint tubing gages are identical and may be used interchangeably. See API *Spec. 5B* for nomenclature.

3.6 lists the chemical requirements, and **Table 3.7** lists the API tubing strength and hardness requirements.

    API Tubing Grade Guidelines. The following guidelines apply to the use of API tubing grades.

• H40—Although an API grade, H40 is generally not used in tubing sizes because the yield strength is relatively low and the cost saving over J55 is minimal. Suppliers do not commonly stock this grade.

• J55—A commonly used grade for most wells when it meets the design criteria. Some operators recommend it be full-length normalized or normalized and tempered after upsetting when used in carbon dioxide or sour service (ring-worm corrosion problems); however, such

TABLE 3.5—PROCESS OF MANUFACTURE AND HEAT TREATMENT
(Reproduced courtesy of the American Petroleum Institute from API *Spec 5CT*[10])

Group	Grade	Type	Manufacturing Process	Heat Treatment Process	Minimum Tempering Temperature
1	H40	–	S or EW	None	–
1	J55	–	S or EW	None*,**	–
1	N80	–	S or EW	*	–
2	L80	1	S or EW	Q&T	1,050°F
2	L80	9 Cr	S or EW	Q&T**	1,100°F
2	L80	13 Cr	S or EW	Q&T**	1,100°F
2	C90	1	S	Q&T	1,150°F
2	C90	2	S	Q&T	1,150°F
2	T95	1	S	Q&T	1,200°F
2	T95	2	S	Q&T	1,200°F
3	P110	–	S or EW†	Q&T	–

*Full-length normalized, normalized and tempered (N&T), or quenched and tempered (Q&T) at the manufacturer's option or if so specialized on the purchase order. ** Type 9 Cr and 13 Cr may be air quenched.
†See SR11.

TABLE 3.6—CHEMICAL REQUIREMENTS BY WEIGHT PER CENT
(Reproduced courtesy of the American Petroleum Institute from API *Spec 5CT*[10])

Group	Grade	Type	Carbon Min.	Carbon Max.	Manganese Min.	Manganese Max.	Molybdenum Min.	Molybdenum Max.	Chromium Min.	Chromium Max.	Nickel Max.	Cooper Max.	Phosphorus Max.	Sulfur Max.	Silicon Max.
1	H40	....	....	....	....	....	....	....	....	....	....	....	0.030	0.030	....
1	J55	....	....	....	....	....	....	....	....	....	....	....	0.030	0.030	....
1	N80	....	....	....	....	....	....	....	....	....	....	....	0.030	0.030	....
2	L80	1	....	0.43*	....	1.90	....	....	....	....	0.25	0.35	0.030	0.030	0.45
2	L80	9Cr	....	0.15	0.30	0.60	0.90	1.10	8.0	10.0	0.5	0.25	0.020	0.010	1.00
2	L80	13Cr	0.15	0.22	0.25	1.00	....	....	12.0	14.0	0.5	0.25	0.020	0.010	1.00
2	C90	1	....	0.35	....	1.00	0.25**	0.75	....	1.20	0.99	....	0.020	0.010	....
2	C90	2	....	0.50	....	1.90	....	n.l.†	....	n.l.†	0.99	....	0.030	0.010	....
2	T95	1	....	0.35	....	1.20	0.25‡	0.85	0.40	1.50	0.99	....	0.020	0.010	....
2	T95	2	....	0.50	....	1.90	....	....	....	....	0.99	....	0.030	0.010	....
3	P110	....	....	....	....	....	....	....	....	....	....	....	0.030§	0.030§	....

Note: Elements shown must be reported in product analysis. *The carbon content for L80 may be increased by 0.50% maximum if the product is oil quenched. **Molybdenum content for Grade C90, Type 1 has no minimum tolerance if the wall thickness is < 0.700 in. †n.l. = no limit.
‡Molybdenum content for Grade T95, Type 1 may be increased to 0.15% minimum if the wall thickness is <0.700 in.
§The phosphorus is 0.020% maximum and the sulfur is 0.010 maximum for EW Grade P110.

heat treatments increase costs. J55 has been the "standard" grade for tubing in most relatively shallow (< 9,000 ft) and low-pressure (< 4,000 psi) wells on land.

• C75—No longer an official API grade and generally not available. It was developed as a higher-strength material for sour service but was replaced by L80 tubing.

• N80—A relatively old grade with essentially open chemical requirements. It is susceptible to H_2S-induced SSC. It is acceptable for sweet oil and gas wells when it meets design conditions. The quenched-and-tempered heat treatment is preferred. The N80 grade is normally less expensive than L80 grades.

TABLE 3.7—API TUBING STRENGTH AND HARDNESS REQUIREMENTS
(Reproduced courtesy of the American Petroleum Institute from API *Spec. 5CT*[10])

Group	Grade	Type	Yield Strength (psi)		Minimum Tensile Strength (psi)	Maximum Hardness		Specific Wall	Allowable Hardness
			Minimum	Maximum		HRC*	BHN**		
1	H40	–	40,000	80,000	60,000	...	...		
1	J55	–	55,000	80,000	75,000	...	...		
1	N80	–	80,000	110,000	100,000	...	...		
2	L80	1,9 Cr, 13 Cr	80,000	95,000	95,000	23	241		
2	C90	1, 2 –	90,000	105,000	100,000	25.4	255**	0.500 or less	3.0
2	C90	1, 2 –	90,000	105,000	100,000	25.4	255**	0.501 to 0.749	4.0
2	C90	1, 2 –	90,000	105,000	100,000	25.4	255**	0.750 to 0.999	5.0
2	C90	1, 2 –	90,000	105,000	100,000	25.4	255	1.000 and greater	6.0
2	T95	1,2	95,000	110,000	105,000	25.4	255**	0.500 or less	3.0
2	T95	1,2	95,000	110,000	105,000	25.4	255**	0.501 to 0.749	4.0
2	T95	1,2	95,000	110,000	105,000	25.4	255**	0.750 to 0.999	5.0
3	P110	–	110,000	140,000	125,000	None			

*Hardness-Rockwell C. **Brinell Hardness Number.

• L80—A restricted yield-tubing grade that is available in Type 1, 9 Cr, or 13 Cr. Type 1 is less expensive than 9 Cr and 13 Cr but more subject to weight-loss corrosion. L80 Type 1 is used commonly in many oil and gas fields because of higher strength than J55. L80 is satisfactory for SSC resistance in all conditions but may incur weight-loss corrosion. Though popular in the past for CO_2- and mild H_2S-contaminated wells, Type 9 Cr largely has been replaced by Type 13 Cr. L80 13 Cr tubing has gained popularity because it has good CO_2-induced weight-loss corrosion resistance properties; however, it is more costly. Type 13 Cr may not be suitable in sour service environments. Typically, the H_2S partial pressure should be less than 1.5 psi for safe use of L80 Type 13 Cr. The user should consult National Assn. of Corrosion Engineers (NACE) MR-01-75.[16]

• C90—A relatively new API grade with two different chemical requirements: Type 1 and Type 2. Only Type 1 is recommended for use in sour service. Typically, this grade must be special ordered; its use has been generally supplanted by T95.

• T95—A high-strength tubular grade that has different chemical requirements: Type 1 and Type 2. Only Type 1 is recommended for sour service. T95 is SSC resistant but not weight-loss resistant.

• P110—The old P105 tubing grade, which allowed a normalized and tempered heat treatment, was discontinued, and the casing P110 grade, which is restricted to quench-and-tempered heat treatment, was adopted. This high-strength tubing typically is used in deep sweet oil and gas wells with high pressures. This grade is sensitive to SSC failures unless the temperatures are relatively high (> 175°F). The P110 grade is slightly more expensive than L80 Type 1 but usually less expensive than the C90 and T95 API restricted-yield grades.

• Q125—Although not a specific API tubing grade, users can order Q125 API tubing. Type 1 chemistry is preferred.

3.3.4 API Markings. API products (tubing, pup joints, and couplings) should be stenciled or a combination of stamping and stenciling as per API *Spec. 5CT*. The sequence of stencil marking is as follows: manufacturer's name, monogram marking, end finish, size designation, weight designation, grade and type, impact test temperature, heat treatment, manufacture process, supplementary requirements, hydrostatic test pressure, type of thread, size of drift, serialization of Grades C-90 and T-95, and plating of coupling. Impact test temperature, heat

TABLE 3.8—API TUBING COLOR CODE
(Reproduced courtesy of the American Petroleum Institute from API *Spec. 5CT*[10])

Group	Grade	Type	Mark	Color Coding	
				Tubing and Pup Joints	Couplings
1	H40	–	H	No color marking or black band	Same
1	J55	–	J	One bright green band	Entire coupling bright green
1	N80	–	N	One red band	Entire coupling red
2	L80	1	L	One red and one brown band	Red with one brown band
2	L80	9 Cr	L9	One red, one brown, and two yellow bands	Red with two yellow bands
2	L80	13 Cr	L13	One red, one brown, and one yellow band	Red with one yellow band
2	C90	1	C90-1	One purple band	Entire coupling purple
2	C90	2	C90-2	One purple band, one yellow band	Purple with yellow band
2	T95	1	T1	One silver band	Entire coupling silver
2	T95	2	T2	One silver band, one yellow band	Silver with one yellow band
3	P110	–	P	One white band	Entire coupling white

TABLE 3.9—TUBING LENGTH AND SIZE TOLERANCES
(Reproduced courtesy of the American Petroleum Institute
from API *Spec. 5CT*[10])

Pipe Size (OD) (in.)	Tolerance (in.)	
2.375 to 3.5	$+\,^3/_{32}$	$-^1/_{32}$
4.0	$+\,^7/_{64}$	$-^1/_{32}$
> 4.0	$+\,^7/_{64}$	-.075%
Wall thickness, t	-12.5%	
Weight		
Single lengths, %	+6.5 and -3.5	
Carload lots, %	-1.75	

Tubing	Drift Mandrel Length (in.)	Minimum ID* (in.)
2⅞ and smaller	42	$-^3/_{32}$
3½ and larger	42	$-^1/_8$

*Minimum inside diameter (ID) is governed by the outside diameter and weight tolerances.

treatment, supplementary requirements, type of thread, and plating of coupling are included if applicable. **Table 3.8** shows tubing color coding.

3.3.5 Tubing Range (Length) and Size Tolerances. API acknowledges two tubing length ranges: Range 1 from 20 to 24 ft and Range 2 from 28 to 32 ft. Range 2 is normally used. Shorter tubing joints (pup joints) are available in 2-, 3-, 4-, 6-, 8-, 10-, and 12-ft lengths with a tolerance of ± 3 in. A complete set of tubing pups with the same connections as the tubing string typically is purchased for each well. **Table 3.9** shows the tolerances on dimensions and weight.

TABLE 3.10—DESIGN FACTOR GUIDELINES

	Range	Suggested
Internal pressure	1.00 to 1.33	1.25
Joint or body yield strength in tension	1.0 to 1.8	1.25*, 1.6**
Collapse resistance	1.0 to 1.25	1.1

*For pulling; **Based on tubing weight in air.

3.3.6 API Test Pressures. API requires that plain-end pipe be tested only to 3,000 psi maximum, except by agreement between the purchaser and the manufacturer. Various tubing grades and sizes can be tested hydrostatically to higher values as listed in API *Spec. 5CT*. The API hydrostatic test pressures specified are inspection test pressures. They do not necessarily have any direct relationship to working pressures but should be considered when establishing design factors. Care should be taken if test pressures are to be exceeded in well operations. The following equation is used to determine the maximum hydrostatic test pressure.

$$p_h = \frac{2 \times (0.8 \times \sigma_y \times t)}{d_o}, \quad\quad\quad\quad (3.1)$$

where p_h = the 80% hydrostatic test pressure (rounded to the nearest 100 psi); σ_y = yield strength for pipe body, psi; t = wall thickness, in.; and d_o = tubing OD, in.

A maximum test pressure during manufacturing of 10,000 psi is imposed because of test equipment limitations. Manufacturers also can conduct hydrostatic tests at a fiber stress not exceeding 80% of the specified minimum yield strength. The hydrostatic test pressures are calculated from Eq. 3.1, except when a lower pressure is required to avoid leakage because of insufficient coupling strength or interface pressure between pipe and coupling threads. The lower pressures are based on formulas given in API *Bull. 5C3*.[7] The production hydrostatic test pressure for threaded pipe are standard pressures listed in the API tables or a higher test pressure as agreed on by the purchaser and the entity performing the threading.

3.4 Tubing Design Factors
A design factor is the specific load rating divided by the specific anticipated load. A design factor less than 1.0 does not necessarily mean the product will fail, and neither does a design factor in excess of 1.0 mean that the product will not fail. As a result, design factors are generally selected on the basis of experience. The designer has the responsibility to select the design factors to suit particular needs and to reflect field experience. The condition of the tubing and the severity of a failure should have a significant effect on the design factors used. Design factors greater than 1.0 are recommended. **Table 3.10** contains design factor guidelines.

The internal-yield pressure rating for tubing is based on an API variation of Barlow's formula and incorporates a 0.875 factor that compensates for the 12.5% reduction tolerance in wall thickness allowed in manufacturing.

$$p_{yi} = \frac{0.875 \times 2 \times \sigma_y \times t}{d_o}. \quad\quad\quad\quad (3.2)$$

**TABLE 3.11—APPROXIMATE MAXIMUM SETTING DEPTHS*
FOR A SINGLE WEIGHT AND GRADE TUBING IN AIR****

Grade	Design Factor			
	1.0	1.25	1.6	1.8
H40	11,200	8,960	7,000	6,222
J55	15,400	12,320	9,625	8,555
N80 and L80	22,400	17,920	14,000	12,444
C90	25,200	20,160	15,750	14,000
T95	26,600	21,280	16,625	14,777
P110	30,800	24,640	19,250	17,111

*In feet. **Based on API minimum yield strength, tube-wall area, and average weight per foot. Assumes no buoyancy and 100% joint/body strength.

In general, these values should not be exceeded in operation. To be on the safe side, a minimum design factor of 1.25 based on the internal-yield pressure rating is suggested; however, some operators use different values.

In medium to high pressure wells, especially in sour service when L80, C90, and T95 API grades are used, the general stress level in the tubing should not exceed the minimum yield strength for L80 or the SSC threshold stress (generally 80% of the minimum yield strength) for C90 and T95 grades.

The joint or body yield strength for the tension design factor varies widely in practice. A simple approach is to assume a relatively high design factor of 1.6 based on the tubing weight in air and ignore other loading conditions. The calculations for loads in tension are usually for static conditions and ignore dynamic loads that may occur in running and pulling the tubing. They also may ignore collapse loads that reduce tension strengths. The pulling or drag loads are not commonly known. These may be relatively high in directional wells. Typically, the highest loads in tension occur in unsetting the packer during pulling operations. In some cases, shear pins in packers result in substantial loads in unsetting that should be accounted for in design.

The condition of the tubing after several years of service in the well is another unknown that needs to be compensated for either in design or by use of a higher tension design factor. When considering all these factors and making adjustments for drag, shear pins, and collapse pressures, a minimum design factor of 1.25 in tension for pulling is suggested. However, field experience has shown, in general, that tubing in new condition (meets API minimum requirements) can be loaded in tension to its minimum yield joint strength during pulling operations without a tension failure. Tension failures during pulling operations should be avoided because the results usually are costly. It is better to cut or back off the tubing rather than have a tension failure. **Table 3.11** shows approximate setting depths for various API grades.

A collapse resistance design of 1.1 is suggested. Collapse resistance for tubing is covered in API *Bull. 5C3*.[7] This standard provides conservative values for design, assuming the tubing cross section is not abnormally elliptical (oval). Any mechanical deformity in the tubing resulting in an out-of-round cross section may cause a considerable reduction in its collapse resistance. The collapse resistance value for a given tubing size, weight, and grade is based on numerous experimental tests and strength of material equations. The minimum value is designated as the API collapse resistance rating. Collapse ratings are reduced by tension loading. For example, a 23% yield stress in tension reduces the collapse resistance by approximately 14%. The biaxial effect should be used to design the tubing for critical tension and collapse conditions. **Fig. 3.2** shows an ellipse of biaxial yield stress.

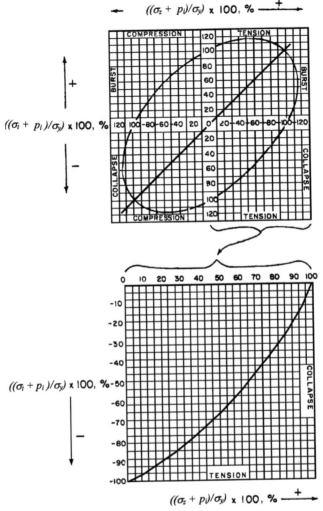

Fig. 3.2—Ellipse of biaxial yield stress.

3.4.1 Tubing Design Considerations. Tubing string design must consider all reasonably anticipated loads imposed during running, producing, stimulation, workovers, and pulling operations. The design must ensure that failures will not occur under these operations; however, the designer typically selects the most economical weight and grade that meets the performance requirements. Computer software is available for tubing design, but the designer must ensure that all design conditions are met adequately.

A reasonable approach must be taken to prevent overdesign. The design need not prevent worst-case scenario failures but rather for all cases that have a reasonable probability of occurring. For instance, assume that there is a shallow tubing leak in which the shut-in tubing pressure is applied in the casing annulus on top of a column of heavy annulus fluid and, subsequently, that the tubing pressure at bottom is reduced quickly to a low value. This event would require tubing with a very high collapse pressure rating. If such a condition is considered to have a reasonable probability of occurring, the tubing string should be designed accordingly or adequate steps should be taken to prevent such a series of events.

The highest tensile loads normally occur at or near the top (surface) of the well. Collapse loads reduce the permitted tension loads, as shown by the biaxial graph in Fig. 3.2, and should be considered when applicable. Fortunately, the casing annulus pressure is normally low at the surface; thus, collapse pressure effects at the surface often can be ignored, but not in all cases. Buoyancy, which reduces the tensile loads, is sometimes ignored on shallow wells, but it should be considered on deeper wells. A condition that frequently determines the required tension yield strength of the tubing occurs when unsetting a partially stuck packer or using a shear-pin-release type packer in wells in which buoyancy is not applicable.

High-burst tubing loads typically occur near the surface with little or no annulus pressure under shut-in tubing conditions or during well stimulation treatments down the tubing. High-burst conditions also may occur deep in the hole with high surface pressures imposed on top of relatively high-density tubing fluid and when the annulus is empty or contains a light-density annulus fluid. Both of these conditions must be evaluated during the design of a tubing string for a specific well.

The burst resistance of the tube is increased because of tension loading up to a certain limit. In tubing- and casing-design practice, it is customary to apply the ellipse of plasticity only when a detrimental effect results. For a conservative design, this increase in burst resistance normally is ignored. Compression loads reduce burst resistance and must be considered when they occur. Such a condition can occur near the bottom of the well with a set-down packer and a relatively high internal tubing pressure and a relatively low annulus pressure. A typical design case in burst is to assume that the tubing is full of produced fluid and that the annulus is empty, which is a common situation for pumped wells.

Because tension loading reduces collapse resistance, the biaxial effect should be used to design for problem regions. A common practice in tubing design is to assume that the tubing is empty and that the annulus is full of fluid. Such conditions are common in low-pressure gas wells or oil wells that may be swabbed to bottom. Typically, the highest collapse pressures are near the bottom of the well. For combination tubing-string design, the collapse and tensile loads should be evaluated at the bottom and top of any tubing size, weight, or grade change.

In directional wells, the effect of the wellbore curvature and vertical deviation angle on the axial stress on the tubing body and couplings/joints must be considered in the tubing design. Current design practice considers the detrimental effects of tubing bending, but the favorable effect (friction while running) is neglected. Wall friction, which is unfavorable for upward pipe movement, generally is compensated for by addition of an acceptable overpull to the free-hanging axial tension. Overpull values are best obtained from field experience but can be calculated with available commercial software computer programs.

3.4.2 Single and Combination/Tapered Tubing Design. Many operators prefer one uniform weight (constant ID) and API grade tubing from top to bottom. Thus, it is not possible to mix different sections of the tubing during running or pulling operations throughout the life of the well. Most relatively shallow (< 9,000 ft), low-pressure (< 4,000 psi) wells have noncombination strings. As the pressures and depths increase, there comes a point at which a higher grade (stronger) or heavier weight (increased wall thickness) tubing must be used to meet load conditions and achieve acceptable design factors. For the same size diameter tubing, a higher grade normally is preferred over an increase in tubing weight. Such a choice is usually less expensive and maintains a constant internal diameter, which simplifies wireline operation inside the tubing.

Unlike casing design, which often has numerous grades and weights in a combination design, tubing design seldom has more than two different grades or weights. Such restriction may increase the cost of the tubing string but simplifies the running and pulling procedures. Deep and high-pressure wells may require more than two weights, grades, or diameters. When more than one grade or weight are used, each should be easily identifiable. To separate different weights and grades, a pup joint or different collar types may be used. For example, one section could use standard couplings and another could use beveled couplings. Painted and stenciled markings on the outside of the tubing are inadequate once the tubing is used because such markings are often obliterated.

The use of two or three different diameter sizes is sometimes advantageous. The larger tubing size may have high-joint-yield strength and permit a higher flow rate. The largest diameter is run on the top and a smaller tubing size on bottom. In such cases, the surface wellhead valves often are sized to permit wireline work in the larger tubing to prevent operational problems. A smaller tubing OD size on bottom may be necessary because of casing diameter restrictions.

3.4.3 Tubing Outside Diameter Limitations. The tubing OD must have adequate clearance with the casing ID. The tubing size selected should permit washover and fishing operations, in case the tubing becomes stuck and requires recovery. A wash pipe must be available that has an outside coupling dimension less than the casing drift diameter and an internal drift diameter that is greater than the tubing coupling OD plus provide a minimum of ⅛-in. clearance for adequate circulation. Also, the tubing OD should permit use of an overshot inside the casing, which limits the tubing OD size and/or the coupling OD. For example, 3½-in. OD tubing with regular API EUE couplings (OD = 4.500 in.) inside 5½-in., 17.00 casing (drift diameter = 4.767 in.) could not be washed over with available wash pipe. Even 3½-in. specialty joint tubing with a joint OD of 3.875 in. would be an impractical, risky washover operation because the couplings would require milling. Nevertheless, special circumstances may require special proprietary tubing in close tolerance applications. Special wash-pipe sizes often can be rented from the tool service companies. The tubing designer should check the success of washover and fishing operations for their particular planned condition and the area of operation.

Multicompletions with parallel tubing strings often result in limiting the tubing and/or coupling size. If two tubing strings are to be run and pulled independently, the sum of the tubing coupling ODs should be less than the casing drift diameter. For example, inside 7-29.00 casing with a drift diameter of 6.059 in., parallel 2⅜-in. tubing strings with EUE couplings may be planned. In such a case, beveled and special-clearance couplings with an OD of 2.910 in. typically are used. The sum of the two ODs is 5.82 in. Experience shows that if the couplings are beveled (top and bottom), these strings can be run and pulled independently. The auxiliary tubing equipment such as gas lift mandrels and safety valves often cause more clearance problems than the tubing couplings.

If two tubing strings are to be run clamped together, then the sum of the smaller tubing body OD and the OD of the coupling of the second or larger string must be less than the casing drift diameter. In these cases, a full-size drawing of the cross sections of the tubulars used may be helpful. The actual clearance may depend on the clamp design. The use of parallel strings of 3½-in. tubing inside 9⅝-in. casing is another common practice, and tubing OD limitations must be considered in such installations.

3.4.4 API Minimum Performance Properties of Tubing. Tubing performance properties are found in API *Bull. 5C2*,[6] and the formulas used in the following examples are found in API *Bull. 5C3*.[7] **Table 3.12** shows minimum tubing performance properties.

Example 3.1 Design a tubing string for a 9,000-ft hydropressured vertical well that is relatively straight, that will be used to flow 500 BOPD, and that will be completed inside 4½-11.60-K55 casing. The well is to be completed with compression-set type packer and 9.0 ppg inhibited salt water in annulus. An overpull to free the packer of 15,000 lbf is anticipated. A maximum surface-treating pressure of 3,000 psi is expected.

TABLE 3.12—MINIMUM PERFORMANCE PROPERTIES OF TUBING (Reproduced courtesy of the American Petroleum Institute from API BULL. 5C2[2])

Column groupings: Columns 2–4 = Nominal Weight (Threaded and Coupled Non-upset / Upset; Integral Joint). Columns 9–13 = Coupling Outside Diameter (Threaded and Coupled Non-upset; Upset Regular / Special Clearance; Integral Joint Drift Diameter / OD of Box). Columns 14–19 = Internal Yield Pressure (Collapse Resistance; Plain End; Threaded and Coupled Nonupset; Upset Regular / Special Clearance; Integral Joint). Columns 20–24 = Joint Yield Strength (F) (Pipe Body Yield; Threaded and Coupled Nonupset; Upset Regular / Special Clearance; Integral Joint).

1	2	3	4	5	6	7	8	9	10	11	12	13	14	15	16	17	18	19	20	21	22	23	24
Size OD, D (in.)	Non-upset (lbm/ft)	Upset (lbm/ft)	Integral Joint (lbm/ft)	Grade	Wall Thickness, t (in.)	d (in.)	Drift Diameter (in.)	Non-upset W (in.)	Regular W (in.)	Special Clearance W_c (in.)	Drift Diameter (in.)	OD of Box (in.)	Collapse Resistance (psi)	Plain End (psi)	Nonupset (psi)	Regular (psi)	Special Clearance (psi)	Integral Joint (psi)	Pipe Body Yield (lbf)	Nonupset (lbf)	Regular (lbf)	Special Clearance (lbf)	Integral Joint (lbf)
1.050	1.14	1.20	—	H-40	.113	.824	.730	1.313	1.660	—	—	—	7,680	7,530	7,530	7,530	—	—	13,320	6,320	13,320	—	—
1.050	—	1.54	—	H-40	.154	.742	.648	—	1.660	—	—	—	10,010	10,270	—	9,420	—	—	17,320	—	17,320	—	—
1.050	1.14	1.20	—	J-55	.113	.824	.730	1.313	1.660	—	—	—	10,560	10,360	10,360	10,360	—	—	18,320	8,690	18,320	—	—
1.050	—	1.54	—	J-55	.154	.742	.648	—	1.660	—	—	—	13,770	14,120	—	12,950	—	—	23,820	—	23,820	—	—
1.050	1.14	1.20	—	L-80	.113	.824	.730	1.313	1.660	—	—	—	15,370	15,070	15,070	15,070	—	—	26,640	12,640	26,640	—	—
1.050	—	1.54	—	L-80	.154	.742	.648	—	1.660	—	—	—	20,020	20,530	—	18,840	—	—	34,640	—	34,640	—	—
1.050	1.14	1.20	—	N-80	.113	.824	.730	1.313	1.660	—	—	—	15,370	15,070	15,070	15,070	—	—	26,640	12,640	26,640	—	—
1.050	—	1.54	—	N-80	.154	.742	.648	—	1.660	—	—	—	20,020	20,530	—	18,840	—	—	34,640	—	34,640	—	—
1.050	1.14	1.20	—	C-90	.113	.824	.730	1.313	1.660	—	—	—	17,290	16,950	16,950	16,950	—	—	29,970	14,220	29,970	—	—
1.050	—	1.54	—	C-90	.154	.742	.648	—	1.660	—	—	—	22,530	23,100	—	21,200	—	—	38,970	—	38,970	—	—
1.050	1.14	1.20	—	T-95	.113	.824	.730	1.313	1.660	—	—	—	18,250	17,890	17,890	17,890	—	—	31,640	15,010	31,640	—	—
1.050	—	1.54	—	T-95	.154	.742	.648	—	1.660	—	—	—	23,780	24,380	—	22,380	—	—	41,140	—	41,140	—	—
1.050	—	1.54	—	P-110	.154	.742	.648	—	1.660	—	—	—	27,530	28,230	—	25,910	—	—	47,630	—	47,630	—	—
1.315	1.70	1.80	1.72	H-40	.133	1.049	.955	1.660	1.900	—	.955	1.550	7,270	7,080	7,080	7,080	—	7,080	19,760	10,920	19,760	—	15,940
1.315	—	2.24	—	H-40	.179	.957	.863	—	1.900	—	—	—	9,410	9,530	—	9,530	—	—	25,560	—	25,560	—	—
1.315	1.70	1.80	1.72	J-55	.133	1.049	.955	1.660	1.900	—	.955	1.550	10,000	9,730	9,730	9,730	—	9,730	27,170	15,020	27,170	—	21,910
1.315	—	2.24	—	J-55	.179	.957	.863	—	1.900	—	—	—	12,940	13,100	—	13,100	—	—	35,150	—	35,150	—	—
1.315	1.70	1.80	1.72	L-80	.133	1.049	.955	1.660	1.900	—	.955	1.550	14,550	14,160	14,160	14,160	—	14,160	39,520	21,840	39,520	—	31,870
1.315	—	2.24	—	L-80	.179	.957	.863	—	1.900	—	—	—	18,810	19,060	—	19,060	—	—	51,120	—	51,120	—	—
1.315	1.70	1.80	1.72	N-80	.133	1.049	.955	1.660	1.900	—	.955	1.550	14,550	14,160	14,160	14,160	—	14,160	39,520	21,840	39,520	—	31,870
1.315	—	2.24	—	N-80	.179	.957	.863	—	1.900	—	—	—	18,810	19,060	—	19,060	—	—	51,120	—	51,120	—	—
1.315	1.70	1.80	1.72	C-90	.133	1.049	.955	1.660	1.900	—	.955	1.550	16,360	15,930	15,930	15,930	—	15,930	44,460	24,570	44,460	—	35,860
1.315	—	2.24	—	C-90	.179	.957	.863	—	1.900	—	—	—	21,170	21,440	—	21,440	—	—	57,510	—	57,510	—	—
1.315	1.70	1.80	1.72	T-95	.133	1.049	.955	1.660	1.900	—	.955	1.550	17,270	16,810	16,810	16,810	—	16,810	46,930	25,940	46,930	—	37,850
1.315	—	2.24	—	T-95	.179	.957	.863	—	1.900	—	—	—	22,340	22,630	—	22,630	—	—	60,710	—	60,710	—	—
1.315	—	2.24	—	P-110	.179	.957	.863	—	1.900	—	—	—	25,870	26,200	—	26,200	—	—	70,290	—	70,290	—	—
1.660	—	—	2.10	H-40	.125	1.410	1.316	—	—	—	1.316	1.880	5,570	5,270	—	—	—	5,270	24,120	—	—	—	22,230
1.660	2.30	2.40	2.33	H-40	.140	1.380	1.286	2.054	2.200	—	1.286	1.880	6,180	5,900	5,900	5,900	—	5,810	26,760	15,480	26,760	—	22,230
1.660	—	3.07	—	H-40	.191	1.278	1.184	—	2.200	—	—	—	8,150	8,050	—	8,050	—	—	35,240	—	35,240	—	—
1.660	—	—	2.10	J-55	.125	1.410	1.316	—	—	—	1.316	1.880	7,660	7,250	—	—	—	7,250	33,170	—	—	—	30,560
1.660	2.30	2.40	2.33	J-55	.140	1.380	1.286	2.054	2.200	—	1.286	1.880	8,490	8,120	8,120	8,120	—	7,990	36,800	21,290	36,800	—	30,560
1.660	—	3.07	—	L-80	.191	1.278	1.184	—	2.200	—	—	—	11,200	11,070	—	11,070	—	—	48,460	—	48,460	—	—
1.660	2.30	2.40	2.33	L-80	.140	1.380	1.286	2.054	2.200	—	1.286	1.880	12,360	11,810	11,810	11,810	—	11,620	53,520	30,960	53,520	—	44,460
1.660	—	3.07	—	L-80	.191	1.278	1.184	—	2.200	—	—	—	16,290	16,110	—	16,110	—	—	70,480	—	70,480	—	—
1.660	2.30	2.40	2.33	N-80	.140	1.380	1.286	2.054	2.200	—	1.286	1.880	12,360	11,810	11,810	11,810	—	11,620	53,520	30,960	53,520	—	44,460
1.660	—	3.07	—	N-80	.191	1.278	1.184	—	2.200	—	—	—	16,290	16,110	—	16,110	—	—	70,480	—	70,480	—	—
1.660	2.30	2.40	2.33	C-90	.140	1.380	1.286	2.054	2.200	—	1.286	1.880	13,900	13,280	13,280	13,280	—	13,070	60,210	34,830	60,210	—	50,010
1.660	—	3.07	—	C-90	.191	1.278	1.184	—	2.200	—	—	—	18,330	18,120	—	18,120	—	—	79,290	—	79,290	—	—
1.660	2.30	2.40	2.33	T-95	.140	1.380	1.286	2.054	2.200	—	1.286	1.880	14,670	14,020	14,020	14,020	—	13,800	63,560	36,770	63,560	—	52,790
1.660	—	3.07	—	T-95	.191	1.278	1.184	—	2.200	—	—	—	19,350	19,130	—	19,130	—	—	83,700	—	83,700	—	—
1.660	—	3.07	—	P-110	.191	1.278	1.184	—	2.200	—	—	—	22,400	22,150	—	22,150	—	—	96,910	—	96,910	—	—
1.900	—	—	2.40	H-40	.125	1.650	1.556	—	—	—	1.556	2.110	4,920	4,610	—	—	—	4,610	27,880	—	—	—	26,940
1.900	2.75	2.90	2.76	H-40	.145	1.610	1.516	2.200	2.500	—	1.516	2.110	5,640	5,340	5,340	5,340	—	5,140	31,960	19,040	31,960	—	26,940
1.900	—	3.73	—	H-40	.200	1.500	1.406	2.200	2.500	—	—	—	7,530	7,370	7,370	7,370	—	—	42,720	—	42,720	—	—
1.900	—	—	2.40	J-55	.125	1.650	1.556	—	—	—	1.556	2.110	6,640	6,330	—	—	—	6,330	38,340	—	—	—	37,040
1.900	2.75	2.90	2.76	J-55	.145	1.610	1.516	2.200	2.500	—	1.516	2.110	7,750	7,350	7,350	7,350	—	7,060	43,950	26,180	43,950	—	37,040
1.900	—	3.73	—	J-55	.200	1.500	1.406	2.200	2.500	—	—	—	10,360	10,130	10,130	10,130	—	—	58,740	—	58,740	—	—
1.900	2.75	2.90	2.76	L-80	.145	1.610	1.516	2.200	2.500	—	1.516	2.110	11,280	10,680	10,680	10,680	—	10,270	63,920	38,080	63,920	—	53,880
1.900	—	3.73	—	L-80	.200	1.500	1.406	2.200	2.500	—	—	—	15,070	14,740	14,740	14,740	—	—	85,440	—	85,440	—	—
1.900	4.42	—	—	L-80	.250	1.400	1.306	2.200	—	—	—	—	18,280	18,420	18,420	—	—	—	103,680	—	—	—	—
1.900	5.15	—	—	L-80	.300	1.300	1.206	2.200	—	—	—	—	21,270	22,110	22,110	—	—	—	120,640	—	—	—	—
1.900	2.75	2.90	2.76	N-80	.145	1.610	1.516	2.200	2.500	—	1.516	2.110	11,280	10,680	10,680	10,680	—	10,270	63,920	38,080	63,920	—	53,880

TABLE 3.12—MINIMUM PERFORMANCE PROPERTIES OF TUBING (continued)

1	2	3	4	5	6	7	8	9	10	11	12	13	14	15	16	17	18	19	20	21	22	23	24
	Nominal Weight							Threaded and Coupled						Internal Yield Pressure					Joint Yield Strength (F_j)				
	Threaded and Coupled							Coupling Outside Diameter			Integral Joint				Threaded and Coupled					Threaded and Coupled			
									Upset							Upset					Upset		
Size OD, D (in.)	Non-upset (lbm/ft)	Upset (lbm/ft)	Integral Joint (lbm/ft)	Grade	Wall Thickness, t (in.)	d (in.)	Drift Diameter (in.)	Non-upset W (in.)	Regular W (in.)	Special Clearance W_c (in.)	Drift Diameter (in.)	OD of Box (in.)	Collapse Resistance	Plain End	Nonupset (psi)	Regular (psi)	Special Clearance (psi)	Integral Joint (lbf)	Pipe Body Yield (lbf)	Nonupset (lbf)	Regular (lbf)	Special Clearance (lbf)	Integral Joint (lbf)
1.900	—	3.73	—	N-80	.200	1.500	1.406	—	2.500	—	—	—	15,070	14,740	—	14,740	—	—	85,440	—	85,440	—	—
1.900	2.75	2.90	2.76	C-90	.145	1.610	1.516	2.000	2.500	—	1.516	2.110	12,620	12,020	12,020	12,020	—	11,560	71,910	42,840	71,910	—	60,610
1.900	—	3.73	—	C-90	.200	1.500	1.406	—	2.500	—	—	—	16,950	16,580	—	16,580	—	—	96,120	—	96,120	—	—
1.900	4.42	—	—	C-90	.250	1.400	1.306	—	—	—	—	—	20,570	20,720	—	—	—	—	116,640	—	—	—	—
1.900	5.15	—	—	C-90	.300	1.300	1.206	—	—	—	—	—	23,930	24,870	—	—	—	—	135,720	—	—	—	—
1.900	2.75	2.90	2.76	T-95	.145	1.610	1.516	2.200	2.500	—	1.516	2.110	13,190	12,690	12,690	12,690	—	12,200	75,910	45,220	75,910	—	63,980
1.900	—	3.73	—	T-95	.200	1.500	1.406	—	2.500	—	—	—	17,890	17,500	—	17,500	—	—	101,460	—	101,460	—	—
1.900	4.42	—	—	T-95	.250	1.400	1.306	—	—	—	—	—	21,710	21,880	—	—	—	—	123,120	—	—	—	—
1.900	5.15	—	—	T-95	.300	1.300	1.206	—	—	—	—	—	25,260	26,250	—	—	—	—	143,260	—	—	—	—
1.900	—	3.73	—	P-110	.200	1.500	1.406	—	2.500	—	—	—	20,720	20,260	—	20,260	—	—	117,480	—	117,480	—	—
2.063	—	—	3.25	H-40	.156	1.751	1.657	—	—	—	1.657	2.325	5,590	5,290	—	—	—	5,090	37,400	—	—	—	35,800
2.063	4.50	—	—	H-40	.225	1.613	1.519	—	—	—	—	—	7,770	7,630	—	—	—	—	52,000	—	—	—	—
2.063	—	—	3.25	J-55	.156	1.751	1.657	—	—	—	1.657	2.325	7,690	7,280	—	—	—	7,000	51,400	—	—	—	49,300
2.063	4.50	—	—	J-55	.225	1.613	1.519	—	—	—	—	—	10,690	10,500	—	—	—	—	71,400	—	—	—	—
2.063	—	—	3.25	L-80	.156	1.751	1.657	—	—	—	1.657	2.325	11,180	10,590	—	—	—	10,180	74,800	—	—	—	71,700
2.063	4.50	—	—	L-80	.225	1.613	1.519	—	—	—	—	—	15,550	15,270	—	—	—	—	103,900	—	—	—	—
2.063	—	—	3.25	N-80	.156	1.751	1.657	—	—	—	1.657	2.325	11,180	10,590	—	—	—	10,180	74,800	—	—	—	71,700
2.063	4.50	—	—	N-80	.225	1.613	1.519	—	—	—	—	—	15,550	15,270	—	—	—	—	103,900	—	—	—	—
2.063	—	—	3.25	C-90	.156	1.751	1.657	—	—	—	1.657	2.325	12,420	11,910	—	—	—	11,460	84,200	—	—	—	80,700
2.063	4.50	—	—	C-90	.225	1.613	1.519	—	—	—	—	—	17,490	17,180	—	—	—	—	116,900	—	—	—	—
2.063	—	—	3.25	T-95	.156	1.751	1.657	—	—	—	1.657	2.325	12,980	12,570	—	—	—	12,090	88,800	—	—	—	85,100
2.063	4.50	—	—	T-95	.225	1.613	1.519	—	—	—	—	—	18,460	18,130	—	—	—	—	123,400	—	—	—	—
2.063	4.50	—	—	P-110	.225	1.613	1.519	—	—	—	—	—	21,380	20,990	—	—	—	—	142,900	—	—	—	—
2.375	4.00	—	—	H-40	.167	2.041	1.947	2.875	—	—	—	—	5,230	4,920	4,920	—	—	—	46,300	30,100	—	—	—
2.375	4.60	4.70	—	H-40	.190	1.995	1.901	2.875	3.063	2.910	—	—	5,890	5,600	5,600	5,600	5,600	—	52,200	35,900	52,200	52,200	—
2.375	4.00	—	—	J-55	.167	2.041	1.947	2.875	—	—	—	—	7,190	6,770	6,770	—	—	—	63,700	41,400	—	—	—
2.375	4.60	4.70	—	J-55	.190	1.995	1.901	2.875	3.063	2.910	—	—	8,100	7,700	7,700	7,700	7,700	—	71,700	49,400	71,700	71,700	—
2.375	4.00	—	—	L-80	.167	2.041	1.947	2.875	—	—	—	—	9,980	9,840	9,840	—	—	—	92,600	60,200	—	—	—
2.375	4.60	4.70	—	L-80	.190	1.995	1.901	2.875	3.063	2.910	—	—	11,780	11,200	11,200	11,200	11,200	—	104,300	71,800	104,300	104,300	—
2.375	5.80	5.95	—	L-80	.254	1.867	1.773	2.875	3.063	2.910	—	—	15,280	14,970	14,970	14,860	11,440	—	135,400	102,900	135,400	135,400	—
2.375	6.60	—	—	L-80	.295	1.785	1.691	—	—	—	—	—	17,410	17,390	—	—	—	—	154,200	—	—	—	—
2.375	7.35	7.45	—	L-80	.336	1.703	1.609	—	3.063	2.910	—	—	19,430	19,810	—	14,860	11,440	—	172,200	—	172,200	141,300	—
2.375	4.00	—	—	N-80	.167	2.041	1.947	2.875	—	—	—	—	9,980	9,840	9,840	—	—	—	92,600	60,200	—	—	—
2.375	4.60	4.70	—	N-80	.190	1.995	1.901	2.875	3.063	2.910	—	—	11,780	11,200	11,200	11,200	11,200	—	104,300	71,800	104,300	104,300	—
2.375	5.80	5.95	—	N-80	.254	1.867	1.773	2.875	3.063	2.910	—	—	15,280	14,970	14,970	14,860	11,440	—	135,400	102,900	135,400	135,400	—
2.375	4.00	—	—	C-90	.167	2.041	1.947	2.875	—	—	—	—	10,940	11,070	11,070	—	—	—	104,200	67,700	—	—	—
2.375	4.60	4.70	—	C-90	.190	1.995	1.901	2.875	3.063	2.910	—	—	13,250	12,600	12,600	12,600	12,600	—	117,400	80,800	117,400	117,400	—
2.375	5.80	5.95	—	C-90	.254	1.867	1.773	2.875	3.063	2.910	—	—	17,190	16,840	16,840	16,720	12,870	—	152,300	115,700	152,300	152,300	—
2.375	6.60	—	—	C-90	.295	1.785	1.691	—	—	—	—	—	19,580	19,560	—	—	—	—	173,500	—	—	—	—
2.375	7.35	7.45	—	C-90	.336	1.703	1.609	—	3.063	2.910	—	—	21,860	22,280	—	16,720	12,870	—	193,700	—	193,700	159,000	—
2.375	4.00	—	—	T-95	.167	2.041	1.947	—	—	—	—	—	11,410	11,690	—	—	—	—	110,000	—	—	—	—
2.375	4.60	4.70	—	T-95	.190	1.995	1.901	2.875	3.063	2.910	—	—	13,980	13,300	13,300	13,300	13,300	—	123,900	85,300	123,900	123,900	—
2.375	5.80	5.95	—	T-95	.254	1.867	1.773	2.875	3.063	2.910	—	—	18,150	17,780	17,780	17,650	13,580	—	160,700	122,200	160,700	160,700	—
2.375	6.60	—	—	T-95	.295	1.785	1.691	—	—	—	—	—	20,670	20,650	—	—	—	—	183,200	—	—	—	—
2.375	7.35	7.45	—	T-95	.336	1.703	1.609	—	3.063	2.910	—	—	23,080	23,520	—	17,650	13,580	—	204,400	—	204,400	167,800	—
2.375	4.60	4.70	—	P-110	.190	1.995	1.901	2.875	3.063	2.910	—	—	16,130	15,400	15,400	15,400	15,400	—	143,400	98,800	143,400	143,400	—
2.375	5.80	5.95	—	P-110	.254	1.867	1.773	2.875	3.063	2.910	—	—	21,010	20,590	20,590	20,430	15,730	—	186,100	141,500	186,100	186,100	—
2.875	6.40	6.50	—	H-40	.217	2.441	2.347	3.500	3.668	3.460	—	—	5,580	5,280	5,280	5,280	5,280	—	72,500	52,700	72,500	72,500	—
2.875	6.40	6.50	—	J-55	.217	2.441	2.347	3.500	3.668	3.460	—	—	7,680	7,260	7,260	7,260	7,260	—	99,700	72,500	99,700	99,700	—
2.875	6.40	6.50	—	L-80	.217	2.441	2.347	3.500	3.668	3.460	—	—	11,170	10,570	10,570	10,570	10,570	—	145,000	105,400	145,000	145,000	—
2.875	7.80	7.90	—	L-80	.276	2.323	2.229	3.500	3.668	3.460	—	—	13,890	13,440	13,440	13,440	11,030	—	180,300	140,700	180,300	180,300	—
2.875	8.60	8.70	—	L-80	.308	2.259	2.165	3.500	3.668	3.460	—	—	15,300	15,000	15,000	14,940	11,030	—	198,700	159,200	198,700	193,100	—

TABLE 3.12—MINIMUM PERFORMANCE PROPERTIES OF TUBING (continued)

1	2	3	4	5	6	7	8	9	10	11	12	13	14	15	16	17	18	19	20	21	22	23	24
	Nominal Weight							Coupling Outside Diameter			Integral Joint				Internal Yield Pressure					Joint Yield Strength (F_j)			
	Threaded and Coupled		Integral Joint						Threaded and Coupled Upset							Threaded and Coupled Upset				Threaded and Coupled	Upset		
Size OD, D (in.)	Non-upset (lbm/ft)	Upset (lbm/ft)	Integral Joint (lbm/ft)	Grade	Wall Thickness, t (in.)	d (in.)	Drift Diameter (in.)	Non-upset W (in.)	Regular W (in.)	Special Clearance W_c (in.)	Drift Diameter (in.)	OD of Box (in.)	Collapse Resistance	Plain End	Nonupset (psi)	Regular (psi)	Special Clearance (psi)	Integral Joint (psi)	Pipe Body Yield (lbf)	Nonupset (lbf)	Regular (lbf)	Special Clearance (lbf)	Integral Joint (lbf)
2.875	9.35	9.45	—	L-80	.340	2.195	2.101	—	3.668	3.460	—	—	16,680	16,560	—	14,940	11,030	—	216,600	—	216,600	193,100	—
2.875	10.50	—	—	L-80	.392	2.091	1.997	—	—	—	—	—	18,840	19,090	—	—	—	—	244,600	—	—	—	—
2.875	11.50	—	—	L-80	.440	1.995	1.901	—	—	—	—	—	20,740	21,430	—	—	—	—	269,300	—	—	—	—
2.875	6.40	6.50	—	N-80	.217	2.441	2.347	3.500	3.668	3.460	—	—	11,170	10,570	10,570	10,570	10,570	—	145,000	105,400	145,000	145,000	—
2.875	7.80	7.90	—	N-80	.276	2.323	2.229	3.500	3.668	3.460	—	—	13,890	13,440	13,440	13,440	13,440	—	180,300	140,700	180,300	180,300	—
2.875	8.60	8.70	—	N-80	.308	2.259	2.165	3.500	3.668	3.460	—	—	15,300	15,000	15,000	14,940	11,030	—	198,700	159,200	198,700	193,000	—
2.875	6.40	6.50	—	C-90	.217	2.441	2.347	3.500	3.668	3.460	—	—	12,360	11,890	11,890	11,890	10,570	—	163,100	118,600	163,100	163,100	—
2.875	7.80	7.90	—	C-90	.276	2.323	2.229	3.500	3.668	3.460	—	—	15,620	15,120	15,120	15,120	11,030	—	202,900	158,300	202,900	202,900	—
2.875	8.60	8.70	—	C-90	.308	2.259	2.165	3.500	3.668	3.460	—	—	17,220	16,870	16,870	16,810	11,890	—	223,600	179,100	223,600	217,300	—
2.875	9.35	9.45	—	C-90	.340	2.195	2.101	3.500	3.668	3.460	—	—	18,770	18,630	—	16,810	12,410	—	243,700	—	243,700	217,300	—
2.875	10.50	—	—	C-90	.392	2.091	1.997	—	—	—	—	—	21,200	21,470	—	—	12,410	—	275,200	—	—	—	—
2.875	11.50	—	—	C-90	.440	1.995	1.901	—	—	—	—	—	23,330	24,100	—	—	12,410	—	302,900	—	—	—	—
2.875	6.40	6.50	—	T-95	.217	2.441	2.347	3.500	3.668	3.460	—	—	12,940	12,550	12,550	12,550	12,550	—	172,100	125,200	172,100	172,100	—
2.875	7.80	7.90	—	T-95	.276	2.323	2.229	3.500	3.668	3.460	—	—	16,490	15,960	15,960	15,960	13,100	—	214,100	167,100	214,100	214,100	—
2.875	8.60	8.70	—	T-95	.308	2.259	2.165	3.500	3.668	3.460	—	—	18,170	17,810	17,810	17,740	13,100	—	236,000	189,100	236,000	229,400	—
2.875	9.35	9.45	—	T-95	.340	2.195	2.101	—	3.668	3.460	—	—	19,810	19,660	—	17,740	13,100	—	257,300	—	257,300	229,440	—
2.875	10.50	—	—	T-95	.392	2.091	1.997	—	—	—	—	—	22,370	22,670	—	—	—	—	290,500	—	—	—	—
2.875	11.50	—	—	T-95	.440	1.995	1.901	—	—	—	—	—	24,630	25,440	—	—	—	—	319,800	—	—	—	—
2.875	6.40	6.50	—	P-110	.217	2.441	2.347	3.500	3.668	3.460	—	—	14,550	14,530	14,530	14,530	14,530	—	199,300	145,000	199,300	199,300	—
2.875	7.80	7.90	—	P-110	.276	2.323	2.229	3.500	3.668	3.460	—	—	19,090	18,480	18,480	18,480	15,160	—	247,900	193,500	247,900	247,900	—
2.875	8.60	8.50	—	P-110	.308	2.259	2.165	3.500	3.668	3.460	—	—	21,040	20,620	20,620	20,540	15,160	—	273,200	218,900	273,200	265,600	—
3.500	7.70	—	—	H-40	.216	3.068	2.943	4.250	—	—	—	—	4,630	4,320	4,320	—	—	—	89,100	65,000	—	—	—
3.500	9.20	9.30	—	H-40	.254	2.992	2.867	4.250	4.500	4.180	—	—	5,380	5,080	5,080	5,080	5,080	—	103,600	79,400	103,600	103,600	—
3.500	10.20	—	—	H-40	.289	2.922	2.797	4.250	—	—	—	—	6,060	5,780	5,780	—	—	—	116,600	92,500	—	—	—
3.500	7.70	—	—	J-55	.216	3.068	2.943	4.250	—	—	—	—	5,970	5,940	5,940	—	—	—	122,500	89,400	—	—	—
3.500	9.20	9.30	—	J-55	.254	2.992	2.867	4.250	4.500	4.180	—	—	7,400	6,990	6,990	6,990	—	—	142,500	109,200	142,500	142,500	—
3.500	10.20	—	—	J-55	.289	2.922	2.797	4.250	—	—	—	—	8,330	7,950	7,950	—	—	—	160,300	127,200	—	—	—
3.500	7.70	—	—	L-80	.216	3.068	2.943	4.250	—	—	—	—	7,870	8,640	8,640	—	—	—	178,200	130,000	—	—	—
3.500	9.20	9.30	—	L-80	.254	2.992	2.867	4.250	4.500	4.180	—	—	10,540	10,160	10,160	10,160	10,160	—	207,200	158,900	207,200	207,200	—
3.500	10.20	—	—	L-80	.289	2.922	2.797	4.250	—	—	—	—	12,120	11,560	11,560	—	—	—	233,200	185,000	—	—	—
3.500	12.70	12.95	—	L-80	.375	2.750	2.625	4.250	4.500	4.180	—	—	15,310	15,000	15,000	15,000	10,660	—	294,600	246,200	294,600	273,100	—
3.500	14.30	—	—	L-80	.430	2.640	2.515	4.250	—	—	—	—	17,240	17,200	—	—	—	—	331,800	—	—	—	—
3.500	15.50	—	—	L-80	.476	2.548	2.423	4.250	—	—	—	—	18,800	19,040	—	—	—	—	361,800	—	—	—	—
3.500	17.00	—	—	L-80	.530	2.440	2.315	4.250	—	—	—	—	20,560	21,200	—	—	—	—	395,600	—	—	—	—
3.500	7.70	—	—	N-80	.216	3.068	2.943	4.250	—	—	—	—	7,870	8,640	8,640	—	—	—	178,200	130,000	—	—	—
3.500	9.20	9.30	—	N-80	.254	2.992	2.867	4.250	4.500	4.180	—	—	10,540	10,160	10,160	10,160	10,160	—	207,200	158,900	207,200	207,200	—
3.500	10.20	—	—	N-80	.289	2.922	2.797	4.250	—	—	—	—	12,120	11,560	11,560	—	—	—	233,200	185,000	—	—	—
3.500	12.70	12.95	—	N-80	.375	2.750	2.625	4.250	4.500	4.180	—	—	15,310	15,000	15,000	15,000	10,660	—	294,600	246,200	294,600	273,100	—
3.500	7.70	—	—	C-90	.216	3.068	2.943	4.250	—	—	—	—	8,540	9,720	9,720	—	—	—	200,500	146,300	—	—	—
3.500	9.20	9.30	—	C-90	.254	2.992	2.867	4.250	4.500	4.180	—	—	11,570	11,430	—	11,430	—	—	233,100	178,700	233,100	207,200	—
3.500	10.20	—	—	C-90	.289	2.922	2.797	4.250	—	—	—	—	13,640	13,010	13,010	—	—	—	262,400	208,100	—	—	—
3.500	12.70	12.95	—	C-90	.375	2.750	2.625	4.250	4.500	4.180	—	—	17,220	16,880	16,880	16,880	12,070	—	331,400	277,000	331,400	273,100	—
3.500	14.30	—	—	C-90	.430	2.640	2.515	4.250	—	—	—	—	19,400	19,350	—	—	—	—	373,200	—	—	—	—
3.500	15.50	—	—	C-90	.476	2.548	2.423	4.250	—	—	—	—	21,150	21,420	—	—	—	—	407,000	—	—	—	—
3.500	17.00	—	—	C-90	.530	2.440	2.315	4.250	—	—	—	—	23,130	23,850	—	—	—	—	445,100	—	—	—	—
3.500	7.70	—	—	T-95	.216	3.068	2.943	4.250	—	—	—	—	8,850	10,260	10,260	—	—	—	211,700	154,400	—	—	—
3.500	9.20	9.30	—	T-95	.254	2.992	2.867	4.250	4.500	4.180	—	—	12,080	12,070	12,070	12,070	12,070	—	246,000	188,700	246,000	246,000	—
3.500	10.20	—	—	T-95	.289	2.922	2.797	4.250	—	—	—	—	14,390	13,730	13,730	—	—	—	276,900	219,600	—	—	—
3.500	12.70	12.95	—	T-95	.375	2.750	2.625	4.250	4.500	4.180	—	—	18,180	17,810	17,810	17,810	12,660	—	349,800	292,400	349,800	324,300	—
3.500	14.30	—	—	T-95	.430	2.640	2.515	4.250	—	—	—	—	20,480	20,430	—	—	—	—	394,000	—	—	—	—
3.500	15.50	—	—	T-95	.476	2.548	2.423	4.250	—	—	—	—	22,330	22,610	—	—	—	—	429,600	—	—	—	—
3.500	17.00	—	—	T-95	.530	2.440	2.315	4.250	—	—	—	—	24,410	25,170	—	—	—	—	469,800	—	—	—	—

TABLE 3.12—MINIMUM PERFORMANCE PROPERTIES OF TUBING (continued)

1	2	3	4	5	6	7	8	9	10	11	12	13	14	15	16	17	18	19	20	21	22	23	24
Size OD, D (in.)	Nominal Weight Threaded and Coupled Nonupset (lbm/ft)	Nominal Weight Threaded and Coupled Upset (lbm/ft)	Nominal Weight Integral Joint (lbm/ft)	Grade	Wall Thick., t (in.)	d (in.)	Drift Diameter (in.)	Coupling OD Upset Nonupset W (in.)	Coupling OD Upset Regular W (in.)	Coupling OD Upset Special Clearance Wc (in.)	Integral Joint Drift Diameter (in.)	Integral Joint OD of Box (in.)	Collapse Resistance	Plain End	Internal Yield Nonupset (psi)	Internal Yield Upset Regular (psi)	Internal Yield Upset Special Clearance (psi)	Internal Yield Integral Joint (psi)	Pipe Body Yield (lbf)	Joint Yield Upset Nonupset (lbf)	Joint Yield Upset Regular (lbf)	Joint Yield Upset Special Clearance (lbf)	Joint Yield Integral Joint (lbf)
3.500	9.20	9.30	—	P-110	.254	2.992	2.867	4.250	4.500	4.180	—	—	13,530	13,970	13,970	13,970	13,970	—	284,900	218,500	284,900	284,900	—
3.500	12.70	12.95	—	P-110	.375	2.750	2.625	4.250	4.500	4.180	—	—	21,050	20,630	20,630	20,630	14,660	—	405,000	338,600	405,000	375,500	—
4.000	9.50	—	—	H-40	.226	3.548	3.423	4.750	—	—	—	—	4,050	3,960	3,960	—	—	—	107,200	72,000	—	—	—
4.000	—	11.00	—	H-40	.262	3.476	3.351	—	5.000	—	—	—	4,900	4,590	—	4,590	—	—	123,100	—	123,100	—	—
4.000	9.50	—	—	J-55	.226	3.548	3.423	4.750	—	—	—	—	5,110	5,440	5,440	—	—	—	147,400	99,000	—	—	—
4.000	—	11.00	—	J-55	.262	3.476	3.351	—	5.000	—	—	—	6,590	6,300	—	6,300	—	—	169,200	—	169,200	—	—
4.000	9.50	—	—	L-80	.226	3.548	3.423	4.750	—	—	—	—	6,590	7,910	7,910	—	—	—	214,400	144,000	—	—	—
4.000	—	11.00	—	L-80	.262	3.476	3.351	—	5.000	—	—	—	8,800	9,170	—	9,170	—	—	246,200	—	246,200	—	—
4.000	13.20	—	—	L-80	.330	3.340	3.215	—	—	—	—	—	12,110	11,550	—	—	—	—	304,400	—	—	—	—
4.000	16.10	—	—	L-80	.415	3.170	3.045	—	—	—	—	—	14,880	14,530	—	—	—	—	373,900	—	—	—	—
4.000	18.90	—	—	L-80	.500	3.000	2.875	—	—	—	—	—	17,500	17,500	—	—	—	—	439,800	—	—	—	—
4.000	22.20	—	—	L-80	.610	2.780	2.655	—	—	—	—	—	20,680	21,350	—	—	—	—	519,800	—	—	—	—
4.000	9.50	—	—	N-80	.226	3.548	3.423	4.750	—	—	—	—	6,590	7,910	7,910	—	—	—	214,400	144,000	—	—	—
4.000	—	11.00	—	N-80	.262	3.476	3.351	—	5.000	—	—	—	8,800	9,170	—	9,170	—	—	246,200	—	246,200	—	—
4.000	9.50	—	—	C-90	.226	3.548	3.423	4.750	—	—	—	—	7,080	8,900	8,900	—	—	—	241,200	162,000	—	—	—
4.000	—	11.00	—	C-90	.262	3.476	3.351	—	5.000	—	—	—	9,590	10,320	—	10,320	—	—	276,900	—	276,900	—	—
4.000	13.20	—	—	C-90	.330	3.340	3.215	—	—	—	—	—	13,620	12,990	—	—	—	—	342,500	—	—	—	—
4.000	16.10	—	—	C-90	.415	3.170	3.045	—	—	—	—	—	16,740	16,340	—	—	—	—	420,700	—	—	—	—
4.000	18.90	—	—	C-90	.500	3.000	2.875	—	—	—	—	—	19,690	19,690	—	—	—	—	494,800	—	—	—	—
4.000	22.20	—	—	C-90	.610	2.780	2.655	—	—	—	—	—	23,260	24,020	—	—	—	—	584,700	—	—	—	—
4.000	9.50	—	—	T-95	.226	3.548	3.423	4.750	—	—	—	—	7,310	9,390	9,390	—	—	—	254,600	171,000	—	—	—
4.000	—	11.00	—	T-95	.262	3.476	3.351	—	5.000	—	—	—	9,980	10,890	—	10,890	—	—	292,300	—	292,300	—	—
4.000	13.20	—	—	T-95	.330	3.340	3.215	—	—	—	—	—	14,380	13,720	—	—	—	—	361,500	—	—	—	—
4.000	16.10	—	—	T-95	.415	3.170	3.045	—	—	—	—	—	17,670	17,250	—	—	—	—	444,000	—	—	—	—
4.000	18.90	—	—	T-95	.500	3.000	2.875	—	—	—	—	—	20,780	20,780	—	—	—	—	522,300	—	—	—	—
4.000	22.20	—	—	T-95	.610	2.780	2.655	—	—	—	—	—	24,560	25,350	—	—	—	—	617,200	—	—	—	—
4.500	12.60	12.75	—	H-40	.271	3.958	3.833	5.200	5.563	—	—	—	4,490	4,220	4,220	4,220	—	—	144,000	104,000	144,000	—	—
4.500	12.60	12.75	—	J-55	.271	3.958	3.833	5.200	5.563	—	—	—	5,730	5,800	5,800	5,800	—	—	198,000	143,500	198,000	—	—
4.500	12.60	12.75	—	L-80	.271	3.958	3.833	5.200	5.563	—	—	—	7,500	8,430	8,430	8,430	—	—	288,000	208,000	288,000	—	—
4.500	15.20	—	—	L-80	.337	3.826	3.701	—	—	—	—	—	11,080	10,480	—	—	—	—	352,600	—	—	—	—
4.500	17.00	—	—	L-80	.380	3.740	3.615	—	—	—	—	—	12,370	11,820	—	—	—	—	393,400	—	—	—	—
4.500	18.90	—	—	L-80	.430	3.640	3.515	—	—	—	—	—	13,830	13,380	—	—	—	—	439,800	—	—	—	—
4.500	21.50	—	—	L-80	.500	3.500	3.375	—	—	—	—	—	15,800	15,560	—	—	—	—	502,600	—	—	—	—
4.500	23.70	—	—	L-80	.560	3.380	3.255	—	—	—	—	—	17,430	17,420	—	—	—	—	554,600	—	—	—	—
4.500	26.00	—	—	L-80	.630	3.240	3.115	—	—	—	—	—	19,260	19,600	—	—	—	—	612,800	—	—	—	—
4.500	12.60	12.75	—	N-80	.271	3.958	3.833	5.200	5.563	—	—	—	7,500	8,430	8,430	8,430	—	—	288,000	208,700	288,000	—	—
4.500	12.60	12.75	—	C-90	.271	3.958	3.833	5.200	5.563	—	—	—	8,120	9,490	9,490	9,490	—	—	324,000	234,800	324,000	—	—
4.500	15.20	—	—	C-90	.337	3.826	3.701	—	—	—	—	—	12,220	11,800	—	—	—	—	396,600	—	—	—	—
4.500	17.00	—	—	C-90	.380	3.740	3.615	—	—	—	—	—	13,920	13,300	—	—	—	—	442,600	—	—	—	—
4.500	18.90	—	—	C-90	.430	3.640	3.515	—	—	—	—	—	15,560	15,050	—	—	—	—	494,800	—	—	—	—
4.500	21.50	—	—	C-90	.500	3.500	3.375	—	—	—	—	—	17,780	17,500	—	—	—	—	565,500	—	—	—	—
4.500	23.70	—	—	C-90	.560	3.380	3.255	—	—	—	—	—	19,610	19,600	—	—	—	—	623,900	—	—	—	—
4.500	26.00	—	—	C-90	.630	3.240	3.115	—	—	—	—	—	21,670	22,050	—	—	—	—	689,400	—	—	—	—
4.500	12.60	12.75	—	T-95	.271	3.958	3.833	5.200	5.563	—	—	—	8,410	10,010	10,010	10,010	—	—	342,000	247,900	342,000	—	—
4.500	15.20	—	—	T-95	.337	3.826	3.701	—	—	—	—	—	12,760	12,450	—	—	—	—	418,700	—	—	—	—
4.500	17.00	—	—	T-95	.380	3.740	3.615	—	—	—	—	—	14,690	14,040	—	—	—	—	467,200	—	—	—	—
4.500	18.90	—	—	T-95	.430	3.640	3.515	—	—	—	—	—	16,420	15,890	—	—	—	—	522,300	—	—	—	—
4.500	21.50	—	—	T-95	.500	3.500	3.375	—	—	—	—	—	18,770	18,470	—	—	—	—	596,900	—	—	—	—
4.500	23.70	—	—	T-95	.560	3.380	3.255	—	—	—	—	—	20,700	20,690	—	—	—	—	658,500	—	—	—	—
4.500	26.00	—	—	T-95	.630	3.240	3.115	—	—	—	—	—	22,880	23,280	—	—	—	—	727,700	—	—	—	—

Solution. Select 2⅜-4.70-J55 EUE tubing (see Table 3.12). The 2⅜-in. size is suitable for the flowing rates (see the chapter on inflow in this section of the handbook), and larger EUE tubing sizes cannot be run and washed over inside this size and weight casing. Smaller OD sizes of tubing will save no significant investment and will complicate wireline work. Select the lightest standard weight available for the initial design and check to ensure that it meets all design conditions. The J55 grade is the most cost-effective grade available. It typically is used as a first selection for most relatively shallow, low-pressure, and low-rate design cases.

Calculate the fluid gradient, g_f.

$$g_f = (0.433 \ \text{psi/ft}/8.32 \ \text{lbm/gal}) \times w_f \ \text{lbm/gal}$$
$$= (0.052 \ \text{psi/ft/lbm/gal}) \times 9.0 \ \text{lbm/gal} = 0.468 \ \text{psi/ft} . \quad\ldots\ldots\ldots\ldots\ldots \quad (3.3)$$

0.052 psi/ft/lbm/gal is obtained from 0.433 psi/ft/8.32 lbm/gal, which is the conversion factor from lb/gal to psi/ft.

Check design conditions for tension. Calculate the resulting hook load for a 9,000-ft length of tubing in air from

$$F_a = L_p \times w_n$$
$$= 9,000 \ \text{ft} \times 4.7 \ \text{lbm/ft} = 42,300 \ \text{lbf} . \quad\ldots\ldots\ldots\ldots\ldots \quad (3.4)$$

The value of w_n is obtained from Table 3.12. This calculation results in a superimposed tubing tension axial (hook) load at the surface in air of 42,300 lbf.

The weight of the tubing string in a fluid is the tubing weight in air minus the axial buoyancy load(s):

$$F_f = F_a - F_b . \quad\ldots\ldots\ldots\ldots\ldots \quad (3.5)$$

The results of the tubing cross-section metal area,

$$A_m = \frac{\pi(d_o^2 - d_i^2)}{4} , \quad\ldots\ldots\ldots\ldots\ldots \quad (3.6)$$

times the hydrostatic pressure at depth,

$$p_{bh} = D_{tV} \times g_f , \quad\ldots\ldots\ldots\ldots\ldots \quad (3.7)$$

are used to calculate the axial buoyancy load,

$$F_b = A_m \times p_{bh} . \quad\ldots\ldots\ldots\ldots\ldots \quad (3.8)$$

In this example,

$$A_m = \frac{\pi(d_o^2 - d_i^2)}{4} = [3.1416 \times (2.375^2 - 1.995^2)]/4 = 1.304 \ \text{in.}^2,$$

$$p_{bh} = D_{tV} \times g_f = 9,000 \ \text{ft} \times 0.468 \ \text{psi/ft} = 4,212 \ \text{psi},$$

$$\text{and } F_b = A_m \times p_{bh} = 1.304 \ \text{in.}^2 \times 4,212 \ \text{psi} = 5,492 \ \text{lbf} .$$

Eq. 3.5 can now be used to calculate the hook load in fluid at surface before setting the packer.

$$F_f = F_a - F_b = 42,300 \text{ lbf} - 5,492 \text{ lbf} = 36,808 \text{ lbf}.$$

Compare these values to the tubing performance properties. With a joint-yield strength rating, F_j, of 71,700 lbf (see Table 3.12) the design factor in tension in air is

$$D_t = F_j / F_a$$
$$= 71,700 / 42,300$$
$$= 1.6, \text{ .... (3.9)}$$

which is an acceptable design factor in tension in air, whereas the design factor in fluid is

$$D_t = F_j / F_f$$
$$= 71,700 / 36,463$$
$$= 1.97, \text{ .... (3.10)}$$

which is an acceptable design factor in tubing considering buoyancy.

Consider pulling conditions. With a stuck packer requiring 15,000 lbf of overpull, F_{op}, at packer to free, assume no buoyancy contribution because the packer is stuck.

$$F_t = F_a + F_{op}$$
$$= 42,300 + 15,000$$
$$= 57,300 \text{ lbf. .... (3.11)}$$

The design factor when considering overpull is

$$D_t = F_j / F_t$$
$$= 71,700 / 57,300$$
$$= 1.25, \text{ .... (3.12)}$$

which is an acceptable design factor in tension during pulling operations.

An overpull any greater than 15,000 lbf would not be acceptable because D_t would be less than 1.25.

Check burst and collapse loads and compare to the tubing performance properties. The maximum allowed internal pressure differential is

$$p_i = p_{yi} / D_b$$
$$= 7,700 / 1.25$$
$$= 6,160 \text{ psi. .... (3.13)}$$

With an internal-yield burst-pressure rating, p_{yi}, of 7,700 psi (see Table 3.12) and a wellhead surface pressure, p_{wh}, of 3,000 psi, calculate the design factor in burst.

$$D_b = p_{yi} / p_{wh}$$
$$= 7,700 / 3,000$$
$$= 2.57, \text{ .... (3.14)}$$

which is an acceptable design factor in burst and is much higher than the 1.25 suggested.

The minimum collapse pressure without axial stress, p_{cr}, = 8,100 psi (See Table 3.12). Assume an annulus full of 9.0 ppg fluid and an empty tubing string. With Eq. 3.7, p_{bh} = 9,000 ft × (9.0 × 0.052) psi/ft = 4,212 psi.

$$D_c = p_{cr} / p_{bh}$$
$$= 8,100 / 4,212$$
$$= 1.92, \quad\quad\quad\quad\quad\quad\quad\quad\quad\quad\quad (3.15)$$

which is an acceptable design factor in collapse and is much higher than the 1.1 suggested.

Check burst at bottom of hole under pumping conditions. Assume tubing filled with 9.0 ppg salt water with 100 psi surface tubing pressure and empty annulus.

$$p_{bh} = D_{tV} \times g_t + p_{wh}$$
$$= 9,000 \text{ ft} \times (9.0 \times 0.052) \text{ psi/ft} + 100 \text{ psi}$$
$$= 4,312 \text{ psi}. \quad\quad\quad\quad\quad\quad\quad\quad (3.16)$$

$$D_b = p_{yi} / p_{bh}$$
$$= 7,700 / 4,312$$
$$= 1.79, \quad\quad\quad\quad\quad\quad\quad\quad\quad\quad\quad (3.17)$$

which is an acceptable design factor in burst.

Select and order tubing material. Order per API *Spec. 5CT*: 9,000 ft plus 300 ft of 2⅜-4.70-J55 EUE-8R, range 2, seamless or electric weld, and one set of pups with standard EUE couplings. In addition, order one container of API-modified thread compound and specify delivery date and shipping instructions.

Example 3.2 Design tubing for relatively deep high-pressure gas well with CO_2 and H_2S. Assume the following conditions: casing designation = 5½-23.00-L80; measured depth, D_m, = 14,000 ft; true vertical depth, D_{tV}, = 13,000 ft; gas rate = 15 MMcf/D, 10 bbl of condensate per MMcf, 40 ppm hydrogen sulfide resulting in a partial pressure of 0.40 psi for the H_2S and a 2% (20,000 ppm) carbon dioxide; p_{wh} = 10,000 psi during stimulation; p_{bh} = 9,000 psi; T_{bh} = 250°F; T_{sf} = 125°F; completion fluid weight = 14.0 ppg of inhibited solids free salt water; fluid gradient = 0.728 psi/ft; anticipated drag on tubing when pulling = 5,000 lbf; and packer shear pins setting = overpull = 25,000 lbf.

Solution. Because of the anticipated rate of 15 MMcf/D, 2⅞-in. tubing will permit flow at a significantly higher rate than 2⅜-in. tubing. The use of 3½-in. tubing is not normally recommended within 5½-in. casing because fishing operations would be difficult. On the basis of experience, the use of 3½-in. tubing rather than 2⅞-in. tubing would not significantly improve the production rate in this case.

Select the tubing weight and grade. Because surface pressures of 10,000 psi are anticipated, the tubing must have a minimum internal-yield pressure greater than 10,000 psi. With a design factor of 1.25 in burst, the required minimum internal-yield pressure is 12,500 psi (1.25 × 10,000). Because the partial pressure of H_2S is 0.40 psi (greater than 0.05 psi), a sour service tubing grade must be used. See NACE MR-01-75.[16]

The obvious choice in the design is 2⅞-7.90-L80 tubing with an inside diameter (ID) of 2.323 in. (For 2⅞-in. tubing, the lightest weight of 6.5 lbm/ft for J55 and L80 grades do not have an adequate internal-yield pressure rating.) See Table 3.12. The 2⅞-7.90-L80 tubing has a

13,440 psi internal-yield pressure value, which is more than adequate. Because of the high gas pressure, a proprietary connection joint with 100% joint strength and with metal-to-metal seals should be considered.

Investigate tension load conditions. Use Eq. 3.4 to calculate $F_a = L_p \times w_n = 14{,}000$ ft $\times 7.9$ lbm/ft $= 110{,}600$ lbf. Use Eq. 3.7 to find the hydrostatic pressure at depth, $p_{bh} = 13{,}000 \times 14 \times 0.052 = 9{,}464$ psi. Use Eq. 3.8 to calculate the buoyancy effect in 14 ppg fluid, $F_b = A_m \times p_{bh} = 2.254$ in.$^2 \times 9{,}464$ psi $= 21{,}332$ lbf. Use Eq. 3.5 to calculate $F_f = F_a - F_b = 110{,}600$ lbf $- 21{,}332$ lbf $= 89{,}269$ lbf. With $F_j = 180{,}300$ lbf, use Eqs. 3.9 and 3.10 to calculate $D_t = F_j/F_a = 180{,}300/110{,}600 = 1.63$, which is an acceptable design factor in tension in air, and $D_t = F_j/F_f = 180{,}300/89{,}269 = 2.02$, which is an acceptable design factor in tension considering buoyancy.

Consider pulling conditions. Buoyancy is neglected because the packer is set.

$$F_t = F_a + F_{op} + F_d$$
$$= 110{,}600 + 25{,}000 + 5{,}000$$
$$= 140{,}600 \text{ lbf}. \quad\text{...} \quad (3.18)$$

This is the required hook load to unset the packer. Use Eq. 3.12 to calculate $D_f = F_j/P_s = 180{,}300/140{,}600 = 1.28$, which is an acceptable design factor in tension.

Check collapse conditions. $p_{cr} = 13{,}890$ psi for 2⅞-7.9-L80 tubing (see Table 3.12). Assume the casing annulus is filled with 14 ppg fluid with no surface pressure and the tubing pressure is bled off after a plug was set in the bottom of the tubing or a tubing safety valve at bottom is closed, which is a reasonable possibility over the life of the well. Use Eq. 3.7 to calculate $p_{bh} = D_{tV} \times g_f = 13{,}000$ ft $\times (14.0 \times 0.052)$ psi/ft $= 9{,}464$ psi, and use Eq. 3.15 to calculate $D_f = p_{cr} / p_{bh} = 13{,}890/9{,}464 = 1.47$, which is an acceptable value. Ensure that the surface annulus pressure is kept less than 3,163 psi $[(13{,}890/1.1) - 9{,}464]$ in the event that the tubing pressure is bled off.

Select and order the tubing material. Request that the tubing meet *API Spec. 5CT*. Order 14,500 ft of 2⅞-7.90-L80 Type 13 Cr, Range 2, seamless tubing with a proprietary connection and one set of pup joints with same type connections as tubing. In addition, order all accessories with the same connection and an appropriate thread lubricant. State the required delivery and follow API *RP 5C1* on tubing handling.

Example 3.3 Design tubing for a relatively deep sweet-oil well. Make a dual grade tubing-string design (to reduce cost). Assume the following conditions: casing designation = 7-26.00-N80; $D_m = 11{,}000$ ft; $D_{tV} = 11{,}000$ ft; desired flow rate under gas lift conditions = 1,500 B/D from 10,000 ft; $p_{ww} = 5{,}000$ psi; $p_{wh} = 5{,}000$ psi; $p_{bh} = 6{,}200$ psi; $T_{bh} = 200°F$; $T_{sf} = 125°F$; completion fluid in annulus, w_f, = 11.0 ppg of inhibited solids free salt water; fluid gradient, g_f, = $0.052 \times w_f = 0.572$ psi/ft; packer shear pins setting = overpull (F_{op}) = 50,000 lbf. The well is relatively straight with small drag forces while pulling, and it is to be circulated with salt water before pulling tubing. Assume $F_d = 0$.

Solution. Select tubing size. Because of the anticipated flow rate, 3½-in. tubing was selected. There is no clearance problem with 3½-in. tubing inside the 7-in. casing. Smaller tubing sizes would result in high friction losses and loss in production rate. Larger tubing sizes would not increase production rates sufficiently and would result in clearance problems inside the 7-in. casing. EUE tubing with modified couplings (see API SR13 seal ring) are selected to provide adequate leak resistance.

Select tubing weight and grade. 3½-9.30-J55 tubing is checked to determine if all design conditions are met.

Check collapse on bottom. p_{cr} = 7,400 psi (see Table 3.12) for the selected tubing. Assume worst/maximum collapse design condition occurs at bottom where annulus is full of 11 ppg fluid and tubing pressure is zero (possible under completion conditions if well is swabbed down.) Use Eq. 3.7 to calculate $p_{bh} = D_{tV} \times g_f$ = 11,000 ft × 0.572 = 6,292, and use Eq. 3.15 to calculate $D_c = p_{cr} / p_{bh}$ = 7,400/6,292 = 1.176, which is adequate because 1.1 is acceptable.

Check burst at bottom. Assume casing annulus is empty and tubing is full of produced water. This is possible under gas lift conditions if the annulus injection pressure is bled off with tubing full of produced fluid plus surface wellhead pressure. Use Eq. 3.16 to calculate the burst pressure on bottom, 11,000 × 0.465 + 100 = 5,115 + 100 = 5,215 psi. With an internal-yield pressure for 3½-9.30-J55 of 6,980 psi, use Eq. 3.17 to calculate 6,980/5,215 = 1.34, which is adequate because 1.25 is acceptable. With a maximum stimulation burst pressure at surface of 5,000 psi, use Eq. 3.14 to calculate D_b = 6,980/5,000 = 1.396, which is adequate for burst.

Check tension loads at surface. For 3½-9.30-J55 or N80 tubing, use Eq. 3.4 to calculate 11,000 ft × 9.3 lb/ft = 102,300 lbf. Use Eqs. 3.7 and 3.8 to calculate the axial buoyancy load, F_b = 2.590 in.^{2} × (11,000 × 11.0 × 0.052) psi = 16,296 lbf. Use Eq. 3.5 to calculate the weight in 11 ppg fluid, 102,300 − 16,296 = 86,004 lbf. For 3½-9.30-J55 EUE tubing (100% joint efficiency), F_j = 142,500 lbf. Use Eq. 3.9 to calculate the design factor in tension, D_t, for 3½-9.30-J55 EUE tubing in air, 142,500/102,300 = 1.39, which does not account for necessary overpull. The recommended design factor for weight in air is 1.6; therefore, the design factor is not adequate. A higher grade at top must be used for adequate tension design conditions.

Check worst possible tension design case. Pull at surface to overcome drag and shear pins in packer with no buoyancy effect on tubing above packer. Use Eq. 3.4 to calculate F_a, and use Eq. 3.18 to calculate F_t = 11,000 × 9.3 + 50,000 + 0 = 102,300 + 50,000 = 152,300 lbf. Use

$$F_a \times D_t = F_{jr} \quad\quad\quad (3.19)$$

to calculate 152,300 × 1.25 = 190,375 lbf. Use Table 3.12 to find F_j = 207,200 lbf for 3½-9.30-N80 tubing, which is acceptable. Suggest the use of as much J55 as feasible to reduce tubing string cost. For maximum pull load on 3½-9.3-J55, applying the acceptable design factor = 142,500/1.25 = 114,000 lbf. Calculate the maximum feet of 3½-9.30-J55 from

$$L_p = (F_a - F_{op}) / w_n$$
$$= (114,000 - 50,000) / 9.3 = 6,882 \text{ ft} . \quad\quad\quad (3.20)$$

Assume L_p = 6,800 ft for 3½-9.30-J55, and L_p = 11,000 − 6,800 = 4,200 ft for 3½-9.30-N80 tubing. Use Eq. 3.12 to calculate the design factor in tension, D_t, for 3½-9.30-N80, 207,200/152,300 = 1.36, which is acccptable. For F_a = 152,300 lbf, the design factor for 3½-9.30-J55 can be calculated as 142,500/(152,300 − 4,200 × 9.3) = 1.26. Do not exceed the 50,000-lbf overpull load, because this would over load the top of the J55 tubing.

Select and order tubing material. Request that tubing meet API *Spec. 5CT*. Order 4,400 ft of 3½-9.30-N80 with EUE modified API SR13 beveled couplings and S or EW, range 2; one set of pup joints for 3½-9.30-N80 EUE modified API SR 13 standard couplings; 7,000 ft of 3½-9.30-J55 with EUE modified API *SR 13* standard couplings and S or EW, range 2; and one container of API modified thread compound as per API *RP 5A3*. Specify delivery date and shipping instructions. Some operators might prefer to use L80 rather than N80 3½ tubing and to heat-treat the J55 after upsetting. Both these options increase the cost of the tubing string but may increase the operating life.

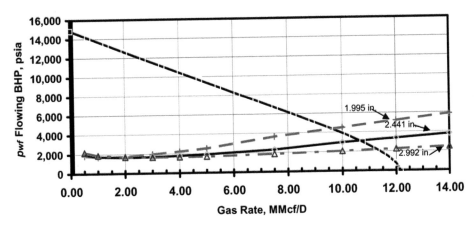

Fig. 3.3—Gas well inflow and outflow for Example 3.4.

Example 3.4 Design tubing for a deep high-pressure gas well. Complete the well with 7-29.00-P110 casing to 13,900 ft and a 5-in. liner (4.031 in. ID) from 13,800 to 16,650 ft. Perforations are to be from 16,530 to 16,570 ft with a permanent packer at 16,500 ft. The bottomhole pressure is estimated to be 14,850 psi with a bottomhole temperature of 340°F and a surface-flowing temperature of 150°F. The well has a surface shut-in pressure of 12,445 psi with a gas gradient, g_g, of 0.146 psi/ft. The well initially will produce approximately 10 MMcf/D of gas with a 10 BC/MMcf and 10 BW/MMcf into a 1,000-psia sales system. The gas gravity is 0.7 and contains 1% of nitrogen and 1% carbon dioxide, but the H_2S is only 1 ppm. The formation may require acid stimulation with a maximum surface-treating pressure of 10,000 psi. Before perforating, the 17.4 ppg mud will be circulated out and replaced with 10 ppg clean inhibited salt water. After perforating, the well will be killed, the packer and tubing installed, and the annulus filled with 10 ppg clean inhibited salt water. If needed, batch inhibition is planned to protect the tubing from erosion/corrosion.

Solution. Select tubing sizes. The type of completion and the size of the tubing string must be selected before making the tubing design. **Fig 3.3** shows an inflow performance and outflow performance graph comparing the production with 2⅜-, 2⅞-, and 3½-in. tubing strings. This graph shows that a full string of 2⅜-in. tubing would restrict production significantly; thus, the amount of 2⅜-in. tubing should be limited. The 2⅞-in. tubing produces the well near its maximum rate, whereas the use of 3½-in. tubing results in only a small production rate increase and will cost substantially more. The 5-in. liner (4.031 in. ID) will make washover and fishing 2⅞-in. tubing difficult; therefore, 2⅜-in. tubing will be used in the liner section of the well. Thus, the top portion of the tubing string will be 2⅞-in. tubing and the lower portion inside the liner will be 2⅜-in. tubing.

Now that the approximate sizes of tubing have been determined, the tubing design can be made for tension, collapse, and burst conditions. In general, select the lowest weight per foot and grade that is acceptable. This will normally result in the most economical design.

Select weights and grades. The most common approach in casing and tubing design is to start at the bottom and work your way back to the surface; however, in this high-pressure well, burst is a major consideration. Draw a pressure-depth graph as shown in **Fig. 3.4**.

To control the shut-in surface tubing pressure of 12,445 psi with a design factor of 1.25, calculate the suggested minimum internal-yield pressure rating required, p_{yi} = 12,445 × 1.25 or 15,556 psi. As Table 3.12 shows, 2⅞-7.90-P110 is suitable, which has an internal yield of

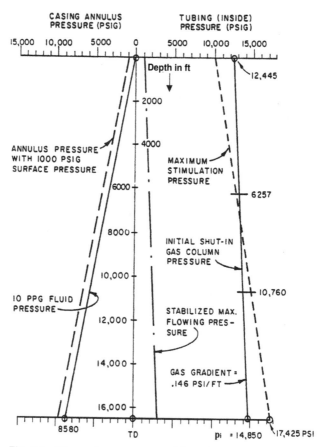

Fig. 3.4—Gas well pressure conditions for Example 3.4.

18,480 psi. API grades C90 and T95 could also be used, but these grades are usually more costly than P110. Because the H$_2$S partial pressure is less than 0.05 psi, the nonsour service grade N80 and P110 can be used.

Because tension reduces the collapse rating and collapse reduces the tension rating, start at the bottom where tension is small and collapse is normally high. Actually, at the bottom (because of buoyancy forces), the tubing is in compression when run in fluid. Draw a schematic tubing depth chart as shown in **Fig. 3.5.**

Check collapse and tension stresses. Start at the bottom of the hole and work to the surface-checking tension and collapse at any size, weight, or grade change. The tensile load increases moving upward, but the collapse differential pressure decreases.

To calculate the collapse differential, use

$$\Delta p_c = g_a \times D_{tV} - g_t \times D_{tV} . \qquad (3.21)$$

With the annulus full of 10 ppg salt water and assuming that the tubing pressure bled to zero, a $0.52 \times 16,500 = 8,580$ psi collapse differential would result on the bottom of the hole. The 2⅜-4.70-N80 tubing has a collapse of 11,780 psi, resulting in a design factor $11,780/8,580 = 1.37$, which is acceptable. Keep the annulus pressure at the surface to a maximum of 1,500 psi

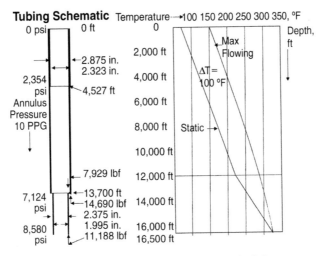

Fig. 3.5—Tubing schematic for Example 3.4.

in normal operations to avoid possible collapse if the tubing pressure at bottom is bled down to zero.

From above the top of the liner at 13,800 ft to the permanent packer at 16,500 ft, 2,700 ft of 2⅜-4.70-N80 tubing is tentatively selected. Use 2,800 ft of 2⅜-in. tubing to avoid interference with the liner top. At 13,700 ft, the tubing size can be increased safely to 2⅞ in., which will allow a higher flow rate. To simplify wireline operations, the tubing weight for all 2⅞-in. tubing is the same.

For burst considerations, the design requires a minimum of 7.9 lbm/ft tubing. There is a –11,188 buoyancy force because of the fluid acting on the bottom tubing area. At 13,700 ft, the 2⅜-in. tubing will have a load of 4.7 lbm/ft × 2,800 ft = 13,160 lbf; however, the tensile load on the tubing is altered slightly because of the tubing area change at 13,700 ft. This results in an axial load at 13,700 ft of 13,160 – 11,188 + 7,929 – 14,690 = –4,789 lbf; thus, the effect of tension on collapse can be neglected because the tubing is in compression.

The maximum burst pressure on bottom may occur during stimulation. Calculate the burst differential from

$$\Delta p_b = p_{wh} + g_t \times D_{tv} - g_a \times D_{tv} \,. \qquad (3.22)$$

Assuming a surface-treating pressure of 10,000 psi, the tubing full of acid (gradient = 0.45 psi/ft), and the annulus full of 10 ppg (gradient = 0.52 psi/ft) salt water, use Eq. 3.22 to calculate a burst differential on bottom of 10,000 + 0.45 × 16,500 – 0.52 × 16,500 = 8,845 psi. The use of a design factor of 1.25 in burst will require an internal-yield pressure of 8,845 × 1.25 = 11,056 psi. The 2⅜-4.70-N80 tubing has an API internal yield of 11,200 psi (see Table 3.12), which is acceptable.

Burst and collapse conditions now need to be checked at all depths where tubing size, weight, or grade changes are planned. Burst is of primary importance. Check burst at the changed over from 2⅜ in. to 2⅞ in. at 13,700 ft. Use Eq. 3.22 to calculate the tubing burst pressure differential during stimulation: 10,000 psi + 0.45 psi/ft × 13,700 ft – 0.52 psi/ft × 13,700 ft = 9,041 psi. The use of a design factor in burst, D_b, 0f 1.25 would require a burst resistance rating of 9,041 psi × 1.25 = 11,301 psi. Thus, at this depth, the 2⅜, 4.7, N80 tubing is acceptable and 2⅞, 7.9, N80 tubing is acceptable because it has an API internal pressure

	Weight	ID		Interval	Quantity
Size Designation	(lbm/ft)	(in.)	Grade	(ft)	(ft)
2⅞	7.9	2.323	P110	0 to 4,527	4,527
2⅞	7.9	2.323	N80	4,527 to 13,700	9,173
2⅜	4.7	1.995	N80	13,700 to 16,500	2,800

TABLE 3.13—SUMMARY OF WEIGHTS AND GRADES FOR EXAMPLE 3.4

rating of 13,440 psi (see Table 3.12.) and a collapse resistance of 13,890 psi. Using a design factor in burst, D_b, of 1.25, the maximum burst differential for 2⅞, 7.9, N80 should not exceed 13,440/1.25 = 10,752 psi.

At the surface during stimulation, 2⅞-in., 7.9, P110 is required as shown previously. The depth of the crossover from P110 to N80 needs to be calculated. This depth is where the burst pressure differential is equal to 10,752 psi for 2⅞-in., 7.9, N80 tubing. The worst case condition is during shut-in when a surface pressure of 12,445 psi occurs and the tubing is full of 0.146-psi/ft gas.

$$L_p = \frac{\left(\dfrac{p_{wh} - p_{br}}{D_b}\right)}{g_a - g_t}, \qquad \text{...} \quad (3.23)$$

where g_a is the annulus fluid gradient and g_t is the tubing fluid gradient.

Using Eq. 3.23, L_p = (12,445 psi – 13,440/1.25 psi)/(0.52 psi/ft – 0.146 psi/ft) = 4,527 ft. Thus, 2⅞-in., 7.9, P110 tubing is to be used from the surface to 4,527 ft and 2⅞-in., 7.9, N80 tubing is to be used from 4,527 to 13,700 ft. **Table 3.13** summarizes the sizes, weights and grades selected.

Calculate the hook load of the tubing string in air and in fluid for the various tubing sizes, weights, and grades.

Hook load in air = 13,700 ft × 7.9 lbm/ft + 2,800 ft × 4.7 lbm/ft = 121,390 lbf.

Hook load in fluid = 121,390 + 7,929 – 14690 – 11,188 = 103,441 lbf.

Body/joint yield strength for 2⅞, 7.9, P110 = 247,900 lbf.

Body/joint yield strength for 2⅞, 7.9, N80 = 180,300 lbf.

Body/joint yield strength for 2⅜, 4.7, N80 = 104,300 lbf.

Maximum allowed hook load at surface for 2⅞, 7.9, P110 tubing = 247,900/1.25 = 198,320 lbf.

Maximum allowed hook load at surface for 2⅞, 7.9, N80 tubing = 4,527 × 7.9 + 180,300/1.25=180,003 lbf.

Maximum allowed hook load at surface for 2⅜, 4.7, N80 tubing = 13,700 × 7.9 + 104,300/1.25= 191,670 lbf.

Thus, the limiting condition is for pulling on the 2⅞, 7.9, N80 tubing, which allows a hook load at the surface of 180,003 lbf. For this string design, an overpull over the weight in fluid would be 180,003 lbf – 103,441 lbf = 76,562 lbf.

Select and order tubing material. Order the tubing to API *5CT* specifications, adding a few hundred feet of each type: seamless, range 2, and a proprietary connection integral joint or threaded and coupled with metal-to-metal seals. Also, order a set of grade P110 pup joints for the 2⅞-in. tubing with the same proprietary connection integral joint. Order an appropriate thread compound. In addition, one special crossover 2⅞-7.90 to 2⅜-4.70 in grade N80 is required. (If an MTC connection is used, the crossover can be a pin × pin with a 2⅞-N80 coupling.)

All auxiliary well equipment should have the same proprietary connection. Tubing should be hydrostatically tested to 80% of yield pressure. Ensure that proper running procedures are used.

Check with the manufacturer on ways to distinguish between the two grades of 2.875-in. OD tubing. Some operators would select 2⅞-7.90-P110 and no 2⅞-7.90-N80 tubing to ensure that accidental mixing of the 2.875-in. OD different grade tubing could not occur and to allow a slightly higher overpull value.

If pressures are greater than 7,000 psi and the depth is greater than 13,000 ft, a pipe-body load analysis should be performed. In sour service for L80, C90, and T95, triaxial stress intensity should be checked and a design factor greater than 1.25 maintained. See *ISO 13679* Sec. B. 5.2.[15]

3.4.5 Stretch in Tubing. When tubing is subject to an axial load, either in tension or compression, that does not exceed the elastic limit of the material, the stretch or contraction may be determined from

$$\Delta L_t = \frac{12 \times F \times L_p}{E \times A_m}, \quad \text{...} \quad (3.24)$$

where ΔL_t = total axial stretch or contraction, in.; F = superimposed tension or compression axial load, lbf; L_p = length of pipe, ft; E = Young's modulus of elasticity for steel = 30 million psi, which is not affected significantly by tubing grade; and A_m = cross-section metal area of pipe, in.^{2} = 0.7854 × ($d_o^2 - d_i^2$).

For multiple sizes or weights, calculate stretch for each section and sum the results. This formula also can be used to determine the length of free pipe by applying a load, F, and measuring the stretch, ΔL_t.

$$L_p = \frac{\Delta L_t \times E \times A_m}{12 \times F}. \quad \text{...} \quad (3.25)$$

Example 3.5 Find free point for a stuck string of 2⅞-6.50 API steel tubing string in an 11,000-ft well.

Solution. With a block-hook load of 60,000 lbf, mark the tubing at the top of rotary table. An additional 10,000-lbf load was picked up and the measured increase in length (stretch) is 20.0 in. Calculate the tubing cross-section area with Eq. 3.6. $A_m = \pi \times (2.875^2 - 2.441^2)/4 = 1.812$ in.^{2} Use Eq. 3.25 to calculate $L_p = \Delta L_t \times E \times A_m / (12 \times F) = 20.0$ in. × 30,000,000 psi × 1.812 in.^{2}/(12 in./ft × 10,000 lbf) = 9,060 ft.

3.4.6 Tubing Buckling. Tubing buckling must be considered in design. See the chapter on completion design in this section of the *Handbook*.

3.4.7 Corrosion Considerations. Tubing selection for corrosive environments is a critical design responsibility. Both the inside and outside of the tubing can be damaged by corrosion. Weight-loss corrosion may be a serious problem with conventional tubing strings in wells producing salt water, especially when the water becomes the wetting phase. Acidity caused by the presence of acid gases (CO_2 and H_2S) normally increases the corrosion rate. When corrosion is minor, the common practice is to use standard API grades and to start batch inhibition when corrosion becomes a problem.

Corrosion/erosion, a major problem with steel tubing, occurs in most high-rate gas-condensate wells in which the gas contains CO_2. The CO_2 attacks the steel tubing, which creates an iron carbonate film (corrosion product); it is removed from the wall by erosion (impingement of well fluids). Rapid deep pit failure may occur from corrosion/erosion. Increasing fluid velocities and CO_2 partial pressure are highly detrimental, as are increasing temperature or increasing brine production. There may be a region of conditions in which frequent batch or continuous inhibition is necessary. Gas wells with CO_2 contents higher than 30 psi partial pressure and gas velocities greater than 40 fps normally require continuous or frequent batch inhibition to protect the steel tubing. CRA material is often the most cost-effective means of combatting erosion/corrosion. Some CRA material is subject to failure in brine water environments.

A different type of tubing design problem is SSC. SSC and/or hydrogen embrittlement causes a brittle-type failure in susceptible materials at stresses less than the tubing yield strength. SSC is a cracking phenomenon encountered with high-strength steels in sour (H_2S) aqueous environment. Cracking also occurs in austenitic stainless steels in caustic or chloride solutions and mild steel in caustic or nitrate solutions. Susceptibility to attack of most low-alloy steels is roughly proportional to its strength. In terms of hardness, most steels are not subject to SSC failure if the hardness is less than 241 Brinell Hardness number or 23 Hardness-Rockwell C. The potential harmful level of H_2S for susceptible materials has been defined as 0.05 psi partial pressure of the H_2S gas phase. Carbonate-induced cracking of mild steel can occur in freshwater environments.

Use of inhibition to prevent SSC is not completely reliable because 100% effective coverage of metal surface generally is not achieved. The best solution for tubulars subject to SSC is to use materials that are not subject to SSC failures. In general, follow NACE guidelines.[16]

Dissimilar metals close to each other can influence corrosion. Because corrosion can result from many causes and influences and can take different forms, no simple or universal remedy exists for its control. Each tubing well problem must be treated individually, and the solution must be attempted in light of known factors and operating conditions.

3.4.8 Internal Coatings. Plastic internal coating of a tubing string is sometimes used to deter corrosion or erosion/corrosion in oil and gas wells and may increase tubing life significantly. Such cases may be in high-water-cut oil wells or gas wells with high CO_2 partial pressures. These coatings are usually thin wall film applications (< 0.01 in. thick) that are baked (bonded) onto the inside walls of the tubing string. The film thickness is small enough to allow normal wireline operations. The key to plastic coatings is selecting the correct material and its proper application. Even if the specifications call for "100% holiday free," eventually the coating comes off and holidays occur because of poor application or handling practices, wireline work, caliper surveys, blisters caused by the environment, or other reasons. Coating should not be expected to stop all weight-loss corrosion over the life of the well. Typically, a few holes may develop in time but the bulk of the tubing stays intact. In such cases, workover costs are usually lowered because the tubing often can be retrieved without major fishing operations. Because such coatings increase the smoothness, they reduce pressure drop slightly in high-rate wells and, in some cases, may be helpful in reducing paraffin and scale problems. Besides thin wall film coatings, there are other kinds of interior coating or liners for tubing that have special application. Plastic liners and cement lining have been used successfully when the reduction in

TABLE 3.14—API MILL PIPE BODY INSPECTION METHODS
(Reproduced courtesy of the American Petroleum Institute from API *Spec. 5CT*[10])

Grade	Visual	Electromagnetic*	Ultrasonic Testing	Magnetic Particle Inspection
H40 and J55	Required	Not Required	Not Required	Not Required
N80 (normalized, normalized and tempered)	Required	Not Required	Not Required	Not Required
N80 (quenched and tempered)	Required	A**	A**	A**
L80 and C95	Required	A**	A**	A**
C90 and T95	Required	B†	C‡	B†
P110	Required	A**	A**	Not Applicable

*Flux leakage or eddy current. **One method or any combination of methods shall be used. †At least one method (excluding the visual method) shall be used in addition to ultrasonic testing to inspect outside surface. ‡Ultrasonic testing shall be used to inspect the inside and outside surface.

ID is not a major problem, primarily for water and carbon dioxide injection tubing or for sour service production.

3.5 Tubing Inspection

API tubing is inspected at the mill in accordance with API *Spec. 5CT*. Physical properties are checked and each length hydrostatically tested, normally to only 3,000 psi in the plain end (unthreaded) condition. Dimensions, weights, straightness, and lengths are also checked. Part of this inspection is to drift all lengths. **Table 3.14** summarizes API *Spec. 5CT*, which specifies pipe body inspection requirements.

Despite all the API specifications and testing, some tubing defects are still found after delivery; thus, some operators do further inspection of new tubing on critical wells. Used tubing frequently requires inspection. See API *RP 5C1*.[5]

There are several types of tubing inspection methods that may be beneficial. The common methods of inspecting the tubing currently in use in field operation are visual, calipers, hydrostatic, electromagnetic, magnetic particle, and ultrasonic. Typical defects are outside and inside pits and longitudinal cuts, transverse laps, and mechanical wear and erosion. API recommends that wall thickness measurements be made with pipe wall micrometers, sonic pulse-echo instruments, or gamma ray devices so that the operator can demonstrate the wall thickness within a 2% accuracy. In addition to the body, the tubing upset and threads often require inspection, typically by magnetic powder and use of thread gauges. The following guidelines are suggested for inspection normally at the well location:

• Visual. The outside of each tubing joint should be inspected visually for mill defects such as seams, slugs, pits, cuts, gouges, dents, or cracks. Each connection should be checked for defective threads and seals. Wall thickness measurements should be considered on critical wells. Internal inspection of tubing requires the use of an optical device and an experienced operator. The operating crews, a manufacturer's representative, the user's personnel, or a service contractor typically does such visual inspections.

• Calipers. Tubing calipers, both multifingered feeler and electronic types, normally are run while the tubing is installed in the well. Where significant wall loss is observed, the tubing can be pulled and the damaged joints replaced.

• Hydrostatic. A commonly used inspection method is to test hydrostatically the tubing body and joint internally with water. Test pressures are usually based on 80% of internal yield.

TABLE 3.15—API COLOR CODING FOR INSPECTED TUBING WALL THICKNESS (Reproduced courtesy of the American Petroleum Institute from *RP 5C1*[5])

Class	Color Band	Loss of Wall Thickness (%)	Remaining Wall Thickness (%)
2	Yellow	0 to 15	85
3	Blue	16 to 30	70
4	Green	31 to 50	50
5	Red	more than 50	less than 50

Hydrostatic tests of the body are performed on the pipe rack on location and the joints checked while running; however, both can be tested while running. A more stringent test of the joints is obtained by the use of nitrogen with a helium tracer rather than water.

• Electromagnetic. To find pits, transverse and/or longitudinal defects in the pipe body, electromagnetic search coils, which find magnetic flux leakage, are typically used. This technique works for a uniform body and will typically not find defects in the upset and/or threaded area of the tube. The inspection equipment must be in good working order and an experienced and qualified operator is required. Eddy-Current, another electromagnetic inspection method, is used for grade verification.

• Magnetic Particle. The magnetic particle inspection methods, both wet and dry, induce either a longitudinal or transverse magnetic field in the tubing and magnetic iron particles dusted on the tubing align at defects. This method is normally used to check the outside surface of upset and end area region for cracks. This method requires a qualified operator, excellent operating environmental conditions, and good operating procedures to be reliable.

• Ultrasonic. Ultrasonic (high frequency sound) is used to find flaws and imperfections in the pipe body wall. The tool is usually stationary and the pipe is rotated and fed mechanically to examine the entire tubing body. The ultrasonic testing equipment must be in good working condition and an experienced and qualified operator is mandatory.

• Hardness Testing. The hardness of tubing is often checked when it is to be used in sour service to ensure the tubing meets API *Spec. 5CT* or to sort mixed grades of tubing.

3.5.1 Inspecting Used Tubing. Used tubing should be classified according to loss of nominal wall thickness. **Table 3.15** shows the API color-coding suggestions. The color coding should consist of a paint band of the appropriate color approximately 2 in. wide around the body of the pipe approximately 1 ft from the box end. There is no standard method for calculating performance properties of used tubing. Tubing reconditioning should be done only in accordance with API specifications.

3.6 Tubing Handling

Tubing can be damaged during shipment, at the wellsite, and during running and pulling. API *RP 5C1*[5] Secs. 2 and 3 should be followed closely. For transportation, slightly different procedures are needed to prevent damage depending on whether shipped by water, rail, or truck. Care must be taken in unloading and storage. Thread protectors must be installed properly and rough handling avoided. Tubing should be stacked on racks following proper procedures, and tubing in storage should be inspected periodically and protected from corrosion. In general, the high-strength materials are more susceptible to handling damage.

Numerous factors must be considered when running and pulling tubing. The operating personnel should ensure that good practices are followed. Each length of tubing should be measured and drifted in compliance with API/ISO specifications. The tubing should be handled with thread protectors, which are not removed, until the tubing is ready to stab. Adequate thread cleaning is essential for proper connection makeup and pressure-tight strings. (See Ref. 16.) Apply a good thread compound but avoid excessive amounts. Collar-type tubing elevators are adequate for API nonbeveled couplings; however, slip-type elevators are recommended when running tubing with beveled couplings, special clearance couplings, and integral joint tubing. Check spider slips to ensure they will not damage the tubing body.

Use of power tongs is necessary to obtain consistent makeup torque. Properly maintained, installed, and calibrated tongs are essential. Follow the API recommended tubing makeup torque in **Table 3.16** for nonupset, external-upset, and integral-joint tubing. Follow the manufacturer's recommendations for specialty joints. However, the makeup torque may vary depending on the thread coatings and lubricant type; thus, adjustments in makeup torque values are sometimes required. Torque values listed in Table 3.16 apply to tubing with zinc-plated or phosphate-coated couplings. For tin-plated couplings, use 80% of the listed values as a guide for proper makeup. To establish the correct torque for API tubing threads, make up the first few joints to the recommended values and examine the connection. There should be no excessive heat, approximately two turns beyond the hand-tight position with all threads buried. Back out the connection (noting torque) and check threads for galling. If needed, adjust torque and repeat. Use the established makeup torque for the remainder of the string. To obtain maximum leak resistance with the API-tapered thread, the pin end of the connection is made up to slightly beyond the point of yielding. Consequently, API EUE connections may make up slightly more on repeated operations. The problem of makeup is to use torque that is sufficient to provide the needed seal without permanently damaging the connection. Good experience has been reported with the torque-turn method with API EUE tubing. In the torque-turn method, the power tongs are calibrated to record both the number of turns and the torque to make up the API tubing coupling to the point of yielding. In many of the proprietary connections, there must be ample makeup torque so that the metal-to-metal seals are energized. Check with the manufacturer for makeup guidelines.

3.6.1 Thread Compound. API-modified thread compound generally has been accepted for a wide range of service conditions over many years. The placement of thread compound at the root of the rounded API threads with the bearing pressure on the thread flanks (the interference fit, power tight makeup) produces the sealing mechanism. The thread compound also provides the lubrication to deter galling. The compound is a mixture of metallic and graphite powders uniformly dispersed in a grease base. API *RP 5A3*[1] and ISO 13678[17] provide the means for evaluating the suitability of thread compounds for use on API round threads in high-pressure service. For specialty connections, consult with the manufacturer on the proper thread compound. Environmentally nondamaging thread compounds meeting API thread-compound performance requirements are available.

3.6.2 Evaluation Procedures for Tubing Connections. Evaluation procedures for casing and tubing connections tests to be performed to determine the galling tendency, sealing performance, and structural integrity of tubular connections, especially for high-pressure application are under study. See ISO/DIS 13679.[15] **Table 3.17** shows example relationships between test classes and service applications. Other relationships may be more appropriate for individual users. Class IV connections are intended for the most severe application, and Class I connections are intended for the least severe application.

TABLE 3.16—API TUBING MAKEUP TORQUE GUIDELINES—ROUND THREAD TUBING
(Reproduced courtesy of the American Petroleum Institute from *RP 5C1*[5])

Size, OD (in.)	Size, OD (mm)	Nominal Weight, Threads and Coupling (lbm/ft)	Grade	Thread	Optimum Torque (ft-lbf)	Optimum Torque (N·m)
1.050	26.7	1.14	H-40	NU	140	190
1.050	26.7	1.14	J-55	NU	180	240
1.050	26.7	1.14	C-75	NU	230	320
1.050	26.7	1.14	L-80	NU	240	330
1.050	26.7	1.14	N-80	NU	250	340
1.050	26.7	1.14	C-90	NU	260	350
1.050	26.7	1.20	H-40	EUE	460	630
1.050	26.7	1.20	J-55	EUE	600	810
1.050	26.7	1.20	C-75	EUE	780	1,060
1.050	26.7	1.20	L-80	EUE	810	1,090
1.050	26.7	1.20	N-80	EUE	830	1,130
1.050	26.7	1.20	C-90	EUE	880	1,190
1.315	33.4	1.70	H-40	NU	210	280
1.315	33.4	1.70	J-55	NU	270	370
1.315	33.4	1.70	C-75	NU	360	480
1.315	33.4	1.70	L-80	NU	370	500
1.315	33.4	1.70	N-80	NU	380	510
1.315	33.4	1.70	C-90	NU	400	540
1.315	33.4	1.80	H-40	EUE	440	590
1.315	33.4	1.80	J-55	EUE	570	770
1.315	33.4	1.80	C-75	EUE	740	1,010
1.315	33.4	1.80	L-80	EUE	760	1,040
1.315	33.4	1.80	N-80	EUE	790	1,070
1.315	33.4	1.80	C-90	EUE	830	1,130
1.315	33.4	1.72	H-40	IJ	310	410
1.315	33.4	1.72	J-55	IJ	400	540
1.315	33.4	1.72	C-75	IJ	520	700
1.315	33.4	1.72	L-80	IJ	530	720
1.315	33.4	1.72	N-80	IJ	550	740
1.315	33.4	1.72	C-90	IJ	580	780
1.660	42.2	2.30	H-40	NU	270	360
1.660	42.2	2.30	J-55	NU	350	470
1.660	42.2	2.30	C-75	NU	460	620
1.660	42.2	2.30	L-80	NU	470	640
1.660	42.2	2.30	N-80	NU	490	660
1.660	42.2	2.30	C-90	NU	510	700
1.660	42.2	2.40	H-40	EUE	530	720
1.660	42.2	2.40	J-55	EUE	690	940
1.660	42.2	2.40	C-75	EUE	910	1,230
1.660	42.2	2.40	L-80	EUE	940	1,270
1.660	42.2	2.40	N-80	EUE	960	1,300
1.660	42.2	2.40	C-90	EUE	1,020	1,380
1.660	42.2	2.10	H-40	IJ	380	520
1.660	42.2	2.33	H-40	IJ	380	520
1.660	42.2	2.10	J-55	IJ	500	680
1.660	42.2	2.33	J-55	IJ	500	680
1.660	42.2	2.33	C-75	IJ	650	890
1.660	42.2	2.33	L-80	IJ	680	920
1.660	42.2	2.33	N-80	IJ	690	940
1.660	42.2	2.33	C-90	IJ	730	1,000
1.900	48.3	2.75	H-40	NU	320	430
1.900	48.3	2.75	J-55	NU	410	560
1.900	48.3	2.75	C-75	NU	540	730
1.900	48.3	2.75	L-80	NU	560	760
1.900	48.3	2.75	N-80	NU	570	780

Notes: 1. It is recommended that the makeup target be based on position, not torque. 2. Under normal circumstances, variations in the listed torque values of ±25% should be considered acceptable.

TABLE 3.16—API TUBING MAKEUP TORQUE GUIDELINES—ROUND THREAD TUBING
(continued)

Size, OD (in.)	(mm)	Nominal Weight, Threads and Coupling (lbm/ft)	Grade	Thread	Optimum Torque (ft-lbf)	(N•m)
1.900	48.3	2.75	C-90	NU	610	830
1.900	48.3	2.90	H-40	EUE	670	910
1.900	48.3	2.90	J-55	EUE	880	1,190
1.900	48.3	2.90	C-75	EUE	1,150	1,560
1.900	48.3	2.90	L-80	EUE	1,190	1,610
1.900	48.3	2.90	N-80	EUE	1,220	1,650
1.900	48.3	2.90	C-90	EUE	1,300	1,760
1.900	48.3	2.40	H-40	IJ	450	600
1.900	48.3	2.76	H-40	IJ	450	600
1.900	48.3	2.40	J-55	IJ	580	790
1.900	48.3	2.76	J-55	IJ	580	790
1.900	48.3	2.76	C-75	IJ	760	1,030
1.900	48.3	2.76	L-80	IJ	790	1,070
1.900	48.3	2.76	N-80	IJ	810	1,100
1.900	48.3	2.76	C-90	IJ	860	1,160
2.063	52.4	3.25	H-40	IJ	570	770
2.063	52.4	3.25	J-55	IJ	740	1,010
2.063	52.4	3.25	C-75	IJ	970	1,320
2.063	52.4	3.25	L-80	IJ	1,010	1,370
2.063	52.4	3.25	N-80	IJ	1,030	1,400
2.063	52.4	3.25	C-90	IJ	1,100	1,490
2.375	60.3	4.00	H-40	NU	470	630
2.375	60.3	4.60	H-40	NU	560	760
2.375	60.3	4.00	J-55	NU	610	830
2.375	60.3	4.60	J-55	NU	730	990
2.375	60.3	4.00	C-75	NU	800	1,090
2.375	60.3	4.60	C-75	NU	960	1,300
2.375	60.3	5.80	C-75	NU	1,380	1,860
2.375	60.3	4.00	L-80	NU	830	1,130
2.375	60.3	4.60	L-80	NU	990	1,350
2.375	60.3	5.80	L-80	NU	1,420	1,930
2.375	60.3	4.00	N-80	NU	850	1,160
2.375	60.3	4.60	N-80	NU	1,020	1,380
2.375	60.3	5.80	N-80	NU	1,460	1,980
2.375	60.3	4.00	C-90	NU	910	1,230
2.375	60.3	4.60	C-90	NU	1,080	1,470
2.375	60.3	5.80	C-90	NU	1,550	2,110
2.375	60.3	4.60	P-105	NU	1,280	1,740
2.375	60.3	5.80	P-105	NU	1,840	2,490
2.375	60.3	4.70	H-40	EUE	990	1,340
2.375	60.3	4.70	J-55	EUE	1,290	1,750
2.375	60.3	4.70	C-75	EUE	1,700	2,310
2.375	60.3	5.95	C-75	EUE	2,120	2,870
2.375	60.3	4.70	L-80	EUE	1,760	2,390
2.375	60.3	5.95	L-80	EUE	2,190	2,970
2.375	60.3	4.70	N-80	EUE	1,800	2,450
2.375	60.3	5.95	N-80	EUE	2,240	3,040
2.375	60.3	4.70	C-90	EUE	1,920	2,610
2.375	60.3	5.95	C-90	EUE	2,390	3,250
2.375	60.3	4.70	P-105	EUE	2,270	3,080
2.375	60.3	5.95	P-105	EUE	2,830	3,830
2.875	73.0	6.40	H-40	NU	800	1,080
2.875	73.0	6.40	J-55	NU	1,050	1,420
2.875	73.0	6.40	C-75	NU	1,380	1,880
2.875	73.0	7.80	C-75	NU	1,850	2,500

Notes: 1. It is recommended that the makeup target be based on position, not torque. 2. Under normal circumstances, variations in the listed torque values of ±25% should be considered acceptable.

TABLE 3.16—API TUBING MAKEUP TORQUE GUIDELINES—ROUND THREAD TUBING (continued)

Size, OD (in.)	(mm)	Nominal Weight, Threads and Coupling (lbm/ft)	Grade	Thread	Optimum Torque (ft-lbf)	(N•m)
2.875	73.0	8.60	C-75	NU	2,090	2,830
2.875	73.0	6.40	L-80	NU	1,430	1,940
2.875	73.0	7.80	L-80	NU	1,910	2,590
2.875	73.0	8.60	L-80	NU	2,160	2,930
2.875	73.0	6.40	N-80	NU	1,470	1,990
2.875	73.0	7.80	N-80	NU	1,960	2,650
2.875	73.0	8.60	N-80	NU	2,210	3,000
2.875	73.0	6.40	C-90	NU	1,570	2,130
2.875	73.0	7.80	C-90	NU	2,090	2,840
2.875	73.0	8.60	C-90	NU	2,370	3,210
2.875	73.0	6.40	P-105	NU	1,850	2,510
2.875	73.0	7.80	P-105	NU	2,470	3,350
2.875	73.0	8.60	P-105	NU	2,790	3,790
2.875	73.0	6.50	H-40	EUE	1,250	1,700
2.875	73.0	6.50	J-55	EUE	1,650	2,230
2.875	73.0	6.50	C-75	EUE	2,170	2,940
2.875	73.0	7.90	C-75	EUE	2,610	3,540
2.875	73.0	8.70	C-75	EUE	2,850	3,860
2.875	73.0	6.50	L-80	EUE	2,250	3,050
2.875	73.0	7.90	L-80	EUE	2,710	3,680
2.875	73.0	8.70	L-80	EUE	2,950	4,000
2.875	73.0	6.50	N-80	EUE	2,300	3,120
2.875	73.0	7.90	N-80	EUE	2,770	3,760
2.875	73.0	8.70	N-80	EUE	3,020	4,090
2.875	73.0	6.50	C-90	EUE	2,460	3,340
2.875	73.0	7.90	C-90	EUE	2,970	4,020
2.875	73.0	8.70	C-90	EUE	3,320	4,380
2.875	73.0	6.50	P-105	EUE	2,910	3,940
2.875	73.0	7.90	P-105	EUE	3,500	4,750
2.875	73.0	8.70	P-105	EUE	3,810	5,170
3.500	88.9	7.70	H-40	NU	920	1,250
3.500	88.9	9.20	H-40	NU	1,120	1,520
3.500	88.9	10.20	H-40	NU	1,310	1,770
3.500	88.9	7.70	J-55	NU	1,210	1,640
3.500	88.9	9.20	J-55	NU	1,480	2,010
3.500	88.9	10.20	J-55	NU	1,720	2,330
3.500	88.9	7.70	C-75	NU	1,600	2,170
3.500	88.9	9.20	C-75	NU	1,950	2,650
3.500	88.9	10.20	C-75	NU	2,270	3,080
3.500	88.9	12.70	C-75	NU	3,030	4,100
3.500	88.9	7.70	L-80	NU	1,660	2,250
3.500	88.9	9.20	L-80	NU	2,030	2,750
3.500	88.9	10.20	L-80	NU	2,360	3,200
3.500	88.9	12.70	L-80	NU	3,140	4,260
3.500	88.9	7.70	N-80	NU	1,700	2,300
3.500	88.9	9.20	N-80	NU	2,070	2,810
3.500	88.9	10.20	N-80	NU	2,410	3,270
3.500	88.9	12.70	N-80	NU	3,130	4,350
3.500	88.9	7.70	C-90	NU	1,820	2,460
3.500	88.9	9.20	C-90	NU	2,220	3,010
3.500	88.9	10.20	C-90	NU	2,590	3,510
3.500	88.9	12.70	C-90	NU	3,440	4,670
3.500	88.9	9.20	P-105	NU	2,620	3,550
3.500	88.9	12.70	P-105	NU	4,060	5,510
3.500	88.9	9.30	H-40	EUE	1,730	2,340

Notes: 1. It is recommended that the makeup target be based on position, not torque. 2. Under normal circumstances, variations in the listed torque values of ±25% should be considered acceptable.

TABLE 3.16—API TUBING MAKEUP TORQUE GUIDELINES—ROUND THREAD TUBING (continued)

Size, OD		Nominal Weight, Threads and Coupling	Grade	Thread	Optimum Torque	
(in.)	(mm)	(lbm/ft)			(ft-lbf)	(N•m)
3.500	88.9	9.30	J-55	EUE	2,280	3,090
3.500	88.9	9.30	C-75	EUE	3,010	4,080
3.500	88.9	12.95	C-75	EUE	4,040	5,480
3.500	88.9	9.30	L-80	EUE	3,030	4,240
3.500	88.9	12.95	L-80	EUE	4,200	5,700
3.500	88.9	9.30	N-80	EUE	3,200	4,330
3.500	88.9	12.95	N-80	EUE	4,290	5,820
3.500	88.9	9.30	C-90	EUE	3,430	4,650
3.500	88.9	12.95	C-90	EUE	4,610	6,250
3.500	88.9	9.30	P-105	EUE	4,050	5,490
3.500	88.9	12.95	P-105	EUE	5,430	7,370
4.000	101.6	9.50	H-40	NU	940	1,260
4.000	101.6	9.50	J-55	NU	1,240	1,660
4.000	101.6	9.50	C-75	NU	1,640	2,200
4.000	101.6	9.50	L-80	NU	1,710	2,280
4.000	101.6	9.50	N-80	NU	1,740	2,330
4.000	101.6	9.50	C-90	NU	1,870	2,500
4.000	101.6	11.00	H-40	EUE	1,940	2,630
4.000	101.6	11.00	J-55	EUE	2,560	3,470
4.000	101.6	11.00	C-75	EUE	3,390	4,600
4.000	101.6	11.00	L-80	EUE	3,530	4,780
4.000	101.6	11.00	N-80	EUE	3,600	4,880
4.000	101.6	11.00	C-90	EUE	3,870	5,250
4.500	114.3	12.60	H-40	NU	1,320	1,780
4.500	114.3	12.60	J-55	NU	1,740	2,360
4.500	114.3	12.60	C-75	NU	2,300	3,120
4.500	114.3	12.60	L-80	NU	2,400	3,250
4.500	114.3	12.60	N-80	NU	2,440	3,310
4.500	114.3	12.60	C-90	NU	2,630	3,570
4.500	114.3	12.75	H-40	EUE	2,160	2,930
4.500	114.3	12.75	J-55	EUE	2,860	3,870
4.500	114.3	12.75	C-75	EUE	3,780	5,130
4.500	114.3	12.75	L-80	EUE	3,940	5,340
4.500	114.3	12.75	N-80	EUE	4,020	5,450
4.500	114.3	12.75	C-90	EUE	4,330	5,870

Notes: 1. It is recommended that the makeup target be based on position, not torque. 2. Under normal circumstances, variations in the listed torque values of ±25% should be considered acceptable.

3.7 Coiled Tubing

Coiled tubing is defined as an electric-welded pipe with one longitudinal seam formed by high-frequency induction welding without the addition of filler material. Coiled tubing is used in special workover cases and as the completion tubing. A common use of coiled tubing is as vent strings, especially in low-rate gas wells. In general, the guidelines for jointed tubing should be followed for coiled tubing. The primary difference between coiled tubing and jointed tubing is that coiled tubing bends because it has no jointed connections (there may be a few butt welds). Coiled tubing is typically thin-wall tubing, which permits spooling and is slightly oval in shape. Coiled tubing has a tendency to coil up during running operations, especially in relatively large casing in deviated holes. As with all tubing operations, coiled tubing's effectiveness depends on good job planning and equipment design along with proper handling, maintenance, and storage procedures. See API *RP 5C7*.[9]

Coiled tubing is currently available in ¾- to 3½-in. OD sizes. The API document covers materials that are high-strength, low-alloy steels with specified minimum yield strengths from

TABLE 3.17—EXAMPLE RELATIONSHIP BETWEEN TEST CLASSES AND APPLICATION

Pressure Range* (psi)	Production Tubular Service Severity		
	High	Normal	Low
More than 12,000	IV	IV	III
8,000 to 12,000	IV	III	II
4,000 to 8,000	III	II	II
0 to 4,000	II	I	I

*The values quoted for differential working pressure range are intended for guidance only. It may be necessary to apply criteria other than differential working pressure such as risk and environmental consideration to select the class of tests appropriate for a particular application.

TABLE 3.18—PROPOSED TENSILE AND HARDNESS REQUIREMENTS FOR COILED TUBING

Grade	Yield Strength* (psi)		Ultimate Tensile (psi)		Maximum Hardness Body Hardness-Rockwell C
	Minimum	Maximum	Minimum	Maximum	
CT60	60,000	75,000	70,000	90,000	22
CT70	70,000	85,000	80,000	100,000	22
CT80	80,000	95,000	90,000	105,000	22
CT90	90,000	105,000	98,000	115,000	23
CT100	100,000	115,000	108,000	125,000	26

*Spooling and unspooling can result in a reduction of the yield strength of approximately 5 to 10%.

60 to 100 kpsi. A flat strip is formed into a round shape, the heat for welding is generated by the resistance to flow of electric current, and the edge is mechanically pressed together. The length of the flat strip material typically ranges from 1,000 to 3,000 ft, and a spool of coiled tubing may be in excess of 25,000 ft, depending mostly on the tubing diameter.

Tapered strings of coiled tubing can be manufactured by changing the wall thickness of the tubing within the length of a spool while maintaining a constant OD. These tapered designs can be manufactured with different weights (same OD but different ID segments) welded together or tapered sections that have a linear change in thickness over the section. Tapered coiled tubing can increase the operating depths and pressures. The manufacturer should provide mechanical properties of coiled tubing for each spool of coiled tubing.

The chemical requirements for API coiled tubing should conform to those listed in API *RP 5C7* Table 3.[9] **Table 3.18** shows tensile and harness requirements for coiled tubing. **Table 3.19** shows the sizes, grades, and ratings.

3.7.1 Coiled Tubing Design Considerations. When used as the permanent well completion tubing, coiled tubing should be designed for the tension, burst, or collapse stresses that typically occur during well operation. With small sizes (< 2⅜ in.) and relatively thin wall thickness,

TABLE 3.19—COILED-TUBING SPECIFICATIONS, REQUIREMENTS, AND PERFORMANCE PROPERTIES
(Reproduced courtesy of the American Petroleum Institute)

			Specification Requirements					Calculated Performance Properties*		
			Wall Thickness		Inside	Hydrostatic		Pipe Body	Pipe Internal	Torsional Yield
Specified			Specified	Minimum	Diameter	Test	D/t_{min}	Yield Load	Yield Pressure	Strength
Diameter	Plain End		t	t_{min}	d	Pressure	Ratio†	L_y‡	p_r***	T§
D (in.)	Weight (lbm/ft**)	Grade	(in.)	(in.)	(in.)	(psi)***		(lbf)	(psi)	(lbf/ft)
.750	.59	CT-55	.083	.078	.584	9,200	9.62	9,060	11,440	138
1.000	.81	CT-55	.083	.078	.834	6,900	12.82	12,430	8,580	268
1.000	.74	CT-70	.075	.070	.850	7,800	14.29	14,320	9,800	316
1.000	.79	CT-70	.080	.075	.840	8,400	13.33	15,260	10,500	332
1.000	.85	CT-70	.087	.082	.826	9,200	12.20	16,550	11,480	353
1.000	.92	CT-70	.095	.090	.810	10,000	11.11	18,010	12,600	376
1.000	.98	CT-70	.102	.097	.796	10,000	10.31	19,260	13,580	395
1.000	1.04	CT-70	.109	.104	.782	10,000	9.62	20,490	14,560	414
1.000	1.17	CT-70	.125	.117	.750	10,000	8.55	22,720	16,380	452
1.000	.74	CT-80	.075	.070	.850	9,000	14.29	16,360	11,200	361
1.000	.79	CT-80	.080	.075	.840	9,600	13.33	17,440	12,000	379
1.000	.85	CT-80	.087	.082	.826	10,000	12.20	18,920	13,120	403
1.000	.92	CT-80	.095	.090	.810	10,000	11.11	20,580	14,400	430
1.000	.98	CT-80	.102	.097	.796	10,000	10.31	22,010	15,520	452
1.000	1.04	CT-80	.109	.104	.782	10,000	9.62	23,420	16,640	473
1.000	1.17	CT-80	.125	.117	.750	10,000	8.55	25,960	18,720	516
1.000	.74	CT-90	.075	.070	.850	10,000	14.29	8,410	12,600	406
1.000	.79	CT-90	.080	.075	.840	10,000	13.33	19,620	13,500	426
1.000	.85	CT-90	.087	.082	.826	10,000	12.20	21,280	14,760	454
1.000	.92	CT-90	.095	.090	.810	10,000	11.11	23,160	16,200	484
1.000	.98	CT-90	.102	.097	.796	10,000	10.31	24,770	17,460	508
1.000	1.04	CT-90	.109	.104	.782	10,000	9.62	26,350	18,720	532
1.000	1.17	CT-90	.125	.117	.750	10,000	8.55	29,210	21,060	581
1.250	1.03	CT-55	.083	.078	1.084	5,500	16.03	15,800	6,860	440
1.250	.94	CT-70	.075	.070	1.100	6,300	17.86	18,160	7,840	517
1.250	1.00	CT-70	.080	.075	1.090	6,700	16.67	19,380	8,400	544
1.250	1.08	CT-70	.087	.082	1.076	7,300	15.24	21,060	9,180	582
1.250	1.17	CT-70	.095	.090	1.060	8,100	13.89	22,960	10,080	623
1.250	1.25	CT-70	.102	.097	1.046	8,700	12.89	24,600	10,860	658
1.250	1.33	CT-70	.109	.104	1.032	9,300	12.02	26,210	11,650	691
1.250	1.50	CT-70	.125	.117	1.000	10,000	10.68	29,150	13,100	762
1.250	1.60	CT-70	.134	.126	.982	10,000	9.92	31,140	14,110	799
1.250	1.82	CT-70	.156	.148	.938	10,000	8.45	35,870	16,580	882
1.250	2.01	CT-70	.175	.167	.900	10,000	7.49	39,770	18,700	944
1.250	.94	CT-80	.075	.070	1.100	7,200	17.86	20,760	8,960	590
1.250	1.00	CT-80	.080	.075	1.090	7,700	16.67	22,150	9,600	622
1.250	1.08	CT-80	.087	.082	1.076	8,400	15.24	24,070	10,500	665
1.250	1.17	CT-80	.095	.090	1.060	9,200	13.89	26,240	11,520	712
1.250	1.25	CT-80	.102	.097	1.046	9,900	12.89	28,110	12,420	752
1.250	1.33	CT-80	.109	.104	1.032	10,000	12.02	29,950	13,310	790
1.250	1.50	CT-80	.125	.117	1.000	10,000	10.68	33,320	14,980	871
1.250	1.60	CT-80	.134	.126	.982	10,000	9.92	35,590	16,130	913
1.250	1.82	CT-80	.156	.148	.938	10,000	8.45	40,990	18,940	1,008
1.250	2.01	CT-80	.175	.167	.900	10,000	7.49	45,460	21,380	1,079
1.250	.94	CT-90	.075	.070	1.100	8,100	17.86	23,350	10,080	664
1.250	1.00	CT-90	.080	.075	1.090	8,600	16.67	24,920	10,800	700
1.250	1.08	CT-90	.087	.082	1.076	9,400	15.24	27,080	11,810	748
1.250	1.17	CT-90	.095	.090	1.060	10,000	13.89	29,520	12,960	801
1.250	1.25	CT-90	.102	.097	1.046	10,000	12.89	31,620	13,970	846
1.250	1.33	CT-90	.109	.104	1.032	10,000	12.02	33,700	14,980	889
1.250	1.50	CT-90	.125	.117	1.000	10,000	10.68	37,480	16,850	980
1.250	1.60	CT-90	.134	.126	.982	10,000	9.92	40,040	18,140	1,028
1.250	1.82	CT-90	.156	.148	.938	10,000	8.45	46,110	21,310	1,134
1.250	2.01	CT-90	.175	.167	.900	10,000	7.49	51,140	24,050	1,214
1.500	1.43	CT-55	.095	.090	1.310	5,300	16.67	21,930	6,600	733
1.500	1.43	CT-70	.095	.090	1.310	6,700	16.67	27,910	8,400	933
1.500	1.52	CT-70	.102	.097	1.296	7,200	15.46	29,930	9,050	988
1.500	1.62	CT-70	.109	.104	1.282	7,800	14.42	31,930	9,710	1,041
1.500	1.84	CT-70	.125	.117	1.250	8,700	12.82	35,580	10,920	1,155
1.500	1.95	CT-70	.134	.126	1.232	9,400	11.90	38,070	11,760	1,216
1.500	2.24	CT-70	.156	.148	1.188	10,000	10.14	44,000	13,810	1,353
1.500	2.48	CT-70	.175	.167	1.150	10,000	8.98	48,950	15,590	1,460
1.500	1.43	CT-80	.095	.090	1.310	7,700	16.67	31,890	9,600	1,066
1.500	1.52	CT-80	.102	.097	1.296	8,300	15.46	34,200	10,350	1,129
1.500	1.62	CT-80	.109	.104	1.282	8,900	14.42	36,490	11,090	1,189

*The performance properties and hydrostatic test pressures shown apply to new pipe, and do not take into account additional deformation, axial load, residual stresses, or ovality caused by spooling or service cycling. **Pipe weight in lb/ft is based on specified dimensions of pipe. ***Barlow's formula is used to calculate the internal yield pressure and the hydrostatic pressure. The minimum wall thickness, the specified minimum yield strength, and the specified OD are used in the calculation. The effect of axial loading on internal yield pressure is not included. †The calculated D/t_{min} ratio is based on the specified OD and minimum wall thickness of the coiled tubing size shown. ‡Pipe body yield load is based on specified OD, minimum wall thickness, and minimum specified yield strength. §Working pressure and working loads should be based on appropriate safety factors, taking into account the serviceability issues.

TABLE 3.19—COILED-TUBING SPECIFICATIONS, REQUIREMENTS, AND PERFORMANCE PROPERTIES (continued)

Specification Requirements							Calculated Performance Properties*		
Specified Diameter D (in.)	Plain End Weight (lbm/ft**)	Grade	Wall Thickness Specified t (in.)	Wall Thickness Minimum t_{min} (in.)	Inside Diameter d (in.)	Hydrostatic Test Pressure (psi)***	D/t_{min} Ratio†	Pipe Body Yield Load L_Y‡ (lbf)	Pipe Internal Yield Pressure p_r,*** (psi)	Torsional Yield Strength T§ (lbf/ft)
1.500	1.84	CT-80	.125	.117	1.250	10,000	12.82	40,670	12,480	1,320
1.500	1.95	CT-80	.134	.126	1.232	10,000	11.90	43,510	13,440	1,389
1.500	2.24	CT-80	.156	.148	1.188	10,000	10.14	50,290	15,790	1,547
1.500	2.48	CT-80	.175	.167	1.150	10,000	8.98	55,950	17,810	1,669
1.500	.43	CT-90	.095	.090	1.310	8,600	16.67	35,880	10,800	1,200
1.500	1.52	CT-90	.102	.097	1.296	9,300	15.46	38,480	11,640	1,270
1.500	1.62	CT-90	.109	.104	1.282	10,000	14.42	41,050	12,480	1,338
1.500	1.84	CT-90	.125	.117	1.250	10,000	12.82	45,750	14,040	1,485
1.500	1.95	CT-90	.134	.126	1.232	10,000	11.90	48,950	15,120	1,563
1.500	2.24	CT-90	.156	.148	1.188	10,000	10.14	56,580	17,760	1,740
1.500	2.48	CT-90	.175	.167	1.150	10,000	8.98	62,940	20,040	1,878
1.750	1.68	CT-55	.095	.090	1.560	4,500	19.44	25,810	5,660	1,026
1.750	1.91	CT-70	.109	.104	1.532	6,700	16.83	37,650	8,320	1,462
1.750	2.17	CT-70	.125	.117	1.500	7,500	14.96	42,020	9,360	1,631
1.750	2.31	CT-70	.134	.126	1.482	8,100	13.89	45,000	10,080	1,721
1.750	2.66	CT-70	.156	.148	1.438	9,500	11.82	52,140	11,840	1,928
1.750	2.94	CT-70	.175	.167	1.400	10,000	10.48	58,140	13,360	2,092
1.750	3.14	CT-70	.188	.180	1.374	10,000	9.72	62,150	14,400	2,197
1.750	1.91	CT-80	.109	.104	1.532	7,600	6.83	43,020	9,510	1,671
1.750	2.17	CT-80	.125	.117	1.500	8,600	14.96	48,020	10,700	1,864
1.750	2.31	CT-80	.134	.126	1.482	9,200	13.89	51,430	11,520	1,967
1.750	2.66	CT-80	.156	.148	1.438	10,000	11.82	59,590	13,530	2,203
1.750	2.94	CT-80	.175	.167	1.400	10,000	10.48	66,440	15,270	2,391
1.750	3.14	CT-80	.188	.180	1.374	10,000	9.72	71,030	16,460	2,511
1.750	1.80	CT-90	.102	.097	1.546	8,000	18.04	45,340	9,980	1,781
1.750	1.91	CT-90	.109	.104	1.532	8,600	16.83	48,400	10,700	1,880
1.750	2.17	CT-90	.125	.117	1.500	9,600	14.96	54,020	12,030	2,097
1.750	2.31	CT-90	.134	.126	1.482	10,000	13.89	57,860	12,960	2,213
1.750	2.66	CT-90	.156	.148	1.438	10,000	11.82	67,040	15,220	2,479
1.750	2.94	CT-90	.175	.167	1.400	10,000	10.48	74,750	17,180	2,690
1.750	3.14	CT-90	.188	.180	1.374	10,000	9.72	79,900	18,510	2,825
2.000	2.20	CT-70	.109	.104	1.782	5,800	9.23	43,360	7,280	1,956
2.000	2.50	CT-70	.125	.117	1.750	6,600	17.09	48,450	8,190	2,189
2.000	2.67	CT-70	.134	.126	1.732	7,100	15.87	51,930	8,820	2,314
2.000	3.07	CT-70	.156	.148	1.688	8,300	13.51	60,280	10,360	2,605
2.000	3.41	CT-70	.175	.167	1.650	9,400	11.98	67,320	11,690	2,839
2.000	3.64	CT-70	.188	.180	1.624	10,000	11.11	72,040	12,600	2,990
2.000	2.20	CT-80	.109	.104	1.782	6,700	19.23	49,560	8,320	2,235
2.000	2.50	CT-80	.125	.117	1.750	7,500	17.09	55,370	9,360	2,502
2.000	2.67	CT-80	.134	.126	1.732	8,100	15.87	59,340	10,080	2,645
2.000	3.07	CT-80	.156	.148	1.688	9,500	13.51	68,890	11,840	2,978
2.000	3.41	CT-80	.175	.167	1.650	10,000	11.98	76,930	13,360	3,245
2.000	3.64	CT-80	.188	.180	1.624	10,000	11.11	82,340	14,400	3,417
2.000	2.50	CT-90	.125	.117	1.750	8,400	17.09	62,290	10,530	2,814
2.000	2.67	CT-90	.134	.126	1.732	9,100	15.87	66,760	11,340	2,976
2.000	3.07	CT-90	.156	.148	1.688	10,000	13.51	77,500	13,320	3,350
2.000	3.41	CT-90	.175	.167	1.650	10,000	11.98	86,550	5,030	3,651
2.000	3.64	CT-90	.188	.180	1.624	10,000	11.11	92,630	16,200	3,844
2.375	2.64	CT-70	.109	.104	2.157	4,900	22.84	51,940	6,130	2,831
2.375	3.00	CT-70	.125	.117	2.125	5,500	20.30	58,100	6,900	3,181
2.375	3.21	CT-70	.134	.126	2.107	5,900	18.85	62,320	7,430	3,371
2.375	3.70	CT-70	.156	.148	2.063	7,000	16.05	72,480	8,720	3,815
2.375	4.11	CT-70	.175	.167	2.025	7,900	14.22	81,090	9,840	4,177
2.375	4.39	CT-70	.188	.180	1.999	8,500	13.19	86,890	10,610	4,413
2.375	2.64	CT-80	.109	.104	2.157	5,600	22.84	59,360	7,010	3,236
2.375	3.00	CT-80	.125	.117	2.125	6,300	20.30	66,400	7,880	3,635
2.375	3.21	CT-80	.134	.126	2.107	6,800	18.85	71,220	8,490	3,853
2.375	3.70	CT-80	.156	.148	2.063	8,000	16.05	82,840	9,970	4,360
2.375	4.11	CT-80	.175	.167	2.025	9,000	14.22	92,670	11,250	4,773
2.375	4.39	CT-80	.188	.180	1.999	9,700	13.19	99,300	12,130	5,043
2.375	2.64	CT-90	.109	.104	2.157	6,300	22.84	66,780	7,880	3,640
2.375	3.00	CT-90	.125	.117	2.125	7,100	20.30	74,700	8,870	4,090
2.375	3.20	CT-90	.134	.126	2.107	7,600	18.85	80,120	9,550	4,334
2.375	3.70	CT-90	.156	.148	2.063	9,000	16.05	93,190	11,220	4,905
2.375	4.11	CT-90	.175	.167	2.025	10,000	14.22	104,260	12,660	5,370
2.375	4.39	CT-90	.188	.180	1.999	10,000	13.19	111,710	13,640	5,673
2.875	3.67	CT-70	.125	.117	2.625	4,600	24.57	70,960	5,700	4,793
2.875	3.92	CT-70	.134	.126	2.607	4,900	22.82	76,170	6,140	5,090
2.875	4.53	CT-70	.156	.148	2.563	5,800	19.43	88,760	7,210	5,789
2.875	5.05	CT-70	.175	.167	2.525	6,500	17.22	99,450	8,130	6,365
2.875	5.40	CT-70	.188	.180	2.499	7,000	15.97	106,680	8,770	6,744
2.875	5.79	CT-70	.203	.195	2.469	7,600	14.74	114,930	9,500	7,167
2.875	3.67	CT-80	.125	.117	2.625	5,200	24.57	81,100	6,510	5,478

*The performance properties and hydrostatic test pressures shown apply to new pipe, and do not take into account additional deformation, axial load, residual stresses, or ovality caused by spooling or service cycling. **Pipe weight in lb/ft is based on specified dimensions of pipe. ***Barlow's formula is used to calculate the internal yield pressure and the hydrostatic pressure. The minimum wall thickness, the specified minimum yield strength, and the specified OD are used in the calculation. The effect of axial loading on internal yield pressure is not included. †The calculated D/t_{min} ratio is based on the specified OD and minimum wall thickness of the coiled tubing size shown. ‡Pipe body yield load is based on specified OD, minimum wall thickness, and minimum specified yield strength. §Working pressure and working loads should be based on appropriate safety factors, taking into account the serviceability issues.

TABLE 3.19—COILED-TUBING SPECIFICATIONS, REQUIREMENTS, AND PERFORMANCE PROPERTIES (continued)

			Specification Requirements					Calculated Performance Properties*		
			Wall Thickness		Inside Diameter	Hydrostatic Test		Pipe Body Yield Load	Pipe Internal Yield Pressure	Torsional Yield Strength
Specified Diameter D (in.)	Plain End Weight (lbm/ft**)	Grade	Specified t (in.)	Minimum t_{min} (in.)	d (in.)	Pressure (psi)***	D/t_{min} Ratio†	L_y‡ (lbf)	p_r*** (psi)	TS§ (lbf/ft)
2.875	3.92	CT-80	.134	.126	2.607	5,600	22.82	87,050	7,010	5,817
2.875	4.53	CT-80	.156	.148	2.563	6,600	19.43	101,430	8,240	6,616
2.875	5.05	CT-80	.175	.167	2.525	7,400	17.22	113,660	9,290	7,274
2.875	5.40	CT-80	.188	.180	2.499	8,000	15.97	121,920	10,020	7,707
2.875	5.79	CT-80	.203	.195	2.469	8,700	14.74	131,340	10,850	8,191
2.875	3.67	CT-90	.125	.117	2.625	5,900	24.57	91,240	7,330	6,163
2.875	3.92	CT-90	.134	.126	2.607	6,300	22.82	97,940	7,890	6,544
2.875	4.53	CT-90	.156	.148	2.563	7,400	19.43	114,110	9,270	7,443
2.875	5.05	CT-90	.175	.167	2.525	8,400	17.22	127,870	10,460	8,183
2.875	5.40	CT-90	.188	.180	2.499	9,000	15.97	137,160	11,270	8,671
2.875	5.79	CT-90	.203	.195	2.469	9,800	14.74	147,760	12,210	9,215
3.500	4.82	CT-70	.134	.126	3.232	4,000	27.78	93,490	5,040	7,736
3.500	5.57	CT-70	.156	.148	3.188	4,700	23.65	109,100	5,920	8,836
3.500	6.21	CT-70	.175	.167	3.150	5,300	20.96	122,410	6,680	9,750
3.500	6.65	CT-70	.188	.180	3.124	5,800	19.44	131,420	7,200	10,357
3.500	7.15	CT-70	.203	.195	3.094	6,200	17.95	141,730	7,800	11,038
3.500	4.82	CT-80	.134	.126	3.232	4,600	27.78	106,850	5,760	8,842
3.500	5.57	CT-80	.156	.148	3.188	5,400	23.65	124,680	6,770	10,099
3.500	6.21	CT-80	.175	.167	3.150	6,100	20.96	139,890	7,630	11,143
3.500	6.65	CT-80	.188	.180	3.124	6,600	19.44	150,190	8,230	11,837
3.500	7.15	CT-80	.203	.195	3.094	7,100	17.95	161,970	8,910	12,615
3.500	4.82	CT-90	.134	.126	3.232	5,200	27.78	120,200	6,480	9,947
3.500	5.57	CT-90	.156	.148	3.188	6,100	23.65	140,270	7,610	11,361
3.500	6.21	CT-90	.175	.167	3.150	6,900	20.96	157,380	8,590	12,536
3.500	6.65	CT-90	.188	.180	3.124	7,400	19.44	168,970	9,260	13,316
3.500	7.15	CT-90	.203	.195	3.094	8,000	17.95	182,220	10,030	14,192

*The performance properties and hydrostatic test pressures shown apply to new pipe, and do not take into account additional deformation, axial load, residual stresses, or ovality caused by spooling or service cycling. **Pipe weight in lb/ft is based on specified dimensions of pipe. ***Barlow's formula is used to calculate the internal yield pressure and the hydrostatic pressure. The minimum wall thickness, the specified minimum yield strength, and the specified OD are used in the calculation. The effect of axial loading on internal yield pressure is not included. †The calculated D/t_{min} ratio is based on the specified OD and minimum wall thickness of the coiled tubing size shown. ‡Pipe body yield load is based on specified OD, minimum wall thickness, and minimum specified yield strength. §Working pressure and working loads should be based on appropriate safety factors, taking into account the serviceability issues.

the overpull allowed will be low, which may be a limiting condition if the tubing becomes stuck or when a packer is used. Collapse pressures will be lowered if the tubing is oval. Care must be taken when tensile loads and collapse pressures are high. Burst rating may need to be reduced for the tubing after several cycles of spooling. Consult with the manufacturers and API RP 5C7.[9] With tapered strings, the design is fixed during the manufacturing to meet the well conditions and, once manufactured, the coiled-tubing design cannot be changed. All coiled tubing is subject to weight-loss corrosion, and plans should be made for corrosion inhibition. If thin-wall coiled tubing is used, pitting may result in an early failure of the tube. Because of spooling, which results in exceeding the body-yield strength and changing the steel properties, coiled tubing is not recommended in sour service.

Nomenclature

A_i = inner pipe area enclosed by ID, L², in.²

A_m = cross-section metal area of tubing, L², in.²

d_i = inside diameter, L, in.

d_o = outside diameter, L, in.

D = depth, L, ft

D_b = design factor in burst

D_c = design factor in collapse

D_m = measured depth, L, ft

D_t = design factor in tension

D_{tV} = true vertical depth, L, ft

E = Young's modulus of elasticity, m/Lt², psi

F = axial load, lbf

F_a = tubing hook load in air, lbf

F_b = axial buoyancy load, lbf

F_d = drag load, lbf

F_f = tubing hook load in fluid, lbf

F_j = joint yield strength, lbf

F_{jr} = minimum joint yield strength required, lbf

F_{op} = overpull load, lbf

F_t = tubing hook load in unsetting packer, lbf

g_a = gradient in the annulus, m/Lt²/L, psi/ft

g_g = gas gradient, m/Lt²/L, psi/ft

g_f = fluid gradient, m/Lt²/L, psi/ft

g_t = gradient in the tubing, m/Lt²/L, psi/ft

g_w = water gradient, m/Lt²/L, psi/ft

L_p = length of tubing ($L_1+L_2...L_n=L_p$), L, ft

n = number of thread turns

p = pressure, m/Lt², psi

p_i = initial pressure, m/Lt², psi

p_{bh} = hydrostatic pressure at depth, m/Lt², psi

p_{br} = burst-pressure rating, m/Lt², psi

p_{ca} = minimum collapse pressure under axial stress, m/Lt², psi

p_{cr} = minimum collapse pressure without axial stress, m/Lt², psi

p_h = hydrostatic test pressure, m/Lt², psi

p_{wf} = bottomhole pressure at the perforations, m/Lt², psi

p_{wh} = wellhead pressure, m/Lt², psi

p_{ww} = wellhead working pressure, m/Lt², psi

p_{yi} = internal yield pressure, m/Lt², psi

t = tube thickness, L, in.

T = temperature, T, °F

T_{bh} = bottomhole temperature, T, °F

T_{sf} = surface flowing temperature, T, °F

w_f = fluid weight, lb/gal

w_n = weight per foot of tubing, lbm/ft

$w_1, w_{2...n}$ = weight of Sec. 1, Sec. 2...n, lbm

γ_g = specific gravity of gas

γ_o = specific gravity of oil

γ_w = specific gravity of water

ΔL_t = total axial stretch or contraction, L, in.

Δp_b = burst differential, m/Lt², psi

Δp_c = collapse differential pressure, m/Lt², psi

ΔT = change in temperature, T, °F

ρ = density, m/L^3, lbm/cu ft

ρ_s = density of steel, m/L^3, 490 lbm/ft^3

ρ_w = density of water, m/L^3, 62.4 lbm/ft^3

σ = unit stress, m/Lt^2, psi

σ_z = axial stress in tubing, m/Lt^2, psi

σ_t = tangential stress in tubing, m/Lt^2, psi

σ_y = minimum yield strength of pipe, m/Lt^2, psi

References

1. *RP 5A3/ISO 13678, Thread Compounds for Casing, Tubing, and Line Pipe*, second edition, API, Washington, DC (2003).
2. *RP 5A5, Field Inspection of New Casing, Tubing, and Plain End Drill Pipe*, sixth edition, API, Washington, DC (1997).
3. *Spec. 5B, Threading, Gauging, and Thread Inspection of Casing, Tubing, and Line Pipe Threads*, 14th edition, API, Washington, DC (1996).
4. *RP 5B1, Threading, Gauging, and Thread Inspection of Casing, Tubing, and Line Pipe Threads*, fifth edition, API, Washington, DC (1999).
5. *RP 5C1, Care and Use of Casing and Tubing*, 18th edition, API, Washington, DC (1999).
6. *Bull. 5C2, Performance Properties of Casing, Tubing and Drill Pipe*, 21st edition, API, Washington, DC (1999).
7. *Bull. 5C3, Formulas and Calculations for Casing, Tubing, Drill Pipe, and Line Pipe Properties*, sixth edition, API, Washington, DC (1994).
8. *RP 5C5/ISO 13679, Evaluation Procedures for Casing and Tubing Connections*, third edition, API, Washington, DC (2003).
9. *RP 5C7, Coiled Tubing Operations in Oil and Gas Well Services*, first edition, API, Washington, DC (2002).
10. *Spec. 5CT/ISO 11960, Casing and Tubing (U.S. Customary Units)*, seventh edition, API, Washington, DC (2002).
11. *Spec. 5CTN, Casing and Tubing (Metric Units)*, fifth edition, API, Washington, DC (1995).
12. *Spec. 15LT, PVC Lined Steel Tubular Goods*, second edition, API, Washington, DC (1999).
13. *RP 15 TL4, Care and Use of Fiberglass Tubulars*, second edition, API, Washington, DC (1999).
14. *ISO/ISO 13680, Petroleum and Natural Gas Industries: Corrosion-Resistant Alloy Seamless Tubes for Use as Casing, Tubing and Coupling Stock—Technical Delivery Conditions*, first edition, ISO, Geneva, Switzerland (2000).
15. *ISO/DIS 13679, Petroleum and Natural Gas Industries: Testing Procedures for Casing and Tubing Connections*, first edition, ISO, Geneva, Switzerland (2002).
16. *MR0175/ISO 15156, Petroleum and Natural Gas Industries—Materials for Use in H2S-Containing Environments in Oil and Gas Production*, first edition, NACE, Houston (2001).
17. *ISO/ISO 13678, Petroleum and Natural Gas Industries: Evaluation and Testing of Thread Compound Systems for Use With Casing, Tubing and Line Pipe*, first edition, ISO, Geneva, Switzerland (2000).

General References

Allen, T.O. and Roberts, A.P.: *Production Operations*, fourth edition, Oil & Gas Consultants Intl. Inc., Houston (1993).

ISO/ISO 10400, Petroleum and Natural Gas Industries: Formulae and Calculation for Casing, Tubing, Drill Pipe and Line Pipe Properties, first edition, ISO, Geneva, Switzerland (1993).

ISO/ISO 10405, Petroleum and Natural Gas Industries: Care and Use of Casing and Tubing, second edition, ISO, Geneva, Switzerland (2000).

ISO/ISO 10422, Petroleum and Natural Gas Industries: Threading, Gauging and Thread Inspection of Casing, Tubing and Line Pipe Threads, first edition, ISO, Geneva, Switzerland (1993).

ISO/ISO 11960, Petroleum and Natural Gas Industries: Steel Pipes for Use as Casing or Tubing for Wells, second edition, ISO, Geneva, Switzerland (2001).

ISO/DIS/CD 15156 Petroleum and Natural Gas Industries: Materials for Use in H₂S Containing Environments in Oil and Gas Production: Parts 1 through 3, first edition, ISO, Geneva, Switzerland (2001).

ISO/DIS 15463 Petroleum and Natural Gas Industries: Field Inspection of New Casing, Tubing and Plain-End Drill Pipe, first edition, ISO, Geneva, Switzerland (2003).

ISO/WD 15464 Petroleum and Natural Gas Industries: Gauging and Inspection of Casing, Tubing and Line Pipe Threads—Recommended Practice, working document, ISO, Geneva, Switzerland (2003).

ISO/DIS 14692, Petroleum and Natural Gas Industries: Glass-Reinforced Plastic (GRP) Piping: Parts 1 through 4, first edition, ISO, Geneva, Switzerland (2002).

SI Metric Conversion Factors

bbl	× 1.589 873	E–01	= m³
ft	× 3.048*	E–01	= m
ft³	× 2.831 685	E–02	= m³
°F	(°F – 32)/1.8		= °C
in.	× 25.4	E+00	= mm
in.²	× 6.451 6*	E+00	= cm²
lbf	× 4.448 222	E+00	= N
lbm	× 4.535924	E–01	= kg
psi	× 6.894 757	E+00	= kPa

*Conversion factor is exact.

Chapter 4
Perforating
George E. King, BP plc

4.1 Flow Path

Perforating is a process used to establish a flow path between the near reservoir and the wellbore. It normally involves initiating a hole from the wellbore through the casing and any cement sheath into the producing zone. The effectiveness of this process depends on the care and design of the perforating procedure. Because a high percentage of current wells use a cased-hole completion, the importance of the design and application of the perforating process cannot be overstated.

Perforations are an elemental piece of the inflow section of the well and have significant impact on the total completion efficiency. This chapter describes the methods of creating the best flow path for a particular completion. It also contains information on completion diagnostics and candidate selection for situations in which reperforating could improve production. The intent of this chapter is to familiarize the engineer with methods and techniques to improve the flow path, not all of which involve perforating equipment.

Establishing an optimum flow path requires the execution of a number of critical steps. These critical operations are identified throughout the chapter and are used in design, quality control inspection, and quality control.

A brief description is needed of the alternative completion methods to cased, cemented, and perforated completions. Openhole completions offer several options that should not be ignored in a quest for a high efficiency flow connection to the reservoir. Key to the completion process is the minimization of pressure drop across the completion, specifically the piece of the flow path from the near reservoir to the wellbore. In many cases, completion requirements extend to the need to modify the flow connection to reduce gas or water coning, to access multiple layers, and to assist in placing fractures. Completion requirements also extend to other aspects that involve initial completion or recompletion of the producing interval. A careful assessment of the benefits offered by both openhole completions and cased and perforated completion methods should be conducted.

4.2 Definitions

Because many of the perforating processes deal with explosive powders and gas expansion methods, a few definitions of the specialized nomenclature are needed.[1]

High explosives are very powerful explosives such as RDX, HMX, PYX, HNS, and others that find common use in the oil industry. High explosives are characterized by extreme energy release in a very short time, some with detonation front movement on the order of 6100+ m/s (20,000+ ft/sec). The detonation of an explosive is a chemical reaction and, like many chemical reactions, certain variables control the speed of the reaction. Peak energy generation with these materials is necessary to perform effectively and can be achieved only if they have high-order initiation. The initiation process for any explosive is critical in oilfield applications.

Gas generators are explosive materials designed to generate energy at a slower rate than the high explosives, and their primary function is to provide quick fluid volume. These materials are used for power fluids (gas drive), fracturing energy, and propulsion energy sources.

Order is a term associated with explosive firing. High order means that the high explosive has been initiated properly and reacts at the maximum speed. Low-order initiation of a high explosive fails to achieve maximum energy; the explosive may react, but the energy level produced is sharply lower than the maximum potential. In perforating charges, a low-order detonation usually means a failure to produce effective perforations, although gas pressure may rise sharply. Burning is one of the low-order reactions, usually producing gas, with no perforation possible. Low-order detonations may expand or burst guns, causing obstructions and fishing or recompletion decisions. Care in design and application of the perforating system can reduce sharply the incidence of low-order firing. Low-order detonations are caused by several factors, but temperature and poor condition of detonating cord are leading causes.

A *primary explosive* is an explosive that is used in initiators or other devices to initiate the explosive sequence. Primary explosives usually are more sensitive to firing (can be initiated more easily) than secondary explosives. Common locations for these explosives are in detonators (also called blasting caps) and some booster devices.

Secondary explosives are the main explosives used in charges. The secondary explosives (usually high explosives) are harder to initiate and must be initiated to get proper response (i.e., a high-order detonation).

Perforation flow efficiency is a measurement of how close flow capacity in the perforated hole approaches the flow capacity of an ideal hole of the same diameter and length. There can be enormous differences in flow rate between a perforated hole and a drilled hole of the same diameter and length. The perforation flow efficiency is a part of the total well flow efficiency. Achieving the highest flow efficiency, by perforation characteristic, by cleanup, or by a breakdown operation, is a critical step. Good perforation flow efficiency is greater than 80%.

Pressure differential toward the formation from the wellbore is overbalance. Pressure differential from the formation to the wellbore is underbalance. Fluid flows from high pressure toward the low pressure in a permeable formation. Special cases of overbalance manipulation include extreme overbalance perforating (EOP).

Phasing is the angle between the charges. The most common phasings are 0°, 180°, 120°, 90°, and 60°. Several specialty guns, offering higher density charge application and guns for sand control or casing protection, may offer phasings that increase the linear distance between the charges in a direct line along the gun body.

Shot density is the measurement of the perforations made per unit length of the gun. Normally given in either shots/ft (SPF) or shots/m (SPM), the ranges of shot density extend from 1 to 27 SPF. The most common shot densities are 4 to 12 SPF (13 to 39 SPM). Shot density requirements are a function of the completion design and the formation production requirements.

Pressure drop is a measurement of the hindrances in the flow system. Rate of fluid flow through a rock is determined by the differential pressure, the permeability of the system, the fluid viscosity, and the length and area of the flow path. To maximize flow rate, the permeability must be high. Crushed rock, debris, and other obstructions result in lower permeability and lower flow rate. In a well system, maximum production is achieved by minimizing pressure drop.

4.3 Perforating History

Bullet guns were the first commercial perforating devices.[2] A hardened steel bullet was fired from a short-barrel gun powered by a gas-producing explosive. These guns first saw commercial use in the early 1930s. The wall thickness and hardness of the casing and the hardness of the formation limit bullet perforating. Bullet guns are still used in some applications, usually in soft formations for deep penetration or brittle formations in which the shattering produced by the bullet can help break down the formation around the perforation.

During the 1930s and 1940s, work in the area of shaped charges progressed in the military arena. The bazooka, with its armor-piercing charges, was one of the first large-scale uses of the technology pioneered by Henry Mohaupt and others. This technology was accepted by the oil industry in the late 1940s and early 1950s and became the most used perforating method by the mid- to late 1950s.

Alternatives to explosives also were implemented, normally with an abrasive slurry of material such as frac sand and a carrier liquid, either sand or water.[3,4] Abrasive perforating methods are slower, require a rig, and contain several wear points in the treating equipment.

Specialty perforators, including laser, hydraulic punches, mechanical punches, water jet, combination bullet/jet guns, and electric arc perforating, have been used. Most of the specialty methods are used for special applications and do not find widespread use. Interesting perforation applications such as underbalanced perforating, tubing-conveyed perforating, and specialty phasings have their roots in much earlier applications, often 15 to 30 years before they became popular.

4.4 Perforating Methods

4.4.1 Bullet Gun Perforating. Projectiles from these guns (bullets) must penetrate the casing, cement, and formation. Bullet speed exiting the barrel is usually approximately 900 m/s (3000 ft/sec). Penetration is easiest in low alloy, thinner walled pipe (H-40, to K-55, and L-80 API casing series pipe grades). Penetration in higher strength casing alloy pipe and harder formations is more difficult in most cases and not feasible in others.[2] When successful, the bullet creates a very round entrance hole but may often create a hole with sharp internal burrs. **Fig. 4.1** shows a bullet-perforated casing from a surface test.

Tunnel length creation with a bullet gun drops sharply with increasing formation strength. Penetration extremes of 15 in. –/+ in soft chalks to 2 to 3 in. in dolomites are common. In contrast to shaped-charge perforating, however, bullets often shatter the rock rather than smoothly push back and compact the rock in their path. The shattering can be a definite advantage when the cracking improves the permeability next to the perforation.

Bullet penetration is primarily a function of the density and strength of the target in its path, as well as gun performance factors. The energy from the bullet is proportional to its mass, the amount of propellant, and the performance of the seal between the bullet and the barrel. Early performance-measuring tests with bullet guns showed a direct correlation between the penetration in a target and the use of new gun barrels. Performance dropped sharply with barrel enlargement and/or wear.

Entrance hole roundness and the pronounced shattering around the perforation tunnel help improve stimulation through bullet-perforated completions. Perforation ball sealers seal quickly and efficiently on bullet perforations. This is partly because of the additional brittle cracking of the formation (increasing permeability), the ability of the ball sealer to create a seal on the perforation, and the reduced number of bullet perforators normally used in a well. The reduced number of bullet perforators used in a well is an indication that a large number of perforations spreads out the flow entering the formation, resulting in a lower flow rate into a given perforation and less tendency to attract and seat a ball sealer.

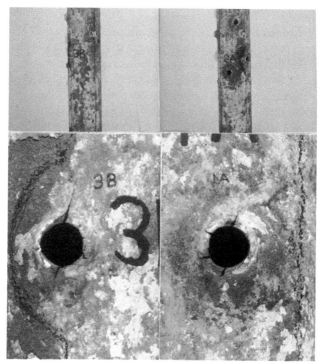

Fig. 4.1—Bullet-perforated casing from a surface test.

Advantages of bullet perforating are high permeability connection to the immediate reservoir and very controlled hole size and shape. Disadvantages are shallow penetration, ineffectiveness in hard formations and high alloy or heavy pipe, leaving a solid mass of steel in the perforation tunnel, and low density perforating.

4.4.2 Abrasive Perforating Methods. Abrasive perforating methods use high-volume flow of abrasive-laden fluid to erode through the target pipe or cut it off when the nozzle or tubing string is rotated.[3,4] Abrasive impingement of hard particles such as sand on steel can cut through 0.25 to 0.3 in. of casing in a matter of minutes. Perforations in the casing or even 15 × 1.2 cm (6 in. × 0.5 in.) slots can be formed within 10 to 20 minutes per slot (hole). Abrasive methods often use a shaped nozzle that focuses the stream on the steel surface. The nozzle helps preserve energy, shorten cutting time, and decrease the effect of clearance distance, but the nozzle wears with use. Clearance distance between the nozzle and the target is important but not as critical as in nonsolids jet cutting.

Perforation depths formed by abrasives are typically short because the returning fluid and solids interfere with the ability of high-pressure fluids to access deeper targets. Depths of 2.54 to 23 cm (1 to more than 8 in.) have been measured in tests performed with backpressure. Abrasive perforating or cutting in surface targets often produces quicker cutting and may achieve deeper perforation depth, but these tests are not a valid representation of tool performance in a well. Adding backpressure on any type of a jetting tool rapidly diminishes its performance because of the reduction of pressure and flow velocity across the nozzle and collapse of bubbles and cavitation that may occur exiting the nozzle on a low-pressure test. Required equipment includes a rig with tubing large enough for the required rate with minimal friction drop. A fixed nozzle for perforating or a rotating nozzle for abrasive cutoff is the main bottomhole assembly.

The type of abrasive varies with the job, but sand is the most common material for perforating and pipe cutoff. Other abrasives such as calcium carbonate, soda glass, and other mineral and synthetic materials can be used. There are some differences in the cutting efficiency of materials. The quickest cutters are harder, more angular materials. Bauxite is the single most erosive material in the abrasive process but is used rarely because of its density and cost.

Liquid selection is less important and usually is dictated by the damage potential to the formation. Because some fluid is lost to the formation in any jetting job, the damage aspect of the carrier fluid should be investigated. The ability of the fluid to lift solids usually is limited to lifting the sand abrasive. The steel removed in the process is too fine to cause significant plugging problems.

Advantages of abrasive-perforating methods include the ability to make perforations with maximum flow area and with minimum damage to the formation or to the integrity of the steel pipe. The perforations are shallow in most cases, limited by the backwash of returning fluids, but are notably undamaged in most tests. The best applications have been in heavy oil completions in which large inflow area in the pipe is a necessity and pipe cutoff is advantageous. Disadvantages of these methods are the time needed to create each perforation, the amount of equipment required (coiled tubing or small tubing), the need to kill or control the well while creating the perforation, and solids cleanup.

4.4.3 Water Jets. Although water jets with pressure impact on the order of 20,000 psi are used as steel cutters in surface applications, they usually are not effective downhole when the backpressure is more than approximately 1,500 psi. The use of these tools is limited sharply by friction pressure drop in the small diameter, long-tubing strings used to supply fluid to the point of cutting. Water jets have been used to create perforation tunnels in openhole completions. A special adaptation of the water jet used a hydraulic punch to open a "door" in the casing through which a flexible water-jet lance was fed to extend a long perforation into the rock. With few exceptions, water-jet perforating is a special application.

4.4.4 Shaped Charges. The shaped charge or "jet" perforator uses a small amount of high explosive and a carefully shaped case and liner to create a focused pressure punch that is highly effective in piercing steel, cement, and rock. The jet is formed through a highly critical, but usually reliable, sequence of events. The sequence begins with the firing of the initiator or detonator cap, which ignites the detonation cord at high energy, followed by the initiation of the charges. The entire sequence of the explosive event must be carried out in high order. Failure to achieve or maintain high-order firing at any point in the explosive sequence will cause all subsequent explosive to initiate low order and burn with very slow energy release.

Fig. 4.2 shows the components of a shaped-charge perforator. **Fig. 4.3** contains an X-ray of a 20-g, steel-cased charge that shows the detail assembly necessary for these charges. The charge case holds the explosive powder and focuses the firing explosive event. The primer area usually holds a small amount of slightly destabilized, secondary high explosive. The primer initiates the main explosive in the charge. As the explosive front moves through the charge, it strikes the apex of the liner deforming the liner and fluidizing part of its mass into a focused jet that punches a hole through the material in its path. **Fig. 4.4** shows a jet formation from a shaped charge. As the jet forms, it stretches out with the jet tip approaching speeds of 6100 m/s (21,000 ft/sec), and the tail of the jet traveling at approximately 3,000 m/s (11,000 ft/sec). For illustration, several unusual targets have been used to capture jet performance with high-speed cameras.[5] In one of the most unusual experiments, the path of a jet through both sides of a crystal wine goblet was captured on ultra-high-speed film and shows full jet development before the goblet shattered. In effect, the hole is placed before the target "knows" that it has been hit.

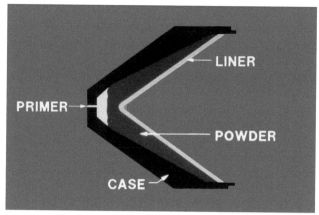

Fig. 4.2—Components of a shaped-charge perforator.

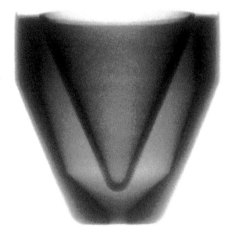

Fig. 4.3—X-ray of a 20-g charge.

Penetration of a shaped-charge jet through a target proceeds with the jet pushing aside everything in its path. The effect is similar to driving a nail through a block of wood. The wood around the nail hole is compacted tightly. Permeability in porous rock is reduced frequently in the compacted zone. There is almost no heat transfer during the jet penetration, although some target heating usually is seen from the post-explosion byproduct gases. Almost any target, including paper, can be perforated with a shaped charge. A classic example of penetration and compaction is the penetration of a jet through a thick telephone book. The area around the perforation tunnel in the paper is highly compacted to a radius of approximately 0.4 in. (1 cm). Straightening out the uncharred paper in the crushed zone revealed that very little of the paper was lost during perforating. Because fluids must flow through this crush zone, understanding how and why it forms and how to remove or bypass it is of primary importance in completion engineering.[6,7]

With shaped charges, the perforation penetration usually is thought to be proportional to the weight of the charge. Although the charge size has an effect on the performance, the shape of the liner, the internal standoff in the gun, and the overall design are also important. In a through-tubing application in which the carriers are small, the charge size will vary from 2 to

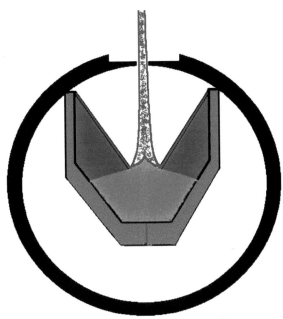

Fig. 4.4—Jet formation from a shaped charge.

approximately 8 g. The smallest charges are used in 1 $\frac{9}{16}$- and 1 $\frac{11}{16}$-in. hollow carriers and the larger sizes are used in expendable strips. In hollow-carrier casing guns with diameters of 3⅛ in. or larger, charge weights of more than 12 g are common (typically 22 to 37 g for 5-in.-diameter guns). Normally, the largest charges are used in the large expendable guns and casing guns in which the charges are more than 50 g. Openhole perforating guns that are designed to reach beyond mud damage in an openhole completion may use charges of 90 g or more.

4.5 Basic Perforating Design—Variables of Flow Through a Perforation

Shaped-charge perforations are used as the model for the rest of this discussion. Perforations are tapering tubes of usually less than 0.8 in. (2 cm) diameter at the entrance hole in the casing and depth of 1 in. (2.5 cm) to more than 30 in. (74 cm). Primary flow from the formation is through the end and walls of the tube. Flow behavior typically is dominated by radial flow with some pseudoradial character in longer perforations. Length, diameter, and permeability of the rock around the perforation control flow through a perforation.[8] Many early studies ignored the damage around the perforation tunnel and focused on the importance of length and entrance hole diameter. Putting damage effects aside, the length of the perforation tunnel is theoretically the most critical factor in a natural completion in which no further stimulation or sand control is planned. Entrance hole diameter becomes more important when some sand control completion designs are planned or fracturing is needed. Because of the early studies that ignored the effects of formation damage, the primary selling points of perforating charges became perforated length and entrance hole diameter. These two elements diminish in significance when the effect of formation damage is studied.[7,9,10]

Perforating charge performance in producing both entrance hole and perforation length is related more closely to charge design than charge size. The charge variables include propellant type, size, and design. The formation variables include formation strength, pressure, porosity, grain size, and fluids in the pores.[11] Perforating charge power is provided by the explosive and focused by the case and liner to produce a jet. The jet may be shaped to maximize either entrance hole or tunnel penetration. The completion type dictates the type of perforation needed

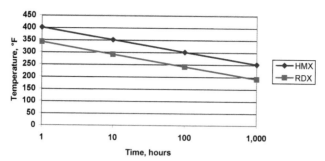

Fig. 4.5—Temperature stability estimates.

and thus the type of charge. No matter which charge is selected, however, the flow path must have a higher flow capacity than the formation can supply. Otherwise, it becomes a restriction in the reservoir-to-wellbore connection. Flow connection should be the primary consideration when selecting a perforating charge. Charge penetration can be optimized for specific nonpermeable targets such as cement and may produce a phenomenally long perforated length and very low flow capacity. Flow capacity should be the requirement in any producing environment.

As the jet penetrates the formation, the material in its path is thrust to the side, creating a zone of lowered permeability. The amount of permeability loss depends on the structure, porosity, and fluid of the formation and the size and design of the charge. Studies of permeability loss in targets and back calculation of damage in relatively homogeneous formations show permeabilities of approximately 35 to 80% of the initial formation permeability. There are three critical requirements to achieving a highly conductive flow path: select the optimum perforating equipment (including, but not limited to, charges) for the completion type, select the fluids and charge for the best formation interaction (minimize damage), and use the application method (underbalance, overbalance, surging, etc.) that provides the best cleanup and flow capacity in the perforations.[8,12–18]

The best-known design considerations for perforating are perforation length, shot-phase angle, perforation density, entrance hole size, and perforating flow efficiency. To design properly for optimum perforating requires preplanning and consideration of parameters such as filtered perforating fluid, amount of underbalance or overbalance, through tubing vs. casing or expendable guns, the method for conveying guns, and gun clearance. Special considerations, such as ultrahigh compressive strength rock (> 30,000 psi UCS), require special charges.[19]

4.6 Temperature Effect

The higher the wellbore temperatures, the shorter the time that the perforating jet charge is stable. **Fig. 4.5** illustrates stable time at temperature for charges made from common types of explosives. Guidelines for high-temperature charge selection vary, but most wireline-conveyed charges should be stable at the temperature for 16 to 24 hours. Tubing-conveyed perforating charges, for operations involving extended time at the bottomhole temperature, must remain stable for approximately 100 hours or more to allow for running the tubing and nippling up the wellhead. Higher temperature charges for operations involving extended time at temperatures greater than 300°F (149°C) are available, although they are more costly. When selecting a high-temperature charge, all parts of the system, including detonator, detonation cord, charges, seals and mechanical components, must be rated for the time at temperature and must work together.

When perforating charges explode low order or burn, large fragments of the charge cases will remain. These fragments are primary evidence of the problem. **Fig. 4.6** shows charged cases removed from a low-order gun. Gun breaches during low-order detonation or burning are common. **Fig. 4.7** shows a burst gun fished from a well after low-order firing. Anytime whole

Fig. 4.6—Charge cases removed from a low-order gun.

Fig. 4.7—Burst gun fished from a well after low-order firing.

charge cases or large sections of charge cases are found in the gun debris, the perforating job quality is highly suspect, and the perforating task should be evaluated or redone.

4.7 Basic Perforating Design—What Is Necessary for the Optimum Flow Path

Before selecting components for a perforating job, the first task is to understand how to get the best flow path possible for the time and money invested and the risk taken. The amount of flow capacity needed must be determined first. Flow capacity needs are a reflection of how much and what type of fluids that the formation can deliver to the wellbore. Inflow performance modeling with representative values of formation permeability and fluid viscosity is necessary. The objective of perforating is to place open perforations at the correct depth that extend through the casing and cement sheath into the formation. To be effective, the perforation tunnel must be in contact with a permeable part of the formation and must not be damaged by any mechanism that would stop or impede the transfer of fluids between the formation and the wellbore.[6,7,20]

Optimizing petroleum production is an exercise in removing pressure drops in a flowing system that stretches from the outer boundaries of the reservoir to the sales line. The perforating process is one element in this engineering exercise. To optimize the whole process, the most severe pressure drops must be examined and removed. As each pressure drop is reduced, the increased flow may change the requirements in another section of the well. Increasing the

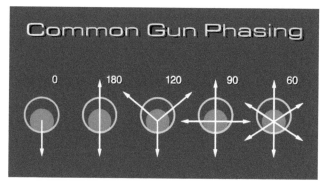

Fig. 4.8—Common perforator phasing.

flow capacity of the reservoir by stimulation or flooding places a greater capacity requirement on the perforations. Other well completion actions, such as gravel packing, change the flow requirement on the perforation by filling the perforation with gravel. Each action changes the criteria for perforation design; therefore, initial perforating designs may not be optimal for later well production. Well design should allow for flexibility in the completion type, which allows for adding perforation density in a zone or perforating other zones after the well has been evaluated or produced.

Phasing is the angle between the charges, and **Fig. 4.8** shows a common perforator phasing. Although there are many possible angles, the five common values are 0°, 180°, 120°, 90°, and 60°. 0° phasing aligns all the shots in a row. The gun should be decentralized, typically against the low side of the casing, so that performance from small charges is maximized by minimizing the clearance between the gun and the casing wall. 0° phasing normally is used only in the smaller OD guns or guns in very large casing. 0° phasing has some drawbacks because putting all the shots in a row lowers tubular yield strength and makes the casing more susceptible to splits and collapse at shot densities greater than 6 SPF. Fracture stimulating in wells that were perforated with 0° phasing may result in a slightly higher incidence of fracturing screenouts than with 60°, 90°, or 120° phasing. It is unknown whether the screenouts result from the smaller entrance holes or from one wing of the fracture wrapping around the pipe.

Of the other common phasing possibilities, 60°, 90°, and 120° are usually the most efficient choices from a fracture stimulation standpoint because they will produce a perforation just a few degrees from any possible fracture direction. These phased carriers may not need to be centralized to give good perforations because, regardless of where they contact the casing, at least two or three optimum perforations per foot should be formed. In small carrier guns in large casing, only 0° phasing should be used because the perforations closest to the gun will be fully developed, while the perforations with the largest gun clearance will be shorter and have a very small diameter. Casing guns offer much better phasing but often cannot be used to add perforations in an existing completion without major intervention.

Perforating phasing is known to affect production in both theoretical and practical applications. Locke, for example, showed that for a 12-in. penetration into the formation, a theoretical productivity ratio of 1.2 is predicted from 90° phasing of 4 SPF, while the productivity ratio is approximately 0.99 when the 4 shots are in 0° phasing.[8] This is ideal behavior and does not consider damage. When damage is considered, the actual formation character and perforation application details may create a much different outcome, although the effect of additional phasing is usually beneficial.

Perforation length usually is thought to be the most important characteristic in a perforation design. Surprisingly, there are several cases in which perforated length does not make a significant difference in well productivity. Only in natural completions does the perforation tunnel

Fig. 4.9—Deep-penetrating and big-hole charge performance from 34-g charges.

length dominate the other factors. Even in natural completions, the flow capacity of the perforated connections is the most important factor. Factors such as hydraulic fracturing or prepacked gravel-pack operations negate the advantages of a few extra inches of perforated length. For hydraulic fracturing or gravel-pack treatments, a large, effective entrance hole through the pipe and cement is more important than total perforation penetration.

Although rarely considered, the perforation diameter also may influence the productivity ratio, especially in high productivity wells. Perforation diameter is dependent on charge design and the clearance of the gun in the casing. In instances such as sand control operations, unstable formations (including some chalks), and wells that are to be hydraulically fracture stimulated, the perforation diameter is important enough to dominate perforator selection. Flow through an open perforation should not be a restriction in the flowing system.

The choice between penetration length and entrance hole size is made available by the size of the charges and an element of the charge design. A charge's design affects the hole diameter and penetration. **Fig. 4.9** shows deep penetrating and big-hole charge performances from 34-g charges.

A deep-penetrating charge has a different shaped liner (and sometimes a different case) from that of a big-hole charge. The deep-penetrating charge spends the bulk of its energy creating a long tunnel, while the big-hole charge focuses its energy on the casing wall and creating hole diameter. Deep-penetrating charges normally are used in natural completions, and big-hole charges are used more for gravel packing and fracturing, in which hole size offers less restriction to wither outflow during fracturing or inflow during production when the perforation is filled with gravel. Big-hole charges may have some disadvantages in both pipe and formation strength. The design of big-hole charges produces maximum force impact at the wall of the casing and can cause damage (and weakening) to the formation adjacent to the entry hole. For completions in weak formations in which sand production could be an issue and gravel packing or frac packing will not be used, deep penetrating charges at high density (12 to 16 SPF or 39 to 54 SPM) are recommended. If the zone collapses, however, reperforating with sufficient density of phased shots is required before gravel-pack operations are instituted.

The number of perforations is always a factor in completion design. Shot densities from 1 to 27 SPF (3 to 88 SPM) are available. High shot densities usually are required for very high flow rate formations, for single point application of fractures in deviated wellbores, and for laminated formations that will not be linked by fracturing. Optimum shot density for a well can best be determined with a nodal analysis simulator; however, judgment is needed when dealing with highly laminated formations or when the formation flow path is suitably inhomogeneous to create limited entry effects in the inflow. Adding perforations is often an excellent diagnostic tool.

Assuming all perforations are open to flow, shot densities of 4 SPF (13 SPM) with 90° phasing and with 13-mm (0.5-in.) holes usually are sufficient to ensure the equivalent of open-hole productivity. However, increased shot densities (greater than 4 per foot) may improve productivity ratios under certain conditions, such as very high flowrate wells or in gravel-packed wells. The real number of open perforations, those producing or taking fluid, is typically only approximately 50% of the total holes in the pipe. (The 50% value was reached after examining hundreds of hours of downhole television recordings in dozens of wells.) The cause of nonfunctioning perforations is usually traced to nonproductive layers in the formation or to damaged perforations. Perforating produces a damage zone around the perforation in which permeability may be reduced substantially below that of the native state formation. Longer perforations are less influenced by the crush zone than are short perforations. Phased perforations, such as 90° phased perforations, are less affected than 0° phased perforations. The damage in the near wellbore, plus the damage in the crushed zone, can cause severe pressure drops. However, most damage from drilling mud is confined near the face of the formation. In cases of nonwater-sensitive sandstones, the damage zone should not be of significance. The crushed zones will be created regardless of damage but may be minimized by underbalance or extreme overbalance perforating.

4.8 Improving Flow Capacity

Creating a perforation is relatively easy. Creating a low-pressure-drop flow path requires considerably more effort. As previously stated, most perforations have a crushed zone and other damage mechanisms that hinder production. To improve flow capacity, underbalanced perforating, extreme overbalanced perforating, surging, or one of several breakdown actions is necessary to clean the perforations and improve flow capacity.

In most cases, overbalanced perforating drives the wellbore fluid into the perforation and has the capacity to create particulate damage in the perforations. Clean fluid becomes a perforating requirement. Studies of the flow rate needed to remove damage report that serious perforation plugging occurs when the pressure is higher in the wellbore than in the formation. The plugs consist of crushed formation, liner particles, case material from the charges, pipe dope, and mud. In many lab and field cases, a plug formed when overbalance perforating in heavy mud is almost impossible to remove by reversing pressure.

Underbalance perforating, or perforating with the pressure in the wellbore lower than the pressure in the formation, generally is acknowledged to be one of the best methods for creating open, undamaged perforations in which the permeability is high enough to create sufficient flow rate to break the crush zone loose and carry it out of the perforation tunnel. In a simplified view, the initial underbalance surge and the subsequent flow clean up the perforations across the interval. In the real world, the initial surge at the moment of perforating opens up the perforations in the highest permeability streaks in the formation. As the pressure quickly equalizes, only a few more perforations may be opened and cleaned. For this reason, long perforated intervals may not be as effectively cleaned by underbalanced perforating as shorter intervals with lower shot density.

The pressure differential required to remove damage from a perforation is affected by pressure, flow rate, and formation integrity. Initially, pressure differentials for underbalanced perforating were established by trial and error, but a connection finally was spotted relating underbalance pressure and flow to formation permeability.[10,11]

The results of underbalance studies of more than 100 wells that were underbalance perforated, tested acidized, and retested are shown in **Fig. 4.10** for oil wells and **Fig. 4.11** for gas wells.[14] The response of an HCl acid job in the sandstone formation showed whether or not the underbalance pressure applied adequately cleaned the perforations.

Although underbalance pressure is of critical importance in generating clean perforations, it is the flow rate created by the underbalance that is responsible for cleaning the perforation.

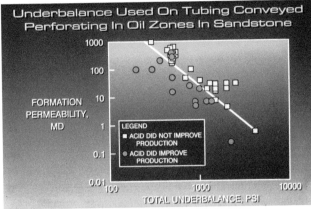

Fig. 4.10—Underbalance pressures used for gas wells.

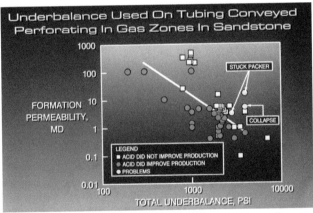

Fig. 4.11—Underbalance pressures used for oil wells.

The importance of flow after underbalance perforating cannot be overemphasized. The flow volume needed from a single perforation to clean debris is estimated at a minimum of 4 gal. In more recent work on deepwater wells in which surge volume is limited by operational and policy guidelines, a 20-bbl surge has shown to be very effective in cleaning the perforations. If the permeability is too low to achieve significant flow rate (< 1 md), underbalance perforating may not be effective. The most frequent causes of failure for underbalance perforating are low formation permeability and lack of flow immediately after the perforating gun fires. Candidate formations with permeabilities of more than 1 md are best, although sandstones are usually much better candidates than carbonates.

EOP is a microfracture-initiating process that is applied at the moment of initial perforating or as a surge process to existing perforations.[21,22] The technique uses stored gas energy in the tubing to break down the zone. Bottomhole pressure equivalents to 1.4 psi/ft and higher are applied instantaneously through the use of a nitrogen gas supercharge contained in the tubing. The energy is isolated in the tubulars of an unperforated well and behind a shear disk or other device in the tubing on a well that has already been perforated. The energy imparted is more sudden than a traditional hydraulic fracturing process and more sustained than an explosive or propellant treatment.

The fracture created by the EOP surge is more likely to fracture more perforations in an exposed zone than a traditional fracture process applied as an all-liquid hydraulic-fracturing process. Work with production logs and radioactive-isotope-tagged sand after EOP jobs indicates that multiple zones tend to break down more evenly when EOP is used. Although a fracture is created during extreme overbalance perforating or surging, its initiation does not appear to be controlled initially by formation stresses or traditional rock mechanics forces, probably because the 1.4 psi/ft gradient is considerably greater than most fracture gradients of 0.7 to 0.9 psi/ft. Because of the very high pressure of the initial surge, the pressure behind the surge is probably greater than the fields of maximum and minimum principal stresses in the formation. As a result, the initial direction of the fracture is in the plane of greatest mechanical near-wellbore weakness: the perforations. After the estimated 6-second life of the pulse, the fracture direction probably is controlled by the traditional stress forces, and subsequent fracture growth goes perpendicular to the plane of least principal stress.

Although treatment designs are still being refined, the initial successes have focused on maximizing the kinetic energy in the job. This is accomplished by minimizing the liquid in the tubing to eliminate friction pressure of liquid movement during the surge. Most job designs focus on filling the tubing with nitrogen and filling the casing below the packer with liquid.

A modification of the EOP process uses explosive propellant to deliver a pressure pulse that achieves the same type of breakdown as the fluid, but with minimum equipment.[23] The propellant is molded into a sleeve that is mounted on the outside of the perforating gun when adding perforations or as a stick when pulsing old perforations. Firing the perforating gun ignites the slower burning propellant, creating a gas pulse that breaks down the perforations. The pressure pulse lasts only a few seconds, but its location at the perforations helps break down crush zone damage. Fractures created by either the EOP or propellant process are not propped and will likely close after the event if not propped. The cleanout benefits of the process, however, have been well documented.

Surging perforations to achieve cleanup is an effective tool provided that the differential pressure is high enough to create enough fluid movement to clean the perforations. Few guidelines exist on surging other than at the local field level. Surges from 500 to 2,000 psi are common and are applied as suddenly as possible. The surges are most effective when the "valve" for the process is close to the formation. Long, small inside diameter tubing strings dampen the surge effectiveness because of high flowing friction resistance during the surge flow. Typically, not all perforations are opened by surging.

4.9 Cement and Casing Damage

Casing and cement damage during perforating has been debated for years.[24–30] There is probably little shattering or cracking damage to a good cement sheath from perforating. Tests have been conducted on more than 50 targets with unconfined compressive strength from 1,500 to more than 9,000 psi. When the perforation is more than approximately 4 in. from a free face (top or bottom of the target), there is almost no instance of cement shattering noted after firing. Splitting (longitudinal) along the perforated planes is seen in some targets but is an artifact of the test. In surface tests, cement cracking following perforating is the result of the test method, not the perforating process.

Either the casing or the carrier must absorb the explosive shock of charge detonation. Air-filled hollow-carrier guns absorb most of the detonation pressure; therefore, there is less possibility of casing splits caused by rupture. This becomes very important when shooting a large number of holes or whenever casing strength is important. The collapse resistance of the casing (and resistance to splits) depends on the number of holes in the pipe, the hole size, and their alignment (shot phasing). Casing guns with staggered phasing have improved the casing collapse resistance loss. These guns, which use deep-penetrating charges, often result in less than 10% casing strength crush resistance loss at shot densities of 16 or more SPF. Perforating with hollow-carrier guns causes only slight reduction in yield or collapse strength of the casing. Expendable and semiexpendable guns cause substantially more damage because the casing must stand the shock of detonation. Casing of low or unknown strength (corroded, old, flawed, or poorly supported casing) definitely should be shot with a hollow-carrier gun.

4.10 Perforating Multiple Strings and Thick Cement

Concentric casing strings reduce the penetration of any perforating charge.[31,32] The thickness of the extra string of casing, as well as the thickness of the two sheaths of cement that must be penetrated, reduces the perforation penetration length. In severe cases of small liners set through larger pipe, such as 5-in. liner cemented in 9⅝-in. casing, perforating both strings is considerably more difficult. For the best chance of perforating multiple strings, the largest, best designed deep-penetrating charge that can be run will generally have the best chance of penetrating through all the strings and into the formation.[29] Through-tubing guns are not recommended for shooting concentric strings because hole size and penetration are reduced with small charges.

In deviated wells in which concentric strings are to be perforated, the perforating gun will ride the low side of the pipe. When a casing gun is used for this operation, shot phasing of 60°, 90°, or 120° should be used to obtain the best chances of making perforations by the charges with the least clearance. The use of centralization techniques (if possible) on the guns run in deviated wells are recommended if hydraulic fracturing is to be used. This allows perforations to be placed near both fracture wings. Centralization also improves the roundness of the holes because the gun clearance will be near ideal. If inadequate perforations are a problem in wells with concentric strings, the innermost casing can be milled out (albeit at great expense) and the completion made through the outer casing.

When casing is run and cemented through washed-out sections, the cement sheath can be sufficiently thick to deny access to the formation with any perforator. When drilling a well into an easily washable pay zone, care must be taken to obtain a gauge or near-gauge hole so that the perforations will reach into the pay.

4.11 Perforating for Different Stimulations

The type of stimulation or ultimate well completion should influence the perforation design. In gravel-packing operations, a large number of phased, big holes usually are desired to enhance gravel placement and reduce the velocity of fluids coming into the wellbore.[33] Although entrance hole diameter is the principal concern, the perforation efficiency must not be overlooked.[34] Effective gravel placement requires leakoff, which is a feature of a high efficiency perforation. Decreased fluid velocity during production will result in less fines movement and plugging in the pack. Because the perforations may be filled with gravel, more perforations are required to generate the same productivity as open perforations.

Fracturing stimulations also require special perforating design.[35] Considerations include sufficient perforations to avoid detrimentally shearing the fluid (lowering the viscosity by degrading the polymer or crosslinked system) and to avoid needless high pumping costs. The viscosity of a fracturing fluid is a designed part of the stimulation treatment, and, if altered, the treatment may not meet expectations of proppant-carrying capacity. If this carrying capacity is destroyed by high shear, the sand may fall out of the fluid too soon, causing a blockage of the wellbore, perforations, or fracture with injected sand (a screenout). For more information, see the chapters on sand control and fracturing in this section of the *Handbook*.

4.12 Perforating in Highly Deviated Wells

The perforating design needed for a cased and cemented highly deviated (greater than approximately 60°) well may be different from the design needed for a vertical well, even in a similar formation. The main factors are placement of guns, cost of perforating in very long sections, need to produce selectively from a certain section of the wellbore, coning control, and need for focusing injected fluid into a single interval when fracturing or acidizing.

The number of perforations needed for well production, either deviated or vertical, depends on the inflow potential. Perforating costs can increase as pay contact increases, leading to reduced perforation density. A better method of perforating cost control is to use logging methods to identify zones of best porosity, oil saturation, and pressure (or flow in which production logging tool data are usable), and concentrate perforations in those areas. Leaving unperforated sections in a highly deviated or horizontal well also gives remedial operations such as plug setting a much better chance for success.

Fracturing in deviated wells requires a decision of whether to perforate the whole zone or to concentrate the perforations to ensure a single fracture breakdown. There is disagreement on the importance of numerous perforations in initiation of "starter fractures" formed in highly perforated zones. Localizing perforations can control the point of fracture initiation. Field performance has shown that perforating at 8 to 16 SPF over a 2- to 5-ft interval is sufficient to initiate a fracture. In field application of multiple fractures in deviated wells, perforating 3 ft (approximately 1 m) of the wellbore before each fracture job has produced good results. Although this approach is effective in providing sufficient wellbore contact with the main fracture to prevent early screenout, it does not address potential inflow from the unfractured matrix pays into the cased and cemented wellbore. Adding perforations along the length after all fracturing is one option, but obtaining any type of cleanup or breakdown of these added perforations can be accomplished only with a straddle packer.

4.13 Perforating Equipment

4.13.1 Guns/Carriers. In shaped-charge perforators, there are two basic carriers: the retrievable hollow carrier and the expendable or semiexpendable carrier. The most important consideration in selecting a perforator is choosing a gun system that matches the requirements dictated by the completion.

Hollow-carrier guns can be run either on wireline or on tubing. They may carry large charges, which normally minimize casing damage. The carrier contains most of the debris from the charge and the alignment system. Hollow-carrier guns are tubes that contain the shaped charges. The guns may be of a small size, able to pass through tubing and restrictions and place initial perforations or add perforations, or of larger sizes that are run through casing, conveyed by either work strings or the production tubing. Both reusable and single-use guns are offered, although higher pressure and more expensive wells typically use the single-use guns to minimize leaks and problems. Single-use guns are designed as expendables because the shaped charge perforates through the gun body. There is usually a "scallop" spot milled in the outside of the hollow-carrier tube at the charge location. The scallop contains the exit burr from the charge firing, which prevents scoring of polished bores if the gun is moved after firing and may minimize gun swelling. The scallop also may minimize the metal thickness penetrated, although this affects the perforation charge performance less than 10%. Keeping the charge exit point within the scallop becomes critical when through-tubing guns are used in which polished bores must be traversed with the gun after firing or when tubing clearances are critical.

There is some distortion (swelling) in the body of almost all hollow-carrier guns after firing. The amount of the distortion is a function of the size of the gun and the type and size of the charge used. The gun diameter, gun wall thickness, charge size, shot density, shot phasing, and well pressure are all factors in the gun distortion. On the larger diameter, thick-walled guns, there is much less distortion than on the small, thin-walled through-tubing guns. In wells in which clearances between the gun and tubulars are critical, the amount of distortion of the gun should be determined from the service company before the gun is used. Gun body swell

Fig. 4.12—Gun swell after firing in a low-pressure test.

ranges from approximately 10% diameter growth in small, 1 $\frac{11}{16}$-in. guns shot in low pressure wells to less than 1% diameter growth in larger guns and those shot at high pressure. **Fig. 4.12** shows a gun swell after firing in a low-pressure test. Gun bowing is often noted in small guns of 2⅛ in. diameter or less, whereas larger guns, because of the increased resistance to bending with increasing diameter, show no evidence of bowing.

Hollow-carrier guns, depending on their diameter and design, may be loaded with 1 to 27 shots/ft and have all the commonly used phase angles as well as specialty phasings. The smaller through-tubing guns should be run through a lubricator and typically are limited to approximately 40 ft in length, less for larger, heavier guns. The advantages of through-tubing guns are low cost, the ability to perforate underbalanced, and the ability to maintain positive well control. The disadvantages of through-tubing guns are limited penetration, small entry hole, and the production limitation of 0° phasing.

Expendable guns have charges that are exposed to well fluids and pressures. The expendable guns are popular for through-tubing applications. They are more vulnerable to damage, but without the bulk of the gun body, larger charges can be run through any given small or buckled tubing restriction. The expendable and semiexpendable carriers normally can use a larger charge for a given tubing or casing size than the hollow-carrier guns because only the skin of the capsule around each charge separates it from the walls of the casing. With expendable guns, there is also more flexibility because some bending can be achieved. The expendable guns are popular for through-tubing applications. The charges are lined together by a common strip, wire/cable, or a linked body design. The expendable guns force the casing to endure a much higher explosive load during firing because the recoil is not contained in a sacrificial shell as in a hollow-carrier gun. Casing splits are sometimes seen with a downhole television camera after perforating with expendable guns in cased holes with poor cement or low-strength casing. Expendable guns are used because their perforating performance is significantly better than hollow-carrier guns in the smaller diameters. When the gun is fired, some or all the linking materials, as well as the charge capsule remnants, are left in the hole. Problems with these guns have centered on misfires from damage to the detonating cord, tubing and surface line plugging from debris, and carrier strip disintegration or severe bending after firing.

Two factors that affect the charge performance in hollow-carrier perforators are standoff and gun clearance. Standoff is the distance between the base of the charge and the inside of the port plug or scallop and is a fixed part of the gun/charge system design. Gun clearance is the distance from the outside of the port plug or scallop to the wall of the casing. The gun clearance distance for a 4-in. hollow carrier, 90° phased gun in 7-in., 23 lbm/ft, N-80 casing can be anywhere from 0 to 2.3 in., depending on the gun position. Unless centralizers are used on the gun, one edge of the gun will contact the casing wall, and maximum clearance will occur at 180° to the wall contact. For this reason, small guns are decentralized purposely by magnets, and the charges are all aligned to fire in the direction of the magnetic positioning (0° phasing). Larger guns with smaller clearance distances use charges phased around the gun. Typically, the maximum gun diameter selected should permit washing over the gun with washpipe in the given casing size.

4.13.2 Detonator Systems.

Once on depth, charges are fired by an initiator or detonator. Detonator systems have been redesigned in recent years to improve safety and to prevent several perforating problems that occur from leaks, pressure problems, and temperature effects.[36,37] Any wireline-conveyed, hollow-carrier gun should have a detonator system that will not allow the charges to fire if the gun is completely or partially filled with water. If a water-filled hollow-carrier gun is fired, the outer body shell may rupture and result in a fishing or milling job. Specialized detonators have methods of preventing wet (fluid-filled) gun firing, as well as offering a number of other safety benefits ranging from resisting stray currents, such as static and radio energy, to pressure switches that prevent accidental surface firing or resafe the gun when a live gun is pulled from a well. The standard explosives detonator (also called a blasting cap) is a mainstay of the construction industry but is not well suited to the petroleum industry. Several accidental discharges of perforating guns have been linked directly to stray currents or poor electrical panel operational procedures. The resistor detonator incorporates resistors that reduce the possibility of discharge from low-power electrical signals. More modern detonators, including flying foil, programmable chips, and other units that are radio safe and allow for extra safety, are available.

4.13.3 Conveyance Systems.

The conveyance system for a perforating gun may be electric line, tubing, coiled tubing, pumpdown, or even slickline. The choice of conveyance depends on the length of the interval to be perforated, the size and weight of guns to be run, the geometry and inclination of the wellbore, and the desire to accomplish other actions such as underbalanced or overbalanced perforating, gravel packing, fracturing, etc. Well control requirements are also a consideration because live-well perforating requires a lubricator or advanced snubbing techniques. There is a significant difference in cost between the conveyance systems. Wireline generally is the lower cost system in wells in which only a few gun runs are necessary to complete the perforating design.

In wells with deviations of less than 50° to 60° and short pay zones, electric line conveyance is the primary conveyance process. Electric line is quickly rigged up with a minimum of equipment, and the short guns fit the standard lubricator lengths. Running a lubricator allows the wells to be perforated live, without the need for expensive and potentially damaging completion fluids. Modifications to lubricator and pressure-control equipment also allow coiled tubing and some snubbing operations to run and retrieve perforating guns. When a well is perforated with a wireline gun with the differential pressure into the well, the flowing fluid tries to move the cable up the hole because of the lift effect produced by fluid drag and the effect of differential pressure on the area of the gun or cable. In normal operations, this drag is minimal and probably will not be noticed unless the well produces several thousand barrels per day.

The magnitude of the drag on the cable depends on the flow. Following perforating, the liquid column used to control the amount of underbalance pressure is lightened by gas production from the formation. The liquid in the tubing also starts to flow upward because of fluid influx from the formation. As more gas enters the casing, there is a period of time in which slugs of water are rapidly lifted by the gas. The velocity increases as the slugs rise because of the expansion of the gas. After all the liquid has been produced from the tubing, the gas flow can be described as quasisteady state. The maximum lift on the cable occurs during the flow of water and gas slugs when the liquid slug velocities are high. After firing underbalanced perforations with a wireline gun, the gun, if possible, should be lowered beneath the perforated zone to minimize the lift force on the gun body. If it is necessary to flow the well as the gun is run or pulled through the tubing, sinker bars will be needed on the gun, and the well should be choked back. Very close clearances between the gun and tubing will result in very high lift forces if the well is flowing.

Because of the need for depth control during perforating, electrical responses from logging tools to confirm depth are the best method. The logging cable may be standard electric line or electric line inside coiled tubing. Alternate conveyance methods such as tubing conveyed, nonelectrical coiled tubing, pumpdown, or slickline also may be used, but a separate method of confirming depth, usually relogging to the set gun or a mechanical option, is required.

Through-tubing, hollow-carrier guns are attractive because they can be run through the production tubing and packer and require only a service truck-based unit. Generally, the phasing for the smaller, through-tubing guns ranges from 0° to a staggered pattern of 15° to 45° either side of the 0° plane (low side of the hole). Complete circumference phasing rarely is used in small, through-tubing guns because increasing clearance from the gun to the casing wall substantially reduces performance of small charges. In 3½-in. and larger outside diameter (OD) tubing, through-tubing hollow-carrier guns with larger charges can be used with 180° phasing to provide adequate penetration.

A major drawback to tubing-conveyed perforating is that there is no way of knowing, except by pulling the guns, how many charges were fired. A signal charge device that either fires a small explosive charge or trips a hammer device a few seconds after the primer cord detonation reaches the bottom of the gun can be used in conjunction with a sensitive sound-recording device to determine that the detonation cord was ignited to the bottom of the gun. Although the detonation of the signal charge will not tell how many charges were fired, it does signify that the primer cord has burned past all the charges. Because the major mechanical problems of tubing-conveyed perforating systems have been in two areas, failure to initiate the guns at the firing head and failure to initiate the next gun at the gun junctions, the use of a bottom-shot detector is very advantageous. The reports of early use of this system indicate it has been very successful on land-based wells but has problems on offshore wells because of the high noise levels associated with platforms.

New perforating methods recently have centered on the use of casing-conveyed perforating.[38] In these methods, the perforating gun is attached to the outside of the casing string, and the guns are deployed during the initial running of the casing string. After the string is cemented in place, the guns may be fired by a signal, from either the surface or inside the casing itself, opening the well to production at initial time or at a later time when a zone is ready to be brought on. This type of perforating could be very beneficial when sequential stimulations of stacked pay zones are planned.

4.13.4 Getting On Depth. No matter how good the perforating system, it is useless if the perforations are not made in the best pay zone. Typical methods of depth control include gamma ray tie-in and correlation to the original openhole gamma ray system. Until the development of sturdy gamma ray logs that could stand the shock of firing, the primary depth control method was to match openhole gamma ray to cased-hole gamma ray strip log and then tie into the collar locator log. When this method was executed properly, the depth control was accurate to within half the length of the collar. Unfortunately, a miscount would result in shooting the gun one joint off depth, which is a complete miss for many zones. With gamma ray logs that run with the gun, the process is simplified and more reliable.

The second piece of the depth-control puzzle is the distance from the gamma ray detector to the top shot of the perforating gun. A record of all the measurements of the gun should be available before the run, and depths should be worked out in advance.

Wireline measurements, even if corrected for stretch, may still be in error. The wheels in the depth-measurement device on logging trucks are calibrated for new cable. Cable wear, cable stretch, and wear of the measurement wheels can all cause inaccuracy. Magnetic marks or depth flags on the cable are helpful but can be thrown off by cable stretch. To account for creep in the wireline and to accurately zero in on the depth, the collar locator should be raised very slowly into the collar above the pay and stopped when the signal for the peak (collar location) is only half formed, which indicates that the tool is exactly in the center of the collar. To find the spot where the tool is centered on the collar and remains without changing may take several very slow passes. Once located, the wireline depth of the collar above the pay can be correlated to the openhole gamma ray log. If the casing (or the tubing in a tubing-conveyed operation) is run with a short joint or pup joint near the pay, it will be much easier to correlate tool depth on repeat runs.

Openhole and cased-hole gamma ray logs rarely agree exactly on depth because of differences in cable and chart paper. The depth correlation is to be made to the openhole log. If two sections are to be perforated and a single shift will not align the cased-hole log to the openhole log, each section should be aligned independently to the openhole log.

Improving depth control is relatively easy if a short pup joint of casing is run near the top of the pay during the initial completion. Recognition of the short joint by the collar locator log is easy and relatively foolproof. Other methods of depth-control assistance are radioactive tags in the threads of one casing coupling joint near the pay. The most common depth-control problem with perforations is shooting them one joint off. The well's plug-back depth (or float collar) also may be "tagged up" with the bottom of the gun in some wells to check depth. If the float collar has been drilled out, it also can be used as a short joint for identification.

4.13.5 Perforating Fluid.
The ideal fluid for perforating operations is a solids-free fluid that will not cause byproducts when exposed to the formation. Acceptable fluids may include 5 to 10% HCl, 10% acetic acid, 2% (or more) KCl water, 2% NH4Cl water, clean brines, and filtered diesel. If a dirty fluid is used, there is a distinct possibility that formation damage will occur because of particle plugging at the surface of the perforation tunnels. Even when a higher pressure differential toward the wellbore is used, clean fluids are still recommended to avoid flow of particles into the perforations in the event of a mechanical breakdown, when formation pressure of productivity is less than expected, or when the well has to be shut in before all the wellbore fluids have been produced.

Occasionally, high-solids-content fluids must be used during perforating, either for well control or because of other restrictions. High particulate fluids such as drilling mud usually are designed to form a mud cake on the face of a permeable formation. If drilling mud is used as a perforating fluid and the pressure differential (either by design or by accident) is toward the formation from the wellbore, a drilling mud cake will form in the perforations that may be difficult to remove unless the formation can be produced at a high drawdown for a long period.

Lighter fluid columns such as oil or diesel may be used as perforating fluids if the full column is diesel or oil, but 6.8 lbm/gal diesel cannot be kept spotted below 9 to 10 lbm/gal brine water. Produced oil and diesel also should be filtered before use. Filtration requirements

Fig. 4.13—Flare produced after explosive cutoff.

may vary with the task, but typically a 2- to 5-μm filter with a beta rating of 1,000 is adequate for most applications.

4.14 Limited Penetration Charges
Tubing puncher charges are used when a hole is needed in tubing for circulation or flow, but damage must be avoided to downhole equipment outside the target pipe. The tubing puncher charge is designed to expend all its energy penetrating the wall without forming additional penetration.

4.15 Pipe Cutoff Methods
Tubing cutoff is important during salvage operations, fishing operations, certain production operations, and any action that requires severing the tubing. The most common pipe cutoff methods involve either explosive or chemical cutters. Explosive cutters use the same explosive technology used in perforating charges. Instead of a cylindrical cone, however, the explosive and the liner are arranged in a wedge so that the explosive front of the device will push out on all sides and sever the pipe. Although the technique is effective in most cases, the external part of the pipe is left with a flare that is often difficult to wash over during pipe recovery operations. Newer explosive cutters have largely reduced this flare to an acceptable level. **Fig. 4.13** shows a flare produced after an explosive cutoff.

Chemical cutting has become one of the most common pipe cutoff methods, especially for tubing. The cutting fluid reacts extremely quickly and generates intense heat. It is sprayed through a nozzle assembly at the walls of the tubing all around the cutoff tool. As the fluid contacts the steel wall, a vigorous reaction occurs and the pipe is separated smoothly without leaving an external flare. **Fig. 4.14** shows an example of a chemical cut pipe. Chemical cutters can produce very smooth cuts but are very dependent on both orientation and even coverage or contact between the cutting chemical and the steel pipe. Heavy walled pipe, higher alloy, increased depth, imperfections in the pipe, scale, paraffin, plastic liner, or incorrect gun sizing can either slow the chemical cut on that side of the pipe or defeat it entirely so that pulling operations are needed to finally separate the pipe. **Fig. 4.15** shows an example of a partial chemical cut.

Radial explosive cutters, either continuous or segmented cutters, produce a pressure wave that is oriented outward and usually produce a flare in the steel at the cut point. **Fig. 4.16** shows an example of a cut produced by a Thermite cutter. The severity of this flare can pro-

Fig. 4.14—Chemical cut pipe.

Fig. 4.15—Partial chemical cut.

vide problems in recovering the pipe or in washing over the stuck section. A mill is often run to dress off the upward-looking connection before running the wash pipe.

Mechanical cutters based on mill design have been used successfully on both jointed and coiled tubing applications to sever pipe. These cutters are considerably slower than the chemical or explosive cutters but can be run on conventional equipment. The mechanical cutters are best used on softer, lower alloy pipes with a thinner wall. High alloy pipes and very thick pipes are more difficult to cut with a mechanical cutter.

Abrasive cutters have been reintroduced recently to the market and have the potential to rapidly sever almost any type of pipe at any depth. These cutters use a particulate such as sand, glass beads, or calcium carbonate pumped through a rotating nozzle, and the abrasion erodes the steel. Cuts through even heavy-walled drillpipe are possible if the cutter can be kept in the same place during the entire cutting operation. Cuts at surface with abrasive cutters are very fast; however, the cutting process is slowed because of backpressure when the cutters are applied downhole. Nonetheless, these cutters are beginning to see extensive use as pipe cutoff tools.

The cutting system necessary for a particular application depends on the well depth, temperature, and size of the tubing and alloy grade and weight of the tubing. However, the most

Fig. 4.16—Cut produced by a thermite cutter.

important factor is any restriction above the cut point and the ability to pull tension on the pipe. Requirements for cutting tubing include knowledge of the specific design of the well and any restrictions above the point to be cut. Once the cut point is selected, the cutting method should be studied carefully to determine if a clean cut can be made that will requiring a minimum of overpull to separate the uncut sections of the pipe. Additional considerations include the conveyance system and the manner of depth control that will place the cutter at the correct position.

References

1. Cook, M.A.: *The Science of High Explosives,* American Chemical Soc. Monograph Series, Krieger Publishing, (1958) 1–17.
2. Kruger, R.F.: "Joint Bullet and Jet Perforation Tests," *API Drilling and Production Practices,* Washington, DC (1956).
3. Pittman, F.C., Harriman, D.C., and St. John, J.C.: "Investigation of Abrasive-Laden-Fluid Method For Perforation and Fracture Initiation," *JPT* (May 1961) 489.
4. McCauley, T.V.: "Backsurging and Abrasive Perforating To Improve Perforation Performance," *JPT* (October 1972) 1207.
5. Aseltine, C.L.: "Flash X-Ray Analysis of the Interaction of Perforators With Different Target Materials," paper SPE 14322 presented at the 1985 SPE Annual Technical Conference and Exhibition, Las Vegas, Nevada, 22–25 September.
6. Saucier, R.J. and Lands, J.F. Jr.: "A Laboratory Study of Perforations in Stressed Formation Rocks," *JPT* (September 1978) 1347.
7. McLeod, H.O. Jr.: "The Effect of Perforating Conditions on Well Performance," *JPT* (January 1983) 31.
8. Locke, S.: "An Advanced Method for Predicting the Productivity Ratio of a Perforated Well," *JPT* (December 1981) 2481.
9. Hong, K.C.: "Productivity of Perforated Completions in Formations With or Without Damage," *JPT* (August 1975) 1027.
10. Klotz, J.A., Krueger, R.F., and Pye, D.S.: "Maximum Well Productivity in Damaged Formations Requires Deep, Clean Perforations," paper SPE 4792 presented at the 1974 SPE Symposium on Formation Damage Control, New Orleans, 7–8 February.
11. Brooks, J.E., Yang, W., and Behrmann, L.A.: "Effect of Sand-Grain Size on Perforator Performance," paper SPE 39457 presented at the 1998 International Symposium on Formation Damage Control, Lafayette, Louisiana, 18–19 February.

12. Bell, W.T.: "Perforating Techniques for Maximizing Well Productivity," paper SPE 10033 presented at the 1982 International Petroleum Exhibition and Technical Symposium, Beijing, 18–26 March.

13. Bell, W.T.: "Perforating Underbalanced Evolving Techniques," *JPT* (October 1984) 1653.

14. King G.E., Anderson, A.R., and Bingham, M.D.: "A Field Study of Underbalance Pressures Necessary to Obtain Clean Perforations Using Tubing Conveyed Perforating," *JPT* (June 1986) 662.

15. Young, W.S. and Zaleski, T.E. Jr.: "Procedural Design Considerations Associated With Tubing-Conveyed Underbalanced Perforating," paper SPE 13646 presented at the 1985 SPE California Regional Meeting, Bakersfield, California, 27–29 March.

16. Halleck, P.M. and Deo, M.: "Effects of Underbalance on Perforation Flow," *SPEPE* (May 1989) 113.

17. Regalbuto, J.A. and Riggs, R.S.: "High Differential Pressure, Radial Flow Characteristics of Gun Perforations," paper SPE 14319 presented at the 1985 SPE Annual Technical Conference and Exhibition, Las Vegas, Nevada, 22–25 September.

18. Bonomo, J.M. and Young, W.S.: "Analysis and Evaluation of Perforating and Perforation Cleanup Methods," *JPT* (March 1985) 505.

19. Smith, P.S., Behrmann, L.A., and Yang, W.: "Improvements in Perforating Performance in High Compressive Strength Rocks," paper SPE 38141 presented at the 1997 SPE European Formation Damage Conference, The Hague, 2–3 June.

20. Behrmann, L.A. *et al.*: "Borehole Dynamics During Underbalance Perforating," paper SPE 38139 presented at the 1997 SPE European Formation Damage Conference, The Hague, 2–3 June.

21. Handren, P.J., Jupp, T.B. and Dees, J.M.: "Overbalance Perforating and Stimulation Method for Wells," paper SPE 26515 presented at the 1993 SPE Annual Technical Conference and Exhibition, Houston, 3–6 October.

22. Behrmann, L.A. and McDonald, B.: "Underbalance or Extreme Overbalance," *SPEPF* (August 1999) 187.

23. Gilliat, J., Snider, P.M., and Haney, R.: "A Review of Field Performance of New Propellant/Perforating Technologies," paper SPE 56469 presented at the 1999 SPE Annual Technical Conference and Exhibition, Houston, 3–6 October.

24. Godfrey, W.K. and Methven, N.E.: "Casing Damage Caused by Jet Perforating," paper SPE 3043 presented at the 1970 SPE Annual Meeting, Houston, 4–7 October.

25. Bell, W.T. and Shore, J.B.: "Casing Damage from Gun Perforators," paper presented at the 1981 IADC Explosive Conference, 9–11 June.

26. Bell, W.T. and Bell, R.M.: The Paradox of Gun Power vs. Completion Efficiency," paper presented at the 1981 IADC Explosive Conference, 9–11 June.

27. King, G.E.: "The Effect of High-Density Perforating on the Mechanical Crush Resistance of Casing," paper SPE 18843 presented at the 1989 SPE Production Operations Symposium, Oklahoma City, Oklahoma, 13–14 March.

28. King, G.E.: "Casing Crush Resistance Loss to High-Density Perforating: Casing Tests," paper SPE 20634 presented at the 1990 SPE Annual Technical Conference and Exhibition, New Orleans, 23–26 September.

29. Godfrey, W.K.: "Effect of Jet Perforating on Bond Strength of Cement," *JPT* (November 1968) 1301.

30. Crump, J.B. and Sabins, F.L.: "Guidelines for Selecting Cement that will be Perforated," Southwestern Petroleum Short Course, Lubbock, Texas, April 1989.

31. King, G.E.: "Perforating Multiple Strings of Casing: Getting Through the Overlap Zone," Southwestern Petroleum Short Course, Lubbock, Texas, April 1989.

32. Regalbuto, J.D., Leidel, D.J., and Sumner, D.R.: "Perforator Performance in High Strength Casing and Multiple Strings of Casing," paper presented at the 1983 API Pacific Coast Meeting, Bakersfield, California, 8–10 November.

33. Venkitaraman, A., Behrmann, L.A., and Chow, C.V.: "Perforating Requirements for Sand Control," paper SPE 65187 presented at the 2000 SPE European Petroleum Conference, Paris, 24–25 October.

34. Snider, P.M. *et al.*: "Perforation Damage Studies in Unconsolidated Sands: Changes in Formation Particle Sizes and the Distribution as a Function of Shaped Charge Design," paper SPE 38635

presented at the 1997 SPE Annual Technical Conference and Exhibition, San Antonio, Texas, 5–8 October.

35. Behrmann, L.A. and Nolte, K.G.: "Perforating Requirements for Fracture Stimulations," *SPEDC* (December 1999) 228.

36. Dickes, R.: "Explosives Safety: Safety Strategies for Operating Electroexplosive Devices in a Radio-Frequency Environment," paper SPE 74178 presented at the 2002 SPE International Conference on Health, Safety, and Environment in Oil and Gas Exploration and Production, Kuala Lumpur, 20–22 March.

37. Motley, J. and Barker, J.: "Unique Electrical Detonator Enhances Safety in Explosive Operations: Case Histories," paper SPE 36636 presented at the 1996 SPE Annual Technical Conference and Exhibition, Denver, 6–9 October.

38. Eller, J.G. *et al.:* "A Case History: Use of a Casing-Conveyed Perforating System to Improve Life of Well Economics in Tight Gas Sands," paper SPE 76742 presented at the 2002 SPE Western Regional/AAPG Pacific Section Joint Meeting, Anchorage, 20–22 May.

SI Metric Conversion Factors

bbl	×	1.589 873	E – 01	= m^3
ft	×	3.048*	E – 01	= m
°F		(°F – 32)/1.8		= °C
gal	×	3.785 412	E – 03	= m^3
in.	×	2.54*	E + 00	= cm
lbm	×	4.535 924	E – 01	= kg
psi	×	6.894 757	E + 00	= kPa

*Conversion factor is exact.

Chapter 5
Sand Control
W.L. Penberthy, Jr. (retired, Exxon Production Research Co.), with contributions from Baker Oil Tools

5.1 Causes of Sand Production

Conventional well completions in soft formations (the compressive strength is less than 1,000 psi) commonly produce formation sand or fines with fluids. These formations are usually geologically young (Tertiary age) and shallow, and they have little or no natural cementation. Sand production is unwanted because it can plug wells, erode equipment, and reduce well productivity. It also has no economic value. Nonetheless, formation sand production from wells is dealt with daily on a global basis. In certain producing regions, sand control completions are the dominant type and result in considerable added expense to operations.

5.1.1 Fluid Flow. Fluid flow from wells is the consequence of the wellbore pressure being smaller than that in the reservoir. The drag force caused by the flow from large to small pressure is related to the velocity-viscosity product at any point around the well. Hence, when fluids flow toward the wellbore, the tendency is for some of the formation material to flow concurrently with the fluids.[1]

5.1.2 Restraining Forces. Opposing the fluid forces are the restraining forces that hold the formation sand in place. These consist of natural cementation (compressive strength), friction between sand grains, fluid pressure in the pores of the rock, and capillary forces. The compressive strength of the rock, the primary restraint, is controlled by intergranular cementation that is a secondary geologic process. As a general rule, old sediments are more consolidated than are younger sediments. Young formations commonly have little cementing material and are referred to as being poorly consolidated. Stated another way, they have low compressive strength. Their compressive strengths are usually less than 1,000 psi and may even be so small that their strengths can not be measured. The frictional forces are related to the confining or overburden stresses. The stress that causes the rock to fail includes the mechanical stress that results from the overburden and the drag forces associated from viscous flow of fluids through the rock matrix. The overburden stress is partially supported by the pore pressure, so the net stress (the cause of rock failure, the effective stress) is the difference between the overburden stress and the pore pressure. Capillary forces also can contribute to sand production; there are numerous examples where sand production occurred when water production began. Sand arches

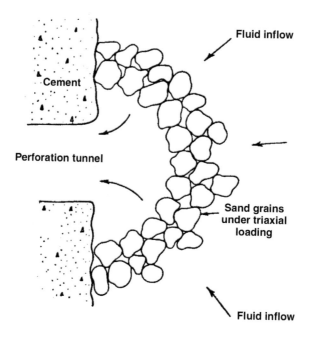

Fig. 5.1—Geometry of a stable arch surrounding a perforation.

form, on occasion, around the perforations. The questions of when and how arches form are related to the flow rate, the compressive strength of the formation, and the size of the sand and the perforations. **Fig. 5.1** portrays an arch and the balance between viscous and restraining forces. Unfortunately, sand arches are not stable, and their transient behavior cannot be relied upon for controlling sand production.

The previous discussion is an oversimplification of the problem, and there are other related factors. Think in terms of sand production being related to the production rate, the pressure reduction around the well, and the compressive strength of the formation. If the forces caused by fluid flow exceed the restraining forces, formation sand is produced.

5.2 Consequences of Sand Production

The consequences of sand production are always detrimental to the short-long-term productivity of the well. Although some wells routinely experience manageable sand production, these are the exception rather than the rule. In most cases, attempting to manage sand production over the life of the well is not an attractive or prudent operating alternative.

5.2.1 Accumulation Downhole.

If the production velocity in well tubulars is insufficient to transport sand to the surface, it will begin to fill the inside of the casing. Eventually, the producing interval may be completely covered with sand. In this case, the production rate will decline until the well becomes "sanded up" and production ceases. In situations like this, remedial operations are required to clean out the well and restore productivity. One cleanout technique is to run a "bailer" on a wireline to remove the sand from the production tubing or casing. Because the bailer removes only a small volume of sand at a time, multiple wireline runs are necessary to clean out the well. Another cleanout operation involves running a smaller diameter tubing string or coiled tubing down into the production tubing to agitate the sand and lift it out of the well by circulating fluid. The inner string is progressively lowered while circu-

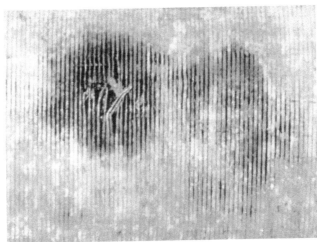

Fig. 5.2—Wire-wrapped screen failure owing to erosion by formation sand (courtesy of Baker Oil Tools).

lating the sand out of the well. This operation must be performed cautiously to avoid the possibility of sticking the inner string inside the production tubing. If the production of sand is continuous, the cleanout operations may be required periodically, as often as monthly or even weekly, resulting in lost production and increased well maintenance costs.

5.2.2 Accumulation in Surface Equipment. If the production velocity is sufficient to transport sand to the surface, the sand may still become trapped in the separator, heater treater, or production flowline. If enough sand becomes trapped in one of these areas, cleaning will be required to allow for efficient production of the well. To restore production, the well must be shut in, the surface equipment opened, and the sand manually removed. In addition to the cleanout cost, the cost of the deferred production must be considered.

5.2.3 Erosion of Downhole and Surface Equipment. If fluids are in turbulent flow, such sand-laden fluids are highly erosive. **Fig. 5.2** is a photograph of a section of eroded well screen exposed to a perforation that was producing sand. **Fig. 5.3** shows a surface choke that failed because of erosion. If the erosion is severe or occurs long enough, complete failure of surface and/or downhole equipment may occur, resulting in critical safety and environmental problems as well as deferred production.

5.2.4 Collapse of the Formation. Collapse of the formation around the well occurs when large volumes of sand are produced. Apparently, when a void is formed and becomes large enough to inadequately support overlying formations, collapse occurs because of a lack of material to provide support. When the collapse occurs, the sand grains rearrange themselves to create a lower permeability than originally existed. This is especially true for formation sand that has a high clay content or wide range of grain sizes. For a formation with a narrow grain-size distribution (well sorted) and/or very little clay, the rearrangement of formation sand causes a decrease in permeability that is not as severe. In the case of the overlying shale collapsing, complete loss of productivity is probable. In most cases, continued long-term production of formation sand usually decreases the well's productivity and ultimate recovery.

The collapse of the formation particularly becomes critical to well productivity if the formation material fills the perforation tunnels. Even a small amount of formation material filling the perforation tunnels will lead to a significant increase in pressure drop across the formation near

Fig. 5.3—Surface choke failure owing to erosion by formation sand (courtesy of Baker Oil Tools).

the wellbore for a given flow rate. Considering these consequences of sand production, the desired solution to sand production is to control it downhole.

Compaction of the reservoir rock may occur as a result of reduced pore pressure leading to surface subsidence. Examples of subsidence, caused by withdrawals of fluids and reduced pore pressure, are found in Venezuela; Long Beach, California; the Gulf Coast of Texas; and in the Ekofisk Field in the central North Sea, where the platforms sank about 10 ft.

5.3 Predicting Sand Production

Predicting whether a well will produce fluids without producing sand has been the goal of many completion engineers and research projects. There are a number of analytical techniques and guidelines to assist in determining if sand control is necessary, but no technique has proven to be universally acceptable or completely accurate. In some geographic regions, guidelines and rules of thumb apply that have little validity in other areas of the world. At the current time, predicting whether a formation will or will not produce sand is not an exact science, and more refinement is needed. Until better prediction techniques are available, the best way of determining the need for sand control in a particular well is to perform an extended production test with a conventional completion and observe whether sand production occurs. Normally, it is not necessary to predict sand production on a well-by-well basis because wells in the same reservoir tend to behave similarly. The prediction required is on a reservoir-by-reservoir basis. However, initial good results may prove misleading, as reservoir and flow conditions change.

5.3.1 Operational and Economic Influences. The difficulty of determining whether sand control is required in a given well is compounded when the well is drilled in a remote area where there is no producing experience and where the various reservoir factors are slightly different from previously exploited regions. Even if the reservoir and formation properties are almost identical to other developments, the operating conditions and risks may be such that different strategies apply. One example might be a subsea project, as opposed to a land development project. Here, the consequences and risks associated with sand production are significantly different because of differing costs and risks associated with remedial well operations; hence, the decision to use a sand-control technique is both an economic and operational decision that must be made with limited data. The decision is complicated by the fact that sand-control techniques, such as gravel packing, are expensive and can restrict well productivity if not performed properly. Therefore, gravel packing cannot be applied indiscriminately when the possibility for sand production from a well is unknown. Making the decision whether to gravel pack is fairly easy if the formation material is either hard (no sand production) or weak (sand production). The difficulty arises when the strength of the formation material is marginal. At that point, the decision normally ceases to be primarily a technical issue but more of an economic and risk management exercise. If there is uncertainty, the conservative approach is to always apply sand-control completions. This obviously will solve the sand production problem but will also increase costs and may reduce well productivity. If sand control was actually unnecessary, the implementation of sand-control completions was a bad economic decision.

5.3.2 Formation Strength. The procedure followed by most, to consider whether sand control is required, is to determine the hardness of the formation rock (i.e., the rock's compressive strength). Because the rock's compressive strength has the same units as the pressure difference between the reservoir and the well (the drawdown), the two parameters can be directly compared, and drawdown limits for specific wells can be determined. Research performed in the early 1970s[1] showed that rock failed and began to produce sand when the drawdown pressure was more than about 1.7 times the compressive strength. As an example, formation sand with a compressive strength of 1,000 psi would not fail or begin to produce sand until the drawdown exceeded 1,700 psi. Others use Brinnell hardness as an indicator of whether to apply sand control. The Brinnell hardness of the rock is related to the compressive strength but is not as convenient to use because the units of hardness are dimensionless and cannot be related to drawdown as easily as compressive strength.

5.3.3 Sonic Log. The sonic log can be used as a way of addressing the sand production potential of wells. The sonic log records the time required for sound waves to travel through the formation, usually in microseconds. The porosity is related to formation strength and the sonic travel time. Short travel times, less than 50 microseconds, indicate low porosity and hard, dense rock; long travel times, 95 microseconds or greater, are associated with soft, low-density, high-porosity rock. A common technique used for determining whether sand control is required in a given geologic area is to correlate incidences of sand production with the sonic log readings above and below the sand production that has been observed. This establishes a quick screening method for the need for sand control. The use of this method requires calibration against particular geologic formations to be reliable.

5.3.4 Formation Properties Log. Certain well logs, such as the sonic log (previously discussed) and density and neutron devices are indicators of porosity and formation hardness. For a particular formation, a low-density reading indicates high porosity. The neutron logs are primarily an indicator of porosity. Several logging companies offer a formation properties log that uses the results of the sonic, density, and neutron logs to determine if a formation will produce formation material at certain levels of drawdown. This calculation identifies weak and strong intervals; the weaker ones are more prone to produce sand. While the formation properties log has been used for over 20 years, experience has shown that this log usually overpredicts the need for sand control.

5.3.5 Porosity. The porosity of a formation can be used as a guideline as to whether sand control is needed. If the formation porosity is greater than 30%, the probability of the need for sand control is high because of the lack of cementation. Conversely, if the porosity is less than 20%, the need for sand control will probably be minimal because the sand has some consolidation. The porosity range between 20 to 30% is where uncertainty usually exists. In natural media, porosity is related to the degree of cementation present in a formation; thus, the basis for this technique is understandable. Porosity information can be derived from well logs or laboratory core analysis.

5.3.6 Drawdown. The pressure drawdown associated with production may be an indicator of potential formation sand production. No sand production may occur with small pressure drawdown around the well, whereas excessive drawdown can cause the formation to fail and produce sand at unacceptable levels. The amount of pressure drawdown is normally associated with the formation permeability and the viscosity of the produced fluids. Low viscosity fluids, such as gas, experience smaller drawdowns, as opposed to the drawdown that would be associated with a 1,000-cp fluid produced from the same interval. Hence, higher sand production is usually associated with viscous fluids.

5.3.7 Finite Element Analysis. The most sophisticated approach to predicting sand production is the use of geomechanical numerical models developed to analyze fluid flow through the reservoir in relation to the formation strength. The effect of formation stress, associated with fluid flow in the immediate region around the wellbore, is simultaneously computed with finite element analysis. While this approach is by far the most rigorous, it requires an accurate knowledge of the formation's strength around the well in both the elastic and plastic regions where the formation begins to fail. Input data on both regions are difficult to acquire with a high degree of accuracy under actual downhole conditions. This is the major difficulty with this approach. The finite element analysis method is good from the viewpoint of comparing one interval with another; however, the absolute values calculated may not represent actual formation behavior.

5.3.8 Time Dependence. The effect of time on the production of formation sand is sometimes considered to be an issue; however, there are no data that suggest that time alone is a factor. There have been undocumented claims that produced fluids could possibly dissolve the formation's natural cementing materials, but the data are not substantiated.

5.3.9 Multiphase Flow. Predicting when multiphase fluid flow will begin can also be an aid. Many cases can be cited where wells produced sand free until water production began, but produced unacceptable amounts afterwards. The reason for the increased sand production is caused by two primary phenomena: the movement of water-wet fines and relative permeability effects. Most formation fines are water wet and, as a consequence, immobile when a hydrocarbon phase is the sole produced fluid because hydrocarbons occupy the majority of the pore space. However, when the water saturation is increased to the point that water becomes mobile, the formation fines begin the move with the wetting phase (water), which creates localized plugging in the pore throats of the porous media. Additionally, when two-phase flow occurs, increased drawdown is experienced because two phases flowing together have more resistance to flow than either fluid alone. These relative permeability effects can increase the drawdown around the well by as much as a factor of 5 per unit of production. See the chapter that discusses relative permeability in the General Engineering section of this *Handbook*. The result of fines migration, plugging, and reduced relative permeability around the well increases the drawdown to the point that it may exceed the strength of the formation. The consequences can be excessive sand production. The severity of fines migration varies from formation to formation and whether gas or liquid is being produced.

5.4 Sand-Control Techniques
There are several techniques available for minimizing sand production from wells. The question of which one to use arises. The choices range from simple changes in operating practices to expensive completions, such as sand consolidation or gravel packing. The sand-control

method selected depends on site-specific conditions, operating practices and economic consider-ations. Some of the sand-control techniques available are maintenance and workover; rate exclusion; selective completion practices; plastic consolidation; high energy resin placement; resin coated gravel; stand-alone slotted liners or screens; and gravel packing.

5.4.1 Maintenance and Workover. Maintenance and workover is a passive approach to sand control. This method basically involves tolerating the sand production and dealing with its ef-fects, if and when necessary. Such an approach requires bailing, washing, and cleaning of surface facilities routinely to maintain well productivity. It can be successful in specific forma-tions and operating environments. The maintenance and workover method is primarily used where there is minimal sand production, low production rates, and an economically viable well service.

5.4.2 Rate Restriction. Restricting the well's flow rate to a level that reduces sand production is a method used occasionally. The point of the procedure is to sequentially reduce or increase the flow rate until an acceptable value of sand production is achieved. The object of this tech-nique is to attempt to establish the maximum sand-free flow rate. It is a trial-and-error method that may have to be repeated as the reservoir pressure, flow rate, and water cut change. The problem with rate restriction is that the maximum flow rate required to establish and maintain sand free production is generally less than the flow potential of the well. Compared to the maximum rate, this may represent a significant loss in productivity and revenue.

5.4.3 Selective Completion Practices. The goal of this technique is to produce only from sec-tions of the reservoir that are capable of withstanding the anticipated drawdown. Perforating only the higher compressive strength sections of the formation allows higher drawdown. The high compressive strength sections will likely have the most cementation and, unfortunately, the lowest permeability. While this approach might eliminate the sand production, it is flawed because the most valuable reserves will not be in communication with the well.

5.4.4 Plastic Consolidation. Plastic consolidation involves the injection of plastic resins that are attached to the formation sand grains. The resin subsequently hardens and forms a consoli-dated mass, binding the sand grains together at their contact points. If successful, the increase in formation compressive strength will be sufficient to withstand the drag forces while produc-ing at the desired rates. The goal of these treatments is to consolidate about a 3-ft radius around the well without appreciably decreasing the permeability of the rock.

Three types of resins are commercially available: epoxies, furans (including furan/phenolic blends), and phenolics. The resins are in a liquid form when they enter the formation, and a catalyst or curing agent is required for hardening. Some catalysts are "internal" because they are mixed into the resin solution at the surface and require time and/or temperature to harden the resin. Other catalysts are "external" and are injected after the resin is in place. The internal catalysts have the advantage of positive placement because all resin will be in contact with the catalyst required for efficient curing. A disadvantage associated with internal catalysts is the possibility of premature hardening in the work string. The amounts of both resin and catalyst must be carefully chosen and controlled for the specific well conditions. Epoxy and phenolics can be placed with either internal or external catalysts; however, the rapid curing times of the furans (and furan/phenolic blends) require that external catalysts be used.

There are two types of plastic consolidation systems. These are called "phase separation" systems and "overflush" systems. Phase separation systems contain only 15 to 25% active resin in an otherwise inert solution. The resin is preferentially attracted to the sand grains, leaving the inert portion that will not otherwise affect the pore spaces. These systems use an internal catalyst. Accurate control of the plastic placement is critical because overdisplacement will result in unconsolidated sand in the critical near-wellbore area.

Phase separation consolidation may be ineffective in formations that contain more than 10% clays. Clays, which also attract the resin, have extremely high surface area in comparison to sands. The clays will attract more resin and because phase separation systems contain only a small percentage of resin, there may not be enough resin to consolidate the sand grains.

Overflush systems contain a high percentage of active resin. When first injected, the pore spaces are completely filled with resin, and an overflush is required to push the excess resin away from the wellbore area to re-establish permeability. Only a residual amount of resin saturation, which should be concentrated at the sand contact points, should remain following the overflush. Most overflush systems use an external catalyst, although some include an internal catalyst.

All plastic consolidations require a good primary cement job to prevent the resin from channeling behind the casing. Perforation density should be a minimum of four shots per foot to reduce drawdown and improve the distribution of plastic; however, each perforation must be treated. Shaley zones should not be perforated because fluids are difficult to place in these low-permeability strata. Clean fluids are essential for plastic consolidation treatments because all solids that are in the system at the time of treatment will be "glued" in place. The perforations should be washed or surged, workover rig tanks should be scrubbed, and fluids should be filtered to 2 microns. Work strings should be cleaned with a dilute HCl acid containing sequestering agents, and pipe dope should be used sparingly on the pin only. A matrix acid treatment, which includes HF and HCl, is recommended for dirty sandstones to increase injectivity.

Both phase separation and overflush systems require a multistage preflush to remove reservoir fluids and make the sand grain oil wet. The first stage, generally diesel oil, serves to displace the reservoir oil. Epoxy resins are incompatible with water; therefore, isopropyl alcohol follows the diesel to remove formation water. The final stage is a spacer (brine) that prevents the isopropyl alcohol from contacting the resin.

Plastic consolidation leaves the wellbore fully open. This becomes important where large OD downhole completion equipment is required. Also, plastic consolidation can be done through tubing or in wells with small-diameter casing. For most applications, the problems associated with plastic consolidation outweigh the possible advantages. The permeability of a formation is always decreased by plastic consolidation. Even in successful treatments, the permeability to oil is reduced because the resin occupies a portion of the original pore space and is oil wet. The amount of resin used is based on uniform coverage of all perforations. However, perforation plugging or permeability variations often cause some perforations to take more plastic than others. In systems that use an external catalyst, there is no sand control in areas that are not contacted by both resin and catalyst.

The primary difficulty in using resin systems is attaining complete and even placement of the chemicals in the formation. In lenticular formations, plastic placement may be uneven because of widely varying permeabilities, and some zones are likely to be untreated. These untreated intervals may break down during subsequent production, and the well will sand up. For this reason, plastic consolidation is suitable for interval lengths less than 10 to 15 ft. Longer intervals can be treated using packers to isolate and treat small sections of the zone at a time, but such operations are difficult and time consuming. Plastic consolidation treatments also do not perform well in formations with permeabilities less than about 50 md. Low permeabilities preclude injecting resins under matrix conditions and cause permeability reductions by the plastic that substantially reduce residual permeability (i.e., well productivity). The resins soften at a temperature greater than 255°F and may not provide sufficient strength at elevated temperature.

Plastic consolidation was used extensively in the late 1950s through the mid-1970s in the Gulf of Mexico; however, this technique currently represents far less than 1% of all sand-control completions worldwide. The reasons for decreased usage include lack of suitable candidates, the placement difficulties already described, as well as tight regulations on the handling of the chemicals, which are generally quite toxic (with the furans being the least toxic of the three). These treatments tend to be costly. The main disadvantage of plastic systems in current operations is its high cost and limited completion interval length for an effective treatment, 15 ft or less. The latter excludes most wells. Because of its current limited use, service companies have difficulty maintaining trained crews.

5.4.5 High-Energy Resin Placement. As previously discussed, one of the main reasons for the lack of acceptance of chemical consolidation techniques has been difficulties in placing the resin uniformly across the entire target interval and restricted length. The uneven coverage is more severe in intervals greater than about 15 ft long. Causes for this are typically attributed to differences in injectivity caused by incomplete perforation clean-up during underbalanced perforating jobs or permeability variations in the formation interval length. See the chapter that discusses under- and overbalanced drilling in the Drilling Engineering section of this *Handbook*. Also see the chapter in the Production Operations Engineering section that discusses underbalanced perforating.

High-energy resin placement addresses some of these problems.[2,3] The technique injects the resin rapidly under highly overbalanced conditions. The resin is surged into the formation at rates that will place the resin before the formation has a chance to fail. Another benefit to the rapid resin placement is that the technique appears to be less affected by permeability contrasts than the matrix treatments. This characteristic leads to more uniform placement over a long perforated interval. This method is still experimental.

Three methods are available for creating the high overbalance pressures that can assist resin placement—propellant gas fracturing, overbalanced perforating, and overbalanced surging. The overbalanced perforating method is currently the preferred method.

Propellant Gas Fracturing. The use of propellant gas fracturing tools involves the conversion of solid propellant by chemical reaction into a gas in the target zone of a wellbore. The chemical propellant is changed into combustion gases by one of two different mechanisms: detonation or flame propagation. Detonation involves a reaction characterized by a shock wave that moves rapidly through the interval to be treated. This shock wave, traveling at velocities between 15,000 and 25,000 ft/sec, induces pressures ranging from 400 to 4,000,000 psi, with pressurization rates up to 100,000 psi. The high-pressure surge places the resin more evenly in long formation intervals where conventional plastic consolidation, pumped at matrix, is impractical.

The reaction products are contained in place by the liquid column in the wellbore above the tool. The rapid generation of gas forces the resin placed in the annular space surrounding the tool out of the perforations and into the formation. For this process, the casing must be in good condition and properly cemented to be successful. Perforations must be clean and clear of debris, and all debris should be removed from the wellbore. Only clean sands should be perforated. Finally, if sand has been produced, the perforations should be prepacked with gravel prior to the treatment, which may be difficult.

The process involved in this type of a treatment is to first inject a preflush of mutual solvent to remove water from the target interval. Furan resin is then placed across the perforations, and the gas-generating propellant tool is placed across the entire perforated interval. Nitrogen overbalance is applied to the work string, and the propellant device is fired to inject resin above fracture pressure. The resin is then followed with an acid post-flush to harden the resin.

An advantage to this system is that resin will be placed in all perforations immediately across from the location of the gas generator tool. However, if multiple tool runs are required to treat an interval longer than about 36 ft, movement of the tool will make it difficult to hold the resin in position. The two other methods, overbalanced perforating and overbalanced surging, are designed to alleviate the problem of maintaining the resin in position.

Overbalanced Perforating or Surging. High-overbalanced perforating resin placement may be used if the well has not been previously perforated. If a well has existing perforations, the interval can be prepacked, and then the resin can be placed with a high-pressure surge.

The composition of the resin solution is furfuryl alcohol resin solvent, a coupling and wetting agent. The resin catalyzes with an acid to form a furan plastic. The resin solution is positioned across an interval of planned perforations. A more dense fluid may proceed below the resin to fill a portion of the wellbore below the zone of interest. A lower density fluid may follow above the resin in the wellbore to keep the resin from floating up above the zone of interest. This technique can ensure more accurate placement of resin across the soon to be perforated interval. Operationally, the pressure in the wellbore fluid, at the depth to be perforated, is increased to a substantially greater level than the pore pressure in the formation. The applied pressure before perforating may be higher than the formation fracturing pressure. Wireline through tubing or casing guns, or tubing conveyed perforating, can all be used for perforating. Resin is forced into the new perforations upon perforating with the overbalanced pressure. Acid is injected into the perforations to convert the liquid resin into a strong plastic that will consolidate the sand.

While the high-energy resin placement techniques offer an advantage over conventional matrix plastic consolidation methods, they are not widely used, and this system is plagued by many of the disadvantages of plastic consolidation—high cost, low success, and lack of longevity. The results of high-energy plastic treatments generally have tended to be disappointing.

5.4.6 Resin-Coated Gravel.
Resin-coated gravel treatments can be pumped in two different ways. The first is a dry, partially catalyzed phenolic resin-coated gravel. Thin resin coating is about 5% of the total weight of the sand. When exposed to heat, the resin cures, resulting in a consolidated sand mass. The use of resin-coated gravel as a sand-control technique involves pumping the gravel into the well to completely fill the perforations and casing. The bottomhole temperature of the well, or injection of steam, causes the resin to complete the cure into a consolidated pack. After curing, the consolidated gravel-pack sand can be drilled out of the casing, leaving the resin-coated gravel in the perforations. The remaining consolidated gravel in the perforations acts as a permeable filter to prevent the production of formation sand. The main use of resin-coated gravel is in prepacked screens, which is discussed later.

Wet resins (epoxies or furans) can also be used. To pump these systems, the well is usually prepacked with gravel; then, the resin is pumped and catalyzed to harden the plastic. After curing, the consolidated plastic-sand mixture is drilled out of the well, leaving the resin-coated sand in the perforations.

Although simple in concept, using resin-coated gravel can be complex. First, and most important, a successful job requires that all perforations be completely filled with the resin-coated gravel, and the gravel must cure. Complete filling of the perforations becomes increasingly difficult, as zone length and deviation from vertical increase. Second, the resin-coated gravel must cure with sufficient compressive strength. While resin-coated systems were used extensively after their development, their use today is limited. Experience with them has shown good initial success but poor longevity, as most wells do not produce sand-free for extended periods of time.

5.4.7 Stand-Alone Slotted Liners or Screens.
Slotted liners or screens have been used as the sole means of controlling formation sand production. In this service, they function as a filter.

Unless the formation is a well-sorted, clean sand with a large grain size, this type of completion may have an unacceptably short producing life before the slotted liner or screen plugs with formation material. When used alone as sand exclusion devices, the slotted liners or screens are placed across the productive interval, and the formation sand mechanically bridges on the slots or openings in the wire-wrapped screen. Bridging theory and laboratory tests show that particles will bridge on a slot, provided the width of the slot is less than two particle diameters. Likewise, particles will bridge against a hole if the perforation diameter does not exceed about three particle diameters.

The slot width, or the screen gauge, is sometimes sized to be equal to the formation sand grain size at the 10-percentile point of the sieve analysis. The theory is that because the larger 10% of the sand grains will be stopped by the openings of the screen, the larger sand will stop the remaining 90% of the formation. The bridges formed will not be stable and may break down from time to time when the producing rate is changed or the well is shut in. Because the bridges can fail or break down, resorting of the formation sand can occur, which, over time, tends to result in plugging of the slotted liner or screen. This design fails for fine-grained sand formations because the slot width is smaller than those available for commercial slotted liners. Wire-wrapped screens can meet the design, but their width is so small that plugging and production reduction is virtually assured. When this technique is used to control formation sand, the slotted liner or screen diameter should be as large as possible to maximize inflow area and minimize the amount of resorting that can occur. Another potential disadvantage of both slotted liners and screens in high-rate wells is the possibility of erosional failure of the slotted liner or screen before a bridge can form.

Using a slotted liner or screen without gravel packing is generally not a good sand-control technique because, in most cases, the screen will eventually restrict well rates because of plugging. There are isolated situations where this use has been successful in openhole completions in high-permeability, well-sorted formations. Selected North Sea wells have performed well. Screens or slotted liners should be avoided in cased-hole completions as the sole sand-control technique because, when the annulus and perforations become filled with formation sand, production rates decrease drastically.

5.4.8 Gravel Packing. Gravel packing consists of placing a screen or slotted liner in a well opposite the completion interval and placing gravel concentrically around it. The gravel is actually large-grained sand that prevents sand production from the formation but allows fluids to flow into the well. The slotted liner or screen retains the gravel. The gravel is sized to be about 5 to 6 times larger than the median formation sand size. Gravel packing creates a permeable downhole filter that allows the production of the formation fluids but restricts the entry and production of formation sand. Schematics of an openhole and cased-hole gravel pack are shown in **Fig. 5.4.** If the gravel is tightly packed between the formation and the screen, the bridges formed are stable, which prevents shifting and resorting of the formation sand. If properly designed and executed, a gravel pack will maintain its permeability under a broad range of producing conditions.

Gravel packing is currently the most widely used sand-control technique for completing wells. More than 90% of all sand-control completions are gravel packs. Because of its flexibility, almost any well at any deviation can be gravel packed. The exception is tubingless completions where clearances do not permit the use of conventional tools. Some tubingless completion gravel packs have been performed, but their success was poor.

5.4.9 Guidelines for Selecting Sand Control. There are many alternatives for sand control. Each alternative has its advantages and disadvantages. Even techniques that are not widely used may have a potential application in which its use might be superior to others. As mentioned before, gravel packing is currently the most widely used technique. The cost to gravel

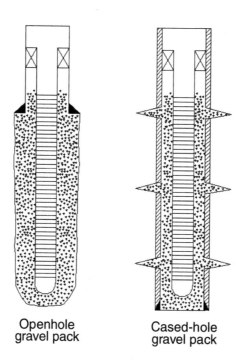

Openhole
gravel pack

Cased-hole
gravel pack

Fig. 5.4—Openhole and ideal cased-hole gravel packs.

pack is directly related to rig costs. Gravel-packed completions from floating drilling rigs may cost in excess of U.S. $2 million. However, should remedial operations be required on a gravel pack, the screen and completion assembly must be removed from the well, which could involve a lengthy fishing job and related problems. Sand consolidation and resin-coated sand are attractive for tubingless completions because no mechanical equipment is left in the hole; however, low permeability, small-interval length, high temperatures, and completion longevity (wells sanded up or low productivity) all present problems with the plastic systems. The right technique must be selected for the well completion at hand. As a first approach, assume that the well will be gravel packed. If it is not appropriate, for whatever reason, review other alternatives.

5.5 Gravel-Pack Design

A gravel pack is simply a downhole filter designed to prevent the production of unwanted formation sand. The formation sand is held in place by properly sized gravel pack sand that, in turn, is held in place with a properly-sized screen. To determine what size gravel-pack sand is required, samples of the formation sand must be evaluated to determine the median grain size diameter and grain size distribution.[4] The quality of the sand used is as important as the proper sizing. The American Petroleum Institute (API) has set forth the minimum specifications desirable for gravel-pack sand in API *RP58, Testing Sand Used in Gravel-Packing Operations.*[5]

5.5.1 Formation Sand Sampling. The first step in gravel-pack design is to obtain a representative sample of the formation. Failure to analyze a representative sample can lead to gravel packs that fail because of plugging or the production of sand. Because the formation sand size is so important, the technique used to obtain a formation sample requires attention. With knowledge of the different sampling techniques, compensation can be made in the gravel-pack sand size selection, if necessary.

Produced Samples. A produced sample of the formation sand is easily contaminated before it reaches the surface. Although such a sample can be analyzed and used for the gravel-pack sand size determination, produced samples will probably have a smaller median grain size than the median of actual formation sand. The well's flow rate, produced fluid characteristics, and completion tubular design influence whether a particular size is produced to surface or settles to the bottom of the well. In many cases, the larger sand grains settle, so a sample that is produced to the surface has a higher proportion of the smaller-size sand grains. This is the reason that the surface sample is not a good representation of the various sizes of formation sand. Also, the transport of sand grains, through the production tubing and surface flow lines, may result in broken sand grains, causing the presence of more fine and smaller grains.

Bailed Samples. Samples collected from the bottom of a well using wireline bailers are also relatively easy to obtain, but these too are probably unrepresentative of the size of the actual formation sand. Bailed samples are generally biased to the larger-size sand grains, assuming that more of the smaller grains are produced to surface. Bailed samples also may be misleading in terms of grain size distribution. When closing the well in to obtain a sample, the larger sand grains settle to the bottom of the well first, and the smaller sand grains fall on top of the larger ones. This results in a sorting of the formation sand grains into a sample that is not representative the formation sand. The use of bailed samples may result in the design of larger than required gravel-pack sand that can result in sand production (small formation particles passing through the gravel pack) or plugging of the gravel pack (small formation particles filling the spaces between the gravel-pack sand grains).

Sidewall Core Samples. Sidewall core samples are obtained by shooting hollow projectiles from a gun lowered into the well on an electric line to the desired depth. The projectiles remain attached to the gun with steel cables, so that when the gun is pulled from the well, the projectiles are retrieved with a small formation sample inside. Taking sidewall core samples is generally included in the evaluation stages of wells in unconsolidated formations; these are the most widely used sample types for gravel-pack sand design. Although more representative than produced or bailed samples, sidewall core samples can also give imprecise results because the volume in each sidewall sample is small. When the projectiles strike the face of the formation, localized crushing of the sand grains occurs, producing broken sand grains and generating more fine particles. The core sample also contains drilling mud solids that can be mistaken for formation material. Experienced lab analysts can separate the effects of crushing and mud solids prior to evaluating the sample, thus improving the quality of the results.

Conventional Core Samples. The most representative formation sample is obtained from conventional cores. In the case of unconsolidated formations, rubber sleeve conventional cores may be required to assure sample recovery. Although conventional cores are the most desirable formation sample, they are not readily available in many wells because of the cost of coring operations. Coring in sand-producing formations is also plagued with poor recovery. If available, small plugs can be taken under controlled circumstances at various sections of the core for a complete and accurate median formation grain size and grain-size distribution determination.

Other Samples. From time to time, operators have no formation sample. In this event, rely on any of the samples from offset wells. If the formation of interest has gravel-pack completions in nearby fields, rely on these. If there is still no information, select a relatively small gravel that will control most formation sand, or consult an expert.

5.5.2 Sieve Analysis. A sieve analysis is a laboratory routine performed on a formation sand sample for the selection of the proper-sized gravel-pack sand. A sieve analysis consists of placing a formation sample at the top of a series of screens that have progressively smaller mesh sizes downwards in the sieve stack. After placing the sieve stack in a vibrating machine, the sand grains in the sample will fall through the screens until encountering a screen through which certain grain sizes cannot pass because the openings in the screen are too small. By

TABLE 5.1—STANDARD SIEVE OPENINGS

U.S. Series Mesh Size	Sieve Opening, in.	Sieve Opening, mm	U.S. Series Mesh Size	Sieve Opening, in.	Sieve Opening, mm
2.5	0.315	8.000	35	0.0197	0.500
3	0.265	6.730	40	0.0165	0.420
3.5	0.223	5.660	45	0.0138	0.351
4	0.187	4.760	50	0.0117	0.297
5	0.157	4.000	60	0.0098	0.250
6	0.132	3.360	70	0.0083	0.210
7	0.111	2.830	80	0.0070	0.177
8	0.0937	2.380	100	0.0059	0.149
10	0.0787	2.000	120	0.0049	0.124
12	0.0661	1.680	140	0.0041	0.104
14	0.0555	1.410	170	0.0035	0.088
16	0.0469	1.190	200	0.0029	0.074
18	0.0394	1.000	230	0.0024	0.062
20	0.0331	0.840	270	0.0021	0.053
25	0.0280	0.710	325	0.0017	0.044
30	0.0232	0.589	400	0.0015	0.037

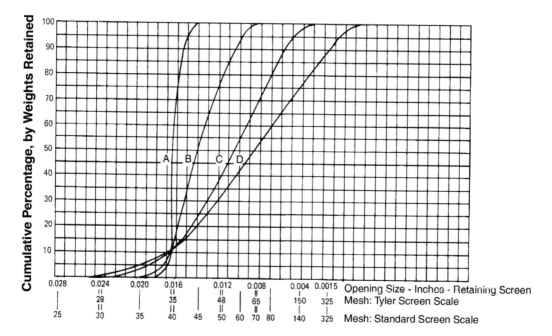

Fig. 5.5—Sand size distribution plot from sieve analysis.[1]

weighing the screens before and after sieving, the weight of formation sample, retained by each size screen, can be determined. The cumulative weight percent of each sample retained can be plotted as a comparison of screen mesh size on semilog coordinates to obtain a sand size-distribution plot, as shown in **Fig. 5.5**. Reading the graph at the 50% cumulative weight gives the median formation grain size diameter. This grain size, often referred to as d_{50}, is the basis of gravel-pack sand size-selection procedures. **Table 5.1** provides a reference for mesh size vs. sieve opening.

If possible, a sample should be taken every 2 to 3 ft within the formation, or at least at every lithology change. The minimum size of the formation sample required for sieve analysis is 15 cm^3. Sieving can be performed either wet or dry. In dry sieving (the most common technique), the sample is prepared by removing the fines (i.e., clays) and drying the sample in an oven. If necessary, the sample is ground with a mortar and pestle to ensure individual grains are sieved rather than conglomerated grains. The sample is then placed in the sieving apparatus that uses mechanical vibration to assist the particles in moving through and on to the various mesh screens. Wet sieving is used when the formation sample has extremely small grain sizes. In wet sieving, water is poured over the sample while sieving to ensure that the particles do not cling together.

5.5.3 Gravel-Pack Sand Sizing. There have been several published techniques for selecting a gravel-pack sand size to control the production of formation sand. The most widely used sizing criterion[4] provides sand control when the median grain size of the gravel-pack sand, D_{50}, is no more than six times larger than the median grain size of the formation sand, d_{50}. The upper case D refers to the gravel, while the lower case refers to the formation sand. The basis for this relationship was a series of core flow experiments in which half the core consisted of gravel-pack sand and the other half was formation sand. The ratio of median grain size of the gravel-pack sand and median grain size of the formation sand was changed over a range from 2 to 10 to determine when optimum sand control was achieved.

The experimental procedure consisted of measuring the pack permeability with each change in gravel size and comparing it to the initial permeability. If the final permeability was the same as the initial permeability, it was concluded that effective sand control was achieved with no adverse productivity effects. If the final permeability was less than the initial permeability, the formation sand was invading and plugging the gravel-pack sand. In this situation, sand control may be achieved, but at the expense of well productivity. **Fig. 5.6** illustrates the results of core flow experiments for a particular gravel/sand combination. As shown in the plot, the permeability of the pack increases up to a median gravel/sand size ratio of 6 but decreases as the ratio increases further. The permeability decreases to a minimum as a 10:12 ratio is reached; then, it increases. The explanation for this behavior is that the permeability increases as the gravel/sand size ratio increases up to a ratio of about 6, which reflects the increasing permeability of the larger gravel (i.e., at a gravel/sand ratio of one, the gravel is the same size as the formation sand). At a gravel/sand size ratio of 6, the formation sand grains bridge on, rather than into the pore structure of the gravel, which is the correct gravel size that provides the highest permeability. However, as the gravel size becomes larger and the ratio increases, the formation begins to bridge within the pore structure of the gravel, thereby decreasing the pack permeability. At a ratio of 10:12, the formation sand has moved well into the pores, decreasing the permeability substantially. As the gravel becomes larger, a reversal occurs because now the formation sand can move both into and through the pore structure of the gravel. At ratios in excess of 15, the formation sand can flow through the gravel with ease. As Fig. 5.6 indicates, at gravel/sand ratios less than 10:12, there is sand control, whereas at ratios larger than 12, there is no sand control.

In practice, the proper gravel-pack sand size is selected by multiplying the median size of the formation sand by 4 to 8 to achieve a gravel-pack sand size range, in which the average is six times larger than the median grain size of the formation sand. Hence, the gravel pack is designed to control the load-bearing material; no attempt is made to control formation fines that make up less 2 to 3% of the formation. This calculated gravel-pack sand size range is compared to the available commercial grades of gravel-pack sand. Select the available gravel-pack sand that matches the calculated gravel-pack size range. In the event that the calculated gravel-pack sand size range falls between the size ranges of commercially available gravel-

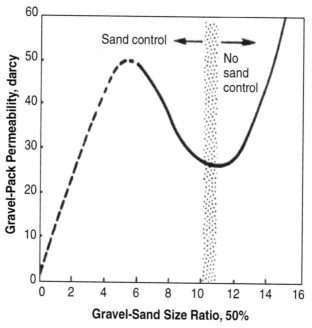

Fig. 5.6—Effect of gravel-sand ratio on sand control permeability.[1]

TABLE 5.2—COMMERCIALLY AVAILABLE SAND SIZES	
Gravel Size, U.S. Mesh	Size Range, in.
8/12	.094–.066
12/20	.066–.033
20/40	.033–.017
40/60	.017–.0098
50/70	.012–.0083

pack sand, select the smaller gravel-pack sand. **Table 5.2** contains information on commercially available gravel-pack sand sizes.

Note that this technique is based solely on the median grain size of the formation sand with no consideration given to the range of sand grain diameters or degree of sorting present in the formation. The sieve analysis plot, discussed earlier, can be used to obtain the degree of sorting in a particular formation sample. A near vertical sieve analysis plot represents good sorting (most of the formation sand is in a very narrow size range) vs. a highly sloping plot, which indicates poorer sorting as illustrated by curves "A" and "D," respectively, in Fig. 5.5. A sorting factor, or uniformity coefficient, can be calculated as

$$C_\mu = \frac{d_{40}}{d_{90}}, \dots\dots\dots\dots\dots\dots\dots\dots\dots\dots\dots\dots\dots\dots\dots\dots (5.1)$$

where

C_μ = sorting factor or uniformity coefficient,

d_{40} = grain size at the 40% cumulative level from sieve analysis plot,

TABLE 5.3—PERMEABILITY OF GRAVEL-PACK SANDS[6,7,8]			
U.S. Mesh Range	Permeability, darcy	Permeability, darcy	Permeability, darcy
6/10	2,703	–	–
8/12	1,969	–	–
10/20	652	500	–
12/20	–	–	668
16/30	–	250	415
20/40	171	119	225
40/60	69	40	69
50/70	–	–	45

and

d_{90} = grain size at the 90% cumulative level from sieve analysis plot.

If C_μ is less than 3, the sand is considered well sorted (uniform); from 3 to 5, it is nonuniform, and if greater than 5, it is highly nonuniform.

5.5.4 Gravel-Pack Sand. The productivity of a gravel-packed well depends on the permeability of the gravel-pack sand and how it is placed. To ensure maximum well productivity, one should use high quality gravel-pack sand. API *RP58, Testing Sand Used in Gravel Packing Operations,* establishes rigid specifications for acceptable properties of sands used for gravel packing. These specifications focus on ensuring the maximum permeability and longevity of the sand under typical well production and treatment conditions. The specifications define minimum acceptable standards for the size and shape of the grains, the amount of fines and impurities, acid solubility, and crush resistance. Only a few naturally occurring sands are capable of meeting the API specifications without excessive processing. These sands are characterized by their high quartz content and consistency in grain size. **Table 5.3** gives the permeability of common gravel-pack sand sizes conforming to API *RP58, Testing Sand Used in Gravel Packing Operations,* specifications (data from Refs. 6, 7, and 8).

Once the sieve analysis has been performed and plotted, the remainder of the gravel-pack sizing can be performed graphically. The gravel-pack sand size is determined by multiplying the median formation grain size by 6. This value is the median gravel grain size. With a straight edge, construct the gravel curve so that its uniformity coefficient, C_μ, is 1.5. The actual gravel size can be determined by the intercept of gravel curve with the 0 and 100 percentile values. Select to the nearest standard gravel size. The screen slot width is typically half the smallest gravel size selected but should not exceed 70% of the smallest grain diameter. While it may appear that this design is conservative, it will not restrict productivity and allows for variances in screen tolerances. The diameter of the screen should allow for at least 0.75-in. clearance from the casing inside diameter (ID). **Fig. 5.7** is an example gravel-pack design.

5.5.5 Gravel-Pack Sand Substitutes. Although naturally occurring quartz sand is the most common gravel-pack material, many alternatives exist. These include: resin-coated sand, garnet, glass beads, and aluminum oxides. Each of these materials offers specific properties that are beneficial for given applications and well conditions. The cost of the materials ranges from 2 to 3 times the price of common quartz sand.

5.6 Slotted Liners and Wire-Wrapped Screens

The slotted liner or screen is the mechanical device that contains the gravel-pack sand in an annular ring between it and the casing wall or open hole. **Fig. 5.8** shows a schematic of its function in an openhole gravel pack.

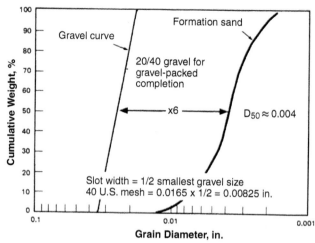

Fig. 5.7—Effect of gravel-sand size ratio on sand control and productivity.[1]

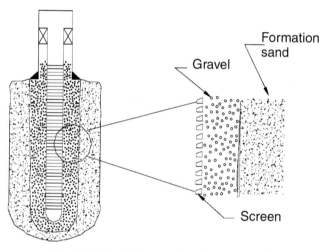

Fig. 5.8—Openhole gravel-pack schematic.[1]

5.6.1 Slotted Liners. Slotted liners are made from tubulars by saw-cutting slot configurations, as shown in **Fig. 5.9.** Slot widths are often referred to in terms of gauge. Slot or screen gauge is simply the width of the opening in inches multiplied by 1,000. For instance, a 12-gauge screen has openings of 0.012 in.

The machining consists of cutting rectangular openings with small rotary saws. Routine slot widths are 0.030 in. or larger. The minimum slot width that can be achieved is about 0.012 in. Slots that cut less than 0.020 in. in width involve high costs because of excessive machine downtime to replace broken saw blades that overheat, warp, and break.

The single-slot staggered, longitudinal pattern is generally preferred because the strength of the unslotted pipe is preserved. The staggered pattern also gives a more uniform distribution of slots over the surface area of the pipe. The single-slot staggered pattern is slotted with an even number of rows around the pipe with a typical 6-in. longitudinal spacing of slot rows.

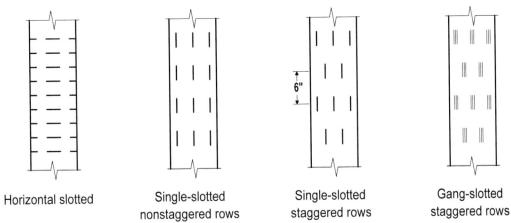

Horizontal slotted

Single-slotted
nonstaggered rows

Single-slotted
staggered rows

Gang-slotted
staggered rows

Fig. 5.9—Slotted-liner geometries (courtesy of Baker Oil Tools).

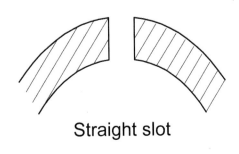

Straight slot

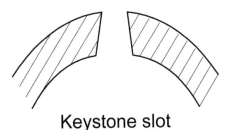

Keystone slot

Fig. 5.10—Straight and keystone-shaped slots (courtesy of Baker Oil Tools).

The slots can be straight or keystone shaped, as illustrated in **Fig. 5.10**. The keystone slot is narrower on the outside surface of the pipe than on the inside. Slots formed in this way have an inverted "V" cross-sectional area and are less prone to plugging because any particle passing through the slot at the outside diameter (OD) of the pipe will continue to flow through, rather than lodging within the slot. While the slotted liners are usually less costly than wire-wrapped screens, they have smaller inflow areas and experience higher pressure drops during production. Slotted liners also plug more readily than screens; they are used where well productivity is small and economics cannot support the use of screens.

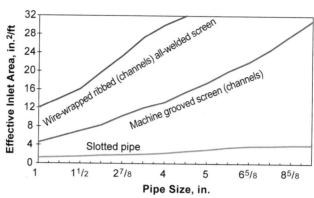

Fig. 5.11—Comparison of effective inlet areas (20-gauge screen).[1]

The length of the individual slots is measured on the ID of the pipe. Usual practice dictates 1½-in. long slots for slot widths of 0.030 in. and under, 2-in. long slots for slot widths between 0.030 to 0.060 in., and 2½-in. long slots for slot widths of 0.060 in. and larger. Slot width tolerance is generally ± 0.003 in. for widths of 0.040 in. and wider and ± 0.002 in. for widths less than 0.040 in.

The primary advantage of a slotted liner over wire-wrapped screens is usually cost; however, small gauge, high-density slot patterns may cost as much as wire-wrapped screens. The disadvantages of the slotted liner are limited flow area (2 to 3%, creating a low tolerance to plugging) and minimum available slot size (approximately 0.012 in.). Slot widths that are less than 0.020 in. and cut in standard carbon steel-pipe grades can rust and will either close or reconfigure the slot opening so that they do not function properly unless they are coated, protected, or stored indoors before use.

5.6.2 Wire-Wrapped Screens. Wire-wrapped screens offer another alternative for retaining the gravel in an annular ring between the screen and the formation. Wire-wrapped screens have substantially more inflow area than a slotted liner, as **Fig. 5.11** illustrates. The screen consists of an outer jacket that is fabricated on special wrapping machines that resemble a lathe. The shaped wire is simultaneously wrapped and welded to longitudinal rods to form a single helical slot with any desired width. The jacket is subsequently placed over and welded at each end to a supporting pipe base (containing drilled holes) to provide structural support. This is a standard-commodity design manufactured by several companies. A schematic of the screen construction is shown in **Fig. 5.12**. Screen tolerances are typically plus 0.001 and minus 0.002 in.; hence, a specified 0.006-in. slot could vary in slot width from 0.004 to 0.007 in.

Because these designs have been used for more than 40 years in worldwide oilfield operations, a great deal is known about the performance of wire-wrapped screens. The typical pipe-base screen fabrication consists of a grade 316L stainless steel jacket placed over a N-80 pipe base; however, other metals can be specified as required for site-specific applications. The inflow area of screens varies from about 6 to 12% (or higher), depending on the slot opening. Screens with the smallest slot openings are typically 6 gauge (0.006 in.). For large gravel, 10 to 20 mesh, screen slot openings are about 18 gauge (0.018 in.).

A version of the wire-wrapped screen is the rod-based screen that consists of the jacket only; however, rod-based screens may have additional heavier rods and a heavier wire wrap than the jackets used on pipe-base screens to provide additional strength. Rod-based screens are commonly used in shallow water-well completions that typically range from a few hundred to maybe a 1,000 ft in depth. Hence, they do not require the strength that is gained by installing the screen jacket over a pipe base. Screen diameters range from 1.5 to 7 in. in

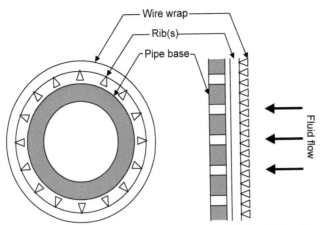

Fig. 5.12—Wire-wrapped screen (courtesy of Baker Oil Tools).

diameter (or larger). This is the diameter of the pipe base. The actual screen diameter is slightly larger (i.e., the actual OD of a 3.5-in. screen is about 4 in.).

5.6.3 Prepacked Screens. Prepacked screens are a modification of wire-wrapped screens; they actually represent a modular gravel pack. They consist of a standard screen assembly with a layer of resin-coated gravel (consolidated) placed around it that is contained in an annular ring supported by a second screen (dual-screen prepack) or outer shroud (single-screen prepack). The resin coating is a partially cured phenolic plastic. Being dry, the resin-coated gravel can be handled like ordinary gravel. After prepacking the screen, the complete unit is heated to cure and harden the resin. The thickness of the gravel layer can be varied to meet special needs. The screens with the lowest profiles are those that contain an annular pack between the jacket and the pipe base. This screen has a thin lattice screen wrapped around it to prevent gravel from flowing through the drill holes in the pipe base before consolidation. Examples of prepacked screens are in **Fig. 5.13**. Prepacked screens have been used with gravel packs instead of standard wire-wrapped screens and in stand-alone applications in horizontal wells. While the prepacked screens have been used in stand-alone service, experience has shown that they are highly prone to plugging, consequently restricting productivity. The inflow area of these screens is about 4 to 6% of the surface area. The exact amount depends on the slot opening and the size of the gravel.

5.6.4 Flow Capacities of Screens and Slotted Liners. Fig. 5.14 shows the pressure drop associated with commercial wire-wrapped screens. Because all have similar designs, there is little difference in performance from one manufacturer to another. These flow capacity tests were performed using water containing no plugging material. The data indicate that all screens have exceptionally high flow capacities. Flow testing with slotted liners revealed that their flow capacity was related to the slot density rather than the screen diameter. Their flow capacities are typically less than half that of wire-wrapped screens with the same diameter. Note that the flow rates were measured in increments of B/D/ft of screen. For flow rates that are typical of most wells, the pressure loss through the screen is negligible, provided that they are not plugged. Slotted liners are more easily plugged than wire-wrapped screens because the slots are usually cut parallel to each other. On the other hand, wire-wrapped screens are fabricated with keystone-shaped wire that allows a particle to pass through the screen if it can traverse the

Dual-screen prepack

Single-screen prepack

Low-profile prepack

Fig. 5.13—Types of prepacked screens (courtesy of Baker Oil Tools).

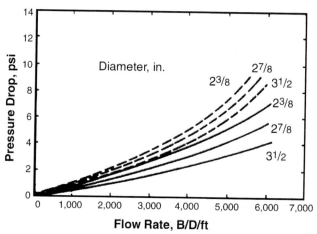

Fig. 5.14—Flow capacity of 12-gauge screens with 20/40 U.S. mesh gravel.[1]

minimum restriction at the OD of the screen. The keystone design can be observed in Fig. 5.10.

5.6.5 Tensile/Collapse Strengths of Wire-Wrapped and Prepacked Screens. Tensile strength test results performed on screens and slotted liners in standard testing equipment showed that standard pipe-base screens have higher tensile ratings than rod-base screens. Testing demonstrated that yielding occurred in the pipe body as well as the coupling. As a consequence, when yielding in the connection caused a thread to separate, the test was terminated. The tensile strength of standard pipe-base screens was about twice that of the rod-base screens.[1] For conservative designs, the tensile strength should be the lesser of 65% of the pipe body or the published joint pull-out strength.

Individual tests demonstrated collapse failures as high as 6,000 to 9,000 psi; however, this represented the simultaneous failure of the screen and the pipe base; screens have a collapse rating of about 3,500 psi, which is the rating for the jacket.

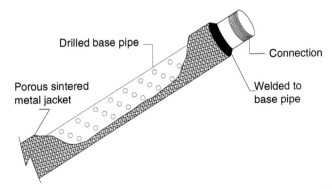

Fig. 5.15—Sintered metal screen schematic (courtesy of Baker Oil Tools).

5.6.6 Proprietary Screen Designs. Proprietary designs were originally developed for stand-alone installations in horizontal wells rather than a gravel-packed completion; however, gravel-pack screen applications should not be ruled out. They are also applicable in this service. Proprietary designs are premium designs that surpass the performance of either a standard wire-wrapped screen or a prepacked screen in their ability to resist plugging and erosion and are equipped with torque-shouldered connections to permit rotation. Because horizontal completions typically consist of a thousand to several thousand feet of completion interval, the main issue is the susceptibility of a particular design to plug with time rather than the flow capacity. These new designs have increased inflow areas to as much as 30% of the surface area of the screens. The materials used and the designs differ from conventional wire-wrapped screens. They consist of designs with lattice, Dutch weave, porous membrane, sintered metal, and corrugated weave filtration sections. The logic used in these designs was that because these screens have inflow areas of 30% compared to about 5% with prepacked screens, their longevity should be extended by about a factor of six when operating under similar downhole conditions. Other issues involve the ability to run the screen without creating damage that would either prevent sand control or restrict productivity. To address this concern, most of the proprietary designs have an outer shroud to protect the screen during installation. Proprietary connections are typically used for horizontal service because of their high strength and the ability to rotate if necessary.

Sintered Metal Screens. The sintered metal screen design was initiated in gravel-pack use in about 1990. The design consists of placing a sintered metal sleeve that is 0.15 to 0.25 in. thick over a drilled pipe base. The sintered metal sleeve contains approximately 30% flow area. The sleeve acts as the filtration medium, while the pipe base provides tensile strength and collapse resistance. **Fig. 5.15** is a schematic of the screen design.

Tensile strength and collapse resistance of this design should be about the same as that for wire-wrapped screens. For conservative designs, the tensile strength capabilities should be the about 65% or the lesser of either the published pipe strength or the joint pull-out of the coupling. The collapse rating should be similar to published values for wire-wrapped screens of about 3,500 psi.

Porous Metal Membrane Screens. This screen design consists of multiple layers (3 or 4) of porous metal membrane (PMM), which contains about 30% open area through variable-sized pore openings. These are between an underlying drainage and overlying protecting mesh screen. They are placed concentrically between a drilled pipe base and a perforated outer shroud. The filter medium for the screen is sintered metal powder that is pressed against a stainless steel lattice screen to provide structural support for the filtration medium. A schematic of the screen's construction is illustrated in **Fig. 5.16**. Test data from the manufacturer show

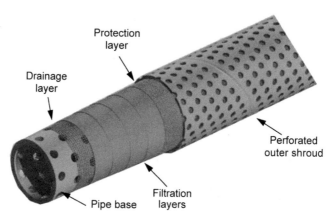

Fig. 5.16—Porous metal membrane screen schematic (courtesy of Baker Oil Tools).

tensile strength testing performed to 110k lbf and a collapse test to about 7,000 psi performed on 2⅞-in. screens, both of which reflect the strength of the pipe base. These data are similar to values for commodity wire-wrapped screens. The tensile strength rating should be less than 65% of the pipe body or connection because physical properties of the screen jacket and perforated shroud should not contribute to these properties significantly.

 Shrouded Multilayer Screens. This screen design consists of three layers of media that form the jacket, which are placed concentrically around a drilled pipe base. The base wrap for the jacket consists of a round stainless steel wire-wrapped support that serves as a drainage layer for the overlying filtration medium. The shroud is placed concentrically over the filtration medium. See **Fig. 5.17** for a schematic of the design.

 The purpose of the base wrap or inner jacket is for support for the overlying filtration medium against high differential pressure. The wrap also promotes using the entire surface area of the filtration medium that optimizes plugging resistance. The openings in the base wrap are typically about 25 microns or larger than the filtration medium to provide secondary sand control. The filtration medium provides pore throat openings that assist in maximizing the inflow area that develops a more permeable filter cake. The design of the filtration medium, a Dutch weave, redirects the flow through it to minimize erosion and extend screen life. The design being offered is rated at a uniform pore-throat opening sizes from 110 to 230 microns. The inflow area for this design is also about 30% of the surface area of the screen. The outer shroud protects the inner filtration section during installation in the well and assists in redirecting the flow stream during production so that erosion of the filtration section is minimized. The strength rating for this screen is a tensile rating of 65% of the pipe body or the published joint pull-out strength and a jacket collapse rating of 3,500 psi.

5.6.7 Plugging and Erosion Tests on Proprietary and Commodity Screens. Prepacked screen designs are more susceptible to plugging than other designs. This stems from their depth filter design. Standard wire-wrapped screens are a surface filter, which are not as susceptible to plugging but are more prone to erosion. Certain proprietary designs are better at resisting plugging and erosion than others. The best designs have large inflow areas and redirected flow through the screen to minimize erosion.

5.7 Gravel-Pack Completion Equipment and Service Tools
There is a myriad of gravel-pack systems available to handle virtually any conceivable well condition. **Fig. 5.18** illustrates typical gravel packs for cased and openhole completions. These employ crossover gravel packing equipment that is state-of-the-art in the industry today. Wash-

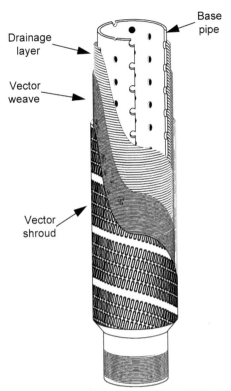

Fig. 5.17—Shrouded multilayer screen (courtesy of Baker Oil Tools).

down and reverse circulation methods are other alternatives that are less expensive and are to be used when costs will not support crossover equipment.

Gravel-pack completion equipment is the equipment that remains in the well after the gravel placement operations are complete. The equipment discussed next does not represent all the types of available equipment, but it does represent a typical gravel-pack completion. Certain well conditions may require compromises in the type and design of gravel-pack equipment that can be used. Another important concept is that there may be several, yet equally effective, ways to complete a well.

5.7.1 Gravel-Pack Base. The first step in installing a gravel-pack completion is to establish a base on which the screen will rest. In cased-hole completions, the most common type base is a sump packer. The sump packer is normally run into the well on an electric wireline before perforating and is set a specified distance (5 to 10 ft) below the lowest planned perforation. The distance below the perforations must accommodate the length of the seal assembly and production screen overlap.

Although sump packers are the preferred gravel-pack base, other options such as a bridge plug or cement plug can be used. In openhole completions, provisions for a debris sump or logging access can be achieved, but these are not routine and may not be feasible in some situations. Therefore, the gravel-pack base is normally a bull plug on the bottom of the screen. The types of common gravel-pack bases are illustrated in **Fig. 5.19**.

5.7.2 Seal Assembly. The seal assembly is required to establish a seal in the bore of the sump packer to prevent gravel-pack sand from filling the bottom of the well during gravel packing.

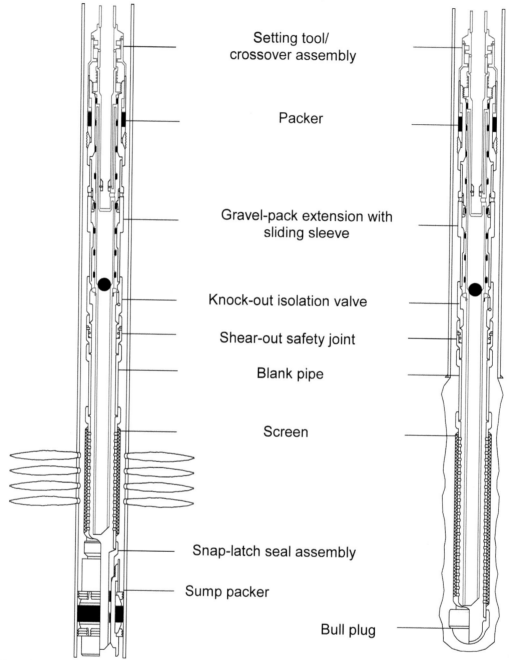

Setting tool/
crossover assembly

Packer

Gravel-pack extension with
sliding sleeve

Knock-out isolation valve

Shear-out safety joint

Blank pipe

Screen

Snap-latch seal assembly

Sump packer

Bull plug

Fig. 5.18—Typical gravel-pack completion equipment in cased- and openholes (courtesy of Baker Oil Tools).

In the case of multiple gravel packs, the seal also provides for zonal isolation. The seal assembly used to engage the sump packer is normally a snap latch type or other type holddown.

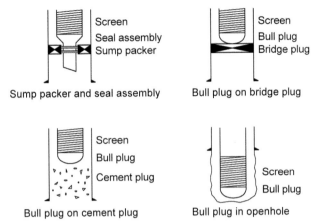

Fig. 5.19—Types of gravel-pack bases (courtesy of Baker Oil Tools).

5.7.3 Gravel-Pack Screen. The purpose of the gravel-pack screen is to create an annulus between the screen and the casing/open hole and to hold the gravel in place during production. As discussed earlier, there are several different types of screens.

Screen Centralization. Filling the annulus between the screen/casing (or open hole) with gravel-pack sand is essential to the control of formation sand production. To ensure that the annulus is filled completely around the screen, centralization of the screen is required. In cased-hole completions, weld-on, blade-type centralizers are normally used. The blades are approximately 6 in. long and are cut from a 0.25- to 0.50-in.-thick plate or steel. The edges of the centralizers are beveled to ensure easy run-in. The centralizers consist of four blades welded to the screen base pipe 90° apart to result in an OD approximately 0.25 in. under the ID of the well's casing. The centralizers are spaced 15 to 20 ft apart and can be positioned at the top, bottom, and/or middle of a screen joint as required.

In openhole gravel packs, centralization is accomplished with bow-spring centralizers. These centralizers consist of a top and bottom collar connected with 4 to 6 steel spring bows. The bows can be compressed (i.e., the centralizer is elongated) for running through restricted IDs. When the centralizer enters a larger ID, the bows attempt to expand to their original position, resulting in a restoring force or centralization. Sufficient centralizers are required such that the combined restoring force is capable of lifting the weight of the screen in the given hole conditions. Computer programs are available for determining optimum centralizer spacing for a specific bow-spring centralizer, hole size, and deviation. See API *Spec. 10D, Specification for Bow-Spring Casing Centralizers.*

5.7.4 Blank Pipe. The purpose of blank pipe is to provide a reservoir of gravel-pack sand above the screen to ensure that the screen remains completely packed in the event of pack settling. During gravel-pack operations, it is possible for minor voids in the annulus pack to occur. In fact, gravel packing with viscous gel transport fluids commonly produces voids, particularly opposite the short lengths of blank pipe between screen joints. Depending on deviation angle, pack settling shortly after gravel placement may fill the voids. It is important to have a sufficient reserve of gravel-pack sand available for this process to occur without uncovering the top of the screen.

Blank Pipe Centralization. As with the screen, the blank pipe must be centralized to ensure even gravel distribution in the blank and casing annulus. Weld-on centralizers are normally used in both cased-hole and openhole completions because the blank pipe is almost always positioned inside the casing. Bow-spring centralizers can be used if desired or required.

Blank Pipe Length. Several rules of thumb exist for determining the length of blank pipe. Perhaps the most scientific method would be to recognize that voids will occur within the length of screen wherever nonscreen regions exist (i.e., at screen joint connections and above the gravel pack). A long-standing guideline for gravel reserve has been to maintain a minimum of 30 ft of packed gravel in the blank pipe above the top of the screen when packing with brine. When viscous fluids are used, blank lengths may be as much as twice the screen length for short completion intervals. This allows for additional settling with these fluids when the gel breaks.

Tell-Tale Screens. Tell-tale screens are short screen sections that are sometimes used to assist with gravel placement and determine when the gravel pack is complete. Their benefit is questionable. There are two types of tell-tale screens: the upper and lower versions.

Upper tell-tale screens are used primarily with brine-pack systems. They are typically located about 30 ft above the main gravel-pack screen. Their function is to indicate, by an increase in pressure, when the dehydrated gravel has reached the tell-tale location. This assures that there is the desired amount of gravel reserve.

Lower tell-tale screens are used when gravel packing with viscous fluids. Their purpose is to assist in ensuring that the gravel slurry reaches the bottom of the gravel pack before the slurry dehydrates. The gravel-pack tools are usually in the lower circulating position when the tell-tale is used in these installations.

5.7.5 Shear-Out Safety Joint. A shear-out safety joint is located just above the blank pipe. It consists of a top and bottom sub connected by shear screws. This device is incorporated in most gravel pack completion assemblies to allow retrieval of the gravel-pack packer and the gravel-pack extension independently of the blank pipe and screen. The joint is parted with straight tension to shear the screws while pulling the packer with a packer-retrieving tool.

5.7.6 Knock-Out Isolation Valve. The knock-out isolation valve is a mechanical fluid-loss device that prevents completion fluid losses and subsequent damage to the formation after performing the gravel pack. The downward closing flapper in the valve is held open by the gravel-pack service tools (normally the washpipe) during the gravel pack. When the service tools are removed from the valve, the flapper closes, preventing fluid loss to the formation. The gravel-pack service tools can be removed from the well and the completion tubing run. When the well is producing, the flapper will open. Alternatively, the flapper is made of a breakable material and can be broken hydraulically or mechanically before producing the well.

5.7.7 Gravel-Pack Extension. Gravel-pack extensions are used with the gravel-pack packer and service tools to provide a flow path from the tubing above the packer and to the screen/casing annulus below the packer. The gravel-pack extension consists of the upper extension (which contains flow ports for the gravel pack fluids), sealbore (sized to match the bore of the gravel-pack packer), and lower extension (to house the gravel-pack crossover tool throughout its range of motion). The length of the gravel-pack extension is designed to work with a particular gravel-pack packer and crossover tool. Gravel-pack extensions are available in two types: perforated or sliding sleeve versions.

5.7.8 Gravel-Pack Packer. At the top of the gravel-pack assembly is a gravel-pack packer. The packer may be permanent or retrievable. However, retrievable type packers are recommended for gravel packing. A retrievable packer expedites workover activities without the potential cost and risk of milling a permanent packer. The retrievable packers used for gravel packing are usually sealbore type packers that can also be used for production; therefore, the packer must be designed for the temperature, pressure, and environmental conditions present in the well.

5.7.9 Gravel-Pack Service Tools. Gravel-pack service tools are the equipment necessary to perform the gravel pack; they are removed from the well after gravel packing. In most cases, the type of gravel-pack equipment used dictates the service tools required for a gravel pack. Further discussion of the service tools is discussed next.

Hydraulic Setting Tool. The hydraulic setting tool is a hydraulic piston that generates the force required to set the gravel-pack packer. It is attached to the top of the crossover tool and has a sleeve shouldered against the setting sleeve of the packer. A setting ball is dropped to the ball seat in the crossover tool to plug off the ID of the work string. Applied pressure to the work string acts on a piston in the hydraulic setting tool to force the sleeve down to compress the slips and packing element of the packer. Special versions of the setting tool are available, which allow for rotation and high-circulating rates while running the gravel-pack assembly.

Gravel-Pack Crossover Tool. The gravel-pack crossover tool creates the various circulating paths for fluid flow during gravel packing. The crossover tool consists of a series of molded seals surrounding a gravel-pack port midway down the tool and a return port near the top of the tool. A concentric tube (washpipe) design in the crossover tool along with the gravel-pack packer and gravel-pack extension allow fluid pumped down the work string above the packer to "cross over" to the screen/casing annulus below the packer. Similarly, return fluids flowing up the washpipe and below the packer can "cross over" to the work string/casing annulus above the packer.

Gravel-pack crossover tools typically have three positions: squeeze, circulating, and reverse circulating, as illustrated in **Fig. 5.20.** The squeeze position is located by positioning to seal the return ports. The squeeze position allows all fluids pumped down the work string to be forced into the formation. It is used to perform squeeze gravel-pack treatments and/or inject acid treatments into the formation. The circulating position is located by picking the crossover tool up approximately 18 in. above the squeeze position. The circulating position works with a properly sized washpipe to provide a flow path to circulate gravel-pack sand to completely fill the screen/casing annulus. The fluids flow down the work string into the crossover tool, out the gravel-pack extension, down the screen/casing annulus into the screen, up the washpipe into the crossover tool again, and up the work string/casing annulus. Special, high-rate, erosion-resistant crossover tools are available for high-rate brine or frac-pack completions.

Washpipe. Washpipe is run below the gravel-pack crossover tool inside the blank pipe and screen to ensure that the return circulation point for the gravel-pack carrier fluid is at the bottom of the screen. The washpipe assists in placing gravel-pack sand at the bottom of the screen and packing from the bottom up. The end of the washpipe should be as close to the bottom of the screen as possible.

Maximizing the washpipe OD increases the resistance to flow, preferentially into the washpipe/screen annulus. The greater resistance to flow forces the gravel-pack transport fluid to flow in the screen/casing annulus and carry the gravel-pack sand to the bottom of the well. That causes the gravel packing of the screen/casing annulus to be more complete. The optimum ratio of washpipe OD to screen base pipe ID should be approximately 0.8. Achieving this ratio in some screen sizes will require the use of special flush-joint washpipe connections.

5.8 Well Preparation for Gravel Packing

Well preparation includes many activities to ensure that the well is completed properly. Some of these items and activities include: appropriate drilling practices, cleanliness, completion fluids, perforating, perforation cleaning, acidizing, and specifications for rig and service company personnel.

5.8.1 Drilling Practices. The productivity of a cased- or openhole gravel-packed completion is determined in part by the condition of the reservoir behind the filter cake, the quality of the filter cake, and the stability of the wellbore. Given this, it can be said that the completion

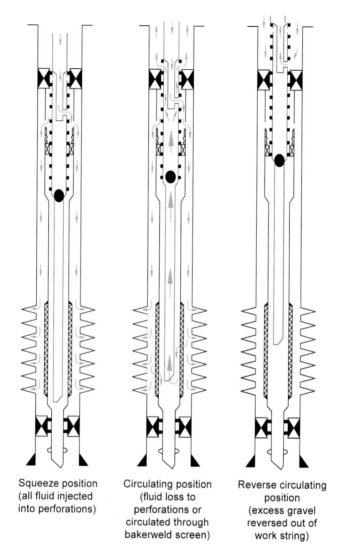

Squeeze position
(all fluid injected
into perforations)

Circulating position
(fluid loss to
perforations or
circulated through
bakerweld screen)

Reverse circulating
position
(excess gravel
reversed out of
work string)

Fig. 5.20—Gravel-pack crossover tool positions (courtesy of Baker Oil Tools).

begins when the bit enters the pay. Thus, it follows that the goal of drilling is to maintain wellbore stability while minimizing formation damage.

5.8.2 Maintaining Wellbore Stability. Wellbore stability in the form of washouts, hole collapse, and fracturing is an effect of large drilling fluid loss, inadequate overbalance, and/or reaction between filtrate and the formation. But, for whatever reason, instability affects both cased- and openhole completions because it can cause loss of the wellbore. Thick cement sheaths in washed-out sections result in poor to no perforation penetration and the lack of cement can make sand placement difficult. Hole collapse can prevent running screens to the bottom of the hole, and failure, in the form of fracturing or collapse, can stop an openhole gravel pack, should failure occur while the pack is in process.

Because stability is an effect of the reaction between the drill-in fluid and the formation, filtrate, filter cake, weight, and rheology become key parameters in building a drill-in fluid.

These variables usually can be addressed by using polymers and fluid-loss agents in a brine-based fluid containing a properly-sized bridging agent like that contained in special drill-in fluids.

5.8.3 Formation Damage. Formation damage, expressed quantitatively in the form of skin, depends on the filtrate used, particle damage, and, for openhole gravel packs, filter cake quality. Skin, in turn, is a reflection of poor productivity; it is expensive to remove or bypass. Preservation of reservoir pore throats requires keeping particles out of pores, minimizing filtrate loss, and employing a filtrate that is compatible with rock and reservoir fluids.

With openhole completions, filtrate must be nondamaging, but it is generally overlooked in cased-hole completions. Frequently, it is assumed that any damage caused by filtrate will be bypassed with perforating. Looking at the occasions when reservoirs are exposed to moderate to high fluid losses, often expressed as a "thirsty mud," it is possible to have filtrate invade 1 to 3 ft from the wellbore. If the filtrate is incompatible with reservoir rock and fluid, there will be a damaged ring beyond which it may be impossible for perforations to penetrate. For openhole completions, the quality of the filter cake is also as important as the other requirements. Because the cake must be gravel packed into place, it is necessary that the cake be thin and friable and have a low breakout pressure.

Again, as with the wellbore stability issue, filtrate and filter cake become key parameters. Proper selection of a filtrate brine base, along with polymers and fluid loss agents containing a properly-sized bridging agent, usually meets these needs.

5.8.4 Cleaning the Casing, Openhole, and Work String. Cleanliness may be one of the most important considerations for gravel packing. Because a gravel pack represents the installation of a downhole filter, any action that promotes plugging the gravel pack is detrimental to well productivity. Many advances have been made in improving the cleanliness of gravel-pack operations, particularly in completion fluids. However, in spite of the fact that clean completion fluids are used, the lack of cleanliness in the casing, work string, lines, pits, and other equipment is a source of potential formation damage. While cleaning the well and rig equipment can be expensive, it is not as expensive as lost productivity or having to rework the entire completion because proper cleaning was neglected in the beginning.

Casing. Reverse circulation is the preferred method of circulation for cleaning the casing. The recommended annular velocity is a minimum of 130 ft/min for casing shoe deviations less than 60° and 300 ft/min for wellbore deviations greater than 60°. Reverse circulation is more effective than conventional circulating, as material is moved downhole with the gravity where it is more efficiently circulated to the surface because of higher velocities in the work string than in the annulus. For an openhole completion, reverse circulation permits cleaning the casing to specifications before addressing the open hole. Planning for a work string that will permit reverse circulation at reasonable bottomhole pressures is required.

Mechanical, hydraulic, and chemical cleaning agents should be employed to clean the casing. Mechanical agents are usually in the form of casing scrapers; most hydraulic agents are push pills and filtered brine. Casing sweeps provide a chemical wash to address polymers, oil, and/or solids adhering to the casing wall.

As a mechanical agent, scrapers remove cement and scale, which will not hinder a bit but will impede a packer. It is prudent to run casing scrapers to the bottom or at least through the interval to be perforated. For openhole completions, the scraper should be run to within 100 ft of the shoe or at least past the proposed packer seat. In displacing the drilling/drill-in fluid, a push pill is pumped first, followed by a casing sweep that is followed by filtered brine. (See **Fig. 5.21.**) Push pills serve as a hydraulic piston by creating a sharp interface between mud and casing sweep. The casing sweep removes polymers and solids adhering to the casing wall. The filtered brine provides turbulence to help remove and wash material from the casing.

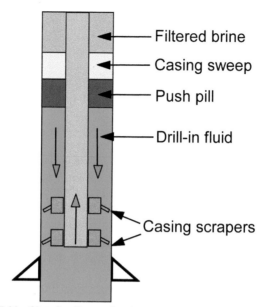

Filtered brine

Casing sweep

Push pill

Drill-in fluid

Casing scrapers

Fig. 5.21—Cleaning the casing (courtesy of Baker Oil Tools).

Push pill volumes should at least be equal to a volume of 300 ft of work string-casing annulus and have the same density as the drill-in fluid and a yield point that is 1.5 to 2.0 times that of the drill-in fluid. Thus, they are easily made from a portion of the drill-in mud by the addition of a viscosifier to raise the yield point. Casing sweeps depend on the chemical employed to remove solids and polymer and, to be effective, will require some contact time at turbulent rates. Calcium hypochlorite (65% active) at 1.5 lbm/bbl and a 5-min contact time effectively removes polymers and fluid-loss agents.

Open Hole. As with the casing, reverse circulation is the preferred method of circulation for an open hole. With the casing cleaned and displaced as previously discussed, all attention can be focused on cleaning the open hole. Wellbore losses and instability can easily be detected and repaired if necessary, and any unrecovered material will be pushed to the bottom out of the way. Recommended annular velocity is 300 ft/min at any deviation to scour the filter cake in preparation for gravel packing and to clean the hole.

Push pills should be used to displace the drill-in fluid from the open hole. The pill should be spotted in the casing and work string annulus above the open hole using forward circulation; then, the work string is run to the bottom and the push pill and drill-in fluid displaced from the open hole with filtered brine using reverse circulation. (See **Fig. 5.22.**) Push pills are sized, as previously discussed in the section on casing cleaning.

Work String. The work string should be sized to permit reverse circulation. It should always be run open ended to minimize backpressure on the formation. The work string contains the same types of debris associated with the casing; however, unlike casing, both the inner and outer surfaces of the work string must be clean because completion fluid is circulated along both surfaces. The work string is usually not a major problem if it has been in use before the completion. Work strings just delivered from storage should be carefully inspected for scale, rust, mill varnish, and other debris. Scraping the work string is usually not as good an option as for the casing, but visual inspections, before it is run into the well, are encouraged to ensure that the string is in good mechanical condition and clean. As a minimum, a "rabbit or drift" with a diameter slightly less than the drift diameter of the work string helps to loosen scale

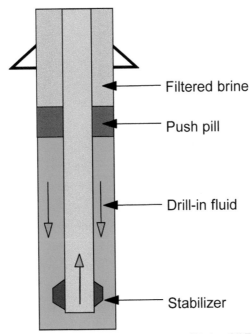

Filtered brine

Push pill

Drill-in fluid

Stabilizer

Fig. 5.22—Cleaning the open hole (courtesy of Baker Oil Tools).

and other debris, as well as providing assurance of the internal diameter of the work string. Once the work string is clean, every effort must be made to keep it clean.

A common source of contamination of the gravel pack is thread dope lubricant. One should use thread dope lubricant sparingly and only on the pin ends during the completion phase. Eliminate the use of thread dope completely on the final run in the hole just before gravel packing the well. Pickling the work string with a pipe dope solvent and a 10% HCl solution before starting a gravel pack is a must. As with any solvent, there is a required contact time and wash rate to dissolve lubricant and carry material out of the work string. Consider the use of a dedicated clean work string strictly for gravel packing, if a number of wells are to be completed.

5.8.5 Surface Facilities. Although they are sometimes ignored, tanks and lines are a common cause of damaging materials, particularly when the rig that drilled the well is used for completing the well. Tanks must be thoroughly scraped and jetted to ensure that any residual solids from the drilling fluids are removed. When possible, tanks should be dedicated to completion fluids when a drilling program involves drilling numerous wells requiring gravel packs. Casing sweep chemicals and seawater are recommended for removing debris from rig lines.

5.8.6 Quality Assurance. If properly filtered brine is used as per the following discussion on filtration, the hole is displaced as recommended, and surface facilities are cleaned, it is easy to obtain returned brine that has less than 20 NTU (nephelometric turbidity units) throughout the entire gravel-pack operation. Again, this is only possible if all of the steps are followed. NTU are measured with turbidity meters that should be carefully calibrated.

5.8.7 Filtration. As stated earlier, gravel-pack completion fluids must be sufficiently clean in order that suspended particles do not plug or reduce the permeability of the formation, perforations, or gravel-pack sand. To achieve a clean fluid requires filtration. Completion fluids are typically filtered to 2 or 10 microns, but in some cases, they are filtered to 1 micron. The fluid can be filtered by either a diatomaceous earth (DE) filter upstream in combination with a car-

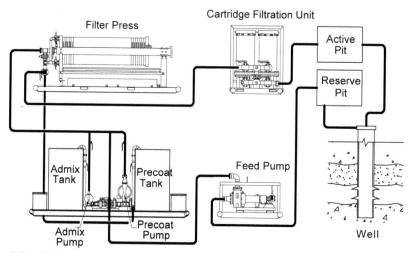

Fig. 5.23—DE filtration system for completion or workover (courtesy of Baker Oil Tools).

tridge filter unit downstream or with a cartridge filter unit alone. A schematic of the filtration system is shown in **Fig. 5.23**. The DE filter unit does a majority of the filtering before the fluid arrives at the cartridge filter unit. Because DE is less expensive than cartridge filters, the use of a DE filter with a cartridge filter downstream is more economical than a cartridge filter unit alone. This is especially true if the completion fluid is dirty, which is usually true at some point during the completion or if large volumes of fluid are required, as in the case of gravel packing.

DE filters are not absolute filters, so a wide variety of particle sizes are capable of "bleeding through" the filter. The DE filter packing itself also will bleed through the filter. DE is capable of plugging the formation and is not acid soluble; therefore, a DE filter should always be used with a downstream cartridge filter to stop the DE and provide additional fluid filtration.

Cartridge filter units can use either nominal or absolute filter cartridges. The nominal filters are typically wound elements designed for bulk solids removal using deep bed filtration. The absolute filters have pleated elements that rely on surface filtration to retain specific size particles. Absolute filters are rated on their efficiencies by their beta rating. The beta rating is defined as the ratio of the concentration of a given particle size entering the filter to the concentration of the same size particle exiting the filter. Commonly used filters have beta ratings from 100 to 5,000. The beta rating depends on flow rate. As an example, a filter that will stop a 2-micron particle at 1 gal/min (gpm) might not stop the same particle at 10 gpm. Also, beta ratio depends on the particle size considered. A cartridge will have a high beta ratio (removal efficiency) for large particles, but a lower beta ratio for smaller particles. For most oilfield operations, filters with beta ratings of 1,000 are all that are required because these remove 99.9% of the particulate material from the fluid passed through it. The equation for calculating removal efficiency from the beta ratio is written as

$$Re_x = 100\left(\frac{\beta_x - 1}{\beta_x}\right), \quad\ldots\ldots\ldots\ldots\ldots\ldots\ldots\ldots\ldots\ldots\ldots\ldots\ldots\ldots\ldots\ldots (5.2)$$

where

Re_x = removal efficiency for particle size "x" (percent),
and

β = beta ratio for particle size "x."

Most completion fluids used for gravel packing are filtered to 2 microns with a removal efficiency of 99.9% or better. Care should be taken while filtering to ensure that the pressure differential through the cartridges does not exceed the cartridge manufacturer's recommendation (typically 30 psi); otherwise, collapse of the cartridge and fluid bypass may occur, destroying the filter's efficiency. Filtration of naturally viscous fluids is difficult because of increased pressure drop required to flow a viscous fluid through the cartridge. If polymers are used, they must be thoroughly sheared to remove unhydrated clusters or "fish eyes." These fluids should be filtered after shearing. Occasionally, you may have to deal with extremely dirty fluids. If time permits, it is advisable to allow the dirty fluid to stand undisturbed overnight to allow solids to settle to the bottom of the holding tank. The clean fluid can then be decanted from the top of the tank and filtered without having to deal with the large volume of settled particles. Oil entrained in the completion fluid also can present filtration problems.

5.8.8 Completion and Gravel-Pack Fluids. The normal sources of completion fluids are produced brine, seawater, or commercially mixed clear brines. In addition to being clean, the fluids used in the well completion must be compatible with the formation and formation fluids. Of particular concern is clay swelling. Additionally, the fluid should be compatible (that is, not cause precipitation on mixing) with formation water. The candidate completion fluids should be tested in the laboratory to ensure their compatibility with the formation and formation fluids because an incompatible completion fluid can cause permanent formation damage.

The overriding design criterion for a good completion fluid is the hydrostatic requirements to maintain well control. Fluid density can be controlled by adding several water-soluble salts such as sodium chloride, sodium bromide, potassium chloride, ammonium chloride, calcium chloride, calcium bromide, zinc bromide and lithium bromide. The densities of these fluids range from 8.33 to as high as about 20 lbm/gal, values that are comparable with the densities of drilling muds. All fluids have their advantages and disadvantages, which depend on the density of the fluid required. High density fluids are expensive.

The fluids used for gravel packing can be water or oil based. The water-based fluids are usually the most desirable, have a higher density, and are more flexible to use than the oil-based systems. Because of this, the water-based fluids are more commonly used. The simplest water-based fluid used for gravel packing is the completion brine itself. Crude oil has been used in the past in preference to water because it was cheaper; however, with the increase in the cost of oil, its use has been largely discontinued in preference to the water-based systems. Crude oil is still a valid alternative in extremely water sensitive formations and when small densities are needed; however, oil is inflammable, and extra precautions are needed to prevent spills.

5.8.9 Perforating for Gravel Packing. Perforating consideration for gravel packing is primarily an exercise in selecting the perforating gun and charge configuration that will provide adequate inflow from the reservoir. Remember that the gravel must be placed in the perforation tunnels. If the gravel porosity is about 35%, this equates to filling 65% of the cross-sectional area of the perforations with gravel. Large-diameter perforations, greater than 0.75 in., fired in high-shot density guns, 12 shots/ft or higher, are the desired configuration to provide a high inflow area. The gravel-pack charges have typical penetrations of 8 to 10 in., which is all that is required for these completions. Deep penetration charge designs are ineffective because they produce an insufficient perforation area for gravel packs. They should be avoided except in special situations, such as having to penetrate two strings of casing, etc. Whether the perforating is performed with wireline or tubing-conveyed guns depends on interval length and other factors. Short, one-gun run completions favor the wireline guns. Intervals with completion lengths greater than 30 ft favor tubing conveyed guns because the entire interval can be perforation underbalanced with a single run of the perforating assembly. Other than these broad guidelines, one should use standard perforating procedures.

5.8.10 Perforation Cleaning. With an impingement pressure approaching 15,000,000 psi, the perforation jet pushes through the casing and cement and into the formation, where it compacts the materials immediately surrounding the perforation. Because the cement and the formation are crystalline, they are compacted. This creates a zone of reduced permeability at the boundary of the perforation that is caused by the high impingement pressure. It is often referred to as the compacted zone. The compacted zone can be up to ½ in. thick and can have a permeability that is substantially less than that of the bulk formation, which can significantly restrict well productivity.

Additionally, the shaped charge creates debris that is deposited in the perforation. The metal from the housing is typically steel and not readily soluble in acid. The liner is usually made of compressed copper that may form a copper slug called a "carrot" after the perforation is created. The carrot may remain inside the hollow carrier and be retrieved, or it could remain in the perforation tunnel or become lodged in the perforation entrance hole in the casing, which is the worst case.

The perforating debris and the compacted zone must be removed to maximize well productivity. Failure to remove the debris and compacted zone can reduce the potential production rate. The methods available for perforation cleaning include acidizing, washing, backsurging, underbalanced perforating, and fracturing. Some recently developed techniques are also available to assist in the operation of cleaning the perforations such as "debris-free" charges. Such charges are not actually debris-free but result in fine-grained material that is acid soluble and easily flowed from the well.

Acidizing. Acidizing perforations involves injecting a predetermined type and volume of acid into the perforations after they have been created to dissolve any acid-soluble material. In most cases, perforating debris is not highly soluble in acid; therefore, acidizing is more effective and better applied when used with other cleaning techniques. Some considerations critical to acidizing are the compatibility of the acid with the formation, the volume of acid being pumped, and the need for uniform placement of the acid into the perforations.

Acid solubility tests should be performed on a formation sample to select the most effective acid. This is important because the acid may actually damage the formation instead stimulating it. The volume of acid to pump is typically determined by the number of perforations and the length of the perforated interval.

Poor placement of acid produces variable and inconsistent results, possibly leading to a decrease in productivity. Ideally, each perforation would receive an equal volume of acid. In reality, the acid tends to flow into the perforations that are unrestricted and do not especially need cleaning. Meanwhile, other perforations that do need cleaning take in little or no acid. To achieve uniform placement of acid into the perforations, use an acid "diverter" to attempt to divert acid from the permeable perforations to the damaged perforations. The usual technique involves pumping several stages of acid separated by diverter slurries consisting of viscous gel and gravel-pack sand. The diverter will flow into the most permeable perforations and fill them with gravel-pack sand. The combination of gravel-pack sand and the high viscosity of the gel reduce the ability of the perforation to accept fluid. The next acid stage should then flow into the other, more resistive perforations, allowing for a more uniform treatment. This technique is referred to as a "staged acid treatment" or an "acid prepack." It can be performed immediately after underbalanced tubing-conveyed perforating (for best results) or just before performing the gravel pack. This will be reviewed further in the discussion on prepacking perforations.

5.8.11 Washing. The goal of washing is to establish communication between several sets of perforations to effectively remove the perforation debris and compacted zone from the well.

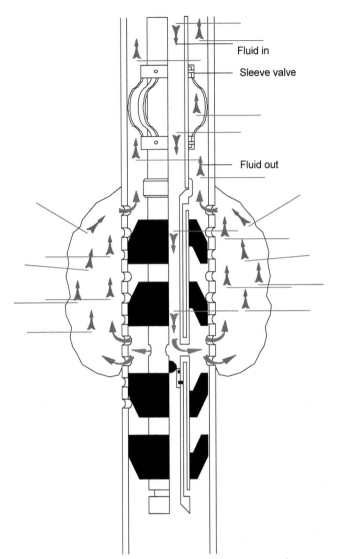

Fig. 5.24—Washing perforations with wash tool.[1]

Unfortunately, perforation washing is commonly performed incorrectly because rig crews may not take time to follow correct procedures. Washing perforations involves running an opposing cup-type tool or pinpoint packers into the well after perforating. The cup tool seals on the inside of the casing and allows a circulation path through the tool and out ports located between the opposing cups. The tool's cup spacing is usually about 1 ft to focus the washing operation over a short interval. The washing consists of pumping filtered, unviscosified completion fluid at the largest rate possible without breaking down the perforations, as **Fig. 5.24** illustrates. Washing should be conducted at the smallest acceptable fluid overbalance.

5.8.12 Backsurging. Backsurging is the running of a surge tool in the well after perforating. The tool has a chamber that contains air at atmospheric pressure. A packer is set, and the lower valve to the chamber is opened to expose the formation to atmospheric pressure, thereby surging the perforation to expel damage. Unfortunately, the technique does not open all plugged perforations and may require several runs in the well to achieve results. Each run is a special trip.

5.8.13 Underbalanced Tubing Conveyed Perforating. Underbalanced-tubing-conveyed perforating is popular for cleaning perforations. It is similar to backsurging but only requires a single trip in that the desired underbalance is set by the amount of fluid in the work string. Upon gun detonation, the formation is immediately surged in proportion to the amount of underbalance. General guidelines for underbalance in unconsolidated sandstone reservoirs are to use 500 psi for oil wells and 1,000 psi for gas wells. In a given field, trial-and-error testing can establish the best underbalance for site-specific conditions.

5.8.14 Fracturing. A relatively new technique is to bypass perforating damage instead of using a cleaning or removal technique. Extreme overbalance perforating is used to perforate and then fracture the formation. The process has been used primarily on consolidated formations with relatively large compressive strengths.

   Frac packing and water fracs also have been successfully used in unconsolidated formations to bypass perforating, drilling, and cementing damage. This procedure is discussed later.

5.8.15 Fluid Loss Control. Fluid loss control is a common consideration when completing unconsolidated formations with a gravel pack, especially in high-permeability formations. In addition to the potential formation damage caused by fluid loss, there is particular anxiety when expensive fluids are involved or when completion fluid reserves are low. The amount of fluid loss that can be tolerated tends to be site-specific, but when losses exceed about 30 bbl/hr, there is concern. Loss rates of 20 to 40 bbl/hr on an offshore rig that has only 100 bbl of reserve fluid is serious. In the latter situation, the rig has about 3 to 4 hours before it either runs out of fluid or has to replenish its supply. Another problematic situation is when fluid losses are high and the completion brine is costly. Hence, managing and minimizing fluid losses can be a major problem.

   The normal methods for controlling fluid loss include: reduced hydrostatic pressure, viscous polymer gels, graded solid particles, and mechanical means. The type of fluid-loss control that is recommended often depends on what phase of the completion process is being executed. Because completion begins as soon as the bit enters the pay and continues through the running of production tubing, excessive fluid loss may become an issue while drilling the reservoir, during openhole gravel packing (especially for a highly deviated hole), immediately after perforating, after prepacking, and after gravel packing.

   When selecting a fluid-loss control technique, the current condition of the well, operations still needing completion, and available remedial techniques for elimination of the deleterious effects of fluid loss control must all be considered. These considerations may lead to different fluid-loss control techniques being used throughout the completion and must not be taken lightly.

5.9 Gravel Placement Techniques

Gravel packing consists of installing a downhole filter in the well to control the entry of formation material but allow the production of reservoir fluids. The gravel-packed completion is perhaps the most difficult and complex routine completion operation because it consists of many interrelated completion practices. There are two primary objectives for gravel packing a well. First, the annulus between the screen and casing must be packed with gravel. Filling the annulus with properly-sized gravel ensures that the formation sand is not produced to surface. The second objective is to pack each perforation with gravel. Filling the perforations with gravel is the key to obtaining high productivity. In an unconsolidated formation, any perforation that is unfilled with gravel will fill with formation sand and severely restrict productivity from such perforations. The following discussion deals with filling the annulus. Perforation packing is discussed later.

The crossover circulating technique is the most common method used to place the gravel around the screen. The gravel-pack equipment and service tools allow circulating the gravel down the work string above the packer and into the screen/casing annulus below the packer. The returns flow up the washpipe and cross over into the work string/casing annulus. The fluid used to transport the gravel can either leak off to the formation or be circulated or reversed out of the hole through the washpipe (as illustrated in **Fig. 5.25**), depending on the position of the service tools.

A variety of fluids has been used as gravel transport fluids such as brine, oil, diesel, crosslinked gels, clarified xanthum gum (XC) gel, hydroxyethylcellulose (HEC) gel, and foam. The most commonly used fluids have been brine and HEC gel. Gravel packs performed with brine are referred to as water/brine packs or conventional packs. Gravel packs performed with HEC gel transport fluids are referred to as slurry packs, gel, or viscous packs. **Table 5.4** is a comparison of HEC gel and brine characteristics that are important to their use as gravel transport fluids. When using HEC, the gravel is suspended by the gel and settles slowly because of the high fluid viscosity. When using brine as a transport fluid, the gravel settles quickly because of the low viscosity. Hence, higher pump rates may be required to cope with particle settling when brines are used.

5.9.1 Historical Background. The earliest gravel packs were performed in shallow, vertical wells, typically by simply pouring gravel into the tubing/casing annulus and allowing the gravel to settle around a screen. Some screens were even washed into place after the gravel was placed. The technique is still employed in water wells but now is seldom used in oil/gas wells. As equipment and technology improved, gravel packing of oil/gas wells was accomplished by mixing sand in brine and pumping the mixture into the hole. Brine represents the simplest of the transport fluids. Before the early 1960s, brine was the most commonly used gravel-pack fluid because other fluid systems had not been developed at that time.

The early equipment used to mix brine and gravel was inefficient and resulted in the "slugging" of gravel into the hole, as opposed to a consistent brine-to-gravel mix ratio. The brine was seldom filtered, and no specifications were in place to ensure the quality of gravel-pack sand. Overall rig housekeeping was poor, and the perforating techniques available were limited to low-shot density, small-diameter guns that produced entrance-hole diameters that were less than 0.5 in. in diameter. The combination of all these factors resulted in unsatisfactory gravel-pack completions that were commonly damaged.

In the late 1960s, research efforts[9-11] by several companies focused on improving gravel packing. The research efforts culminated in the introduction of viscosified gravel transport fluids, HEC being the fluid of choice. One of the most attractive features of viscous fluids is that it permits the transport of high gravel concentrations (up to 15 lbm/gal). HEC gel provided a reasonably clean medium for transporting the gravel-pack sand, the gel allowed consistent batch mixing, and it protected the gravel from crushing and contamination during pumping. Because of its apparent advantages, HEC fluids rapidly replaced brine as the gravel packing fluid of choice. HEC gels remained the "state-of-the-art" gravel transport fluid for many companies until the early 1990s.

Despite the advances in gravel quality, wellbore cleanliness, fluid filtration, and perforation quality, gravel-packed wells were not, in general, producing as efficiently as theoretically possible. Gravel-pack skins from 20 to 100 were common when gels were used. Also, it became common knowledge that gravel packs performed with gelled fluids commonly produced voids in the packs. HEC was evidently not as nondamaging as originally assumed, and as a consequence, improved shear mixing procedures were developed.[5,12,13] Despite better mixing, damage because of residual gel remained likely. Research also indicated that HEC did not pack perfora-

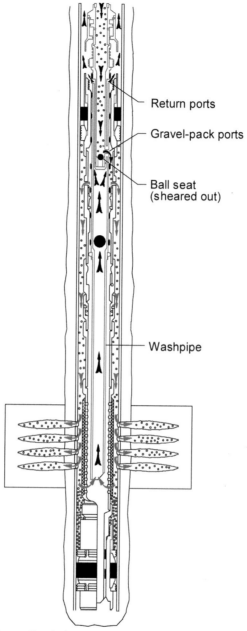

Return ports

Gravel-pack ports

Ball seat
(sheared out)

Washpipe

Fig. 5.25—Flow paths during gravel packing (courtesy of Baker Oil Tools).

tions efficiently in deviated wells with a large interval zone length.[6] Alternatives to HEC, such as crosslinked (XC) polymers and other special gels, were proposed as the ideal gravel-pack fluid but were never completely accepted.

Research[14] and operating data presented in the early 1990s showed that water was a general-purpose gravel transport fluid that produced low-porosity packs that did not contain voids and was capable of efficiently prepacking perforations, provided that fluid loss was acceptable. Improved mixing equipment was developed for handling brine-sand mixtures in water-pack systems. The equipment allowed consistent mixing of gravel in brine and redirected attention

TABLE 5.4—COMPARISON OF HEC AND BRINE GRAVEL-PACK CARRIER FLUIDS		
	HEC Gel	Brine
Fluid viscosity	300–750 cp	1–2 cp
Typical gravel concentration	10–5 lbm/gal	1–3 lbm/gal
Typical pump rate	1–4 bbl/min	4–5 bbl/min
Tell-tale screen used	yes	no

to brine as the gravel transport fluid of choice. Coupled with research data and positive field results, these developments initiated the trend for most of the industry to accept brine as a gravel-pack carrier fluid.[14,15] Although gel represented an improvement in technology at the time and is still applicable for certain well situations, brine is the most widely used gravel-pack fluid in the industry today. However, gelled fluids are used extensively for frac packing.

Continued evolution of procedures saw the introduction of DE filtration systems (circa 1980) that were able to filter large quantities of brine quickly at a reasonable cost. Coupled with the increasing use of clear brine, DE filtration systems resulted in substantially cleaner wellbores than previously had been possible.

In 1986, the API introduced specifications for gravel-pack sand (API *RP58, Testing Sand Used in Gravel-Packing Techniques*) that established rigorous requirements.[5] The API specifications called for gravel, sieved to strict tolerances with low crush resistance and acid solubility, that was capable of passing through pumping equipment with little or no degradation. Finally, in the early 1980s, underbalanced-tubing-conveyed perforating became a common and well-established technique for achieving the high-shot density, large-hole diameter, clean perforations required for maximum gravel-packed well productivity. All of these improvements, developments, and changes significantly improved the gravel-packing systems that are now offered on a routine service.

5.9.2 Physical Model Observations. Field-scale model studies[14] with water and gelled transport fluids in a 22-ft-long clear plastic gravel-pack model revealed many significant facts concerning gravel placement. The model simulated a 7-in. casing with a 2⅜-in. screen that had a perforation shot density from 0 to 12 shots/ft. The model could be rotated to simulate well deviations from 0 to 110° from vertical. The following discussion deals primarily with cased-hole completions. It also applies to openhole completions for gravel packing the annulus between the screen and the open hole.

Brine Transport Fluids. Simulations with brine transport fluids were performed at deviations from 0 to 110°. The gravel-packing sequence at well deviations from 0 to 45° were highly controlled by gravity and packed from the bottom of the well upwards, as **Fig. 5.26** portrays. As long as finite leakoff occurred through the perforations, they were packed with gravel. The gravel did not begin filling the perforation tunnels until the level of the gravel in the annulus reached the perforation entrance. At this point, the gravel would divert into the perforations (if the perforation was experiencing leakoff) and completely pack the perforation as the annular pack level rose. The result was a tight annular pack that completely prepacked the perforations experiencing leakoff. Well deviations of 45 to 60° from vertical were also completely packed, but the packing began on the low side of the hole and filled the annulus with a series of dunes propagated up and down the length of the model. At about 60° well deviation, the gravel is in transition between falling to the bottom of the interval or remaining at the top of the interval on the low side of the hole. As a consequence, the packing is random, as shown in **Fig. 5.27**. The reason for this behavior is that at about 60°, it represents the complement of the angle of repose for gravel that is about 28°, as illustrated in **Fig. 5.28**.

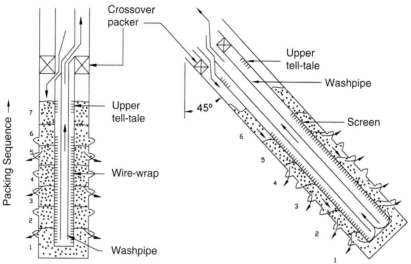

Fig. 5.26—Packing sequence with brine carrier fluids in wells less than 45°.[14]

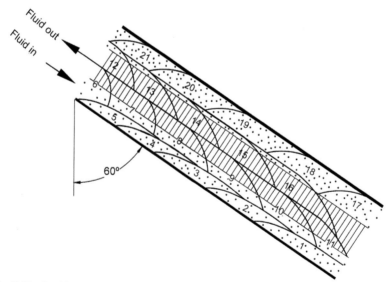

Fig. 5.27—Packing sequence with brine carrier fluids in wells at 60° deviation.[14]

As the well deviation exceeds 60°, a gravel dune forms initially at the top of the completion interval and is propagated sequentially downwards from the top to the bottom of the completion interval. This occurs because the angle of repose has been exceeded, and gravity becomes a more dominant force that causes a gravel dune to form in the completion interval. To ensure propagation of the dune, the ratio of the washpipe OD to the screen ID must be larger than 0.70. The purpose of the large-diameter washpipe is to divert flow from the annulus between the washpipe and the screen to the annulus outside the screen. Testing and field experience has confirmed that the ideal ratio is probably in the range of 0.70 to 0.80. Additionally, the return flow rate to the cross-sectional area ratio (between the screen and the casing) should

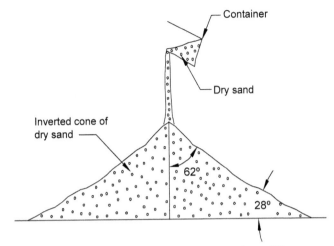

Fig. 5.28—Angle of repose for gravel-pack sand.[14]

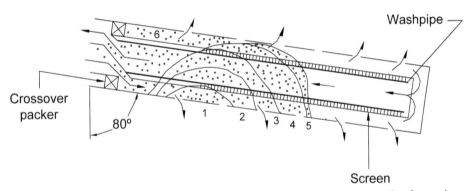

Fig. 5.29—Failed packing sequence with brine carrier fluid in a high-angle well, resulting from a low-rate and small-diameter washpipe.[14]

be at least 1 ft/sec to supply sufficient transport velocity. This is referred to as the superficial velocity. If the ratio of washpipe OD to screen ID is too small, excess fluid will divert into in the annulus between the screen and the washpipe and the gravel dune will stall high in the completion interval, resulting in a "premature sandout" (see **Fig. 5.29**). **Fig. 5.30** shows the effect of washpipe to screen diameter ratios on gravel placement efficiency. If the ratio of washpipe OD to screen ID is too large, sticking the washpipe is a concern, as well as potentially high pump pressures during the final stages of gravel placement. A schematic of the gravel packing process, in wells greater than 60° when a large diameter washpipe is used, is illustrated in **Fig. 5.31**. This figure shows the dune deposited and propagated along the low side of the hole (sequences 1 to 10) until it reaches the end of the completion interval (alpha wave). At this point a secondary deposition (beta wave) backfills and packs the volume above the alpha wave to complete the gravel pack.

Gel Transport Fluids. Simulations with gel transport fluids were also performed at the same well deviations previously discussed. The packing mechanisms with gel were more complex than with brine because viscous forces were stronger. At 0 to 45°, the high viscosity of the gel allows radial packing around the gravel-pack screen and node buildup at the perforations. At screen connections, voids were commonly observed. But the voids where typically

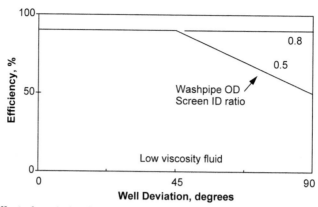

Fig. 5.30—Effect of washpipe OD to screen ID ratios on gravel placement efficiency.[14]

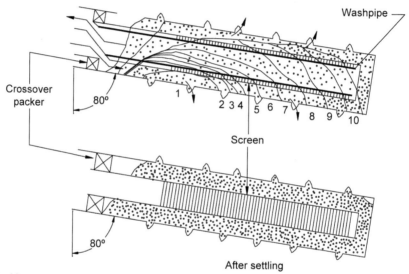

Fig. 5.31—Packing sequence with brine carrier fluid in a high-angle well using a high-rate and large-diameter washpipe.[14]

filled by gravel settling after a few hours, provided that the well deviation was less than about 60°. As with brine, perforation packing was complete but occurred only if the perforation experienced fluid leakoff. At deviations greater than 60°, voids persisted in areas where incomplete slurry dehydration occurred (opposite screen joint connections or unperforated sections of the interval). Unlike the lower deviation simulations, gravel pack, settling at deviations greater than 60°, resulted in voids along the top of the gravel pack, as **Fig. 5.32** shows. When the voids occurred opposite the perforations, gravel-pack sand placed in the perforations would be unloaded into the voids when production occurred. Under actual conditions, these phenomena result in either sand production or localized filling of the perforation tunnels with formation sand that will severely restrict productivity. Observations were that gravel packing with brine produces a pack with a porosity of about 37%. The porosity of gel packs is about 42% and can be higher if there are voids.

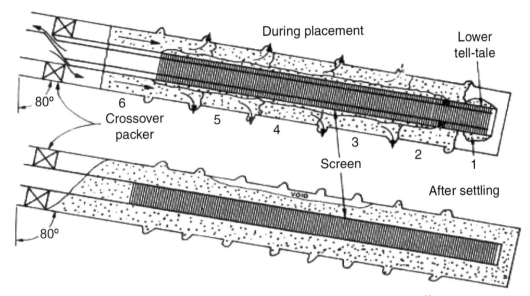

Fig. 5.32—Gravel-pack sequence with viscous fluids showing voids.[14]

Transport Fluid Summary. Based on the results of laboratory testing and field experience, brine exhibits more complete packing of the perforations and annulus under a wide variety of well conditions and is considered by most to be a general-purpose gravel-pack fluid. Gel transport fluids should be limited to use in wells with deviations less than 45° and gross zone lengths less than 50 ft in length.

5.9.3 Field Results. The main objective of annular gravel placement is to effectively pack the annulus between the screen and the casing or the open hole. For cased-hole completions, an added objective is to pack the perforations with gravel because the latter significantly improves well productivity and longevity. In addition to perforation packing, the quality of the pack in the screen/casing annulus is important, regardless of whether the well is completed cased or openhole. Gravel-pack evaluation logs have demonstrated the superiority of brines over gels in that lower pack porosities are achieved. Brine packs are also more uniform and do not contain voids common with gels that have been verified by post-gravel-pack evaluation logs.

5.9.4 Gravel Packing With Shunts. Because viscous fluids are still used for gravel packing, particularly in frac-pack applications, there is concern about void formation in the annular gravel pack. A shunt system has been developed that may help solve the problems associated with these high-viscosity fluids (voids).[16] The shunts are actually channels or conduits that are designed to transport gravel through the shunt when bridges are formed in the annulus. **Fig. 5.33** is an example of a shunt activating when a bridge forms in the annulus. Note that the shunt (there can be a single or multiple shunt tubes) is attached to the outside of the screen.

The shunt can be run either in cased- or openhole configurations. For cased-hole applications, the shunt screens are usually run unprotected, but in openhole horizontals, an outer shroud is added to protect the shunts when running in the hole. The shroud may also provide centralization for openhole completions. The horizontal shunt-screen gravel packs are commonly performed in the squeeze mode (no returns), and fracturing is believed to be occurring during the packing process. Reports are that when gravel packing with shunt screens up to

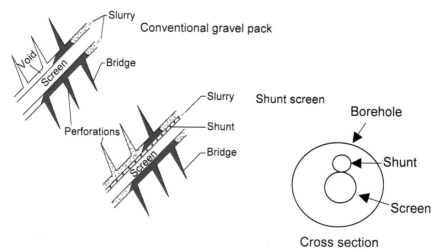

Fig. 5.33—Gravel packing with viscous fluids with and without shunts.

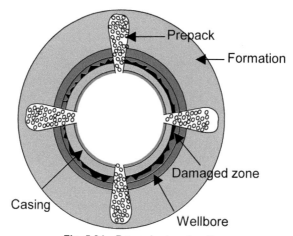

Fig. 5.34—Prepacked perforations.

35%, excess gravel is pumped over the hole volume. Whether this means that the excess packed washouts occurred because of fracturing is not clear.

The burden of the additional hardware is increased weight, drag, and dimensional concerns; this limits the diameter of the hole in which it can be run. For example, for a 4-in. pipe-base screen, a 7-in. shroud encases the screen and the shunts. Hence, the minimum hole diameter in which the screen assembly can be run is 8.5 in. For smaller diameters such as 6.125 in., which is probably the most common horizontal openhole diameter, a 4.5- to 5-in. shroud would be required. For this shroud diameter, the screen diameter (pipe base) would probably have no more than 2 in.—meaning the washpipe and shunt dimensions are also reduced. Hence, washpipe and shunt friction pressure limit the length of the lateral that can be gravel packed for the small hole sizes.

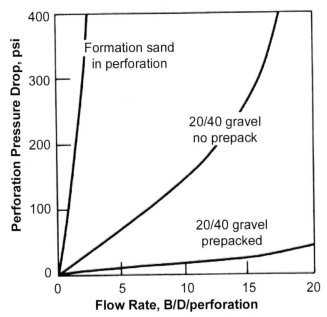

Fig. 5.35—Effect of perforation packing (0.5-in. perforation on pressure loss).[1]

TABLE 5.5—PRESSURE LOSSES IN A PACKED PERFORATION (FORMATION SAND, 1,000 md)			
	Pressure Drop, psi		
Flow Rate, B/D/Perforation	⅜-in. Diameter Perforation	½-in. Diameter Perforation	¾-in. Diameter Perforation
1	450	190	64
10	27,760	9,280	2,091

5.10 Prepacking the Perforations

5.10.1 Cased-Hole Gravel Packs. Gravel packing cased-hole completions in vertical and deviated wells are more common than openhole completions, particularly in shaley reservoirs. Reasons for this are several-fold: cased-hole completions are the norm in almost any development because the reservoir is usually easier to manage, so remedial operations are simplified; wellbore stability issues are minimal; and if multiple intervals are involved, openhole completions will not provide the necessary isolation.

However, cased-hole gravel packs have an important requirement that is easily overlooked. The perforations must be prepacked with gravel if productivity and completion longevity is desired.[1] Not until the late 1980s was the importance of prepacking fully appreciated. The illustration shown in **Fig. 5.34** is an example of prepacked perforations. Note that the gravel is packed through each perforation and into the perforation tunnel beyond the cement sheath. **Fig. 5.35** shows the benefit of prepacking. This information was taken from large-scale laboratory testing studies that illustrated the pressure drop across perforations filled with 1-darcy formation sand, 20:40 gravel and 20:40, gravel that was prepacked in the perforations.[1] **Tables 5.5 and 5.6** provide additional information. The lowest pressure drop through the perforations oc-

Flow Rate, B/D/Perforation	⅜-in. Diameter Perforation	½-in. Diameter Perforation	¾-in. Diameter Perforation
1	2	1	0.4
10	55	21	6
25	272	99	25

TABLE 5.6—PRESSURE LOSSES IN A PACKED PERFORATION (20:40 GRAVEL, 119,000 md) / Pressure Drop, psi

TABLE 5.7—GRAVEL-PACK PRODUCTIVITY FROM MIOCENE RESERVOIRS, VENUZUELA[1]

	Productivity Index, BOPD, psi	
	Interval 1	Interval 2
Openhole gravel pack	48.4 (14)	6.4 (13)
Gun perforated casing	36.6 (20)	5.2 (14)
Cased-hole gravel pack (with prepack)	12.9 (19)	3.2 (12)
Cased-hole gravel pack (without prepack)	4.0 (14)	1.7 (3)

( ) = Number of wells

curs when they are prepacked. Lower pressure losses across the perforation not only affect flow from the reservoir, but the larger wellbore pressure provides additional inflow pressure to lift fluids to the surface. Cased-hole gravel packs that have not been prepacked are usually damaged. There is no remedial treatment that can remove the damage (a frac pack can bypass the damage), leading to a well that will be permanently restricted unless a workover is performed to prepack the completions and complete the well properly. **Table 5.7** verifies this scenario with field data and shows the superiority of wells that were prepacked.

Prepacking can be defined as any method that intentionally places gravel into the perforation tunnels. Filling of perforation tunnels can be accomplished either with a dedicated operation before performing the gravel pack or simultaneously with it. The technique used is normally dictated by well parameters, such as excessive fluid loss, an extended rathole area, reservoir acid sensitivity, zone length, etc. An additional concern that must be addressed is the question of what transport fluid to use for the prepacking operation. Regardless of the technique selected, to effectively pack the perforations, one critical condition must be met: there must be fluid loss through the perforation. **Fig. 5.36** shows the effects of the leakoff rate on the amount of gravel prepacked. Data also show that the well deviation is not a factor on the amount of gravel placed.

5.10.2 Choice of Fluids. Provided that there is leakoff, any fluid can be used. The packing sequences, 1 to 7, when brine and viscous fluids are used, are shown in **Figs. 5.37 and 5.38**. The two are slightly different because of the viscosity of the fluid. Viscous fluids suspend and transport the gravel completely to the end of the perforation tunnel and then pack back toward the entrance of the perforation. Note the node at the entrance of the perforation caused by viscous forces in Fig. 5.37. With brine, the gravel is initially deposited at the entrance of the perforation, and subsequent packing takes place over the top of the dune until it reaches the

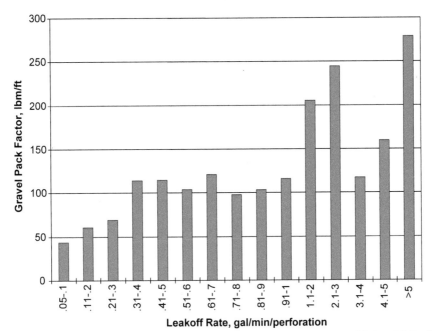

Fig. 5.36—Effect of leakoff rate to perforation filling efficiency (courtesy of Baker Oil Tools).

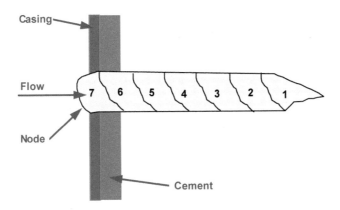

Fig. 5.37—Perforation filling with viscous transport fluid.[14]

end of the perforation. The last volume to be prepacked is that over the dune. The obvious question at this point is which fluid should be used, or which is the best? The question has many operating implications. However, field data from prepacking operations, conducted at matrix rates, show that brines are superior because they pack more gravel.

5.10.3 Prepacking Below Fracture Pressure. To prepack below fracture pressure, the perforations must be clean and contain no debris. There must be leakoff into the formation. A void outside the perforation is desirable.

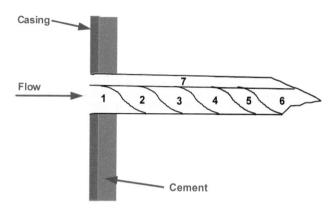

Fig. 5.38—Perforation filling with brine transport fluid.[14]

Viscous Fluid Gravel Packs. These completions consist of gravel packing with viscous gels —slurry packs in which there is no dedicated procedure to prepack the perforations. Any prepacking that occurs is simultaneous with the gravel pack. Example field results using this approach (**Fig. 5.39a**[17]) for a project in southeast Asia reflect the performance in terms of the skin factors measured after completion.[18] Some wells performed exceptionally well (i.e., the skin factor was small), while others were disappointing. Completion success was inconsistent. The average of the data indicated a skin factor of about 24 or a flow efficiency of 25%, which is common for gel packs. Whether the problem with well performance was a lack of prepacking or damage caused by other factors is not known. Acidizing is probably the only alternative for restoring production for this example, but it will never restore reservoir capacity if the perforations are not prepacked.

Acid Prepacking. Acid prepacking has been used to improve productivity. A critical aspect of a successful damage removal procedure is that the acid must come into contact with the entire interval. In addition, it has been commonly thought that contact time must be sufficient to allow all of the damage to be dissolved. With these assumptions, during the mid-1980s, acid prepacking quickly evolved into a process in which a diverted acid treatment was pumped at a low rate. Several studies indicated that one of the most effective diverters for acid prepacking is to carry relatively small quantities of sand in an HEC gel. While this combination did provide good diversion, the well test results, shown in Fig. 5.39b, tended to be inconsistent. Poor perforation filling from injecting a sand/gel slurry into the perforations at a low rate, coupled with formation damage, resulting from the use of HEC, are the most likely causes for the elevated skins. The detrimental effects of questionable perforation filling can easily overpower any benefit obtained from using the acid.

Dedicated Prepack Operations. High matrix injection rates and the use of nonviscous transport fluids are two techniques that have been demonstrated to improve perforation filling. The traditional acid prepacking techniques violate both of these conditions. If the perforation filling is indeed critical for cased-hole gravel packs, completion methods that focus on filling perforations should prove superior to those that sacrifice perforation filling for damage removal. **Fig. 5.40** illustrates this point. Here the skin factors from 55 Gulf of Mexico wells[19] are shown, 42 of which were prepacked at matrix rates with a 20 lbm/1,000 gal HEC (slickwater) fluid. Typical prepack volumes were about 40 lbm/ft. An annular brine gravel pack followed prepacking. The remaining wells were completed with a water prepack and an annular brine pack. The wells completed with the gel prepack required post-gravel-pack acid to achieve the perfor-

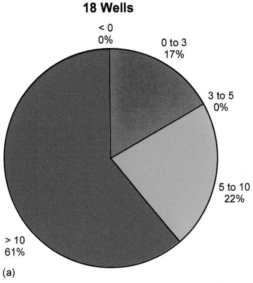

18 Wells

< 0
0%

0 to 3
17%

3 to 5
0%

5 to 10
22%

> 10
61%

(a)

Fig. 5.39a—Distribution of gel-pack skins.[16]

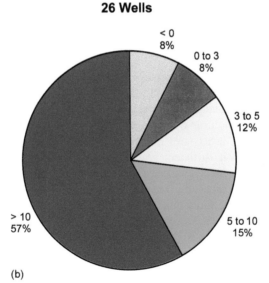

26 Wells

< 0
8%

0 to 3
8%

3 to 5
12%

5 to 10
15%

> 10
57%

(b)

Fig. 5.39b—Distribution of conventional acid prepack skins.[16]

mance reported in Fig. 5.40. However, the transport fluid was able to easily leak off to the formation, and high injection rates were used to enhance placement of gravel in the perforation tunnels. The data presented indicate that not only are the average skin factors reduced compared to slurry packing and acid prepacking (Figs. 5.39b and 5.40), but the overall consistency was also improved (especially for high-permeability thick formations). These data demonstrate that when prepacking below fracture pressure, it is more important to ensure that as many perforations as possible are completely filled with gravel-pack sand than for the damage to be

55 Wells

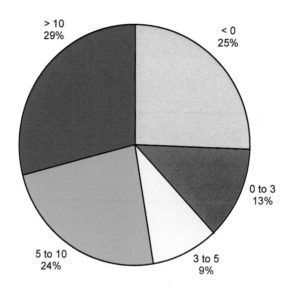

Fig. 5.40—Distribution of dedicated brine-pack skins.[16]

removed. However, it must be remembered that improved well performance will result if damage can be effectively removed without jeopardizing the filling of the perforations.

5.10.4 Prepacking Above Fracture Pressure. One of the main detriments to prepacking below fracture pressure is that gravel can only be placed into voids created during underbalanced perforating or perforation cleanup. If the amount of penetration into the formation does not extend completely through the near-wellbore damaged zone, restricted well productivity results. To overcome this difficulty, it becomes necessary to remove the damage with acid. This is not always easily accomplished if sufficient gravel has not been prepacked. Another technique to eliminate the effects of the damaged zone is to bypass it rather than to attempt to remove it. This is accomplished by hydraulically inducing a fracture in which the orientation is normal to the least principal stress in the formation.

Techniques available to create these fractures include brine fracturing or a frac pack. To allow frac packing and water fracs to be distinguished, a description of these techniques is discussed next.

Frac Pack. A fracture with a length of about 100 ft can be created with a viscous transport fluid, but typical lengths are usually shorter. High pump rates are typically used (15 to 20 bbl/min), with proppant concentration increasing from 12 to 15 lbm/gal. The total amount of gravel pumped is typically in excess of 1,000 lbm/ft. Horsepower requirements may exceed 5,000 hydraulic horsepower (hhp) but are commonly lower.

Water Frac. A fracture with a length between 5 and 15 ft can be created with a low-viscosity (brine) transport fluid. Pump rates are higher than for conventional gravel packing but usually lower than a frac pack. Typical pump rates are in the range of 8 to 12 bbl/min. Proppant loading is held constant between 1 and 2 lbm/gal, and total job size is typically from 100 to 150 lbm/ft. These treatments can be multistaged to further enhance the ability to effectively treat several sand subintervals with a single treatment. Horsepower requirements are typically about 1,000 hhp.

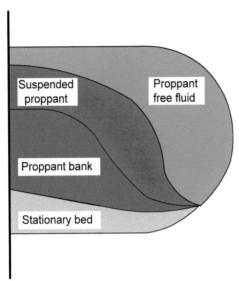

Fig. 5.41—Equilibrium bank formation within a fracture (courtesy of Baker Oil Tools).

Treatment Comparison. From the description of these prepacking treatments, frac packs are significantly larger than water fracs. The frac packs appear to reach much farther out in the reservoir as a consequence of the longer fracture lengths, while the water fracs focus is near the wellbore. The amount of fracture length required is a question that arises. Many propose that bigger is better.[20]

When water is used as the fracturing fluid, short, narrow fractures are created because of the fluid's low viscosity that results in a hydraulic fluid efficiency less than 5%. With frac packs, the fluid efficiency is in the range of about 25% because viscosified fluids reduce leakoff. Also, frac packs are designed for a tip screenout that ceases fracture length extension before the end of the treatment. Continued pumping with high gravel concentrations is intended to increase the width of the fracture to increase fracture conductivity.

The gravel placement geometry in a water-frac treatment forms an equilibrium gravel bank similar to that shown in **Fig. 5.41**. Frac packs pumped in viscous fluids at high gravel concentrations also probably have a small equilibrium gravel bank, but substantially more of the gravel tends to be suspended in the fracture at higher concentrations, which provides for the wide fractures after closure.

Both treatments can be pumped in either a single step or two steps. In the single-step approach, the formation is fractured and subsequently gravel packed in one pumping sequence. In the two-step method, the fracturing and the annular gravel are performed separately. Of the two alternatives, the single-step method is preferred because it is less expensive and time consuming.

There are proponents of both fracture prepacking methods. Some prefer the frac packs because they believe that the longer, wider fractures provide less risk of a low-productivity well. Proponents of water fracs cite lower costs and operations conducted with platform-based equipment as advantages. From the standpoint of productivity improvement (stimulation) in the high-permeability wells, long fractures are not required, and fracture conductivity is more significant than length, provided the fracture extends past the damage.

Probably the best way to compare the benefits of the various prepack treatments is to compare their relative performance based on experience in the field. **Figs. 5.42 and 5.43** compare frac packs and water fracs. Because there is a wide discrepancy in their designs and fracture

23 Wells

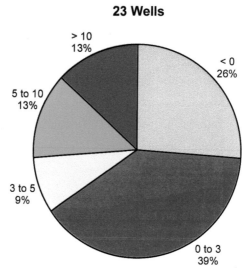

Fig. 5.42—Distribution of water-frac skins.[16]

57 Wells

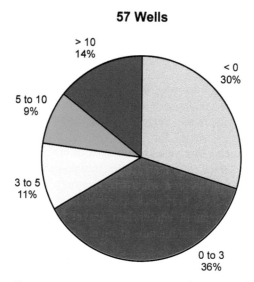

Fig. 5.43—Distribution of frac-pack skins.[16]

geometry, one might think that the frac packs with long, wide fractures would provide a superior result. While there are similarities between the techniques, comparing the results of the frac packs to the water fracs reveals that the skin distributions are almost identical. These data strongly suggest that the main benefit of either treatment is perforation prepacking and damage bypass, regardless of which prepack technique is implemented. Credence to this viewpoint is that neither of the fracture prepack methods produces completions with large negative skin factors that have been achieved with conventional fracturing in consolidated formations. Skin factors below –1 are rare for any cased-hole gravel pack.

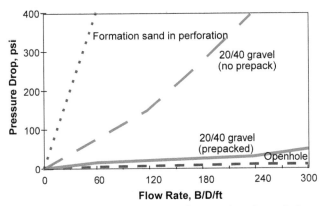

Fig. 5.44—Comparison of pressure drawdowns for cased- and openhole gravel packs.[1]

5.11 Openhole Gravel Packing

Openhole completions provide another opportunity for sand control. Many engineers do not routinely think of performing an openhole completion when confronted with selecting a completion. This is true probably because cased-hole completions are so widely accepted and because they are not familiar with selection criteria and procedures. However, openhole completions provide excellent, high-productivity completions, but they must be applied under the right reservoir conditions. They avoid the difficulties and concerns of perforation packing and reduce the gravel-placement operations to the relatively simple task of packing the screen/openhole annulus. Because openhole gravel packs have no perforation tunnels, formation fluids can converge toward and through the gravel pack radically from 360°, eliminating the high pressure drop associated with linear flow through perforation tunnels. The reduced pressure drop through an openhole gravel pack virtually guarantees that it will be more productive than a cased-hole gravel pack in the same formation, provided they are executed properly. **Fig. 5.44** illustrates the theoretical pressure drops experienced in openhole and cased-hole gravel packs. It reveals that openhole gravel packs result in virtually no additional pressure drop as the formation fluids converge at the wellbore.

5.11.1 Guidelines for Selecting Openhole Gravel-Pack Candidates. Despite their potential for creating high-productivity wells, openhole gravel packs are not suitable for all reservoirs and formations. One disadvantage of the openhole completion (including openhole gravel packs) is the inability to always isolate unwanted water and/or gas production. Unlike cased-hole completions that can be precisely and selectively perforated in the zones of interest, openhole completions sometimes offer less control over fluids (water, oil, and gas) exposed to the wellbore. Furthermore, remedial operations (such as squeeze cementing, plugbacks, or straddle packoffs) to isolate unwanted fluid production can be carried out with a reasonably good chance of success with little to no planning in a cased-hole well. Such remedial operations in an openhole well (with the exception of a plugback) require additional planning to isolate undesirable fluids. With this in mind, openhole completions are best suited for thick reservoir sands rather than multiple sand reservoirs where there is water and/or gas to contend with.

Maintaining borehole stability during drilling and completion is an essential requirement for openhole gravel packs. Concern over the lack of borehole stability is a primary reason that openhole gravel packs are not used more often in unconsolidated, dilatant formations. Unstable boreholes make running of the gravel-pack assembly difficult and may prevent proper gravel placement if the formation flows in around the screen. Fortunately, state-of-the-art drill-in flu-

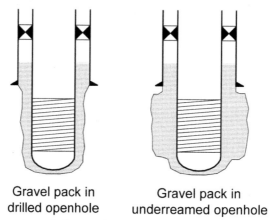

Gravel pack in
drilled openhole

Gravel pack in
underreamed openhole

Fig. 5.45—Top set openhole gravel-pack completion (courtesy of Baker Oil Tools).

ids are usually effective in maintaining borehole stability while performing a horizontal completion in dilatant-type formations.

Openhole gravel packs should be avoided in formations with several sand and shale laminations if the shales are prone to uncontrollable eroding and/or sloughing. During gravel placement, the shale can intermix with the gravel-pack sand, resulting in reduced gravel permeability and impaired well performance. Again, proper drill-in fluid selection can alleviate some of the problems associated with laminated sand and shale formations. The guidelines for selecting openhole gravel-pack candidates are listed next.

- Formations where cased-hole gravel packing has unacceptable productivity.
- Wells where increased productivity is required.
- Reservoirs where long, sustained single-phase hydrocarbon flow is anticipated.
- Situations where workovers for isolating gas or water cannot be accomplished.
- Wells where high water/oil or gas/oil ratios can be tolerated.
- Reservoirs with single uniform sands (avoid multiple sands interspersed with troublesome shale layers or water sands).
- Formations that can be drilled and completed maintaining borehole stability in the completion interval.
- Wells where cased-hole completions are significantly more expensive (i.e., long horizontal wells).

5.11.2 Top-Set Openhole Gravel Pack. The most common type of openhole completion is referred to as "top set," which is illustrated in **Fig. 5.45**. While this figure shows a vertical completion, this discussion is also pertinent to openhole horizontal wells. In this completion, the production casing is set at the top of the completion interval to isolate overlying strata. Once the casing is cemented, the productive formation is drilled to total depth; the hole is cleaned and displaced; and the gravel pack is installed. Critical issues in top-set openhole gravel packs include: selecting the casing seat, drilling the open hole, underreaming if necessary, and cleaning the hole and gravel packing. See the chapter on completion design in this section of the *Handbook*.

5.11.3 Selecting the Casing Seat. Selecting the casing seat at the proper depth can have a significant impact on the success and cost of an openhole completion. Normally, the casing should be set at the top of the reservoir, just barely into the productive interval. If the overlying formation is an unstable or sloughing (heaving) shale, failure to isolate the shale behind casing may cause problems and delays throughout the remainder of the completion. Well logs should be run to ensure that all offending strata have been penetrated and will be cased before running the casing. In some instances, several logging runs may be required as the well is deepened to determine exactly when the casing should be run. In the case of logging while drilling, the casing point can be easily picked without multiple logging runs. Alternatively, the well can be drilled to total depth and logged to determine the appropriate casing depth. Then a sand plug can be placed across the productive interval before cementing the casing.

5.11.4 Drilling the Open Hole. Several options are available for drilling the openhole completion interval. How this is performed and the type of fluids used depend on the mineral and fluid content of the formation (i.e., whether it is sensitive to the drilling and/or completion fluid). Another factor is whether to enlarge the hole by underreaming. The fluid used for drilling the open hole is critical to the success of the completion. The general requirements of an ideal drill-in (or underreaming) fluid, which apply to any openhole completion and are not specific to gravel packs, are compatibility with the reservoir rock and fluids (nondamaging); good suspension properties; low friction loss; low fluid loss; easily controlled density; ready availability; low cost; ease of mixing and handling; nontoxicity; and thin friable filter cakes with low breakout pressure.

While most fluids do not have all of these properties, some, such as calcium carbonate brine fluids, have performed well as drill-in and underreaming fluids. The critical issue is that the drill-in fluid should do minimal irreversible damage to the face of the formation. The solid-laden fluids should quickly form a filter cake to minimize filtrate losses. The filter cake should be easily removable before or after gravel packing. The ease with which it is removed is reflected in a low breakout pressure. Breakout pressure is reached when drawdown pressure, required to initiate production after the formation, has been mudded off with the drill-in fluid. In rare cases, clear brines have been acceptable as nondamaging drill-in fluids. If the open hole is to be underreamed, standard drilling mud may be used as a drill-in fluid, provided that the underreaming operation, using calcium carbonate brine-based systems, removes the mud-invaded, damaged portion of the formation.

5.11.5 Underreaming. Underreaming is the operation of enlarging the hole size below the casing shoe. One reason for underreaming an open hole is to remove damage present in the pilot hole. Underreaming may be unnecessary if the pilot hole is drilled with a nondamaging fluid. The larger-diameter hole also enhances the well productivity slightly, but in most cases, this is insignificant. Underreaming may be performed simply to provide greater clearance between the screen and the open hole. In any event, underreaming should be performed with a nondamaging fluid that keeps the hole stable. Traditional drilling muds should be used only as a last alternative, and damage-removal treatments should be planned before placing the well on production if these muds are used.

Underreaming is usually more of an annoyance than an incremental time, cost, or productivity issue because a cased-hole completion also requires changing over to a clean fluid before perforating. Perforating, of course, is unnecessary. Underreaming and perforating usually offset each other in incremental costs.

In the event that running a liner across the completion interval at a later date is an option to isolate unwanted fluids, underreaming probably should be avoided. The cement sheath in an underreamed hole will be much thicker than normal and will interfere with effective perforating or make perforating operations more difficult. The difficulties are that perforating, or ineffective perforations, will adversely affect gravel packing and, subsequently, will restrict well productivity.

5.11.6 Hole Cleaning. Solids can be drill-in fluids, drill solids, and gravel-pack sand. The importance of cleaning the hole and the filter cake is shown in **Fig. 5.46**. This bar graph is

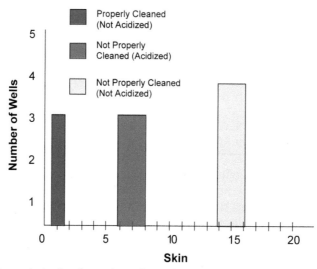

Fig. 5.46—Proper hole cleaning reduces formation damage (courtesy of Baker Oil Tools).

based on field data collected from 10 wells and shows the relationship between completion skin and hole cleaning. This relationship is not too surprising, but what is often overlooked is that once a well is damaged, subsequent acid treatments increase productivity but will not yield an undamaged well. Before running the screen in the hole and gravel packing, it is necessary to remove the drill-in fluid, drill solids from the hole, clean the hole, and scour the filter cake to its dynamic thinness.

5.11.7 Set-Through Openhole Gravel Pack. When accurately setting the casing depth is difficult or secondary pay zones exist above the primary target, set-though openhole completions can be applied. In this type of completion, the casing is run through all formation pay zones and cemented in place. Cased- and openhole well logs are used to determine the exact location of the pay zones behind the casing, and windows are milled (with a nondamaging fluid) opposite the completion interval to create an "openhole" environment. The well can then be gravel packed. Schematics of example set-through-type completions are shown in **Fig. 5.47**. Because of the amount of debris created by milling casing windows, it is recommended that all set-through openhole completions be underreamed to expose a clean, nondamaged formation face. A requirement in applying set-through-type completions is a good cement job. The casing must be securely cemented to facilitate milling operations and maintain alignment between the upper casing and the lower casing sections. Because a sump packer can be used, a set-through gravel pack assembly is basically the same as a cased-hole type. The only exception would be the use of bow-spring-type centralizers in long openhole sections. Set-through-type completions are especially well suited for recompletions in existing wells.

5.11.8 Gravel Packing Openhole Completions. To gravel pack an openhole completion, follow the well preparation and gravel placement guidelines previously discussed.

5.12 Sand Control in Horizontal and Long-Throw Highly-Deviated Wells
Horizontal well completions have been attempted in a myriad of reservoir situations to increase well productivity, improve reservoir management, and access incremental reserves that could not be developed economically with vertical wells. While the first horizontal wells were drilled in competent formations, eventually soft formations were completed horizontally. Practically all horizontal wells drilled in soft formations have been completed openhole. Most of these bore-

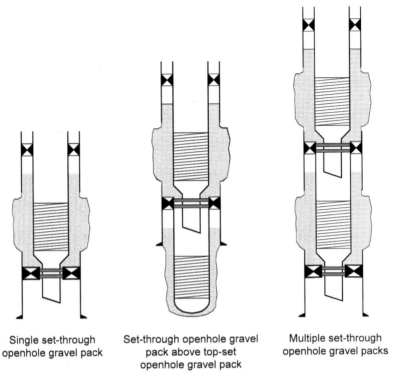

Single set-through
openhole gravel pack

Set-through openhole gravel
pack above top-set
openhole gravel pack

Multiple set-through
openhole gravel packs

Fig. 5.47—Examples of set-through-type openhole gravel-pack completions (courtesy of Baker Oil Tools).

holes did not collapse; however, because many of these completions were in formations, where conventional sand-control applications were practiced, slotted liners and wire-wrapped or prepacked screens were run to prevent hole collapse and sand production because horizontal gravel-pack technology was not yet available.

5.12.1 Stand-Alone Slotted Liner and Screen Completions. The typical procedure for completing horizontal wells with slotted liners and screens is to drill the well to the casing seat, set casing, drill the horizontal section, displace the hole, run the screen, and then produce the well. It is not always this simple, but the intent should be to follow these guidelines.

Sand-control horizontal wells were originally dealt with by using stand-alone slotted liners, screens, and, more recently, proprietary screens. The initial productivity of these completions was usually acceptable, and some were outstanding; however, in most applications, the stand-alone devices either plugged or cut out (eroded) with time. The consequences are either unacceptably low well rates or excessive sand production. The acknowledged stand-alone screen failure rate in the Gulf of Mexico was estimated to be about 25% in 1996. Since that time, numerous additional failures have occurred, and the failure rate has increased substantially. Hence, in most applications, the use of stand-alone screens as retention devices has been disappointing because the stand-alone screen approach forces them to perform as filters (see **Fig. 5.48**). Their use in horizontals confirmed previous stand-alone experience in vertical wells —they plugged. Many screen designs were progressively used to determine if particular designs would improve performance: slotted liners, wire-wrapped screens, prepacked screens, and the high inflow-area proprietary screens. As might be expected, these completions experienced a wide range of reservoir situations. Some stand-alone applications have performed exceptionally well. The exceptional wells (mainly in the North Sea) had formation permeabilities in the

Plugging with poorly sorted material   **Bridging with well sorted material**

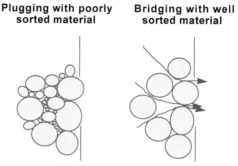

Fig. 5.48—Screens and slotted liners without gravel packing (courtesy of Baker Oil Tools).

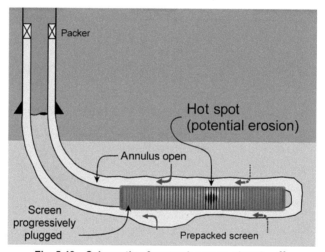

Fig. 5.49—Schematic of prepack screen plugging.[20]

range of 10 to 12 darcy and were well sorted. Experience in the Gulf of Mexico with stand-alone screen completions has been disappointing; the failure rate from these completions has been well over 70% as of 2000.

In many horizontal wells where stand-alone screens have been used, there are implications that the formation does not collapse around the screen. When this happens, there is an open annulus that serves as a conduit for fluid and particulate transport along the entire length of the screen. There are many examples in which a stand-alone screen completion produced extremely well for a period of time and, then, abruptly lost productivity. The screens appear to be progressively plugging; however, because of the high flow capacity per foot of screen, a short section of unplugged screen can handle enormous flow rates. When the last few increments of screen plug, either production ceases or the screen erodes. **Fig. 5.49** displays an example.

To combat these problems, technology has been developed to gravel pack horizontal wells because gravel packing can sustain productivity. Gravel packing has always been the state-of-the-art technology for vertical wells. Gravel-pack technology was not available for horizontal wells until 1995, but its acceptance has been steadily increasing and is now the preferred technique. In this service, the screen functions as a gravel-retention device, and the gravel placed around the screen fills and stabilizes the borehole. The streamlines into the screen are now normal because the annulus between the screen and the open hole is filled with gravel, as **Fig. 5.50** suggests. The result is sustained productivity.

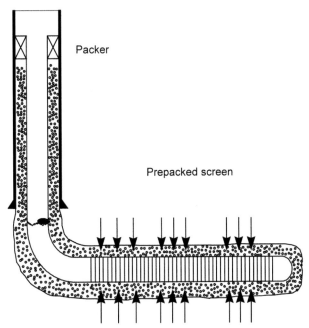

Fig. 5.50—Horizontal openhole gravel-pack completion (courtesy of Baker Oil Tools).

TABLE 5.8—COMPARISON OF ACTIVE AND FAILED SAND EXCLUDING HORIZONTAL COMPLETIONS			
Well Description	Total Wells	Active Wells	Failed Wells
Job count	43	28	15
Initial screen drawdown, psi	679	545	875

5.12.2 Horizontal Gravel Packing. Gravel packing offers another option for completing a horizontal well when sand production represents a problem. The original perception was that technology was not available for gravel packing long, horizontal completions, and other alternatives, such as stand-alone screens, had to suffice. This is contrary to the fact that the performance of stand-alone screens had been unacceptable in conventional wells. One of the most disturbing examples, portrayed in **Table 5.8**, shows failure statistics and average pressure drops across 43 stand-alone screen completions in horizontal wells in the Gulf of Mexico. Of these, 15 (35%) were classified as failures, but the remaining active wells are producing at an average pressure drop of 545 psi. Taken from the perspective of the flow capacities of screens that were previously discussed, the remaining wells, while still producing and not reported as failures, are also plugged.

Horizontal gravel-pack technology was developed[21] in the mid-1990s. Studies were performed in a field-scale model that was 1,500 ft long and instrumented with data acquisition; they also contained visual observations of the packing process through high-strength plastic sections in the model. A typical plot of the location of the alpha and beta waves (see the section on gravel placement techniques), as a function of time for a horizontal gravel pack, is illustrated in **Fig. 5.51**. The figure demonstrates that the entire 1,500-ft model was packed with

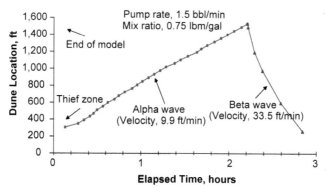

Fig. 5.51—Gravel dune location (alpha-beta wave).[20]

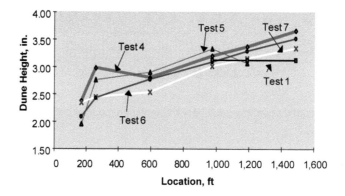

Fig. 5.52—Dune height in a wellbore.[20]

gravel. Testing clearly revealed that the height of the alpha wave was not constant with pack length, as had been implied from studies conducted in short models. Instead, the height of the alpha wave was inclined upward from the heel to the toe of the model as **Fig. 5.52** illustrates. The reason for the inclination is a result of fluid loss that reduces the annular flow velocity and increases the gravel concentration, thereby reducing the gravel transport efficiency. The consequence was an increase in the alpha-wave dune height with length. Having this data provided valuable information for designing horizontal gravel packs. If the top of the borehole interferes with deposition over the top of the alpha wave, deposition stalls, and beta-wave deposition begins at the stall location (**Fig. 5.53**). To avoid a premature stall, the superficial annular velocity must be maintained above 1 ft/sec, based on return flow through the washpipe. The superficial velocity is defined as the ratio of the return flow rate through the washpipe to the annular area between the washpipe and the wellbore. Provided that the design of the gravel pack is correct and a superficial velocity of 1 ft/sec is maintained, gravel packing a long horizontal gravel pack can be performed with routine procedures. Gravel deposition (alpha-beta wave) will proceed to the toe of the well, as **Fig. 5.54** shows.

Horizontal gravel designs are available that utilize the concept illustrated in **Fig. 5.55**, which shows pressure plotted as a function of pump rate. The fracture pressure is identified, and a treating pressure is shown. Note that at low rates, there is insufficient transport to initiate alpha-wave transport, but at slightly higher pump rates, the alpha wave will prematurely stall. However, at an acceptable pump rate, the entire alpha-beta wave deposition can be performed

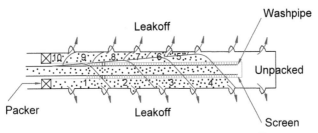

Fig. 5.53—Horizontal gravel pack (partial).[20]

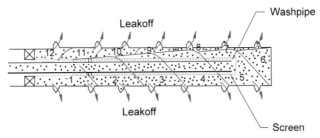

Fig. 5.54—Horizontal gravel pack (complete pack).[20]

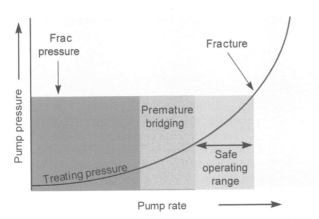

Fig. 5.55—Horizontal gravel-pack design criteria.[20]

to complete the gravel pack without fracturing the formation. Fracturing is manifest by a reduction in return through the wash pump and will stall the transport process.

5.12.3 Field Results. As of the year 2001, over 400 horizontal gravel packs have been performed. Most of these completions had horizontal lengths of 1,500 to 2,000 ft. The longest horizontal gravel pack performed as of mid-2001 has been 7,000 ft. The volume of gravel pack in these completions is typically 20 to 30% greater than the theoretical volume, indicating that the annulus is completely filled with gravel. The pack volume being greater than 100% is accounted for by hole irregularities that are larger than the bit diameter. Similar experience has been noted in vertical openhole gravel packs. In several applications of this technology, gravel packs were run behind failed stand-alone screen completions that lost productivity. After the screen was removed and the hole was displaced, new equipment was run, and the well was gravel packed. The performance of the horizontal gravel packs has demonstrated that they maintain productivity compared to the stand-alone screen experience.

Nomenclature

$$C_\mu = \text{sorting factor or uniformity coefficient}$$
$$d_{40} = \text{formation sand diameter, 40 percentile}$$
$$d_{50} = \text{formation sand diameter, 50 percentile}$$
$$d_{90} = \text{formation sand diameter, 90 percentile}$$
$$d = \text{formation sand diameter}$$
$$D_{50} = \text{median grain size of the gravel-pack sand}$$
$$D = \text{gravel diameter}$$
$$Re_x = \text{removal efficiency for particle size "x" (percent)}$$
$$\beta = \text{beta ratio for particle size "x"}$$

References

1. Penberthy, W.L. Jr. and Shaughnessy, C.M.: *Sand Control,* Monograph Series, SPE, Richardson, Texas (1992) **1,** 11–17.
2. Hollabough, G.S. and Dees, J.M.: "Propellant Gas Fracture Stimulation of a Horizontal Austin Chalk Wellbore," paper SPE 26584 presented at the 1993 SPE Annual Technical Conference and Exhibition, Houston, 3–6 October.
3. Dees, J.M. and Handren, J.M.: "A New Method of Overbalanced Perforating and Surging of Resin for Sand Control," *JPT* (May 1994) 431.
4. Saucier, R.J.: "Considerations in Gravel-Pack Design," *JPT* (February 1974) 205.
5. *RP 58, Recommended Practice for Testing Sand Used in Gravel Packing Operations,* first edition, API, Washington DC (1986).
6. Sparlin, D.D.: "Sand and Gravel—A Study of Their Permeabilities," paper SPE 4772 presented at the 1974 SPE International Symposium on Formation Damage Control, New Orleans, 7–8 February.
7. Gurley, D.G., Copeland, C.T., and Hendrick, J.O. Jr.: "Design, Plan, and Execution of Gravel-Pack Operations for Maximum Productivity," *JPT* (October 1977) 1259.
8. Cocales, B.: "Optimizing Materials for Better Gravel Packs," *World Oil* (December 1992) 73.
9. Sparlin, D.: "Fight Sand With Sand—A Realistic Approach to Gravel Packing," paper SPE 2649 presented at the 1969 SPE Annual Meeting, Denver, 28 September–1 October.
10. Lybarger, J.H., Scheuerman, R.F., and Willard, R.O.: "Water-Base, Viscous Gravel-Pack System Results in High Productivity in Gulf Coast Completions," paper SPE 4774 presented at the 1974 SPE International Symposium on Formation Damage Control, New Orleans, 7–8 February.
11. Novotny, R.J. and Matson, R.P.: "Laboratory Observations of Gravel Placement Techniques," paper SPE 5659 presented at the 1975 SPE Annual Meeting, Dallas, 28 September–1 October.
12. Roll, D.L. *et al.:* "Effects of Pumping Equipment on Sand-Laden Slurries," *SPEPE* (November 1987) 291.
13. Ashton, J.P. and Nix, C.A.: "Polymer Shear Mixer: A Device for Improving the Quality of Polymer Viscosified Brines," paper SPE 14829 presented at the 1986 SPE International Symposium on Formation Damage Control, Lafayette, Louisiana, 26–27 February.
14. Penberthy, W.L. and Echols, E.E.: "Gravel Placement in Wells," *JPT* (July 1993) 612, 670.
15. Johnson, M.H., Montagna, J.N., and Richard, B.M.: "Studies, Guidelines, and Field Results of Nonviscosified Completion Brine Gravel-Pack Carrier Fluids," paper SPE 23774 presented at the 1992 SPE International Symposium on Formation Damage Control, Lafayette, Louisiana, 26–27 February.
16. Jones, L.G. *et al.:* "Alternate Path Gravel Packing," paper SPE 27359 presented at the 1991 SPE Annual Technical Conference and Exhibition, Dallas, 6–9 October.

17. Mathis, S.P. and Saucier, R.J.: "Water-Fracturing vs. Frac-Packing: Well Performance Comparison and Completion Type Selection Criteria," paper SPE 38593 presented at the 1997 SPE Annual Technical Conference and Exhibition, San Antonio, Texas, 5–8 October.

18. Welling, R.W.F.: "Improving Gravel-Packing Techniques in Brunei Darussalam Field Trial Results," paper SPE 25363 presented at the 1993 SPE Asia Pacific Oil and Gas Conference, Singapore, 8–10 September.

19. Barrilleaux, M.F., Ratterman, E.E., and Penberthy, W.L. Jr.: "Gravel-Pack Procedures for Productivity and Longevity," paper SPE 31089 presented at the 1996 SPE International Symposium on Formation Damage Control, Lafayette, Louisiana, 14–15 February.

20. Morales, R.H. *et al.:* "Optimum Fractures in High Permeability Formations," paper SPE 36417 presented at the 1996 SPE Annual Technical Conference and Exhibition, Denver, 6–9 October.

21. Penberthy, W.L. Jr. *et al.:* "Gravel Placement in Horizontal Wells," paper SPE 31147 presented at the 1997 SPE International Symposium on Formation Damage Control, Lafayette, Louisiana, 14–15 February.

SI Metric Conversion Factors

bbl	× 1.589 873	E–01	= m
bbl/min	× 2.649 788	E–03	= $m^3 s^{-1}$
cp	× 1.0*	E–03	= Pa s
ft	× 3.048*	E–01	= m
ft/sec	× 3.048	E–01	= m sec^{-1}
°F	(F – 32)/1.8		= °C
gal	× 3.785 412	E–03	= m^3
hp	× 7.460 43	E–01	= kW
in.	× 2.54*	E+00	= cm
lbm	× 4.535 924	E–01	= kg
psi	× 6.894 757	E+00	= kPa

*Conversion factor is exact.

Chapter 6
Formation Damage
Mukul M. Sharma, SPE, U. of Texas at Austin

6.1 Introduction

Any unintended impedance to the flow of fluids into or out of a wellbore is referred to as formation damage. This broad definition of formation damage includes flow restrictions caused by a reduction in permeability in the near-wellbore region, changes in relative permeability to the hydrocarbon phase, and unintended flow restrictions in the completion itself. Flow restrictions in the tubing or those imposed by the well partially penetrating a reservoir or other aspects of the completion geometry are not included in this definition because, although they may impede flow, they either have been put in place by design to serve a specific purpose or do not show up in typical measures of formation damage such as skin.

Over the last five decades, a great deal of attention has been paid to formation damage issues for two primary reasons: (1) the ability to recover fluids from the reservoir is affected very strongly by the hydrocarbon permeability in the near-wellbore region, and (2) although we do not have the ability to control reservoir rock properties and fluid properties, we have some degree of control over drilling, completion, and production operations. Thus, we can make operational changes, minimize the extent of formation damage induced in and around the wellbore, and have a substantial impact on hydrocarbon production. Being aware of the formation damage implications of various drilling, completion, and production operations can help in substantially reducing formation damage and enhancing the ability of the well to produce fluids.

In this chapter, we discuss methods to measure and to quantify the extent of formation damage and provide criteria that can be used to identify various types of formation damage. The goal is to define the mechanisms involved better so that an operator can recommend and design the correct remedial action and/or make changes to drilling, completion, and production operations to minimize damage in the future. It is generally true that, whenever possible, preventing formation damage is more effective than remedial treatments such as acidizing and fracturing. We do not discuss such treatments in this chapter. However, for each type of damage mechanism, potential remedial treatments are suggested.

6.2 Quantifying Formation Damage

A commonly used measure of well productivity is the productivity index, J, in barrels per pounds per square inch:

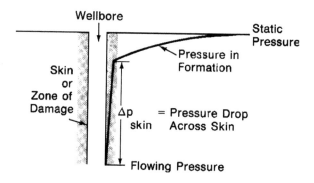

Fig. 6.1—Pressure profile in the near-wellbore region for an ideal well and a well with formation damage.[7]

$$J = \frac{q_o}{\overline{p}_R - p_{wf}}. \tag{6.1}$$

The most commonly used measure of formation damage in a well is the skin factor, S. The skin factor is a dimensionless pressure drop caused by a flow restriction in the near-wellbore region. It is defined as follows (in field units):

$$S = \left(\frac{kh}{141.2\ q\mu B}\right)\Delta p_{skin}. \tag{6.2}$$

Fig. 6.1 shows how flow restrictions in the near-wellbore region can increase the pressure gradient, resulting in an additional pressure drop caused by formation damage (Δp_{skin}). In 1970, Standing[1] introduced the important concept of well flow efficiency, F, which he defined as

$$F = \frac{\overline{p}_R - p_{wf} - \Delta p_{skin}}{\overline{p}_R - p_{wf}} \quad \frac{\text{ideal drawdown}}{\text{actual drawdown}}. \tag{6.3}$$

Clearly, a flow efficiency of 1 indicates an undamaged well with $\Delta p_{skin} = 0$, a flow efficiency > 1 indicates a stimulated well (perhaps because of a hydraulic fracture), and a flow efficiency < 1 indicates a damaged well. Note that, to determine flow efficiency, we must know the average reservoir pressure, p_R, and skin factor, S. Methods to measure these quantities are discussed in Sec. 6.3.

The impact of skin on well productivity can be estimated by the use of inflow performance relationships (IPRs) for the well such as those proposed by Vogel,[2] Fetkovich,[4] and Standing.[1] These IPRs can be summarized as follows[5]:

$$\frac{q}{q_{max}} = FY(x + 1 - FYx), \tag{6.4}$$

where

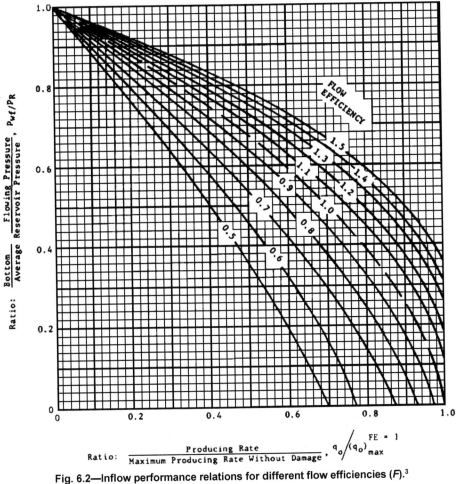

Fig. 6.2—Inflow performance relations for different flow efficiencies (F).[3]

$$Y = 1 - \frac{p_{wf}}{\overline{p}_R} . \quad \dots\dots\dots\dots\dots\dots\dots\dots\dots\dots\dots\dots\dots\dots\dots\dots\dots\dots (6.5)$$

When $x = 0$, a linear IPR model is recovered; when $x = 0.8$, we obtain Vogel's IPR; and when $x = 1$, Fetkovich's IPR model is obtained. An example of a plot for the dimensionless hydrocarbon production as a function of the dimensionless bottomhole pressure (IPR) is shown in **Fig. 6.2** for different flow efficiencies. It is evident that, as flow efficiency decreases, smaller and smaller hydrocarbon rates are obtained for the same drawdown $(\overline{p}_R - p_{wf})$.

The choice of the IPR used depends on the fluid properties and reservoir drive mechanism. Standing's IPR is most appropriate for solution-gas-drive reservoirs, whereas a linear IPR is more appropriate for waterdrive reservoirs producing at pressures above the bubblepoint and for hydrocarbons without substantial dissolved gas. A more detailed discussion of this is provided in Ref. 3.

6.3 Determination of Flow Efficiency and Skin

It is evident that, to quantify formation damage and to study its impact on hydrocarbon production, one must have reasonable estimates of the flow efficiency or skin factor. Several methods have been proposed to evaluate these quantities for oil and gas wells. The most common methods are multirate tests, isochronal gas-well tests, and transient well tests (pressure-buildup analysis).

6.3.1 Multirate Tests. Multirate tests can be conducted on both oil and gas wells. In these tests, several stabilized flow rates, q_i, are achieved at corresponding stabilized flowing bottomhole pressures, p_{wf}. The simplest analysis considers two different stabilized rates and pressures. The IPR can be written as

$$\frac{q_1}{q_2} = \frac{FY_1(x+1-FY_1x)}{FY_2(x+1-FY_2x)} . \hspace{2cm} (6.6)$$

Simplifying and solving for the flow efficiency, F, we obtain

$$F = \left(\frac{x+1}{x}\right)\left(\frac{q_1Y_2 - q_2Y_1}{q_1Y_2^2 - q_2Y_1^2}\right), \hspace{2cm} (6.7)$$

where $x \neq 0$.

The above equation clearly shows that it is possible to obtain flow efficiency rather simply with two stabilized bottomhole pressures and two stabilized flow rates. A similar analysis can be performed to obtain an expression for a linear IPR ($x = 0$).

6.3.2 Multirate Tests in Gas Wells: Inertial Effects. For many gas wells and some oil wells, flow rates are sufficiently high that turbulent or inertial pressure drops near the wellbore can be significant. In such cases, the additional pressure drop measured by the skin can be confused with the pressure drop because of non-Darcy or inertial flow. It is very important to separate out the pressure drop caused by turbulent flow from that caused by physical skin because it has a significant impact on the stimulation recommendations made on the well. To analyze high-rate gas or oil wells, the following equation is needed.[6]

Darcy's law for high-rate gas wells can be written as

$$q_{sc} = \frac{703 \times 10^{-6} \ kh\left[m(\overline{p}_R) - m(p_{wf})\right]}{T\left[\ln\left(\frac{r_e}{r_w}\right) - 0.75 + S + Dq_{sc}\right]} . \hspace{2cm} (6.8)$$

Here,

$$m(p) = \int_{p_b}^{P} \frac{2p}{\mu_g z}dp . \hspace{2cm} (6.9)$$

This equation can be rearranged to obtain

$$m(\overline{p}_R) - m(p_{wf}) = Aq_{sc} + Bq_{sc}^2 . \hspace{2cm} (6.10)$$

Here, Aq_{sc} represents a laminar pressure drop and Bq_{sc}^2 represents an inertial or non-Darcy pressure drop (sometimes referred to as a turbulent pressure drop). Note that A contains the physical skin, S, and B is directly proportional to the non-Darcy coefficient, D. By plotting multirate test data as a plot of $\dfrac{m(\overline{p}_R) - m(p_{wf})}{q_{sc}}$ vs. q_{sc}, we obtain A and B as an intercept and slope, respectively. It is then possible to compare the magnitude of the pressure drop caused by S with that caused by inertial effects, Dq_{sc}.

If $S > Dq_{sc}$, a stimulation treatment would be recommended. However, if $Dq_{sc} > S$, the well may need to be reperforated or fractured to increase the inflow area and to reduce inertial effects.

6.3.3 Isochronal Test in Gas Wells. In gas wells in which it takes a long time to achieve stabilized rates, wells are shut in and produced for a fixed time interval (Δt) at several different rates. These isochronal tests are then interpreted by the following "deliverability" relation,

$$q_{sc} = c\left(\overline{p}_R^2 - p_{wf}^2\right)^n, \dots\dots\dots\dots\dots\dots\dots\dots\dots (6.11)$$

where the exponent n lies between 0.5 and 1. An exponent closer to 0.5 indicates that non-Darcy effects are important; an exponent close to 1 indicates that they are not.[7]

It should be noted that the "deliverability" equation is a variation of the equation derived in the previous section.

6.3.4 Pressure-Buildup Analysis. The most common method for determining skin is a pressure-buildup test.[7,8] In this test, a well that has been producing for a time, t_p, is shut in for time Δt. The pressure buildup is recorded as a function of time. By constructing a Horner plot[7,8] like the one shown in **Fig. 6.3**, we can compute the skin and the product of the permeability and formation thickness, kh, of the reservoir (in field units).

$$S = S = 1.151\left[\frac{p_{wf} - p_{ws,\,1\,hr}}{m} - \log\left(\frac{k}{\mu c r_w^2}\right) + 3.23\right]\dots\dots\dots\dots (6.12)$$

and

$$kh = \frac{162.6q\mu B}{m}. \dots\dots\dots\dots\dots\dots\dots\dots\dots\dots (6.13)$$

Here, m is the slope of the straight-line portion of the Horner plot, and $p_{ws,1hr}$ is the extrapolated shut-in pressure at a shut-in time of 1 hour.

It is also possible to obtain the average reservoir pressure with the Matthew, Brons, and Hazelbrook method from the pressure-buildup data.[9] Knowing both the average reservoir pressure and skin, we can calculate the flow efficiency of the well. This method provides a direct and quantitative measure of the extent of formation damage in a well.

Methods following the same principle have been developed for deviated and horizontal wells. Equations for analysis are more complex and are not discussed in this chapter. The same methods can also be used to analyze data from gas wells and from wells on artificial lift.

The short discussion presented above shows how near-wellbore formation damage can be quantified by measurements made on oil and gas wells. Such measurements are essential for determining the extent and magnitude of the formation damage and its impact on hydrocarbon

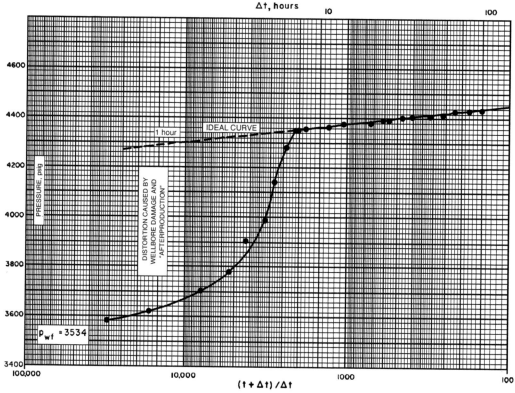

Fig. 6.3—Horner plot from a pressure-buildup test.[7]

production. However, these measures do not provide us with any clues on the reasons for the formation damage. In subsequent sections in this chapter, reasons and mechanisms for formation damage and strategies to minimize the impact of drilling and completion operations on well productivity are discussed.

6.4 Formation Damage vs. Pseudodamage

Formation damage mechanisms can be broken down into two broad classes: near-wellbore permeability reduction and near-wellbore relative permeability changes. These changes can occur under a variety of different circumstances. The following sections deal with different ways in which permeability and relative permeability in the near-wellbore region are altered by drilling, completion, and production operations.

Before we discuss formation damage mechanisms, it is important to clearly distinguish formation damage from well completion and reservoir effects that are a consequence of how the wellbore penetrates the reservoir and where the perforations are placed (sometimes referred to as pseudoskin effects)[10–13] and permeability loss as a result of depletion.[14] Reservoir engineering models for limited-entry flow in partially penetrating wells are presented in several reservoir engineering texts such as Dake.[10]

The second major cause of pseudoskin is high-velocity flows near the wellbore, which induces turbulence or inertial effects. As discussed in the previous section, turbulence or inertial effects can lead to an additional turbulent pressure drop that needs to be clearly distinguished from the pressure drop induced by a reduction in permeability. Finally, flow restrictions in the wellbore itself such as chokes, scale buildup, wax, or asphaltene deposits can often result in tubing pressure drops that are substantially larger than anticipated. This reduction in well productivity is not commonly referred to as formation damage. Other types of production impairment caused within the tubing are collapsed tubing or flow restrictions caused by mechanical restrictions such as corrosion products; poor cement jobs, resulting in commingling of produced fluids from different zones; and insufficient tubing diameter or improper design of artificial-lift systems. This partial list provides some examples of flow restrictions caused primarily in the tubing and should not typically be categorized as formation damage. They do not show up in measures of formation damage such as skin, which are primarily measures of flow restrictions in the near-wellbore region.

In this chapter, flow restrictions in the completion itself such as the compacted zone around perforation tunnels and plugged gravel packs are included in the discussion of formation damage because they typically are measured as a well skin (Section 6.3).

6.5 Drilling-Induced Formation Damage

Drilling fluids serve to balance formation pressures while drilling to ensure wellbore stability. They also carry cuttings to the surface and cool the bit. The drilling engineer traditionally designs drilling fluids with two primary goals in mind: to ensure safe, stable boreholes, which is accomplished by operating within an acceptable mud-weight window, and to achieve high rates of penetration so that rig time and well cost can be minimized. Note that these primary considerations do not include well productivity concerns. Over the past decade, a growing recognition of the importance of drilling-induced formation damage has led operators to mesh the objectives of the drilling engineer with those of the production and reservoir engineers. This can be achieved only if the design of the drilling program is a coordinated effort between drilling and production engineers. The use of drill-in fluids (fluids used to drill through the pay zone) that minimize formation damage has become widespread.

Drilling and well productivity concerns are addressed in the design of drill-in fluids. To meet well productivity objectives (i.e., to minimize formation damage), the drill-in fluid must meet the following additional objectives: minimize the extent of solids invasion into the formation by bridging across the pores and forming a thin, low-permeability, filter cake; minimize the extent of filtrate and polymer invasion into the formation through the formation of an external filter cake; and ensure ease of removal of the external filter cake during flowback to maximize the inflow area during production and to avoid plugging gravel packs. To achieve these goals, various strategies have been adopted. In this section, we address these strategies in terms of the basic mud formulations being used. Traditional water-based muds, oil-based muds, and some special formulations of drill-in fluids for fractured formations and unconsolidated sands are discussed. This is followed by a discussion of formation damage caused by drilling in deviated and horizontal wells and the use of drill-in fluids for such applications.

6.5.1 Formation Damage Caused by Water-Based Muds. The vast majority of drilling fluids consist of bentonite mixed with polymers to enhance the rheology (or, more specifically, the cuttings-carrying capacity of the fluid), starches to control fluid loss, dissolved salts such as potassium chloride or sodium chloride, and perhaps a pH buffer to maintain the pH of the mud to the desired level. A great deal of work has been done in the last three decades on evaluating the formation damage potential of water-based drilling fluids.[15–19] The following factors have been observed to have an impact on the depth of invasion of solids and filtrate and therefore on the extent and depth of formation damage or permeability impairment: the state of dispersion of solids in the mud, the size and concentration of solids and polymers in the mud, the pore throat size or permeability of the formation, the pH and salinity of the filtrate, and the water sensitivity of the formation.

In most instances, the invasion of solids into the formation is limited to 2 or 3 in. from the wellbore wall, which implies that the productivity of perforated wells with relatively shallow depth of damage will not be significantly affected. **Fig. 6.4** shows the productivity index (PI)

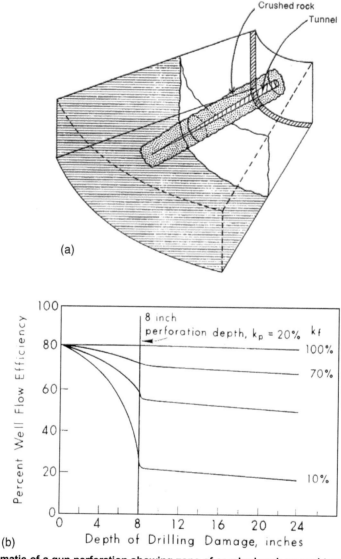

Fig. 6.4—(a) Schematic of a gun perforation showing zone of crushed rock around tunnel.[56] (b) Effect of damage by mud while drilling on well productivity when perforated with a nondamaging fluid is permeability of crushed zone around perforated tunnel as a percent of initial permeability.[56]

of a well for different depths of damage assuming an 8-in.-long perforation. It is evident that as long as the depth of damage is smaller than the perforation length, the well PI is not significantly affected. Wells that are completed openhole without stimulation are particularly susceptible to this kind of damage.

In some instances, deep penetration of drill solids can occur. **Fig. 6.5** shows the depth of invasion of formation damage when a 300-md Berea sandstone core is subjected to dynamic circulation of different water-based drilling fluids across its face.[20] It is evident that, in overtreated muds (containing too much thinner or dispersant), dispersed bentonite particles can penetrate through > 8 in. of rock and cause severe and irreversible damage. The other extreme, flocculated muds (too little thinner or too much salt), will limit solids invasion but will result in thick, high-permeability filter cakes. Filter cakes can result in such problems as stuck pipe

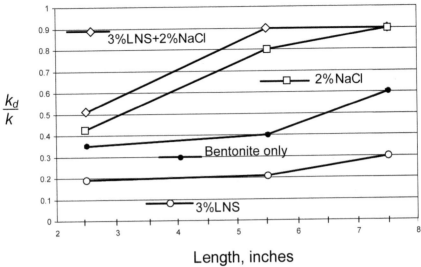

Fig. 6.5—Depth of permeability damage caused by mud invasion for muds with different degrees of bentonite dispersion. All muds contain 4% bentonite by weight.[20]

and large filtrate loss. The use of salts and thinners is, therefore, a critical part of the design of drilling fluids for a given application. Appropriately conditioned muds must be used to eliminate the possibility of solids invasion and to minimize filtrate invasion. As discussed later, using sized bridging solids is a powerful tool for reducing solids and polymer invasion.

Although solids invasion clearly is detrimental to well productivity, filtrate invasion can also lead to substantial formation damage and to greater depths in some instances. It has been shown, for example,[20,21] that the use of freshwater muds can result in filtrates that can be damaging to water-sensitive sandstones. In such instances, the simple process of increasing the salinity of the filtrate can prevent fines migration induced by filtrate leakoff. The loss of aqueous filtrates also results in a reduction in the relative permeability to the hydrocarbon phases.[21] Such relative permeability effects are referred to as water-blocks and are discussed in the section on formation damage resulting from emulsion and sludge formation.

Similarly, the use of polymers is widespread but can, in some instances, lead to formation damage. Its been shown that the use of improper mixing producers in dissolving polymers into brines can result in the formation of "fish eyes," or unhydrated aggregates of polymer that can be several microns in diameter. These particulate gels are very effective as plugging agents and can lead to irreversible damage if not broken up and completely hydrated in the mud. Proper conditioning and dispersal of polymers is of critical importance in the field.[22–25]

There is a limited database on the formation damage caused by starches and other polymers such as xanthan or carboxymethylcellulose. These data indicate that the flow of such polymers can induce a substantial reduction in permeability as a result of constriction of pore throats, particularly in low-permeability formations.

6.5.2 Formation Damage Caused by Oil-Based Muds. Oil-based muds consist of water droplets dispersed in a continuous oil phase. The water droplets are stabilized by emulsifiers and organophilic clays. Standard API fluid loss tests show that the fluid leakoff rate in oil-based muds is substantially lower than for water-based muds. However, as shown elsewhere,[26] when tests are conducted on oil-saturated cores (not filter paper), leak-off rates for oil-based muds can be comparable to those for water-based muds. One important conclusion of this study is that API fluid leakoff tests should not be used to determine filtration rates in oil-based muds. Instead, dynamic filtration tests conducted on oil-saturated cores are much more representative. The relative permeability to oil in oil-saturated zones is high, leading to large leakoff rates in the productive zone.[26]

The invasion of solids and oil droplets into the formation is determined largely by the effectiveness of the external filter cake formed by organophilic bentonite and water droplets. The structure of the filter cake formed is substantially different from that of water-based muds. Water droplets bridge across the pore throats to form the external filter cake. Because the droplets are deformable, they can form very impermeable filter cakes, leading to good leakoff control. However, if the overbalance pressure exceeds the capillary pressure needed to squeeze the water droplets into the pores, a significant loss in productivity can result. To prevent this from happening, large overbalance pressures should be avoided.

Experimental studies have shown that the accumulation of drill solids in the mud results in the introduction of fines that can be much more damaging than clean mud. Drill-solids control, therefore, is an important issue in oil-based muds. In general, however, oil-based muds prove to be excellent (albeit expensive) candidates for drilling gauge hole and providing high-productivity wells.[26,27]

It is important to recognize and identify damage caused by oil-based muds because the recommended treatment procedures for stimulating wells damaged by oil-based muds can be quite different from those for wells damaged with water-based muds. Acidizing wells with conventional acid formulations may not be successful and in fact may result in additional damage as a result of the presence of emulsifiers in the filtrate. Solvent preflushes may need to be designed on the basis of compatibility tests between the mud, crude oil, and acid formulation.

6.5.3 The Concept of Minimum Underbalance Pressure. It is clear from the preceding discussion that the formation of an external mud cake is important in protecting the formation from solids and filtrate invasion. Are there conditions under which an external mud cake will not form across the face of the formation? Yes, there are at least two situations in which an external filter cake does not form across of the face of the formation: (1) lost circulation and (2) drilling overbalanced below the minimum overbalance pressure.

When drilling through very-high-permeability rocks or fractured formations, solids present in the drilling fluid may not be able to bridge across the face of the pores or fractures, resulting in leakoff of whole mud into the formation.[13] This leakoff can result in very severe, irreversible damage to the fracture or matrix. In general, bridging solids are added to the drilling fluid to bridge across the pores or fractures. Sizing of these solids is discussed in more detail in Ref. 18.

The second case in which filter cakes do not form is less intuitively obvious. To form a mud cake, solids in the mud are pushed against the formation by a hydrodynamic force that is proportional to the leakoff velocity. In addition, because of mud circulation, particles are constantly being sheared away from the face of the external cake. This balance between the hydrodynamic shearing action resulting from mud circulation and the fluid leakoff into the formation results in an equilibrium cake thickness.[28,29] Because the leakoff is proportional to the overbalance pressure, smaller overbalance pressures will lead to smaller leakoff rates and thinner external filter cakes, resulting in a minimum overbalance pressure below which no external filter cake is formed at all. Alternatively stated, there is a minimum permeability for a fixed overbalance pressure below which no external filter cake will form. This suggests that we must always drill either underbalanced or above the minimum overbalance pressure to ensure that an external cake is formed and available to protect the formation when drilling through the productive zone. Additional details for calculating the minimum overbalance pressure are provided in Ref. 29.

6.5.4 Mud-Induced Damage in Fractured Reservoirs. When drilling through fractured formations, large quantities of whole mud can be lost to the fracture network, resulting in fracture plugging. Because fractures contribute almost all the productivity of such wells, it is important to keep these fractures open as much as possible. In such cases, underbalanced drilling is recommended and frequently used. Underbalanced drilling allows fluids from the fracture to flow into the wellbore, keeping the fractures relatively undamaged. If, however, because of safety and regulatory constraints, underbalanced drilling is not possible, bridging additives need to be added to the mud system to ensure that large-enough particles are available to bridge across the fracture face. The bridging additives most commonly used to ensure the formation of a bridge across the fracture face are calcium carbonate and fibrous additives such as cellulosic fibers and acid-soluble fibers.[30,31] Sizing of these granular or fibrous additives has been discussed in detail in Refs. 30 and 31.

6.5.5 Formation Damage in Horizontal Wells. Horizontal wells are more susceptible to formation damage than vertical wells for the following reasons.[32,33]

1. The pay zone in a horizontal wellbore comes into contract with a drilling fluid for a much longer period than a vertical pay zone (days compared with hours).

2. Most horizontal wells are openhole completions, which means that even shallow damage that in a cased perforated completion would be bypassed by the perforations becomes significant.

3. Because the fluid velocity and pressure gradient during flowback are usually small, cleanup of internal and external cakes is not as effective as in vertical wellbores. Thus, only a fraction of the wellbore contributes to flow when the well is returned to production.

4. Removing mud-induced formation damage by acidizing horizontal wells is often very difficult and expensive because of the large volumes of acid required and the difficulty in placing the acid in the appropriate wellbore locations.

Studies conducted on a simulated horizontal wellbore indicated that the heel is more damaged than the toe and that the upper part of the well is less damaged than the bottom of the wellbore where the drillpipe rests.[32] The damage zone around the horizontal wellbore can therefore be modeled as an eccentric cone around the wellbore with a significantly larger depth of penetration at the heel and a shallower depth of penetration at the toe.[33]

Because the drilling fluid is in contact with the producing zone for an extended period of time, drill-in fluids have been devised to minimize the potential formation damage. Sized calcium carbonate and sized salt fluids are the drill-in fluids used most often in such applications. Oil-based muds have also been evaluated for this purpose. A more detailed discussion of their formation damage potential is provided in Refs. 34 through 41.

6.6 Formation Damage Caused by Completion and Workover Fluids

When completion or workover operations are conducted on a well (perforating, gravel packing, etc.), the fluid present in the wellbore must minimize the impact on the near-wellbore permeability. Several decades ago, engineers realized that the use of drilling fluids during completions was inappropriate because fluids caused severe damage to the productive zone. A wide variety of fluids are now available as completion or workover fluids. A list of these fluids is provided in **Table 6.1.** Our discussion here focuses on formation damage issues related to these different types of completion and workover fluids.

Water-based fluids usually consist primarily of clear brines. The only problem with clear brines is that they are not ever really clear.[42-44] They always contain some solids, including corrosion products, bacteria, and debris from the wellbore and surface tanks. The density of the brine is maintained large enough so that the bottomhole pressure exceeds the reservoir pressure by a safe margin (typically 300 to 600 psi). Substantial amounts of solids can be pushed into the formation, resulting in a loss of permeability in the near-wellbore region. **Fig. 6.6** shows the loss in permeability observed when brines with differing quantities of solids are injected

TABLE 6.1—COMPLETION AND WORKOVER FLUIDS
Water-based fluids
• Clear brines
• Oil-soluble resins and waxes
• Polymer fluids
• Water-soluble solids (sodium chloride)
• Acid-soluble particles
• Biodegradable polymers
Emulsions
• Usually oil in water (12.5 lbm/gal)
Oil-based fluids
• Lease crude
• Invert-emulsion muds
• Asphalt pitches
Foams

into a core. Rapid reductions in permeability are observed even with relatively clean fluids. Surface filtration facilities are often used to clarify and filter completion brines, which can help to reduce the permeability impairment substantially. Most of the high-density brines used can be quite expensive. Large volumes of fluid loss can add substantially to the cost of a completion operation. An important fact to keep in mind with completion and workover fluids is that, unlike drilling fluids, they do not contain drill solids. This means that there is no effective bridging material available to reduce fluid leakoff.

When fluid-leakoff rates are very high, fluid-leakoff-control additives may be used to minimize leakoff and formation damage. Use of acid-soluble granular additives such as calcium carbonate is the most common strategy.[45–51] If this method proves to be ineffective, viscosifying polymers are used to reduce the amount of fluid loss. Hydroxyethylcellulose (HEC) is commonly used because it is soluble in hydrochloric acid. HEC is a poor viscosifier at higher (> 250°F) temperatures, and unbroken and unhydrated HEC in the form of fisheyes can be damaging.

Polymer fluids suffer from similar drawbacks. Severe formation damage can occur if large amounts of polymer are lost to the formation. This problem is particularly acute if the polymer is not completely hydrolyzed in the brine.

If the density requirements of the completion fluid are relatively modest, emulsions can be used as completion fluids. In these instances, the droplets that form the dispersed phase act as a filtration-control agent. Both water and oil-external emulsions have been used when reservoir pressures are low.

Oil-based fluids such as crude oil and invert-emulsion muds can be used as completion fluids. It is important to ensure that the crude oil does not contain asphaltenes or paraffins that might precipitate under changes in pressure and temperature as the fluid is circulated into the well. Refs. 45 through 52 provide a more detailed discussion of some of the issues summarized in this section. In addition, crude oil is flammable and messy to handle.

6.7 Damage During Perforating and Cementing

When cement is bullheaded into the annulus to displace mud, the differential pressure between the cement and the formation fluid can lead to a significant loss of cement filtrate into the formation. If, however, large volumes of cement filtrate invade the rock, the possibility of formation damage exists.

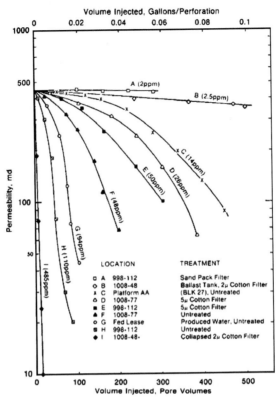

Fig. 6.6—Apparent permeability reduction in Cypress sandstone cores injected with treated and untreated bay water from offshore Louisiana.[48]

The major constituents in the aqueous phase in contact with hydrating cement are calcium silicates, calcium aluminates, calcium sulfates, calcium carbonates or bicarbonates, and alkali sulfates. Depending on the specific composition of the cement and its pH, the filtrate may be supersaturated with calcium carbonate and calcium sulfate. As the cement filtrate invades the formation and reacts with the formation minerals, its pH is reduced from > 12 to a pH buffered by the formation minerals. This rapid change in pH can result in the formation of inorganic precipitates such calcium carbonate and calcium sulfate.

Evidence of formation damage induced by cement filtrates has been clearly demonstrated in experimental studies presented in Refs. 53 and 55. Cunningham and Smith[53] investigated the influence of cement filtrates on formation permeability and concluded that there was little evidence of fines migration or clay swelling induced by the cement filtrate. They observed severe permeability reductions of 60% to 90% in cores invaded by cement filtrate. Yang and Sharma[54] investigated the impact of cement additives such as lignin derivatives, cellulose derivatives, organic acids, and synthetic polymers on the extent of permeability reduction in cores exposed to cement filtrate. In that study, cement filtrate was injected immediately after filtration into a sandstone core. Reductions in permeability of 40% to 80% were observed up to 6 in. into the core. Most of the damage observed was attributed to the precipitation of insoluble material such as calcium carbonate and calcium sulfate in the core. The quantity of precipitate and rate of precipitation relative to fluid convection were important factors that controlled the extent and depth of permeability damage. Cement filtrates that showed fast rates of precipitation tended to damage the upstream end of the core, whereas filtrates with slow precipitation rates tended to plug the downstream end of the core or not plug the core at all. The composition of the cement played an important role in determining both the quantity and the rates of precipitation. For example, the addition of lignin derivatives or polymer reduced the quantity of precipitate and resulted in less damage to the rock. The addition of cellulose derivatives, on the other hand, increased the rate and quantity of precipitation by an order of magnitude and resulted in more damage.[54]

If the depth of invasion of the cement filtrate can be restricted to ≈ 4 in., cement-filtrate-induced damage should not be a major concern because the perforation tunnels will bypass the damage. However, in some situations in which large volumes of cement filtrate may be lost, this form of damage should be seriously considered. In such cases, the use of fluid-loss-control additives and polymers in the cement slurry needs to be evaluated carefully so that the cement is properly designed to minimize both the leakoff rate and the amount of insoluble precipitates formed in the formation.

The process of perforating is critical to well productivity because the perforation is the only channel of communication between the wellbore and the formation. During underbalanced perforating, the surge flow of fluid into the wellbore should clean the perforation tunnel of all disaggregated rock and liner debris. Any remaining debris in the tunnel could plug gravel packs during production. Even clean perforation tunnels show a narrow region of reduced permeability around them. The nature of this crushed or compacted zone around perforation tunnels created during perforating has been widely studied.[56–79] It is now well recognized that it consists of shattered grains and fines generated by the perforation charge and perhaps fines that flow in from the formation during underbalanced surge flow. The reduction in permeability in the compacted region is typically of the order of 20 to 50% but can be larger in some cases.[79] Using an optimal underbalance pressure results in better perforation performance.[58] The reasons for this are not completely understood. It is likely that too low an underbalance results in insufficient perforation cleaning and too large an underbalance results in the generation and migration of additional fines. This explanation is consistent with the observation that the optimum underbalance pressure is higher for lower-permeability formations.

6.8 Formation Damage Caused by Fines Migration

Fines migration is a recognized source of formation damage in some production wells, particularly in sandstones.[80,81] Direct evidence of fines-induced formation damage in production wells is often difficult to come by. Although most other forms of formation damage have obvious indicators of the problem, the field symptoms of fines migration are much more subtle. Indirect evidence such as declining productivity over a period of several weeks or months is the most common symptom. This reduction in productivity can usually be reversed by mud-acid treatments. A large number of wells around the world follow these patterns of reduction of productivity followed by significant improvements when subjected to a mud-acid treatment. This behavior most often suggests a buildup of fines in the near-wellbore region over a period of time. Field studies and laboratory experiments have indicated that the fines causing the permeability reduction include clays, feldspars, micas, and plagioclase. Because the mobile fines are made up of a wide variety of minerals, the clay content of the reservoir may not always be a good indicator of the water sensitivity of the formation.

Core flow tests conducted in the laboratory clearly show that if low-salinity (< 2%) brines are injected into water-sensitive rocks, large reductions in permeability (up to a factor 500) are obtained (**Fig. 6.7**).[82–85] It is now well established that this dramatic reduction in permeability is almost entirely a result of fines migration. Evidence is shown clearly in Fig. 6.7. Reversal of flow results in a temporary increase in permeability as the fines plug pores in the reverse flow direction.

Fine-grained minerals are present in most sandstones and some carbonates. They are not held in place by the confining pressure and are free to move with the fluid phase that wets them (usually water). They remain attached to pore surfaces by electrostatic and van der Waals

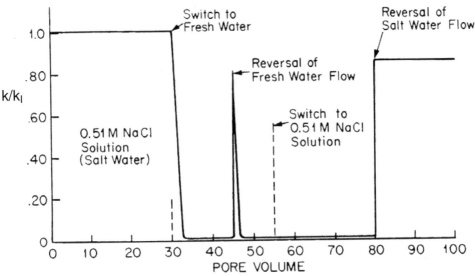

Fig. 6.7—Permeability reduction. Temporary and permanent permeability gain illustrating fines migration in Berea sandstone.[82]

forces. At "high" (> 2%) salt concentrations, the van der Waals forces are sufficiently large to keep the fines attached to the pore surfaces. As the salinity is decreased, the repulsive electrostatic forces increase because the negative charge on the surfaces of the pores and fines is no longer shielded by the ions. When the repulsive electrostatic forces exceed the attractive van der Waals forces, the fines are released from pore surfaces.[86] There is a critical salt concentration below which fines are released.[82,86] The typical magnitude of the critical salt concentration is in the range of 5,000 to 15,000 ppm (1.5%) sodium chloride. For divalent ions, this concentration is significantly lower. If a water-sensitive sandstone is exposed to brine with a salinity below the critical salt concentration, fines are released, and significant reductions in permeability are observed (Fig. 6.7).

Fines migration can also be induced by mechanical entrainment of fines, which can occur when the fluid velocity is increased above a critical velocity.[85–90] Gruesbeck and Collins,[85] among others, have measured the critical velocity for sandstones. Typical reported values of critical velocities are in the range of 0.02 m/s. This translates into modest well flow rates for most oil and gas wells.

It has been experimentally observed that critical flow velocities for fines migration are lower when the brine phase is mobile. Critical velocities are an order of magnitude higher when the brine is at a residual saturation. This implies that fines migration will be more important with the onset of water production in a well, which is indeed the case. It is often observed that well productivities decline much more rapidly after the onset of water production. In such instances, more frequent acid treatments are needed to maintain production after water breakthrough.

The extent of permeability reduction observed is also a function of the wettability of the rock. More oil-wet rocks tend to show less water sensitivity, maybe because the fines are partially coated with oil and are not as readily accessible to the brine. Significantly smaller reductions in permeability are observed when the rock is made less water-wet.[84,90]

The above observations imply that fines migration can be induced by any operation that introduces "low" (< 2%) -salinity or "high" (> 9%) -pH fluids into a water-sensitive formation. Fines migration can also be induced by "high" flow rates in the near-wellbore region, particularly in wells producing water. Examples of such operations include loss of freshwater-mud filtrate or completion fluid to the formation, steam injection in a huff 'n' puff operation for recovering heavy oil, water injection from a freshwater source, high well production rates (flow velocities above the critical velocity), and water breakthrough in production wells.

6.9 Formation Damage Caused by Swelling Clays

Swelling clays, although relatively abundant in shales, do not occur as commonly in producing intervals. Thus, problems with swelling clays are not nearly as common as those associated with fines migration. The most common swelling clays found in reservoir rock are smectites and mixed-layer illites. It was earlier thought that much of the water and rate sensitivity observed in sandstones was caused by swelling clays. However, it is now well accepted that the water-sensitive and rate-sensitive behavior in sandstones is more commonly the result of fines migration and only rarely of swelling clays.[91,92] Swelling clays reduce formation permeability by peeling off the pore surfaces and plugging pore throats, not by reducing porosity alone. Should this happen to any extent, large reductions in permeability are observed.

The presence of swelling clays is generally associated with drilling problems (i.e., hole quality and stuck pipe). This can result in poor cement jobs and sensitivity to completion fluids. Poor hole quality in the producing interval can result in significant migration of fluids behind pipe, resulting in reduced fluids control in the wellbore. These problems are encountered if either the producing formation or the intervening shales contain substantial quantities of swelling clays. When swelling clays are present in the producing interval, formation damage problems can occur because of rate sensitivity or water sensitivity. Care must be exercised to ensure that production rates and drawdowns in such wells are maintained so that the critical velocity is not exceeded in the near-wellbore region.

Clay minerals, such as smectites and mixed-layer illites, can expand in volume up to 20 times their original volume through adsorption of layers of water between their unit cells. Such 2:1 clay minerals are particularly prone to swelling because there is no hydrogen bonding between the octahedral layers of the unit cells.

Swelling is known to occur in three steps. In the first step, referred to as crystalline swelling, layers of water enter the interlayer space in the clay mineral, resulting in an increase in the C spacing of the clay mineral in steps. The size of these steps is observed to be approximately equal to the diameter of the water molecule. Extremely large swelling pressures can be generated through such an expansion of the clay lattice. The next stage in swelling is referred to as hydration swelling. This is thought to occur through the hydration and dehydration of ions entering the interlayer region. Several theories have been proposed to explain the observed repulsive hydration force observed in the presence of different cations.[93] Finally, when the interlayer spacing is ≈ 50 Å or so, free swelling occurs. This is driven primarily by the balance between electrostatic and van der Waals forces between the layers of clay. In this stage of swelling, the clay layers are sufficiently far apart that very little mechanical integrity exists in the clay. Such clay minerals are liable to be dispersed in the flowing fluid and to plug pore throats.

To prevent fines migration and clay swelling, various chemical treatments have been designed. These include polymers containing quaternary ammonium salts,[94] hydrolyzable metal ions such as zirconium oxychloride,[95] hydroxy-aluminum,[96] and polymerizable ultrathin films.[97]

Each of these methods relies on coating the fines (which are usually negatively charged) with large polyvalent cations that can attach irreversibly to the mineral surfaces. When the electrostatic charges on the fines are neutralized, the likelihood of fines migration is reduced significantly. Fines-stabilizing chemicals have been used in treatments such as acidizing, gravel packing, and fracturing. The effectiveness of such treatments is discussed extensively in Ref. 98.

6.10 Formation Damage in Injection Wells

Water is commonly injected into formations for three primary reasons: pressure maintenance, water disposal, or waterflooding. In such projects, the cost of piping and pumping the water is determined primarily by reservoir depth and the source of the water. However, water treatment costs can vary substantially, depending on the water quality required. In most cases, the well injectivity is a crucial factor in determining the cost of water injection. Maintaining high injectivities over long periods of time is extremely important for all water injection projects.

Historically, a great deal of expense and effort have been expended in treating water to ensure that very-high-quality water is being injected so that the injectivity of the well can be maintained over a long period of time.

There are two main properties of injection water that determine the formation damage or the injectivity of water injection wells: the total dissolved solids in the injection water and the total suspended solids (solids and oil droplets) in the injection water.[99–104]

The salinity and ion content in the injection water control two types of formation damage in an injection well: freshwater sensitivity of the formation and precipitation of inorganic scale.

In water-sensitive formations, if fresh water is being injected from a nearby lake or river, caution must be exercised to ensure that fines migration is not a major factor. This can be achieved by ensuring that the salinity is above the critical salt concentration for the rock. Injection wells are usually less susceptible to fines-migration problems than production wells because the fines being generated are pushed away from the wellbore, leading to less severe impairment in the near-wellbore region and therefore relatively small losses in injectivity. In some instances in which the reservoir contains large proportions of clays and fines, severe injectivity losses may be experienced when injecting below the critical salt concentration.

The precipitation of inorganic scale is a major concern when injecting brines with a high concentration of divalent ions. The hardness of the injection water is a good indicator of its scaling tendency. Should the water analysis indicate large concentrations of calcium, magnesium, iron, or barium, a water treatment facility that softens the water may be required. This is also an issue when injecting seawater into formations that contain brines with high salinity.

Large persistent drops in injectivity are expected when inorganic scales are formed in injection wells. Most field experience, however, indicates that the injection fluid quickly displaces the native brines away from the near-wellbore region with very little mixing. Inorganic scale precipitation resulting from incompatibility between the injection and reservoir brine is therefore not usually an issue for most injection wells. Geochemical interactions between injected fluids and the reservoir minerals can sometimes result in the formation of insoluble precipitates. Scale precipitation can also be induced by changes in pH, temperature, and state of oxidation of the brine. The formation of insoluble iron precipitates as a result of corrosion is a common source of damage in injection wells. These precipitates, mixed with other organic material, can result in severe and irreversible reductions in well injectivity. Careful analysis of both the formation brines and injected fluids and a check of the reservoir mineralogy are necessary. Checking for compatibility and ensuring that inorganic scale precipitation does not occur at reservoir temperature and pressure conditions are important when any water injection program is planned.

The presence of solids and oil droplets in the injection fluid can result in severe and rapid declines in injectivity.[99–104] If the injection pressure is below the fracture gradient and if fracturing is undesirable from a reservoir engineering or environmental point of view, small concentrations of solids can result in rapid reductions in well injectivity. As an example, 5 ppm of solids being injected into a well at 10,000 B/D computes to 45 kg of solids being injected every day. This large volume of solids can result in severe and rapid plugging of the injection well in a relatively short duration. Field experience in many parts of the world suggests that matrix injection of clean brines containing 3 to 5 ppm of suspended solids results in injection

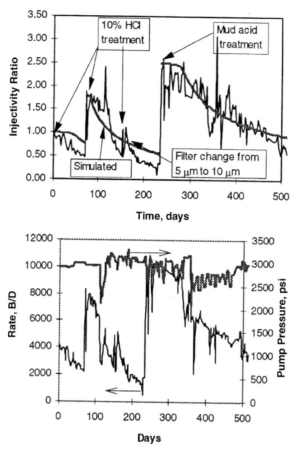

Fig. 6.8—Behavior of Well A10: (a) injectivity decline; (b) pressure and rate data.[101]

well half-lives (time it takes for injectivity to decline to half its value) of 3 to 6 months. **Fig. 6.8** shows the injectivity of a well in the offshore Gulf of Mexico. Seawater was being injected into this well at the rates indicated.[101] As the figure shows, despite the relativity good quality of the water, a rapid reduction in injectivity was observed in this and other wells in this field. This reduction led to costly stimulation and workover operations in these subsea wells.

In other field experiences, water has been injected into injection wells with minimal impact on injectivity. A good example of this type of injection well behavior is the injection of produced water in Prudhoe Bay field in Alaska, where 2,000 ppm oil plus solids in the injection water has been routinely injected with relatively little impact on well injectivity. The apparent lack of formation damage is a consequence of thermally induced injection well fractures that propagate hundreds of meters into the formation.[105–111] A great deal of work has been done to study the impact of water quality on the growth of fractures in water injection wells and the impact of injection well fractures on reservoir sweep and oil recovery.[112,113] This discussion is outside the scope of this chapter.

When fracturing injection wells is undesirable or unacceptable, the quality of the injection water plays an important role in determining well injectivity or formation damage in injection wells. Various water clarification devices such as sedimentation tanks, sand filters, cartridge filters, flotation devices, and hydrocyclones are available. These facilities significantly prolong the life of water injection wells and significantly reduce the formation damage. An economic analysis is thus necessary to ensure that the benefits are greater than the costs.

TABLE 6.2—GROSS COMPOSITION OF CRUDE OILS			
Average Value	Normal Producible Crude Oil (n=517)*	All Crude Oil (n=636)*	Disseminated Bitumen (n=1057)*
Saturated HC	57.2	53.3	29.2
Aromatic HC	28.6	28.2	19.7
Resins + asphaltenes	14.2	18.5	51.1
Aromatic sulfur, % aromatic fraction**	2.07		1.85

Values are wt% of the fraction boiling >210°C.
*n means number of samples.
**Number of samples for aromatic sulfur: 230 and 88, respectively.

6.11 Formation Damage Resulting From Paraffins and Asphaltenes

Perhaps the most common formation damage problem reported in the mature oil-producing regions of the world is organic deposits forming both in and around the wellbore. These organic deposits fall into two broad categories, paraffins and asphaltenes.

Crude oils contain three main groups of compounds: saturated hydrocarbons or paraffins, aromatic hydrocarbons, and resins and asphaltenes. **Table 6.2** shows the gross composition of crude oils, tars, and bitumens obtained from various sources. It is evident that crude oils contain substantial proportions of saturated and aromatic hydrocarbons with relatively small percentages of resins and asphaltenes. More degraded crudes, including tars and bitumens, contain substantially larger proportions of resins and asphaltenes.

6.11.1 Paraffin Deposition.

Paraffins are high-molecular-weight alkanes (C^{20+}) that can build up as deposits in the wellbore, in feed lines, etc. These organic deposits can act as chokes within the wellbore, resulting in a gradual decrease in production with time as the deposits increase in thickness. This can result in producing problems unless some remedial action is taken on a systematic and periodic basis. Deposits vary in consistency from soft accumulations to hard, brittle deposits. Usually the deposits are firmer and harder as the molecular weight of the paraffin deposits increases. Sometimes paraffins and asphaltenes occur together in organic deposits.

The primary cause of wax or paraffin deposition is simply a loss in solubility in the crude oil.[114,115] This loss of solubility is usually a result of changes in temperature, pressure, or composition of the crude oil as a result of loss of dissolved gases. Paraffins that have the highest melting point and molecular weight are usually the first to separate from solution, with lower-molecular-weight paraffins separating as the temperature decreases further. For example, a C^{60} alkane with a melting point of about 215°F will deposit at a much higher temperature than a C^{20} alkane with a melting point of 98°F.

The ability of the crude oil to hold the paraffin in solution is generally quantified with two indicators: a pour point and a cloud point. The procedure for measuring the pour point and cloud point may be found in ASTM manuals (D2500-66 for cloud points and D97-66 for pour points). The cloud point is defined as the temperature at which paraffins begin to come out of solution and a clear solution of hydrocarbons turns cloudy. Obviously, it is difficult to measure the cloud point for dark crude oil because cloudiness is not visible. In such cases, the presence of paraffin crystals may have to be detected with a polarizing light microscope. The pour point is defined as the temperature at which the crude oil no longer flows from its container. As the temperature is lowered, wax crystals form an interlocking network that supports the hydrocarbon liquid within it. This network of paraffin crystals is quite shear sensitive and loose when first formed but can harden and become extremely rigid as fluid is lost from it. Pour points are relatively easy to measure in the field and provide a good indication of conditions under which large quantities of paraffin will fall out of solution in crude oils.

The most common cause of loss of solubility of the paraffin in the crude oil is a decrease in temperature, which may occur for a variety of reasons[116]: cooling produced by the crude oil and associated gas expanding through the perforations, gas expansion while lifting fluids to the surface, radiation of heat from the tubing to the surrounding formation induced by intrusion of water into or around the wellbore, and loss of lighter constituents in the crude oil because of vaporization. Several other possible reasons for a decrease in temperature can be envisioned. In offshore installations, for example, paraffin problems are usually associated with the rapid change in temperature as the crude oil from the wellbore enters subsea pipelines that are immersed in seawater at 4°C. Large volumes of paraffins can be deposited on the surfaces of the pipelines, which requires periodic pigging.

Pressure itself has little or no influence on the solubility of paraffin in crude oil. However, it does have a significant impact on the composition of the crude oil. Reductions in pressure usually lead to loss of volatiles from the crude oil and can induce the precipitation of paraffins. This is the primary reason why paraffin problems are more common in the more mature regions of the world. As the reservoir pressure is depleted and the lighter components of the crude oil are produced in preference to the heavier fractions, the likelihood of paraffin precipitation is significantly increased.

For paraffin deposition to be a significant problem, the paraffin must deposit on the pore walls or the tubing surface. If the paraffin remains entrained in the crude oil, it usually offers few production problems. Several factors influence the ability of paraffin to deposit on the pipe walls:

1. The presence of water wetting the surfaces of the pipe tends to inhibit paraffin deposition. In addition, water has a higher specific heat than oil, which increases flowing temperatures.

2. Pipe quality plays an important role. Rusty pipes with large surface area and numerous sites for paraffin crystal formation offer an ideal location for paraffin deposition. Paraffin adheres to rough surfaces better than smooth surfaces.

3. The temperature profile in the near-wellbore region or within the pipe plays an important role in determining whether the paraffin will deposit on the walls or will continue to be entrained with the fluid.

The injection of fluids such as stimulation fluids or injection water into the wellbore can often induce paraffin deposition problems. This is particularly true if the surface temperature is significantly colder than the reservoir temperature. Field cases documenting paraffin precipitation during fracture stimulation are provided in Ref. 114.

6.11.2 Removal of Paraffin Deposits. Paraffin accumulations are removed by methods that can be broadly placed into three categories: (1) mechanical removal of paraffin deposits, (2) the use of solvents to remove paraffin deposits, and (3) the use of heat to melt and remove the wax. Mechanical methods such as scrapers, knives, and other tools are most commonly used to remove paraffin deposits in the wellbore. They can be very effective and are relatively inexpensive.

The most common solvent used to remove paraffin from tubulars and the near-wellbore region is crude oil. Hot oiling is the least expensive method, commonly used on stripper wells to remove paraffin deposits. Lease crude taken from stock-tank bottoms is heated to temperatures of 300°F or more. This heated oil is then injected or gravity fed into the tubing or annulus (more common). The high temperature induces solubilization of the paraffin deposits in the injected crude, which is then produced back to the surface. Hot oiling has been used successfully to remove paraffin deposition but can result in formation damage. The use of hot salt water to melt the paraffin may be a safer approach.

Solvents, both organic and inorganic, have been used in the past. These include crude oil, kerosene, diesel, and surfactant formulations that can solubilize the paraffin. Organic solvents that consist of a blend of aromatics are usually used to remove mixtures of paraffin and asphaltene deposits. However, the cost of such treatments can be significantly higher than that of hot oil or water treatments.

Steam has been used in a number of cases in which severe paraffin problems have resulted in plugged tubulars. The lack of solubility of paraffin in hot water necessitates the use of surfactants with steam or hot water so that the melted paraffin can be removed.

6.11.3 Methods for Preventing Paraffin Deposition.

Several mechanical adjustments can be made in the production string that can minimize the likelihood of paraffin deposition. In general, these steps are designed to minimize the cooling of the crude oil as it is produced to the surface. This can be accomplished by designing pumping wells or tubing sizes and gas lift systems that maximize the flow of oil to the surface and minimize the heat lost to the surrounding formations. Use of more expensive methods such as plastic coatings on tubulars and electrical heaters is severely limited by economics.

Paraffin inhibitors are a class of compounds that consist of crystal modifiers that prevent the deposition of paraffin onto pipe surfaces. These surface-active materials retard paraffin deposition by inhibiting the adhesion of paraffin to sites on the tubing walls. Surfactants used in these applications include wetting agents, dispersants, and crystal modifiers.[116,117] Each of these chemicals needs to be tested for a specific crude oil to evaluate its effectiveness.

6.11.4 Asphaltene Precipitation.

High-molecular-weight constituents of crude oil containing nitrogen, sulfur, and oxygen (N, S, and O) compounds are referred to as asphaltenes. This broad class of compounds is clearly not hydrocarbon because these compounds contain a large portion of heteroatoms in their structure. Lower-molecular-weight NSO compounds are referred to as resins. The separation of crude oil into resins and asphaltenes and other constituents is based primarily on solubility. Asphaltenes and resins are generally defined as the pentane-insoluble fraction of the crude oil.[118]

The average molecular structure of an example asphaltene fraction from a crude oil from Venezuela is shown in **Fig. 6.9**.[118] It consists primarily of condensed aromatic rings associated with aliphatic tails. The polynuclear aromatic rings associate with each other through their π electron systems to form clusters of stacked rings, as shown in the figure. In crude oils, these asphaltene structures are dispersed and maintained in suspension by the action of resins. If sufficient quantities of resin molecules are present in the crude oil, the asphaltenes remain dispersed and in solution. However, the addition of large quantities of alkanes or removal of the resin fraction can result in a loss of solubility because the asphaltene molecules associate with each other, forming large aggregates or micelles, and precipitate out. These micelles or aggregates are visible under optical microscopes as dark, solid aggregates. Precipitation of asphaltenes occurs through the formation of such aggregates. The solubility of asphaltenes is therefore a function of temperature, pressure, and the composition of the crude oil. Any action that affects the compositional balance of the crude oil can affect the ability of the oil to maintain the asphaltenes in solution.

A very common example of the change in composition of a crude oil is what occurs during pressure depletion in a reservoir. As shown in **Fig. 6.10**, the solubility of asphaltene is a minimum at the bubblepoint pressure.[119] This has important consequences for predicting where asphaltene precipitation will occur in a reservoir. As the reservoir is depleted and the bubblepoint pressure is achieved lower in the tubing or even in the formation itself, the possibility of asphaltene deposition occurs at these locations. Indeed, in studies published in the literature, the location of asphaltene deposition is observed to move from the top of the tubing to the

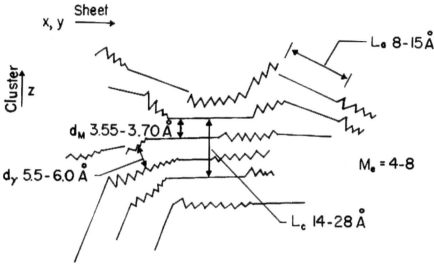

Fig. 6.9—Cross-sectional view of an asphaltene model based on X-ray diffraction. Zigzag line represents configuration of a saturated carbon chain or loose net of naphthenic rings; straight line represents the edge of flat sheets of condensed aromatic rings.[118]

bottom and into the reservoir over a period of time as the reservoir pressure is depleted and the location where the bubblepoint pressure is reached moves further out toward the reservoir.

Asphaltene deposition can also be induced by changes in composition of the crude oil through injection of fluids such as CO_2 or lean gas.[120,121] Several studies have documented the possibility of asphaltene precipitation during lean gas and CO_2 injection (Refs. 38 and 39). Large changes in temperature can also induce asphaltene deposition.[122,123] In such cases, deposits of paraffin and asphaltene are commonly observed together. The asphaltene particles frequently act as nucleation sites for paraffin crystals.

6.11.5 Removal of Asphaltene Deposits. Removal of asphaltene deposits also requires the use of solvents or mechanical devices. However, the solvents used for asphaltene removal are quite different from those used for paraffins. Because asphaltenes are soluble in aromatic solvents, mixtures of aromatic solvents such as xylene have been used to remove asphaltene deposits.[124] It should be noted that solvents such as diesel and kerosene that are primarily straight-chain alkanes should not be used because they may induce asphaltene precipitation.

6.12 Formation Damage Resulting From Emulsion and Sludge Formation

The presence of emulsions at the surface does not imply the formation of emulsions in the near-wellbore region. Most often, surface emulsions are a result of mixing and shearing that occur in chokes and valves in the flow stream after the fluids have entered the well. It is uncommon to have emulsions and sludges form in the near-wellbore region without the introduction of external chemicals.[125] The mixing of two immiscible fluids at a high shear rate in the formation can sometimes result in the formation of a homogeneous mixture of one phase dispersed into another. Such emulsions usually have a higher viscosity than either of the constituent fluids and can result in significant decreases in the ability of the hydrocarbon phase to flow.

Crude-oil/brine emulsions are stabilized by the presence of surfactants and colloidal particles such as clays, paraffins, and asphaltenes. In general, organophilic particles such as paraffins and asphaltenes favor the formation of oil-external emulsions and sludges. Water-wet solids such as clays favor the formation of water-external emulsions. It is important to mini-

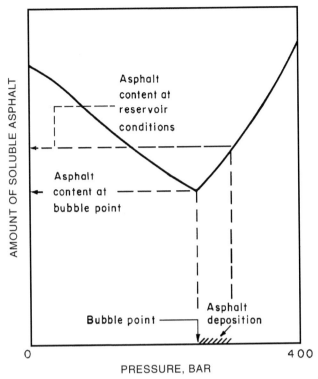

Fig. 6.10—Pressure dependence of asphalt solubility for a North Sea crude oil showing the possibility of asphalt deposition in the well tubing.[119]

mize the loss of surface-active materials into the near-wellbore region to ensure that emulsions do not form. For example, large volumes of surfactants are used as corrosion inhibitors and dispersants in acid treatments. A significant cause of failure of acid treatments is the formation of sludges and emulsions during an acid treatment as a result of the presence of these surfactants. The compatibility of crude oil with the acid package needs to be evaluated before it is pumped into the well. It has also been observed that the presence of iron enhances the formation of these sludges. It is therefore recommended that iron be removed from the tubing by circulating a slug of acid to the surface to ensure that the iron-rich acid is not squeezed into the formation during an acid treatment.

In general, it is difficult to remove emulsions and sludges once they are formed. Thus, it is imperative to prevent the formation of such emulsions. Use of mutual solvents such as alcohols and surfactants (demulsifiers) is the most common way to remove these deposits from the near-wellbore region. However, because of the unfavorable mobility ratio of the injected fluid, placing the treatment fluids in the plugged zones can be difficult. Again, laboratory tests with the crudes should be conducted to ensure compatibility.

6.13 Formation Damage Resulting From Condensate Banking

As shown in **Fig. 6.11**, gas/condensate reservoirs are defined as reservoirs that contain hydrocarbon mixtures that on pressure depletion cross the dewpoint line. In such instances as when the bottomhole pressure is reduced during production, the dewpoint pressure of the gas is reached in the near-wellbore region. This results in the formation of liquid hydrocarbons near the wellbore and in the reservoir. As the liquid hydrocarbon saturation in the near-wellbore region increases, the gas relative permeability is decreased, resulting in significant declines in well productivity.[126,127] An example of this is shown by the data in **Fig. 6.12**. Here, a substan-

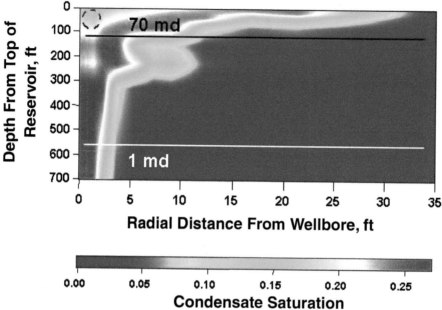

Fig. 6.11—Illustration of condensate dropout in near-wellbore region. Buildup of liquid hydrocarbons in this region can cause large reductions in gas relative permeability.[133]

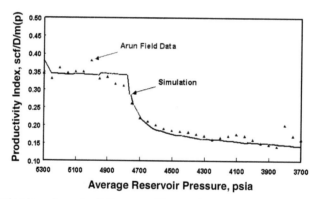

Fig. 6.12—Reduction in well productivity caused by condensate buildup, Arun field, Indonesia.[133]

tial reduction in well productivity is obtained as the average reservoir pressure declines below the dewpoint for a well in the Arun gas field. This mechanism of formation damage is related primarily to changes in fluid saturation in the near-wellbore region, resulting in decreases in gas relative permeability.

The buildup of the condensate bank and its consequences on well productivity have been well studied in the literature (Refs. 128 through 138). Early predictions of productivity loss because of condensate dropout indicated that a loss in PI by a factor of 5 to 8 would be expected because of liquid buildup.[130-132] However, the decline in PI observed in many of the fields is much smaller (a factor of 2 to 4). Further investigation of this problem indicated that the high gas flow rates in the near-wellbore region can result in stripping out of the liquid hydrocarbon phase in regions around the wellbore. This stripping-out effect has been quantified through capillary-number-dependent models for relative permeability of the gas phase.[129,138]

With this phenomenon properly accounted for, good agreement with field observations is obtained (Fig. 6.12).

In addition to liquid dropout, several other important phenomena can play an important role in determining well productivity and need to be carefully evaluated. Because of the high flow rates of gas in the near-wellbore region, non-Darcy effects may be significant and may need to be accounted for.[133–136] The combination of non-Darcy flow, capillary-number-dependent relative permeability, and phase behavior makes the problem rather complex, and numerical simulations are needed to fully capture all the physics of the problem. Clearly distinguishing the effects of liquid dropout from non-Darcy effects from production performance and pressure-transient tests can be challenging and may require compositional numerical models. Such models are widely available and have been used in estimating gas-well productivity, including condensate dropout.

The most direct method of reducing condensate buildup is to reduce the drawdown so that the bottomhole pressure remains above the dewpoint. In cases when this is not desirable, the impact of condensate formation can be reduced by increasing the inflow area and achieving linear flow rather than radial flow into the wellbore. This minimizes the impact of the reduced gas permeability in the near-wellbore region. Both of these benefits can be achieved by hydraulic fracturing.

Hydraulic fracture stimulation is the most common method used to remedy condensate buildup problems. The creation of a fracture results in a significant decrease in the drawdown needed to produce the well. In addition, buildup of a liquid hydrocarbon phase on the faces of the fracture does not affect well productivity as significantly as in radial flow around the wellbore. Additional details of this are available elsewhere.[137]

Recently, the use of solvents and surfactants such as methanol has been suggested as a way to stimulate gas/condensate wells in which hydraulic fracturing is not the preferred option.[139,140] The use of methanol results in removal of the condensate and water banks around a wellbore. This allows gas flow to be unimpeded through the near-wellbore region, resulting in smaller drawdown and slower accumulation of condensate. Within certain ranges of temperature and pressure, the presence of a residual methanol phase in the near-wellbore region can also result in the inhibition of condensate formation for a period of time.

6.14 Formation Damage Resulting From Gas Breakout

In solution-gas-drive reservoirs, as the reservoir fluid pressure drops below the bubblepoint, a gas phase is formed. If this event occurs in the wellbore, the gas bubbles formed help to lift the liquid hydrocarbons to the surface. However, if the bubblepoint is reached in the near-wellbore region, a significant gas saturation builds up around the wellbore resulting in a decrease in the oil relative permeability. As might be expected, this form of damage is more likely to occur later in the life of the reservoir as the average reservoir pressure is depleted below the bubblepoint.

This type of damage can be diagnosed if the production engineer has a good understanding of and access to phase behavior data. In many cases, however, lack of access to these data can result in an incorrect diagnosis of the reduction in well productivity. Such a misdiagnosis can lead to inaccurate recommendations for stimulation treatments.

In typical relative permeability curves, the change in the relative permeability to oil can be rather drastic as the gas saturation increases. This decrease in oil permeability can have a dramatic effect on well productivity. Oil flow rates can decrease while gas flow rates may increase rapidly over a relatively short duration.

The most common method to address gas breakout problems is to hydraulically fracture the well in an attempt to reduce the drawdown needed to produce at a given rate. Repressurizing the reservoir is also an excellent alternative. The economics of reservoir repressurization need to be carefully evaluated in such applications. It should be noted that in cases in which the average reservoir pressure drops below the bubblepoint throughout most of the reservoir, a gas cap may begin forming in the reservoir. This can, over a long time period, result in increased gas production into the wellbore from the gas cap.

6.15 Formation Damage Resulting From Water Blocks

If large volumes of water-based drilling or completion fluids are lost to a well, a region of high water saturation around the wellbore forms. In this region, the relative permeability to the hydrocarbon phases is decreased, resulting in a net loss in well productivity.[141,142]

Regions of high water saturation, or water blocks around the wellbore, are expected to dissipate with time as the hydrocarbon fluids are produced. In general, when the viscous forces are significantly larger than the capillary forces, the water block will clear up rather rapidly. If, however, the capillary forces holding the water in place are larger than the viscous forces, for example, in tight gas reservoirs, water blocks may persist for a very long period of time. A capillary number, defined as the ratio of capillary to viscous forces, can be used to quantify this effect. When capillary forces are larger than or comparable to viscous forces, water blocks are hard to remove. On the other hand, when viscous forces dominate, water blocks will clear up in a matter of a few hours or days.[143] Water blocks will generally be more troublesome for low-permeability, depleted gas wells in which the capillary number is significantly less than 1.[144,145]

There are three primary methods used to remove water blocks: (1) surging or swabbing the wells to increase the capillary number temporarily; (2) reducing surface tension through the addition of surfactants or solvents, which also has the net effect of increasing the capillary number by reducing the interfacial tension between the hydrocarbon and water phases so that the water block may be cleaned up during flowback, and (3) the use of solvents or mutual solvents such as alcohols to solubilize the water and remove it through a change in phase behavior.[146,147] All of these three methods have been successfully applied in the field. The benefit of one method over another depends on the specific conditions of reservoir permeability, temperature, and pressure.

6.16 Formation Damage Resulting From Wettability Alteration

Converting a rock from water-wet to oil-wet results in a substantial reduction in the relative permeability to the hydrocarbon phase and an increase in relative permeability to the water (Fig. 6.12). Wettability alteration to less water-wet conditions is therefore clearly undesirable.

The loss of surfactants in drilling and completion fluids,[148–150] corrosion inhibitors and dispersants in stimulation fluids, and the use of resins for sand control can cause changes in wettability in the near-wellbore region. Care must be exercised when oil-wetting surfactants are used in the wellbore to ensure that these fluids are not lost to the productive zone. Alteration of wettability in a region around the wellbore can result in an additional pressure drop because of the reduction in oil permeability. This additional pressure drop or skin is hard to distinguish from mechanical skin caused by physical plugging of pore throats. In effect, wettability alteration has the same net result as changing the effective permeability to the hydrocarbon phase in a region around the wellbore.

The use of solvents and water-wetting surfactants may be recommended in cases in which large volumes of oil-wetting surfactants such as oil-based muds have been lost to the formation.

6.17 Bacterial Plugging

Anaerobic bacteria are ubiquitously present in and around oil and gas wells.[151] Under most producing conditions, their growth is not stimulated because of the high temperature and pressure conditions. However, in some instances, injection of water-based fluids can induce the growth of microbial populations and can result in significant declines in productivity or injectivity.[152] The growth of sulfur-reducing bacteria can also result in the generation of hydrogen sulfide gas and the fouling of flowlines and facilities.

The use of a bactericide (such as sodium hypochlorite or mixtures of other strong oxidizing agents and antibacterial agents) is sometimes an effective, albeit expensive, method of reducing this problem.

6.18 Conclusions

This chapter has presented methods to measure and quantify formation damage in oil and gas wells. Several different mechanisms responsible for causing formation damage were discussed. A better understanding of these mechanisms allows us to make recommendations for drilling, completion, and production operations that will reduce the extent of formation damage and maximize well productivity.

Nomenclature

$$
\begin{aligned}
A &= \text{contains the physical skin, } S \\
Aq_{sc} &= \text{laminar pressure drop} \\
B &= \text{proportional to the non-Darcy coefficient, } D \\
Bq_{sc}^2 &= \text{inertial or non-Darcy pressure drop} \\
c &= \text{compressibility} \\
Dq_{sc} &= \text{inertial effects} \\
F &= \text{well flow efficiency} \\
J &= \text{productivity index} \\
k &= \text{overall permeability, md} \\
k_I &= \text{initial permeability, md} \\
kh &= \text{permeability and formation thickness} \\
m &= \text{slope} \\
n &= \text{exponent} \\
p &= \text{pressure} \\
p_b &= \text{bubblepoint pressure} \\
p_R &= \text{average reservoir pressure} \\
p_{wf} &= \text{flowing bottomhole pressure} \\
p_{ws,1hr} &= \text{extrapolated shut-in pressure at a shut-in time of 1 hour} \\
\Delta P_{skin} &= \text{additional pressure drop caused by formation damage} \\
q &= \text{flow rate} \\
q_i &= \text{flow rates} \\
q_o &= \text{oil flow rate} \\
q_{sc} &= \text{volumetric flow rate, surface conditions} \\
r_e &= \text{external boundary radius} \\
r_w &= \text{well radius} \\
S &= \text{skin factor} \\
T &= \text{temperature} \\
t &= \text{time} \\
t_p &= \text{well that has been producing for a time} \\
\Delta t &= \text{fixed time interval} \\
z &= \text{real gas compressibility factor} \\
\mu &= \text{viscosity} \\
\mu_g &= \text{gas viscosity}
\end{aligned}
$$

References

1. Standing, M.B.: "Inflow Performance Relationships for Damaged Wells Producing by Solution Gas Drive Reservoirs," *JPT* (November 1970) 1399.
2. Vogel, J.V.: "Inflow Performance Relationships for Solution Gas Drive Wells," *JPT* (January 1968) 83.
3. Brown, K.E.: *Technology of Artificial Lift Methods,* volume 1, PennWell Publishing Co., Tulsa, Oklahoma.
4. Fetkovich, M.J.: "The Isochronal Testing of Oil Wells," paper SPE 4529 presented at the 1973 SPE Annual Meeting, Las Vegas, Nevada, 30 September–3 October.
5. Peters, E.J.: Class notes. Department of Production Engineering, University of Texas at Austin (1990).
6. Jones, L.G., Blount, E.M., and Glaze, O.H.: "Use of Short Term Multiple Rate Flow Tests to Predict Performance of Wells Having Turbulence," paper SPE 6133 presented at the 1976 SPE Annual Technical Conference and Exhibition, New Orleans, 3–6 October.
7. Matthews, C.S. and Russell, D.G.: *Pressure Buildup and Flow Tests in Wells,* Monograph Series, SPE, Richardson, Texas (1967) **1**, 110.
8. Horner, D.R.: "Pressure Build-Up in Wells," *Proc.,* Third World Pet. Cong., The Hague (1951) Sec. II, 503–523. Also *Pressure Analysis Methods,* Reprint Series, SPE, Richardson, Texas (1967) 25–43.
9. Matthews, C.S., Brons, F., and Hazelbrook, P.: "A Method for Determination of Average Pressure in a Bounded Reservoir," *Trans.,* AIME (1954) **201**, 182–191. Also *Pressure Analysis Methods,* Reprint Series, SPE, Richardson, Texas (1967) 51–60.
10. Dake, L.P.: *Fundamentals of Reservoir Engineering,* Elsevier Scientific Publishing Co., New York City (1978).
11. Jones, L.G. and Watts, J.W.: "Estimating Skin Effect in a Partially Completed Damaged Well," *JPT* (February 1971) 249.
12. Odeh, A.S.: "Steady-State Flow Capacity of Wells with Limited Entry to Flow," *SPEJ* (March 1968) 43.
13. Weeks, S.G.: "Formation Damage or Limited Perforating Penetration? Test-Well Shooting May Give a Clue," *JPT* (September 1974) 979.
14. Ben Marek, F.: "Permeability Loss in Depletion of Reservoirs," paper SPE 8433 presented at the 1979 SPE Annual Technical Conference and Exhibition, Las Vegas, Nevada, 23–26 September.
15. Abrams, A.: "Mud Design To Minimize Rock Impairment Due to Particle Invasion," *JPT* (May 1977) 586.
16. Nowak, T.J. and Krueger, R.F.: "The Effect of Mud Filtrates and Mud Particles upon the Permeabilities of Cores," *API Drill. Prod. Prac.* (1951) 164–181.
17. Glenn, E.E. and Slusser, M.L.: "Factors Affecting Well Productivity, II: Drilling Fluid Particle Invasion Into Porous Media," *JPT* (May 1957) 132; *Trans.,* AIME, **210.**
18. Suri, A. and Sharma, M.M.: "Strategies for Sizing Particles in Drilling and Completion Fluids," paper SPE 68964 presented at the 2001 SPE European Formation Damage Conference, The Hague, The Netherlands, 21–22 May.
19. Ladva, H.K.J. *et al.:* "Multiphase Flow and Drilling Fluid Filtrate Effects on the Onset of Production," paper SPE 58795 presented at the 2000 SPE International Symposium on Formation Damage Control, Lafayette, Louisiana, 23–24 February.
20. Di, J. and Sharma, M. M.: "Formation Damage Caused by Static and Dynamic Filtration of Water-Based Muds," paper SPE 23823 presented at the 2001 SPE European Formation Damage Conference, The Hague, The Netherlands, 21–22 May.
21. Roy, R. and Sharma, M.M.: "The Relative Importance of Solids and Filtrate Invasion on the Flow Initiation Pressure," paper SPE 68949 presented at the 2001 European Formation Damage Conference, The Hague, The Netherlands, 21–22 May.
22. Hodge, R.M. *et al.:* "Evaluation and Selection of Drill-in Fluid Candidates To Minimize Formation Damage," paper SPE 31082 presented at the 1996 SPE International Symposium on Formation Damage Control, Lafayette, Louisiana, 14–15 February.

23. Browne, S.V. and Smith, P.S.: "Mudcake Cleanup To Enhance Productivity of High Angle Wells," paper SPE 27350 presented at the 1994 SPE International Symposium on Formation Damage Control, Lafayette, Louisiana, 7–10 February.

24. Ryan, D.F., Browne, S.V., and Burnham, M.P.: "Mud Clean-up in Horizontal Wells," paper SPE 30528 presented at the 1995 SPE Annual Technical Conference and Exhibition, Dallas, 22–25 October.

25. Francis, P.: "Dominating Effects Controlling the Extent of Drilling-Induced Formation Damage," paper SPE 38182 presented at the 1997 SPE European Formation Damage Conference, The Hague, The Netherlands, 2–3 June.

26. Jiao, D. and Sharma, M.M.: "Dynamic Filtration of Invert-Emulsion Muds," *SPEDC* (September 1993) 165.

27. McKinney, L.K. and Azar, J.J.: "Formation Damage Due to Synthetic Oil Mud Filtrates at Elevated Temperatures and Pressures," paper SPE 17162 presented at the 1988 SPE Formation Damage Control Symposium, Bakersfield, California, 8–9 February.

28. Di, J. and Sharma, M.M.: "Mechanism of Cake Buildup in Cross-Flow Filtration of Colloidal Suspensions," *J. Colloid and Interface Science* (1994) **162,** 454.

29. Di, J. and Sharma, M.M.: "Investigation of Dynamic Mud Cake Formation: The Concept of Minimum Overbalance Pressure," paper SPE 26323 presented at the 1993 SPE Annual Technical Conference and Exhibition, Houston, 3–6 October.

30. Di, J. and Sharma, M.M.: "Mud Induced Formation Damage in Fractured Reservoirs," *SPEDC* (March 1996).

31. Singh, T. and Sharma, M.M.: "Development of an Acid Degradable Drill-In Fluid for Fractured Reservoirs," paper SPE 38153 presented at the 1997 SPE European Formation Damage Symposium, The Hague, The Netherlands, 2–3 June.

32. Thomas, B. and Sharma, M.M.: "Distribution of Mud Induced Damage Around Horizontal Wellbores," paper 39468 presented at the 1998 SPE International Symposium on Formation Damage Control, Lafayette, Louisiana, 18–19 February.

33. Frick, T.P. and Economides, M.J.: "Horizontal Well Damage Characterization and Removal," *SPEPF* (February 1993).

34. Longeron, D.G., Alfenore, J., and Salehi, N.: "Experimental Approach to Characterize Drilling Mud Invasion, Formation Damage and Cleanup Efficiency in Horizontal Wells With Openhole Completions," paper SPE 58737 presented at the 2000 SPE International Symposium on Formation Damage Control, Lafayette, Louisiana, 23–24 February.

35. Bailey, L. *et al.:* "Filtercake Integrity and Reservoir Damage," paper SPE 39429 presented at the 1998 SPE International Symposium on Formation Damage Control, Lafayette, Louisiana, 18–19 February.

36. Ali, S. *et al.*: "Alternative Methods Clean Up Filter Cake," *Oil & Gas J.* (1 February 1999) 54.

37. Browne, S.V. and Smith, B.P.: "Mudcake Cleanup To Enhance Productivity of High-Angle Wells," paper SPE 27350 presented at the 1994 SPE International Symposium on Formation Damage Control, Lafayette, Louisiana, 7–10 February.

38. Browne, S.V. *et al.*: "Simple Approach to the Cleanup of Horizontal Wells With Pre-Packed Screen Completions," *JPT* (September 1995) 794.

39. Zain, Z. and Sharma, M.M.: "Cleanup of Wall-Building Filter Cakes," paper SPE 56635 presented at the 1999 SPE Annual Technical Conference and Exhibition, Houston, 3–6 October.

40. Zain, Z. and Sharma, M.M.: "A Simple Model for Filter Cake Lift-Off," *Oil & Gas J.* (1 November 1999) 70–75.

41. Burton, B.: "Estimate Formation Damage Effects on Horizontal Wells," *Pet. Eng. Intl.* (August 1995) 29.

42. Morgenthaler, L.N.: "Formation Damage Tests of High-Density Brine Completion Fluids," *SPEPE* (November 1986) 432; *Trans.*, AIME, **281.**

43. Eaton, B.A. and Smithy, M.: "Formation Damage From Workover and Completion Fluids," paper SPE 3707 presented at the 1971 SPE California Regional Meeting, Los Angeles, California, 4–5 November.

44. Azari, M. and Leimkuhler, J.: "Formation Permeability Damage Induced by Completion Brines," *JPT* (April 1990) 486.

45. Mahajan, N.C. and Barron, B.M.: "Bridging Particle Size Distribution: A Key Factor in the Designing of Non-Damaging Completion Fluids," paper SPE 8792 presented at the 1980 SPE Symposium on Formation Damage Control, Bakersfield, California, 28–29 January.

46. Darley, H.C.H.: "Chalk Emulsion: A New Completion Fluid," *Pet. Eng.* (July 1972) 45.

47. Priest, G.G. and Allen, T.O.: "Non-Plugging Emulsions Useful as Completion and Well Servicing Fluids," *JPT* (March 1958) 11.

48. Tuttle, R.N. and Barkman, J.H.: "New Non-Damaging and Acid-Degradable Drilling and Completion Fluids," *JPT* (November 1974) 1221.

49. Sloan, J.P., Brooks, J.P., and Dear, S.F. III: "A Nondamaging Acid-Soluble Weighting Material," *JPT* (January 1975) 15–20.

50. Mondshine, T.C.: "Completion Fluid Uses Salt for Bridging, Weighting," *Oil & Gas J.* (22 August 1977) 124.

51. Priest, G.G. and Morgan, B.E.: "Emulsions for Use as Non-Plugging Perforating Fluids," *JPT* (June 1957) 177; *Trans.,* AIME, **210.**

52. Patton, J.T. and Phelan, P.F.: "Well Damage Hazards Associated with Conventional Completions Fluids," paper SPE 13800 presented at the 1985 SPE Production Operations Symposium, Oklahoma City, Oklahoma, 10–12 March.

53. Cunningham, W.C. and Smith, D.K.: "Effect of Salt Cement Filtrate on Subsurface Formations," *JPT* (March 1968) 259.

54. Yang, X. and Sharma, M.M.: "Formation Damage due to Cement Filtrates in Sandstone Cores," *SPEJ* (1991) 399.

55. Jones, R.R., Carpenter, R.B., and Conway, M.W.: "A Study of Formation Damage Potential During Cementing Operations," paper SPE 22777 presented at the 1991 SPE Annual Technical Conference and Exhibition, Dallas, 6–9 October.

56. Klotz, J.A., Krueger, R.F., and Pye, D.C.: "Effects of Perforation Damage on Well Productivity," *JPT* (November 1974) 1303; *Trans.,* AIME, **257.**

57. Crawford, H.R.: "Underbalanced Perforating Design," paper SPE 19749 presented at the 1989 SPE Annual Technical Conference and Exhibition, San Antonio, 8–11 October.

58. King, G.E., Anderson, A., and Bingham, M.: "A Field Study of Underbalance Pressures Necessary To Obtain Clean Perforations Using Tubing Conveyed Perforating," *JPT* (June 1986) 662.

59. Bartusiak, R., Behrmann, L.A., and Halleck, P.M.: "Experimental Investigation of Surge Flow Velocity and Volume Needed To Obtain Perforation Cleanup," *J. Pet. Sci & Eng.* (1997) **17,** 19–28.

60. Tariq, S.M.: "New, Generalized Criteria for Determining the Level of Underbalance for Obtaining Clean Perforations," paper SPE 20636 presented at the 1990 SPE Annual Technical Conference and Exhibition, New Orleans, 23–26 September.

61. Behrmann, L.A.: "Underbalance Criteria for Minimum Perforation Damage," paper SPE 30081 presented at the 1995 SPE European Formation Damage Conference, The Hague, The Netherlands, 15–16 May.

62. McLeod, H.O. Jr.: "The Effect of Perforating Conditions on Well Performance," *JPT* (January 1983) 21.

63. Suman, G.O. Jr.: "Perforations: A Prime Source of Well Performance Problems," *JPT* (April 1972) 399.

64. Pettijean, L. *et al.:* "Well Productivity Improvement Using Extreme Overbalance Perforating and Surging-Case History," paper SPE 30527 presented at the 1995 SPE Annual Technical Conference and Exhibition, Dallas, 22–25 October.

65. Halleck, P.M.: "Advances in Understanding Perforator Penetration and Flow Performance," paper SPE 27981 presented at the 1994 SPE Petroleum Engineering Symposium, Tulsa, 29–31 August.

66. Hsia, T-Y. and Behrmann, L.A.: "Perforating Skins as a Function of Rock Permeability and Underbalance," paper SPE 22810 presented at the 1991 SPE Annual Technical Conference and Exhibition, Dallas, 6–9 October.

67. Halleck, P.M., Poyol, E., and Santarlli, F.J.: "Estimating Perforation Flow From Variation in Indentation Hardness," paper SPE 24769 presented at the 1992 SPE Annual Technical Conference, Washington, DC, 4–7 October.

68. Kooijman, A.P., Hoek, P.J.V., and Kenter, C.J.: "Horizontal Wellbore Stability and Sand Production in Weakly Consolidated Sandstones," paper SPE 36419 presented at the 1996 SPE Annual Technical Conference and Exhibition, Denver, 6–9 October.

69. Pearson, J.R.A. and Zazovsky, A.F.: "A Model for the Transport of Sand Grains From a Perforation During Underbalance Surge," paper SPE 38634 presented at the 1997 SPE Annual Technical Conference and Exhibition, San Antonio, Texas, 5–8 October.

70. Zhang, J., Rai, C.S., and Sondergeld, C.H.: "Mechanical Strength of Reservoir Materials: Key Information for Sand Prediction," paper SPE 49134 prepared for presentation at the 1998 SPE Annual Technical Conference and Exhibition, New Orleans, 27–30 September.

71. Behrmann, L.A. *et al.:* "Measurement of Additional Skin Resulting From Perforation Damage," paper SPE 22809 presented at the 1991 SPE Annual Technical Conference and Exhibition, Dallas, 6–9 October.

72. Behrmann, L.A., Pucknell, J.K., and Bishop, S.R.: "Effects of Underbalance and Effective Stress on Perforation Damage in Weak Sandstone: Initial Results," paper SPE 24770 presented at the 1992 SPE Annual Technical Conference and Exhibition, Washington, DC, 4–7 October.

73. Bird, K. and Blok, R.H.J.: "Perforating in Tight Sandstones: Effect of Pore Fluid and Underbalance," paper SPE 36860 presented at the 1996 SPE European Petroleum Conference, Milan, Italy, 22–24 October.

74. Pucknell, J.K. and Behrmann, L.A.: "An Investigation of the Damaged Zone Created by Perforating," paper SPE 22811 presented at the 1991 SPE Annual Technical Conference and Exhibition, Dallas, 6–9 October.

75. Brooks, J.E., Yang, W., and Behrmann, L.A.: "Effect of Sand-Grain Size on Perforator Performance," paper SPE 39457 presented at the 1998 SPE International Symposium on Formation Damage Control, Lafayette, Louisiana, 18–19 February.

76. Behrmann, L.A. *et al.:* "Borehole Dynamics During Underbalance Perforating," paper SPE 38139 presented at the 1997 SPE European Formation Damage Conference, The Hague, The Netherlands, 2–3 June.

77. Halleck, P.M., George, J., and Bast, M.: "The Character and Distribution of Damage Around Perforations: Comparison of Balanced and Underbalanced Conditions," paper presented at the 1999 SPE Eastern Regional Meeting, West Virginia, 20–22 October.

78. Venkitaraman, A. and Behrmann, L.A.: "Qualitative Analysis of Perforation-Induced Gravel-Pack Impairment Experiments," paper SPE 38144 presented at the 1997 SPE European Formation Damage Conference, The Hague, The Netherlands, 2–3 June.

79. Arora, D. and Sharma, M.M.: "The Nature of the Compacted Zone Around Perforation Tunnels," paper SPE 58720 presented at the 2000 SPE International Symposium on Formation Damage Control, Lafayette, Louisiana, 23–24 February.

80. Gray, D.H. and Rex, R.W.: "Formation Damage in Sandstones Caused by Clay Dispersion and Migration," *Clays, Clay Minerals* (1966) **14,** 355.

81. Muecke, T.W.: "Formation Fines and Factors Controlling Their Movement Through Porous Media," *JPT* (February 1979) 144.

82. Khilar, K.C. and Fogler, S.H.: "Water Sensitivity of Sandstones," *SPEJ* (February 1983) 55.

83. Vaidya, R.N. and Fogler, H.S.: "Fines Migration and Formation Damage: Influence of pH and Ion Exchange," *SPEPE* (November 1992) 325.

84. Sarkar, A.K. and Sharma, M.M.: "Fines Migration in Two-Phase Flow," *JPT* (May 1990) 646–652; *Trans.,* AIME, **289.**

85. Gruesbeck, C. and Collins, R.E.: "Entrainment and Deposition of Fine Particles in Porous Media," *SPEJ* (December 1982) 847.

86. Sharma, M.M., Yortsos, Y.C., and Handy, L.L.: "Deposition and Release of Clays in Sandstones," paper SPE 13572 presented at the 1985 SPE Symposium on Oilfield and Geothermal Chemistry, Phoenix, Arizona, 9–11 April.

87. Das, S.K., Sharma, M.M., and Schechter, R.S.: "Adhesion and Hydrodynamic Removal of Colloidal Particles From Surfaces," *Particle Science and Technology* (1995) **13,** 227.

88. Chamoun, H. *et al.:* "Factors Controlling the Hydrodynamic Detachment of Particles from Surfaces," *J. Colloid and Interface Science* (1992) **147,** No. 4.

89. Sharma, M.M. and Yortsos, Y.C.: "Fines Migration in Porous Media," *AIChE J.* (1987) **33,** No. 10, 1654.

90. Freitas, A.M. and Sharma, M.M.: "Effect of Surface Hydrophobicity on the Hydrodynamic Detachment of Particles From Surfaces," *Langmuir* (1999) **15,** 2466.

91. Jones, F.O. Jr.: "Influence of Chemical Composition of Water on Clay Blocking of Permeability," *JPT* (April 1964) 441.

92. Mungan, N.: "Permeability Reduction Through Changes in pH and Salinity," *JPT* (December 1965) 1449; *Trans.,* AIME, **254.**

93. Israelachvili, J.: *Intermolecular and Surface Forces,* John Wiley and Sons, New York City (1993).

94. Borchardt, J.K., Roll, D.L., and Rayne, L.M.: "Use of a Mineral Fines Stabilizer in Well Completions," paper SPE 12757 presented at the 1984 SPE California Regional Meeting, Long Beach, California, 11–13 April.

95. Peters, F.W. and Stout, C.M.: "Clay Stabilization During Fracturing Treatments with Hydrolyzable Zirconium Salts," *JPT* (1977) 187.

96. Coppel, C.P., Jennings, H.Y., and Reed, M.G.: "Results From Wells Treated with Hydroxy-Aluminum," *JPT* (1978) 1108.

97. Sharma, B.G. and Sharma, M.M.: "Polymerizable Ultra-Thin Films: A New Technique for Fines Stabilization," paper SPE 27345 presented at the 1994 SPE Symposium on Formation Damage Control, Lafayette, Louisiana, 7–10 February.

98. Borchardt, J.K.: "Cationic Organic Polymer Formation Damage Control Chemicals," *ACS Symposium Series* (1989) **396.**

99. Barkman, J.H. and Davidson, D.H.: "Measuring Water Quality and Predicting Well Impairment," *JPT* (July 1972) 865.

100. Eylander, J.G.R.: "Suspended Solids Specifications for Water Injection from Core-Flood Tests," *SPERE* (1988) 1287.

101. Sharma, M.M. *et al.:* "Injectivity Decline in Water Injection Wells: An Offshore Gulf of Mexico Case Study," *SPEPF* (February 2000) 6.

102. Van Oort, E., Van Velzen, J.F.G., and Leerlooijer, K.: "Impairment by Suspended Solids Invasion: Testing and Prediction," *SPEPF* (August 1993) 178.

103. Wennberg, E. and Sharma, M.M.: "Determination of the Filtration Coefficient and Transition Time or Water Injection Wells," paper SPE 38181 presented at the 1997 SPE European Formation Damage Symposium, The Hague, The Netherlands, 2–3 June.

104. Pang, S. and Sharma, M.M.: "A Model for Predicting Injectivity Decline in Water Injection Wells," *SPEFE* (September 1997) 194.

105. Perkins, T.K. and Gonzalez, J.A.: "The Effect of Thermoelastic Stresses on Injection Well Fracturing," *SPEJ* (February 1985) 78.

106. Detienne, J.L. *et al.:* "Thermally Induced Fractures: A Field-Proven Analytical Model," *SPEREE* (February 1998) 30.

107. Martins, J.P. *et al.:* "Produced-Water Reinjection and Fracturing in Prudhoe Bay," *SPERE* (August 1995) 176; *Trans.,* AIME, **299.**

108. van den Hoek, P.J. *et al.:* "Simulation of Produced Water Re-Injection Under Fracturing Conditions," paper SPE 36846 presented at the 1996 SPE European Petroleum Conference, Milan, Italy, 22–24 October.

109. Paige, R.W. and Murray, L.R.: "Re-Injection of Produced Water: Field Experience and Current Understanding," paper SPE 28121 presented at the 1994 SPE/ISRM Rock Mechanics in Petroleum Engineering Conference, Delft, The Netherlands, 29–31 August.

110. Van Velzen, J.F.G. and Leerlooijer, K.: "Impairment of a Water Injection Well by Suspended Solids: Testing and Prediction," paper SPE 23822 presented at the 1992 SPE Symposium on Formation Damage Control, Lafayette, Louisiana, 26–27 February.

111. Suarez, R. *et al.:* "An Experimental Investigation of Fracture Propagation During Water Injection," paper SPE 73740 presented at the 2002 SPE International Symposium on Formation Damage Control, Lafayette, Louisiana, 20–21 February.

112. Gadde, P.B. and Sharma, M.M.: "Growing Injection Well Fractures and Their Impact on Waterflood Performance," paper SPE 71614 presented at the 2001 SPE Annual Technical Conference and Exhibition, New Orleans, 30 September–3 October.

113. Gadde, P.B. and Sharma, M.M.: "Role of Fracture Face and Formation Plugging in Injection Well Fracturing and Injectivity Decline," paper SPE 52731 presented at the 1999 SPE/EPA Exploration and Production Environmental Conference, Austin, Texas, 28 February–3 March.

114. McClaflin, G.G. and Whitfill, D.L.: "Control of Paraffin Deposition in Production Operations," paper SPE 12204 presented at the 1983 SPE Annual Technical Conference and Exhibition, San Francisco, 5–8 October.

115. Thomas, D.C.: "Selection of Paraffin Control Products and Applications," paper SPE 17626 presented at the 1988 SPE International Meeting on Petroleum Engineering, Tianjin, China, 1–4 November.

116. Newberry, M.E. and Barker, K.M.: "Formation Damage Prevention Through the Control of Paraffin and Asphaltene Deposition," paper SPE 13796 presented at the 1985 SPE Production Operations Symposium, Oklahoma City, Oklahoma, 10–12 March.

117. Houchin, L.R. and Hudson, L.M.: "The Prediction Evaluation and Treatment of Formation Damage Caused by Organic Deposition," paper SPE 14818 presented at the 1986 SPE International Symposium on Formation Damage Control, Lafayette, Louisiana, 26–27 February.

118. Yen, T.F.: "Structure of Petroleum Asphaltene and Its Significance," *Energy Sources* (1974) **1**, No. 4, 447.

119. Hirschberg, A. *et al.:* "Influence of Temperature and Pressure on Asphaltene Flocculation," *SPEJ* (June 1984) 283.

120. Monger, T.G. and Fu, J.C.: "The Nature of CO_2-Induced Organic Deposition," paper SPE 16713 presented at the 1987 SPE Annual Technical Conference and Exhibition, Dallas, 27–30 September.

121. Monger, T.G. and Trujillo, D.E.: "Organic Deposition During CO_2 and Rich-Gas Flooding," *SPERE* (February 1991) 17.

122. Leontaritis, K.J.: "Asphaltene Deposition: A Comprehensive Description of Problem Manifestations and Modeling Approaches," paper SPE 18892 presented at the 1989 SPE Production Operations Symposium, Oklahoma City, Oklahoma, 13–14 March.

123. Kawanaka, S., Park, S.J., and Mansoori, G.A.: "Organic Deposition From Reservoir Fluids: A Thermodynamic Predictive Technique," *SPERE* (May 1991) 185.

124. Schantz, S.S. and Stephenson, W.K.: "Asphaltene Deposition: Development and Application of Polymeric Asphaltene Dispersants," paper SPE 22783 presented at the 1991 SPE Annual Technical Conference and Exhibition, Dallas, 6–9 October.

125. Schechter, R.S.: *Oil Well Stimulation,* Prentice Hall, Englewood Cliffs, New Jersey (1991).

126. Afidick, D., Kaczorowski, N.J., and Bette, S.: "Production Performance of a Retrograde Gas: A Case Study of the Arun Field," paper SPE 28749 presented at the 1994 SPE Asia Pacific Oil and Gas Conference, Melbourne, Australia, 7–10 November.

127. Barnum, R.S. *et al.:* "Gas Condensate Reservoir Behavior: Productivity and Recovery Reduction Due to Condensation," paper SPE 30767 presented at the 1995 SPE Annual Technical Conference and Exhibition, Dallas, 22–25 October.

128. Boom, W. *et al.:* "On the Use of Model Experiments for Assessing Improved Gas-Condensate Mobility Under Near-Wellbore Flow Conditions," paper SPE 36714 presented at the 1996 SPE Annual Technical Conference and Exhibition, Denver, 6–9 October.

129. Boom, W. *et al.:* "Experimental Evidence for Improved Condensate Mobility at Near-Wellbore Flow Conditions," paper SPE 30766 presented at the 1995 SPE Annual Technical Conference and Exhibition, Dallas, 22–25 October.

130. Asar, H. and Handy, L.L.: "Influence of Interfacial Tension on Gas/Oil Relative Permeability in a Gas-Condensate System," *SPERE* (February 1988) 257.

131. Hartman, K.J. and Cullick, A.S.: "Oil Recovery by Gas Displacement at Low Interfacial Tension," *J. Petroleum Science and Engineering* (1994) **10**, 197.

132. Henderson, G.D. *et al.:* "Measurement and Correlation of Gas Condensate Relative Permeability by the Steady-State Method," *SPEREE* (April 1998) 134.

133. Narayanaswamy, G., Pope, G.A., and Sharma, M.M.: "Predicting Gas-Condensate Well Productivity Using Capillary Number and Non-Darcy Effects," paper SPE 51910 presented at the 1999 SPE Reservoir Simulation Symposium, Houston, 14–17 February.

134. Wang, X. and Mohanty, K.K.: "Multiphase Non-Darcy Flow in Gas Condensate Reservoirs," paper SPE 56486 presented at the 1999 SPE Annual Technical Conference and Exhibition, Houston, 3–6 October.

135. Coles, M.E. and Hartman, K.J.: "Non-Darcy Measurements in Dry Core and the Effect of Immobile Liquid," paper SPE 39977 presented at the 1998 SPE Gas Technology Symposium, Calgary, 15–18 March.

136. Narayanaswamy, G., Sharma, M.M., and Pope, G.A.: "Effect of Heterogeneity on the Non-Darcy Flow Coefficient," *SPEREE* (June 1999) 296.

137. Kumar, R.: "Productivity Improvement in Gas Condensate Reservoirs Through Fracturing," MS thesis, U. of Texas at Austin (2000).

138. Pope, G.A. *et al.:* "Modeling Relative Permeability Effects in Gas-Condensate Reservoirs with a New Trapping Model," *SPEREE* (April 2000) 171.

139. Du, L. *et al.:* "Use of Solvents to Improve the Productivity of Gas Condensate Wells," paper SPE 62935 presented at the 2000 SPE Annual Technical Conference and Exhibition, Dallas, 1–4 October.

140. Al Anazi, H., Pope, G.A., and Sharma, M.M.: "Laboratory Measurement of Condensate Blocking and Treatment for Both High and Low Permeability Rocks," paper SPE 77546 presented at the 2002 SPE Annual Technical Conference and Exhibition, San Antonio, Texas, 29 September–2 October.

141. Tannich, J.D.: "Liquid Removal From Hydraulically Fractured Gas Wells," *JPT* (November 1975) 1309.

142. Abrams, A. and Vinegar, H.J.: "Impairment Mechanisms in Vicksburg Tight Gas Sands," paper SPE 13883 presented at the 1985 SPE/DOE Low Permeability Gas Reservoirs Symposium, Denver, 19–22 May.

143. Holditch, S.A.: "Factors Affecting Water Blocking and Gas Flow From Hydraulically Fractured Gas Wells," *JPT* (December 1979) 1515.

144. Cimolai *et al.:* "Mitigating Horizontal Well Formation Damage in a Low-Permeability Conglomerate Gas Reservoir," paper SPE 26166 presented at the 1993 SPE Gas Technology Symposium, Calgary, 28–30 June.

145. Kamath, J. and Laroche, C.: "Laboratory Based Evaluation of Gas Well Deliverability Loss Due to Waterblocking," paper SPE 63161 presented at the 2000 SPE Annual Technical Conference and Exhibition, Dallas, 1–4 October.

146. McLeod, H.O. and Coulter, A.W.: "The Use of Alcohol in Gas Well Stimulation," paper SPE 1663 presented at the 1966 SPE Eastern Regional Meeting, Columbus, Ohio, 10–11 November.

147. Jagannathan, A. and Sharma, M.M.: "Clean-up of Water Blocks in Low Permeability Formations," paper SPE 84216 presented at the 2003 SPE Annual Technical Conference and Exhibition, Denver, 5–8 October.

148. Sharma, M.M. and Wunderlich, R.: "Alteration of Rock Properties Due to Interaction With Drilling Fluid Components," *J. Petroleum Science and Engineering* (1987) **1,** 127.

149. Yan, J. and Sharma, M.M.: "Wettability Alteration Caused by Oil-Based Muds and Mud Components," *SPEDC* (March 1993) 35.

150. Yan, J. and Sharma, M.M.: "Wettability Alteration and Restoration for Cores Contaminated With Oil Based Muds," *J. Petroleum Science and Engineering* (1989) **2,** No. 2, 63.

151. Carlson, V., Bennett, E.O., and Rowe, J.A. Jr.: "Microbial Flora in a Number of Oilfield Water-Injection Systems," *SPEJ* (June 1961) 71.

152. Raleigh, J.T. and Flock, D.L.: "A Study of Formation Plugging with Bacteria," *JPT* (February 1965) 201.

SI Metric Conversion Factors

Å	× 1.0*	E–01	= nm
bbl	× 1.589 873	E–01	= m³
ft	× 3.048*	E–01	= m
°F	(°F – 32)/1.8		= °C
gal	× 3.785 412	E–03	= m³
in	× 2.54*	E+00	= cm
lbm	× 4.535 924	E–01	= kg
psi	× 6.894 757	E+00	= kPa

*Conversion factor is exact.

Chapter 7
Matrix Acidizing
Harry O. McLeod, SPE

7.1 Introduction

This chapter is organized to help perform acidizing on a well candidate in a logical step-by-step process and then select and execute an appropriate chemical treatment for the oil/gas well. The guidelines are practical in intent and avoid the more complicated acid reaction chemistries, although such investigations and the use of geochemical models are recommended for more complicated formations or reservoir conditions. Effective acidizing is guided by practical limits in volumes and types of acid and procedures so as to achieve an optimum removal of the formation damage around the wellbore.

Most of this chapter is an outgrowth of field case studies and of concepts derived from experimental testing and research. Justification for the practices and recommendations proposed herein are contained in the referenced documents. The reader is referred to the author's previous papers on matrix acidizing for references published before 1990. Concepts and techniques presented have been examined during repeated presentation of the Society of Petroleum Engineering (SPE) Short Course titled "Matrix Acidizing to Improve Well Performance."[1] Recent research has fine-tuned many of the concepts and acid types that are incorporated into proprietary software of various service companies. These programs are available through service company stimulation specialists who can assist with particular formation characteristics and reservoir conditions. The reader should use this chapter as an introduction to significant and necessary concepts and practices. Improved procedures and products can be selected by the company engineer in partnership with the stimulation specialist using proprietary software. The objective in the following discussion is to provide reasonable procedures and guidelines and to offer cautions suggested by particular formation compositions and reservoir conditions.

7.2 Two Basic Acidizing Treatments

Acidizing is used to either stimulate a well to greater than ideal matrix reservoir flow or to remove damage. These are two distinct and different purposes, the field applications and results of which are often merged or confused. Basically, there are two types of acid treatments that are related to injection rates and pressures. Injection rates resulting in pressures below fracture pressure are termed "matrix acidizing," while those above fracture pressure are termed "fracture acidizing."

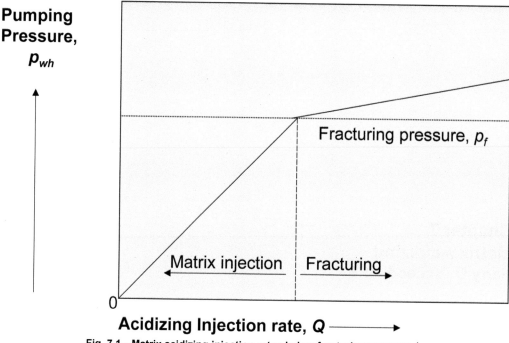

Fig. 7.1—Matrix acidizing injection rates below fracturing pressure.[1]

Fig. 7.1 shows the increase in pressure linearly with rate until parting pressure is attained, at which time rate can continue to increase with little change in pressure above parting pressure. Matrix acidizing is used primarily for damage removal, while fracture acidizing is used to enlarge the effective wellbore by creating an acid-etched fracture deep into the wellbore for relatively low-permeability formations to improve well productivity several-fold. This chapter focuses on matrix acidizing.

7.3 Purposes/Applications

A matrix treatment restores permeability by removing damage around the wellbore, thus improving productivity in both sandstone and carbonate wells. Although the acid systems used in sandstone and carbonate differ, the same practices apply to both. In the absence of damage, the large volume of acid that is required to improve the formation permeability in the vicinity of the wellbore may not justify the small incremental increase in production, especially in sandstone. In carbonate rock, hydrochloric acid enlarges the wellbore or tends to bypass damage by forming wormholes. The permeability increase is much larger in carbonate than in sandstone. The effect of damage on well productivity and flow is illustrated in **Figs. 7.2 and 7.3**.[1]

Severe damage (k_D/k less than 0.2) is usually close to the wellbore, within 12 in., as in Fig. 7.2. More moderate damage (k_D/k greater than 0.2) may occur much deeper (3 ft from the wellbore or more), as described in Fig. 7.3. Oilwell flow behavior is greatly affected by the geometry of radial flow into the wellbore; 25% of the pressure drop takes place within 3 ft of the wellbore if no damage is present, as shown in **Fig. 7.4**.[2] Because of the small flow area, any damage to the formation at that point may account for most of the total pressure drop (drawdown) during production and, thereby, dominate well performance.

7.4 Effects of Acidizing: Undamaged Well

Matrix acidizing is applied primarily to remove damage caused by drilling, completion, and workover fluids and solids precipitated from produced water or oil (i.e., scale or paraffin). Re-

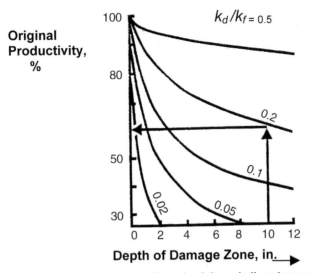

Fig. 7.2—Effect of damage on well productivity—shallow damage.[1]

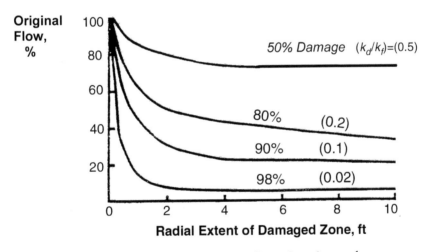

Fig. 7.3—Effect of damage zone on flow—deep damage.[1]

moval of severe plugging in carbonate or sandstone can result in very large increases in well productivity. On the other hand, if there is no damage, a matrix treatment seldom increases natural production more than 50%, depending on the size of the treatment and the penetration depth of live acid, as demonstrated in **Fig. 7.5.**[1]

Wormholes are small, continuous channels formed by acid preferentially enlarging pores in carbonate, usually around 2 to 5 mm in diameter. In radial flow, wormholes form a dendritic pattern, like the roots of a tree. Gdanski[3] developed a practical model for wormholing during matrix acidizing in carbonates, which shows that practical limits for effective penetration of hydrochloric (HCl) acid varies from about 1 to 5 ft. Penetration is limited by injection rate and volume. The maximum rate allowed is a function of the carbonate permeability. Radial penetration is so limited in low-permeability carbonate that it is a better candidate for fracture acidizing.

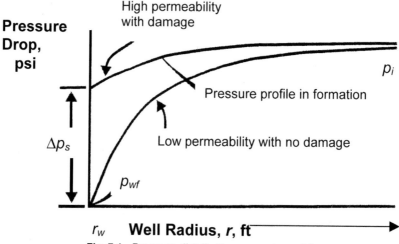

Fig. 7.4—Pressure distribution around a well.[2]

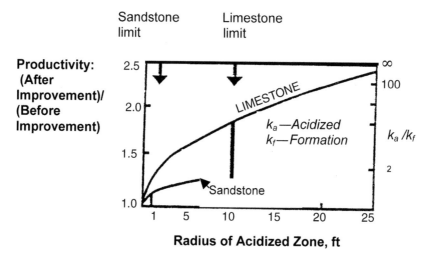

Fig. 7.5—Effects of acidizing an undamaged well.[1]

When there is no damage present, improper or poorly executed acid treatments can reduce the natural formation permeability and reduce well productivity, as in new wells with low reservoir permeability. Gidley[4] presented the results of an extensive statistical review of one company's acidizing success in sandstone reservoirs in the U.S. He found that only 54% of 507 wells increased in production following hydrofluoric (HF) acid stimulation. More recently, Nitters et al.[5] stated that past programs resulted in only 25% success. Where better evaluation and quality control have been implemented, the percentage of successful treatments has improved to 75 to 90%. Such a program was developed by Brannon et al.,[6] who successfully acidized 35 of 37 wells (95% success) for an average production increase of 343 BOPD. Other areas and formations still suffer from poor acidizing responses, which implies that opportunities for technology development still exist.

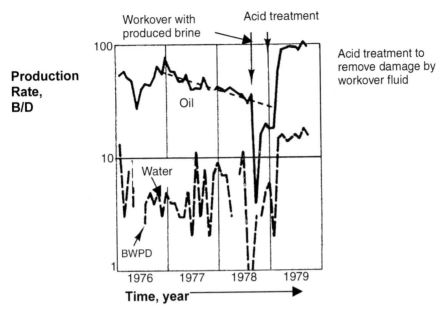

Fig. 7.6—Production history graph—sudden change (workover).[7]

7.5 Selecting Successful Acidizing Candidates

Wells may perform poorly or less well than expected because of three different factors: (1) an inefficient mechanical system (wrong size tubing in a flowing well or inefficient artificial lift equipment for pumping or gas lift wells), (2) low reservoir permeability, or (3) wellbore restriction because of formation damage or incomplete perforating. A good matrix acidizing candidate is any well producing from a formation with permeability greater than 10 md and the permeability of which in the near-wellbore or near-perforation region has been reduced by solid plugging. This plugging is either mechanical or chemical. Mechanical plugging is caused by either the introduction of suspended solids in a completion or workover fluid or the dispersion of in-situ fines by incompatible fluids and/or high interstitial velocities. Chemical plugging is caused by mixing incompatible fluids that precipitate solids. If formation damage is the cause for poor production, the well is a good candidate for acidizing. Several methods can be used to evaluate the presence of damage: production history plots that show sudden change, slope change, and gradual change; offset well comparison; pressure buildup tests; and well performance analysis.

7.6 Production History Plots

Production rate/time plots are normally available for oil/gas wells that show change of rate with time and that note significant events such as workovers and stimulation treatments. Damage is revealed by at least three different characteristics as previously listed. The first is a sudden change in productivity following an event like a workover, as shown in **Fig. 7.6**.[7] An unfiltered produced brine was used to kill the well during a workover to repair a tubing leak. In this example, formation damage is obvious in the reduced productivity immediately after the workover. This lowered productivity persisted until an acid treatment removed the damage. Many times the analysis of a damaged condition is not so obvious.

A depletion-type history curve may decline at a certain rate, as shown in **Fig. 7.7**.[8] This well followed a certain decline rate and then began to decline faster as shown by the change in slope. This is often characteristic of scale buildup around the wellbore from produced water.

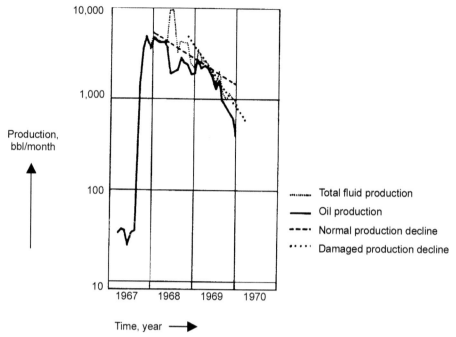

Fig. 7.7—Production history graph—change in slope: scale buildup (after Farina[8]).

This well was diagnosed and treated with HCl acid to dissolve calcium carbonate scale, and production rate was restored.

Some changes occur so slowly over time that productivity change is difficult to detect. Overlaying history curves of different wells will reveal this change in productivity. **Fig. 7.8** shows this overlay for two California wells. Increasing water production called attention to one well, and testing revealed a casing leak in this well.[7]

7.7 Offset Well Comparison

Often acidizing candidates are selected on the basis of offset well comparisons. The productivities of offset wells are compared, and the poorer-performing wells are selected for acidizing. Many times, this selection is made without sufficient well testing. Pressure buildup testing may be too expensive in terms of lost production during long shut-ins, or well interference may circumvent reliable long-time pressure data. **Table 7.1** shows such an offset comparison.[9]

On the basis of production only, three wells are acidizing candidates. However, when one compares the formation potential through log analysis, as expressed by net porosity feet, only one well is a reliable acidizing candidate: Well B-1. Acidizing all three wells on the basis of production rate alone may provide only a 33% success. In waterfloods, it is also important to compare effective reservoir pressures around each well or to compare the injection rates from adjacent water injection wells. If a well's water injectivity is low, production will be less in the offset producing well.

7.8 Pressure Buildup Tests

Where wells flow naturally, as in natural gas wells or new oil wells, pressure buildup tests provide a reliable measure of reservoir permeability and wellbore condition (skin factor, S). The skin factor, S, when positive, indicates restricted flow; however, the restriction is not necessarily formation damage. A skin factor of 5 to 20 or more can result from inadequate perforation size and/or low shot density when combined with either non-Darcy or two-phase

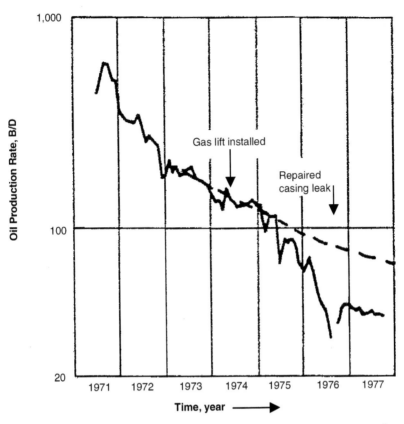

Fig. 7.8—Production history graph—overlaying graphs to detect damage.[7]

	Production		Gas/Oil Ratio,	Log Potential
Well Number	Oil, B/D	Water, B/D	scf/D	Porosity, ft
B-1	30	5	600	4.0
B-2	30	0	800	2.0
B-3	50	10	500	3.0
B-4	10	0	1,000	0.5

TABLE 7.1—OFFSET WELL COMPARISON[7]

fluid flow. Two-phase flow effects and non-Darcy flow cause high skin factors by themselves and can amplify the restriction caused by limited perforating. Such an example is shown in the buildup test in **Fig. 7.9**.[9] See the chapter on fluid flow in the reservoir engineering section of this handbook for more details on this type of plot.

This gas well was perforated with sufficient underbalance to achieve clean undamaged perforations, yet the skin factor from the pressure buildup test was 11. Well flow analysis showed that this skin was caused mainly by high-velocity flow of gas into small perforations created by the small through-tubing perforating gun used in this well.

Other wells have been identified with high skin factors that were the result of limited perforating and two-phase-flow effects. One gas condensate well had a skin factor of 29, which was

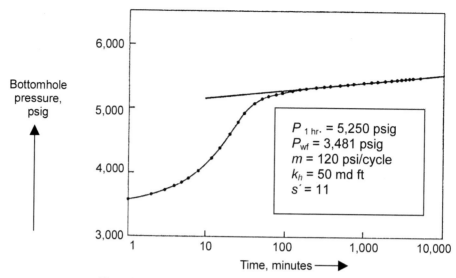

Fig. 7.9—Pressure buildup of a south Texas gas well.[9]

TABLE 7.2—WHEN TO QUESTION A POSITIVE SKIN FACTOR, S, AS AN INDICATOR OF DAMAGE[9]
Formation damage may not exist when pressure buildup tests show a positive skin factor, S. High skin factor may be caused by incomplete or low shot density perforating and velocity or two-phase flow effects.   If any of the following conditions exist, you might not have damage and must perform a production system analysis and review reservoir fluid properties to pinpoint whatís going on. High liquid/gas ratio (LGR) > 100 bbl/MMft^3/D (gas well). High gas/oil ratio (GOR) $\geq$ 1,000 scf/bbl. Three-phase production (water, oil, and gas). High-pressure drawdown $\left(\overline{P}_r - P_{wf}\right)$ > 1,000 psi. High flow rate $\frac{q}{h}$ > 20 B/D/ft, and $\frac{q}{N}$ > 5 B/D/perf. Perforations < 4 SPF. Perforated zero-degree phasing. Perforated with small through-tubing gun (gun diameter less than 2 in.). Reservoir pressure > bubblepoint pressure, and wellbore pressure < bubblepoint pressure.

the result of liquid saturation buildup and non-Darcy flow around the wellbore after a compressor was installed to pull the well harder. Another well in a deep, overpressured oil reservoir had a positive skin factor even after fracturing because of a solution gas/oil ratio (GOR) over 1,200 scf/bbl and a high pressure drawdown. Acidizing such wells have caused productivity decreases because acidizing sometimes produces damage where no damage existed before acidizing; therefore, use the checklist shown in **Table 7.2** before selecting acidizing candidates on the basis of high skin factors alone.[9]

7.9 Well Flow Analysis
A skin factor can be analyzed by well flow analysis to show when it is caused by the previously described effects or when it is the result of permeability damage. An example of such a damaged well is shown in **Fig. 7.10**.[9] This figure shows predicted gravel-pack pressure drop

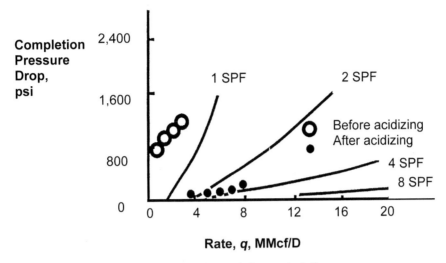

Fig. 7.10—Well completion analysis.[9]

vs. flow rate for different effective shots per foot (perforations). This well was perforated adequately and should have produced much better after completion. Review of the completion procedure showed that formation damage probably occurred during completion, and a standard acidizing treatment was used to dissolve the damage. Performance significantly improved, as shown by the reduction of completion pressure drop and increase of flow rate in this gas well.

7.10 Formation Damage Diagnosis

Well testing and well test analysis generate a skin factor and well completion efficiency. This is insufficient alone for formation damage diagnosis. Well performance analysis has provided a beneficial tool to identify the location and thickness of damage at flow points in the near wellbore area. Models of flow into perforations and gravel-packed tunnels provide a way to relate the location and severity of damage to the completion procedure that preceded it.

Well diagnosis is not just an evaluation of whether a well is damaged. Picking a potentially successful acidizing candidate involves not only the fact that a well is damaged but what kind of damage and where it is located around the wellbore. Damage is often most severe and localized at the point of flow entry into the wellbore. The improvement in damage analysis through well performance is rather recent, as evidenced by the work of several authors.[10–20] Most of this occurred through emphasis on improving gravel-packed completions in high-rate oil wells by means of multirate testing and improved wellbore models. Some of this work has focused on identifying specific damage mechanisms.[17–19]

7.11 Identify Extent/Type of Damage

To select the appropriate acid, one must diagnose the probable type of damage and the extent of penetration into the formation. Drilling solid infiltration is shallow (less than one in.); drilling fluid filtrate can invade the formation 3 ft or more. Perforation damage is shallow and varies in severity according to the perforating procedure. Water injection well damage can be quite deep when moderately clean fluids are injected over long periods of time with small unfiltered solids in the fluid. Likewise, incompatible fluids may precipitate deeper in the formation. Repeated acid treatments also may leave damage deeper in the formation. Shallow damage can be quite severe in that thin filter cakes or internal bridging under high differential pressure can have very low permeability. Deep damage is usually more moderate but can be quite difficult to reach with reactive fluids like acid and, thus, may require deep treatments like hydraulic fracturing or acid fracturing.

Familiarity with all sources of damage and damaging operations is a requisite tool for an engineer selecting the best remedial acid treatment and is beyond the scope of this chapter. Sparlin and Hagen[21] provide good information on damage mechanisms and damage analysis in their SPE Short Course on formation damage. Ref. 1 provides a damage check list. More information on damaging mechanisms and analysis is provided in the chapter on formation damage in this handbook. Recent examples of damage analysis and removal are provided by Fambrough *et al.,*[22] Zhu *et al.,*[23] and Guoynes *et al.*[24] A recent article concerning well completion post-audits provides a means of pinpointing the time of occurrence and the operation that caused damage in a particular completion by analysis of fluid loss and injection data.[25]

7.12 Damage Removal by Chemical Solvents

Selection of a chemical for any particular application depends on which contaminants are plugging the formation. HCl acid and other acids do not dissolve pipe dope, paraffin, or asphaltenes. Treatment of these solids or plugging agents requires an effective organic solvent (usually an aromatic solvent like toluene, xylene, or orthonitrotoluene). Acetic acid effectively dissolves calcium carbonate scale; however, it does not dissolve ferric oxide (iron oxide) scale. HCl acid dissolves calcium carbonate scale quite easily but has little affect on calcium sulfate scales. Calcium sulfate can be converted to calcium carbonate or calcium hydroxide by treatment with potassium hydroxide or sodium carbonate. HCl acid then can be used to dissolve the converted scale. Several cycles of such treatment may be necessary to remove all the scale. Calcium sulfate also can be dissolved in one step with the sodium salt of ethylene diamine tetra acetic acid (EDTA), but at a higher cost. HF acid must be used to dissolve formation clay minerals or drilling-mud solids when they plug pore throats in the formation.

Because different plugging solids require different solvents for their removal, there is no universal solvent for wellbore damage. Treatment based on such a premise often yields disappointing results. Never pump solvent or acid into a well until the probable causes of damage and the best chemical to remove the damage have been defined. A summary solvent selection table is given in **Table 7.3** for the type of damage.[1]

7.13 Formation Response to Acid

Even though damage has been identified and an appropriate acid or other cleaning agent is available to remove the damage, one must evaluate the probable response of the formation (its fluids and minerals) to either the acid or spent acid. There are many incompatibilities possible in acidizing various formations. These incompatibilities result in solid precipitates, which can plug pore throats so as to offset the improvement by acid dissolving pre-existing, damaging solids. Results can range from no bad effects and complete cleanup of damage to less than optimum improvement to plugging of the formation with acid-generated precipitates. As an example, a gas well producing 4 MMft³/D from a sandstone reservoir was acidized to improve production. The well flowed only 2 MMft³/D after acidizing. Post-treatment analysis showed that production was restricted by the small perforations (small inflow area) created with a through-tubing gun in underbalanced perforating; however, no permeability damage was present. Subsequent detailed petrographic core analysis indicated that a combination of acid-released fines and spent-acid precipitates damaged the formation during the acid treatment. Such incompatibilities are discussed next.

7.14 Formation Properties

One can prevent acid-induced damage by predicting and dealing with formation response before acidizing. While it is sometimes easy to dissolve plugging solids, the real test of success is dissolving the solids without injecting or creating other damaging solids in the process. If

TABLE 7.3—TYPE DAMAGE VS. SOLVENT[1]

Damaging Material	Solvent							
	Acetic Acid A	Hydrochloric Acid B	Hydrofluoric Acid C	Aromatic Solvent D	EDTA E	Two-Step Conversion F	Surfactant Cleaning G	Insoluble H
Calcium hydroxide	✓	✓						
Zinc hydroxide	✓	✓	*					
Calcite $CaCO_3$	✓	✓	*					
Dolomite (CaMg) CO_3	✓	✓	*					
Siderite $FeCO_3$	✓	✓	*					
Zinc or copper (pipe dope)	✓	✓						
Gelling agents (HEC, Guar)								
Iron oxides, magnetite, hematite, limonite		✓						
Iron sulfide		✓						
Clay minerals			✓					
Kaolinite			✓					
Smectite			✓					
Illite			✓					
Chlorite		P	✓					
Feldspar			✓					
Silica			✓					
Cement solids								
Asphaltenes				✓				
Paraffin wax				✓				
Gypsum ($CaSO_4$)					✓	✓		
Bacteria insoluble, loosened						✓	✓	
Barite ($BaSO_4$)								✓
Graphite (pipe dope)								✓
Lead (pipe dope)								✓
Organic materials (seaweed, paper, rope, rubber, plastic, etc.)								✓
Oil-wetting chemicals (drilling, fluids, completion fluids, chemical treatments)							✓	

Note: (*) –HF will dissolve these minerals, but reaction products will precipitate and damage formation. Do not use HF acid on carbonate formations. P = partially soluble.

potential incompatibilities between acid and formation solids or fluids are identified, precipitation of reaction products in the formation can be prevented or controlled.

Three properties of the formation are important: (1) Formation fluid analysis helps select appropriate displacement fluids to isolate formation fluids that are incompatible with either the acid or the spent acid products. (2) Formation matrix characterization identifies potential problems with acid treatments. (3) Formation mineralogy helps select the type of acid and its concentration.

7.14.1 Formation Fluid Compatibility. Formation fluid compatibility with both acid and spent acid must be considered in the treatment with acid. Formation water analysis is a standard test in laboratories, and chromatography is standard to identify gas compositions. Crude-oil analysis is much more complicated, so emulsion tests and sludge tests have been developed to identify incompatible crude oils.

7.14.2 Sulfate Ion Content. High sulfate-ion content exists in some formation waters. Spending HCl acid on carbonate generates a high concentration of calcium ions, which precipitates calcium sulfate when spent acid mixes with formation water containing more than 1,000 ppm sulfate ion. This can be prevented by preflushing the formation water away from the wellbore. In limestone acidizing, KCl or NaCl brines will work. In sandstone acidizing, NH_4Cl brine must be used (KCl and NaCl are incompatible with spent HF acid). Such a preflush, combined with quick return of spent acid from the formation by swabbing, has improved response to acidizing in the San Andres dolomite formation in eastern New Mexico.

7.14.3 Bicarbonate Ion Content. High bicarbonate-ion content in formation waters causes precipitation of acid-dissolved scale. Treatment with an acid form of EDTA both removes calcium carbonate scale and prevents the recurrence of the scale for several months.

7.14.4 Crude-Oil Incompatibility (Sludge and Asphaltenes). Some oils, particularly black asphaltic oils (less than 30°API), react with acid to form either damaging sludge (precipitated asphaltenes) or stable emulsions. Sometimes sludge preventers and emulsion breakers cannot prevent the formation of stable emulsions. Dissolved iron also creates more stable sludge and emulsions with these crude oils. Some difficult crudes need a preflush buffer of hydrocarbon solvent between crude oil and acid that is mutually compatible with both the crude oil and the acid. The buffer reduces contact between acid and the oil and prevents or reduces the problems with sludge and emulsions. Using this technique in one Wyoming oil field increased treatment success from 25 to 75%. Asphaltene particles can precipitate during production, and aromatic solvents can loosen and partially or completely dissolve them and also help acid dissolve solids. Presoaks with an aromatic solvent and producing back before acidizing have been helpful in treating wells drilled with oil-based mud. Organic skin damage in oil-producing wells is a major factor in the loss of productivity and revenue. Paraffin and asphaltene deposition in the formation around the wellbore creates a barrier to oil flow. Better methods of problem identification and programs to remediate these problems have been developed in recent years. The potential sources of organic damage, problem identification test techniques, chemical selection, and application methods are discussed.[26,27]

7.14.5 Hydrogen Sulfide. Hydrogen sulfide can be present in the oil, gas, and/or water in any producing or injection well. Sulfide scavengers are effective in preventing incompatibilities and precipitation of iron sulfide.[28]

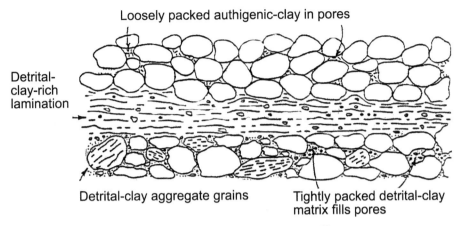

Loosely packed authigenic-clay in pores

Detrital-clay-rich lamination

Detrital-clay aggregate grains

Tightly packed detrital-clay matrix fills pores

Fig. 7.11—Clay minerals in sandstone.[29]

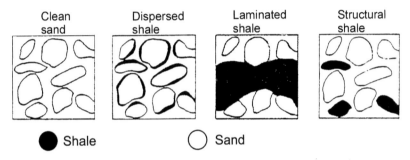

Clean sand   Dispersed shale   Laminated shale   Structural shale

● Shale   ○ Sand

Fig. 7.12—Forms of shale by distribution.[30]

7.15 Formation Matrix Properties

Formation matrix analysis is more involved and can be critical to acidizing success. The most significant properties are the grain size distribution, cementation, and clay content, which control permeability. Formation permeability is needed to estimate the matrix injection rate and the risk of acid fracturing. Clay distribution is also important, as illustrated in **Figs. 7.11 and 7.12**.[29,30]

Fig. 7.11 depicts clean sand, dispersed shale or clay, laminated shale, and structural shale. The preferred formation is a clean, uniform size, pure quartz sand that is the simplest to acidize because no incompatibilities exist, and acid mostly dissolves damage like drilling mud or other solids. Dispersed clay exists as grain coatings, bridging clays, or pore-filling clays, as illustrated in **Figs. 7.12 and 7.13**.[31] These clays are highly reactive with HF acid and sometimes HCl acid (chlorite clay). All clays are much more reactive above 250°F. Clays control the HF acid spending rate and the undesired secondary and tertiary reaction products that are characteristic of HF acidizing in clay-rich sandstone. Laminated shale or clay is more isolated from HF reaction because it is impermeable. It prevents vertical flow of acid from perforations and also restricts near-perforation flow. Structural shale is rare but is present in some Pleistocene or recent sands and can cause matrix collapse and reduced permeability when acid softens the shale grains.

The distribution and type of clay are characterized by petrographic analysis: thin sections, scanning electron microscopy, and x-ray diffraction analysis.[32] These tests are standard with most core-analysis companies and stimulation-service companies. When no cores are available,

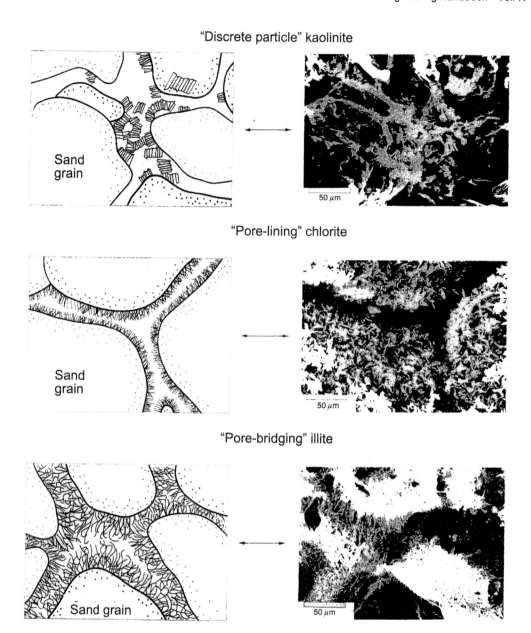

Fig. 7.13—Three general types of dispersed clay.[31]

analyses are possible using drill cuttings. Permeability may also be analyzed with mercury injection testing of drill cuttings, and estimates of permeability can be made by statistical analysis of thin sections and scanning electron microscope (SEM) photographs. Permeability may also be estimated by certain log analysis programs and are based on porosity and clay content and water saturation (as an indicator of grain size).

7.16 Formation Mineralogy

Carbonates usually have no formation-compatibility problem because HCl acid dissolves carbonate easily and leaves a formation compatible brine as a reaction product. However, where

TABLE 7.4—ACID USE GUIDELINES[34]

Situation	Concentration
Carbonate Acidizing:	
Perforating fluid	5% acetic
Damaged perforations	9% formic
	10% acetic
	15% HCl
Deep wellbore damage	15%
	28%
	Emulsified HCl
Sandstone Acidizing:	
HCl solubility $\geq$ 20%	Use HCl only
High permeability (100 md plus)	
High quartz (80%), low clay (<5%)	12.0% HCl/3.0% HF[1]
High feldspar (> 20%)	13.5% HCl/1.5% HF[1]
High clay (> 10%)	6.5% HCl/1.0% HF[2]
High iron chlorite clay	3.0% HCl/0.5% HF[2]
Low permeability (10 md or less)	
Low clay (< 5%)	6.0% HCl/1.5% HF[3]
High chlorite	3.0% HCl/0.5% HF[4]

Notes: [1]Preflush with 15% HCl. [2]Preflush with sequestered 5% HCl. [3]Preflush with 7.5% HCl or 10% acetic. [4]Preflush with 5% acetic acid.

anhydrite (a lower water content than gypsum) occurs in certain dolomitic carbonates, anhydrite dissolves in proportion to HCl-acid concentration and precipitates as acid spends. Even though a weaker HCl-acid concentration to reduce dissolution of anhydrite or calcium sulfate inhibitors are used, fluid recovery after treatment still must be rapid. Sandstone is more complicated because many minerals may exist with different precipitating products.

In sandstone acidizing, formation mineral content is important to the design of the HCl acid preflush, HF acid treatment, and overflush. Where high HCl-acid solubility exists (20% or more), HF acid should not be used. Formation damage often can be loosened by dissolving HCl-acid soluble compounds producing the released insoluble compounds. The use of HF acid in sandstone with a high-carbonate content produces voluminous solid precipitates. Gdanski and Schuchart[33] questions HF acid use in formations with more than 10% carbonate.

Compounds of calcium carbonate, magnesium carbonate, and iron compounds are soluble in hydrochloric acid. Sufficient volumes of hydrochloric acid must be injected ahead of HF acid to dissolve all these acid-soluble materials before the HF acid or spent HF acid reaches them. The HF acid concentration is selected to prevent or reduce damaging precipitates as guided by recommendations in **Table 7.4.**[34]

Some minerals such as sodium feldspar will automatically precipitate fluoride compounds when more than 3% HF acid is used. Potassium fluosilicate will precipitate when more than 1.5% HF acid reacts with potassium feldspar. When HF acid is used in clay containing sandstone, hydrous silica precipitates. An overflush (displacement by compatible brine) displaces precipitated hydrous silica 3 to 5 ft away from the wellbore, where it will do the least amount of damage. As long as the precipitates move, the likelihood of permanent damage is reduced. Shutting in a well after HF-acid injection can result in the formation of more silica gel. When the well is returned to flow soon after the acid treatment, some of the precipitate near the wellbore may be produced and help clean up the formation. If too little hydrochloric acid preflush is used in formations with 5 to 15% carbonate, residual carbonate near the wellbore will react with spent HF acid (fluosilicic acid or aluminum fluoride) and cause excessive precipitation.

These hydrated precipitates occupy more volume than that of the original clay and carbonate dissolved.

Dissolved iron minerals can precipitate in the formation. Ferric iron precipitates before acid spends to its normal pH of about 4. The precipitation of up to 10,000 ppm iron in solution may be prevented by adequate treatment with a complexing agent such as NTA, EDTA, citric acid, or combinations of acetic and citric acid. Damage from precipitated iron minerals is compounded by the high iron concentration that comes off the surface of the tubing during acid injection. New manufactured tubing has a crust of mill scale or magnetite, which is a form of ferric/ferrous oxide. This mill scale is loosened by the acid during acid injection. Particles of mill scale can then be injected into the perforations and may be trapped there. Injected acid continues to dissolve the mill, scale creating ferric chloride that enters the formation. This iron combines with iron from iron-oxide minerals, iron-rich chlorite clay, or other iron compounds in the formation to create more iron-hydroxide precipitates. This damage is lessened by pickling new tubing to remove mill scale and then circulating the pickling acid back out of the well before acidizing the formation. Older steel tubing stored outdoors (especially in coastal or marine environments) develop a coating of iron oxide (rust), which dissolves much faster in hot acid than does mill scale (iron magnetite).

7.17 Methods of Controlling Precipitates

Methods to control the precipitates caused by acidizing are acid staging, lower acid concentrations, and overflushing.

7.17.1 Preflush.
Preflush with either 5 to 15% HCl or 5 to 10% acetic acid. In formations with over 1% carbonate, an HCl or acetic acid preflush dissolves the carbonate to prevent waste of HF acid and formation of the insoluble precipitate calcium fluoride. Calcium and sodium chloride workover brine also must be flushed away from the wellbore with HCl acid or ammonium chloride brine. Preflushes also displace and isolate incompatible formation fluids (either brine or crude oil). Higher concentrations of ammonium chloride (> 3%) are recommended where swellable smectite and mixed layer clays are present.[33,35]

7.17.2 Treatment.
Treat with an adequate volume of proper concentration HF acid. For successful HF acidizing, more than 120 gal/ft of HF/HCl acid is usually required. Less may be used where only shallow, moderate damage exists (e.g., 25 to 75 gal/ft is sometimes used on new perforations to remove damage or as a spearhead treatment in perforation breakdown prior to hydraulic fracturing in tight sandstone). The concentration, 3% HF to 12% HCl acid (often referred to as regular mud acid), is the usual concentration for damage removal in clean, quartzose sands. Concentrations of 0.5 to 1.5% HF are more effective in other clay containing sands. When the combined percentage of clay and feldspar is more than 30%, use 1.5% HF or less. In some low-permeability sandstone, HF concentrations as low as 0.5% HF have been used (e.g., the Morrow formation in Texas and New Mexico). If in doubt, consider an acid response test on a typical core or a geochemical acidizing simulator. See Table 7.4 for suggested acid concentrations that may be modified according to the information presented in the following sections.

7.17.3 Postflush or Overflush.
An overflush displaces unreacted HF acid into the formation, displaces HF-acid reaction products away from the wellbore, cleans corrosion inhibitors to restore a water-wet condition and good oil/gas effective permeability, and re-establishes oil/gas saturation near the wellbore.

Typical overflushes for HF acid treatments are 3% ammonium chloride brine, weak acid (3 to 7.5% HCl acid) and filtered diesel oil or aromatic solvent (oil wells only) or nitrogen (gas wells only). The volume of overflush should be equal to or greater than the HF acid stage

TABLE 7.5—PREVENTING ACID INCOMPATIBILITIES: A SUMMARY[37]			
Acid	Fluid/Mineral	Precipitate	Prevention
HCl	Zeolite	Hydrous aluminosilicate	Use acetic acid
HCl	Chlorite	Hydrous aluminosilicate	Use acetic acid
HCl	Anhydrite	Calcium sulfate	Scale inhibitor
HCl	Ferric oxide	Ferric hydroxide	Iron complexing agent and/or reducing agent
HCl	Asphaltic crude oil	Asphaltenes	Hydrocarbon preflush
Spent HCl	Formation water with bicarbonate or sulfate ions	Calcium carbonate or calcium sulfate	Compatible brine preflush—prefer 3% ammonium chloride
HF	Carbonate	Calcium fluoride	HCl preflush
HF	Potassium feldspar	Potassium silicofluoride	Use 1½% HF max
Spent HF	Clay mineral	Hydrous silica	Disperse with proper overflush
Spent HF	Carbonate	Calcium fluoride hydrous aluminosilicate	Sufficient HCl preflush

volume. For most wells, an overflush of at least 200 gal/ft displaces spent acid past the critical flow radius of 3 to 5 ft. This large overflush reduces near wellbore precipitation of amorphous silica. At formation temperatures of 200°F or more, this precipitation occurs while the HF acid is being pumped into the formation. This precipitate is somewhat mobile at first but may setup as a gel after flow stops. Overflushing with 3% ammonium chloride or weak acid dilutes and disperses precipitate away from the wellbore. Often, the overflush is 3% ammonium chloride with 10% ethylene glycol monobutyl ether (EGMBE) and a polyquarternary amine clay stabilizer. However, high-cation capacity clays may swell as a result of injecting preflushes or overflushes of brines or acid with concentrations lower than 4%. Where significant quantities of smectite and mixed layer clays are found, Gdanski and Schuchart[33] recommend the use of 5% ammonium chloride brine. This is supported by the work of Al-Anazi et al.[35] Gidley et al.[36] state that carbon dioxide preflushes and overflushes also have proven effective in some wells. Other chemicals can be added to acid to prevent or reduce the precipitation of some compounds (e.g., iron complexing agents, sulfate scale inhibitors, and sludge preventers). **Table 7.5** summarizes the steps to prevent or control incompatibilities in acidizing different formations and formation fluids.[37]

Recent work has provided additional field cases of new types of acid damage from minerals in the formation such as zeolite,[38] chlorite,[39,40] and carbonate minerals precipitating aluminum fluoride complexes created by HF acid.[36] The experimental works of Shuchart and others[41–43] provide a better understanding of HF acid chemistry and precipitation of HF acid reaction products. Shuchart[42] summarized HF acid reactions into primary, secondary, and tertiary reactions. The primary reaction for HF acid dissolves damage and whole clay with no precipitation.

In the secondary reaction, fluosilicic acid (a product of the primary dissolution of clay or silica by HF acid) dissolves clay in formation and precipitates hydrous silica. This reaction can reduce clay damage deeper in the formation. Stronger acid (12% HCl and 3% HF acid) creates higher silica concentrations from the primary dissolution of clays and silica, which precipitate in subsequent reactions deeper in the formation. In higher-temperature formations, this silica precipitates closer to the wellbore and reduces permeability.

In the tertiary reaction, HCl acid and aluminum fluoride complexes react slowly to dissolve clays and precipitate hydrous silica but proceed faster at temperatures in excess of 00°F. This reaction exacerbates post-acid scale precipitation. The slower tertiary reactions occur in most acid treatments in the 8- to 24-hour time period that the acid system typically remains in the formation.

7.18 Acid Treatment Design
Once you determine that a well is a good candidate for matrix acidizing and have selected appropriate acids, you are ready to design the treatment. Essentially, the design process is a systematic approach to estimating and calculating injection pressure and rate, volumes, and concentrations. Live HF acid usually penetrates only about 6 to 12 in. into the sandstone before spending. If acid can easily reach nearby plugging solids, small volumes of 25 to 50 gal/ft of HF-type acid can dissolve this damage; however, with more severe damage, more time and volume are needed to reach the plugging solids. Effective acid diversion reduces acid volumes needed.

7.19 Matrix Acidizing Design Guidelines
The recommended steps in treatment design are given next.
• Estimate safe injection pressures: determine present fracturing gradient, determine present bottomhole fracturing pressure, and determine allowable safe injection pressure at both the wellbore (at least 200 psi below fracturing pressure) and at the surface (tubing and wellhead pressure limitations).
• Estimate safe injection rate into the damage-free formation.
• Estimate safe injection rate into damaged formation.
• Select stages required for fluid compatibility.
• Calculate volume of each stage required: crude oil displacement, formation brine displacement, acetic acid stage, hydrochloric acid stage, hydrofluoric acid (HF and HCl acid) stage, and overflush stage.
• Select acid concentrations according to formation mineralogy. More detailed procedures with a calculated example are available in Ref. 1. **Table 7.6** provides a one-page summary and guide to selecting fluid stages and volume.

7.20 Acid Type and Concentration
Permeability and mineralogy determine the compatible concentration of HCl or acetic acid in the preflush stage and HF and HCl acid in the HF-/HCl-acid stage. Guidelines for proper concentrations are provided in Table 7.4. The background for the acid-use guidelines in Table 7.4 is given in Ref. 9. These guidelines are not absolutes and probably should be modified according to more recent research. These guidelines were provided as a fairly conservative approach to avoid problems that could occur with 12% HCl and 3% HF that were regularly used prior to 1985. These guidelines helped when no previous experience existed in acidizing a particular formation. Evaluated experience provides the most reliable information. Acid flow tests with cores are reliable when long cores are used.[44] These tests are expensive and, therefore, seldom performed.

Gdanski[43] recommends 13.5% HCl to 1.5% HF acid for high-feldspar sandstone and 9% HCl to 1% HF acid for clay-rich formations to prevent unwanted precipitation of fluoride scales. With more reactive clays and a higher carbonate content, acetic acid must be added to the acid mixtures to maintain a lower pH and reduce the amount of post-acid precipitation. For

TABLE 7.6—SUMMARY CHART—ACIDIZING STAGES, ACID DESIGN

Stage Number	Stage Name	Reason for Stage	Information Source	Stage Composition	Stage Volumes*	
I	Crude-oil displacement	Prevent oil sludging by acid	Acid/crude oil sludging test	Aromatic solvent (xylene, toluene)	Radial displacement: 3 ft (Fig. 7.3)	
II	Formation water displacement	Prevent scale deposition HCO$_3$, SO$_4$ content	Formation water analysis	Sandstone: 3% NH$_4$Cl; carbonate: 2% KCl and 3% NaCl	Radial displacement: 3 ft (Fig. 7.3)	
III	Acetic acid stage	Iron compounds in formation pyrite, siderite, hematite, chlorite clay	X-ray analysis	10% acetic acid	%CaCO$_3$ 0–5 5–10 10–15 15–20	gal/ft 25 50 75 100
IV	Hydrochloric acid	CaCO$_3$ or other HCl soluble minerals	X-ray analysis or HCl acid solubility test	According to core mineralogy 3 to 15% HCl	Sandstone: % HCl soluble < 5 5–10 10–20 Limestone: 25–100 gal/ft	% of HF stage volume 50 100 200
V	Hydrofluoric acid (not used on carbonates and sandstones when HCl solubility > 20%)	Clay damage	X-ray analysis, SEM analysis	According to formation mineralogy 0.5 to 3% HF and 3 to 13.5% HCl	75 to 150 gal ft	
VI	Overflush	To spend acid/to flush spent acid from perfs	Always use	(a) 3% NH$_4$Cl (all wells), (b) nitrogen (gas wells), (c) diesel oil (oil wells), (d) 5% HCl (water wells)	Same volume as HF acid or volume to displace to 5 ft radially	

*Minimum stage volumes: 500 gal.

chlorite-rich sandstone, Simon and Anderson[39] show the benefit of preflushing with 10% acetic acid and dissolving chlorite with 10% acetic and 1% HF acid. At temperatures higher than 200°F, Wehunt et al.[40] recommend decreasing HF-acid concentration to 0.1% HF in 10% acetic acid at 380°F. However, at low temperature (less than 125°F), stronger acids are required to remove damage, and secondary and tertiary reaction precipitates are minor.

The guidelines in Table 7.4 do not specifically address permeability between 10 and 100 md, a range where field results have been erratic. Some treatments are very successful, and some result in little or no change. Proper selection is assisted by detailed petrographic studies, realistic core flow studies and/or reliable geochemical modeling. Pore throat sizes in these moderate-permeability formations are small enough to screen dispersed, undissolved clay-sized fines or spent acid precipitates and cause internal pore plugging. Recent research has helped to better define formation response to acids; however, as a practical matter, small hydraulic fracturing treatments are simpler and more cost-effective than matrix acidizing in some of these formations with permeability less than 50 md.

The guidelines for low permeability (less than 10 md) were based on treatments in which breakdown with acid probably occurred to open damaged perforations. The lower concentrations prevented massive precipitation in the formation and damage to the isolating cement yet were sufficient to clean up some perforation damage. Such treatments are probably obviated now by the advent of tubing-conveyed perforating.

7.21 Retarded HF Acids

Retarded HF (RHF) acids offer alternatives to the acids in Table 7.4, are less reactive with sandstone, and normally result in deep acid penetration into the formation. Three RHF acids that are based on boric acid, aluminum chloride, and a phosphoric acid were examined recently with guidance for their use.[45,46] A newer retarded sandstone acid is based on fluosilicic acid for deeper clay dissolution.[47] Fluosilicic acid can be injected by itself into a sandstone reservoir without causing any damage as long as it is blended into HCl acid or an organic acid. These acid mixtures improved the performance of two Brazilian water-injection wells by removing deep clay damage. A preflush of HCl or acetic acid must be used to dissolve carbonates ahead of the fluosilicic acid to prevent tertiary precipitation of calcium/aluminum fluoride complexes. In sandstone formations with more than 1% carbonate, the cost of sufficient acid preflush may prohibit treatment of damage beyond 2 ft in depth.

7.22 Geochemical Models

Several geochemical models exist today that provide guidance on acid type and concentration. The acidizing model of Thomas and Fannin[48] predicts dissolution of rock to increase porosity and permeability and incorporates the resistance of a diverting agent to ensure good acid coverage in a layered sandstone formation. The model does not consider precipitation and relies on an expert system to choose appropriate acid types and concentrations. The model of Davies *et al.*[49] is based on equilibrium chemistry and predicts the improvement in porosity and permeability by rock dissolution. It also predicts the porosity decrease by precipitation of species and the final permeability of the rock around the wellbore as a result of net dissolution. It helps select the volumes of acid required and the optimum acid types and concentrations to maximize well performance.

Gdanski and Schuchart[33] developed a geochemical model for sandstone acidizing that is helpful to engineers dealing with acidizing of sandstone containing sensitive minerals like zeolite and chlorite clay and for formation temperatures above 200°F. Above 200°F, various organic acids are recommended for certain minerals.

Quinn *et al.*[50] report on the application of a complex kinetic geochemical model to explore the importance of the formation minerals, mineral precipitation, and the effect of acid and injection rate. A new permeability prediction model relates the permeability of a permeable medium to the porosity, grain-size distribution, and the amounts and identities of all detrital minerals present and predicts productivity improvement. The optimal matrix stimulation is a compromise between maximizing the dissolution of the damaging minerals and minimizing secondary precipitation.

An integrated matrix stimulation model by Bartko *et al.*[51] for sandstone and carbonate formations assists in determining formation damage, selection, and optimization of fluid volumes; provides a pressure skin response of the acid treatment; and forecasts well productivity.

Single zone (shallow damage)

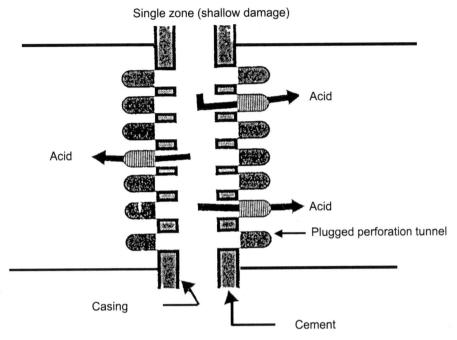

Fig. 7.14—Acid entry into formation through perforations.[9]

7.23 Acid Placement and Coverage

A leading cause of unsuccessful acid treatment is failure to contact all the damage with the acid. Fluids pumped into a formation take the path of least resistance. In a typical treatment, most acid enters the formation through the least damaged perforation tunnels, as the schematic in **Fig. 7.14** shows.[9]

When this happens, it is easy to conclude that acidizing is very expensive and does not work well. Acidizing works well to remove damage when the type of damage is known, the treatment is designed properly, and it is properly executed. Extreme damage may require more than what is discussed. Actions required may include a chemical soak and swabbing the soak back before acidizing or reperforating, and/or fracturing to bypass damage.

Numerous methods help control acid placement. Selection is based on wellbore hardware, formation characteristics, and field experience. Additional guidelines are provided in Ref. 1. The four main types of zone coverage techniques in matrix acidizing are mechanical, particulate, viscosity, and density segregation. These methods also can be combined in treatments.

7.24 Mechanical Techniques

7.24.1 Opposed Cup Packer or Perforation Wash Tool. This perforation wash tool allows selective injection of acid into closely spaced perforations in high-permeability formations. High rate and/or pressure should be avoided when using either this tool or closely spaced straddle packers. High pressures can cause the cups to leak or turn over or the tool to separate at the port (the weakest part). High pressure can also establish communication behind the pipe between the point of injection and nearby perforations without removing damage from the plugged perforation. This type of isolation is best used for removing damage from severely plugged perforations in high-permeability formations. A field example of this technique in a Gulf Coast sandstone is given by McLeod and Crawford.[13]

7.24.2 Squeeze Packer and Retrievable Bridge Plug. A good method of isolating perforated intervals is to use a retrievable bridge plug and a squeeze packer. The bridge plug is set in blank sections of casing between perforated sections. The treatment usually begins with the lower set of perforations and finishes with the upper set. Straddle packers may be used in a similar way and have been used successfully in the Permian Basin to better clean damaged perforations.

7.24.3 Ball Sealers. Ball sealers can be divided into two categories: those heavier (sinkers) and those lighter (floaters) than the fluid. Successful use requires a good cement job on the installed casing and round good quality perforation holes. Sinkers have been used the longest and usually require 200% excess ball sealers and a high pump rate (greater than 5 bbl/min). The high pump rate usually prohibits their use in sandstone matrix acidizing, but they may be used in fracture acidizing or perforation breakdown. Floaters, or neutral-density ball sealers, provide excellent mechanical isolation for matrix acidizing at injection rates of 1 bbl/min or higher. The density or specific gravity of these ball sealers is matched to the fluid being pumped so better ball action will take place. Surface flowback equipment must be modified to catch the floating ball sealers during flowback.

Ball sealers are limited in their use. They are not used in long intervals with high-perforation density, wells perforated with more than 4 shots/ft, low-rate treatments (¼ to ½ bbl/min), and gravel-packed wells. Regardless of the type of treatment or ball used, treatment will be more effective when density of the ball is very close to the density of the fluid used in the treatment.

7.25 Particulates

7.25.1 Pregravel-Pack Acid Treatments. One effective way to divert acid in a treatment before gravel packing is to use slugs of hydroxyethylcellulose (HEC) gel and gravel-pack sand. Ammonium chloride brine mixed with HEC at a concentration of 90 lbm/1,000 gal can be mixed in 5-bbl batches with 100 lbm of correctly sized gravel-pack sand. The combination of viscosity and sand packing helps divert acid to other perforations. The unique feature of this method, as opposed to other "particulate diverters," is that the perforation tunnel is packed with gravel-pack sand instead of some other material that would prevent gravel-pack slurry from entering the perforations during later slurry placement.

7.25.2 Soluble Particulate Diverters. Selection of the optimal particulate diverter is based on the kind of fluid injected and/or produced. The diverter must be temporary and easily removed; otherwise, there will be a new kind of damage to be treated and removed. Oil-soluble resin (OSR) is one of today's more common diverting agents. OSR is slowly soluble in toluene, xylene, condensate, crude oil, and EGMBE (mutual solvent). OSR should be mixed on site with a blender and immediately pumped or added to the acid "on the fly" with a chemical injection pump. If OSR diverters are mixed off location or are allowed to stand for an hour or more, they will clump and may cause pump failure or plug perforations. OSR diverters should not be used with solvent-acid mixtures, which dissolve the resin enough to reduce its effectiveness. The chart in **Fig. 7.15** shows the application of high concentrations of OSR to achieve significant pressure increases by more effective diverter action. The annular pressure (static column of fluid between the well tubing and coil tubing) shows pressure increases when diverter concentration increases.[4] Please refer to Ref. 6 for a full explanation. Shown in **Fig. 7.16** are gamma ray logs before and after using radioactive tracers with OSR diverters in a California well.[9] Such tracers are excellent diagnostic tools to find where the acid is going. In this case, radioactive intensity shows that most of the acid bypassed the preferred interval and went behind the casing and entered a thief zone behind the pipe.

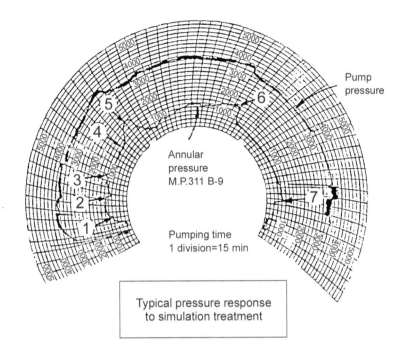

Pump pressure

Annular pressure
M.P.311 B-9

Pumping time
1 division=15 min

Typical pressure response
to simulation treatment

(1) Xylene at formation

(2) 10% acetic acid at formation

(3) 10% HCl acid at formation

(4) Raise volume of diverter from $1/2$ to 1%

(5) $7\frac{1}{2}$% HCl/$1\frac{1}{2}$% HF acid at formation

(6) 3% NH4 Cl at formation

(7) Xylene at formation

Fig. 7.15—Pressure response to acidizing using OSR diverter.[6]

Benzoic acid flakes or powder are soluble in toluene, xylene, alcohol, and some condensate fluids. They dissolve very slowly in water/gas. Benzoic acid is often used because it is soluble in the fluids normally encountered in oil/water wells; however, if not well dispersed or mixed, it will plug perforations. Benzoic acid plugs do not dissolve fast because not enough fluid can flow by it to dissolve the plug. One well took 6 months to return to normal productivity after being treated with caked benzoic acid powder delivered to the location.

7.26 Viscous Acid
Thickening the acid through use of soluble polymers, nitrogen and foaming agents, or dispersing oil (either as loose two-phase mixtures or with emulsifiers) is useful in high-permeability formations with deep damage. Design is difficult; therefore, experience and on-site flexibility are important for success. Excellent results have been obtained with staged foam slugs between

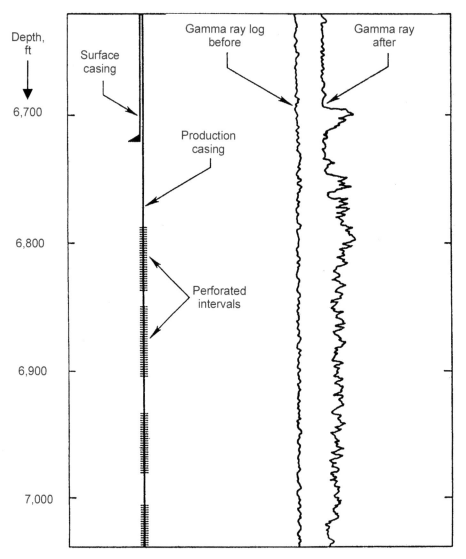

Fig. 7.16—OSR diverter evaluation radioactive tracer.[9]

acid stages in high-permeability Gulf Coast gas wells to remove near-wellbore damage. This technique is so promising because the diverter (gas and fluid) disappears when the foam breaks with little chance of damage as with slowly dissolving particulates. See Gdanski and Behanna[52] for useful guidelines.

Fadele *et al.*[53] show that diverters often need not be used in gas wells because of the natural viscous diversion. Water and acid are 100 times more viscous than gas, and this provides a natural diversion for acid entering a gas formation. This may be one reason acidizing works better in gas wells than in oil wells. Other recent papers offer further improvements with viscous acids and diverters.[54-56]

Other significant factors are the rathole below the lowest perforation and the space just above the top perforation and below the packer. Rathole fluid should be heavier than the acid, and fluid above the top perforation should be lighter than the acid. If not, acid can end up in the rathole rather than the formation. Acid left in the borehole can cause casing leaks below the treated interval. Spotting acid over the perforations before injecting is very important in low to moderate permeability (10 to 50 md), and density segregation must be planned to achieve the best contact of acid with damaged perforations in these formations. Concentric tubing helps to achieve accurate placement of the acid in the wellbore to take advantage of density segregation.

7.26.1 Concentric Tubing. Concentric tubing is preferred for matrix acid treatments because it allows the rathole to be circulated clean, permits better placement for acid contact with all perforations, bypasses production or injection tubing debris, can be acid cleaned on surface before running into the hole, and limits pump rate to 0.5 to 1 bbl/min because of fluid friction pressure in small tubing (1 to 1.5 in.).

7.27 Advances in Acid Diversion

The design and implementation of diverting systems has been advanced by recent design techniques but still relies on guidelines and field experience. Hill and Rossen[57] have provided a better means to compare diverting methods and design diverting treatments. Gdanski and Behenna[52] have provided some appropriate guidelines for foamed acids or foamed-diverter stages.

Hill and Rossen compared the techniques of injection rate diversion, coined MAPDIR (maximum pressure differential and injection rates); particulate diverting agents; viscosified fluids; and foamed acid. MAPDIR results in effective treatment of lower-permeability layers but at the expense of much larger volumes of acid. It may also be limited in use by pump and tubing capacities. Wells can clean up faster because no particulates are used. Also, treatment time is less to achieve the same reduction in skin factor as other techniques. The particulate diverting is most efficient in terms of volumes of acid and, thereby, is generally more economic if treating time is not a large economic factor. Oil soluble resins are not completely oil soluble, and sometimes plugging by these resins may not be temporary. Better quality assurance/quality control (QA/QC) is required for successful implementation. Quality assurance is the pretreatment planning to ensure that proper materials and procedures are used. Quality control is on-site supervision and testing to ensure that quality treatment is performed. Foam diversion is nondamaging in that surfactants are soluble and removable in produced water and nitrogen is recovered. Foams are most difficult to design and are not completely understood in terms of their behavior in different formations; however, guidelines for designing and implementing foam treatments are provided by Gdanski and Behenna.[52] Foams tend to be more stable in high-permeability layers and, therefore, reduce the acid losses in these layers. They also tend to be more stable in water zones and less stable in oil layers, providing some selectivity in treating wells with high water cuts or nearby bottom water. Viscosified fluids are similar to foam but provide a more consistent fluid hydrostatic pressure when well pressure limitations are present. The viscous behavior of these fluids in different formations is not well defined. These systems may be combined with MAPDIR when rate is limited by equipment.

7.28 Horizontal Wells

Horizontal wells are special cases, which have been covered by Frick and Economides.[58] They emphasize how damage control and removal is just as important in horizontal wells as in vertical completions. Moderate damage can reduce horizontal well productivity to that below the productivity of an undamaged vertical well. The authors provide a stimulation technique employing coiled tubing. They also provide a design strategy for calculating volumes of acid required and the rate of coiled-tubing withdrawal during acid placement. A method of optimization for completion and stimulation of horizontal wells is also presented. Other papers have further advanced the planning, design, diversion, execution, and evaluation of acidizing horizontal wells employing similar methods to those used in vertical wells.[59,60]

7.29 Acid Additives

An acid additive is any material blended with acid to modify its behavior. Because acid is so naturally corrosive, the development of an additive to reduce acid attack on steel pipe was the first requirement for successful acidizing. Development of a suitable corrosion inhibitor started the acidizing service industry in 1932. Comprehensive testing and application of corrosion inhibitors is still necessary in successful acidizing. Many acid additives are available, but those that are usually necessary are corrosion inhibitors, surfactants, and iron control agents. Any other additives are optional and should not be used unless specific well conditions dictate their use and have been thoroughly tested for compatibility with the formation fluids and the necessary additives. A mutual solvent in the overflush may be beneficial.

7.29.1 Corrosion Inhibitor. By nature of its adsorption on solid surfaces, the corrosion inhibitor is a surface-active agent with a unique purpose—to protect pipe rather than to change acid behavior in the formation. Corrosion inhibitors do not stop corrosion; they greatly reduce the reaction rate of acid with steel. Proper selection and application of corrosion inhibitors also reduce pitting (the tendency of acid to corrode or dissolve metal deeply in specific sites). Corrosion inhibitors are cationic and oil wetters. This is the mechanism by which they adsorb (plate out) on a metal surface and form an oil-wet film to protect the iron from exposure to acid. Plating out and oil wetting also occur in the formation, especially on clay minerals. To compensate for this, other additives, such as surfactants and mutual solvents, are used to restore water-wetness and maximize permeability to oil.

Pitting corrosion is very detrimental to the integrity of pipe. Reasons for pitting are inhibitor breakdown with time and temperature, insufficient inhibitor for wellbore conditions, and metal impurities in pipe. Factors that affect corrosion are pipe metallurgy, type acid, acid concentration, temperature, inhibitor solubility in the acid, inhibitor concentration, contact time with steel, inhibitor aids, and compatibility with other acids and additives such as organic acid, surfactants, alcohol, and solvent in the acid.

Service companies perform extensive lab testing in combination with additives to provide data to estimate the time of protection of pipe during the course of acid exposure to tubing in an acid treatment. The type of inhibitors and conditions in which they are used are many and complex. The engineer works closely with the stimulation specialist to ensure the proper selection and use of corrosion inhibitors in oil/gas wells. Usually, less than 5 mils of tubing corrosion should be allowed by the inhibitor in an acid treatment (equivalent to 0.025 lbm/ft^2 of tubing surface area) at temperatures less than 200°F.

7.29.2 Surface Active Agents. Surface active agents are molecules composed of an oil-soluble group and a water-soluble group. These chemicals lower the interfacial tension between the immiscible fluids. They also adsorb on rock surfaces and can alter the natural wettability of rock. Surfactants are classified into four major groups depending on the nature of the water-soluble part of the molecule. These divisions are anionic (water-soluble end is anionic), cationic (water-soluble end is cationic), nonionic (do not ionize—one end of molecule is water-soluble, the other is oil-soluble), and amphoteric (water-soluble end may be anionic, cationic, or uncharged depending on the pH of the system).

The primary use of surfactants is in emulsion prevention in acid/oil interactions. Other uses are as wetting agents, penetrating agents, sludge preventers and foaming agents, acid solvent dispersant, mud dispersants, emulsion breakers, retarders, and suspending agents. Surfactants should be tested for performance as emulsion breakers for crude/oil acid systems in both live acid and spent acid.

7.29.3 Iron-Control Agents. Iron control uses several different products to keep iron in solution: iron complexing agents, iron reducing agents, and hydrogen sulfide scavengers.

7.29.4 Iron-Complexing Agents. Iron in solution has two forms: ferric and ferrous. Ferric iron is often called iron (III), and ferrous iron is often called iron (II). The oxidized form, iron (III), precipitates in spent acid around a pH of 1 to 2. Iron (II) does not precipitate as ferrous hydroxide until a pH of 7 is reached, well beyond the final equilibrium of spent HCl acid, which is around a pH of 5. Normally, the ferrous iron is not a problem in acid treatments; however, there are three exceptions. If acid is pumped into a new well that has been drilled with caustic water-based mud, the mud filtrate in the formation may still have a pH of 11 or higher. Mixing of spent acid with this mud filtrate precipitates ferrous hydroxide. Ferrous iron also precipitates in a sour environment where hydrogen sulfide is dissolved in the brine, oil, or natural gas. The only effective remedy to keep iron (II) in solution where hydrogen sulfide exists is to use a hydrogen sulfide scavenger to make the sulfide unavailable for precipitating ferrous sulfide at a pH of 2. Complexing agents do not prevent the precipitation of iron sulfide.[28] A third problem long term is the presence of iron (II) in the presence of undissolved calcium carbonate. Iron (II) can precipitate slowly as ferrous carbonate—a slowly forming carbonate scale. This usually does not impede flow in carbonate rocks but may in sandstone with excess carbonate because the sand grain matrix can screen the precipitate. Addition of acetic acid to the preflush maintains a low-pH environment to prevent the iron carbonate precipitation.

Ferric oxide and ferrous sulfide are frequently found in water-injection wells in surface pipe, tubing and borehole, and in the formation. The iron oxide is present from air contamination in the injected water. Iron sulfide is present from bacterial action in the injected water or formation. Ferric oxide is common in all acid treatments. The main source is a coating of mill scale or rust on the surface of the tubing or piping used in stimulation. This is usually the source of the most damaging iron concentrations in acid. Iron-complexing agents can only complex iron concentrations of up to 10,000 ppm. Acid can dissolve iron from tubing walls as high as 100,000 ppm. No complexing agent can complex this much iron. Two important steps in controlling iron in acidizing are pickling treating strings prior to acidizing and using iron reducing agents. Acid pickling treatments are covered later in the section on job execution; however, the purpose of pickling tubing is to clean the tubing of easily dissolved iron and bring it back to the surface for disposal. This procedure reduces the amount of ferric iron in solution during the subsequent injection of acid into the formation.

7.29.5 Iron-Reducing Agents. The most common iron-reducing agent is erythorbic acid—a cousin to vitamin C. Erythorbic acid is added to the acid to reduce any ferric ion to ferrous iron before it enters the formation. The use of a reducing agent does not take the place of acid pickling the treating string. Even though pickling removes most of the easily dissolvable iron oxide from the tubing, enough iron oxide remains after pickling so that a reducing agent is still necessary during the acid treatment. Some formations contain iron oxide in the formation so that iron complexing agents are still needed along with the reducing agent as a safeguard. The complexing agents most commonly used are shown in **Table 7.7**.[61] One of the favorite iron-control agents is the combination of citric and acetic acid. Citric acid by itself is limited to 15 lbm/1,000 gal of acid because of limited solubility in the acid. Acetic acid permits mixing higher loadings of citric acid (up to 100 lbm/1,000 gal) and also maintains a low pH in spent acid to keep iron (III) in solution. Improved techniques and procedures have advanced the control of dissolved iron in acid treatments.[62,63,28]

7.29.6 Hydrogen Sulfide Control. Common chelating agents are ineffective for iron control in sour environments. Systems containing hydrogen sulfide contain only ferrous iron [iron (II)] species. The only effective method of preventing precipitation of iron sulfide during sour-well acid treatments is to remove hydrogen sulfide from the fluid with sulfide scavenger products. If there is any possibility of ferric iron [iron (III)] being injected from surface containers or pipe, a reducing agent should be added in the acid to reduce the dissolved iron (III) to iron (II).

TABLE 7.7—IRON-CONTROL AGENTS[61]	
Iron Control Additive	Concentration: Pounds/1,000 gal Acid
NTA (nitrilotetraacetic acid)	50–300
Tetra-sodium EDTA	30–60
Erythorbic acid	2–15
Citric acid (to 150°F	15
Combination:	
Citric acid	50 lbm/1,000 gal
Acetic anhydride	10 gal/1,000 gal

TABLE 7.8—MUTUAL SOLVENT GUIDELINES[1]
A. Ethylene glycol monobutyl ether (EGME). Use 10% vol/vol (100 gal EGMBE/1,000 gal in overflush).
B. Methanol (methyl alcohol). Do not exceed 25% vol/vol (250 gal/1,000 gal of acid).
C. Isopropyl alcohol (IPA). Do not exceed 20% vol/vol (200 gal/1,000 gal of acid).

7.29.7 Other Additives. The "other" category of additives consists of those that are optional for special conditions and are not commonly needed in all treatments. They should not be used unless they have been thoroughly tested for compatibility with all formation fluids. These additives are mutual solvents, clay stabilizers, acid diverting agents, calcium sulfate scale inhibitors, and gelling agents.

7.29.8 Mutual Solvents. A mutual solvent is soluble in either oil or water. For this reason, it is very effective in sandstone acidizing, in which it is important to keep all solids water-wet. Mutual solvents are either EGMBE or other modified glycol ethers. They improve the solubility of corrosion inhibitors in the spent acid in the formation and compatibility of inhibitors with emulsion preventers and other additives. The most important property is to reduce the adsorption of corrosion inhibitors on residual clay particles in the formation and to help maintain water-wetting for maximum oil/gas flow after acidizing. A mutual solvent also reduces residual water saturation (spent acid) following a treatment. Gas wells clean up better by keeping surfactants in solution rather than adsorbing on sand and clay too near the wellbore.

Alcohol. Methyl alcohol and isopropyl alcohol have been used for many years to aid in cleaning up water-blocked gas wells. On occasion, 10 to 20% alcohol is used in acid to stimulate moderately low-permeability (5 to 50 md) gas sands to speed the cleanup of spent acid. The normal concentrations of mutual solvents and alcohol are listed in the **Table 7.8.**[1]

7.29.9 Clay Stabilizers. Clay minerals or other fines may move in the formation, particularly during water production. Also, some clays can be dispersed or swell when contacted with fresh water or low-salinity brines.

Cationic polymers are sometimes used in brine or acid to stabilize clays. These cationic polymers do not oil-wet sands because the end of the molecule projecting from the adsorbed end is water soluble. Clay stabilizers used include polyquaternary amines, polyamines, and cationic surfactants. Polyquaternary amines have been the most effective, with polyamines second. The use of cationic surfactants for clay control is not recommended except in water-

TABLE 7.9—DIVERTERS[64]

Pre-Gravel-Pack Acid Treatments	Perforated Completions	Gravel-Packed Wells

5 bbl of a 90 lbm/1,000-gal HEC gelled 3% ammonium chloride with 100 lbm of correctly-sized gravel-pack sand	A. Ball sealers
	  1. Neutral density or floaters: 50% excess
	  2. Sinkers: 200% excess
	
	B. Oil-soluble resin or polymer: 0.5 to 5 gal/1,000 gal
	C. Benzoic acid: 1 lbm/ft of perforations
	D. Rock salt: 0.5 to 2 lbm/ft (do not use with HF acid)
	E. Unibeads (wax beads): 1 to 2 lbm/ft
	F. Naphthalene flakes or moth balls: 0.25 to 1 lbm/ft (do not use in water-injection wells)
		Oil-soluble resins may be used as in II.B.; however, they must be well mixed and added to the acid as it is pumped or else the diverter may plug the screen or gravel pack.

TABLE 7.10— SOLVENTS FOR DIVERTING AGENTS AND FLUID LOSS CONTROL AGENTS

Diverter	Solvent
Oil soluble resin	Toluene, xylene, condensate, and oil
Liquid polymer (dispersed OSR)	Toluene, xylene, condensate, and oil
Salt	Water and dilute HCl acid
Wax beads	Toluene, xylene, and some oil
Napthalene flakes	Toluene, xylene, some condensate, and gas
Benzoic acid (powder or flakes)	Toluene, xylene, some condensate, gas, and water (very slowly)
Paraformaldehyde	Hot water and HCl acid
Calcium carbonate	HCl
Polymer and silica fines	HF/HCl acid
Sand	None
Paper or other organic fiber	None

injection wells in water-sensitive formations. A wide variance in opinion exists as to how to best apply these products. Clay stabilizers are most often used in the overflush following an HF-acid treatment in sandstone formations. Most of the clay stabilizers are not affected by HCl acid but are dislodged by HF acid. It is not recommended to use more than 20 gal/1,000 gal.

Acid Diverters. Diverting agents (discussed earlier) are best used in acidizing damaged perforations so that acid is distributed more evenly to all perforations regardless of the degree of plugging or variations in permeability. The diverting agents should ideally be either degradable or partially soluble in produced oil and/or water. Uses in gas wells are limited and difficult to clean up; foamed acid is a better means of diversion in gas wells. Some guidelines for diverter use are listed in **Tables 7.9[64] and 7.10.**

7.29.10 Calcium Sulfate Inhibitors. When acidizing formations with a high-sulfate-ion content in the formation water (usually greater than 1,000 ppm) or rock containing anhydrite, it is advisable to include a calcium sulfate inhibitor in the acid. The inhibitor is usually phosphonic acid, polyacrylate, or other material.

7.29.11 Gelling Agents. Acids may be thickened for diversion during acidizing with soluble polymers such as xanthan (a biopolymer) or acrylamide polymers. Higher viscosity may be obtained with crosslinking metal ions or ligands. Certain surfactants may be used to thicken acid through the formation of surfactant micelles.

7.29.12 Summary Remarks. In 1999, Coulter and Jennings[65] updated industry experience in the use of acids and additives. Many chemical additives are proprietary compositions, but the service company has detailed instructions for mixing and use. It also has facilities and personnel to carry out acid and additive testing for well treatment. The operating engineer's knowledge of the well and the reservoir and the service company engineer's knowledge of chemical products and treatment processes are required to recommend appropriate treatment fluids. This partnering improves the quality of acid treatments.

7.30 Job Supervision
The key to successful job execution is thorough and effective job supervision. The operating company responsible for supervising the job must prepare the well before the service company administers the acid treatment; monitor the progress of the project before, during, and after the treatment; and properly evaluate the results. The most important tasks associated with job supervision are those related to safety, well preparation, and quality control.

7.31 Safety and Environment Protection

7.31.1 Safety. The main safety precautions for those on site during an acid treatment concern detection of leaks and proper handling of acid. Pressure tests are performed with water or brine to ensure the absence of leaks in pressure piping, tubing, and packer. Leaks on the surface can endanger service personnel, and subsurface leaks can cause subsequent corrosion of tubing and casing in the annulus. Anyone around acid tanks or pressure connections should wear safety goggles for eye protection. Those handling chemicals and valves should wear protective gauntlet-type, acid-resistant gloves. Fresh water and spray washing equipment should be available at the job site. In case of acid contact with the eyes, immediately flush eyes with clean water and consult a physician. If acid contacts the skin, wash the area of contact with water for 15 minutes. Consult a physician immediately after flushing if hydrofluoric acid comes in contact with skin or eyes. Wear self-contained, full-face, fresh-air masks when potential hydrogen sulfide gas hazards exist. Also, testing equipment and appropriate safety equipment should be on hand to monitor the working area and protect personnel in the area. Special scrubbing equipment may be required for removal of toxic gases. Further information on safety with acid can be found in API *Bull. D15, Recommendations for Proper Usage and Handling of Inhibited Oilfield Acids*[66] and in *Data Sheet 634, Safe Well Stimulation by Acidizing* from the National Safety Council.[67]

7.31.2 Environment Protection. Proper handling and disposal of acid and spent acid products should be observed. Often, environmental hazards can be reduced or prevented by the proper choice of chemical additives at optimum concentrations. The acid flowbacks are normally processed in a test separator. Oil goes to the water/oil separation system, and the aqueous phase is filtered and treated with activated carbon for overboard disposal in accordance with regulatory guidelines of oil and grease measurements. This process, used in many offshore operations, is described in an article by Ali.[68] Regulatory guidelines[69] are available to control and monitor discharges of well workover fluids containing oil or grease. Overboard discharges must meet 42 mg/L daily maximum and 29 mg/L monthly average oil and grease limits. There are no acute and chronic toxicity measurement requirements at present.

7.32 Well Preparation

Treating fluids must leave surface tanks, travel through surface pipe and well tubing, enter a wellbore, and pass through the perforations into the formation so that the solvent can react with the damaging solids. Each of these components through which the fluid travels must be properly cleaned before pumping acid into the formation. Surface tanks must be cleaned before being filled with acid. The best tanks are rubber lined and cleaned of any formerly contained materials before the new acid and additives are added to the tank. Surface lines through which the acid is pumped should be cleaned with acid before the treatment. A small amount of acid can be flushed through the lines and into waste containment before final hookup for the well treatment. This also can be accomplished in the step for acid cleaning well tubing.

7.32.1 Borehole Cleanout.
The well should be adequately prepared before the service company arrives on site to perform the acid treatment. If possible, wellbore fill should be circulated out to remove any solids and sludge that have accumulated in the rathole and/or isolated by placing a heavy brine in the rathole prior to acidizing. If the formation pressure is very low, care must be taken to prevent the loss of accumulated sludge and other materials to the formation. Any fluid-loss additives selected should dissolve in the produced well fluids, such as oil-soluble resins or benzoic acid particulates.

Fluids used to load the well prior to injecting acid should be filtered to a "superclean" state to prevent any damage during injection testing before acidizing—typically to less than 50 ppm for solids and less than 2 microns for size. No produced lease water should be used because these produced waters usually are contaminated with emulsion breakers or corrosion inhibitors often found in water/oil separation facilities and may also contain suspended solid hydrocarbons and clay particles. Emulsion breakers and corrosion inhibitors in produced water can oil-wet the formation and reduce productivity, and suspended solids are very damaging.

7.32.2 Acid Cleaning Tubing.
In addition to borehole cleanout, acid clean the tubing and surface piping before injecting acid into the formation to prevent plugging of the perforations by solids released from the tubing. **Fig. 7.17** shows the characteristics of acid being pumped down tubing in a well.[7]

Pumping acid through tubing releases solids deposited on the pipe surface. Acid-insoluble solids like pipe dope, paraffin, asphalt, and gypsum or barite scales may plug the perforations and even fill the wellbore. Acid-soluble solids like calcium carbonate may just spend the acid, whereas dissolved iron oxide or iron sulfide may precipitate as the acid spends on other minerals in the formation. Either acid cleaning the tubing and reversing to surface containment or bypassing the production tubing with an acid-cleaned concentric tubing string prevents perforation plugging from tubing deposits.

The dissolution of mill scale and/or rust in the tubing can theoretically lead to concentrations as high as 75,000 ppm in acid, and field acid cleaning tests confirmed this. Iron complexing agents can prevent ferric hydroxide precipitation from acid with up to 10,000 ppm iron.

For high-pressure reservoirs, acid may be pumped down the tubing close to the bottom and then flowed back to the surface containment. If the reservoir pressure will not hold the acid hydrostatic column, foamed acid may be used to clean the tubing, or a work string can be run with a packer, isolation valve, and circulating tool to isolate the formation while acid cleaning

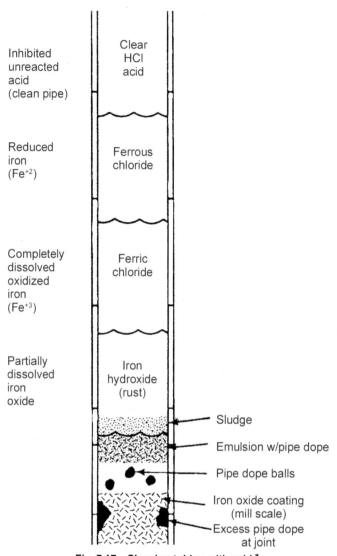

Fig. 7.17—Cleaning tubing with acid.[7]

the tubing. If a work string is not used and if the production tubing cannot be cleaned proper-ly, it should be bypassed using a concentric tubing string to pump the acid.

A concentric tubing string can be used to circulate accumulated sludge below the perforated interval with clean brine before acid injection. Injection wells may have accumulated corrosion deposits and/or bacterial slimes. Producing wells may have loose scale deposits, hydrocarbon solids, or produced formation fines. Recent papers[70–73] have provided additional guidance on tubing cleaning and pickling.

7.33 Quality Control
Quality control checks before, during, and after pumping increase the probability of acidizing success. Onsite supervisors are encouraged to check the equipment.

• Inspect all tanks that will be used to hold acid or water. The tanks must be clean. Small amounts of dirt, mud, or other debris can destroy any acid job.

• Make sure the service company has the equipment to circulate the acid tank prior to pumping. This must be done to avoid emulsion problems and to protect the tubing. Acid corrosion inhibitors and other additives can separate to the top of the tank in as little as 2 hours.

• The line to the pit or tank should be laid and ready to connect to the wellhead so the acid can be backflowed immediately after the end of the overflush.

Field supervisors are focusing more on acid quality control. Guidelines are provided by King and Holman[64] and elsewhere.[34]

7.33.1 Injection Testing. When in doubt that the formation will take acid, inject a compatible "superclean" filtered brine to test the ability of the formation to take fluid. If the test shows severe damage, the operation may be changed to include an acid minisqueeze prior to the main acid job to make sure that the formation is open to fluid. Zhu and Hill[74] showed that a pretreatment test could be used to evaluate permeability and skin factor prior to treatment. The monitoring program followed evolution of skin even with diversion effects. The program is reliable and flexible for acquiring and processing data, calculating skin, and diagnosing matrix acidizing treatments.

7.33.2 Sampling and Titration. Sampling of all pumped fluids for solids content and acid titration for HCl- and HF-acid concentration should be performed on site as a quality control measure. Samples of spent acid should be analyzed for pH immediately and then kept in air-tight containers for chemical analysis. Large variations in acid concentrations delivered to the well site have been found. Delivered acid concentrations are usually more accurate and consistent when a known on-site titration program is to be used. Premixed acid should be rolled and circulated to make sure that all additives are properly dispersed and that none, especially corrosion inhibitors, have separated and floated to the top of acid tanks or have sunk to the bottom. Titration of acid is an excellent test to see whether acid is well mixed. In one case, 15% HCl acid was sampled and titrated to show 6% HCl acid. The acid tank was "rolled" to mix well and titrated again. This time, it titrated as 15% HCl acid. Poorly-mixed acid can result in highly varied acid concentrations (5 to 25% in an average 15% HCl-acid mix) with similar variations in corrosion inhibitors and other additives. Such a variable mix will exacerbate corrosion, emulsion problems, and acid/formation interactions. Also, high acid strength can harm tubing and certain formations. Surfactants should be checked to ensure that they leave the rock minerals in a water-wet condition for optimum oil flow.

7.34 Injection-Rate Control and Monitoring

The main acid job should be circulated in place with HCl acid placed across the formation before the packer is set or before the bypass valve is closed. All perforations should be covered by acid before injection starts. Injection should start at a predetermined injection rate and the pressure observed to determine the condition of the wellbore. If the pressure rises close to the pressure limit, the rate should be cut in half until the pressure stabilizes at a level below the formation fracturing pressure. When the HF acid stage reaches the formation, a pressure drop is normally observed. The rate should not be changed as long as a positive pressure is observed at the wellhead. If the well goes on vacuum, the rate should be instantly raised until a positive pressure is observed at the wellhead. Hold the new rate steady as the acid is injected. Nevertheless, the constant injection rate of HF acid into the wellbore should not exceed an optimum ½ bbl/min unless the perforated interval is greater than 25 ft. If the formation is very thick, the rate can be 0.02 bbl/min per foot of net pay. Other authors have different opinions on allowable injection rates, as discussed later.

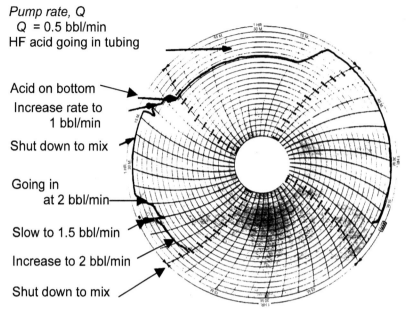

Pump rate, Q
 Q = 0.5 bbl/min
HF acid going in tubing

Acid on bottom

Increase rate to
    1 bbl/min

Shut down to mix

Going in
    at 2 bbl/min

Slow to 1.5 bbl/min

Increase to 2 bbl/min

Shut down to mix

Fig. 7.18—Acid treatment with poor rate control.[7]

7.35 Pressure Behavior During Acid Injection

Two pressure responses are often observed during acid treatment. **Fig. 7.18** shows one response.[7] In this well, when acid hit the formation, pressure dropped immediately. As the pressure dropped, the rate was increased; then the pressure began to rise. The rate was reduced, and then the well was shut in while another batch of acid was mixed on site. Injection was restarted at a rate of 2 bbl/min, then cut back to 1.5 bbl/min and stabilized at 2 bbl/min for the final injection of overflush. Rate should be held constant for a period of time at least until the pressure stabilizes. Haphazard changes in rate make it impossible to determine on site what the quantitative response of the well is to the acid treatment, unless newer computer models and monitoring equipment are available, as discussed later. A better-controlled acid treatment is shown in **Fig. 7.19**.[7] Here, the rate is stabilized at 0.55 bbl/min. When the HF acid stage entered the formation, the pressure slowly declined but stayed above 0 psi. This rate was continued as long as the pressure was observed and is the type of response that one should observe when a well is treated to remove wellbore damage.

When the overflush reaches the formation, the rate may be increased as fast as allowed, as long as the pressure stays below the fracturing pressure. The faster overflush rate will push the spent acid deeper into the formation and overdisplace the spent acid reaction products more efficiently away from the wellbore. This safely finishes the treatment and allows the spent acid to be produced back sooner. The well should be flowed immediately, unloaded with nitrogen, swabbed back, or put on artificial lift.

7.36 On-Site Evaluation of Acid Treatment Effectiveness

The pressure and rate chart of the acid treatment show the effect of acid volume on the formation as the acid treatment proceeds. The papers of McLeod and Coulter,[75] Paccaloni et al.,[76] and Prouvost and Economides[77] are significant to the on-site evaluation of acidizing treatments. On-site data monitoring follows and evaluates the progress of damage removal by acid. **Fig. 7.20**[76] shows injection rate and pressure plotted on a precalculated chart of pressure vs. rate and crossplotted with a family of skin-factor curves based on steady-state injection. The successive points clearly show the reduction in skin factor. These plots may be somewhat misleading

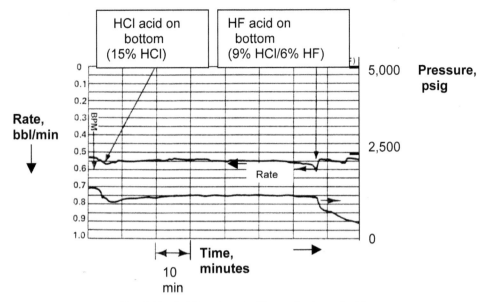

Fig. 7.19—Acid treatment with good rate control.[7]

because pressure transients are ignored after rate changes; however, no on-site computer is required.

Fig. 7.21[77] shows rates, pressures (both measured and simulated), and skin-factor change during acidizing, as presented by Prouvost and Economides.[77] This method requires an onsite computer but considers pressure transient effects when rate is changed. Such plots are a tremendous help in analyzing on-site acidizing performance and in follow-up well analysis. More information is also available in the excellent text on stimulation by Economides and Nolte.[78] McLeod and Coulter[75] presented the first example of injection pressure buildup analysis before and after acidizing cleanup in **Figs. 7.22 and 7.23.** Calculation to obtain formation permeability before and after acidizing are shown with data in **Tables 7.11 through 7.14.**

Hill and Zhu[79] advanced the monitoring of acidizing treatments, building on the earlier contributions of McLeod and Coulter,[75] Paccaloni et al.,[76] and Prouvost and Economides.[77] The use of the inverse injectivity diagnostic plot permits the real-time evaluation of treatments and further assists in post-treatment evaluations. Montgomery et al.[80] proposed more active treatment monitoring into standard acidizing practice.

Refs. 81 and 82 provide good field examples of monitoring acid treatments with concurrent skin evolution for both diverted and nondiverted treatments. Monitored on-site evaluation was later confirmed with well-flow analysis of post-treatment well performance. However, more work is needed on evaluating causes of treatment failures or skin increases.

7.37 Spent Acid Production Control

The well should be produced first at the same rate before acidizing. As soon as the well has cleaned up and all spent acid has been recovered or reduced to zero water cut, the producing rate may be increased. In formations with moveable fines, the rate should be increased once each week to finally reach the optimum producing rate for that well. Increasing the rate gradually helps the return of any dispersed solids and prolongs the improvement for the acid treatment.

Ali et al.[83] discussed a method to minimize production facility upsets offshore by special handling of the returned acids at the surface. The cost of fluid handling is further reduced by

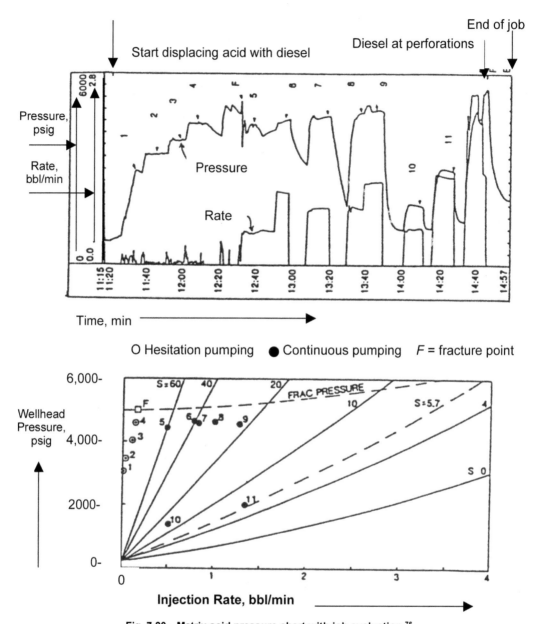

Fig. 7.20—Matrix acid pressure chart with job evaluation.[76]

optimizing use of additives with improved laboratory testing procedures.[84] This was stimulated by the work of Bansal.[85]

7.38 Produced Fluid Sampling

Spent acid samples should be collected at the surface to properly analyze the response of the well to the acid treatment. These samples should be analyzed for pH immediately and then kept in airtight containers for chemical analysis. Chemical analysis of these samples can provide information for use in evaluating why a well did not respond to acid treatment. If precipitates or emulsions are a problem, the return samples will show the reason. Whatever

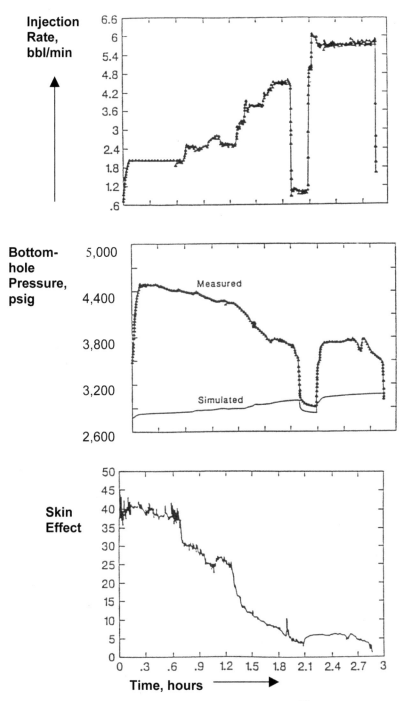

Fig. 7.21—Skin evolution during acid job.[77]

solids are precipitating to cause possible damage to the rock around the wellbore may be present in these collected samples. Steps can be taken to reduce precipitation by changes in acid concentration, preflush fluids, and/or additives in the next scheduled treatment.

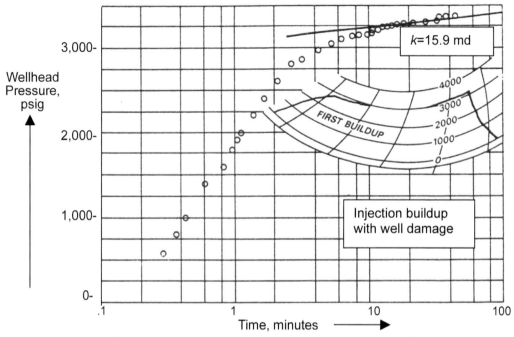

Fig. 7.22—Injection pressure buildup with wellbore damage.[34]

Analysis of well flowback may indicate problems and concerns not readily evident otherwise. Such problems may arise from acid or spent acid mixing with lost completion brines and/or formation water, significant dissolution of carbonates, and total consumption of acid. The insight obtained helps to design optimum formulations for future treatments.[63]

A comprehensive HF acidizing radial flow model was modified by Gdanski and Schuchart[33] to account for deep-matrix mixing and back production of sandstone-acidizing treating fluids. Deep matrix mixing may require back production of at least two treatment volumes of aqueous fluid to recover the spent injected acids. Matching the ionic return profiles can provide information about formation mineralogy and excess precipitation.

To summarize, on-site supervision of acid treatments is critical to successful acidizing. Long treatments can best be controlled by two persons—one to coordinate the acid schedule and rate and pressure control, and the other to check materials; titrate acid; and monitor volumes, rates, and pressures. The engineer who recommended and designed the job and the supervisor who prepared the well for acidizing make a good combination. Good data and record keeping greatly help the job of evaluating acidizing results.

7.39 Evaluation of Acid Treatments

The evaluation process encompasses six major areas on which to focus when assessing job performance and acid treatment success:

• Injection rate and pressure.
• Final fall-off pressure record.
• Well production analysis (nodal analysis).
• Produced fluid samples.
• Post-treatment investigation concerning damage incurred during injection, acid removal of damage, post-treatment damage (precipitates), and verbal communications.

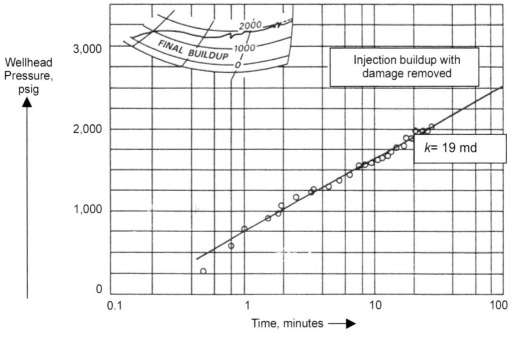

Fig. 7.23—Injection pressure buildup with damage removed.[34]

TABLE 7.11—ACID TREATMENT EVALUATION DATA[34]	
Assumed Well Data	Buildup Data
μ = 1 cp	Before acidizing:
φ = 0.25	h = 27 ft
$c = (10)^{-5} psi^{-1}$	q = 0.35 bbl/min or 502 B/D
B = 1.0	m = 190 psi/cycle
r_w = 0.4 ft	k = 15.9 md
	After acidizing:
	q = 2 bbl/min or 2,800 B/D
	m = 910 psi/cycle
	k = 19 md

• Recommendations for continuous improvement.

The most important measure of the treatment is the productivity of the well after treatment. When the productivity stabilizes at the same production rate as before treatment, the flowing bottomhole pressure should be estimated from fluid levels or from measured flowing pressures. Static bottomhole pressure should be measured following any long shut-in periods. A well flow analysis should show whether the designed productivity was obtained. The pressure charts from the treatment, including both accurate injection rates and recorded injection pressures, can be analyzed using transient pressure analysis to determine when or if the wellbore damage was removed by the treatment. An injectivity index can be calculated for the well both before and after the HF-acid stage. The final overflush injection pressures and rates should give a fairly accurate measure of the well productivity before the well is ever returned to production. A useful source of information is the final pressure falloff after the treatment. If the pressure ex-

TABLE 7.12—INJECTION PRESSURE BUILDUP ANALYSIS
BEFORE ACIDIZING*

$$kh = \frac{162.6\,qB}{m}$$

$$= \frac{162.6(502)(1)(1)}{190} = 430\,\text{md/ft},$$

and

$$kh = \frac{kh}{h} = \frac{430}{27} = 15.9\,\text{md}.$$

$$S = 1.151\left(\frac{p\,1\,\text{hr} - p_w}{m} - \log\frac{k}{\varphi\mu c r_w{}^2} + 3.23\right)$$

$$= 1.151\left[\frac{3{,}400 - 0}{190} - \log\frac{15.9}{(0.25)(1)(10)^{-5}(0.4)^2} + 3.23\right]$$

$$= 1.15(17.89 - 7.60 + 3.23)$$

$$= 15.6.$$

*From Fig. 7.22. m = 190 psi/cycle.

TABLE 7.13—INJECTION PRESSURE BUILDUP ANALYSIS
AFTER ACIDIZING*

$$kh = \frac{162.6\,q\mu B}{m}$$

$$= \frac{162.6(2{,}880)(1)(1)}{910} = 514\,\text{md/ft},$$

and

$$k = \frac{514}{27} = 19.0\,\text{md}.$$

$$S = 1.151\left[\frac{2{,}375 - 0}{910} - \log\frac{19}{(0.25)(1)(10)^{-5}(0.4)^2} + 3.23\right]$$

$$= 1.15(2.61 - 7.67 + 3.23)$$

$$= 1.15(-1.83) = -2.1.$$

*From Fig. 7.23. m = 910 psi/cycle.

ists at the wellhead, the falloff pressures should be recorded on site until the well goes on vacuum. If the well goes on vacuum too soon, fluid levels can be shot with a sonolog device until the level falls to near the static bottomhole pressure. These final falloff pressures can be used to estimate the wellbore condition after the acid treatment. If this analysis shows that the acid treatment removed all wellbore damage, the treatment is potentially successful if later well production analysis shows that no post-acid precipitation occurred. An example of this type analysis is shown in the example provided by McLeod.[34]

If the well injectivity or productivity (after the well returns to injection or production) is not close to that predicted by the falloff analysis, some damage probably occurred to the formation after the acid treatment ended. Subsequent damage after the treatment may be caused by

TABLE 7.14—STABILIZED WATER INJECTION RATE*

$$q = \frac{0.00707\, kh\, \Delta p}{\mu B\left[\ln\left(\dfrac{re}{rw}\right) + S - 0.75\right]}$$

$$= \frac{0.00707(19)(27)(1{,}940)}{(1)(1)\left(\ln\dfrac{660}{0.4} - 2.1 - 0.75\right)}$$

$$= 1{,}540 \text{ BWPD.}$$

*Calculated expected injection rate at a pressure difference of 1,940 psi.

precipitation of acid reaction products in the formation or by return of fines to the wellbore with internal pore plugging at or near perforations. This is especially true in gravel-packed wells.

First, it is important to know that the treatment removed the damage in the wellbore during treatment as intended. If damage occurred after the treatment, steps can be taken to prevent that damage in a later treatment of that well or others in the reservoir by such steps as utilizing different additives to keep reaction products in solution, overflushing the reaction products deeper into the formation, using different acids or acid concentrations to prevent the excess precipitation of acid reaction products, or using stabilizers to prevent fines from returning to the wellbore and reducing productivity.

If the anticipated productivity was achieved, the acid treatment worked as designed. If not, the entire treatment should be reviewed to analyze the causes. Often, unsatisfactory performance results from imperfect coverage during the treatment. A change in the acid placement technique may be necessary for the next acid treatment in the field. If solid diverting agents were employed, changes in concentrations may be necessary, or perhaps another diversion technique would work better. Feasibility and economic analysis from the expected well production increase determine whether these changes are worthwhile.

The engineer evaluating the treatment should individually discuss the treatment with the service company supervising engineer and the operating company supervisor. Their observations lead to future treatment improvements.

The acid treatment report and the pressure/rate treatment charts are the best sources of information. The engineer can observe and follow the injectivity during the entire process to see whether the injectivity decreased during the treatment. Plugging or reduced injectivity during the first injection into the wellbore can be traced to solids suspended in injected fluids at the beginning of the treatment. The condition of the well, well preparation, and QC sampling can reveal the source of these plugging solids.

Usually, the damage during an acid treatment occurs at the time the first acid hits the formation. This first acid damage is usually caused by solids removed from the tubing walls prior to the acid reaching the formation. Also, acid may react adversely with some of the minerals in the formation, and perhaps a different acid or solvent (such as acetic acid or an aromatic solvent) should be used to first contact the formation. Many acid failures are caused by the elimination of needed wellbore preparations prior to the acid treatment.

7.40 Continuous Improvement

Nitters *et al.*[5] present a systematic approach for candidate selection, damage evaluation, and treatment selection and design using a recently developed integrated software package. They recognize the importance of evaluating skin factors from well tests to determine what could be improved. After identifying damage mechanisms, they used an expert system and geochemical simulator to select appropriate treatment fluids. They also developed software for the evaluation and design of acid placement.

Hashem *et al.*[86] produced an excellent example of a complete strategy for acidizing. Well analysis and sampling identified the damage mechanisms that were removed by the appropriate acid systems and additives that were selected using formation mineralogy, extensive laboratory testing with core flood studies, and acid and additive testing. Well preparation, job supervision, and on-site monitoring played key roles in the success of the acid treatments. Treatment evaluations were performed to identify problems with some acid treatments, which led to improved additive formulations and improved spent-acid cleanup procedures. These steps resulted in an 86% success rate in treatment of water-injection wells and significantly improved water injectivity.

To summarize, successful acidizing is assured by proper treatment design, well preparation, and execution, which includes significant practices: acid cleaning of tubing; acid type and concentration designed for the mineralogy and the permeability of the formation; acids, additives, and solvent flush designed for proper acid/reservoir fluid compatibility; properly prepared wellbore and effective acid coverage; sufficient time provided for acid contact and penetration of all perforations; and precipitation prevented or flushed away from the wellbore.

Treatment evaluation leads to problem identification and to continuously improved treatments. The prime source of information on which to build an evaluation are the acid treatment report and the pressure and rate data during injection and falloff.

The tasks of execution and evaluation go hand in hand. Proper execution, quality control, and record keeping are prerequisites to the task of accurate evaluation. Evaluation of unsatisfactory treatments is essential to recommending changes in chemicals and/or treating techniques and procedures that will provide the best treatment for acidizing wells in the future. This implies a program for continuous improvement.

Summary
One may feel overwhelmed by the details in executing successful acid treatments. This is true of any complex oilfield operation such as cementing, perforating, gravel packing, or hydraulic fracturing. Acidizing has often been treated with a cavalier attitude because the treatments can be relatively inexpensive in some areas. Past acid treatments have been successful without much care. That was true because completions were so bad in the early days of acidizing that some production improvement was fairly easy. Today, completions are much better planned and executed, and there is less tolerance for poor stimulation processes. Experience with acid in a field is a starting point. If a particular formation or reservoir has a history of successful acidizing with a particular system and products, many of the recommendations herein may not be necessary. Modern completion analysis programs can evaluate the success of past jobs and can establish whether improvements are needed. If acidizing has been unsuccessful in certain areas, the systematic process presented in this chapter may provide solutions to that lack of success.

Nomenclature
B = formation volume factor (reservoir volume/stock tank volume)
c = fluid compressibility, vol/vol/psi
F = fracture initiation pressure, psi
h = formation thickness, ft
H = formation thickness, ft
k = permeability, md
k_a = acidized formation permeability, md
k_d = damaged formation permeability, md

k_f = formation reservoir permeability, md

kh = product of k and h, md ft

K = permeability, md

m = slope of pressure buildup on semilog paper, pressure change per log cycle of time, psi/cycle

$p_{1\,hr}$ = pressure at time of 1 hour on pressure buildup line, psi

p = pressure, psi

p_f = fracturing pressure, psi

p_i = injection pressure, psi

p_{wf} = flowing wellbore pressure, psi

P_r = static reservoir pressure, psi

q = flow rate or injection rate, B/D

Q = injection rate, bbl/min

r = radial distance from wellbore, ft

r_w = wellbore radius, ft

S = skin factor

S' = apparent skin factor (includes effect of non-Darcy flow in gas flow)

Δp_s = additional pressure drop from damaged zone, or skin, psi

μ = fluid viscosity, cp

ϕ = formation porosity, fraction

References

1. McLeod, H.O.: "Matrix Acidizing to Improve Well Performance," *Short Course Manual,* SPE, Richardson, Texas (1986).
2. Earlougher, R.C. Jr.: *Advances in Well Test Analysis,* Monograph Series, SPE, Richardson, Texas (1977) **5,** 8 and 14.
3. Gdanski, R.: "A Fundamentally New Model of Acid Wormholing in Carbonates," paper SPE 54719 presented at the 1999 European Formation Damage Conference, The Hague, The Netherlands, 31 May–1 June.
4. Gidley, J.L.: "Acidizing Sandstone Formations: A Detailed Examination of Recent Experience," paper SPE 14164 presented at the 1985 SPE Annual Technical Conference and Exhibition, Las Vegas, Nevada, 22–25 September.
5. Nitters, G. *et al.:* "Structured Approach to Advanced Candidate Selection and Treatment Design of Stimulation Treatments," paper SPE 63179 presented at the 2000 SPE Annual Technical Conference and Exhibition, Dallas, 1–4 October.
6. Brannon, D.H., Netters, C.K., and Grimmer, P.J.: "Matrix Acidizing Design and Quality-Control Techniques Prove Successful in Main Pass Area Sandstone," *JPT* (August 1987) 931.
7. McLeod, H.O., Ledlow, L.B., and Till, M.V.: "The Planning, Execution, and Evaluation of Acid Treatments in Sandstone," paper SPE 11931 presented at the 1983 SPE Annual Technical Conference and Exhibition, San Francisco, 5–8 October.
8. Farina, J.R.: "An Approach to Estimating Skin Damage and Appropriate Treatment Volumes," *Proc.,* 18th Annual Southwestern Petroleum Short Course Association, Lubbock, Texas (1971) 53–57.
9. McLeod, H.O.: "Significant Factors for Successful Matrix Acidizing," paper SPE 20155 presented at the 1989 Centennial Symposium—Petroleum Technology into the Second Century, New Mexico Tech., Socorro, New Mexico, 16–19 October.
10. McLeod, H.O.: "The Effect of Perforating Conditions on Well Performance," *JPT* (January 1983) 31.
11. Unneland, T. and Waage, R.I.: "Experience and Evaluation of Production through High-Rate Gravel-Packed Oil Wells, Gullfaks Field, North Sea," *SPEPF* (May 1993) 108.

12. Unneland, T. and Larsen, L.: "Limitations of the Skin Concept and Its Impact on Success Criteria Used in Sand Control," paper SPE 30093 presented at the 1995 SPE European Formation Damage Control Conference, The Hague, The Netherlands, 15–16 May.

13. McLeod, H.O. and Crawford, H.R.: "Gravel Packing for High-Rate Completions," paper SPE 11008 presented at the 1982 SPE Technical Conference and Exhibition, New Orleans, 26–29 September.

14. Landrum, W.R. et al.: "Heidrun Results From Precompleted Wells Using Innovative Gravel-Packing Techniques," paper OTC 8087 presented at the 1996 Offshore Technology Conference, Houston, 6–9 May.

15. Burton, R.C., Rester, S., and Davis, E.R.: "Comparison of Numerical and Analytical Inflow Performance Modeling of Gravel-Packed and Frac-Packed Wells," paper SPE 31102 presented at the 1996 SPE Formation Damage Control Symposium, Lafayette, Louisiana, 14–16 February.

16. Burton, R.C. et al.: "Evaluating Completion Damage in High-Rate, Gravel-Packed Wells," paper SPE 31091 presented at the 1996 SPE Formation Damage Control Symposium, Lafayette, Louisiana, 14–16 February.

17. McLeod, H.O. and Minarovic, M.J.: "The Monitoring and Analysis of Gravel-Packing Procedures to Explain Well Performance," paper SPE 27356 presented at the 1994 SPE Formation Damage Control Symposium, Lafayette, Louisiana, 9–10 February.

18. Blok, R.H.J. et al.: "Experimental Investigation of the Influence of Perforating on Gravel-Pack Impairment," paper SPE 36481 presented at the 1996 SPE Annual Technical Conference and Exhibition, Denver, 6–9 October.

19. Rajah, B., Linder, R., and Todd, B.: "Experiences and Results of Acid Prepacking and Gravel Packing Wells in the West Lutong Field in Sarawak, Malaysia," paper SPE 29290 presented at the 1995 SPE Asia Pacific Oil and Gas Conference, Kuala Lumpur, 20–22 March.

20. McLeod, H.O.: "The Application of Spherical Flow Equations to Gravel-Pack Evaluation," paper SPE 23769 presented at the 1992 SPE Formation Damage Control Symposium, Lafayette, Louisiana, 26–27 February.

21. Sparlin, D.D. and Hagen, R.W.: "Formation Damage Prevention," Short Course Manual, International Completion Consultants Inc., Houston (2004).

22. Fambrough, J.D., Lane, R.H., and Braden, J.C.: "A Comprehensive Approach for Stimulating Produced Water Injection Wells at Prudhoe Bay, Alaska," paper SPE 28976 presented at the 1995 SPE International Symposium on Oilfield Chemistry, San Antonio, Texas, 14–17 February.

23. Zhu, D., Radjadhyax, N., and Hill, A.D.: "Using Integrated Information to Optimizing Matrix Acidizing," paper SPE 68930 presented at the 2001 European Formation Damage Conference, The Hague, The Netherlands, 21–22 May.

24. Guoynes, J. et al.: "Damage-Specific Stimulation Techniques Provide Maximum Deliverability Improvement in Four Gas-Storage Reservoirs—A Case Study," paper SPE 54726 presented at the 1999 European Formation Damage Conference, The Hague, The Netherlands, 31 May–1 June.

25. McLeod, H.O. and Pashen, M.A.: "Well-Completion Audits to Evaluate Gravel-Packing Procedures," paper SPE 31088 presented at the 1996 Formation Damage Control Symposium, Lafayette, Louisiana, 14–15 February.

26. Newberry, M.E. and Barker, K.M.: "Organic Formation Damage Control and Remediation," paper SPE 58723 presented at the 2000 SPE International Symposium on Formation Damage Control, Lafayette, Louisiana, 23–24 February.

27. King, S.R. and Worley, H.W.: "Have We Forgotten Oil Is Not Inert? Guidelines for Enhancing Stimulation Success," paper SPE 59541 presented at the 2000 SPE Permian Basin Oil Recovery Conference, Midland, Texas, 21–23 March.

28. Brezinski, M.M.: "Chelating Agents in Sour-Well Acidizing: A Methodology or Mythology,"paper SPE 54721 presented at the 1999 European Formation Damage Conference, The Hague, The Netherlands, 31 May–1 June.

29. Pittman, E.D. and Thomas, J.B.: "Some Applications of Scanning Electron Microscopy to the Study of Reservoir Rock," paper SPE 7550 presented at the 1978 SPE Annual Technical Conference and Exhibition, Houston, 1–3 October.

30. Poupin, A.: "Log Analysis of Sand Shale Sequences—A Systematic Approach," JPT (July 1970) 867.

31. Neasham, J.W.: "The Morphology of Dispersed Clay in Sandstone Reservoirs and Its Effect on Sandstone Shaliness, Pore Space, and Fluid Flow Properties," paper SPE 6858 presented at the 1977 SPE Annual Technical Conference and Exhibition, Denver, 9–12 October.

32. Kalfayan, L.J. and Metcalf, A.S.: "Successful Sandstone Acid Design Case Histories: Exceptions to Conventional Wisdom," paper SPE 63178 presented at the 2000 SPE Annual Technical Conference and Exhibition, Dallas, 1–4 October.

33. Gdanski, R.D. and Schuchart, C.E.: "Advanced Sandstone-Acidizing Designs With Improved Radial Models," *SPEPF* (November 1998) 272.

34. McLeod, H.O.: "Matrix Acidizing," *JPT* (December 1984) 2055.

35. Al-Anazi, H.A.: "Matrix Acidizing of Water Injectors in a Sandstone Field in Saudi Arabia: A Case Study," paper SPE 62825 presented at the 2000 SPE/AAPG Regional Meeting, Long Beach, California, 19–23 June.

36. Gidley, J., Brezovec, E.J., and King, G.E.: "An Improved Method for Acidizing Oil Wells in Sandstone Formations," paper SPE 26580 presented at the 1993 SPE Annual Technical Conference and Exhibition, Houston, 3–6 October.

37. McLeod, H.O.: "Acidizing Incompatibilities—A Review," paper presented to the SPE Production Operations Study Group, Houston (27 February 1991).

38. Underdown, D.R., Hickey, J.J., and Kalra, S.K.: "Acidization of Analcime Cemented Sandstone, Gulf of Mexico," paper SPE 20624 presented at the 1990 SPE Annual Technical Conference and Exhibition, New Orleans, 23–26 September.

39. Simon, D.E. and Anderson, M.S.: "Stability of Clay Minerals in Acid," paper SPE 19422 presented at the 1990 SPE Formation Damage Control Symposium, Lafayette, Louisiana, 22–23 February.

40. Wehunt, C.D. *et al.:* "Laboratory Acidization of an Eolian Sandstone at 380°F," paper SPE 25211 presented at the 1993 SPE International Symposium on Oilfield Chemistry, New Orleans, 2–5 March.

41. Shuchart, C.E. and Ali, S.A.: "Identification of Aluminum Scale with the Aid of Synthetically Produced Basic Aluminum Fluoride Complexes," *SPEPF* (November 1993) 291.

42. Shuchart, C.E.: "HF Acidizing Returns Analyses Provide Understanding of HF Reactions," paper SPE 30099 presented at the 1995 SPE European Formation Damage Conference, The Hague, The Netherlands, 15–16 May.

43. Gdanski, R.D.: "Fluosilicate Solubilities Impact HF Acid Compositions," *SPEPF* (November 1994) 225.

44. Gdanski, R.D.: "Fractional Pore Volume Acidizing Flow Experiments," paper SPE 30100 presented at the 1995 SPE European Formation Damage Control Conference, The Hague, The Netherlands, 15–16 May.

45. Al-Dahlan, M.N., Nasr-El-Din, H.A., and Al-Qahtani, A.A.: "Evaluation of Retarded HF Acid Systems," paper SPE 65032 presented at the 2001 SPE International Symposium on Oilfield Chemistry, Houston, 13–16 February.

46. Stanley, F.O. *et al.:* "An Economic, Field-Proven Method for Removing Fines Damage from Gravel Packs," paper SPE 58790 presented at the 2000 SPE International Symposium on Formation Damage Control, Lafayette, Louisiana, 23–24 February.

47. Da Motta, E.P. and Dos Santos, J.A.C.M.: "New Fluosilicic Acid System Removes Deep Clay Damage," paper SPE 54729 presented at the 1999 SPE European Formation Damage Conference, The Hague, The Netherlands, 31 May–1 June.

48. Thomas, R.L. and Fannin, V.: "A Sandstone Matrix Acidizing Simulator for Engineered Treatment Designs: A Field Study," *Proc.,* Indonesian Petroleum Assn., Jakarta (1993) 187–211.

49. Davies, D.R. *et al.:* "A Novel Procedure to Increase Well Response to Matrix Acidizing Treatments," paper SPE 23621 presented at the 1992 SPE Latin American Petroleum Engineering Conference, Caracas, 8–11 March.

50. Quinn, M.A., Lake, L.W., and Schechter, R.S.: "Designing Effective Sandstone Acidizing Treatments Through Geochemical Modeling," *SPEPF* (February 2000) 33.

51. Bartko, K.M. *et al.:* "Development of a Stimulation Treatment Integrated Model," paper SPE 35991 presented at the 1996 SPE Petroleum Computer Conference, Dallas, 2–5 June.

52. Gdanski, R.D. and Behenna, R.R.: "Experience and Research Show Best Designs for Foam Diverted Acidizing," *Oil &Gas J.* (1993) **91,** No. 36, 85.

53. Fadele, O., Zhu, D., and Hill, A.D.: "Matrix Acidizing in Gas Wells," paper SPE 59771 presented at 2000 SPE/CER Gas Technology Symposium, Calgary, 3–5 April.

54. Chang, F., Qu, Q., and Frenier, W.: "A Novel Self-Diverting Acid Developed for Matrix Stimulation of Carbonate Reservoirs," paper SPE 65033 presented at the 2001 SPE International Symposium on Oilfield Chemistry, Houston, 13–16 February.

55. Buijse, M.A. and van Domelen, M.S.: "Novel Application of Emulsified Acids to Matrix Stimulation of Heterogeneous Formations," paper SPE 65355 presented at the 1998 SPE International Symposium on Formation Damage Control, Lafayette, Louisiana, 18–19 February.

56. Saxon, A., Chariag, B., and Rahman, M.R.A.: "An Effective Matrix Design Technique for Carbonate Formations," paper SPE 62173 presented at the 1997 Middle East Oil Show, Bahrain, 15–18 March.

57. Hill, A.D. and Rossen, W.R.: "Fluid Placement and Diversion in Matrix Acidizing," paper SPE 27982 presented at the 1994 U. of Tulsa Centennial Petroleum Engineering Symposium, Tulsa, 29–31 August.

58. Frick, T.P. and Economides, M.J.: "State of the Art in the Matrix Stimulation of Horizontal Wells," paper SPE 26997 presented at the 1994 SPE Latin American/Caribbean Petroleum Engineering Conference, Buenos Aires, 27–29 April.

59. Zhu, D., Hill, A.D., and Looney, M.D.: "Evaluation of Acid Treatments in Horizontal Wells," paper SPE 59804 presented at the 2000 SPE Permian Basin Oil Recovery Conference, Midland, Texas, 21–23 March.

60. Eckerfield, L.D. *et al.*: "Fluid Placement Model for Horizontal Well Stimulation," *SPEDC* (September 2000) 185.

61. Hall, B.E. and Dill, W.R.: "Iron Control Additives for Limestone and Sandstone Acidizing of Sweet and Sour Gas Wells," paper SPE 17157 presented at the 1988 SPE Formation Damage Symposium, Bakersfield, California, 8–9 February.

62. Taylor, K.C., Nasr-El-Din, H.A., and Al-Alawi, M.J.: "Systematic Study of Iron Control Chemicals Used During Well Stimulation," paper SPE 54602 presented at the 1998 SPE International Symposium on Formation Damage Control, Lafayette, Louisiana, 18–19 February.

63. Al-Dahlan, M.N. and Nasr-El-Din, H.A.: "A New Technique to Evaluate Matrix Acid Treatments in Carbonate Reservoirs," paper SPE 58714 presented at the 2000 SPE International Symposium on Formation Damage Control, Lafayette, Louisiana, 23–24 February.

64. King, G.E. and Holman, G.B.: "Quality Control at Well Site Optimizes Acidizing Economics," *Oil & Gas J.* (1985) **83**, No. 11, 139.

65. Coulter, G.R. and Jennings, A.R.: "A Contemporary Approach to Matrix Acidizing," *SPEPF* (May 1999) 150.

66. *Bull. D15, Recommendation for Proper Usage and Handling of Inhibited Oilfield Acids*, first edition, API, Washington, DC (1985).

67. *Data Sheet 634, Safe Well Stimulation by Acidizing*, National Safety Council.

68. Ali, S.A. *et al.*: "Process, Optimized Acidizing Reduce Production Facility Upsets," *Oil & Gas J.* (1997) **95**, No. 6, 44.

69. *GMG290000, General Permit for the Western Portion of the Outer Continental Shelf (OCS) of the Gulf of Mexico*, NPDES, Federal Register, Washington, DC (December 1993) **58**, No. 231.

70. Saylors, S.E.: "Iron: Minimizing Problems and Maximizing Treatment Effectiveness," *Proc.*, 33rd Annual Southwestern Petroleum Short Course Assn., Lubbock, Texas (1986) 148–156.

71. Smith, B.: "Proper Treatment of Tubulars Key to Iron Control," *Proc.*, 37th Annual Southwestern Petroleum Short Course Association, Lubbock, Texas (1990) 115–122.

72. Loewen, K.: "A Well Stimulation Acid Tube Clean Methodology," paper CIM/SPE 47 presented at the 1990 CIM Petroleum Society/SPE International Technology Meeting, Calgary, 10–13 June.

73. Ashford, D.I.: "Effective Acid Pickling Increases Production," paper 13 presented at the 1987 CIM Petroleum Society Conference, Regina, Saskatchewan, 6–8 October.

74. Zhu, D. and Hill, A.D.: "Field Results Demonstrate Enhanced Matrix Acidizing Through Real-Time Monitoring," *SPEPF* (November 1998) 279.

75. McLeod, H.O. and Coulter, A.W.: "The Stimulation Treatment Pressure Record—An Overlooked Formation Evaluation Tool," *JPT* (August 1969) 952.

76. Paccaloni, G., Tambini, M., and Galoppini, M.: "Key Factors for Enhanced Results of Matrix Stimulation Treatments," paper SPE 17154 presented at the 1988 SPE Formation Damage Control Symposium, Bakersfield, California, 8–9 February.

77. Prouvost, L.P. and Economides, M.J.: "Applications of Real-Time Matrix Acidizing Evaluation Method," paper SPE 17156 presented at the 1988 SPE Formation Damage Control Symposium, Bakersfield, California, 8–9 February.

78. Economides, M.J. and Nolte, K.G.: *Reservoir Stimulation*, third edition, John Wiley and Sons, Ltd., West Sussex, England (2000) 20-4–20-8.

79. Hill, A.D. and Zhu, D.: "Real-Time Monitoring of Matrix Acidizing Including the Effects of Diverting Agents," paper SPE 28548 presented at the 1994 SPE Annual Technical Conference and Exhibition, New Orleans, 25–28 September.

80. Montgomery, C.T., Jan, Y.-M., and Niemeyer, B.L.: "Development of a Matrix Stimulation Treatment Evaluation and Recording System (MASTERS)," paper SPE 26579 presented at the 1993 SPE Annual Technical Conference and Exhibition, Houston, 3–6 October.

81. Zhu, D., Hill, A.D., and Morgenthaler, L.N.: "Assessment of Matrix Acidizing Treatment Responses in Gulf of Mexico Wells," paper SPE 52166 presented at the 1999 SPE Mid-Continent Operations Symposium, Oklahoma City, Oklahoma, 28–31 March.

82. Hill, A.D. and Zhu, D.: "Real-Time Monitoring of Matrix Acidizing Including the Effects of Diverting Agents," *SPEPF* (May 1996) 95.

83. Ali, S.A. *et al.*: "Process Optimized Acidizing Reduces Production Facility Upsets," *Oil & Gas J.* (1997) **95,** No. 6, 44.

84. Ali, S.A., Durham, D.K., and Elphingstone, E.A.: "Testing Identifies Acidizing Fluid/Crude Compatibility Problems," *Oil & Gas J.* (March 1994) **92,** No. 13, 47.

85. Bansal, K.M.: "Effect of Nonproduced Fluids on Produced Water Treatment Equipment Efficiency," paper SPE 25199 presented at the 1993 SPE International Symposium on Oilfield Chemistry, New Orleans, 2–5 March.

86. Hashem, M.K., Nasr-El-Din, H.A., and Hopkins, J.A.: "An Experience in Acidizing Sandstone Reservoirs: A Scientific Approach," paper SPE 56528 presented at the 1999 SPE Annual Technical Conference and Exhibition, Houston, 3–6 October.

SI Metric Conversion Factors

°API	$\times$ 141.5/(131.5 + °API)		= g/cm^3
bbl	$\times$ 1.589 873	E – 01	= m^3
cp	$\times$ 1.0*	E – 03	= Pa·s
ft	$\times$ 3.048*	E – 01	= m
ft^3	$\times$ 2.831 685	E – 02	= m^3
°F	(°F – 32)/1.8		= °C
gal	$\times$ 3.785 412	E – 03	= m^3
in.	$\times$ 2.54*	E + 00	= cm
lbf	$\times$ 4.448 222	E + 00	= N
lbm	$\times$ 4.535 924	E – 01	= kg
psi	$\times$ 6.894 757	E + 00	= kPa

*Conversion factor is exact.

Chapter 8
Hydraulic Fracturing
Stephen A. Holditch, Texas A&M U.

8.1 Introduction

The first hydraulic fracturing treatment was pumped in 1947 on a gas well operated by Pan American Petroleum Corp. in the Hugoton field.[1] Kelpper Well No. 1, located in Grant County, Kansas, was a low-productivity well, even though it had been acidized. The well was chosen for the first hydraulic fracture stimulation treatment so that hydraulic fracturing could be compared directly with acidizing. Since that first treatment in 1947, hydraulic fracturing has become a common treatment for stimulating the productivity of oil and gas wells.

Hydraulic fracturing is the process of pumping a fluid into a wellbore at an injection rate that is too great for the formation to accept in a radial flow pattern. As the resistance to flow in the formation increases, the pressure in the wellbore increases to a value that exceeds the breakdown pressure of the formation open to the wellbore. Once the formation "breaks down," a fracture is formed, and the injected fluid begins moving down the fracture. In most formations, a single, vertical fracture is created that propagates in two directions from the wellbore. These fracture "wings" are 180° apart and normally are assumed to be identical in shape and size at any point in time; however, in actual cases, the fracture wing dimensions may not be identical. In naturally fractured or cleated formations, it is possible that multiple fractures can be created and propagated during a hydraulic fracture treatment.

Fluid that does not contain any propping agent (called the "pad") is injected to create a fracture that grows up, out, and down, and creates a fracture that is wide enough to accept a propping agent. The purpose of the propping agent is to prop open the fracture once the pumping operation ceases, the pressure in the fracture decreases, and the fracture closes. In deep reservoirs, man-made ceramic beads are used to hold open or "prop" the fracture. In shallow reservoirs, sand is normally used as the propping agent.

This chapter discusses the processes used to design and pump a hydraulic fracture treatment and provides an overview of the theories, design methods, and materials used in a hydraulic fracture treatment.

8.1.1 Objectives of Hydraulic Fracturing.

In general, hydraulic fracture treatments are used to increase the productivity index of a producing well or the injectivity index of an injection well. The productivity index defines the rate at which oil or gas can be produced at a given pressure differential between the reservoir and the wellbore. The injectivity index refers to the rate at which fluid can be injected into a well at a given pressure differential.

There are many applications for hydraulic fracturing. Hydraulic fracturing can increase the flow rate of oil and/or gas from low-permeability reservoirs, increase the flow rate of oil and/or gas from wells that have been damaged, connect the natural fractures and/or cleats in a formation to the wellbore, decrease the pressure drop around the well to minimize sand production, enhance gravel-packing sand placement, decrease the pressure drop around the well to minimize problems with asphaltine and/or paraffin deposition, increase the area of drainage or the amount of formation in contact with the wellbore, and connect the full vertical extent of a reservoir to a slanted or horizontal well. There could be other uses, but most of the treatments are pumped for these reasons.

A low-permeability reservoir is one that has a high resistance to fluid flow. In many formations, chemical and/or physical processes alter the reservoir rock over geologic time. Sometimes, these diagenetic processes restrict the openings in the rock and reduce the ability of fluids to flow through the rock. Low-permeability rocks are normally excellent candidates for stimulation by hydraulic fracturing.

Regardless of the permeability, a reservoir rock can be damaged when a well is drilled through the reservoir and when casing is set and cemented in place. Damage occurs because drilling and/or completion fluids leak into the reservoir and alter the pores and pore throats. When the pores are plugged, the permeability is reduced, and the fluid flow in this damaged portion of the reservoir may be substantially reduced. Damage can be especially severe in naturally fractured reservoirs. To stimulate damaged reservoirs, a short, conductive hydraulic fracture is often the desired solution.

In many cases, especially for low-permeability formations, damaged reservoirs, or horizontal wells in a layered reservoir, the well would be uneconomical unless a successful hydraulic fracture treatment is designed and pumped. The engineer in charge of the economic success of such a well must design the optimal fracture treatment and then go to the field to be certain the optimal treatment is pumped successfully.

8.1.2 Candidate Selection. The success or failure of a hydraulic fracture treatment often depends on the quality of the candidate well selected for the treatment. Choosing an excellent candidate for stimulation often ensures success, while choosing a poor candidate normally results in economic failure. To select the best candidate for stimulation, the design engineer must consider many variables. The most critical parameters for hydraulic fracturing are formation permeability, the in-situ stress distribution, reservoir fluid viscosity, skin factor, reservoir pressure, reservoir depth, and the condition of the wellbore. The skin factor refers to whether the reservoir is already stimulated or is damaged. If the skin factor is positive, the reservoir is damaged, and the well could be an excellent candidate for stimulation.

The best candidate wells for hydraulic fracturing treatments have a substantial volume of oil and gas in place and need to increase the productivity index. Such reservoirs have a thick pay zone, medium to high pressure, in-situ stress barriers to minimize vertical height growth, and either a low-permeability zone or a zone that has been damaged (high skin factor).

Reservoirs that are poor candidates for hydraulic fracturing are those with little oil or gas in place because of thin reservoirs, low reservoir pressure, or small areal extent. Reservoirs with extremely low permeability may not produce enough hydrocarbons to pay all the drilling and completion costs, even if successfully stimulated; thus, such reservoirs would not be good candidates for stimulation.

8.1.3 Developing Data Sets. For most petroleum engineers, developing a complete and accurate data set is often the most time-consuming part of fracture treatment design. The data required to run both the fracture design model and the reservoir simulation model can be divided into two groups: data that can be "controlled" by the engineer and data that must be measured or estimated, but cannot be controlled.

The primary data that can be controlled by the engineer are the well completion details, treatment volume, pad volume, injection rate, fracture fluid viscosity, fracture fluid density, fluid-loss additives, propping agent type, and propping agent volume. The data that must be measured or estimated are formation depth, formation permeability, in-situ stresses in the pay zone, in-situ stresses in the surrounding layers, formation modulus, reservoir pressure, formation porosity, formation compressibility, and reservoir thickness. There are three thicknesses that are important to the design engineer: the gross thickness of the reservoir, the net thickness of the oil- or gas-producing interval, and the permeable thickness that will accept fluid loss during the hydraulic fracture treatment.

The most critical data for the design of a fracture treatment (roughly in order of importance) are the in-situ stress profile, formation permeability, fluid-loss characteristics, total fluid volume pumped, propping agent type and amount, pad volume, fracture fluid viscosity, injection rate, and formation modulus. In hydraulic fracture treatment design, the two most important parameters are the in-situ stress profile and the permeability profile of the zone to be stimulated, plus the layers of rock above and below the target zone that will affect fracture height growth.

In new fields or reservoirs, most operating companies are normally willing to run logs, cut cores, and run well tests to determine important factors such as the in-situ stress and the permeability of the reservoir layers. With such data, along with fracture-treatment and production records, accurate data sets for a given reservoir normally can be compiled. These data sets can be used on subsequent wells to optimize the fracture treatment designs. It is normally not practical to cut cores and run well tests on every well. Thus, the data obtained from cores and well tests from a few wells must be correlated to log parameters, so the logs on subsequent wells can be used to compile accurate data sets.

To design a fracture treatment, most use pseudo-three-dimensional (P3D) models. To use a P3D model, the data must be entered by reservoir layer. **Fig. 8.1** illustrates the important data profiles required by a P3D model. For the example in Fig. 8.1, the fracture treatment would be started in the sandstone reservoir. The fracture would typically grow up and down until a barrier is reached to prevent vertical fracture growth. In many cases, thick marine shale is a barrier to vertical fracture growth. In some cases, coal seams prevent fractures from growing vertically. Many coal seams are highly cleated, which means that they contain an abundance of small natural fractures. When the fracture fluid enters a highly cleated coal seam, there will be very high fluid leakoff into the coal cleats. In thick, highly cleated coal seams, the fracture is likely to be contained within the coal seam.

The data used to design a fracture treatment can be obtained from several sources, such as drilling records, completion records, well files, openhole geophysical logs, cores and core analyses, well tests, production data, geologic records, and other public records, such as publications. In addition, service companies provide data on their fluids, additives, and propping agents. **Table 8.1** illustrates typical data needed to design a fracture treatment and possible sources for the data.

8.1.4 Fracture Treatment Optimization. The goal of every fracture treatment design should be to attain the optimum fracture treatment for each and every well. In 1978, Holditch *et al.*[2] discussed the optimization of both the propped fracture length and the drainage area (well spacing) for low-permeability gas reservoirs. **Fig. 8.2** illustrates the method used to optimize the size of a fracture treatment[3,4] and clearly shows the following:

• As the propped length of a fracture increases, the cumulative production will increase, and the revenue from hydrocarbon sales will increase.

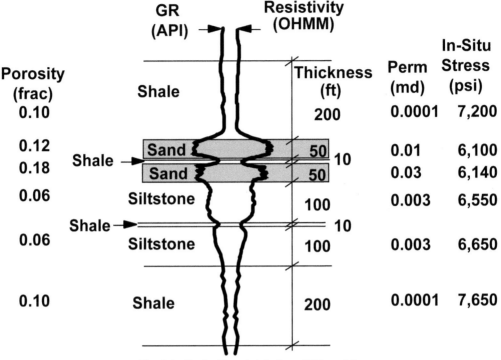

Fig. 8.1—Typical input data for a P3D model.

• As the fracture length increases, the incremental benefit (amount of revenue generated per foot of additional propped fracture length) decreases.

• As the treatment volume increases, the propped fracture length increases.

• As the fracture length increases, the incremental cost of each foot of fracture (cost/ft of additional propped fracture length) increases.

• When the incremental cost of the treatment is compared with the incremental benefit of increasing the treatment volume, an optimum propped fracture length can be found for every situation.

Additional economic calculations can be made to determine the optimum fracture treatment design. However, in all cases, the design must consider the effect of the fracture on flow rates and recovery, the cost of the treatment, and the investment guidelines of the company that owns and operates the well.

8.1.5 Field Considerations. After the optimum fracture treatment has been designed, it must be pumped into the well successfully. A successful field operation requires planning, coordination, and cooperation of all parties. Treatment supervision and the use of quality control measures will improve the successful application of hydraulic fracturing. Safety is always the primary concern in the field, and it begins with a thorough understanding by all parties of their duties. A safety meeting is always held to review the treatment procedure, establish a chain of command, ensure everyone knows his/her job responsibilities for the day, and establish a plan for emergencies.

The safety meeting also should be used to discuss the well completion details and the maximum allowable injection rate and pressures, as well as the maximum pressures to be held as backup in the annulus. All casing, tubing, wellheads, valves, and weak links, such as liner

TABLE 8.1—DATA SOURCES

Data Item and Unit	Sources
Formation permeability, md	Cores, well tests, correlations, production data
Formation porosity, %	Cores, logs
Reservoir pressure, psi	Well tests, well files, regional data
Formation modulus, psi	Cores, logs, correlations
Formation compressibility, psi	Cores, logs, correlations
Poisson's ratio	Cores, logs, correlations
Formation depth, ft	Logs, drilling records
In-situ stress, psi	Well tests, logs, correlations
Formation temperature, °F	Logs, well tests, correlations
Fracture toughness, psi - $\sqrt{in.}$	Cores, correlations
Water saturation, %	Logs, cores
Net pay thickness, ft	Logs, cores
Gross pay thickness, ft	Logs, cores, drilling records
Formation lithology	Cores, drilling records, logs, geologic records
Wellbore completion	Well files, completion prognosis
Fracture fluids	Service company information
Fracture proppants	Service company information

tops, should be tested thoroughly before starting the fracturing treatment. Mechanical failures during a treatment can be costly and dangerous. All mechanical problems should be discovered during testing and repaired before pumping the fracture treatment.

Before pumping the treatment, the engineer in charge should conduct a detailed inventory of all the equipment and materials on location. The inventory should be compared with the design and the prognosis. After the treatment has concluded, another inventory of all the materials left on location should be conducted. In most cases, the difference in the two inventories can be used to verify what was mixed and pumped into the wellbore and the hydrocarbon-bearing formation.

In addition to an inventory, samples of the base fracturing fluid (usually water) should be taken and analyzed. Typically, a water analysis is done on the base fluid to determine the minerals and type of bacteria present. The data from the water analysis can be used to select the additives needed to mix the viscous fracture fluid required to create a wide fracture and to transport the propping agent into the fracture. In addition, samples of the additives used during a treatment and the fracture fluid after all additives have been added should be taken and saved in case future analyses are required.

8.2 Fracture Mechanics

Fracture mechanics has been part of mining engineering and mechanical engineering for hundreds of years. In petroleum engineering, fracture mechanics theories have been used for only approximately 50 years. Much of what is used in hydraulic fracturing theory and design was developed by other engineering disciplines many years ago. However, certain aspects, such as poroelastic theory, are unique to porous, permeable underground formations. Three important parameters of fracture mechanics are in-situ stress, Poisson's ration, and Young's modulus.

8.2.1 In-Situ Stresses. Underground formations are confined and under stress. **Fig. 8.3** illustrates the local stress state at depth for an element of formation. The stresses can be divided

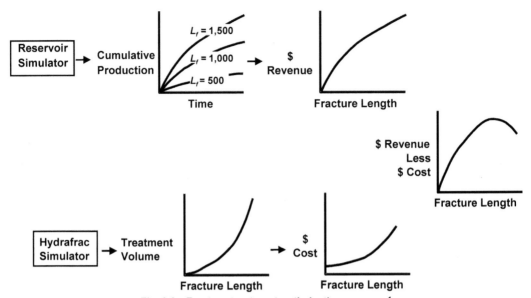

Fig. 8.2—Fracture treatment optimization process.[1]

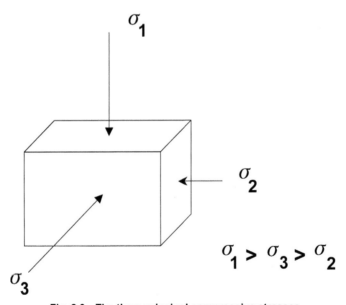

Fig. 8.3—The three principal compressive stresses.

into three principal stresses. In Fig. 8.3, σ_1 is the vertical stress, σ_2 is the minimum horizontal stress, and σ_3 is the maximum horizontal stress. These stresses are normally compressive, anisotropic, and nonhomogeneous,[5] which means that the compressive stresses on the rock are not equal and vary in magnitude on the basis of direction. The magnitude and direction of the principal stresses are important because they control the pressure required to create and propagate a fracture, the shape and vertical extent of the fracture, the direction of the fracture, and the stresses trying to crush and/or embed the propping agent during production.

TABLE 8.2—TYPICAL RANGE OF VALUES FOR YOUNG'S MODULUS		
Lithology	Young's Modulus (psi)	Poisson's Ratio
Soft sandstone	$0.1\text{-}1 \times 10^6$	0.2 to 0.35
Medium sandstone	$2\text{-}5 \times 10^6$	0.15 to 0.25
Hard sandstone	$6\text{-}10 \times 10^6$	0.1 to 0.15
Limestone	$8\text{-}12 \times 10^6$	0.30 to 0.35
Coal	$0.1\text{-}1 \times 10^6$	0.35 to 0.45
Shale	$1\text{-}10 \times 10^6$	0.28 to 0.43

A hydraulic fracture will propagate perpendicular to the minimum principal stress.[6] For a vertical fracture, the minimum horizontal stress can be estimated with

$$\sigma_{min} \cong \frac{v}{1-v}(\sigma_1 - \alpha p_p) + \alpha p_p + \sigma_{ext}, \dots\dots\dots\dots\dots\dots\dots\dots\dots\dots\dots\dots\dots (8.1)$$

where
    σ_{min} = the minimum horizontal stress,
    v = Poisson's ratio,
    σ_1 = overburden stress,
    α = Biot's constant,
    p_p = reservoir fluid pressure or pore pressure, and
    σ_{ext} = tectonic stress.
Poisson's ratio can be estimated from acoustic log data or from correlations based on lithology. **Table 8.2** presents typical ranges for Poisson's ratio. The overburden stress can be computed with density log data. Normally, the value for overburden stress is approximately 1 psi/ft of depth. The reservoir pressure must be measured or estimated. Biot's constant is usually 1.0, but can be less than 1.0 on occasion.

Poroelastic theory is often used to estimate the minimum horizontal stress.[7–9] Eq. 8.1 combines poroelastic theory with a term that accounts for any tectonic forces that are acting on a formation. The first term on the right side of Eq. 8.1 is a linear elastic term that converts the effective vertical stress on the rock grains into an effective horizontal stress on the rock grains. The second term in Eq. 8.1 represents the stress generated by the fluid pressure in the pore space. The third term is the tectonic stress, which could be zero in tectonically relaxed areas, but can be important in tectonically active areas.

In tectonically active areas, the effects of tectonic activity must be included in the analyses of the total stresses. To measure the tectonic stresses, injection tests are conducted to measure the minimum horizontal stress. The measured stress is then compared with the stress calculated by the poroelastic equation to determine the value of the tectonic stress.

8.2.2 Basic Rock Mechanics. In addition to the in-situ or minimum horizontal stress, other rock mechanical properties are important when designing a hydraulic fracture. Poisson's ratio is defined as "the ratio of lateral expansion to longitudinal contraction for a rock under a uniaxial stress condition."[5] The value of Poisson's ratio is used in Eq. 8.1 to convert the effective vertical stress component into an effective horizontal stress component. The effective stress is defined as the total stress minus the pore pressure.

The theory used to compute fracture dimensions is based on linear elasticity. When applying this theory, the modulus of the formation is an important parameter. Young's modulus is defined as "the ratio of stress to strain for uniaxial stress."[5] The modulus of a material is a measure of the stiffness of the material. If the modulus is large, the material is stiff. In hydraulic fracturing, a stiff rock results in more narrow fractures. If the modulus is low, the fractures are wider. The modulus of a rock is a function of the lithology, porosity, fluid type, and other variables. Table 8.2 illustrates typical ranges for modulus as a function of lithology.

8.2.3 Fracture Orientation. A hydraulic fracture will propagate perpendicular to the least principle stress (see Fig. 8.3). In some shallow formations, the least principal stress is the overburden stress; thus, the hydraulic fracture will be horizontal. Horizontal fractures have been documented.[10] In reservoirs deeper than approximately 1,000 ft, the least principal stress will likely be horizontal; thus, the hydraulic fracture will be vertical. The azimuth orientation of the vertical fracture will depend on the azimuth of the minimum and maximum horizontal stresses. Lacy and Smith provided a detailed discussion of fracture azimuth in Ref. 11.

Injection Tests. The only reliable technique for measuring in-situ stress is by pumping fluid into a reservoir, creating a fracture, and measuring the pressure at which the fracture closes.[5] The well tests used to measure the minimum principal stress are in-situ stress tests, step-rate/flowback tests, minifracture tests, and step-down tests. For most fracture treatments, minifracture tests and step-down tests are pumped ahead of the main fracture treatment. As such, accurate data are normally available to calibrate and interpret the pressures measured during a fracture treatment. In-situ stress tests and step-rate/flowback tests are not run on every well; however, it is common to run such tests in new fields or new reservoirs to help develop the correlations required to optimize fracture treatments for subsequent wells.

In-Situ Stress Tests. An in-situ stress test can be either an injection-falloff test or an injection-flowback test. The in-situ stress test is conducted with small volumes of fluid (a few barrels) and injected at a low injection rate (tens of gal/min), normally with straddle packers to minimize wellbore storage effects, into a small number of perforations (1 to 2 ft). The objective is to pump a thin fluid (water or nitrogen) at a rate just sufficient to create a small fracture. Once the fracture is open, the pumps are shut down, and the pressure is recorded and analyzed to determine when the fracture closes. Thus, the term "fracture-closure pressure" is synonymous with minimum in-situ stress and minimum horizontal stress. When the pressure in the fracture is greater than the fracture-closure pressure, the fracture is open. When the pressure in the fracture is less than the fracture-closure pressure, the fracture is closed. **Fig. 8.4** illustrates a typical wellbore configuration for conducting an in-situ stress test. **Fig. 8.5** shows typical data that are measured. Multiple tests are conducted to ensure repeatability. The data from any one of the injection-falloff tests can be analyzed to determine when the fracture closes. **Fig. 8.6** illustrates how one such test can be analyzed to determine in-situ stress.

Minifracture Tests. Minifracture tests are run to reconfirm the value of in-situ stress in the pay zone and to estimate the fluid-loss properties of the fracture fluid. A minifracture test is run with fluid similar to the fracture fluid that will be used in the main treatment. Several hundred barrels of fracturing fluid are pumped at fracturing rates. The purpose of the injection is to create a fracture that will be of similar height to the one created during the main fracture treatment. After the minifracture has been created, the pumps are shut down, and the pressure decline is monitored. The pressure decline can be used to estimate the fracture-closure pressure and the total fluid leakoff coefficient. Data from minifracture treatments can be used to alter the design of the main fracture treatment, if required.

Step-Down Tests. For any injection-falloff test to be conducted successfully, a clean connection between the wellbore and the created fracture is needed. The main objective of an in-situ stress test and the minifracture test is to determine the pressure in the fracture when the frac-

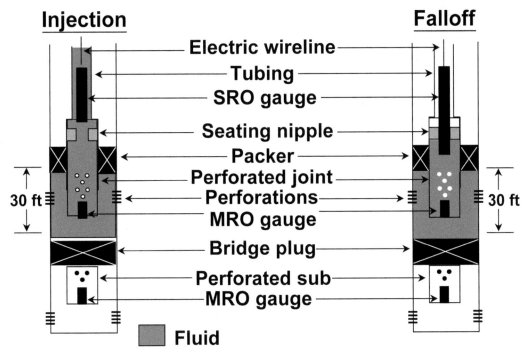

Fig. 8.4—Wellbore hardware required for an in-situ stress test.

ture is open and the pressure when the fracture is closed. If there is excess pressure drop near the wellbore because of poor connectivity between the wellbore and the fracture, the interpretation of in-situ stress test data can be difficult. In naturally fractured or highly cleated formations, multiple fractures that follow tortuous paths are often created during injection tests. When these tortuous paths are created, the pressure drop in the "near-wellbore" region can be very high, which complicates the analyses of the pressure falloff data. To determine the cause of near-wellbore pressure drop, step-down tests are run.[12]

A step-down test is pumped just before the minifracture treatment. A step-down test is pumped at fracturing rates with linear fluids, the friction pressures of which are well known. The pressure at the bottom of the hole during the injection is a function of the net pressure in the fracture and the near-wellbore pressure drop. To measure the near-wellbore pressure drop, the net pressure in the fracture needs to be relatively constant during the step-down portion of the test. To do this, the step-down test is started by injecting into the well for 10 to 15 minutes. Experience has shown that, in most cases, the net pressure is relatively stable after approximately 10 to 15 minutes of injection. The injection rate is then "reduced in steps" to a rate of zero. The injection rate at each step should be held constant for approximately 1 minute so the stabilized injection pressure can be measured. The injection rate should be stepped from the maximum value to zero, in three to five steps, in less than 5 minutes. The objective of the step-down test is to measure the near-wellbore pressure drop as a function of injection rate. If the net pressure in the fracture is relatively stable, then the change in bottomhole injection pressure as the injection rate is reduced will be a function of the near-wellbore pressure drop.

The key to analyzing a step-down test is that the two main causes of near-wellbore pressure drop can be distinguished easily as the data are analyzed. When the pressure drop near the wellbore is caused by perforation friction, the near-wellbore pressure drop will be a function of the injection rate squared, as Eq. 8.2 shows.

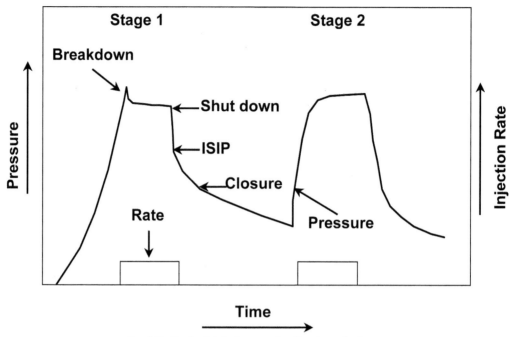

Fig. 8.5—Typical data from an in-situ stress test.

$$p_{pfr} = \frac{0.2369 i_{pf}^2 \rho}{d_{pf}^4 \alpha^2} \cdot \text{...} \quad (8.2)$$

If the near-wellbore pressure drop is caused by tortuosity, then the near-wellbore pressure drop will be a function of the injection rate raised to a power of one-half (0.5), as Eq. 8.3 shows.

$$\Delta p_\tau = a \times Q^{0.5} \cdot \text{...} \quad (8.3)$$

A graph of the value of near-wellbore pressure drop vs. injection rate will provide a clear indication of what is causing the near-wellbore pressure drop. **Fig. 8.7** illustrates that the graph of pressure drop vs. injection rate will be concave upward when the pressure drop is dominated by tortuosity and will be concave downward when the pressure drop is dominated by perforation friction.

8.2.4 Net Pressure. The reason for computing values of in-situ stress and conducting stress tests, minifracture tests, and step-down tests is to compute the net pressure in the fracture. The net pressure is the difference between the actual pressure in the fracture and the minimum in-situ stress, σ_{min}.

$$p_n = p_f - \sigma_{min} \cdot \text{...} \quad (8.4)$$

The net pressure is generated by both tip effects and the pressure drop down the fracture caused by viscous fluid flow. **Fig. 8.8** illustrates the net pressure profile down a typical fracture. In many formations, the pressure drop down the fracture is dominated by the pressure

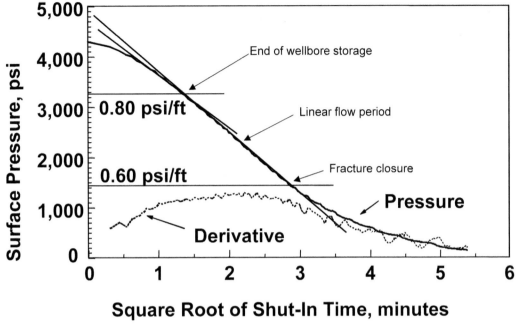

Fig. 8.6—Closure pressure analysis.

increases near the tip of the fracture as propagation occurs. The net pressure profile controls both the fracture height and fracture width distribution along the fracture length.

The value of net pressure is important because the engineer needs to know for which value to design the main fracture treatment, to perform onsite analyses of the fracturing pressures, and to perform postfracture analyses of the fracturing pressures. One of the best methods to analyze a fracture treatment is to use a fracture propagation model to analyze the net pressures measured during a fracture treatment.

8.3 Fracture Propagation Models

The first fracture treatments were pumped just to see if a fracture could be created and if sand could be pumped into the fracture. In 1955, Howard and Fast[13] published the first mathematical model that an engineer could use to design a fracture treatment. The Howard and Fast model assumed the fracture width was constant everywhere, allowing the engineer to compute fracture area on the basis of fracture fluid leakoff characteristics of the formation and the fracturing fluid.

8.3.1 Two-Dimensional Fracture Propagation Models. The Howard and Fast model was a 2D model. In the following years, other 2D models were published.[14–17] With a 2D model, the engineer fixes one of the dimensions, normally the fracture height, then calculates the width and length of the fracture. With experience and accurate data sets, 2D models can be used in certain formations with confidence, assuming the design engineer can estimate the created fracture height accurately.

Figs. 8.9 and 8.10 illustrate two of the most common 2D models used in fracture treatment design.[18] The Perkins-Kern-Nordgren (PKN) geometry (Fig. 8.9) is normally used when the fracture length is much greater than the fracture height, while the Kristonovich-Geertsma-Daneshy (KGD) geometry (Fig. 8.10) is used if fracture height is more than the fracture length.[19] In certain formations, either of these two models can be used successfully to design hydraulic fractures. The key is to use models (any model) to make decisions, rather than trying

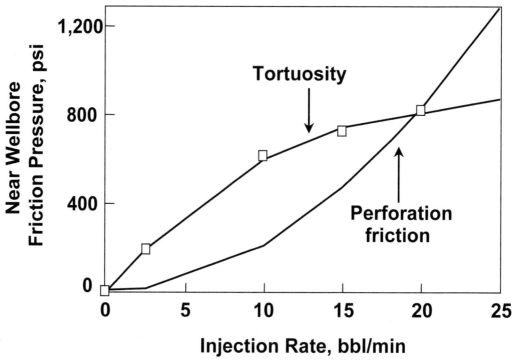

Fig. 8.7—Effects of perforations and tortuosity on the near-wellbore pressure drop.

to calculate precise values for fracture dimensions. The design must always compare actual results with the predictions from model calculations. By "calibrating" the 2D model with field results, the 2D models can be used to make design changes and improve the success of stimulation treatments. If the correct fracture height value is used in a 2D model, the model will give reasonable estimates of created fracture length and width if other parameters, such as in-situ stress, Young's modulus, formation permeability, and total leakoff coefficient, are also reasonably known and used.

To illustrate how certain variables affect fracture propagation, Eqs. 8.5 through 8.7 conform to the PKN fracture geometry assumptions. For fluid flow down an elliptical tube,

$$\frac{\partial \Delta p}{\partial x} = \frac{64}{\pi} - \frac{Qu}{Hw^3} \; . \dots\dots\dots\dots\dots\dots\dots \text{(8.5)}$$

The PKN fracture mechanics equation is

$$w_{(x, t)} = \frac{(1 - v)H\Delta p_{(x, t)}}{G}, \; \dots\dots\dots\dots\dots\dots \text{(8.6)}$$

and the PKN width equation is

$$w_{(o, t)} = 2.52\left[\frac{(1 - v)Q\mu L}{G}\right]^{1/4} \; . \dots\dots\dots\dots\dots \text{(8.7)}$$

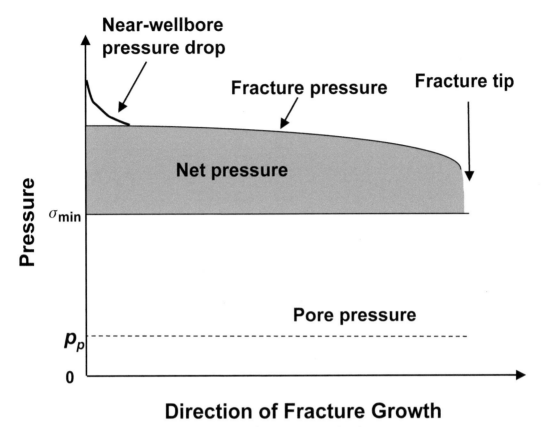

Fig. 8.8—Pressure profile in a propagating fracture.

Eq. 8.5 is the relationship used to compute the pressure distribution down the fracture for any given combination of injection rate, fracture fluid viscosity, fracture height, and fracture width. This equation, given certain physical dimensions and constraints, provides the pressure distribution in the fracture.

Eq. 8.6 provides the relationship between a given pressure distribution and what the dimensions of the fracture will be on the basis of rock mechanics theory. This equation, given a certain pressure distribution, provides the fracture width distribution. Eq. 8.5 and Eq. 8.6 are solved simultaneously to generate Eq. 8.7. By reviewing Eq. 8.7, one can observe that the fracture width will increase when the injection rate increases, the fracture fluid viscosity increases, the fracture length increases, or the formation modulus decreases. Similar equations have been derived by a number of authors. A complete discussion concerning the equations that describe the various 2D fracture models can be found in Refs. 18 and 19.

Three-Dimensional Fracture Propagation Models. 2D models have been used for decades with reasonable success. Today, with high-powered computers available to most engineers, P3D models are used by most fracture design engineers. P3D models are better than 2D models for most situations because the P3D model computes the fracture height, width, and length distribution with the data for the pay zone and all the rock layers above and below the perforated interval.

Clifton[20] provides a detailed explanation of how 3D fracture propagation theory is used to derive equations for programming 3D models, including P3D models. **Figs. 8.11 and 8.12** illustrate typical results from a P3D model. P3D models give more realistic estimates of fracture

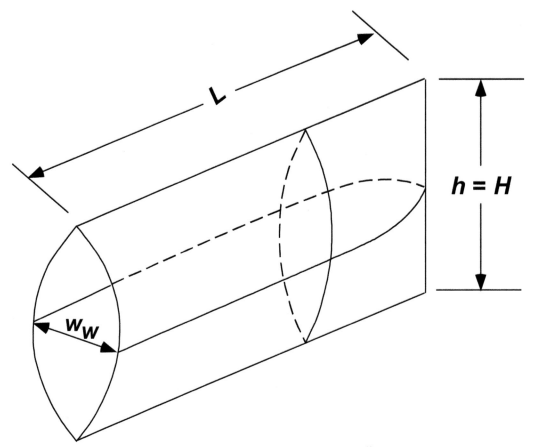

Fig. 8.9—PKN geometry for a 2D fracture.[18]

geometry and dimensions, which can lead to better designs and better wells. P3D models are used to compute the shape of the hydraulic fracture as well as the dimensions. The key to any model, including 3D or P3D models, is to have a complete and accurate data set that describes the layers of the formation to be fracture treated, plus the layers of rock above and below the zone of interest. In most cases, the data set should contain information on 5 to 25 layers of rock that will or possibly could affect fracture growth. It is best to enter data on as many layers as feasible and let the model determine the fracture height growth as a function of where the fracture is started in the model. If the user only enters data on three to five layers, it is likely that the user is deciding the fracture shape rather than the model.

8.4 Fracturing Fluids and Additives

To create the fracture, a fluid is pumped into the wellbore at a high rate to increase the pressure in the wellbore at the perforations to a value greater than the breakdown pressure of the formation. The breakdown pressure is generally believed to be the sum of the in-situ stress and the tensile strength of the rock. Once the formation is broken down and the fracture created, the fracture can be extended at a pressure called the fracture-propagation pressure. The fracture-propagation pressure is equal to the sum of the in-situ stress, plus the net pressure drop, plus the near-wellbore pressure drop. The net pressure drop is equal to the pressure drop down the fracture as the result of viscous fluid flow in the fracture, plus any pressure increase caused by tip effects. The near-wellbore pressure drop can be a combination of the pressure drop of the

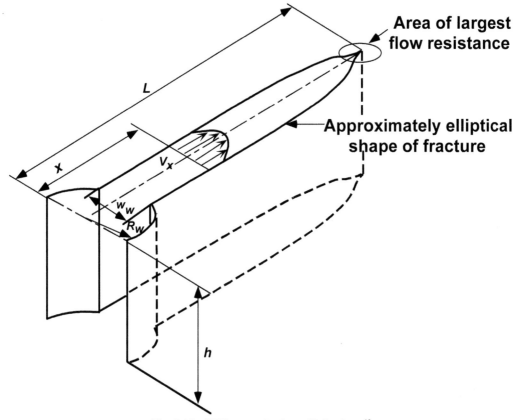

Fig. 8.10—KGD geometry for a 2D fracture.[18]

viscous fluid flowing through the perforations and/or the pressure drop resulting from tortuosity between the wellbore and the propagating fracture. Thus, the fracturing-fluid properties are very important in the creation and propagation of the fracture.

8.4.1 Properties of a Fracturing Fluid. The ideal fracturing fluid should be compatible with the formation rock and fluid, generate enough pressure drop down the fracture to create a wide fracture, be able to transport the propping agent in the fracture, break back to a low-viscosity fluid for cleanup after the treatment, and be cost-effective. The family of fracture fluids available consist of water-based fluids, oil-based fluids, acid-based fluids, and foam fluids. **Table 8.3** lists the types of fracturing fluids that are available and the general use of each type of fluid. For most reservoirs, water-based fluids with appropriate additives will be best. In some cases, foam generated with N_2 or CO_2 can be used to stimulate shallow, low-pressure zones successfully. When water is used as the base fluid, the water should be tested for quality. **Table 8.4** presents generally accepted levels of water quality for use in hydraulic fracturing.

The viscosity of the fracture fluid is important. The fluid should be viscous enough (normally 50 to 1000 cp) to create a wide fracture (normally 0.2 to 1.0 in.) and transport the propping agent into the fracture (normally hundreds to thousands of feet). The density of the fluid is also important. Water-based fluids have densities near 8.4 ppg. Oil-base fluid densities will be 70 to 80% of the densities of water-based fluids. Foam-fluid densities can be substantially less than those of water-based fluids. The fluid density affects the surface injection pressure and the

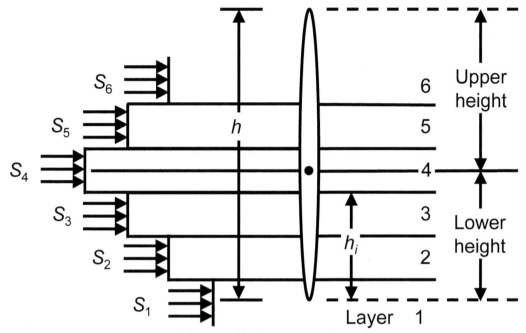

Fig. 8.11—Width and height from a P3D model.

ability of the fluid to flow back after the treatment. In low-pressure reservoirs, low-density fluids, like foam, can be used to assist in the fluid cleanup.

A fundamental principle used in all fracture models is that "the fracture volume is equal to the total volume of fluid injected minus the volume of fluid that leaks off into the reservoir."[13] The fluid efficiency is the percentage of fluid that is still in the fracture at any point in time, when compared with the total volume injected at the same point in time. The concept of fluid loss was used by Howard and Fast to determine fracture area.[13] If too much fluid leaks off, the fluid has a low efficiency (10 to 20%), and the created fracture volume will be only a small fraction of the total volume injected. However, if the fluid efficiency is too high (80 to 90%), the fracture will not close rapidly after the treatment. Ideally, a fluid efficiency of 40 to 60% will provide an optimum balance between creating the fracture and having the fracture close down after the treatment.

In most low-permeability reservoirs, fracture-fluid loss and efficiency are controlled by the formation permeability. In high-permeability formations, a fluid-loss additive is often added to the fracture fluid to reduce leakoff and improve fluid efficiency. In naturally fractured or highly cleated formations, the leakoff can be extremely high, with efficiencies down in the range of 10 to 20%, or less. To fracture treat naturally fractured formations, the treatment often must be pumped at high injection rates with fluid-loss additives.

8.4.2 Fracture-Fluid Additives. Typical additives for a fracture fluid have been described in detail by Ely.[21] Typical additives for a water-based polymer fluid are briefly described next. **Table 8.5** presents additional information on additives.

Polymers are used to viscosify the fluid. Crosslinkers are used to change the viscous fluid to a pseudoplastic fluid. Biocides are used to kill bacteria in the mix water. Buffers are used to control the pH of the fracture fluid. Surfactants are used to lower the surface tension. Fluid-loss additives are used to minimize fluid leakoff into the formation. Stabilizers are used to

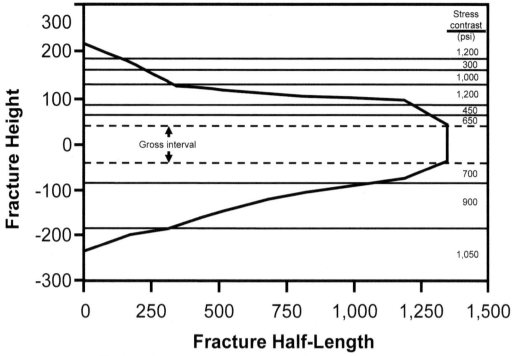

Fig. 8.12—Length and height distribution from a P3D model.

keep the fluid viscous at high temperature. Breakers are used to break the polymers and crosslink sites at low temperature.

The operator of an oil or gas well normally does not own the equipment, fluids, or additives required to pump a fracture treatment. The operator hires a service company to mix and pump the fracture treatment. Each service company has its own research department for developing fracture fluids and additives. Each service company obtains its additives from various suppliers. As such, there are no "rules" one can use to select the specific additives for a fracture fluid without first consulting with the service company that will mix and pump the fluid into the well. Many times, pilot tests of the fracture fluids must be conducted to be certain all the additives will work properly at the temperature in the reservoir and for the duration of the treatment.

8.5 Propping Agents and Fracture Conductivity
Propping agents are required to "prop open" the fracture once the pumps are shut down and the fracture begins to close. The ideal propping agent is strong, resistant to crushing, resistant to corrosion, has a low density, and is readily available at low cost.[22] The products that best meet these desired traits are silica sand, resin-coated sand (RCS), and ceramic proppants.

8.5.1 Types of Propping Agents.
Silica sand is obtained from sand mining. There are several sources in the United States and a few outside the United States. The sand must be tested to be sure it has the necessary compressive strength to be used in any specific situation. Generally, sand is used to prop open fractures in shallow formations. Sand is much less expensive per pound than RCS or ceramic proppants.

RCS is stronger than sand and is used where more compressive strength is required to minimize proppant crushing. Some resins can be used to form a consolidated pack in the fracture,

TABLE 8.3—FRACTURING FLUIDS AND CONDITIONS FOR THEIR USE

Base Fluid	Fluid Type	Main Composition	Used For
Water			
	Linear	Guar, HPG, HEC, CMHPG	Short fractures, low temperature
	Crosslinked	Crosslinker + Guar, HPG, CMHPG or CMHEC	Long fractures, high temperature
	Micellar	Electrolite + Surfactant	Moderate length fractures, moderate temperature
Foam			
	Water based	Foamer + N_2 or CO_2	Low-pressure formations
	Acid based	Foamer + N_2	Low-pressure, carbonate formations
	Alcohol based	Methonal + Foamer + N_2	Low-pressure, water-sensitive formations
Oil			
	Linear	Gelling agent	Short fractures, water-sensitive formations
	Crosslinked	Gelling agent + Crosslinker	Long fractures, water-sensitive formations
	Water emulsion	Water + Oil + Emulsifier	Moderate length fractures, good fluid loss control
Acid			
	Linear	Guar or HPG	Short fractures, carbonate formations
	Crosslinked	Crosslinker + Guar or HPG	Longer, wider fractures, carbonate formations
	Oil emulsion	Acid + Oil + Emulsifier	Moderate length fractures, carbonate formations

which will help to eliminate proppant flow back into the wellbore. RCS is more expensive than sand, but it has an effective density that is less than sand.

Ceramic proppants consist of sintered bauxite, intermediate-strength proppant (ISP), and lightweight proppant (LWP). The strength of a ceramic proppant is proportional to its density. Also, the higher-strength proppants, like sintered bauxite, cost more than ISP and LWP. Ceramic proppants are used to stimulate deep (> 8,000 ft) wells where large values of in-situ stresses will apply large forces on the propping agent.

8.5.2 Factors Affecting Fracture Conductivity. The fracture conductivity is the product of propped fracture width and the permeability of the propping agent, as **Fig. 8.13** illustrates. The permeability of all the commonly used propping agents (sand, RCS, and the ceramic proppants) will be 100 to 200+ darcies when no stress has been applied to the propping agent. However, the conductivity of the fracture will be reduced during the life of the well because of increasing stress on the propping agents, stress corrosion affecting the proppant strength, proppant crushing, proppant embedment into the formation, and damage resulting from gel residue or fluid-loss additives.

The effective stress on the propping agent is the difference between the in-situ stress and the flowing pressure in the fracture, as **Fig. 8.14** illustrates. As the well is produced, the effective stress on the propping agent will normally increase because the value of the flowing

TABLE 8.4—ACCEPTABLE LEVELS FOR MIX WATER

Item	Value
pH	6 to 8
Iron	< 10 ppm
Oxidizing agents	None
Reducing agents	None
Carbonate*	< 300 ppm
Bicarbonate*	< 300 ppm
Bacteria	None
Cleanliness	Reasonable

*Higher carbonate/bicarbonate content requires further pilot testing on gel break and crosslinking.

TABLE 8.5—SUMMARY OF CHEMICAL ADDITIVES

Type of Additive	Function Performed	Typical Products
Biocide	Kills bacteria	Gluteraldehyde carbonate
Breaker	Reduces fluid viscosity	Acid, oxidizer, enzyme breaker
Buffer	Controls the pH	Sodium bicarbonate, fumaric acid
Clay stabilizer	Prevents clay swelling	KCl, NHCl, KCl substitutes
Diverting agent	Diverts flow of fluid	Ball sealers, rock salt, flake boric acid
Fluid loss additive	Improves fluid efficiently	Diesel, particulates, fine sand
Friction reducer	Reduces the friction	Anionic copolymer
Iron Controller	Keeps iron in solution	Acetic and citric acid
Surfactant	Lowers surface tension	Fluorocarbon, Nonionic
Gel stabilizer	Reduces thermal degradation	MEOH, sodium thiosulphate

bottomhole pressure will be decreasing. However, as Eq. 8.1 shows, the in-situ stress will decrease with time as the reservoir pressure declines. This phenomenon of decreasing in-situ stress as the reservoir pressure declines was proven conclusively by Salz.[9] **Fig. 8.15** illustrates the differences in fracture conductivity as effective stress increases on the propping agent for a variety of commonly used propping agents. The data in Fig. 8.15 clearly show that for shallow wells, where the effective stress is less than 6,000 psi, sand can be used to create high-conductivity fractures. As the effective stress increases to larger and larger values, then the higher-strength, more-expensive propping agents must be used to create a high conductivity fracture.

When choosing a propping agent, a proppant that will maintain enough conductivity after all crushing and embedment occurs must be chosen. The effects of non-Darcy flow, multiphase flow, and gel residue damage should also be considered.

8.5.3 Proppant Transport. To create a hydraulic fracture, fluid is injected at high rate and pressure into a wellbore and into a formation that is open to the wellbore. Viscous fluid flow within the fracture and tip effects create the net pressure required to generate the created width profile and the created fracture height. The volume of fluid pumped will affect the created fracture length. However, without pumping a propping agent into the fracture, the created fracture will close once the pumping operation ceases. The flow of oil and gas from the formation

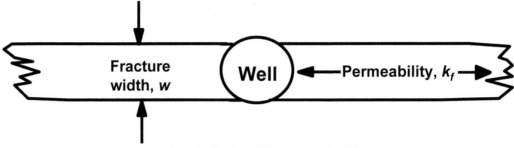

Fig. 8.13—Definition of fracture conductivity.

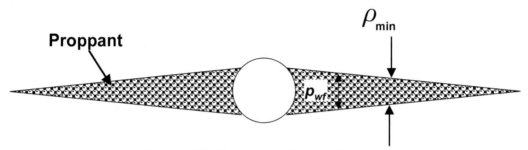

Fig. 8.14—Effective stress on the propping agent.

into the fracture is dependent on the propped fracture dimensions. The really important charac-teristics of a fracture are the propped width, height, and length distributions; therefore, prop-pant transport considerations are very important in designing a hydraulic fracture treatment. **Fig. 8.16** illustrates the difference between the created fracture dimensions and the propped fracture dimensions.

The first fluid pumped into a well during a fracture treatment is called the "prepad." The prepad is used to fill the casing and tubing, test the system for pressure, and break down the formation. Next, the pad fluid, which is the viscous fracturing fluid used during the treatment, is pumped. No propping agent has been added to the pad. The purpose of the pad is to create a tall, wide fracture that will accept the propping agent. Following the pad, the fluid containing propping agent, which is called the slurry, is pumped. The slurry moves into the fracture, trans-porting the propping agent. The particles move up, out, and down the fracture with the slurry. The particles also can settle in the fracture as a result of gravitational forces.

Daneshy[23] provided a thorough summary of proppant transport issues. The effects of gravi-ty on proppant settling can be computed by beginning with Stokes' law. Eq. 8.8 is Stokes' law for a single spherical particle of diameter d_p and density ρ_p settling in a Newtonian fluid with a density of ρ_f and a viscosity of μ.

$$v_t = \frac{g d_p^2 (\rho_p - \rho_f)}{18\mu} . \qquad (8.8)$$

Eq. 8.8 shows that the settling velocity will increase as the diameter and density of the prop-ping agent increase and as the density and viscosity of the fracturing fluid decrease. To

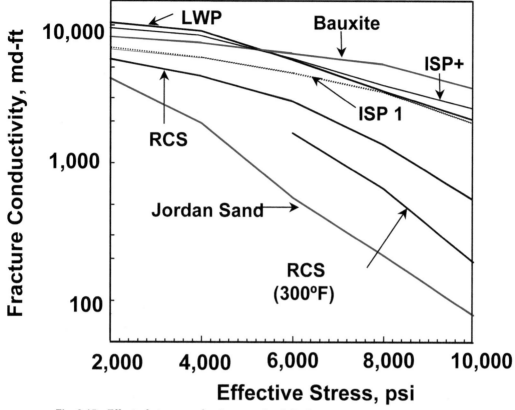

Fig. 8.15—Effect of stress on fracture conductivity from common propping agents.

minimize proppant settling, propping agents that are smaller in diameter and/or less dense, as well as a more viscous fluid, can be used.

However, Stokes' law must be modified with the use of non-Newtonian fluids and to account for the other particles in suspension in the slurry during the pumping operation. Ref. 23 provides a complete discussion on the factors that affect proppant transport and how Stokes' law has been modified to account for many important factors. For example, at low proppant concentrations (1 to 3 ppg), the viscosity of the slurry is relatively unchanged. At high proppant concentrations (8 to 14 ppg), the slurry viscosity can be 3 to 10 times more than the viscosity of the clean fluid. Such factors must be recognized and included in any fracture-propagation design model.

There are other factors that must be included when trying to compute the propped fracture dimensions. The type of fracture fluid will affect proppant transport. Linear fracture fluid will not transport proppants as well as fluids with structure, such as crosslinked fluids or viscoelastic surfactant fluids. Geologic realities also must be considered. For example, no fracture is exactly vertical, and the walls of a fracture are rarely smooth. If there are turns and ledges along the fracture walls, these geologic features tend to reduce proppant settling when compared with the theoretical equations for transport in smooth-wall, parallel-plate systems. Smith et al.[24] discussed other issues and presented several case histories in which fracture-treatment data were analyzed to determine the propped fracture dimensions. Smith stated that fracture height growth during and after pumping operations, fluid loss in layered formations, and slurry viscosity all affect the propped fracture dimensions.

Created
fracture dimensions

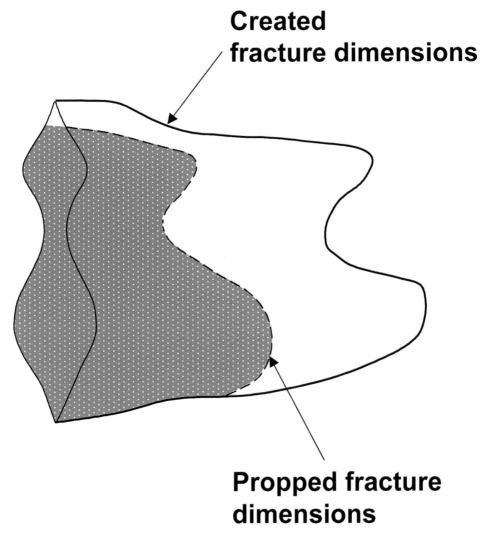

Propped fracture
dimensions

Fig. 8.16—Difference between created and propped fracture dimensions.

8.6 Fracture Treatment Design

8.6.1 Data Requirements. The most important data for designing a fracture treatment are the in-situ stress profile, formation permeability, fluid-loss characteristics, total fluid volume pumped, propping agent type and amount, pad volume, fracture-fluid viscosity, injection rate, and formation modulus. It is very important to quantify the in-situ stress profile and the permeability profile of the zone to be stimulated, plus the layers of rock above and below the target zone that will influence fracture height growth.

There is a structured method that should be followed to design, optimize, execute, evaluate, and reoptimize the fracture treatments in any reservoir. The first step is always the construction of a complete and accurate data set. Table 8.1 lists the sources for the data required to run fracture propagation and reservoir models. The design engineer must be capable of analyzing logs, cores, production data, and well-test data and be capable of digging through well files to obtain all the information needed to design and evaluate the well that is to be hydraulically fracture treated.

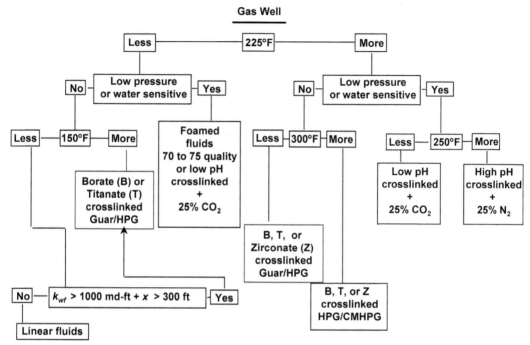

Fig. 8.17—Process for selecting a fracture fluid.

Design Procedures. To design the optimum treatment, the effect of fracture length and fracture conductivity on the productivity and the ultimate recovery from the well must be determined. As in all engineering problems, sensitivity runs need to be made to evaluate uncertainties, such as estimates of formation permeability and drainage area. The production data obtained from the reservoir model should be used in an economics model to determine the optimum fracture length and conductivity. Then a fracture treatment must be designed with a fracture propagation model to achieve the desired length and conductivity at minimum cost. The most important concept is to design a fracture with the appropriate data and models that will result in the optimum economic benefit to the well operator, as Fig. 8.2 shows.

A hydraulic fracture propagation model should be run to determine what needs to be mixed and pumped into the well to achieve the optimum values of propped fracture length and fracture conductivity. The base data set should be used to make a base case run. The engineer then determines which variables are the most uncertain. The values of in-situ stress, Young's modulus, permeability, and fluid-loss coefficient often are not known with certainty and must be estimated. The design should acknowledge these uncertainties and make sensitivity runs with the fracture-propagation model to determine the effect of these uncertainties on the design process. As databases are developed, the number and magnitude of the uncertainties will diminish.

In effect, the design engineer should fracture treat the well many times on his or her computer. Sensitivity runs lead to a better design and educate the design engineer on how certain variables affect the values of both the created and propped fracture dimensions.

Fracturing Fluid Selection. The selection of the fracture fluid for the treatment is a critical decision. Economides *et al.*[25] developed a flow chart that can be used to select the category of fracture fluid on the basis of factors such as reservoir temperature, reservoir pressure, the expected value of fracture half-length, and water sensitivity. **Fig. 8.17** presents the fluid-selection flow chart for a gas well. The information in Fig. 8.17 is compatible with the information in Table 8.3.

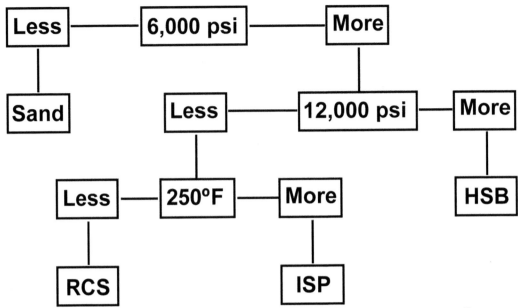

Fig. 8.18—Proppant selection based on closure pressure (after Economides and Nolte).[25]

To use Fig. 8.17, one must follow a path that depends on formation temperature, reservoir pressure, and an intangible variable called water sensitivity. For a low-temperature, high-pressure reservoir, the desired fracture conductivity and the desired fracture length must be considered. Economides *et al.* suggest that Fig. 8.17 can also be used to select a fluid to fracture treat an oil reservoir that is not water sensitive.

The definition of what comprises a water-sensitive reservoir and what causes the damage is not always clear. Most reservoirs contain water, and most oil reservoirs can be waterflooded successfully. Thus, most fracture treatments should be pumped with suitable water-base fracture fluids. Acid-base fluids can be used in carbonates; however, many deep carbonate reservoirs have been stimulated successfully with water-base fluids containing propping agents. Oil-base fluids should be used only in oil reservoirs when water-base fluids have proved conclusively to not work. Pumping oil-base fluids is more dangerous than pumping water-base fluids, and special care should be taken in the field.

Propping-Agent Selection. **Fig. 8.18** presents a flow chart created by Economides and Nolte[25] for selecting propping agents. To use Fig. 8.18, the maximum effective stress on the propping agent must be determined. The effective stress is defined in Fig. 8.14. The maximum effective stress depends on the minimum value of flowing bottomhole pressure expected during the life of the well. If the maximum effective stress is less than 6,000 psi, then Fig. 8.18 recommends that sand be used as the propping agent. If the maximum effective stress is between 6,000 and 12,000 psi, then either RCS or intermediate-strength proppant should be used, depending on the temperature. For cases in which the maximum effective stress is greater than 12,000 psi, high-strength bauxite should be used as the propping agent.

Fig. 8.18 should be used only as a guide, because there will be exceptions. For example, even if the maximum effective stress is less than 6,000 psi, the designer may choose to use RCS or other additives to "lock" the proppant in place when proppant flowback becomes an issue. In high-flow-rate gas wells, non-Darcy pressure drops can lead to the use of ceramic proppants to maximize fracture conductivity.

For fracture treatments in countries that do not mine sand for fracturing, the largest cost of the proppant is often the shipping charges. If the propping agent must be imported, intermediate-strength proppants may be selected, even for relatively shallow wells, because the cost differential between the intermediate strength proppants and sand is not much of a factor.

To confirm exactly which type of propping agent should be used during a specific fracture treatment, the designer should factor in the estimated values of formation permeability and optimum fracture half-length. Cinco-Ley[26] published an equation that can be used to determine the optimum fracture conductivity. The dimensionless fracture conductivity is defined as

$$C_{fD} = \frac{\pi k L_f}{C_f} . \quad\text{..} \quad (8.9)$$

To minimize the pressure drop down the fracture, the value of C_{fD} should be approximately 10 or greater. The required fracture conductivity can be computed as

$$C_{fD} = 31.4159 k L_f, \quad\text{..} \quad (8.10)$$

where k = the formation permeability (md) and L_f = the fracture half-length (ft). For example, if the formation permeability is 25 md and the optimum fracture half-length is 50 ft, then the optimum fracture conductivity would be 3,927 md-ft. The treatment must be designed to create a fracture wide enough, and pump proppants at concentrations high enough, to achieve the conductivity required to optimize the treatment. However, in many low-permeability reservoirs, the dimensionless fracture conductivity, C_{fD}, must be 50 to 100 for the fracture fluid to clean up after the treatment. As such, the "optimum" value of C_{fD} = 10 is considered a minimum value, and C_{fD} should be even larger than 10 when fracture fluid cleanup issues are a problem. In high-permeability formations, C_{fD} values of 10 or greater are often not feasible.

Some tend to compromise fracture length and conductivity in an often unsuccessful attempt to prevent damage to the formation around the fracture. Holditch[27] showed that substantial damage to the formation around the fracture can be tolerated as long as the optimum fracture length and conductivity are achieved. However, damage to the fracture or the propping agents can be very detrimental to the productivity of the fractured well. Ideally, the optimum fracture length and conductivity can be created while minimizing damage to the formation. If the opposite occurs—that is, the formation is not damaged, but the fracture is not long enough or conductive enough—then the well performance usually will be disappointing.

8.6.2 Evaluating Risks in the Design. The well operator always should evaluate risks such as mechanical risks, product price risks, and geologic risks. Uncertainties in the data can be evaluated by making sensitivity runs with both reservoir models and fracture propagation models. One of the main risks in hydraulic fracturing is that the entire treatment will be pumped and/or paid for (i.e., the money is spent), but, for whatever reason, the well does not produce at the desired flow rates nor achieve the expected cumulative recovery. In some cases, mechanical problems with the well or the surface equipment cause the treatment to fail. Other times, the reservoir does not respond as expected.

To evaluate the risk of mechanical or reservoir problems, 100% of the costs and only a fraction of the revenue can be used in the economic analyses. For example, one in every five fracture treatments in a certain formation is not successful; therefore, 80% of the expected revenue and 100% of the expected costs can be used to determine the optimum fracture length. **Fig. 8.19** illustrates how such an analysis can alter the desired fracture length.

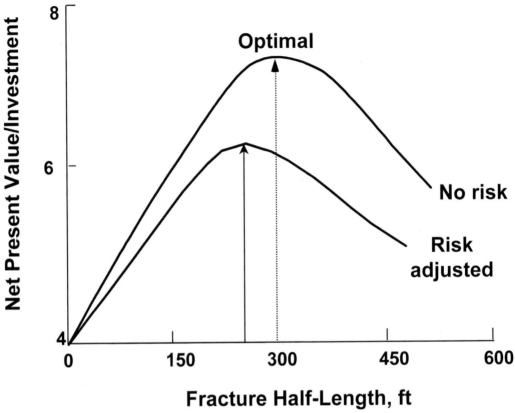

Fig. 8.19—Optimizing the fracture design considering risks.

Finally, after the optimum, risk-adjusted fracture treatment has been designed, it is extreme-ly important to be certain the optimum design is pumped correctly into the well. For this to occur, the operator and the service company should work together to provide quality control before, during, and after the treatment is pumped. The best engineers spend sufficient time in the office designing the treatment correctly, and then go to the field to help supervise the field operations or provide on-site advice to the supervisor.

8.7 Acid Fracturing

Designing an acid-fracturing treatment is similar to designing a fracturing treatment with a prop-ping agent. Ref. 28 presents a thorough explanation of the fundamentals concerning acid fracturing. The main difference between acid fracturing and proppant fracturing is the way frac-ture conductivity is created. In proppant fracturing, a propping agent is used to prop open the fracture after the treatment is completed. In acid fracturing, acid is used to "etch" channels in the rock that comprise the walls of the fracture. Thus, the rock has to be partially soluble in acid so that channels can be etched in the fracture walls. As such, the application of acid frac-turing is confined to carbonate reservoirs and should never be used to stimulate sandstone, shale, or coal-seam reservoirs. Long etched fractures are difficult to obtain because of high leakoff and rapid acid reaction with the formation.

8.7.1 Acid-Fracturing Candidate Selection. In general, acid fracturing is best applied in shal-low, low-temperature carbonate reservoirs. The best candidates are shallow, in which the reservoir temperature is less than 200°F and the maximum effective stress on the fracture will be less than 5,000 psi. Low temperature reduces the reaction rate between the acid and the formation, which allows the acid to penetrate deeper into the fracture before becoming spent. Because limestone reservoirs are ductile, a low effective stress on the fracture is required to maintain adequate fracture conductivity over the life of the well. In deep limestone reservoirs, in which problems exist with high bottomhole temperature and high effective stress on the fracture, water-based fluids with propping agents can be used successfully to stimulate the formation.[29] In deep dolomite reservoirs that are less ductile than limestones, acid fracturing may work satisfactorily; however, proppant fracturing with water-based fluids may work also.

Acid-fracture fluids with propping agents are not recommended. When the acid reacts with the carbonate formation, fines are always released. If a propping agent is used with acid, the fines plug up the propping agent, resulting in very low fracture conductivity. When deciding to stimulate many carbonate reservoirs, the costs and benefits of an acid-fracture treatment should be compared with a treatment that uses water-based fluids carrying a propping agent. It should not be assumed that acid fracturing works best because the formation is a carbonate.

There could be a few applications in which acid fracturing could be the preferred treatment in a deep, high-temperature carbonate reservoir. For example, if a high-permeability carbonate reservoir is damaged as a result of drilling operations or non-Darcy flow effects, then a stimulation treatment can be applied to improve the productivity index. In such cases, injecting acid at fracturing rates can improve the permeability near the wellbore, which will reduce the pressure drop caused by skin and/or non-Darcy flow.[30]

In other cases, especially in deep dolomites that contain an abundance of natural fractures, acid fracturing may work better than proppant fracturing. In such reservoirs, it is common that multiple fractures are opened when pumping begins. With multiple fractures, no single fracture ever gains enough width to accept large concentrations of propping agent. Near-wellbore screenouts often occur as the proppant concentration is increased to more than 2 to 3 ppg. In such cases, acid fracturing may work better than proppant fracturing.

Other considerations when selecting acid-fracturing candidates are cost and safety. In deep, hot reservoirs, the cost of an acid-fracturing treatment can exceed the costs of a proppant-fracture treatment. In hot reservoirs, expensive chemicals are required to inhibit the acid-reaction rate with the steel tubular goods and to retard the reaction rate with the formation. Acid must be handled with extreme care in the field. When pumping large volumes of high-strength acid, at high injection rates and at high pressures, safety should be the top concern of everyone in the field.

8.7.2 Acid Fluids Used in Fracturing. The most commonly used fluid in acid fracturing is 15% hydrochloric acid (HCl). To obtain more acid penetration and more etching, 28% HCl is sometimes used as the primary acid fluid. On occasion, formic acid (HCOOH) or acetic acid (CH_3COOH) is used because these acids are easier to inhibit under high-temperature conditions. However, acetic and formic acid cost more than HCl. Hydrofluoric acid (HF) should never be used during an acid fracturing treatment in a carbonate reservoir.

Typically, a gelled water or crosslinked gel fluid is used as the pad fluid to fill the wellbore and break down the formation. The water-based pad is then pumped to create the desired fracture height, width, and length for the hydraulic fracture. Once the desired values of created fracture dimensions are achieved, the acid is pumped and fingers down the fracture to etch the walls of the fracture to create fracture conductivity. The acid is normally gelled, crosslinked, or emulsified to maintain fracture width and minimize fluid leakoff. Because the acid is reactive with the formation, fluid loss is a primary consideration in the fluid design. Large amounts of fluid-loss additives are generally added to the acid fluid to minimize fluid leakoff. Fluid-loss control is most important in high permeability and/or naturally fractured carbonate formations; thus, long etched fractures are difficult to obtain.

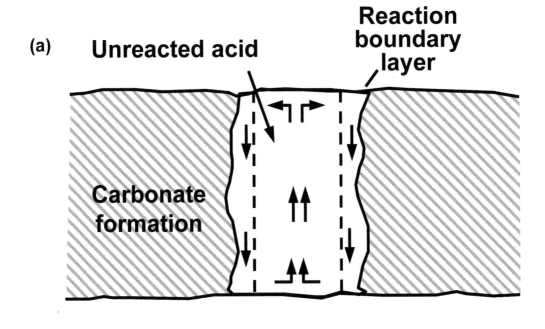

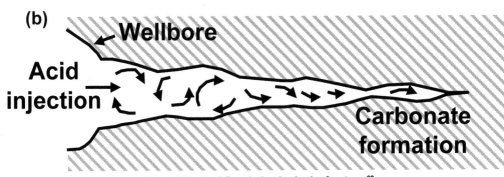

Fig. 8.20—Acid-flow behavior in the fracture.[28]

8.7.3 Acid-Fracture Design Considerations. In addition to Ref. 28, two papers[31,32] provide the technology commonly used today to design acid fracture treatments. There are several unique considerations to be understood when designing acid fracture treatments. Of primary concern is acid-penetration distance down the fracture. The pad fluid is used to create the desired fracture dimensions. Then the acid is pumped down the fracture to etch the fracture walls, which creates fracture conductivity. When the acid contacts the walls of the fracture, the reaction between the acid and the carbonate is almost instantaneous, especially if the temperature of the acid is 200°F or greater. As such, the treatment must be designed to create a wide fracture, with minimal leakoff, with viscous fluids. **Fig. 8.20**[28] illustrates why the design engineer should be striving to create a wide fracture. If a wide fracture is created with a viscous acid and minimal fluid loss, then a boundary layer of spent acid products will reduce the rate at which the live acid contacts the formation at the walls of the fracture. However, as the flow in the fracture becomes more turbulent and less laminar, the live acid will contact the walls of the fracture more easily, and the acid will not penetrate very far into the fracture before becoming spent.

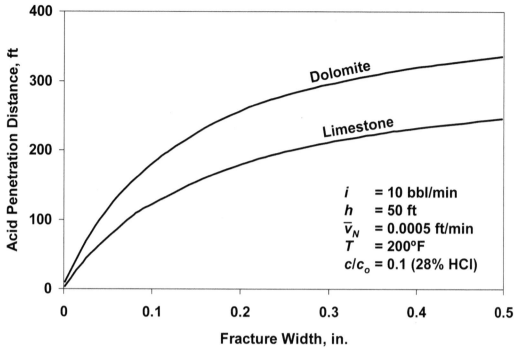

Fig. 8.21—Effect of fracture width on acid-penetration distance.[28]

Factors such as fracture width, injection rate, acid viscosity, and reservoir temperature all affect acid penetration. **Figs. 8.21 and 8.22**[28] illustrate how fracture width and formation temperature affect acid penetration in the fracture, respectively. In Fig. 8.21, as the fracture width increases, the distance that unspent acid will reach in the fracture also increases. The distance increases because, in a wide fracture, there is less turbulence. This results in less mixing as the live acid moves down the fracture; therefore, the viscous and leakoff properties of the fracture fluid should be controlled to maximize fracture width. Fig 8.22 contains information concerning the effects of reservoir temperature, acid strength, and formation lithology. It is clear that the use of higher-strength acid increases the penetration distance in the fracture before the acid spending. Also, as temperature increases, the acid penetration distance decreases. As the temperature increases, the reaction rates between the acid and the formation increase substantially. In fact, the reaction rate doubles every time the temperature increases 18°F.[28] Fig. 8.22 also shows that dolomite is less reactive with HCl than limestone; therefore, acid fracturing may work slightly better in reservoirs that are more highly dolomitized.

The problem with acid fracturing that prevents its successful application in many reservoirs involves sustaining fracture conductivity over time. When the acid etches the fracture walls, the resulting fracture conductivity can be several orders of magnitude more conductive than similar treatments that use water-based fluids and propping agents. **Fig. 8.23** presents data concerning fracture conductivity as a function of effective stress on the fracture and rock embedment strength.[28] The embedment strength is easily measured and can be correlated with the compressive strength of the rock. As the compressive strength increases, the rock embedment strength increases. The data in Fig. 8.23 show that, when the embedment strength is less than 100,000 psi, large fracture conductivities, on the order of 10 to 50,000 md-ft, can be created during an acid-fracture treatment, as long as the effective stress on the fracture is 1,000 psi or less. However, once the effective stress on the fracture exceeds 5,000 psi, the fracture conductivity decreases substantially. As such, in deep limestone reservoirs in which the maximum effective

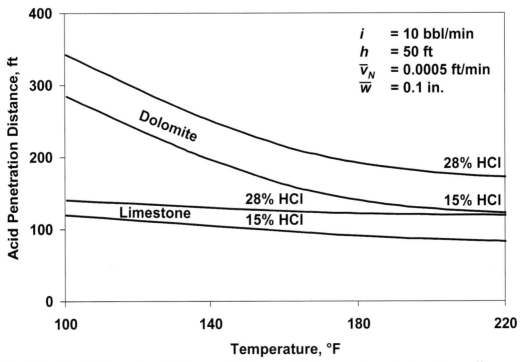

Fig. 8.22—Effect of temperature, lithology, and acid concentration on acid-penetration distance.[28]

stress on the fracture is much greater than 5,000 psi, an acid fracture will not stay open as the well is produced. In such cases, water-based fluids carrying propping agents should be considered as an alternative to acid fracturing.

8.8 Fracturing High-Permeability Formations

Smith and Hannah[33] documented the evolution of hydraulic fracturing in high-permeability reservoirs since the 1950s. The first fracture treatments in the 1950s were pumped in moderate- to high-permeability formations. Those treatments were designed to remove formation damage that usually occurred during the drilling and completion operations. Low-permeability reservoirs were fracture treated in the 1950s and 1960s, but, at low oil and gas prices, low-permeability reservoirs were generally not economic, even after a successful fracture treatment.

The values of high, moderate, and low permeability need to be defined on the basis of both the formation permeability and the reservoir fluid viscosity, or the k/μ ratio, where k is the formation permeability in md, and μ is the formation fluid viscosity in cp. For a gas well, the average viscosity of the gas is assumed to be approximately 0.02 cp. For a typical gas well, a low-permeability formation might be where $k < 0.1$ md, a medium-permeability reservoir might be $10 > k > 1$ md, and a high-permeability reservoir might be 25 md $> k$. If the formation contains oil with a fluid viscosity of 2 cp, then all the permeability values must be multiplied by a factor of 100 to determine what is a low-, moderate-, and high-permeability formation. This example illustrates that the definition of "high permeability" also depends on the value of the reservoir-fluid viscosity. In heavy-oil plays, in which the reservoir fluid viscosity is several thousand centipoises, then formations with several Darcies permeability would be considered a low-permeability reservoir. From this point forward, we assume that the formation fluid is either gas or light oil; thus, a formation with a permeability of several hundred millidarcies or more will be considered high permeability.

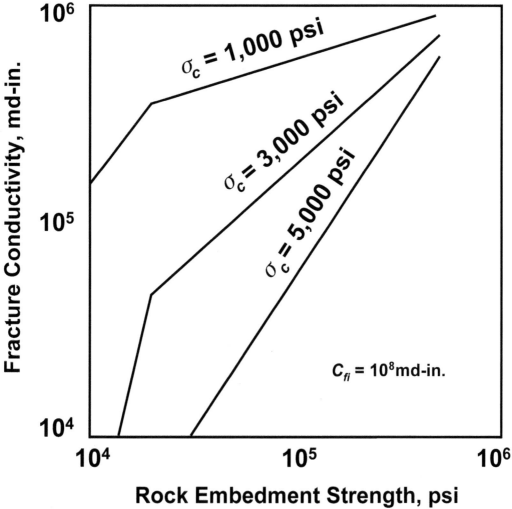

Fig. 8.23—Fracture conductivity in a carbonate reservoir as a function of effective stress on the fracture and embedment strength.[28]

8.8.1 Candidate Selection Criteria for High-Permeability Formations.
The main reasons for fracture treating high-permeability formations are to improve both the reservoir and wellbore communication, to bypass formation damage, to reduce the drawdown around the wellbore, to increase the back stress on the formation, to control sand production, to reduce fines migration, to reduce asphaltene deposition, and to reduce water coning.[34] As mentioned, the early fracture treatments were pumped to break through damage near the wellbore and increase the productivity index of the formation. Today, fracture treatments in high-permeability wells are pumped to bypass damage, but other reasons have become just as important. For example, many treatments are pumped for sand-control purposes. By creating a short, highly conductive fracture connecting the reservoir to the wellbore, the productivity index is increased; thus, more oil and gas can be produced with a lower drawdown. As the drawdown is reduced, the tendency of a poorly consolidated reservoir to produce sand is also reduced. The reduction in drawdown also helps to deter fines migration, asphaltene deposition, and water coning in certain formations.

8.8.2 Design Considerations for High-Permeability Formations. Most fracture treatments in high-permeability formations are designed to achieve a tip screenout.[35] A tip screenout design is one in which the pad volume is designed carefully so that the pad leaks off during the treatment, causing the propping agent to bridge at the tip of the fracture near the end of the job. At this point, the fracture quits growing in length, but pumping continues. As pumping continues, the pressure in the fracture increases, which leads to increasing width and, sometimes, increasing height. The fracture continues to inflate and is packed with the propping agent. The purpose of a tip-screenout design is to create a short, extremely wide fracture that is completely packed with the propping agent.

Smith and Hannah[33] documented that Amoco successfully combined hydraulic fracturing and gravel packing in the Hackberry field south of Lake Charles, Louisiana, in 1984. Hannah et al.[36] described a combination fracture treatment and gravel pack in an offshore field in 1994. Since the early 1990s, "frac-pack" treatments have become standard for many producing areas worldwide. Frac-pack treatments tend to reduce the skin factors from very high numbers (10 to 50) to essentially a skin of zero. In other words, the damage to the formation surrounding the wellbore during the drilling and completion of the well is negated by the frac-pack operations. In many cases, the productivity index is increased by a factor of three or more by the frac-pack treatments.[36]

Park[37] provided information concerning the design criteria for tip screenout treatments that are part of a frac-pack operation. In general, the designed fracture lengths for a frac-pack treatment are from 10 to 50 ft. The treatments are designed to create as wide a propped fracture as possible; thus, treatments are designed for proppant concentrations as high as 17 to 20 lbm/ft^2. Many unconsolidated or poorly consolidated sands have values of Young's modulus that range from 90,000 to 200,000 psi, which theoretically can result in created fracture widths of 3 in. and propped fracture widths of 2 in. As the value of modulus increases, the rock becomes stiffer, the created fractures become narrower, and the amount of propping agent that can be placed in the fracture decreases. Tip screenout treatments can be designed with almost any fracture-treatment-design model. Just like any design, the engineer must have data that describe the reservoir and the treatment conditions accurately. Some fracture design models have special features to optimize the size of the pad volume, the leakoff characteristics of the fluid, and other variables that affect tip screenout designs.

Early frac-pack treatments were pumped with the equipment, fluids, and gravel commonly used in gravel-packing operations. For example, the fluid most commonly used was hydroxyethyl cellulose gel because it is clean and should not significantly damage the reservoir. Also, 40- to 60-mesh gravel was used as the propping agent. As the technology has evolved, other fluids such as hydroxypropyl guar crosslinked with borates and viscoelastic surfactant fluids have been used successfully to pump a frac-pack treatment. Because fracture conductivity is so important, the use of 20- to 40-mesh proppants is now common.

In summary, fracture treatment technology was first developed in the 1950s to break through damage in high-permeability reservoirs. In the 1960s, gelled water fluids were used successfully to fracture treat both low- and high-permeability oil and gas wells. The technology evolved in the 1970 and 1980s; the industry was pumping massive hydraulic fracture treatments in microdarcy reservoirs. Massive treatments in tight reservoirs are still being pumped today and will become even more important in the future. However, in the 1990s, because of the tip screenout design process and frac-pack operations, stimulation of high-permeability reservoirs is once again an important aspect of hydraulic fracturing to reduce the effects of formation damage and to enhance gravel packing.

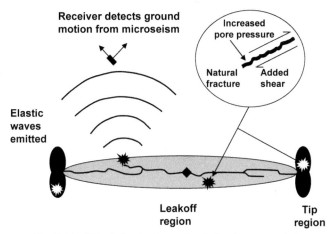

Fig. 8.24—Principle of microseismic fracture mapping.

8.9 Fracture Diagnostics

Fracture diagnostics involves analyzing the data before, during, and after a hydraulic fracture treatment to determine the shape and dimensions of both the created and propped fracture. Fracture diagnostic techniques are divided into several groups.[38]

8.9.1 Direct Far-Field Techniques. Direct far-field methods consists of tiltmeter-fracture-mapping and microseismic-fracture-mapping techniques. These techniques require sophisticated instrumentation embedded in boreholes surrounding the well to be fracture treated. When a hydraulic fracture is created, the expansion of the fracture causes the earth around the fracture to deform. Tiltmeters can be used to measure the deformation and to compute the approximate direction and size of the created fracture. Surface tiltmeters are placed in shallow holes surrounding the well. Downhole tiltmeters are placed in vertical wells at depths near the zone to be fracture treated. As with surface tiltmeters, downhole tiltmeter data are analyzed to determine the orientation and dimensions of the created fracture.

Microseismic fracture mapping relies on a downhole receiver array of accelerometers or geophones to locate microseisms or microearthquakes that are triggered by shear slippage in natural fractures surrounding the hydraulic fracture. **Fig. 8.24** illustrates the principle of microseismic fracture mapping.[38] In essence, noise is created in a zone surrounding the hydraulic fracture. With sensitive arrays of instruments, the noise can be monitored, recorded, analyzed, and mapped.

Although direct far-field techniques can be used to map hydraulic fractures, the technology is still under development. When the technology is used in a field, the data and knowledge gained are often used on subsequent wells to spread out the costs. Knowing the fracture orientation is useful in planning field development and in optimizing future fracture treatments.

8.9.2 Direct Near-Wellbore Techniques. Direct near-wellbore techniques are run in the well that is being fracture treated to locate or image the portion of fracture that is very near (within inches of) the wellbore. Direct near-wellbore techniques consist of tracer, temperature, production, borehole image, downhole video, and caliper logs. If a hydraulic fracture intersects the wellbore, these direct near-wellbore techniques can be of some benefit in locating the hydraulic fracture.

However, these near-wellbore techniques are not unique and cannot supply information on the size or shape of the fracture once the fracture is two to three wellbore diameters in distance from the wellbore. In naturally fractured reservoirs, in which multiple fractures are likely to exist, the reliability of direct near-wellbore techniques are even more speculative. As such, direct near-wellbore techniques are used only to find where the hydraulic fracture exited the wellbore and to map the fracture that is essentially connected directly to the wellbore.

8.9.3 Indirect Fracture Techniques. Indirect fracture techniques consist of hydraulic fracture modeling of net pressures, pressure-transient-test analyses, and production-data analyses. Because the fracture-treatment data and the post-fracture production data are normally available on every well, the indirect fracture diagnostic techniques are the most widely used methods to determine the shape and dimensions of both the created and the propped hydraulic fracture.

The fracture-treatment data can be analyzed with a P3D fracture propagation model to determine the shape and dimensions of the created fracture. The P3D model is used to history match the fracturing data, such as injection rates and injection pressures. Data, such as the in-situ stress and permeability in key layers of rock, can be varied (within reason) to achieve a history match of the field data.

Post-fracture production and pressure data can be analyzed with a 3D reservoir simulator to estimate the shape and dimensions of the propped fracture. Values of formation permeability, fracture length, and fracture conductivity can be varied in the reservoir model to achieve a history match of the field data.

The main limitations of these indirect techniques are that the solutions may not be unique and may require as much fixed data as possible. For example, if the engineer has determined the formation permeability from a well test or production test before the fracture treatment, so that the value of formation permeability is known and can be fixed in the models, the solution concerning values of fracture length become more unique. Most of the information in the literature concerning post-fracture analyses of hydraulic fractures has been derived with these indirect fracture diagnostic techniques.

Limitations of Fracture Diagnostic Techniques. Warpinski discussed many of these same fracture diagnostic techniques.[39] **Table 8.6** lists certain diagnostic techniques and their limitations.[39] Fracture diagnostic techniques do work and can provide important data when entering a new area or a new formation. In most cases, however, fracture diagnostics is expensive, which limits its widespread use in industry. In the future, if costs are reduced, fracture diagnostics may become more widely applied.

8.9.4 Net-Pressure Analysis. Net pressure is defined as the pressure in the fracture minus the in-situ stress. Nolte and Smith[40] published a classic paper that can be used to interpret net-pressure behavior in the field or after the treatment to determine estimates of fracture growth patterns. Their analysis method uses the PKN theory, which assumes that as long as the fracture height is contained, the net pressure will increase with time according to

$$p_n \propto \Delta t^e, \quad\quad\quad\quad\quad\quad\quad\quad\quad\quad\quad\quad\quad\quad\quad\quad\quad (8.11)$$

where $\frac{1}{8} < e < \frac{1}{5}$, and slope $e = \frac{1}{5}$ for low leakoff and $\frac{1}{8}$ for high leakoff.

When Nolte and Smith began analyzing bottomhole pressure data collected during fracture treatments, they found that the PKN theory held for certain situations, but other fracture propagation modes were observed. **Fig. 8.25** summarizes their findings. In Fig. 8.25, Mode I conforms to Eq. 8.11; however, three other modes were identified by analyzing field data.

Mode II conforms to either stable height growth or increased fluid loss. Mode II fracturing is not unusual, nor is it cause for concern. Lateral fracture growth during Mode II is less than Mode I, but the fracture is still being propagated and can be filled with proppant.

When the slope of the graph of $\log(p_n)$ vs. $\log(\Delta t)$ increases to a unit slope (Mode III), then the fracture has stopped propagating in length, and the fracture is being inflated as the net

TABLE 8.6—LIMITATIONS OF FRACTURE DIAGNOSTIC TECHNIQUES[39]		
Parameter	Technique	Limitations
Fracture height		
	Tracer logs	Shallow depth of investigation; shows height only near the wellbore
	Temperature logs	Difficult to interpret; shallow depth of investigation; shows height only near wellbore
	Stress profiling	Does not measure fracture directly; must be calibrated with in-situ stress tests
	P3D models	Does not measure fracture directly; estimates vary depending on which model is used
	Microseismic	Optimally requires nearby offset well; difficult to interpret; expensive
	Tiltmeters	Difficult to interpret; expensive and difficult to conduct in the field
Fracture length		
	P3D models	Length inferred, not measured; estimates vary greatly depending on which model is used
	Well testing	Large uncertainties depending on assumptions and lack of prefracture well test data
	Microseismic	Optimally requires nearby offset well; difficult to interpret; expensive
	Tiltmeters	Difficult to interpret; expensive and difficult to conduct in the field
Fracture azimuth		
	Core techniques	Expensive to cut core and run tests; multiple tests must be run to assure accuracy
	Log techniques	Requires openhole logs to be run; does not work if natural fractures are not present
	Microseismic	Analysis intensive; expensive for determination of azimuth
	Tiltmeters	Useful only to a depth of 5,000 ft; requires access to large area; expensive

pressure increases. This is the desired behavior if a tip screenout treatment has been designed. During Mode III, it is still possible to pack the fracture with proppant; however, the pressure has to be monitored closely to be certain the maximum allowable surface injection pressure is not exceeded. Mode IV occurs when the fracture height is increasing rapidly. Normally, rapid height growth is not desirable, and the fracture treatment should be flushed and terminated if Mode IV is reached during the treatment.

The pressures analyzed in a "net pressure graph," such as Fig. 8.25, are bottomhole pressures and should be corrected for near-wellbore pressure drops. **Fig 8.26** shows the pressures in the entire system. During every fracture treatment, the surface pressure can be measured. On certain wells, the bottomhole treating pressure (BHTP), which is the pressure inside the wellbore at the perforations, can be measured. If the BHTP is not measured directly, then that value must be computed with the surface pressure and the estimates of pipe friction and hydrostatic head. The hydrostatic head can be estimated accurately, even when propping agents are being added, because a densitometer is used to measure the density of the slurry as it is pumped. Problems may occur in trying to estimate the pipe friction when using crosslinked polymer fluids containing propping agents. Significant errors can occur in the pipe friction estimates when high proppant concentrations (> 4 ppg) are being pumped.

If the BHTP is computed or measured successfully, the near-wellbore pressure drop must be subtracted to determine the pressure in the fracture near the wellbore, p_f. The pressure in the

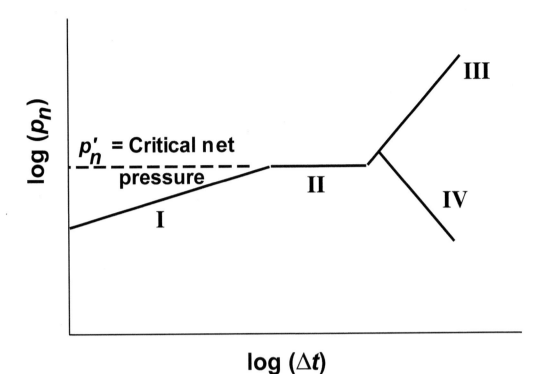

Fig. 8.25—Interpretation of fracturing pressures.[28]

fracture near the wellbore is the value that must be known and analyzed to determine the width, height, and length of the fracture with either net pressure theory or P3D fracture propagation models. The near-wellbore pressure drop is composed of two parts: the perforation friction and tortuosity. By running a step-down test before the main fracture treatment, the near-wellbore pressure drop often can be estimated accurately. One problem is that the perforation friction and the tortuosity pressure drop can change during the treatment as the propping agent is introduced. The propping agent can erode perforations or plug some of the pathways that are causing the tortuosity pressure drops. At the end of the treatment, the pressure data need to be analyzed as the pumps are shut down to determine if the near-wellbore pressure drop has changed during the treatment.

8.10 Post-Fracture Well Behavior
There are many factors that the engineer must consider when analyzing the behavior of a well after it has been fracture treated. The engineer should analyze the productivity index of the well both before and after the fracture treatment. Other factors of importance are ultimate oil and gas recovery and calculations to determine the propped fracture length, the fracture conductivity, and the drainage area of the well. Post-fracture treatment analyses of the fracture treatment data, the production data, and the pressure data can be very complicated and time consuming. However, without adequate post-fracture evaluation, it will be impossible to continue the fracture treatment optimization process on subsequent wells.

8.10.1 Productivity Index Increase. Many of the early treatments in the 1950s were designed to increase the productivity index of damaged wells. These treatments were normally pumped

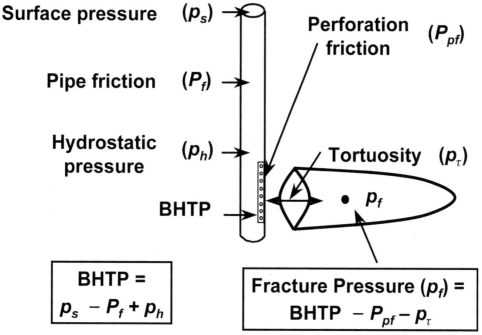

Fig. 8.26—Wellbore and near-wellbore hydraulics.

to break through damage in moderate- to high-permeability wells. The productivity index of an oil well is

$$J = \frac{q_o}{\left(p_e - p_{wf}\right)} \, . \quad \dots\dots\dots\dots\dots\dots\dots\dots\dots\dots\dots\dots\dots\dots\dots\dots\dots\dots \text{(8.12)}$$

For a gas well,

$$J = \frac{q_g \bar{\mu}\bar{z}}{\left(p_e^2 - p_{wf}^2\right)}, \quad \dots\dots\dots\dots\dots\dots\dots\dots\dots\dots\dots\dots\dots\dots\dots\dots\dots \text{(8.13)}$$

where $\bar{\mu}$ and $\bar{z}$ are evaluated at the average pressure of

$$\bar{p} = \frac{\left(p_e + p_{wf}\right)}{2} \, . \quad \dots\dots\dots\dots\dots\dots\dots\dots\dots\dots\dots\dots\dots\dots\dots\dots\dots \text{(8.14)}$$

J is the productivity index in terms of barrels per psi per day or mcf-cp per psi squared per day. Viscosity and compressibility are included in the equation describing the productivity index of a gas well, because they are pressure dependent. McGuire and Sikora[41] published a procedure (**Fig. 8.27**) that was the first tool a fracture-treatment design engineer could use to determine the fracture length and fracture conductivity required to achieve a certain fold of increase in the productivity index. The McGuire and Sikora graph can be used to draw the following conclusions:

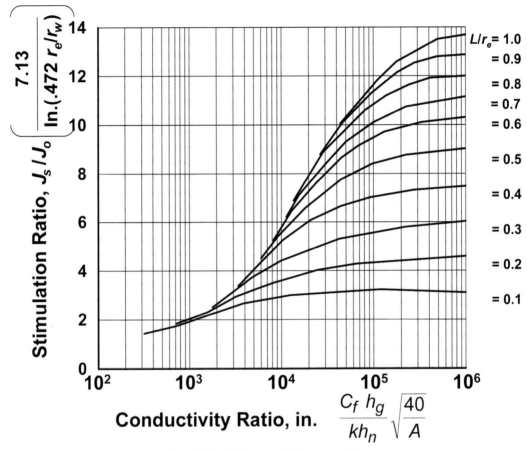

Fig. 8.27—McGuire and Sikora graph.[41]

• For high-permeability reservoirs, fracture conductivity is more important than fracture length.

• For low-permeability reservoirs, fracture length is more important than fracture conductivity.

• For a given fracture length, there is an optimum value of conductivity ratio.

• Most fracture treatments in undamaged formations should result in stimulation ratios of 2 to 14.

These conclusions have allowed engineers to design successful fracture treatments for more than 40 years.

At approximately the same time as the classic McGuire and Sikora paper was published, Prats[42] published another classic paper. Assuming J is the productivity index for a fractured well at steady-state flow, and J_o is the productivity index of the same well under radial flow conditions, Prats found that

$$\frac{J}{J_o} = \frac{\ln\left(\dfrac{r_e}{r_w}\right)}{\ln\left(\dfrac{r_e}{0.5\,L_f}\right)}, \qquad\qquad\qquad\qquad (8.15)$$

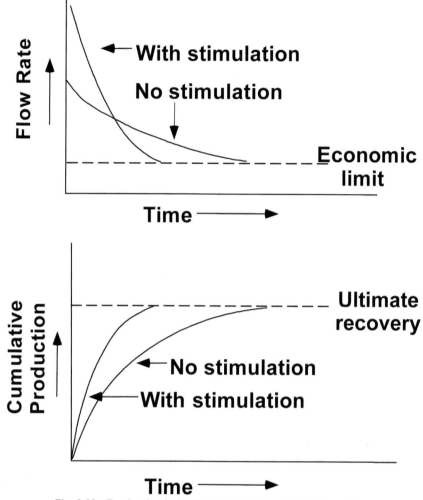

Fig. 8.28—Production behavior in a high-permeability formation.

for a well containing an infinite conductivity fracture whose fracture half-length is L_f. Prats explained that a well with a fracture half-length of 100 ft will produce as if the well had been drilled with a 100-ft diameter drill bit. In other words, the hydraulic fracture, if conductive enough, acts to extend the wellbore and stimulate flow rate from the well. If the dimensionless fracture conductivity, C_{fD} (Eq. 8.9), is equal to 10 or greater, the hydraulic fracture will essentially act as if it is an infinitely conductive fracture.

8.10.2 Ultimate Recovery for Fractured Wells. Hydraulic fracturing should always increase the productivity index of a well; and, under certain circumstances, the hydraulic fracture can increase the ultimate recovery. **Figs. 8.28 and 8.29** illustrate the differences that sometimes occur between low-permeability and high-permeability reservoirs. In Fig. 8.28, when a high-permeability well is fracture treated, the drainage volume and the recovery efficiency in the reservoir are not significantly altered. The fracture treatment increases the flow rate, increases the decline rate, and decreases the producing life of the well. The ultimate recovery is not changed. The same reserves are recovered in a shorter period of time, which reduces overall operating costs. Accelerating the recovery of a fixed volume of reserves is often beneficial. If

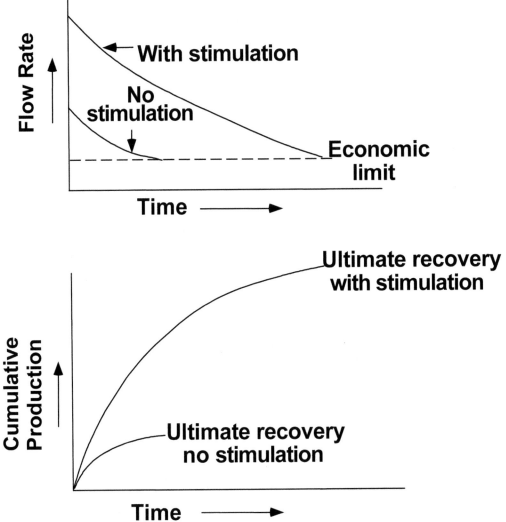

Fig. 8.29—Production behavior in a low-permeability formation.

the well is located in the Arctic or offshore in deep water, where operating costs are very high, then recovering the reserves sooner is very advantageous.

Fig. 8.29 illustrates the normal situation in low-permeability reservoirs. Without a fracture treatment, most low-permeability wells will flow at low rates and recover only modest volumes of oil and gas before reaching their economic limit. By definition, a low-permeability well will not be economic unless a successful fracture treatment is both designed and pumped into the formation. When the stimulation treatment is successful, the flow rate will increase, the ultimate recovery will increase, and the producing life will be extended. In fact, many low-permeability wells will produce for 40 or more years, given adequate product prices and minimal operating costs. It is usually very easy to justify fracture treatments in low-permeability wells when the fracture treatment substantially increases the ultimate recovery.

8.10.3 Post-Fracture Well-Test Analyses. Post-fracture well-test analyses are used to compute estimates of the propped fracture length, fracture conductivity, and drainage area of the formation. It is important to keep good records of the flow rates of oil, gas, and water, as well as the flowing pressures after the fracture treatment. If possible, a pressure-buildup test should be run after the well cleanup following the fracture treatment. Lee[43] presented a complete discussion on how to analyze production and pressure data after a fracture treatment to estimate fracture properties.

Nomenclature

a = constant (solved for)
A = area, L^2, acres
B = Borate crosslinker
c = acid concentration
c_o = original acid concentration
C_f = fracture conductivity, md-ft
C_{fD} = dimensionless fracture conductivity
d_p = proppant diameter, L
d_{pf} = perforation diameter, L, in.
g = gravitational constant
G = Shear modulus, m/L^3
h = fracture height, L
h_g = gross height, L
h_i = fracture height, L
h_n = net pay, L
H = fracture height, L
i = injection rate, L^3/t
i_{pf} = specific injection rate, bbl/min-perforation
J = productivity index, STB/D/psi
J_o = productivity index of unfractured well, STB/D/psi
J_s = productivity index of stimulated well, STB/D/psi
k = formation permeability, L^2, md
k_f = fracture permeability, L^2, md
L = fracture half-length, L, ft
L_f = fracture half-length, L, ft
n = number for perforations
p_e = pressure at the extremity of the reservoir, psi
P_f = pipe friction
p_f = actual pressure in the fracture, m/Lt^2
p_h = hydrostatic head
p_n = net pressure, m/Lt^2
p'_n = critical net pressure, m/Lt^2
p_p = pore pressure (reservoir pressure), m/Lt^2
p_{pfr} = perforation friction, psi
p_s = surface pressure, m/Lt^2
p_t = pressure drop because of tortuosity
p_{wf} = flowing bottomhole pressure, m/Lt^2
P_e = stress on proppant
P_{pf} = perforation friction
q_g = gas flow rate, Mcf/D
q_o = oil flow rate, STB/D

$$Q = \text{injection rate, L}^3/\text{t}$$
$$r_e = \text{drainage radius, ft}$$
$$r_w = \text{wellbore radius, ft}$$
$$S_{1-6} = \text{in-situ stresses in layers 1–6, m/L}^2$$
$$t = \text{time, t}$$
$$T = \text{temperature, T, °F}$$
$$u = \text{viscosity, cp}$$
$$\bar{u} = \text{average gas viscosity, cp}$$
$$v = \text{Poisson's ratio}$$
$$\bar{v}_n = \text{velocity in the fracture, L/t}$$
$$v_t = \text{terminal settling velocity, ft/min}$$
$$v_x = \text{velocity down the fracture}$$
$$w = \text{fracture width, L}$$
$$\bar{w} = \text{average fracture width, L}$$
$$w_w = \text{fracture width at the wellbore, L}$$
$$x = \text{distance, L}$$
$$z = \text{gas compressibility factor}$$
$$\alpha = \text{Biot's constant}$$
$$\alpha = \text{discharge coefficient, usually 0.9 (in Eq. 8.2)}$$
$$\Delta t = \text{change in time, t}$$
$$\Delta p_\tau = \text{pressure drop near perforations wellbore because of tortuosity, m/Lt}^2$$
$$\partial \Delta p = \text{change in net pressure in the fracture, m/Lt}^2$$
$$\partial_x = \text{incremental distance down the fracture, L}$$
$$\mu = \text{fluid viscosity, m/Lt}$$
$$\rho = \text{fracturing-fluid density, m/L}^3$$
$$\rho_p = \text{proppant density, m/L}^3$$
$$\rho_{\min} = \text{minimum in-situ stress, m/L}^2$$
$$\rho_f = \text{fluid density, m/L}^3$$
$$\sigma_c = \text{closure stress on the fracture}$$
$$\sigma_{\text{ext}} = \text{tectonic stress, m/Lt}^2$$
$$\sigma_{\min} = \text{minimum horizontal stress (in-situ stress), m/Lt}^2$$
$$\sigma_{ob} = \text{overburden stress, m/Lt}^2$$
$$\sigma_1 = \text{vertical (overburden) stress, m/Lt}^2$$
$$\sigma_2 = \text{minimum horizontal stress, m/Lt}^2$$
$$\sigma_3 = \text{maximum horizontal stress, m/Lt}^2$$

References

1. Veatch, R.W. Jr., Moschovidis, Z.A., and Fast, R.C.: "An Overview of Hydraulic Fracturing," *Recent Advances in Hydraulic Fracturing*, J.L. Gidley *et al.* (eds.), Monograph Series, SPE, Richardson, Texas (1989) **12,** Chap. 1.
2. Holditch, S.A. *et al.*: "The Optimization of Well Spacing and Fracture Length in Low-Permeability Gas Reservoirs," paper SPE 7496 presented at the 1978 SPE Annual Technical Conference and Exhibition, Houston, 1–4 October.
3. Veatch, R.W. Jr.: "Overview of Current Hydraulic Fracture Design and Treatment Technology —Part I," *JPT* (April 1983) 677.

4. Britt, L.K.: "Optimized Oilwell Fracturing of Moderate-Permeability Reservoirs," paper SPE 14371 presented at the 1985 SPE Annual Technical Conference and Exhibition, Las Vegas, Nevada, 22–25 September.

5. Warpinski, N.R. and Smith, M.B.: "Rock Mechanics and Fracture Geometry," *Recent Advances in Hydraulic Fracturing*, J.L. Gidley *et al.* (eds.), Monograph Series, SPE, Richardson, Texas (1989) **12,** Chap. 3, 57–63.

6. Hubbart, M.K. and Willis, D.G.: "Mechanics of Hydraulic Fracturing," *Trans.*, AIME (1957) **210**, 153.

7. Whitehead, W.S., Hunt, E.R., and Holditch, S.A.: "The Effects of Lithology and Reservoir Pressure on the In-Situ Stresses in the Waskom (Travis Peak) Field," paper SPE 16403 presented at the 1987 SPE/DOE Low Permeability Reservoir Symposium, Denver, 18–19 May.

8. Salz, L.B.: "Relationship Between Fracture Propagation Pressure and Pore Pressure," paper SPE 6870 presented at the 1977 SPE Annual Technical Conference and Exhibition, Denver, 9–12 October.

9. Veatch, R.W. Jr. and Moschovidis, Z.A.: "An Overview of Recent Advances in Hydraulic Fracturing Technology," paper SPE 14085 presented at the 1986 SPE International Meeting on Petroleum Engineering, Beijing, 17–20 March.

10. Reynolds, J.J., Scott, J.B., and Coffer, H.F.: "Hydraulic Fracture—Field Test To Determine Areal Extent and Orientation," *JPT* (April 1961) 371.

11. Lacy, L.L. and Smith, M.B.: "Fracture Azimuth and Geometry Determination," *Recent Advances in Hydraulic Fracturing*, J.L. Gidley *et al.* (eds.), Monograph Series, SPE, Richardson, Texas (1989) **12,** Chap. 16, 341.

12. Cleary, M.P. *et al.*: "Field Implementation of Proppant Slugs To Avoid Premature Screenout of Hydraulic Fractures with Adequate Proppant Concentration." paper SPE 25892 presented at the 1993 SPE Rocky Mountain Regional/Low Permeability Reservoirs Symposium, Denver, 12–14 April.

13. Howard, G.C. and Fast, C.R.: "Optimum Fluid Characteristics for Fracture Extension," *Drill. & Prod. Prac.* (1957) **24,** 261.

14. Perkins, T.K. and Kern, L.R.: "Widths of Hydraulic Fractures," *JPT* (September 1961) 937.

15. Geertsma, J. and de Klerk, F.: "A Rapid Method of Predicting Width and Extent of Hydraulically Induced Fractures," *JPT* (December 1969) 1571.

16. Nordgren, R.P.: "Propagation of a Vertical Hydraulic Fracture," *SPEJ* (August 1972) 306.

17. Daneshy, A.A.: "On the Design of Vertical Hydraulic Fractures," *JPT* (January 1973) 83; *Trans.*, AIME, **255.**

18. Geertsma, J.: "Two-Dimensional Fracture-Propagation Models," *Recent Advances in Hydraulic Fracturing*, J.L. Gidley *et al.* (eds.), Monograph Series, SPE, Richardson, Texas (1989) **12,** Chap. 4, 81.

19. Geertsma, J. and Haafkens, R.: "A Comparison of the Theories to Predict Width and Extent of Vertical, Hydraulically Induced Fractures," ASME *J. Energy Res. Tech.* (1979) **101,** 8.

20. Clifton, R.J.: "Three-Dimensional Fracture-Propagation Models," *Recent Advances in Hydraulic Fracturing*, J.L. Gidley *et al.* (eds.), Monograph Series, SPE, Richardson, Texas (1989) **12,** Chap. 5, 95.

21. Ely, J.W.: "Fracturing Fluids and Additives," *Recent Advances in Hydraulic Fracturing*, J.L. Gidley *et al.* (eds.), Monograph Series, SPE, Richardson, Texas (1989) **12,** Chap. 7, 131.

22. Holditch, S.A.: "Criteria of Propping Agent Selection," prepared for the Norton Co. (1979a).

23. Daneshy, A.: "Proppant Transport," *Recent Advances in Hydraulic Fracturing*, J.L. Gidley *et al.* (eds.), Monograph Series, SPE, Richardson, Texas (1989) **12,** Chap. 10, 210.

24. Smith, M.B. *et al.*: "Enhanced 2D Proppant Transport Simulation: The Key To Understanding Proppant Flowback and Post-Frac Productivity," paper SPE 38610 presented at the 1997 SPE Annual Technical Conference and Exhibition, San Antonio, Texas, 5–8 October.

25. Economides, M.J. and Nolte, K.G.: *Reservoir Stimulation,* third edition, John Wiley & Sons Ltd., West Sussex, England (2000).

26. Cinco-Ley, H., Samaniego, V.F., and Dominquez, N.: "Transient Pressure Behavior for a Well with a Finite-Conductivity Vertical Fracture," *SPEJ* (August 1978) 253.

27. Holditch, S.A.: "Factors Affecting Water Blocking and Gas Flow From Hydraulically Fractured Gas Wells," *JPT* (December 1979) 1515.

28. Williams, B.B., Gidley, J.L., and Schechter, R.S.: *Acidizing Fundamentals*, Monograph Series, SPE, Richardson, Texas, 1979) **6.**
29. Kozik, H.G., Bailey, B.G., and Holditch, S.A.: "A Case History of Massive Hydraulic Fracturing the Cotton Valley Lime Matrix, Fallon and Personville Field—Limestone County, Texas," *JPT* (February 1981) 229.
30. Pathak, P. *et al.*: "The Arun Gas Field in Indonesia: Resource Management of a Mature Field," paper SPE 87042 presented at the 2004 SPE Asia Pacific Conference on Integrated Modelling for Asset Management, Kuala Lumpur, 29–30 March.
31. Roodhart, L.P., Kamphuis, H., and Davies, D.R.: "Improved Acid-Fracturing Treatment Designs Based on In-Situ Temperature Calculations," paper SPE 26185 presented at the 1993 SPE Gas Technology Symposium, Calgary, 28–30 June.
32. Settari, A.: "Modeling of Acid-Fracturing," *SPEPF* (February 1993) 30.
33. Smith, M.B. and Hannah, R.R.: "High-Permeability Fracturing: The Evolution of a Technology," *JPT* (July 1996) 628.
34. Valko, P.P., Oligney, R.E., and Economides, M.J.: "High Permeability Fracturing of Gas Wells," *Petroleum Engineering Intl.* (January 1998) 75.
35. Smith, M.B., Miller, W.K. II, and Haga, J.: "Tip Screenout Fracturing: A Technique for Soft, Unstable Formations," *SPEPE* (May 1987) 95.
36. Hannah, R.R.: "Combination Fracturing/Gravel Packing Completion Technique on the Amberjack, Mississippi Canyon 109 Field," *SPEPF* (November 1994) 262.
37. Park, E.I.: "Frac Pack Maximize Well Productivity in Sand Control Developments," *Petroleum Engineer Intl.* (August 1995) 22.
38. Cipolla, C.L. and Wright, C.A.: "State of the Art in Hydraulic Fracture Diagnostics," paper SPE 64434 presented at the 2000 SPE Asia Pacific Oil and Gas Conference, Brisbane, Australia, 16–18 October.
39. Warpinski, N.R.: "Hydraulic Fracture Diagnostics," *JPT* (October 1996) 907.
40. Nolte, K.G. and Smith, M.B.: "Interpretation of Fracturing Pressures," *JPT* (September 1981) 1767.
41. McGuire, W.J. and Sikora, V.T.: "The Effect of Vertical Fractures on Well Productivity," *JPT* (October 1960) 72; *Trans.*, AIME (1960) **219,** 401.
42. Prats, M.: "Effect of Vertical Fractures on Reservoir Behavior—Incompressible Fluid Case," *SPEJ* (June 1961) 105; *Trans.,* AIME (1961) **222.**
43. Lee, W.J.: "Postfracture Formation Evaluation," *Recent Advances in Hydraulic Fracturing*, J.L. Gidley *et al.* (eds.), Monograph Series, SPE, Richardson, Texas (1989) **12,** Chap. 15, 317.

SI Metric Conversion Factors

bbl	× 1.589 873	E – 01	= m^3
cp	× 1.0*	E – 03	= Pa·s
°F	(°F – 32)/1.8		= °C
ft	× 3.048*	E – 01	= m
ft^2	× 9.290 304*	E – 02	= m^2
in.	× 2.54*	E + 00	= cm
lbm	× 4.535 924	E – 01	= kg
psi	× 6.894 757	E + 00	= kPa

*Conversion factor is exact.

Chapter 9
Well Production Problems
Raymond Jasinski, SPE, Schlumberger Ltd. (retired)

9.1 Introduction

Oil, gas, water, steel, and rock are not always chemically inert under oil/gas production conditions. Their mutual interactions, induced in part by changes in pressure and temperature, can lead to the accumulation of solids, both organic and inorganic (scaling) within the production system, as well as deterioration of the metals that the fluids contact (corrosion).

This chapter discusses these effects in terms of root causes, the operational difficulties resulting, and the principles/methods that have been used to cope. Case histories are not presented in any detail, but references are given to specific papers dealing with cause/effect/cure examples. It is assumed that the reader is not an expert in things chemical but does have a passing acquaintance with the jargon of chemistry and with some of the general principles underlying chemical processes.

"Well production problems" are taken as starting when fluids enter the wellbore and end when fluids reach the storage/treatment facilities. Problems arising from adverse chemistry, occurring in the formation, are discussed elsewhere in the literature. The disposal of toxic coproduction [e.g., H_2S, Hg, and naturally occurring radioactive materials (NORM)] is mentioned briefly in this chapter and is discussed in the chapter on facilities in the Facilities and Construction Engineering section of this *Handbook*. This chapter also does not treat the flow engineering problems, multiple-phase production problems, and the in-situ measurement/control problems attendant to producing hydrocarbons.

9.1.1 Hydrocarbon-Related Problems. *Asphaltenes.*

Certain crude oils deposit solid asphaltenes during production. These deposits may plug the wellbore tubing and valves, as well as coat surface safety and process control equipment.[1] Asphaltenes can accumulate in separators and in pipelines, a problem discussed elsewhere. The tendencies of crudes to deposit asphaltenes do not correlate with the quantity of dissolved asphaltenes present in the reservoir fluid. Some oils with 1% asphaltene or less will form deposits in tubulars, while others with 10% or more asphaltenes will form no deposits. Asphaltenes chemistry varies with field. Asphaltenes contained in oil from a well in the North Sea are chemically different from asphaltenes found in the Venezuela fields, or another North Sea well. The chemistry controlling these depositions is not well defined. Nevertheless, some generalities are possible, which can aid in the design of prevention and remediation technology for a given well.

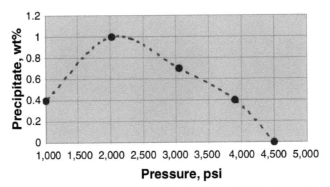

Fig. 9.1—Pressure dependence of asphaltene precipitation (cumulative) at constant temperature, 100°C (data from Ref. 2).

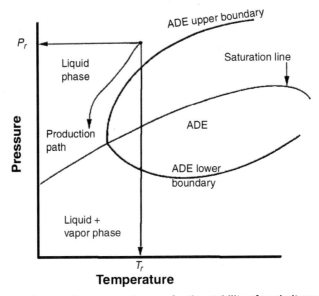

Fig. 9.2—A pressure/temperature phase diagram for the stability of asphaltenes in a crude oil.[3]

Asphaltene precipitation as changing pressure and temperature is illustrated in **Figs. 9.1 and 9.2**. The first figure is a plot of weight percent asphaltene precipitated as a function of pressure at reservoir temperature. A plot of saturation level, rather than percent asphaltene, gives the same form (data obtained from Ref. 2). The observed general scenario is as follows. There is no asphaltene precipitation on pressure reduction until a critical "onset pressure" is reached—here, nominally 4,500 psi; for the well described in Fig. 9.1, the reservoir pressure is in excess of 5,000 psi. The total amount deposited increases with decreasing pressure, reaching a maximum at nominally the saturation pressure. Asphaltene deposits can then redissolve as pressure falls, at least partially, possibly reaching zero deposition at low pressure ("dissolution pressure"). Not all crudes will show a dissolution pressure at accessible temperatures.

Fig. 9.2 shows an asphaltene deposition envelope (ADE), a plot of such onset pressures (upper boundary) and dissolution pressures (lower boundary) as a function of temperature, overlaid with a saturation pressure/temperature (PT) curve.[3] The sense of the ADE region is that asphaltenes precipitate for PT values between the boundaries. The precipitation problem will be

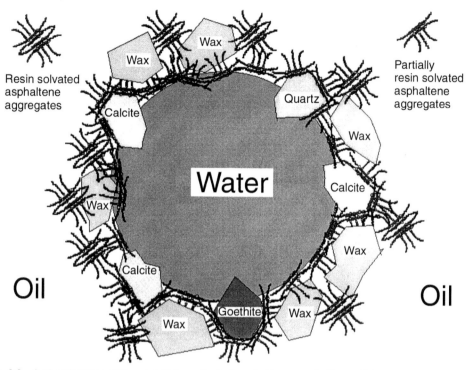

Fig. 9.3—A visualization of the stabilizing effect of asphaltenes and other solids on water droplets.[7]

greater the closer the PT values are to the saturation line (as indicated in Fig. 9.1). A possible PT route to avoid asphaltene deposition during production is also shown in the figure.

Pressure and temperature changes are not the only drivers for asphaltene deposition. Combining certain crudes can deposit asphaltenes at the point of mixing (e.g., in the wellbore, flowlines, headers, pipelines, and oil treatment facilities.) Gas lift would favor deposition of asphaltenes from the heavy oil. ADE diagrams can be drawn for such compositional variations as well.[3,4] Shear effects[5] and electrokinetic effects during flow have been claimed as additional mechanisms for asphaltene precipitation.[6] [It is claimed that asphaltenes are electrically charged and the electrical potential generated by flow of these ions through small orifices (similar chemistry to electro-osmosis) can overcome charge stabilization, causing flocculation.] Increases in asphaltene problems with water-production onset are generally observed, as is the decrease in problems with larger water cuts; the definition of "large" varies with field. The presence of other solids with water in the produced fluid can exacerbate the consequences of asphaltene precipitation, generating a greater mass of solids and/or stable emulsions. A rationale for this exacerbation is shown schematically in **Fig. 9.3**.[7] The surface-active resin/asphaltene aggregates adsorb with wax and other solids onto water droplets, stabilizing an emulsion that can be sufficiently strong to plug production.

Definition of Asphaltenes. Asphaltenes are a compound class, not a single compound, concentrated in the high-temperature distillation residue of petroleum (> 530°C). Other components are heavy oils, resins, and high-molecular-weight waxes.[8] The asphaltene class is defined in accord with the solubility sequence illustrated in **Fig. 9.4**.

The quantity, and possibly chemistry, of the asphaltene mixture depends on, at least, the final solvent used after the initial separation (e.g., *n*-pentane vs. *n*-heptane). (Data are from Ref. 9.) An asphaltene mixture using *n*-C_5 as a precipitant will contain more material than an

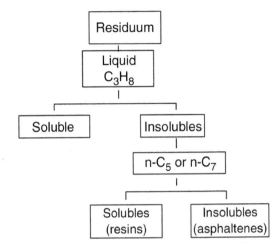

Fig. 9.4—Solubility sequence used to define asphaltenes.

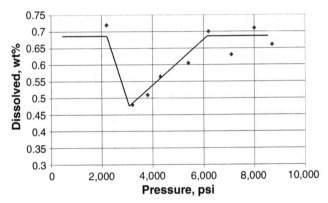

Fig. 9.5—Amount of asphaltene left in the crude oil vs. pressure, at constant temperature (after Infochem Computer Services).

asphaltene mixture using n-C_7. Asphaltenes precipitated from a cyclopentane addition would be very small in quantity, compared with those precipitated by n-pentane.

Asphaltene phase separation and deposition in the field generally involve only a portion of the asphaltene fraction generated from the crude oil in the laboratory by n-C_5 fractionation (nominally 30 to 50% of the asphaltenes present are precipitated).[10] An example is shown in **Fig. 9.5**—a plot of the quantity of asphaltene dissolved (as per n-C_5 precipitation) vs. pressure at constant temperature.[11]

The asphaltene mixtures precipitated by either the n-C_5 or n-C_7 addition are dark brown to black, amorphous solids. The resins tend to be lighter in color and less viscous.[12] Resins have H/C ratios ranging from 1.3 to 1.6; asphaltenes range from 1.0 to 1.3. An asphaltene molecule consists of clusters of condensed aromatic and naphthenic rings. Each cluster contains not more than 5 to 6 rings, connected by paraffin linkages, which may also contain oxygen and sulfur atoms (as sulfides and disulfides). The resins and asphaltenes contain about half the total nitrogen and sulfur in the crude oil. Nitrogen atoms are present predominantly as primary amines and pyridines (bases). It is these nitrogen atoms that can react with stimulation acid, potentially forming sludges. Oxygen is present predominantly in the form of acidic functional groups (car-

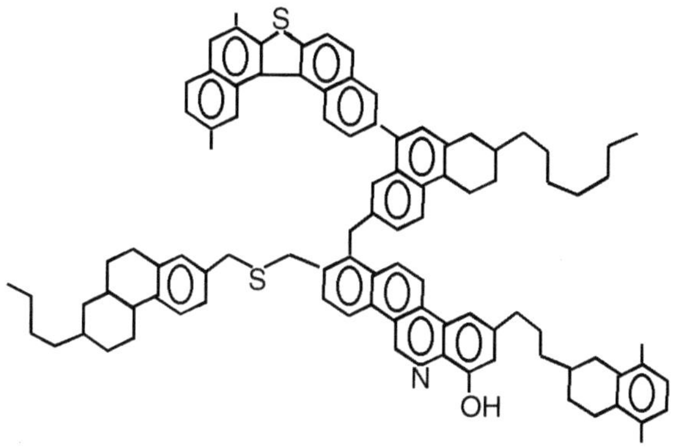

Fig. 9.6—Hypothetical/generic structure of an asphaltene.

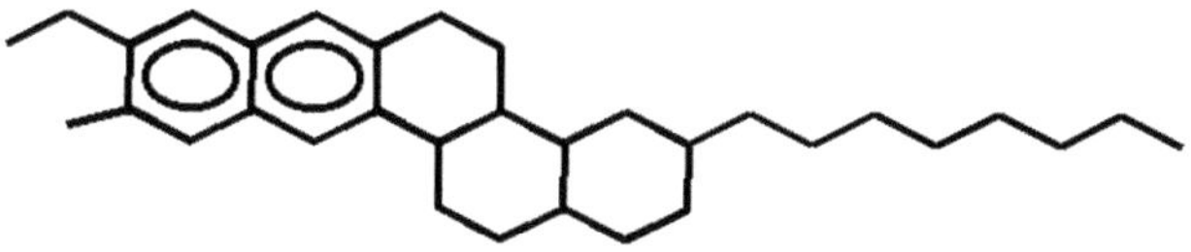

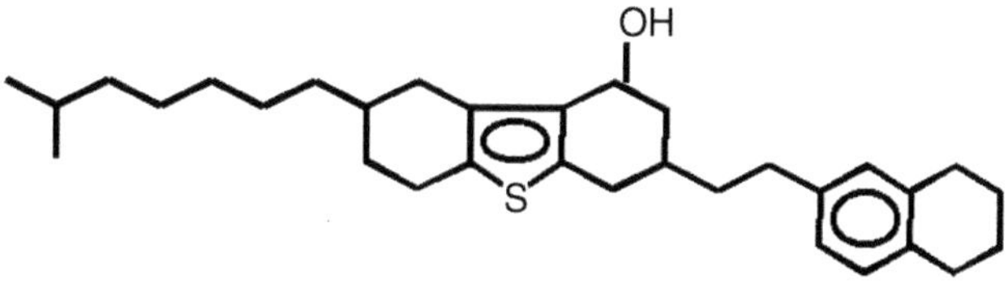

Fig. 9.7—Structures of crude-oil resins.

boxylic acids and phenols). These oxygen atoms can form chelants (salts) with iron, potentially forming sludges. Additional compositional details are given in Ref. 13. An example of an asphaltene molecule is given in **Fig. 9.6**.[12]

Asphaltene molecules form aggregates with themselves, nominally 35 to 40Å in size, while remaining dissolved in oil.[13] The specific nature of the chemical bonding between the monomer asphaltene molecules within the aggregates has not been well defined, which complicates anticipation (computer simulation) of their deposition tendencies. Various polar interactions are possible in principle, as well as acid-based interactions between the basic nitrogen and acidic carboxyl functions.

The asphaltene molecules and aggregates in a given crude cover a range of molecular weights;[14] the smaller-molecular-weight asphaltenes are the most polar.[12] The difficulties in quantifying asphaltene molecular weight result from the aggregation problem.[8,13] For example, molecular weight ranges of 935 to 16,840 were found for one crude, depending on the instrumental techniques used; others have reported ranges of 1,000 to 2,000,000.[14]

There is ample evidence that resin molecules play a major role in solvating the asphaltenes in oil. Petroleum resins are nominally C_{30} compounds and are different from nonpetroleum resins, which tend to be a 3- to 5-membered condensed aliphatic ring structure. **Fig. 9.7** is a depiction of the structure of two resins derived from a crude oil; the aliphatic side chains are the nonpolar groups; the condensed aromatic rings are the polar groups.[15]

"Common wisdom" is that resins attach themselves to the asphaltene aggregates by polar-group interactions. The nonpolar "tails" of the resin molecules provide compatibility (solvation) with the nonpolar components in crude oil. The concept that resins are the sole solvating oil constituents for the asphaltenes is an oversimplification. Naphthenes precipitate less asphaltenes[9] than the low-carbon-number paraffins (solvate asphaltenes better than paraffins); xylene is used as a solvent for asphaltene removal, which is discussed later. Both classes of compounds (naphthenes and aromatics) are present in oil. The amounts vary depending on the source of the crude.

When this bonding chemistry between asphaltene aggregates and the solvating entities in the crude oil is disrupted, the aggregates come out of solution and flocculate to form larger particles. These flocs are the source of the operational problems. Only after flocculation occurs does deposition occur.[6] The sequence of forms for the asphaltene during oil production is soluble → colloidal particles → flocculated → deposit.

Modeling Asphaltene Deposition. Preventing and/or mitigating asphaltene deposition is facilitated by the availability of the ADE for the particular well. The direct measurement of this stability envelope is difficult, tedious, expensive, and not always possible, particularly with crudes from old exploratory wells. Computer simulations of asphaltene precipitation tendencies are an option, whereby the computer takes "key information" about oil composition and asphaltene properties in order to generate the stability diagram. A problem in establishing a workable model is defining the relevant key information in terms of readily measurable oil and asphaltene parameters. The model is to specify the operating envelope of pressure; temperature under which asphaltenes will and will not deposit; how much asphaltene will deposit; how these parameters vary with liquid composition, particularly in the context of mixing oils from different reservoirs and/or using gas lift to assist production; and how to best remove the asphaltene deposit (e.g., which solvents will be most effective for a particular asphaltene deposit). Not all models available specify all of these items.

There are two broad classes of models for asphaltene dissolution and flocculation, variously labeled as the molecular-thermodynamic approach and thermodynamic-colloidal approach. The scope, limitations, and details of the concepts underlying these model classes are reviewed in Refs. 6 and 12.

The thermodynamic-colloidal approach holds that the asphaltene micelles are composed of an insoluble aromatic core, onto the surface of which resin molecules adsorb, thereby providing a steric stabilization against their flocculation and precipitation.[6,12] Here, the major focus of the computation is on the resin. The additional solvation, because of other chemical components of the oil, is nevertheless taken into account in the present versions of such simulators.[16]

The molecular-thermodynamic approach[2,12,17,18] envisions that the asphaltenes are monodispersed polymeric entities soluble in the host oil. Conventional polymer theory (e.g., the Flory-Huggins model) has been used to describe the situation.[17,18] The dissolution/deposition process is taken as reversible. The oil is assigned a solvating power (i.e., the resins are not treated as unique entities but as members of the bulk solvent, in which naphthenes and aromatics, for example, are also members).

All models require establishing at least four input parameters (two characteristic of the oil and two characteristic of the asphaltene). One version of the molecular–thermodynamic approach[17,18] uses the molar volume and solubility parameter of the solvent crude oil as a function of pressure, as well as the molecular weight and solubility parameter of the precipitating asphaltene. Correlations with component class analysis (paraffins, aromatics, resins, and asphaltenes), as well as other measured oil parameters, are often used to generate the four input parameters.[16] Model accuracy is improved by calibration to one experimental onset pressure.

Given the uncertainties in asphaltene precipitation chemistry discussed, these computer models should be validated by the operator with comparisons of predicted onset pressures with experimental values for the fields of interest. These models are then best applied to new wells within the field by applying this correlation.

Coping With Asphaltene Deposition. The most effective procedure is configuring the production conditions to stay out of the precipitation envelope established for the well. This involves minimizing pressure drops within the production system—possibly fracturing the formation to minimize drawdown.[19] The use of pressure maintenance by water injection might be appropriate if the field is of sufficient size.[10] If prevention cannot be achieved, it may be possible to move the deposition to a location more easily treated (e.g., at the choke rather than at the perforations).

Chemical inhibitors can be used to prevent asphaltene precipitation. The inhibitors must be placed in the oil before asphaltene precipitation has taken place. In completion systems where capillary ("macaroni") tubing already exists, a continuous injection of an inhibitor can be used. Continuous injection of an inhibitor into pipelined crude is straightforward, as well as the injection of inhibitors immediately before the mixing of asphaltene in incompatible oils. Asphaltene inhibitors can be squeezed into the formation, similar to inorganic-scale inhibitors. However, because of necessity, these inhibitors are oil soluble, resulting in a short functional lifetime for the inhibitor.

Asphaltene inhibitors are generally resinous organic polymers.[20] Their functional groups interact with the asphaltenes in much the same way natural resins keep the asphaltenes dissolved. It is claimed that the strength of the interaction is stronger than with natural resins, keeping the asphaltene dissolved over a broader range of pressure and temperature. Given the variability in the asphaltene structure, it is important that the polymer inhibitor be evaluated on the specific crude in which it will be placed. In principle, it is possible that these polymers could also cause formation damage by altering the wetting properties of the rock. It is obviously prudent to evaluate this possibility on core samples before treatment.

Asphaltene deposits are generally removed manually if present in readily accessible equipment, such as separators and other surface equipment. For tubular and flowline deposits, removal techniques involve chemical methods such as solvent soaks with or without dispersants. Combining solvents and heating may also be effective (see the section on wax removal). Physical methods can be used depending on the hardness of the deposit (e.g., pigging, hydroblasting, and drilling). Pigging (cutting) is appropriate for removing pipeline deposits—often, mixtures of waxes and asphaltenes.

The traditional solvent of choice has been xylene. Refs. 12 and 21 describe the use of certain refinery cuts as solvents for asphaltene deposits—mixtures cheaper and more effective than xylene. It is to be expected, given the variability of asphaltene chemistry described, that the refinery-solvent mixture will have to be tailored to the specific well—one mixture will not necessarily cure all. A logic for deriving such mixtures is discussed in Ref. 22.

Terpenes (more-expensive natural products) have been used effectively as solvents, replacing xylene because of health, safety, and environment (HSE) considerations. Certain alkylbenzene compounds will stabilize (dissolve or disperse) asphaltenes in simple aliphatic solvents (e.g., heptane). Also, the highly polar and readily available *p-* (*n*-dodecyl) benzenesulfonic acid is a highly effective compound.[23]

The prevention-by-well-design scenario, albeit initially potentially expensive, may be more cost effective throughout the life of the well vs. cleaning/dissolving. As with the removal of inorganic scale, which is discussed later, the costs of the treatments involve not only the chemical itself but the deferred and/or lost oil production attendant to the well's downtime for the treatment. A methodology for asphaltene control in the field, including all aspects previously described, is illustrated in Ref. 19.

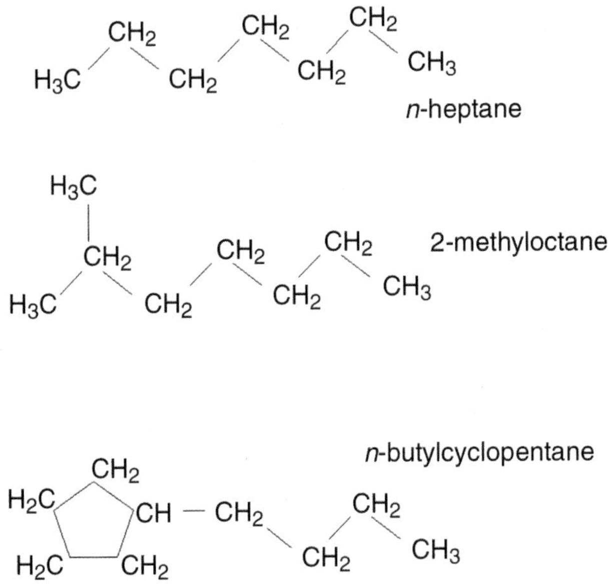

CH_2 structures (figure)

Fig. 9.8—Structures of hydrocarbon classes involved in wax deposition.

9.1.2 Waxes. Many crudes contain dissolved waxes that can precipitate and deposit under the appropriate environmental conditions. Paraffin wax produced from crude oil consists primarily of long chain, saturated hydrocarbons (linear alkanes/n-paraffins) with carbon chain lengths of C_{18} to C_{75+}, having individual melting points from 40 to 70°C. This wax material is referred to as "macrocrystalline wax." Naphthenic hydrocarbons (C_{18} to C_{36}) also deposit wax, which is referred to as "microcrystalline wax." Macrocrystalline waxes lead to paraffin problems in production and transport operations; microcrystalline waxes contribute the most to tank-bottom sludges.[24] **Fig. 9.8** shows the generic molecular structures of n-paraffins, iso-paraffins, and naphthenes. The n-heptane structure is an example of a "normal" paraffin; 2-methyloctane is an "iso" paraffin and n-butylcyclopentane is a naphthene. These specific n-paraffins and naphthenes are too small to crystallize as wax deposits (i.e., outside the carbon-number range specified above). The drawings illustrate the type of structures involved.

Waxes isolated from crudes can contain various amounts of all classes: n-paraffins, naphthenes, and iso-paraffins. For example, waxes derived from several Venezuelan crudes[24] showed n-paraffin/(cyclo + iso paraffin) ratios ranging from 1.28 to 0.23. The iso-paraffins of the 2-methyloctane type (Fig. 9.8) are more likely to be included in a wax deposit than the more highly branched alkanes.

A "clean waxy crude" is defined as a crude oil that consists of only hydrocarbons and wax as the heavy organic constituents. "Regular waxy crudes" contain other heavy organics in addition to the waxes (e.g., asphaltenes and resins). These heavy organics have interactions with the crude, which can either prevent wax-crystal formation or enhance it.

Phenomenology. As the temperature of the crude drops below a critical level and/or as the low-molecular-weight hydrocarbons vaporize, the dissolved waxes begin to form insoluble crystals. The deposition process involves two distinct stages: nucleation and growth. Nucleation is the forming of paraffin clusters of a critical size ("nuclei") that are stable in the hydrocarbon fluid. This insoluble wax itself tends to disperse in the crude.

Wax deposition onto the production system ("growth") generally requires a "nucleating agent," such as asphaltenes and inorganic solids. The wax deposits vary in consistency from a soft mush to a hard, brittle material. Paraffin deposits will be harder if longer-chain n-paraffins are present. Paraffin deposits can also contain asphaltenes, resins, gums, fine sand, silt, clays, salt, and water.[25] High-molecular-weight waxes tend to deposit in the higher-temperature sections of a well, while lower-molecular-weight fractions tend to deposit in lower-temperature regions. Prior to solidification, the solid wax crystals in the liquid oil change the flow properties from a Newtonian low viscosity fluid to a very-complex-flow behavior gel with a yield stress.

Coping With Waxes. The primary chemical parameter to establish is the critical temperature at which these wax nuclei form—the "wax appearance temperature" (WAT). The WAT (or "cloud point") is highly specific to each crude. The WAT value is a function of oil composition; cooling rate during measurement; pressure; paraffin concentration; molecular mass of paraffin molecules; occurrence of nucleating materials such as asphaltenes, formation fines, and corrosion products; water/oil ratio; and shear environment.[26] A variety of experimental methods have been used to obtain this number. Among these are differential scanning calorimetry (DSC), cross polarization microscopy (CPM), filter plugging (FP), and Fourier transform infrared energy scattering (FTIR).

DSC measures the heat released by wax crystallization. CPM exploits the fact that insoluble wax crystals rotate polarized light, but liquid hydrocarbons do not. FP measures the increase in differential pressure across a filter, which can be attributed to wax-crystal formation. FTIR detects the cloud point by measuring the increase in energy scattering associated with wax solidification. Each of these techniques has its advantages and disadvantages. A comparison/review of these methods is found in Ref. 27. In testing, cloud points, measured by each of the four methods, agreed with the average value of all methods within 3 to 5°F.

The second, and more important, question is how well do laboratory-measured cloud points anticipate WATs found in the field. Measured cloud-point data should only match field results for wells producing at low shear (high shear rates tend to delay the deposition of waxes). Another inherent problem is that the cloud-point measurement sees the precipitation of the most insoluble paraffin, not the mass of lower-molecular-weight paraffins that might contribute the major amount of wax deposit. Nevertheless, CPM measurements have been found to correlate well with the temperature at field deposition, more so than optical techniques that required a greater mass of wax to register a signal.[26] A major problem in correlating these measurements and simulations (discussed later) with field experience is the acquisition of good field data.[27] Illustrative of the state of the art in interpreting these measurements is that closer agreement is found between stock-tank oil measurements and field experience, even though it is live oil that is being produced.

An alternative to the measurement of cloud point is its prediction from compositional data by thermodynamic models. These models can predict cloud point as the temperature at which the first infinitesimal amount of wax appears, as well as predicting that mass of wax precipitating out of solution that, from experience, corresponds to field deposition.[28] Models that use detailed *n*-paraffin composition input data, as obtained from high-pressure gas chromatography, generally outperform models based on less specific information like compositions to C_{7+} [the numbers are more generally available in the routine pressure/volume/temperature (PVT) reports].

Simulation of Deposition During Production. Given the cloud point, what is the propensity for wax precipitation during the production and, in particular, the pipelining and processing of the crude? This is the regime of "paraffin deposition models." These are engineering simulators used to predict wax buildup in flowing systems, taking into account such parameters as heat transfer, phase behavior of the crude, flow regime, wax deposition kinetics, shear rate, diffusivity, wall conditions (roughness, coatings, scale), and produced-water/oil ratio. One such model currently in use is "ParaSim™" (AEA Technology, U.K.). More extensive programs are under development.[29]

Prevention/Inhibition. As with other solids-depositing problems, prevention can be more cost effective than removal. One key to wax-deposition prevention is heat. Electric heaters can be employed to raise the crude-oil temperature as it enters the wellbore. The limitations are the maintenance costs of the heating system and the availability of electrical power. And, as with the hydrate problem, which is discussed below, maintaining a sufficiently high production level may also keep the upper-wellbore temperature above the WAT. In addition, high flow rates tend to minimize wax adherence to metal surfaces because of the shearing action of the flowing fluid. Insulated pipelines are also an alternative to minimize, if not eliminate, the problem; costs can be prohibitive for long pipelines.

Wax deposition can be prevented, delayed, or minimized by the use of dispersants or crystal modifiers. As with asphaltenes, the paraffin-wax characteristics vary from well to well. Thus, chemicals that are effective in one system are not always successful in others, even for wells within the same reservoir. "For this reason it is of fundamental importance to establish a good correlation between oil composition and paraffin inhibitors efficiency, leading to an adequate product selection for each particular case, avoiding extremely expensive and inefficient 'trial-and-error' procedures."[24]

Paraffin-crystal modifiers are chemicals that interact with the growing crude-oil waxes by cocrystallizing with the native paraffin waxes in the crude oil that is being treated. These interactions result in the deformation of the crystal morphology of the crude-oil wax. Once deformed, these crystals cannot undergo the normal series of aggregation steps. Types of paraffin-crystal modifiers include maleic acid esters, polymeric acrylate and methacrylate esters, and ethylene vinyl acetate polymers and copolymers.

Dispersants act to keep the wax nuclei from agglomerating. Dispersants are generally surfactants and may also keep the pipe surface water wet, minimizing the tendency of the wax to adhere. Some water production is required, of course. High levels of water alone may maintain the system in a water-wet state. As with scale prevention, a smooth surface tends to decrease wax adherence. However, the operational problem is to maintain such a surface for an extended period of time. Various forms of erosion are highly detrimental.

Obviously, these inhibitors must be delivered into the crude oil at temperatures above the WAT. This need not cause a problem for surface equipment; it could cause a problem for wellbore treatment, if the bottomhole temperatures are low.

Removal. Removal of wax deposits within a wellbore is accomplished by cutting, drilling, chemical dissolution, or melting—the use of hot oil, hot water, or steam. Of these, the use of hot oil has been the most popular, normally pumped down the casing and up the tubular. It is intended that the high temperature of the liquid phase heat and melt the wax, which then dissolves in the oil phase. Using the bottom-up delivery approach, hot oil first reaches those waxes most difficult to melt. The higher in the tubular the hot oil proceeds, the lower its temperature becomes, thereby reducing its wax-carrying capacity. Hot oiling can cause permeability damage if the fluid containing the melted wax enters the formation.[25]

Hot water, hot-water/surfactant combinations, and steam are alternatives to hot oiling. Plain hot-water treatments do not provide the solvency required to remove the wax, hence the use of surfactants to disperse the wax. The advantage of water is its greater heat capacity.

Chemical generation of heat has also been proposed as a method of melting wax deposits. One field-tested scheme uses the thermochemical process of reacting two specific nitrogen salt solutions, acidic ammonium chloride and sodium nitrite;[30] an orgainc solvent is included to keep the wax in solution after the system has cooled.

Various aromatic solvents can be used to dissolve the wax. These are generally not heated, relying solely on the solvency properties of the fluid. As with asphaltene dissolution, *o*-xylene has been one of the more effective solvents for waxes; kerosene and diesel tend to be poor solvents. However, as with asphaltenes dissolution, one solvent does not necessarily work equally well on all wax deposits; an example of solvent screening procedures is given in Ref. 31.

Pigging is the primary mechanical method of removing wax buildup from the internal walls of pipelines. The pig cuts the wax from the pipe walls; a bypass can be set with a variable-flow pass, allowing the pig to prevent wax buildup in front. Pig sizing can vary, and multiple pig runs with pigs of increasing size can be used. For subsea pigging, a looped flowline is required or a subsea pig launcher for a single flowline. The major uncertainty in this operation is the wax hardness as it is formed in the pipeline.

Coiled tubing with the appropriate cutters at the end also can be used for wax removal—the drawback for pipeline cleaning being the limited reach of the coiled tubing. For wellbore cleaning this is obviously less of a problem.

9.1.3 Toxic-Materials Production. Various toxic materials are coproduced with the hydrocarbons. Their removal and disposal will be discussed elsewhere in more detail. A brief overview is given here.

Hydrogen sulfide is highly toxic. If the oil or gas is sour, there is no alternative but to produce the H_2S and, because it generally has minimal economic value, dispose of the gas in a safe and cost-effective manner. The treatment procedure and treatment location depend on the concentration of H_2S. Caustic scrubbing can be used for the removal of high concentrations.[32] Treatment of the low-concentration H_2S (nominally < 150 ppm) is made using nonregenerative chemical technology that is more efficient at low H_2S concentrations. Chlorine dioxide and nitrite ion[33,34] are two such low-cost treatment chemicals.

Mercury is also is a naturally occurring contaminant found primarily in natural gas. As with hydrogen sulfide, there is little alternative but to produce it and then remove it—generally at a central treating plant rather than on site. The occurrence of mercury in quantity and location is discussed in Ref. 35. Regulations exist restricting the amount present in natural gas for sale.

NORM, such as radium and radon, are generally not considered a serious well-production problem. The sources of NORM in oil and gas production are sedimentary rocks.[36] Radon gas and radium are to be expected in many formation waters. Radium is similar in chemistry to calcium and, particularly, barium. Radium sulfate coprecipitates with barium sulfate and is concentrated in barite scale. The radioactive daughter product, radon, is also trapped within the barite deposit. Coprecipitated radium sulfate can require radioactivity decontamination procedures during scale removal. About 30% of the producing wells in the U.S. are contaminated with radioactive salts. Radioactive scales also are found in oil/gas fields in the North Sea, in practically all main producing areas of the former Soviet Union, as well as other regions of the world.[37] Radioactive lead (Pb^{210}) has been found in southern U.K. gas fields as metallic lead and lead sulfide.[38] Prevention of barite precipitation is preferred for minimizing the consequences of NORM.[36,39]

9.2 Water-Related Production Problems

All oil fields under waterdrive, either from waterflood or a natural aquifer, eventually produce water along with oil. Even gas-cap and depletion reservoirs may produce some water. This coproduction of water causes an additional set of problems: corrosion, scale/salts deposition, gas-hydrate formation, and disposal of the water itself. Water coproduction also tends to exacerbate hydrocarbon-solids deposition. Discussed first in this section is the gas-hydrate problem: the possibility of solids formation because of the coproduction of water and light ends. This is followed by a discussion of water control: avoiding lifting unnecessary water and disposing of the water. The final portions of this section deal with inorganic-scale deposition and metal corrosion.

9.2.1 Hydrates. Natural-gas hydrates are ice-like solids that form when free water and natural gas combine at high pressure and "low" temperature. This can occur in gas and gas/condensate

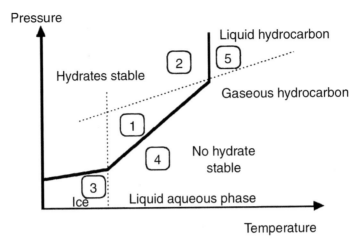

Fig. 9.9—Schematic phase diagram for a water/hydrocarbon/hydrate system [after E'tudes et Productions Schlumberger, *Gas Hydrates Production* (January 1998)].

wells, as well as in oil wells. Location and intensity of hydrate accumulations in a well vary and depend on the operation regime, design, geothermal gradient in the well, fluid composition, and other factors. Detailed reviews of gas-hydrate chemistry, physics, and oilfield engineering are found in Refs. 40 and 41.

At the appropriate combinations of temperature, pressure, and low-molecular-weight gases, water molecules arrange themselves into coplanar 5- or 6-membered rings, which then form three-dimensional (3D) polyhedra around the gases (tetradecahedrons, dodecahedrons, and hexadeca-hedrons). These individual polyhedra then combine to form specific crystalline lattices. In these solids, one volume of water in the hydrate state may "enclathrate" 70 to 300 volumes of gas. Such solids can be formed with N_2, H_2S, CO_2, C_1, C_2, C_3, and iso-butane. Larger molecules like *n*-butane and cyclopentane require the presence of some smaller molecules. Natural-gas hydrates are to be distinguished from the common inorganic-salt hydrates such as $CuSO_4 \cdot 5H_2O$.

A general phase diagram for water, hydrocarbon, and solid hydrate is shown in **Fig. 9.9**. There are essentially five regions: 1) hydrate + gaseous hydrocarbon (+ excess liquid water); 2) hydrate + liquid hydrocarbon (+ excess liquid water); 3) ice + gaseous hydrocarbon; 4) liquid water + gaseous hydrocarbon; and 5) liquid water + liquid hydrocarbon.

The temperatures at which gas hydrates form are significantly higher than the temperatures at which water ice will form. The exact PT values for this equilibrium vary with hydrocarbon-gas composition and with the dissolved salt content in the liquid water phase. (This salt will not enter the gas-hydrate crystal structure, but it will control the chemical activity of the water from which the hydrate forms.) Hydrates can form more readily (i.e., at higher temperatures) from oil than in pure methane.[41]

Shut-in gas wells are particularly prone to serious hydrate problems if the well has been producing some water. Subsequent equilibration of the tubular and its contents with cold zones of the rock can lower the temperature into the hydrate-formation region. Hydrate nuclei form from the films of water on the tubular walls. The subsequent crystallization can result in large plugs of hydrate tens or hundreds of meters long.

Hydrate formation also can take place within a shut-in oil well, generating a slurry of solid that is capable of accumulating and plugging the pipe.[40] The logic is that oil will dissolve some water—generally small amounts. Under high-temperature/high-pressure (HT/HP) conditions, the amounts can be 5 to 10 mol% (at 300°F). The oil is produced up the wellbore, temperature falls, and liquid water comes out of solution, remaining in suspension as micro-

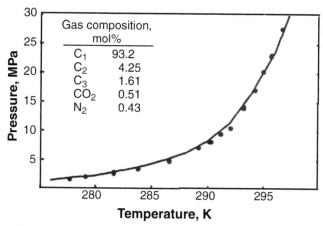

Fig. 9.10—Simulated and experimental gas hydrate equilibrium diagram for a natural-gas mixture (points are experimental).

droplets. In a static condition, the microdroplets gradually coalesce and precipitate. This liquid water is saturated with gas so that hydrates can form at the appropriate PT values.

Coping With Hydrate Formation. The first step in controlling hydrate formation is to understand which pressure and temperature conditions/locations in the specific system are conducive to gas-hydrate formation. A number of computer simulators are available for this purpose,[42–45] usually as adjuncts to more general phase PVT simulators. The models vary in how well they compute the chemical activity of the water phase, the effect of higher-molecular-weight hydrocarbons, and the effect of hydrate inhibitors (see the discussion that follows). A comparative assessment of models is given in Ref. 46. **Fig. 9.10** shows the results of simulations with one of the models—the line is computed, the dots are experimental points.[44] Besides the dissociation PT points for the hydrate, the information required and derivable from such models is the amount of hydrate formed, the composition of all phases, and the distribution of inhibitors throughout all phases.

The second control step is the comparison of this information with the measured or expected PT profile within the production system. A method of coping with hydrate formation is then selected (e.g., producing the hydrocarbons under conditions that avoid the hydrate PT formation zone or using a suitable inhibition method. The simulator should also be capable of evaluating the consequences of the inhibitor strategy. An example of adjusting production conditions to avoid hydrate formation is PT curves for producing wet gas at various rates.[47]

The alternative to production control is the use of inhibitors. These are classified as environmental inhibitors, thermodynamic inhibitors, and kinetic inhibitors. The conceptually simplest "environmental inhibition" method is to dry the gas before it is cooled—remove the water and hydrates so they cannot form. This involves adsorption onto, for example, silica gel, or cooling and condensation, absorption of water into alcohols, or adsorption onto hydroscopic salts.

"Thermodynamic inhibition" has been the most common method for controlling gas hydrates. There are a number of alternatives: heating the gas, decreasing pressure in the system, injecting salt solutions, and injecting alcohol or glycol.

One method of providing heat to the hydrate-formation zone is the use of electrical-resistance heating via cables connected to a transformer.[41] Another is placing the choke in a sufficiently hot zone of the production system. The injection of salts (primarily $CaCl_2$) reduces hydrate formation by lowering the chemical activity of water, and by lowering the solubility of gas in water.

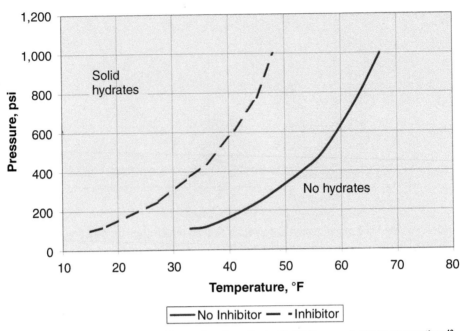

Fig. 9.11—A general phase diagram illustrating the effect of inhibitors on hydrate prevention.[48]

Alternative four is used more frequently now with a transition from methanol to ethylene glycols for HSE reasons. The general effect of such inhibitors is shown in **Fig. 9.11** (not a total removal of the problem but a shift of the hydrate-formation curve to lower temperatures, ostensibly outside the PT production regime). It is possible to compute this phase diagram for gas/water/methanol or the glycols with reasonable accuracy. The major drawback to this inhibition technique is the large quantity of methanol or glycol required. This impacts both operating costs and logistics, particularly important for offshore wells and pipelines.[48]

Such problems have resulted in the search for kinetic hydrate inhibitors[49]—low-dosage chemicals that, as with asphaltenes, waxes, and inorganic scales, prevent the growth of hydrate nuclei or prevent the agglomeration of nuclei into large crystals (also called "threshold hydrate inhibitors"). Ref. 50 describes the field testing of such inhibitors. The compounds were primarily quaternary ammonium salts; polymeric n-vinyl-2-pyrrolidone was particularly effective. The application of kinetic hydrate inhibitors to black-oil flowlines is described in Ref. 51. The additive here was a methanol-based solution of the polymer *n*-vinyl, *n*-methyl acetamide-covinyl caprolactam ("VIMA-VCap"). In the example given, the dose rate was low (0.5 gal/D in 16 B/D of produced water). Nonpolymeric gas-hydrate inhibitors have been successfully field tested on an offshore platform containing gas lift injection wells,[52] and they have been used in long wet-gas subsea pipelines.[52] A novel gas-hydrate inhibitor controlling hydrate formation during startup uses a borate-crosslinked gel system;[53] this inhibited gel system ostensibly also exhibits fracturing-fluid performance equal to that of more conventional borate-gel systems.

Removal of Solid Hydrates. Solid hydrates are removed with many of the same chemicals and technology used to inhibit hydrate formation. The simplest method is, if possible, to reduce pressure above the hydrate plug sufficiently enough to reverse the equilibrium reaction. Addition of solvents, such as alcohols and glycols, is the most common technique (well completions will often provide for a methanol-injection line). An example of hydrate-plug removal with coiled-tubing jetting from a deepwater test well is given in Ref. 54. Chemical heating, such as described for wax removal, has been used.[40]

9.2.2 Water Control. The material presented in this section that deals with water control technology has been abstracted from a recent review of water problems and control technology.[55] This review contains the references to the original literature. Water disposal is discussed elsewhere.

The Problem. The present worldwide daily water production from oil wells is roughly 3 BWPD per barrel of oil. It costs money to lift water and then dispose of it. In a well producing oil with 80% water cut, the cost of handling water can double normal lifting costs. Yet, wells with water cuts in excess of 90% may still produce sufficient hydrocarbons to be economical (e.g., certain wells in the North Sea Shell Expro Brent fields and in the BP-Amoco Forties fields). "Water control technology" is intended to reduce the costs of producing water.

It is not necessary, nor desirable, to completely shut off the coproduced water. The logic here is the distinction between "good" (necessary) and "bad" (excess) water.[55] "Good" water is that water produced at a rate below the water/oil economic limit (i.e., the oil produced can pay for the water produced). "Good" water, then, is that water that cannot be shut off without reducing oil production. The fractional water flow is dictated by the natural mixing behavior that gradually increases water/oil ratio (WOR). "Good" water is also caused by converging flowlines from the injector to the producer wellbore. Water breakthrough on injection occurs initially along the shortest (least resistant) flow path between injector and producer, while oil is still being swept along other flow paths.

"Bad" water is water produced into the wellbore that produces no oil or insufficient oil to pay for the cost of handling the water. The remainder of this discussion deals with "bad" water.

Phenomenology. There is no one mechanism for "bad" water intrusion, and there is no one technology that will shut off water intrusion. There are 10 basic types of water problems.[55] The first four problems, which are listed next, are relatively easily controlled; the next two are more difficult but control is still feasible. The last four problems do not lend themselves to simple and inexpensive near-wellbore solutions and require completion or production changes as part of the reservoir management strategy (e.g., multilateral wells, sidetracks, coiled-tubing isolation, and dual completions). Mechanisms for water intrusion are as follows:

• Casing, tubing, or packer leaks.

• Channel flow behind the casing from primary cementing that does not isolate water-bearing zones from the pay zone.

• Moving oil/water contact (OWC).

• Watered-out layer without crossflow—this is a common problem with a multilayer production and high-permeability zone isolated with flow barriers (e.g., a shale bed) above and below the zone. It is shown schematically in **Fig. 9.12**.[55]

• Fractures or faults between injector and producer.

• Fractures or faults from a water layer. Water can be produced from fractures that intersect a deeper water zone.

• Coning or cusping. Coning occurs in a vertical well when there is an OWC near the perforations with a relatively high vertical permeability driving high flow rates.

• Edge water from poor areal sweep. Areal permeability anisotropy causes this problem.

• Gravity-segregated layer. In a thick reservoir layer with high-vertical permeability, water, either from an aquifer or injector, slumps downward in the permeable formation and sweeps only the lower part of the reservoir (**Fig. 9.13**).[55]

• Watered-out layer with crossflow. This is difficult, if not impossible, to treat.

Effective water control is generally predicated on knowing the position and mechanism (source) of the intruding water. These parameters may be established from direct measurement, the well's production logs, and production history.

"Accurate production logs...can show water entry into the wellbore. The tool can determine flow and holdup for each fluid phase in vertical, deviated and horizontal wells. The addition of

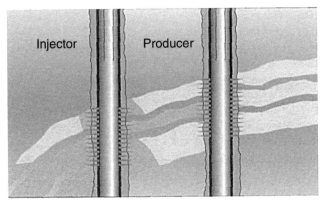

Fig. 9.12—Watered-out layer without crossflow (after Bailey[55]).

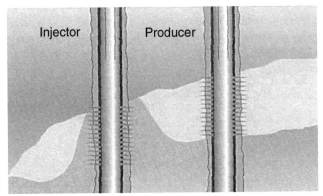

Fig. 9.13—Gravity segregated layer (after Bailey[55]).

new optical and electrical sensors incorporating local probe measurements and phase velocity measurements have resulted in major improvements in the diagnosis in both complex and simple wells with three-phase flow. Such advances in reliable and accurate production logging, particularly in deviated wells with high water cuts represent a major step forward in identifying and understanding water problem types. A production log can be turned into a multilayer production log or a 'multilayer test' by measuring the production rate of each layer at several different producing pressures with station measurements positioned between each layer. In this way, crossflow potential can be measured. Wireline formation pressure measurements such as those with the MDT [modular formation dynamics tester] tool or the repeat formation tester (RFT) tool can show if the layers are in communication. A vertical interference test performed with the MDT tool will show vertical permeability near the wellbore. Log correlations can demonstrate whether extensive shale permeability exists across a field. A production log (spinner) may detect wellbore crossflow during well shut-in."[55]

Production history can be used in a number of ways. First, there is the "recovery plot": a semilog plot of WOR vs. cumulative production, allowing extrapolation to the WOR economic limit (where producing water equals the value of the oil produced). If extrapolated production is approximately equal to the expected reserves, the well is producing acceptable ("good") water and no water control is necessary. Next, there is the production history itself—a log/log plot of oil/water rates vs. time. Good candidates for water control show an increase in water production and a decrease in oil production at about the same time. Also, there is the decline-curve analysis: a semilog plot of oil production vs. cumulative oil. A sudden increase in decline may indicate a water problem or severe pressure depletion caused by damage buildup. And finally, there are diagnostic plots: log/log plots of WOR vs. time. Three basic signatures (patterns) distinguish between different water-breakthrough mechanisms (**Fig. 9.14**).[55]

Shut-in and choke-back analysis of the fluctuating WOR data can, sometimes, provide clues to the problem type. Water-entry problems such as coning or a single fracture intersecting a deeper water layer will lead to a lower WOR during choke-back or shut-in. Fractures or a fault intersecting an overlying water layer have the opposite effect.

Injector Problems. There can be additional problems associated with the injector well—primarily because of unplanned and uncontrolled fracturing of the receiving reservoir. One mechanism arises from the buildup of solids because of, for example, filtration, bacterial action, scale buildup, or changes in reservoir wettability. Pressure is increased to maintain injectivity and fracturing may occur. Thermal fracturing is often encountered offshore because of the stress reduction in the injection zone from cool-down. The zone with the highest injectivity cools down first and fractures, taking even more injection fluid—hence, poor sweep efficiency. One strategy to control this problem is to deliberately fracture all receiving zones, increasing sweep efficiency.

Coping With Water Production. Mechanical or inflatable plugs are often the solution of choice for the near-wellbore problems: casing leaks, flow behind casing, rising bottom water, and watered-out layers without crossflow. These plugs can be deployed on coiled tubing or wireline to ensure shutoff in cased and openhole environments. When the wellbore must be kept open to levels deeper than the water entry, a through-tubing patch may be deployed inside the casing. One technology involves placing a flexible, inflatable composite cylinder made of, for example, carbon fiber, thermosetting plastics, and a rubber skin opposite the area to be treated. A pump then inflates the sleeve and injects well fluid, which heats the resins, turning on the polymerization process. After the resins have set, the sleeve is deflated and extracted.

Rigid gels are highly effective for near-wellbore shutoff of excess water. Unlike cement, gels can be squeezed into the target formation to give complete shutoff of that zone or to reach shale barriers. They have operational advantages over cement treatments because they can be jetted rather than drilled out of the wellbore. Commercial gels can be bullheaded into the formation to treat problems such as flow behind casing and watered-out layers without crossflow, or they can be selectively placed in the water zones using coiled tubing and a packer.

Certain crosslinked polymers can also have long working times before becoming rigid. They are injected into small faults or fractures but only penetrate formations with permeabilities greater than 5 darcy. Large volumes (1,000 to 10,000 bbl) of these inexpensive fluids often successfully shut off extensive fracture systems surrounding waterflood injector or producing wells.

Gel treatments are not generally successful for combating coning/cusping problems for prolonged times because they require very large volumes to be effective. An alternative is to drill one or more lateral drainholes near the top of the formation to take advantage of the greater distance from the OWC and decreased drawdown. Another approach is a dual drain (**Fig. 9.15**).[55]

Gel treatments are also not likely to work on the "gravity-segregated-layer" problem. Lateral drainholes may be effective in accessing the unswept oil. Infill drilling is often the best approach to improving the areal sweep efficiency edgewater problem. A large, likely uneconomic treatment of gel would be required to divert the injected water away from the pore space that has already been swept by water.

Treatments for water problems in horizontal wells are most effective when the treatment zone is isolated from the remainder of the wellbore. In cased holes, this is achieved mechanically with packers. However, when a screen or liner has been run but left uncemented, such

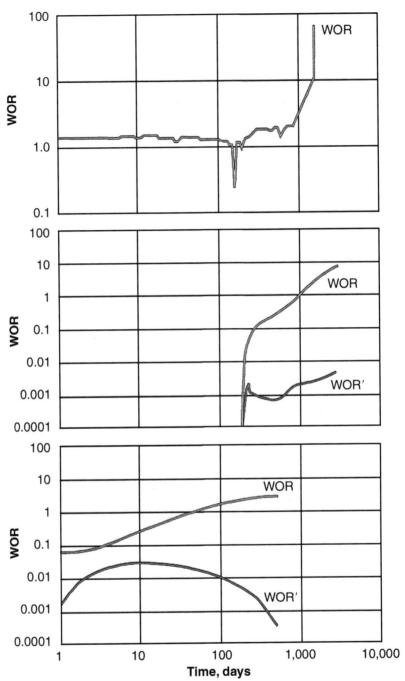

Fig. 9.14—Idealized profiles characterizing water-breakthrough mechanisms. An open flow path shows a very rapid breakthrough [e.g., through a fault, fracture, channel behind casing (top)]. Edgewater flow (middle) generally shows a rapid increase at breakthrough, followed by a straight-line curve. A gradual increase in water (bottom) indicates the buildup of a water cone early in the well's life (The WOR' curves are the time derivatives of the WOR plots.) (after Bailey[55]).

mechanical devices are not effective in isolating the open annular space behind the pipe. One product developed for such situations is the annular chemical packer (**Fig. 9.16**).

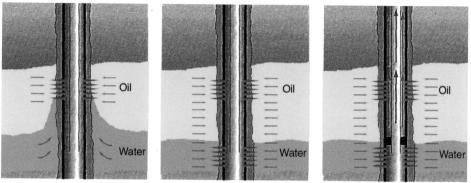

Fig. 9.15—The coning problem is on the left; perforating the water leg eliminates the coning (middle). Alternatively, the water can be coproduced separately through tubing and annulus (after Bailey[55]).

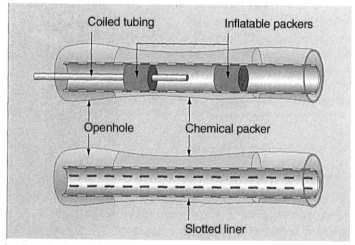

Fig. 9.16—This technology involves placement of a cement-based fluid into the annular space between an uncemented liner and the formation. The fluid is conveyed into the treatment zone using coiled tubing and injected between an inflatable packer assembly to fill the annulus over a selected interval. It is designed to sit in this position forming a permanent, impermeable, high-strength plug, fully isolating the volume of the annulus (after Schlumberger *Oilfield Review*).

Proactive water control includes choking back zones with high permeability to create a more uniform sweep. This means sacrificing early cash flow for an uncertain return because of incomplete knowledge of heterogeneity. The production (and injection) profile can be improved through selective stimulation of zones with lower permeability. Coiled tubing is used to precisely place these small hydraulic fractures.

Disposal. Whether water production is minimized or not, some water (e.g., "good" water) will be produced and must be disposed. To minimize costs, the water should be removed as early as possible (e.g., with a downhole separator if possible); see **Fig. 9.17**.[55] The method for disposal at the surface will be discussed elsewhere.

9.2.3 Inorganic-Scale Formation. Wells producing water are likely to develop deposits of inorganic scales. Scales can and do coat perforations, casing, production tubulars, valves, pumps and downhole completion equipment, such as safety equipment and gas lift mandrels. If

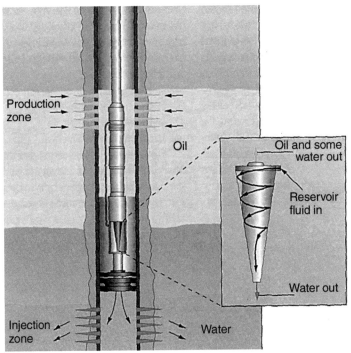

Fig. 9.17—Such downhole separators, coupled with electrical submersible pumps, allow up to 50% of the water to be separated and injected into another formation (after Bailey[55]).

allowed to proceed, this scaling will limit production, eventually requiring abandonment of the well. Technology is available for removing scale from tubing, flowline, valving, and surface equipment, restoring at least some of the lost production level. Technology also exists for preventing the occurrence or reoccurrence of the scale, at least on a temporary basis. "Temporary" is generally 3 to 12 months per treatment with conventional inhibitor "squeeze" technology, increasing to 24 or 48 months with combined fracture/inhibition methods. (See the discussion that follows.)

Phenomenology. As brine, oil, and/or gas proceed from the formation to the surface, pressure and temperature change and certain dissolved salts can precipitate. This is called "self-scaling." If a brine is injected into the formation to maintain pressure and sweep the oil to the producing wells, there will eventually be a commingling with the formation water. Additional salts may precipitate in the formation or in the wellbore (scale from "incompatible waters"). The chemical formulae and mineral names for most oilfield scales are shown in **Table 9.1.**

The most common oilfield scales are calcite, barite, celestite, anhydrite, gypsum, iron sulfide, and halite. "Exotic" scales such as calcium fluorite, zinc sulfide, and lead sulfide are sometimes found with HT/HP wells. Many of these scaling processes can and do occur simultaneously. Scales tend to be mixtures.[56] For example, strontium sulfate is frequently found precipitated together with barium sulfate.

Calcite deposition is generally a self-scaling process. The main driver for its formation is the loss of CO_2 from the water to the hydrocarbon phase(s) as pressure falls. This removes carbonic acid from the water phase, which had kept the basic calcite dissolved. Calcite solubility also decreases with decreasing temperature (at constant CO_2 partial pressure).

Halite scaling is also a self-scaling process. The drivers are falling temperature and evaporation. Halite solubility in water decreases with decreasing temperature, favoring halite dropout

TABLE 9.1—OILFIELD MINERAL SCALES	
Mineral	Formula
Calcite	$CaCO_3$
Aragonite	$CaCO_3$
Vaterite	$CaCO_3$
Anhydrite	$CaSO_4$
Gypsum	$CaSO_4$
Barite	$BaSO_4$
Celestite	$SrSO_4$
Mackinawite	FeS
Pyrite	FeS_2
Halite	$NaCl$
Fluorite	CaF_2
Sphaerlite	ZnS
Galena	PbS

during the production of high-total-dissolved solids brines to the surface. (Falling pressure has a much smaller effect on decreasing halite solubility.) Evaporative loss of liquid water is generally the result of gas breakout from undersaturated condensate and oil wells, as well as the expansion of gas in gas wells. This increase in water vapor can leave behind insufficient liquid water to maintain halite solubility in the coproduced brine phase. Halite self-scaling is found with both high-temperature and low-temperature wells [e.g., with 125 and 350°F bottomhole temperature (BHT) gas/gas condensate wells].

Barite scales are generally the result of mixing incompatible waters. For example, seawater is often injected into offshore reservoirs for pressure maintenance. Seawater has a high-sulfate content; formation waters often have high-barium contents. Mixing these waters results in barite deposition. If this mixing/precipitation occurs within the reservoir far removed from a vertical wellbore, there will generally be little impact on the production of hydrocarbons. Mixing/precipitation near or within the wellbore will have a significant impact on production. Mixing of incompatible waters within the sandpack of a hydraulically fractured well can also be detrimental to production. Furthermore, after the initial, large deposition of scale, this water continues to be saturated in barite and additional barite scale will continue to form in the wellbore as pressure and temperature fall.

Waterfloods combining ground waters with high calcium and high sulfate contents can deposit anhydrite or gypsum by much the same "incompatible waters" mechanism discussed for barite. However, calcium sulfate scale solubility, unlike that of barite scale, actually increases with decreasing temperature (until about 40°C). This can decrease the likelihood of scale after the initial mixing deposition. The reversal in solubility falloff below 40°C accounts for the gypsum scaling observed in surface equipment. This inverse temperature effect can result in the generation of anhydrite scale when injecting seawater. Anhydrite solubility falls as pressure falls; data could not be found for gypsum solubility vs. pressure.

Iron sulfide scales are almost ubiquitous when hydrogen sulfide is produced—frequently the result of tubular corrosion in the presence of H_2S. A review of the iron sulfide chemistry and phases occurring in production equipment is contained in Refs. 57 and 58. Suffice it to say, the chemistry is complicated; more than one iron sulfide phase can be present. The physical properties of the phases vary (sometimes dense, sometimes not), and the phase composition can change with time.

These multistep scale/water chemistries can be simulated with present day computer software. Some of the programs are commercial; some operators have their own in-house programs. In effect, the code sets up a series of equilibrium equations for each possible scale and solution ion/ion reaction, as well as solution-gas reaction, then solves them simultaneously as a function of input pressure, temperature, gas composition, and water-phase composition. These are referred to as "thermodynamic models." As of 2001, the software had not yet reached a level of sophistication sufficient to say, reliably, how fast these solids can form during production. This has resulted in a series of "rules-of-thumb," correlating an operator's field experience with the thermodynamic simulator's output. Such rules of thumb are much less necessary for formation scaling, particularly if the mineral is naturally present in the formation (e.g., calcite). Computer simulation of scaling tendencies for produced oilfield brines has found considerable acceptance and application. Examples of this technology, applied to halite and calcite scaling in HT/HP wells, are in Refs. 59 and 60.

Scaling Economics. Scale remediation and prevention come at a cost, and a major theme in the oil patch has always been to "cut costs." It is becoming more appropriate to think of scale control in terms of "value added"—obviating the consequences of not remediating or preventing scale formation, and so increasing the total revenue from a well, as well as possibly extending its lifetime.[61] The effects of scale can be quite expensive and rapid. In one North Sea well (Miller field), production fell from 30,000 B/D to zero in just 24 hours because of scaling. The cost for cleaning out the single well and putting it back on production was approximately the same as the chemical costs to treat the entire field.[62] While not all wells are susceptible to such momentous penalties for allowing scaling to initiate, there is no question that scale formation, remediation, and prevention have associated costs. The cost savings because of less deferred/lost oil can result in substantially increased revenue over the life of the well, as well as more oil.[61]

It is anticipated that oilfield scaling problems will continue to worsen and become more expensive.[63] The new drivers are the tendencies to longer tiebacks; the use of smart wells (integrity more critical); more gas production (gas-well formations tend to be more delicate); the need to use greener chemicals; and the increasing large amounts of produced water.

Coping With Scale Production. Scale control has tended to be reactive rather than proactive. There are a variety of methods of removing the effects of scale on production. The first step is to determine which scales are forming and where they are forming. Some of this information can be reliably inferred from the computer simulation procedures discussed, particularly for self-scaling processes. The simplest method of physically detecting scale in the wellbore is to run calipers down the wellbore and measure decreases in the tubing inner diameter. Gamma ray log interpretation has been used to indicate barium sulfate scale because naturally radioactive radium (Ra226) precipitates as an insoluble sulfate with this scale. An example of this technology is shown in **Fig. 9.18**. Visual observation with the appropriate wireline tools has also been used to show the presence of calcite and halite solids within the wellbore.

The onset of water production coinciding with simultaneous reduction in oil production is a sign of potential scale problems. It is quite possible, particularly with gas wells, to produce water below the limit of detection of surface analysis (nominally 1 or 2%). This water will evaporate and leave its dissolved solids behind, as scale. Because the amounts of water are small, the amounts of solids per unit volume of water will be small, but the solids will accumulate with time. The same idea applies to the appearance at the surface of liquid "fresh" water when the reservoir brine is known to be brackish. This can be condensed water because of falling temperature. When a few percent of liquid water is produced, it is prudent to track the dissolved ion content with time. Injection-water breakthrough is generally signaled by dramatic changes in the concentrations of scaling ions, such as barium or sulfate, which coincide with reduced oil production.

Early warning of scaling conditions downhole would be valuable. Wells with intelligent completions and permanent monitoring systems are being designed to contain scale sensors. The function of the scale sensor is double duty—not only to provide early warning about the

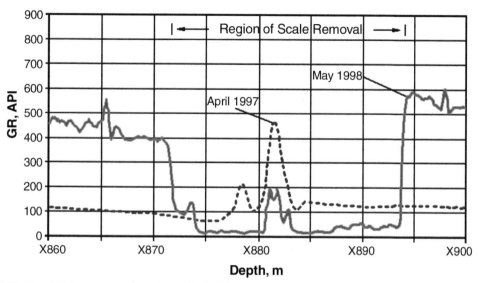

Fig. 9.18—The 1997 gamma ray log shows the buildup on the lower side-pocket mandrel one year before treatment. The 1998 log was measured after the scale was removed from the zone between X872 and X894 m (after Schlumberger *Oilfield Review*).

initiation of production impairment by scale generation but also to provide information about possible impairment of the smart-well sensors and valves by films of scale.

Scale remediation techniques must be quick and nondamaging to the wellbore, tubing, and the reservoir. If the scale is in the wellbore, it can be removed mechanically or dissolved chemically. Selecting the best scale-removal technique for a particular well depends on knowing the type and quantity of scale, its physical composition, and its texture. Mechanical methods are among the most successful methods of scale removal in tubulars. When pulling costs are low (e.g., readily accessible and shallow land locations), often the least expensive approach to scaling is to pull the tubing and drillout the scale deposit.

Scales are generally brittle. One of the earliest methods used to break off the thin brittle scale from pipes was explosives: a strand or two of detonation cord ("string shot") placed with an electronic detonation cap at the appropriate location in the wellbore, most effectively at the perforations. Thicker scales require more stringent means. Impact bits and milling technologies have been developed to run on coiled tubing inside tubulars using a variety of chipping bits and milling configurations. Such scale-removal rates are generally in the range of 5 to 30 linear ft/hr of milling.[64]

An alternative to milling and drilling is jetting.[64] Fluid jetting systems have been available for many years to remove scales in production tubing and perforations. These tools can be used with chemical washes to attack soluble deposits where placement is critical. Water jetting can be effective on soft scale, such as halite, but is less effective on some forms of medium to hard scales such as calcite and barite. The use of abrasive slurries greatly improves the ability of jets to cut through scale but can damage the steel tubulars and valves.

"Sterling beads" is an alternative abrasive material for scale removal by jetting.[64] This material matches the erosive performance of sand on hard, brittle scales, while being 20 times less erosive of steel. Sterling beads do not damage the well if prolonged jetting occurs in one spot. The beads are soluble in acid and have no known toxicity, simplifying use and cleanup. Hard scales, such as barite, are removed at rates > 100 ft/hr. This tool is capable of descaling config-

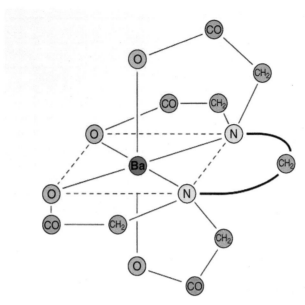

Fig. 9.19—A representation of a chelant/scale dissolver molecule, ethylenediaminetetraacetic acid (after Crabtree *et al.*[64]).

urations other than wellbore tubing (e.g., removing hard barite scale deposits on two gas lift valves in a multiple-mandrel gas lift completion).

Dissolution. Chemical dissolution of certain wellbore scales is generally relatively inexpensive and is used when mechanical removal methods are ineffective or costly. Carbonate minerals are highly soluble in hydrochloric acid; therefore, they can easily be dissolved. Bullheaded "acid washes" are commonly used to remove calcite accumulations within the wellbore.

Sulfate scale is more difficult to remove from the wellbore because the scale has a low solubility in acid. Chelants (scale dissolvers) have a high thermodynamic driving force for dissolving sulfate scales such as barite, isolating and locking up the scale metallic ions within their closed cage-like structures (**Fig. 9.19**). These chemicals are successful at removing films of sulfate scale from the wellbore. However, they are slow in dissolving the larger particle-sized wellbore scales and plugs—the reaction rates are surface-area limited; treatments are time-consuming, thus expensive.

Iron sulfides are soluble in hydrochloric acid. Many HCl corrosion inhibitors are also effective in inhibiting the iron sulfide from dissolution, as well as the tubular steel. There are now exceptions: inhibitors that protect the steel and not the scale, as well as being compatible with scavengers for the toxic hydrogen sulfide that is generated.[65]

For halite, dilution with low-salinity water is sufficient to prevent its accumulation in the wellbore and to dissolve halite that may have accumulated in the wellbore. This requires a source of fresh or brine-treated water to help prevent other scaling problems, which can be expensive. A case in point is the use of a desulfation plant to remove sulfate ion from the halite wash water for the Heron field production.[66]

Some scales and scaling situations are "chemically difficult." Fluorite scale, found with some HT/HP brines, has no known solvent (as of the date of this writing). Access of the scale-dissolver chemical to the inorganic scale can be blocked by organic deposits (e.g., asphaltenes).

Inhibition. Inhibitors are typically used after remediation to prevent further scaling. Obviously, this same technology can be used to do pre-emptive scale control. The effectiveness of inhibition is related to the degree of scale supersaturation—the higher this value, the more diffi-

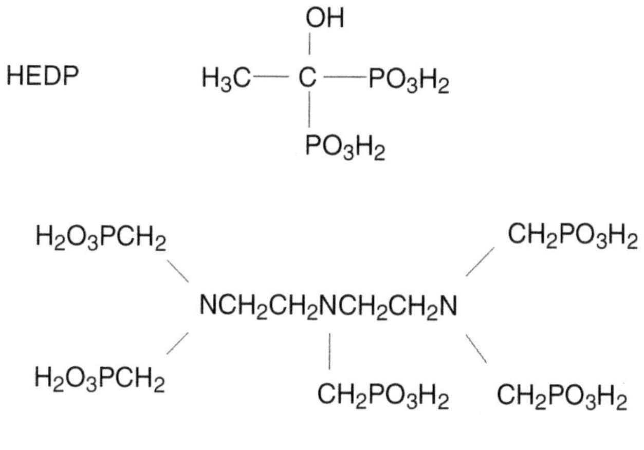

OH
|
HEDP   H₃C— C —PO₃H₂
|
PO₃H₂

Fig. 9.20—The chemical structure of two phosphonate inhibitor molecules [hydroxyethylenediphosphonic acid (HEDP) and diethylenetriaminepenta (methylenephosphonic) acid (DTPMP)].

cult it is to inhibit. For example, barite solutions with saturation indices > 350 are particularly difficult to inhibit.

Scale precipitation can be avoided by chelating the scaling cation. This is costly because the reactions are "stoichiometric," (e.g., one chelant molecule per one scaling cation). More effective are chemicals that poison the growth of scale. These are "threshold" inhibitors, effectively inhibiting mineral scale growth at concentrations of 1,000 times less than a balanced stoichiometric ratio. Most inhibitors for inorganic scales are phosphorous compounds: inorganic polyphosphates, organic phosphate esters, organic phosphonates, organic aminophosphates, and organic polymers. A variety of such chemicals is well-known, and they are available from many companies. Two chemical structures are shown in **Fig. 9.20**. These are used for the various carbonate and sulfate scales. Recently, the successful use of a nonphosphorus compound to inhibit halite precipitation has been described and field tested at moderate temperatures;[67] more classical amine-based halite salt inhibitors are also available for halite inhibition.[68]

Delivering the inhibiting solution to the scaling brine in the tubular has been done by a number of means: continuous injection into the wellbore via a "macaroni string" (a narrow-diameter tubing reaching to the perforations); injection into a gas lift system;[69] and slow dissolution of an insoluble inhibitor placed in the rat hole.[70,71] These delivery methods are straightforward to implement but not necessarily without problems. For example, gas injection requires the inhibitor solution to be atomized properly and not to deposit subsequently on the tubular walls immediately adjacent to the injection point;[72] narrow tubing can plug.

The most frequently used method of delivering the inhibiting solution to the scaling brine has been the "inhibitor squeeze." Here an inhibitor-containing solution is forced into the formation, whereby the inhibitor then resides on the rock surface, slowly leaching back into the produced-water phase at or above the critical concentration needed to prevent scaling [the minimum inhibitor concentration (MIC)]. It is intended that the released inhibitor protect the tubulars, as well as the near wellbore. It is required, obviously, that the inhibitor adsorb on the formation rock with sufficient capacity to provide "long-term" protection. It is also required that the inhibitor be relatively stable to thermal degradation under downhole conditions and be compatible in the particular brine system. And it is also required that the inhibitor treatment not cause a significant permeability reduction and reduced production (see discussion that follows). These requirements are generally achievable, but again, one chemical does not necessarily fit all field situations.[73]

Two types of inhibitor squeeze treatments are routinely carried out where the intention is either to adsorb the inhibitor onto the rock by a physico-chemical process —an "adsorption squeeze"—or to precipitate (or phase separate) the inhibitor within the formation pore space onto the rock surfaces—a "precipitation squeeze."

Adsorption of inhibitors is thought to occur through electrostatic and van der Waals interactions between the inhibitor and formation minerals. The interaction may be described by an adsorption isotherm, which is a function of pH, temperature, and mineral substrate and involves cations such as Ca^{+2}. The adsorption process for retaining inhibitor in the formation is most effective in sandstone formations. Treatment lifetimes are generally on the order of 3 to 6 months.

The "precipitation squeeze" process is based on the formation of an insoluble inhibitor/calcium salt. This is carried out by adjusting the calcium ion concentration, pH, and temperature of polymeric and phosphonate inhibitor solutions. Also used are calcium salts of phosphino-polycarboxylic acid or a polyacrylic acid scale inhibitor. The intent is to place more of the inhibitor per squeeze, extending the treatment lifetime. Normally, the precipitation squeeze treatment lifetime exceeds one year, even when high water production rates are encountered.

The engineering design of such adsorption and precipitation squeeze treatments into real-world multilayer formations is generally done with an appropriate piece of software. This simulator takes core flood data and computes the proper pre-flushes, inhibitor volumes, post flushes, and potential squeeze lifetime. Computer simulation of such chemistry is described in Refs. 74 and 75.

The sequence of pumping steps involved in squeezing inhibitors is listed next.

• Acid cleans the scale and debris out of the wellbore to "pickle" the tubing (this fluid should not be pushed into the formation).

• A "spearhead" package (a demulsifier and/or a surfactant) increases the water wetness of the formation and/or improves injectivity.

• A dilute inhibitor preflush pushes the spearhead into the formation and, in some cases, cools the near-wellbore region.

• The main scale-inhibitor treatment, which contains the inhibitor chemical, is normally in the concentration range of 2.5 to 20%.

• A brine overflush pushes the main treatment to the desired depth in the formation away from the wellbore.

• A shut-in or soak period (usually approximately 6 to 24 hours)—the pumping stops and the inhibitor adsorbs (phosphonate/polymers) or precipitates (polymers) onto the rock substrate.

• The well is brought back to production.

Fig. 9.21 illustrates a typical inhibitor return curve that shows the concentration of an inhibitor dissolved in the water phase as the well is brought back on production.

A large amount of inhibitor returns immediately after turning on the well. This is nonadsorbed inhibitor or weakly adsorbed inhibitor. It is "wasted" in the sense that it is not available for use late in the life of the squeeze. This wasted inhibitor does not otherwise impose a serious financial burden on the treatment—the inhibitors can be the cheapest part of the inhibition treatment. The plateau (or slowly declining) portion of the return curve is the critical data that describe the effectiveness of the treatment. As long as the curve is above the MIC, scale deposition is not taking place in the formation or wellbore. Immediately below the MIC, scale formation may start to occur.

The x-axis in Fig. 9.21 is given in terms of time (months). The lifetime parameter is more correctly volumes of water produced. Obviously, a high rate of water passing over a given amount of inhibitor will maintain the MIC for a shorter period of time than a low rate of water passing over the same amount of inhibitor.

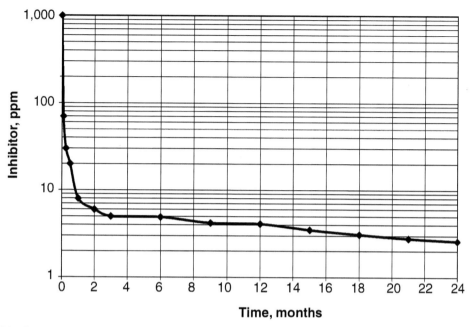

Fig. 9.21—General concentration vs. time (return) curves for various scale inhibitors (after Schlumberger *Oilfield Review*).

Scale-inhibitor squeeze treatments can sometimes bring undesirable side effects. These side effects include: process upsets, poor process and discharged water quality on initial flowback, extended cleanup period, deferred oil, and the potential for a permanent decrease in oil production combined with an increase in water production. The first three side effects listed are functions primarily of the oil, brine, and squeeze chemicals. Most of these problems can by avoided or at least minimized by prior laboratory testing. Deferred oil is an intrinsic problem in well intervention. The improved production must pay for the deferred oil.

Permanent decreases in production after inhibitor squeeze treatments are usually associated with pumping large amounts of water-based chemicals into water-sensitive zones, assuming an otherwise proper treatment design and the use of clean fluids. Clay swelling and in-situ emulsions are damage mechanisms; low pH-inhibitor solutions are often detrimental to clays, in particular to chlorites.[76] Handling the scale inhibition of water-sensitive reservoirs is not a solved problem. Several routes are being investigated. One solution is the use of oil-soluble inhibitors.[77] Another is the use of water-in-oil emulsion ("invert emulsions"), similar to the invert emulsions used for time-delayed acidization. A third solution is the use of a mutual solvent preflush.[78] Here, the mutual solvent is the first chemical seen by the sensitive formation, and it is the last seen as the well is put back on production. Also used are "clay stabilizers" in the preflush.[79] As of this writing, no single approach solves all problems.

New inhibitor chemistry is also being developed to handle the harsher scaling environments such as particularly high supersaturated barium sulfate solutions (saturation indices > 350).[80] A case in point is the barite scaling problem in the North Sea Miller field.[81] "Harsh" conditions also include HT/HP reservoirs with severe thermal stability requirements.[82,83]

Combined Treatments. Well intervention to place the scale inhibitor is particularly costly with high-volume wells because of large amounts of deferred oil; intervention at remote locations (e.g., offshore platforms and subsea completions) adds to the cost. It is often possible to place a scale inhibitor as part of the scale-removal step, providing both treatments with one setup and intervention. One of these techniques is the inclusion of a scale inhibitor with the

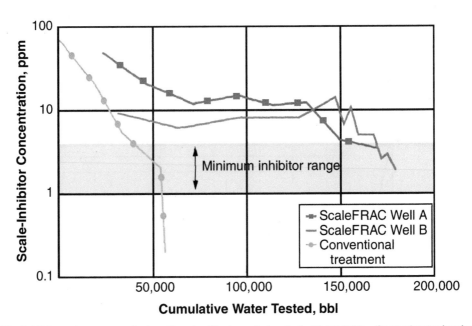

Fig. 9.22—Inhibitor return curves for two Permian Basin wells treated with inhibition/fracturing technology and a companion well treated by a conventional squeeze (after Wigg and Fletcher[62]).

acid stimulation process for dissolving calcite scale.[84] The advantages are in cost and in putting the inhibitor into exactly the same zone opened up by the acid treatment.

A second dual-treatment technique consists of placing a scale inhibitor along with a hydraulic fracture stimulation. Inhibitors can be injected into the pumped gel/sand mixture with calcium ion to form a sufficiently insoluble and immobile scale-inhibitor material within the proppant pack. DTPMP acid (Fig. 9.20) has been used, as well as polyphosphates.[85,86] Other inhibitor formulations can generate a "glaze" on the proppant pack.[64] The concept has been effective with calcite and barite scales. This technology has been practiced since the early 1990s on the Alaskan North Slope and, more recently, in west Texas; lifetimes of nominally two years are now claimed.[85,64] Shown in **Fig. 9.22** are return curves for such a treatment together with a return curve for a conventional squeeze. Here, lifetime is expressed in terms of quantity of water protected from scaling. There are also a few important ancillary advantages to the method greater than extended lifetime—the well returns to production faster because adsorption time shut-in is not required, and there is little opportunity for changes in the formation wettability and its attendant problems. The concept is illustrated schematically in **Fig. 9.23**.

A newer dual-treatment technique consists of deploying an inhibitor impregnated into porous ceramic proppant along with conventional proppant in hydraulic fracture stimulation.[87] Upon production, any water flowing over the surface of the impregnated proppant will cause dissolution of the scale inhibitor. Dry oil will not release the inhibitor from the beads or the insoluble inhibitor. Field examples of this technology are given in Refs. 88 and 89. The advantages are similar to those of the nonencapsulated inhibitor/frac concept already discussed but with a potentially longer lifetime (e.g., 4 years). This comes at an additional cost that must be offset by savings in deferred oil and setup/intervention costs.[88] The targets are high-volume wells in remote locations, such as the North Sea and deep Gulf of Mexico. Both inhibitor/proppant techniques also protect the fracture itself from plugging with scale. This scaling occurs primarily when incompatible waters mix near the wellbore.

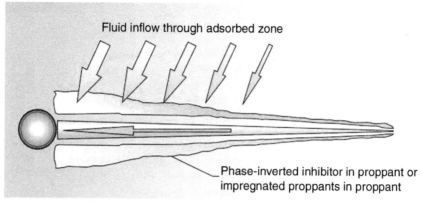

Fig. 9.23—Schematic representation of the mode of operation for a combined hydraulic fracture and scale inhibitor treatment (after Schlumberger *Oilfield Review*).

9.2.4 Corrosion. Corrosion control in oil/gas production is reviewed in depth in Refs. 90 through 92, from which some of the following material is abstracted.

Corrosion Chemistry of Steels. Iron is inherently (thermodynamically) sufficiently active to react spontaneously with water (corrosion), generating soluble iron ions and hydrogen gas. The utility of iron alloys depends on minimizing the corrosion rate. Corrosion of steel is an "electro-chemical process," involving the transfer of electrons from iron atoms in the metal to hydrogen ions or oxygen in water. The corrosion reaction of iron with acid is described by the equation

$$Fe + 2\ H^+ = Fe^{++} + H_2 \ . \qquad\qquad (9.1)$$

This reaction is made up of two individual processes, which are

$$Fe = Fe^{++} + 2\ e^- \qquad\qquad (9.2)$$

[the generation of soluble iron and electrons (this is the "anodic" process—the oxidation of the metal)] and

$$2\ H^+ + 2\ e^- = H_2 \qquad\qquad (9.3)$$

[the consumption of the electrons by acid to generate hydrogen gas (this is a "cathodic" process —the reduction of protons)].

This separation of the overall corrosion process into two reactions is not an electrochemical nuance; these processes generally do take place at separate locations on the same piece of metal. This separation requires the presence of a medium to complete the electrical circuit between anode (site of iron dissolution) and cathode (site for corrodant reduction). Electrons travel in the metal phase, but the ions involved in the corrosion process cannot. Ions require the presence of water; hence, corrosion requires the presence of water. This overall process is shown schematically in **Fig. 9.24**.[92] The space between the anode and cathode may be small or large depending on a number of factors.

Acid is not the only corrodant possible. Another common cathodic process is the reduction of oxygen, which is written as

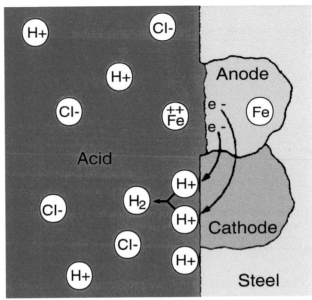

Fig. 9.24—A representation of the separation in position of anodic and cathodic corrosion sites (after Schlumberger *Oilfield Review*).

$$O_2 + 4 \ H^+ + 4 \ e^- = 2 \ H_2O \ . \ \text{..} \ (9.4)$$

This reaction can also take place at a location different from that of iron dissolution.

The other chemical constituents in the vicinity of the anodic sites determine the ultimate chemical fate of the Fe^{++} ion, such as the precipitation of iron-containing solids on or near the corroding surface.

The net rate of corrosion is determined by how fast the corrodant arrives at the iron-atom/water interface, how much corrodant is present, the electrical potential (energy) of the corrodant (oxygen has a higher potential than do protons), and the intrinsic rate of the cathodic reactions—electron transfer processes involving protons and oxygen are not instantaneous and depend on the nature of the solid surface on which they occur.

"How fast the corrodants arrive" has two aspects: mass transport in the corroding fluid and permeating surface barriers between the iron metal and the water phase. Surface barriers are placed barriers, such as paint or plastic coatings, passivating oxide films inherent to the metal (discussed later), and low-permeability corrosion products (e.g., siderite, as formed in the presence of certain oils and/or inhibitors).

The Nature of Steels. Alloying iron with carbon (usually 0.2 to 1%) forms steel (low-alloy steel)—a far stronger metal than iron, hence, suitable for oilfield use. Other components can be added to iron to enhance corrosion-resistance properties.

Some of the carbon added is insoluble, forming iron carbide (Fe_3C), which accelerates the cathodic processes necessary for corrosion to take place, accelerating the corrosion rate. One of the major, ubiquitous impurities in steel is sulfur, and it is a major source of corrosion instability. This element is highly insoluble in iron and precipitates in the form of insoluble sulfide inclusions, in particular MnS and (Mn, Fe)S. These inclusions are generally the sites of pitting (discussed later).[93]

Grain boundaries are also areas that are chemically active.[92] When iron solidifies during casting, the atoms, which are randomly distributed in the liquid state, arrange themselves in a crystalline array. This ordering usually begins simultaneously at many points in the liquid, and as these blocks of crystals and grains meet, there is a mismatch in the boundaries. There are areas of higher energy. Chemical impurities in the melt tend to accumulate at these grain boundaries and are more susceptible to chemical attack than the iron surface itself.

Plain carbon steels are processed by one of four heat treatments: annealing, normalizing, spherodizing, and quench and tempering. These treatments determine, in part, the physical and corrosion properties of the metal. Annealing or normalizing results in greater corrosion resistance than spherodizing or quench and tempering. The logic is that these treatments determine, in large, part of the physical dimensions and distribution of the impurities and inclusions in the metal.

The corrosion products formed in oxygen-containing water on mild steel are $FeOOH$, likely amorphous, and magnetite.[94] Below 200°C, these oxides, in the absence of reactive inclusions, are protective. In the presence of dissolved CO_2, $FeCO_3$ films form, which can sometimes be protecting (discussed later).

The compositions of corrosion-resistant alloys (CRAs) are chosen to spontaneously generate surface oxide films that will be stable and impermeable in the presence of the more aggressive corrodants. In oilfield use, it is also required that these films spontaneously reform if ruptured, as, for example, during and after erosion by sand or scratching by wireline/caliper tools. CRAs include the ferrous stainless steels and nonferrous nickel and cobalt alloys. Stainless steels contain at least 12% chromium. These alloys passivate in oxidizing environments through the formation of a thin layer of chromium oxide—containing film on the surface of the alloy. The crystallinity of this film decreases with increasing Cr content in the steel, becoming more glass-like and more protective.[94] Again, various inclusions can be weak points in the passivating film. The surfaces of nickel-based CRAs, such as Incoloy 800™, are a passivating nickel ferrite ($Ni_{0.8}Fe_{2.2}O_4$).

There are four classes of stainless steels that are based on chemical content, metallurgical structure, and mechanical properties. These classes are martensitic, ferritic, austenitic, and duplex. The manufacturing processes for CRAs are more complex than those producing low-alloy steels. Stainless steels are less costly than the nickel and cobalt alloys, though they are 1.5 to 20 times more expensive than low-alloy steels.

Oilfield Corrosion. Oilfield corrosion can be divided into categories.

Corrosion because of oxygen is found with surface equipment and can be found downhole with the oxygen introduced by waterflooding, pressure maintenance, gas lifting, or completion and/or workover fluids. It is the major corrodant of offshore platforms, at and below the tide line. The chemistry of this process follows the equations previously given.

"Sweet" corrosion is generally characterized first by simple metal dissolution followed by pitting. The corrodant is H^+, derived from carbonic acid (H_2CO_3) and the dissolution of CO_2 in the produced brine. The pitting leaves distinctive patterns (e.g., "mesa" corrosion), attributable to the metallurgical processing used in manufacturing the tubing. "Ringworm" corrosion is caused when welding is not followed by full-length normalizing of the tubular after processing. Corrosion inhibitors and CRAs are effective in mitigating sweet corrosion. Naphthenic acids and simple organic acids indigenous to crude oil also contribute to corrosion.

"Sour" corrosion (H_2S) results in the formation of various insoluble iron sulfides on the metal surface. Not only is H_2S an acidic corrodant, it also acts as a catalyst for both the anodic and cathodic halves of the corrosion reaction. Galvanic corrosion (bimetallic corrosion) is caused by the coupling of a corrosive and noncorrosive metal in the presence of a corrodant. Erosion is yet another category of corrosion. Erosion corrosion is the acceleration of corrosion because of the abrasion of metal surfaces by particulates (e.g., sand). Finally, there is corrosion caused by acids—those used to stimulate wells (HCl and HF).

Oilfield corrosion can take specific forms: metal wastage, pitting, crevice corrosion, intergranular corrosion, stress corrosion cracking (SCC), blistering, embrittlement, sulfide stress

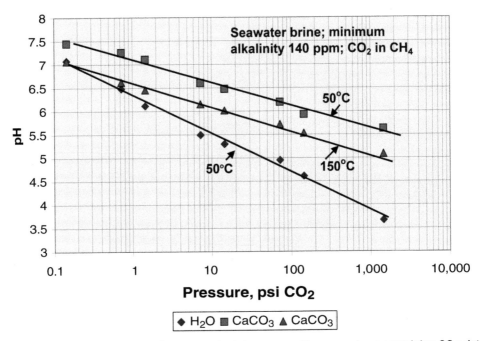

Fig. 9.25—Computed pH vs. pressure for a seawater brine exposed to a gas phase containing CO_2; data are shown for seawater alone at 50°C and for calcite-saturated seawater at 50 and 150°C.

cracking (SSC), and corrosion fatigue. The first five forms involve primarily carbonic acid and/or dissolved oxygen as corrodants. Items 6 through 8 are induced primarily by H_2S.

Corrosive failure by uniform loss of metal is only infrequently seen during the production of oil and gas. It is, however, the first step in corrosive failure of steels by means of localized corrosion. A circumstance for severe metal wastage is the pumping of poorly inhibited matrix stimulation acids.

Pitting is the common failure mode of sweet corrosion and corrosion because of dissolved oxygen. All passivating/protecting films on steel contain weak spots that will preferentially dissolve and form pits. As mentioned, these areas are generally the sulfide inclusions. Chloride ion weakens the repassivating film, allowing continued dissolution. The decreasing pH within the pit also enhances continued corrosion. The driver for theses processes is the large cathodic area of the metal oxide surface vs. the small anodic pit. Pitting is particularly dangerous because penetration through a tubular can occur relatively fast. Other corrosion mechanisms, such as SCC, frequently start at pits. Oxygen scavengers are typically used to remove this gas in an attempt to minimize the pitting problem. However, small amounts may remain (e.g., 20 ppb), and these can be sufficient to induce corrosion.

Carbonic acid, the driver for sweet corrosion, is a weak acid. The pH of the formation water depends on the CO_2 partial pressure, temperature, and alkalinity (controlled primarily, but not exclusively, by the presence or absence of carbonate minerals in the formation). Shown in **Fig. 9.25**, as a function of CO_2 partial pressure, are computed pH values for a seawater brine (containing 140 ppm alkalinity) and a seawater brine saturated in calcite at 50 and 150°C (substantially higher alkalinities). For the common case of carbonate-containing reservoirs and moderate temperatures, produced waters should have pH values of 6 or greater. Waters exposed to greater amounts of CO_2 in noncarbonate-containing reservoirs can have pH values of 4 or less.

Fig. 9.26—Scanning-electron-microscope micrographs (X10K) of the surface of N-80 steel coupons after a 24-hour exposure at 186°F to brine and 760-psi CO_2, without crude oil (upper left), with 95 vol% crude oil E (upper right), with 95 vol% crude oil F (lower left), and with 95 vol% crude oil B (lower right); all deposits are siderite (courtesy of the Electrochemical Society).

Such corrosion induced by CO_2 is a function not only of CO_2 partial pressure and temperature but also of the crude oil. Crude oil contains surface-active chemicals—some oils contain more than others. These chemicals (e.g., resins and asphaltenes) can impact the corrosion process, at least for low-alloy steels. For a fixed brine composition, WOR, temperature, and pressure, corrosion in the presence of some crudes can be negligible, while in the presence of others, it can be extreme under identical environmental conditions.[95,96] Sweet corrosion generally results in the deposition of insoluble $FeCO_3$ (siderite) on the steel surface. It has been suggested that this selectivity to oil composition relates to the physical morphology of the $FeCO_3$ corrosion product—a compact, tight film can protect the steel; a loose, poorly adherent film does not.[96] An example is shown in **Fig. 9.26**. The average uniform corrosion rate for steel in Crude B was 0.6 mil/yr; the corrosion rate in Crude E was 26 mil/yr. Many corrosion inhibitors apparently act by the same mechanism (i.e., the generation of siderite films similar, and/or more compact than those formed from Crude B).[96]

Alternatively, it has been suggested that wettability plays the dominant role, whereby the surface-active components in the crude oil provide for a water-wet surface (high corrosion rates) or an oil-wet surface (low corrosion rates).[97] Regardless of the mechanism, crude oil can modify the corrosion rate. The penalty for ignoring the effect of crude-oil chemistry is the cost of overtreating or using more expensive alloys than are required.

A crevice, such as the junction space under a bolt or the physical junction of two metal parts, is in effect a pit. Uniform corrosion can initiate (in the presence of a corrodant) within the crevice and continue, driven by the large cathodic area outside the pit or crevice.

Stress corrosion cracking is intergranular corrosion, but it takes place only when the metal is under stress and in the presence of a corrodant. The corrodant can be specific—not all corrodants induce SCC on all alloys. Metal wastage is generally small; SCC is often preceded by pitting. High-strength steels are more susceptible to SCC than low-strength alloys. The severity of intergranular corrosion generally depends on the metallurgical history of the steel. Austenitic steels (common stainless steels) are particularly susceptible to intergranular attack.

Blistering, as well as embrittlement and sulfide stress cracking, a subclass of SCC, all stem from the same cause: the presence of H_2S in the system and at the metal surface. The roots of

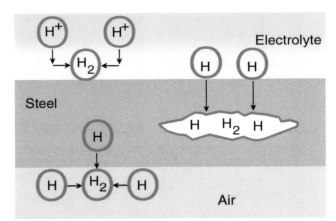

Fig. 9.27—The alternatives for hydrogen atoms formed by the corrosion process: combination in the water phase to make gas, diffusion into the metal to make gas or embrittle steel, penetration through the metal, recombining to make gas (a phenomenon also used to measure corrosion) (after Schlumberger *Oilfield Review*).

the problem are in the mechanism for the cathodic discharge of hydrogen. The mechanism already discussed for the cathodic portion of the acid-induced corrosion process itself, involves two steps.

$$H^+ + e^- = H^{\cdot}, \dots\dots\dots\dots\dots\dots\dots\dots\dots (9.5)$$

and

$$2\ H^{\cdot} = H_2 \dots\dots\dots\dots\dots\dots\dots\dots\dots\dots (9.6)$$

(i.e., the proton is first reduced to a hydrogen atom on the metal surface (H$^{\cdot}$), followed by the combination of two hydrogen atoms to yield hydrogen gas). Hydrogen sulfide inhibits the combination of hydrogen atoms (as does arsenic and some other corrosion inhibitors). Accordingly, the hydrogen atoms can penetrate into the metal where they cause the corrosion problems that were already listed. This is shown schematically in **Fig. 9.27.**[91]

This hydrogen entry into low-strength steels can result in hydrogen blisters, if there is a macroscopic defect in the steel such as an inclusion. Such a void can provide a space for the hydrogen atoms to form hydrogen gas. Pressure builds and blisters form resulting in rupture and leakage.

Embrittlement (hydrogen-induced cracking and hydrogen embrittlement cracking) causes failure at stresses well below the yield strength. This phenomenon usually occurs only with high-strength, hard steels, generally those having yield strengths of 90,000 psi or higher. Tubing and line pipe (electric welded and seamless) are susceptible to this effect. The dominating factor is the metallurgical structure of the steel relating to its method of manufacture.

SSC cracking failure requires only low concentrations of H$_2$S. The time to failure decreases as stress increases. Cracking tendency increases as pH decreases. SSC can be thought of in the same language as that used in describing hydraulic fracturing. There is a critical "stress intensity factor" below that at which a fracture (crack) will not propagate. This factor is related linearly to tensile strength. Some of this problem has been attributed to the effects of cold working on the alloys. Alloys that were stress relieved were found to increase in resistance to SSC.[98]

Wells producing hydrocarbon liquids, with the hydrogen sulfide, are less susceptible to SSC, pitting, and weight loss. For example, certain Canadian condensate wells have produced fluids with 40 mol% H_2S and 10% CO_2 for 30 years without serious corrosion problems. Stability is associated with a protective iron sulfide film, wetted by the oil/liquid hydrocarbon. These wells also had a BHT of 90°C; iron sulfide films are less effective in preventing corrosion above 110°C.

Steels, repeatedly stressed in a cyclical manner, may fail in time (corrosion fatigue). It is required for failure that the stress be above a critical value called the "endurance limit" (nominally 40 to 60% less than the tensile strength). The presence of a corrodant substantially reduces the fatigue life of a metal. Cyclic stress can be looked upon as a method of accelerating failure because of the other mechanisms previously described.

Bimetallic corrosion/galvanic corrosion can occur when two metals are coupled (in electrical contact) and a corrodant is present. The more reactive metal corrodes faster, while the less-reactive metal shows little or no corrosion. The more-reactive metal cathodically protects the less-reactive metal (exploiting cathodic protection to prevent corrosion is discussed later). In general, the total corrosion of the anodic material is proportional to the exposed area of the cathodic material. Thus, steel rivets in monel corrode very rapidly, while monel rivets in steel cause little damage.

Weld-related corrosion is a variant of galvanic corrosion. When a metal is welded, the welding process can generate a microstructure different from that of the parent metal. As a result, the weld may be anodic vs. the parent metal and may corrode more rapidly. This corrosion may take the form of localized metal wastage; if H_2S is present, there is SSC cracking of hard zones in the metal or in the heat-affected zone. Similar problems can arise with electric-resistance-welded pipe.

Metal wastage in sweet systems is avoided by using weld consumable with a higher alloy content than that of the base metal; recourse is made to laboratory measurements to achieve the proper weld-metal/base-metal combination. Welding procedure standards are available to avoid hard zone SSC. Chemical inhibition is also effective in protecting welded pipe.

Coping With Corrosion. The paths to obviating corrosion problems are conceptually straightforward: isolate the metal from the corrodant; employ a metal alloy that is inherently resistant to corrosion in the corrosive medium; chemically inhibit the corrosion process; move the electrical potential of the metal into a region where the corrosion rate is infinitesimally small ("cathodic protection"); or live with the corrosion and replace the corroded component after failure.

Isolation is the regime of paints, coatings, and liners. An introduction to the subject is given in Ref. 92, from which some of the following discussion is abstracted; a detailed discussion of these subjects is in Ref. 99. For any coating to be effective, it must be sufficiently thick to completely isolate the item being protected from the environment. Small holes in the coating ("holidays") result in the rapid formation of pits. Considerable care and quality control is required to guarantee the generation of holidays during service.

Organic coatings, such as asphalt enamel and coal tar enamel, are used to protect equipment concerned with the handling of oil and gas. Baked thin-film coatings, such as thermosetting phenolics and epoxies (applied in multiple coats), can be used to protect tubular goods. External protection of pipelines frequently involves use of adhesive tapes made of polyethylene or similar materials. Fusion bonded epoxy has been used successfully to protect a 150-km seawater-injection line (oxygen was the corrodant, much of which, but not all, was removed by scavenging chemicals).[100]

Inorganic coatings include both sacrificial coatings, which furnish cathodic protection (see below for mechanism) at small breaks in the coating, and nonsacrificial coatings, which protect only the substrates actually coated. Sacrificial coatings include galvanizing or coating with other metals anodic to the substrate and heavy suspensions of anodic metals (e.g., zinc particles, in silicates or organic vehicles). Zinc-silicate coatings (paints) are often used to coat the splash zone of drilling and production platforms. The zinc metal provides for cathodic protection of the steel substrate. Below the water line, the most economical approach to corrosion control is cathodic protection (see below). The pH of the environment is important— highly basic or acidic environments can remove coatings.

Nonsacrificial inorganic coatings include metal platings such as nickel and nonmetallic coatings such as ceramics. Nickel can be applied by electroplating or electroless plating. Ceramic coatings, when properly applied, are highly effective; they are also costly and fragile. Other systems, while not truly coatings, perform the same function (e.g., Portland cement and plastic liners). Plastic liners have been used for internal protection of tubing and lined pipe. Some liners are sealed into individual joints of pipe and tubing; some are fused into one continuous close-fitting liner through the entire pipe. Both cement and plastic liners are suitable for water lines.

The proper application of coatings is, in large part, an art form. Accordingly, it is also not possible to overemphasize the need for close inspection of the coating process, good quality control, and testing that the coating has been complete.

From a cost point of view, low-alloy steels are preferred. In certain cases, "minor" alterations in alloy composition can minimize corrosion. For example, L-80 steel with a tempered martensitic structure and a chromium content > 0.5% has been used without problems in 20-ppb oxygen-containing environments, while a similar steel with < 0.1% Cr has shown serious corrosion.[101]

The choice of using CRAs or chemical means to solve the more severe corrosion problem comes down to economics (available capital vs. long-term operating costs). Remoteness of operation becomes an important consideration in determining operating costs, as does downtime and deferred/lost oil because of repeated intervention for inhibitor application. Availability and cost of platform space is a consideration for offshore facilities.

The corrosion-control effectiveness of CRAs depends on the chemical severity of the environment. Crevice corrosion, pitting attack, and SCC are the primary concerns. The corrosion resistance of annealed austenitic stainless steels, such as 304 and 316, is affected by the presence of chlorides and temperature; type 304 is less corrosion resistant than type 316. Both materials are susceptible to SCC when the temperature is above 150°F. Both alloys are also low-strength steels. Alloys 654 SMo and AL6XN can be manufactured to higher strengths and are more resistant to SCC. Austenitic stainless steels are probably the most susceptible of all ferrous alloys to pitting.

Martensitic stainless steels have had the widest range of use of any of the available CRAs. Such steels may be manufactured through heat treatment into tubular products with acceptable yield strengths for downhole tubing. Many millions of feet of tubing type (grade L-80) 13Cr are in corrosive well service; it is considered the material of choice for deep sweet-gas wells with temperatures less than 150°C. About 35% of the L-80 13Cr usage was for oil wells. The passivity of 13Cr is destroyed by high chloride levels, particularly at high temperature, which can lead to pitting and crevice corrosion.

Duplex stainless steels are high-strength alloys achieved by means of cold working. Such steels are more corrosion resistant than martensitic steels but are similar in resistance to SSC. Cold-worked duplex has been used to 0.3 psi H_2S. Annealed duplex is more resistant to H_2S and SSC than the cold-worked versions. Annealed duplex line pipe has been used in wet CO_2 service (99%) without problems. 22Cr duplex steel has been used where pH_2S was between 0.5 and 1 psi. Such steels have been used successfully in HT/HP wells (e.g., 350°F and 14,000 psi), producing no H_2S. However the copresence of chloride, stress, and dissolved oxygen can induce SSC. Wells not exposed to even small amounts of oxygen have operated successfully.[102]

The material most commonly used for sour service is AISI Type 4130 steel, modified by microalloy additions with a quenched and tempered microstructure (martensite).[103] C-110 steel has been used as casing in North Sea wells (30 to 60 bar CO_2 and 30 to 50 millibar H_2S).[104] An overview of CRAs and their use in sour service is given in Ref. 90.

Nickel and cobalt alloys are used in the most severely corrosive conditions (high pressure, high temperature, and high H_2S contents). C-276, a nickel-based alloy, can be used to 8,000 psi H_2S and 400°F. Nickel alloys have found extensive use in the Mobile Bay fields. They are less expensive than the cobalt alloy MP35N previously used for such extreme conditions. Nickel alloys are also used as weld cladding for wellhead and valve equipment.

As with scale problems, the appropriate addition of chemicals can often inhibit corrosion problems, including some effects of H_2S. The delivery techniques are often the same, but the inhibition mechanisms and types of chemicals are different.

Neutralizing inhibitors reduce the hydrogen ion in the environment. Typically, they are amines, ammonia, and morpholine. They are effective in weak acid systems but are stoichiometric reactants: one molecule equivalent of inhibitor per molecule of acid. They have found minimal use in the oil field.

Scavenging inhibitors are compounds that also remove the corrodant. Oxygen scavengers are commonly used in the oil field (e.g., in removing oxygen during water injection).

The majority of the corrosion inhibitors employed during production form thin barrier layers between the steel surface and the corroding fluid. The concept is that the organic inhibitor will strongly adsorb on the metal wall to form a barrier, possibly only a few molecules thick, which will prevent access to the corrodant and possibly leave the surface oil-wet (further retarding access of the corrodant). The generic name given to these compounds is "filming amines." This name is qualitatively correct in that most inhibitors are indeed nitrogen-containing, and the inhibitor does finally reside on the surface. The specific mechanism can be more complicated. For example, the inhibitor can interact with the corrosion product to increase its adherence and to lower its permeability. Such layers are likely to be far thicker than a few molecules.[96]

Regardless of the specific mechanisms involved, the inhibitor must contact the metal substrate. The general procedures are tubing displacement; displacement from the annulus; continuous injection; squeeze into the reservoir as liquid or gas; weighed liquids/capsules/sticks; and vapor-phase inhibitors.

The first two batch treatments are operated by pushing the inhibitor-containing fluid across the face of the production tubulars top-down (Item 1) or bottom-up (Item 2). The inhibitor film then persists on the metal surface for some period of time ranging from days to months, depending on the specific environment and materials.

Continuous injection is done if the well completion allows for a "macaroni string" reaching to the perforations. This technique often includes a simple-to-complicated valving system; it is to be remembered that valves can plug. Injection through the annulus has also been used.

Inhibitor squeezing into the formation is an alternative. Here, the mechanism is different than that of scale inhibitor squeezes. The large amount of inhibitor that returns initially is not wasted but is intended to coat the tubular and production equipment with an adsorbed, persistent film of inhibitor. The small amounts of inhibitor that subsequently desorb from the formation are intended to repair holes that are generated in the initial film.

Weighed liquids/capsules/sticks are all variations on the theme of placing inhibitor in the rathole where it is slowly released into the wellbore fluid, continuously depositing and/or repairing the protective film.

Vapor-phase corrosion inhibitors are organic compounds that have a high vapor pressure, generating volatile corrosion inhibitors (such as some amines) that allow this inhibitor material to migrate to distant, and often otherwise inaccessible, metal surfaces within the container. Such inhibitors have been used on the Trans-Alaska pipeline to protect low-flow areas, dead legs, and the annular space in road casings and contingency equipment. The concept has also been applied to storage tank protection.[105]

Filming-amine inhibitors are intended to protect steels from the action of "natural" corrodants in the produced hydrocarbon and water phases. They are generally not effective in protecting the steels from the acids used to stimulate wells or from the partially spent acids returning from such treatments. These tasks are accomplished by the inclusion of large dosages of different inhibiting chemicals with the stimulation acids. Such inhibitor systems are also available to handle low-alloy steels and CRAs in HT/HP conditions.[106] Concern for stability of CRAs during matrix stimulation of deep hot wells has resulted in the use of organic acids such as acetic acid and formic acid rather than HCl. Inhibitor systems have been developed for these chemicals as well.

Cathodic Protection. This technology is used to protect pipelines, offshore platforms, and surface equipment and is discussed more fully in the Facilities and Construction Engineering section of this *Handbook*. As previously discussed, corrosion is an electrochemical process: iron atoms give up electrons; the electrons flow through the metal to the corrodant; ion movement in the water film contacting both corrodant and iron metal completes the electrical circuit. In certain important cases, it is possible to reverse this current flow out of the steel surface by the application of an external power supply (i.e., make the surface to be protected cathodic rather than anodic). The technology involved in employing cathodic protection must take into account the quantity of current required; composition and configuration of the impressed current anode; resistivity of the corroding medium; size of the item being protected; accessibility of the surface being protected; and length of the item being protected.

Nomenclature

P_r = reservoir pressure
T_r = reservoir temperature

Acknowledgments

The data for Fig. 9.5 are used with permission of Infochem Computer Services, London. Fig. 9.9 is used with permission of Études et Productions Schlumberger, Clamart, France. Figs. 9.12 through 9.19, 9.21 through 9.24, and Fig. 9.27, copyright Schlumberger *Oilfield Review,* are used with permission. Fig. 9.26 is courtesy of the Electrochemical Society.

References

1. Thawer, R., Nicoll, D., and Dick, G.: "Asphaltene Deposition in Production Facilities," *SPEPE* (November 1990) 475.
2. Burke, N., Hobbs, R., and Kashoue, S.: "Measurement and Modelling of Asphaltene Precipitation," *JPT* (November 1990) 1440.
3. Leontaritis, K., Amaefule, J., and Charles, R.: "A Systematic Approach for the Prevention and Treatment of Formation Damage Caused by Asphaltene Deposition," *SPEPF* (August 1994) 157.
4. Ngheim, L., Coombe, D., and Farouq Ali, A.M.: "Compositional Simulation of Asphaltene Deposition and Plugging," paper SPE 48996 presented at the 1998 SPE Annual Technical Conference and Exhibition, New Orleans, 27–30 September.
5. Limanowka, W., Voytechek, M., and Limanowka, R.: "Asphaltene Deposition Problems in Oil Industry with Focus on Electric Submersible Pump Applications," paper SPE 56662 presented at the 1999 SPE Annual Technical Conference and Exhibition, Houston, 1–6 October.
6. Leontaritis, K.: "Asphaltene Deposition: A Comprehensive Description of Problem Manifestations and Modeling Approaches," paper SPE 18892 presented at the 1989 SPE Production Operations Symposium, Oklahoma City, Oklahoma, 9–17 March.

7. Sarbar, M. and Wingrove, M. : "Physical and Chemical Characterization of Saudi Arabian Crude Oil Emulsions," paper SPE 38817 presented at the 1997 SPE Annual Technical Conference and Exhibition, San Antonio, Texas, 5–8 October.

8. Hunt, J.: *Petroleum Geochemistry and Geology,* W. Freeman and Co., New York City (1996).

9. Mitchell, D. and Speight, J.: "The Solubility of Asphaltenes in Hydrocarbon Solvents," *Fuel* (1973) **52,** No. 4, 149.

10. Colmenares, R.: "Short and Long-Term Management of the El Furial Field," paper SPE 38782 presented at the 1997 SPE Annual Technical Conference and Exhibition, San Antonio, Texas, 5–8 October.

11. Edmonds, B.: *Technical Update—Asphaltene Deposition,* Infochem Computer Services Ltd., London (1999).

12. Cimino, R., Correra, S., Lockhart, T.: "Solubility and Phase Behavior of Asphaltenes in Hydrocarbon Media," *Asphaltene Fundamentals and Applications,* E. Sheu and O. Mullins (eds.) Plenum Press, New York City (1995) Chap. 3, 97–130.

13. Calemma, V. *et al.:* "Structural Characterization of Asphaltenes of Different Origins," *Energy & Fuels* (1995) **9,** No. 2, 225.

14. Kawanka, S. *et al.:* "Thermodynamic and Colloidal Models of Asphaltene Flocculation," *Oil Field Chemistry,* Symposium 390, ACS, Toronto (1989) Chap. 24.

15. Suzuki, T. *et al.:* "Chemical Structure of Tar-Sand Bitumens by 13-C and 1-H NMR Spectroscopy Method," *Fuel* (1982) **61,** No. 1, 40.

16. Leontaritis, K.: "PARA-Based Reservoir Oil Characterizations," paper SPE 37252 presented at the 1997 SPE International Symposium on Oilfield Chemistry, Houston, 16–21 February.

17. Hirschberg, A. *et al.:* "Influence of Temperature and Pressure on Asphaltene Flocculation," *SPEJ* (June 1984) 283.

18. DeBoer, R. *et al.:* "Screening of Crude Oils for Asphalt Precipitation: Theory, Practice and Selection of Inhibitors," *SPEPF* (February 1995) 55.

19. Alf, J., Betancourt, J., and Avila, C.: "A Methodology for Asphaltene Control in Production Facilities in North of Managas Venezuela," paper SPE 56572 presented at the 1999 SPE Annual Technical Conference and Exhibition, Houston, 3–6 October.

20. Allenson, S. and Walsh, M.: "New Chemicals and Treatment Methods that Prevent Asphaltene Deposition Problems Found in Oil Production," *Proc.,* IBC U.K. Conference, Aberdeen (1997).

21. Del Bianco, A., Stroppa, F., and Bertero, L.: "Tailoring Hydrocarbon Streams for Asphaltene Removal," paper SPE 28992 presented at the 1995 International Symposium on Oilfield Chemistry, San Antonio, Texas, 14–17 February.

22. Minssieux, L.: "Removal of Asphalt Deposits by Covalent Squeezes: Mechanisms and Screening," paper SPE 39447 presented at the 1998 SPE International Symposium on Formation Damage Control, Lafayette, Louisiana, 18–19 February.

23. Chang, C. and Folger, S.H.: "Stabilization of Asphaltenes in Aliphatic Solvents Using Alkylbenzene Derived Amphiphiles," *Langmuir* (1994) **10,** No. 1, 749.

24. Garcia, M. *et al.:* "Correlation Between Oil Composition and Paraffin Inhibitors Activity," paper SPE 49200 presented at the 1998 SPE Annual Technical Conference and Exhibition, New Orleans, 27–30 September.

25. Allen, T. and Roberts, A.: "Paraffins and Asphaltenes," *Production Operations*, Oil and Gas Consultants Intl. Inc., Tulsa (1982) 2.

26. Hammami, A. and Raines, M.: "Paraffin Deposition From Crude Oils: Comparison of Laboratory Results to Field Data," paper SPE 38776 presented at the 1997 SPE Annual Technical Conference and Exhibition, San Antonio, Texas, 5–8 October.

27. Monger-McClure, T., Tackett, J., and Merrill, L.: "DeepStar Comparisons of Cloud Point Measurements and Paraffin Prediction Methods," paper SPE 38774 presented at the 1997 SPE Annual Technical Conference and Exhibition, San Antonio, Texas, 5–8 October.

28. Calange, S., Ruffier-Meray, V., and Behar, E.: "Onset Crystallization Temperature and Deposit Amount for Waxy Crudes: Experimental Determination and Thermodynamic Modelling," paper SPE 37239 presented at the 1997 International Symposium on Oilfield Chemistry, Houston, 18–21 February.

29. Brill, J.: "Experimental Investigation of Paraffin Deposition Prediction in Single-Phase and Multiphase Flowlines and Wellbores," *Proc.,* IBC U.K. Conference, Aberdeen (1997).

30. Khalil, C., Rocha, N., and Silva, E.: "Detection of Formation Damage Associated to Paraffin in Reservoirs of the Reconcavo Baiano, Brazil," paper SPE 37238 presented at the 1997 International Symposium on Oilfield Chemistry, Houston, 18–21 February.

31. Ferworn, K., Hammami, A., and Ellis, H.: "Control of Wax Deposition: An Experimental Investigation of Crystal Morphology and an Evaluation of Various Chemical Solvents," paper SPE 37240 presented at the 1997 International Symposium on Oilfield Chemistry, Houston, 18–21 February.

32. Cassinis, R. and Farone, W.: "Improved H_2S Caustic Scrubber," paper SPE 38273 presented at the 1997 SPE Western Regional Meeting, Long Beach, California, 25–27 June.

33. Sturman, P., Goeres, D., and Winters, M.: "Control of Hydrogen Sulfide in Oil and Gas Wells with Nitrite Injection," paper SPE 56772 presented at the 1999 SPE Annual Technical Conference and Exhibition, Houston, 3–6 October.

34. Wilson, D.: "Hydrogen Sulphide Scavengers: Recent Experience in a Major North Sea Field," paper SPE 36943 presented at the 1996 SPE European Petroleum Conference, Milan, Italy, 22–24 October.

35. Wilhelm, M.: "Removal and Treatment of Mercury Contamination at Gas Processing Facilities," paper SPE 29721 presented at the 1995 SPE/EPA Environmental and Protection Conference, Houston, 27–29 March.

36. Smith, A.: "Radioactive-Scale Formation," *JPT* (June 1987) 697.

37. Takhautdinov, S. *et al.:* "Influence of Radon and Decay Products on Field Equipment Service Personnel," paper SPE 35867 presented at the 1996 SPE International Conference on Health, Safety, and Environment, New Orleans, 9–12 June.

38. Hartog, F. *et al.:* "Lead Deposits in Dutch Natural Gas Systems," paper SPE 68316 presented at the 2001 SPE International Symposium on Oilfield Scale, Aberdeen, 29–30 January.

39. Oddo, J. *et al.:* "The Chemistry, Prediction and Treatment of Scale Containing Naturally Occurring Radioactive Materials (NORM) in Antrim Gas Fields, Michigan," paper SPE 25485 presented at the 1993 Production Operations Symposium, Oklahoma City, Oklahoma, 21–23 March.

40. Makogon, Y.: *Hydrates of Hydrocarbons,* PennWell Books, Tulsa (1997).

41. Sloan, E.: *Clathrate Hydrates of Natural Gases,* Marcel Dekker Inc., New York City (1990).

42. Edmonds, B., Moorwood, R., and Szczepanski, R.: "A Practical Model for the Effect of Salinity on Gas Hydrate Formation," paper SPE 35569 presented at the 1996 European Production Operations Conference and Exhibition, Stavanger, 16–17 April.

43. Hendriks, M.: "Hydrate Structure Stability in Simple and Mixed Hydrates," *Fluid-Phase Equilibria* (1996) **117,** No. 1–2, 193.

44. Tohidi, B.: "Measurement and Prediction of Hydrate-Phase Equilibria for Reservoir Fluids" *SPEPF* (May 1996) 69.

45. Behar, E.: "Hydrates Problem Within the Framework of Multiphase Production and Transport of Crude Oils and Natural Gases: Part 1—Physical Chemistry of Hydrates Formation and Dissociation," *Review IFP* (1994) **49,** No. 3, 265.

46. Sawyer, W. *et al.:* "Comparative Assessment of Natural Gas Hydrate Production Models," paper SPE 62513 presented at the 2000 SPE/CERI Gas Technology Symposium, Calgary, 3–5 April.

47. Makogon, Y.: *Hydrates of Hydrocarbons,* PennWell Books, Tulsa (1997) 262.

48. Yousif, M. and Dunayevsky, V.: "Hydrate Plug Remediation: Options and Applications for Deep Water Drilling Operations," paper SPE/IADC 37624 presented at 1997 SPE/IADC Drilling Conference, Amsterdam, 4–6 March.

49. Mitchell, G. and Talley, L.: "Application of Kinetic Hydrate Inhibitor in Black-Oil Flowlines," paper SPE 56770 presented at the 1999 SPE Annual Technical Conference and Exhibition, Houston, 3–6 October.

50. Klomp, U., Kruka, V., and Reijnhart, R.: "Low Dosarge Ihibitors: (How) Do They Work?," *Proc.,* IBC U.K. Conference, Aberdeen (1997).

51. Pakulski, M., Prukop, G., and Mitchell, C.: "Field Testing and Commercial Applications of High Efficiency Nonpolymeric Gas Hydrate Inhibitor in Offshore Platforms," paper SPE 49210 presented at the 1998 SPE Annual Technical Conference and Exhibition, New Orleans, 27–30 September.

52. Argo, C. *et al.:* "Commercial Deployment of Low-Dosage Hydrate Inhibitors in a Southern North Sea 69 km Wet-Gas Subsea Pipeline," paper SPE 63017 presented at the 2000 SPE International Symposium on Oilfield Chemistry, Houston, 18–21 February.

53. Nelson, R. *et al.:* "A Novel Gas-Hydrate Inhibitor for Deepwater Frac-Pack and Subsea Environments," paper SPE 58764 presented at the 2000 International Symposium on Formation Damage Control, Lafayette, Louisiana, 23–24 February.

54. Reyma, E. and Stewart, S.: "Case History of the Removal of a Hydrate Plug Formed During Deep Water Well Testing," paper SPE 67746 presented at the 2001 SPE/IADC Drilling Conference, Amsterdam, 27 February–1 March.

55. Bailey, B.: "Water Control," *Oilfield Review* (2000) **12,** No. 1, 30.

56. Carrell, K.: "The Occurrence, Prevention and Treatment of Sulphate Scales in Shell Expro," paper SPE 16538 presented at the 1987 Offshore Europe Conference, Aberdeen, 8–11 September.

57. Nasr-El-Din, H.A. and Al-Humaidan, A.Y.: "Iron Sulphide Scale: Formation and Prevention," paper SPE 68315 presented at the 2001 SPE International Symposium on Oilfield Scale, Aberdeen, 30–31 January.

58. Cowan, J. and Weintritt, D.: *Water-Formed Scale Deposits,* Gulf Publishing Co., Houston (1976) 187–188.

59. Jasinski, R., Sablerolle, W., and Amory, M.: "ETAP: Scale Prediction and Control for the Heron Cluster," paper SPE 38769 presented at the 1997 SPE Annual Technical Conference and Exhibition, San Antonio, Texas, 5–8 October.

60. Jasinski, R.: "Calcite Scaling Tendencies for North Sea HT/HP Wells: Prediction, Authentication and Application," paper SPE 49198 presented at the 1998 SPE Annual Technical Conference and Exhibition, New Orleans, 27–30 September.

61. Tjomsland, T., Grotle, M., and Vikane, O.: "Scale Control Strategy and Economical Consequences of Scale at Veslefrikk," paper SPE 68308 presented at the 2001 International Symposium on Oilfield Scale, Aberdeen, 29–30 January.

62. Wigg, H. and Fletcher, M.: "Establishing the True Cost of Downhole Scale Control," paper presented at the 1995 International Conference on Oilfield Scaling, Aberdeen, 20–21 November.

63. Frigo, D.: "The Costs of Scale—a R&D Perspective," plenary lecture, 2001 SPE International Symposium on Oilfield Scale, Aberdeen, 29–30 January.

64. Crabtree, M. *et al.:* "Fighting Scale—Removal and Prevention," *Oilfield Review* (1999) **11,** No. 3, 30.

65. Nasr-El-Din, H. *et al.:* "An Experimental Study Removing Iron Sulphide Scale From Well Tubulars," paper SPE 60205 presented at the SPE 2000 International Symposium on Oilfield Scale, Aberdeen, 22–27 January.

66. Weston, R. and Michaluk, P.: "Scale Control in Heron Cluster Field Using Sulphate Removal Membranes," paper SPE 60207 presented at the 2000 SPE International Symposium on Oilfield Scale, Aberdeen, 26–27 January.

67. Frigo, D. *et al.:* "Chemical Inhibition of Halite Scaling in Topsides Equipment," paper SPE 60191 presented at the 2000 SPE International Symposium on Oilfield Scale Aberdeen, 26–27 January.

68. Earl, S. and Nahm, J.: "Use of Chemical Salt Precipitation Inhibitors to Maintain Supersaturated Salt Muds for Drilling Salt Formations," paper SPE 10097 presented at the 1981 SPE Annual Technical Conference and Exhibition, San Antonio, Texas, 5–7 October.

69. Poggesi, G., Brazy, J.L., and Hurtevent, C.: "Scale Inhibitor Injection via the Gas Lift in High Temperature Block 3 Fields in Angola," paper SPE 68301 presented at the 2001 SPE International Symposium on Oilfield Scale, Aberdeen, 29–30 January.

70. Hsu, J. and Henderson, A.: "Encapsulated Scale Inhibitor Treatments Experience in the Ghawar Field Saudi Arabia," paper SPE 60209 presented at the 2000 SPE International Symposium on Oilfield Scale, Aberdeen, 26–27 January.

71. Bourne, H., Heath, S., McKay, S.: "Effective Treatment of Subsea Wells with a Solid Scale Inhibitor System," paper SPE 60207 presented at the SPE 2000 Intl. Symposium on Oilfield Scale, Aberdeen, 26–27 January.

72. Cowie, L. *et al.:* "Delivering Chemicals into Production Wells via Gas Lift—Where Are We?" paper presented at the 1999 SPE International Symposium on Oilfield Scale, Aberdeen, 27–28 January.

73. Graham, G. *et al.:* "Scale Inhibitor Selection for Continuous and Downhole Squeeze Application in HP/HT Conditions," paper SPE 49197 presented at the 1998 SPE Annual Technical Conference and Exhibition, New Orleans, 27–30 September.

74. Shuler, P.: "Mathematical Model for the Scale-Inhibitor Squeeze Process Based in the Langmuir Adsorption Isotherm," paper SPE 25162 presented at the 1993 SPE International Symposium on Oilfield Chemistry, New Orleans, 2–5 March.

75. Yuan, M.D. *et al.:* "The Modeling of Adsorption and Precipitation Scale Inhibitor Squeeze Treatments in North Sea Fields," paper SPE 25163 presented at the 1993 SPE International Symposium on Oilfield Chemistry, New Orleans, 2–5 March.

76. Jordan, M. *et al.:* "Phosphonate Scale Inhibitor Adsorption/Desorption and the Potential for Formation Damage in Reconditioned Field Core," paper SPE 27389 presented at the 1994 SPE International Symposium on Formation Damage Control, Lafayette, Louisiana, 7–10 February.

77. Asheim, T. *et al.:* "Inhibitor Squeeze Treatment for Preventive Carbonate Scale Control in a Subsea Completed Well on Smorbukk," paper SPE 60201 presented at the 2000 SPE International Symposium on Oilfield Scale, Aberdeen, 26–27 January.

78. Poynton, N., Tidswell, R., and Steels, J.: "Squeezing Aqueous Based Scale Inhibitors into a Water Sensitive Reservoir—Development of a Squeeze Strategy," paper SPE 60219 presented at the 2000 International Symposium on Oilfield Scale, Aberdeen, Scotland, 26–27 January.

79. Shuler, P. *et al.:* "Clay-Induced Permeability Damage from Injected Scale Inhibitor Solutions," paper SPE 27370 presented at the 1994 SPE Symposium on Formation Damage Control, Lafayette, Louisiana, 7–10 February.

80. Singleton, M. *et al.:* "Developments on PhosphoMethylated PolyAmine (PMPA) Scale Inhibitor Chemistry for Severe BaSO4 Scaling Conditions," paper SPE 60216 presented at the 2000 SPE International Symposium on Oilfield Scale, Aberdeen, 26–27 January.

81. Bourne, H. and Williams, G.: "Increasing Squeeze Life on Miller with New Inhibitor Chemistry," paper SPE 60198 presented at the 2000 Intl. Symposium on Oilfield Scale, Aberdeen, 26–27 January.

82. Graham, G., Dyer, S., and Shone, P.: "Potential Application of Amine Methylene Phosphonate Based Inhibitor Species in HP/HT Environments for Improved Carbonate Scale Inhibitor Performance," paper SPE 60217 presented at the 2000 SPE International Symposium on Oilfield Scale, Aberdeen, 26–27 January.

83. Pirri, R., Hurtevent, C., and Leconte, P.: "New Scale Inhibitor for Harsh Field Conditions," paper SPE 60218 presented at the 2000 SPE International Symposium on Oilfield Scale, Aberdeen, 26–27 January.

84. Smith, P., Cowie, I., and Bourne, H.: "Field Experience with a Combined Acid Stimulation and Scale Inhibitor Treatment," paper SPE 23809 presented at the 2001 SPE International Symposium on Oilfield Scale, Aberdeen, 29–30 January.

85. Martins, J. *et al.:* "Scale Inhibition of Hydraulic Fractures in Prudhoe Bay," paper SPE 23809 presented at the 1992 Symposium on Formation Damage Control, Lafayette, Louisiana, 26–27 February.

86. Powell, R. *et al.:* "Controlled-Release Scale Inhibitor for Use in Fracturing Treatments," paper SPE 28999 presented at the 1995 SPE International Symposium on Oilfield Chemistry, San Antonio, Texas, 14–17 February.

87. Collins, I.R.: "Scale Inhibitor Impregnated Particles—Field Applications?" paper presented at the 1997 IBC Solving Oilfield Scaling Conference, Aberdeen, 22–23 January.

88. Webb, P. *et al.:* "Advantages of a New Chemical Delivery System for Fractured and Gravel-Packed Wells," *SPEPF* (August 1999) 14.

89. Norris, M., Bourne, H., and Heath, S.: "Maintaining Fracture Performance through Active Scale Control," paper SPE 68300 presented at the 2001 SPE International Symposium on Oilfield Scale, Aberdeen, 29–30 January.

90. Treseder, R. and Tuttle, R.: "Corrosion Control in Oil and Gas Production," Item No. 37741, NACE, Houston (1998).

91. Brondel, D. *et al.:* "Corrosion in the Oil Industry," *Oilfield Review* (April 1994) 4.

92. "Corrosion Control in Petroleum Production," NACE, Houston (1979) TPC No. 5, Chap. 7.

93. Szklarska-Smialowska, Z.: *Pitting Corrosion of Metals,* NACE, Houston (1986) 69–96.

94. Krueger, J.: "Passivity and Breakdown of Passivity," *Electrochemistry in Industry,* U. Landau, E. Yeager, and D. Kortas (eds.) Plenum Press, New York City (1982) Chap. 5, 317–330.

95. Efird, K.D. and Jasinski, R.: "Effect of Crude Oil on Corrosion of Steel in Crude Oil/Brine Production," *Corrosion* (1989) **45,** No. 2, 165.

96. Jasinski, R.: "Corrosion of Low Alloy Steel in Crude Oil/Brine/CO_2 Mixtures," *Proc.,* The Electrochemical Society: Surfaces, Inhibition and Passivation, Princeton (1986) **86,** No. 7, 139–148.

97. Smart, J.S.: "Wettability—A Major Factor in Oil and Gas Corrosion," *Materials Performance* (2001) **40,** No. 4, 54.

98. Treseder, R. and Badrak, R.: "Effect of Cold Working on SSC Resistance of Carbon and Low Alloy Steels—A Review," paper 21 presented at NACE Corrosion 97, Houston (March 1997).

99. "Coatings and Linings for Immersion Service," NACE International, Houston (1998) TPC No. 2.

100. Chen, E. and Ahmed T.: "Why Internally Coated Piping is Used for the World's Largest Seawater Injection System," paper SPE 49211 presented at the 1998 SPE Annual Technical Conference and Exhibition, New Orleans, 27–30 September.

101. Nice, P. and Ueda, M.: "The Effect of Microstructure and Chromium Alloying Content to the Corrosion Resistance of Low-Alloy Steel Well Tubing in Sea Water Injection Service," paper 3 presented at NACE Corrosion 98, Houston (March 1998).

102. Mowat, D., Edgerton, M., and Wade, E.: "Erskine Field HT/HP Workover and Tubing Corrosion Failure Investigation," paper SPE 67779 presented at the 2001 SPE/IADC Drilling Conference, Amsterdam, 27 February–1 March.

103. Echaniz, C., Morales, C., and Pereze, T.: "The Effect of Microstructure on the K_{ISSC} Low Alloy Carbon Steels," paper 120 presented at NACE Corrosion 98, Houston (March 1998).

104. Linne, C.: "Heavy Wall Casing in C-110 Grade for Sour Service," paper 117 presented at NACE Corrosion 98, Houston (March 1998).

105. Gandhi, R.: "Storage Tank Bottom Protection Using Volatile Corrosion Inhibitors," *Materials Performance—Supplement* (January 2001) 28.

106. Frenier, W., Hill, D., and Jasinski, R.: "Corrosion Inhibitors for Acid Jobs," *Oilfield Review* (1994) **1,** No. 2, 15.

SI Metric Conversion Factors

Å	× 1.0*	E – 10	= m
°API	141.5/(131.5 + °API)		= g/cm³
bbl	× 1.589 873	E – 01	= m³
bar	× 1.0*	E + 05	= Pa
ft	× 3.048*	E – 01	= m
°F	(°F – 32)/1.8)		= °C
gal	× 3.785 412	E – 03	= m³
psi	× 6.894 757	E + 00	= kPa

*Conversion factor is exact.

Chapter 10
Artificial Lift Selection
James F. Lea, U. of Oklahoma

10.1 Introduction

Artificial lift is a method used to lower the producing bottomhole pressure (BHP) on the formation to obtain a higher production rate from the well. This can be done with a positive-displacement downhole pump, such as a beam pump or a progressive cavity pump (PCP), to lower the flowing pressure at the pump intake. It also can be done with a downhole centrifugal pump, which could be a part of an electrical submersible pump (ESP) system. A lower bottomhole flowing pressure and higher flow rate can be achieved with gas lift in which the density of the fluid in the tubing is lowered and expanding gas helps to lift the fluids. Artificial lift can be used to generate flow from a well in which no flow is occurring or used to increase the flow from a well to produce at a higher rate. Most oil wells require artificial lift at some point in the life of the field, and many gas wells benefit from artificial lift to take liquids off the formation so gas can flow at a higher rate.

To realize the maximum potential from developing any oil or gas field, the most economical artificial lift method must be selected. The methods historically used to select the lift method for a particular field vary broadly across the industry. The methods include operator experience; what methods are available for installations in certain areas of the world; what is working in adjoining or similar fields; determining what methods will lift at the desired rates and from the required depths; evaluating lists of advantages and disadvantages; "expert" systems to both eliminate and select systems; and evaluation of initial costs, operating costs, production capabilities, etc. with the use of economics as a tool of selection, usually on a present-value basis.

These methods consider geographic location, capital cost, operating cost, production flexibility, reliability, and "mean time between failures." This chapter discusses some of the most commonly used methods. In most cases, what has worked best or which lift method performs best in similar fields serve as selection criteria. Also, the equipment and services available from vendors can easily determine which lift method will be applied. However, when significant costs for well servicing and high production rates are a part of the scenario, it becomes prudent for the operator to consider most, if not all, of the available evaluation and selection methods. If the "best" lift method is not selected, such factors as long-term servicing costs, deferred production during workovers, and excessive energy costs (poor efficiency) can reduce drastically the net present value (NPV) of the project. Typically, the reserves need to be produced in a timely manner with reasonably low operating costs. Conventional wisdom considers the best artificial lift method to be the system that provides the highest present value for the life of the project. Good data are required for a complete present-value analysis, and these data are not always broadly available.

In some situations, the type of lift already has been determined and the task is to best apply that system to the particular well. The more basic question, however, is how to determine the proper type of artificial lift to apply in a given field for maximum present value profit (PVP). This chapter briefly reviews each of the major types of artificial lift before examining some of the selection techniques. Some less familiar methods of lift also are mentioned. Preliminary factors related to the reservoir and well conditions that should be considered are introduced.

Environmental and geographical considerations may be overriding issues. For example, sucker-rod pumping is, by far, the most widely used artificial lift method in onshore United States operations. However, in a densely populated city or on an offshore platform with 40 wells in a very small deck area, sucker-rod pumping might be a poor choice. Also, deep wells producing several thousands of barrels per day cannot be lifted by beam lift; therefore, other methods must be considered. Such geographic, environmental, and production considerations can limit the choices to only one method of lift; however, determining the best overall choice is more difficult when it is possible to apply several of the available lift methods.

10.2 Reservoir Pressure and Well Productivity

Among the most important factors to consider when selecting an artificial lift system are current and future reservoir pressure and well productivity. If producing oil or liquid rate is plotted (X axis) against producing BHP (Y axis), one of two inflow performance relationships (IPR) usually is seen. Above the bubblepoint pressure, the liquid rate vs. pressure drop below the reservoir pressure (drawdown) is linear. Below the bubblepoint pressure, a relationship similar to that described by Ref. 1 occurs. **Fig. 10.1** illustrates production vs. drawdown relationships as a single IPR with a bubblepoint of 750 psig and an average reservoir pressure of 2,000 psig. If the necessary data are available, a single-phase IPR expression for either gas or liquid flow is available from radial-flow equations. Gas-deliverability curves show a nonlinear dependence of gas rate similar to the liquid rate vs. pressure on a Vogel curve.[1] Liquid-rate IPR curves can have a gas-to-liquid ratio associated with the liquid rate, and gas-deliverability curves can have a liquid production (e.g., bbl/MMscf/D) associated with the gas rates. This chapter focuses on IPRs with liquid production as a function of the flowing BHP.

Some types of artificial lift can reduce the producing sandface pressure to a lower level than other artificial lift methods. For pumping wells, achieving a rate that occurs below the bubblepoint pressure requires measures to combat possible gas interference because gas bubbles (free gas) will be present at the intake of the downhole artificial lift installation. In addition to setting the pump below the perforations, such measures include the use of a variety of other possible gas-separation schemes and the use of special pumps to compress gas or reduce effects of "fluid pound" in beam systems. However, the artificial lift method of gas lift is assisted by the production of gas (with liquids) from the reservoir.

The reward for achieving a lower producing pressure will depend on the IPR. With the IPR data available, a production goal may be set. For low-rate wells, the operator would want to produce the maximum rate from the well. For high-rate wells, the production goal can be set by the capacity or horsepower limit of a particular artificial lift method.

In addition to radial flow and IPR expressions for vertical wells, there are several IPR models[2] for horizontal wells. Horizontal wells typically produce several multiples of what a vertical well would produce in the same formation. Artificial lift usually is installed in the near vertical portion of a horizontal well, rarely into the horizontal portion, to reduce slugging and to achieve maximum drawdown.

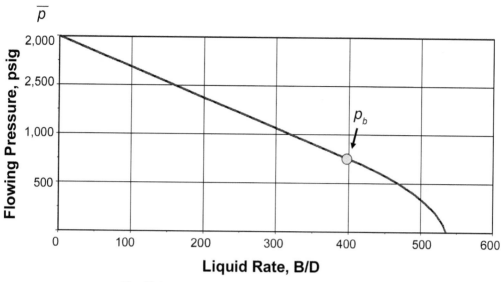

Fig. 10.1—IPR with bubblepoint pressure of 750 psi.

IPRs can be generated to represent the expected well conditions as the shut-in pressure depletes. When correlated to a reservoir model or a tank material balance, time can be associated with future IPRs. **Fig. 10.2** shows future IPR curves as the reservoir pressure drops as a result of depletion. This particular model shows the productivity index (PI) remaining constant above the bubblepoint as the reservoir depletes. The bubblepoint would not necessarily remain constant with time as modeled here. Reservoir models may be used to predict expected inflow conditions of the wells for the life of the project. Usually this is done only for larger projects. IPR expressions can be modified to show damage or stimulation effects. A test rate or absolute open flow for an IPR increase due to skin removal can be found by multiplying by approximately $(7+s)/7$ in which s is the nonrate dependent initial "skin" of the well and the final skin is zero. This approximate ratio is determined by dividing a radial-flow rate equation with no skin by a radial-flow equation with skin. The "7" is approximately the log of 0.472 times the drainage radius over the wellbore radius. More complex relationships show the effects of rate-dependent skin or turbulence. For more discussion, see the chapter on formation damage in this volume of the *Handbook*.

10.3 Reservoir Fluids
The characteristics of the reservoir fluid also must be considered. Paraffin buildup can be attacked mechanically when sucker-rod pumping is used but may require a thermal or chemical method when other artificial lift methods are used. Sand- or solids-laden production, which can rule out the use of plunger lift, also can cause wear with sucker-rod pumps, reciprocating hydraulic pumps, and jet pumps. Gas lift and PCPs produce moderate volumes of solids with only minor problems. The producing gas/liquid ratio is very important to the lift designer. If the percentage of free gas at intake conditions is high, gas interference is a potential detriment to all methods of lift, but it is a benefit to gas lift. High-fluid viscosity hinders most major forms of lift, but the PCP may produce low temperature, shallow, viscous fluids with little difficulty.

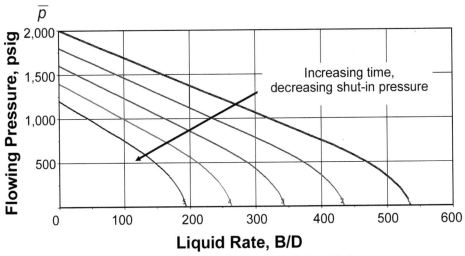

Fig. 10.2—IPR with shut-in pressure declining with time.

10.4 Long-Term Reservoir Performance and Facility Constraints

Two approaches frequently are taken to account for long-term reservoir performance: design on the basis of anticipated performance and design on the basis of current conditions.

If future reservoir performance can be predicted, artificial lift equipment can be installed that can produce up to the largest rate anticipated over the life of the well. This philosophy leads to the installation of oversized equipment, perhaps in anticipation of ultimately producing large quantities of water. Because most artificial lift methods operate at poor efficiency when underloaded, oversized equipment installed because of anticipated high short-term production rates can lead to high energy or operational costs over a significant fraction of the life of the field.

Another extreme is to design only for current conditions without anticipating future production profiles. This can lead to multiple required changes in the size or type of installed lift equipment. Operating efficiently during the short term may be possible, but large amounts of capital for changing equipment may be required later. For example, changing reservoir conditions with time, as shown in Fig. 10.2, would have to be considered carefully in sizing artificial lift equipment for current conditions and for some future date. Ref. 3 addresses some of the concerns of timing related to artificial lift methods.

The operator should consider both long-term and short-term aspects of an artificial lift plan. The goal is to maximize the PVP of the operation over the life of the field. Frequently, the lift method that produces the most oil is the method that provides maximum PVP. However, if operational costs are significantly high for a particular method, a method that can only produce a lower rate but produces more reliably may be more economical. Changes in a lift method usually are not considered worthwhile, but if conditions change drastically, other lift methods may need to be implemented.

10.5 Types of Artificial Lift

The major forms of artificial lift are sucker-rod (beam) pumping, ESP, gas lift, and reciprocating and jet hydraulic pumping systems. Also, plunger lift and PCP are becoming more common. There are other methods, which are mentioned as appropriate, such as the electrical submersible progressive cavity pump (ESPCP) for pumping solids and viscous oils, in deviated wells. This system has a PCP with the motor and some other components similar to an ESP.

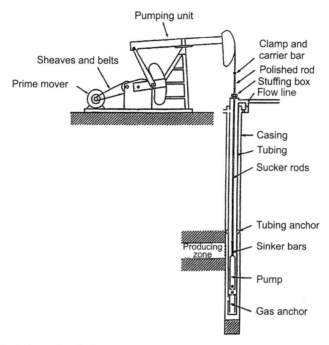

Fig. 10.3—Schematic of a beam-pumping system. (Courtesy of Harbison-Fischer.)

Other methods include modifications of beam pump systems, various intermittent gas-lift methods, and various combination systems.

Artificial lift method selection should be a part of the overall well design. Once the method is selected, the wellbore size required to obtain the desired production rate must be considered. Many times, a casing program has been designed to minimize well-completion costs, but it is later found that the desired production could not be obtained because of the size limitation on the artificial lift equipment. This can lead to an ultimate loss of total reserves. Even if target production rates can be achieved, smaller casing sizes can lead to higher long-term well-servicing problems. If oil prices are low, it is tempting to select a small casing size to help with current economics. Obviously, wells should be drilled and completed with future production and lift methods in mind, but this is often not the case.

Secs. 10.5.1 through 10.5.6 introduce the major methods of artificial lift. The advantages and disadvantages of each method of lift are presented. This information is a tool for any artificial lift selection process.

10.5.1 Sucker-Rod Pumping. Sucker-rod pumping systems are the oldest and most widely used type of artificial lift for oil wells. **Fig. 10.3** shows a schematic of a rod pumping system. System details are found in the chapter on sucker-rod pumping in this section of the *Handbook*.

There are approximately 2 million oil wells in operation worldwide. More than 1 million wells use some type of artificial lift. More than 750,000 of the lifted wells use sucker-rod pumps. In the U.S., sucker-rod pumps lift approximately 350,000 wells. Approximately 80% of all U.S. oil wells are stripper wells making less than 10 B/D with some water cut. The vast majority of these stripper wells are lifted with sucker-rod pumps. Of the nonstripper "higher" volume wells, 27% are rod pumped, 52% are gas lifted, and the remainder are lifted with ESPs, hydraulic pumps, and other methods of lift. These statistics[4] indicate the dominance of rod pumping for onshore operations. For offshore and higher-rate wells around the world, the use of ESPs and gas lift is much higher.

Major Considerations for Sucker-Rod Pumping Systems. Sucker-rod pumping systems should be considered for new, lower volume stripper wells because they have proved to be cost effective over time. In addition, operating personnel usually are familiar with these mechanically simple systems and can operate them efficiently. Inexperienced personnel also can operate rod pumps more effectively than other types of artificial lift. Sucker-rod pumping systems can operate efficiently over a wide range of production rates and depths. Most of these systems have a high salvage value.

Sucker-rod systems should be considered for lifting moderate volumes from shallow depths and small volumes from intermediate depths. It is possible to lift up to 1,000 B/D from approximately 7,000 ft and 200 bbl from approximately 14,000 ft. Special rods may be required, and lower rates may result depending on conditions.

Most of the sucker-rod pumping system parts are manufactured to meet existing standards, which have been established by the American Petroleum Institute (API). Numerous manufacturers can supply each part, and all interconnecting parts are compatible. Many components are manufactured and used that are not API certified, such as large-diameter downhole pumps extending to more than 6 in. in diameter.

The sucker-rod string is the length of the rods from the surface to the downhole pump, and it continuously is subjected to cyclic load fatigue typical of sucker-rod pump systems. The system must be protected against corrosion, as much as any other artificial lift system, because corrosion introduces stress concentrations that can lead to early failures. Frequent rod failures must be avoided for an economical system operation.

Sucker-rod pumping systems often are most incompatible with deviated (doglegged) wells, even with the use of rod protectors and rod and/or tubing rotators. However, deviated wells with smooth profiles and low dogleg severity may allow satisfactory sucker-rod pumping, even if the angle at the bottom of the well is large (approximately 30 to 40°, up to 80°). Some high-angle hole systems use advanced methods of protecting the tubing and rod string with rod protectors and "roller-rod protectors," while other installations with high oil cuts, smooth profiles, and lower angles of deviation use only a few of these devices. Plastic-lined tubing has proven to be effective in reducing rod/tubing wear.

The ability of sucker-rod pumping systems to produce sand-laden fluids is limited, although there are several special filters and sand-exclusion devices available. Some pumps are designed either to exclude the sand or continue to operate as the sand travels through the barrel-plunger clearance. Special metallurgies are used for sand wear.

Paraffin and scale can interfere with the efficient operation of sucker-rod pumping systems. Special wiper systems on the rods and hot water/oil treatments are used to combat paraffin. Hard scales can cause early failures.

Free gas entering the downhole pump reduces hydrocarbon production and causes other problems. This problem and various recommended solutions are detailed in the chapter on sucker-rod pumping in this section of the *Handbook*.

One of the disadvantages of a beam-pumping system is that the polished-rod stuffing box, in which a polished rod with the rods hung below enters the well at the surface through a rubber packing element, can leak. This can be minimized with special pollution-free stuffing boxes that collect any leakage. Good operations, with such practices as "don't over tighten" and "ensure unit alignment with standard boxes," with standard boxes are also important.

Continuous production with the system attempting to produce more than the reservoir will produce leads to incomplete pump filling of the pump, fluid pound, mechanical damage, and low energy efficiency. Many systems are designed to produce 120 to 150% more than the reser-

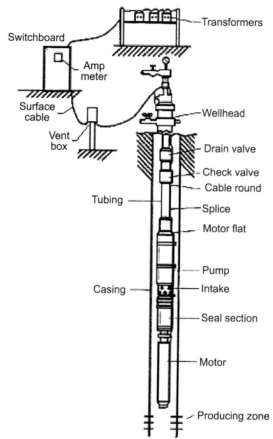

Fig. 10.4—Schematic of typical ESP system. [Courtesy of Schlumberger (REDA).]

voir will produce, but when the well is pumped down, a pumpoff controller will stop pumping temporarily to allow fluid entry into the casing-tubing annulus over the pump.

In general, sucker-rod pumping is the method of artificial lift that should be used if the system can be designed without overloading the prime mover, gearbox, unit structure, and the calculated fatigue loading limits of the rods. This system should be considered very carefully in the selection process and, in many cases, should be the artificial lift system of choice.

10.5.2 Electrical Submersible Pumping. As an example area in which ESPs are applied extensively, THUMS Long Beach Co. was formed in April 1965 to drill, develop, and produce the 6,479-acre Long Beach unit in Wilmington field, Long Beach, California. It was necessary to choose the best method to lift fluids from the approximately 1,100 deviated wells over a 35-year contract period from four man-made offshore islands and one onshore site. ESPs have been the primary system in this environment for the contract period.

Fig. 10.4 shows a schematic of a typical ESP system. The chapter on ESP in this section of the handbook contains more complete details of this mechanical-electrical-hydraulic system.

Major ESP Advantages. ESPs provide a number of advantages.
• Adaptable to highly deviated wells; up to horizontal, but must be set in straight section.
• Adaptable to required subsurface wellheads 6 ft apart for maximum surface-location density.
• Permit use of minimum space for subsurface controls and associated production facilities.

• Quiet, safe, and sanitary for acceptable operations in an offshore and environmentally conscious area.

• Generally considered a high-volume pump.

• Provides for increased volumes and water cuts brought on by pressure maintenance and secondary recovery operations.

• Permits placing wells on production even while drilling and working over wells in immediate vicinity.

Major ESP Disadvantages. ESPs have some disadvantages that must be considered.

• Will tolerate only minimal percentages of solids (sand) production, although special pumps with hardened surfaces and bearings exist to minimize wear and increase run life.

• Costly pulling operations and lost production occur when correcting downhole failures, especially in an offshore environment.

• Below approximately 400 B/D, power efficiency drops sharply; ESPs are not particularly adaptable to rates below 150 B/D.

• Need relatively large (greater than 4½-in. outside diameter) casing size for the moderate- to high-production-rate equipment.

Long life of ESP equipment is required to keep production economical. Improvements and recommendations based on experience are in the chapter on ESP in this section of the *Handbook* and in Ref. 4.

10.5.3 The PCP and the Electrical Submersible Progressive Cavity Pump. **Fig. 10.5** shows a schematic of a PCP with a rotating metal rotor and a flexible rubber-molded stator. The stator forms a cavity that moves up as the rotor turns. The pump is well suited for handling solids and viscous fluids because the solids that move through the pump may deflect the rubber stator but do not abrade, wear, or chemically deteriorate the stator or rotor to any appreciable degree. Most PCPs are powered by rotating rods driven from the surface with a hydraulic or electric motor. The system shown in Fig. 10.5 has a pump small enough that the entire pump can be inserted with rods.

Introduced in 1936, the PCP is of simple design and rugged construction. Its low (300 to 600 rev/min) operating speeds enable the pump to maintain long periods of downhole operation if not subjected to chemical attack or excessive wear or it is not installed at depths greater than approximately 4,000 to 6,000 ft. The pump has only one moving part downhole with no valves to stick, clog, or wear out. The pump will not gas lock, can easily handle sandy and abrasive formation fluids, and is not normally plugged by paraffin, gypsum, or scale.

With this system, the rotating rods wear and also wear the tubulars. The rotating rods "wind" up on start and "unwind" on the shutdown. Rotating rods must be sealed at the surface, and many installations have oil leaks at the surface. These problems must be addressed during system design.

To alleviate problems inherent with the conventional rotating-rod PCP systems, the ESPCP system is available. While the number installed is still small, this is not a new system. It has been run in Russia for a number of years and also was available from an ESP vendor a number of years ago. The newer ESPCP system (**Fig. 10.6**) has some advantages over the rotating sucker-rod systems.

There is a problem of rotating the eccentric rotor with the motor shaft because of possible vibration; therefore, a flexible connection is used. There is a seal section, as in an ESP assembly, to protect the underlying motor from wellbore fluids and to accommodate an internal thrust bearing. Because the PCP usually rotates at approximately 300 to 600 rev/min, and the ESP motor rotates at approximately 3,500 rev/min under load, there must be a way of reducing speed before the shaft connects to the PCP. Methods available from various manufacturers include the use of a gearbox to reduce the motor to acceptable speeds (less than approximately 500 rev/min). Another method is to use higher pole motors with lower synchronous speeds to

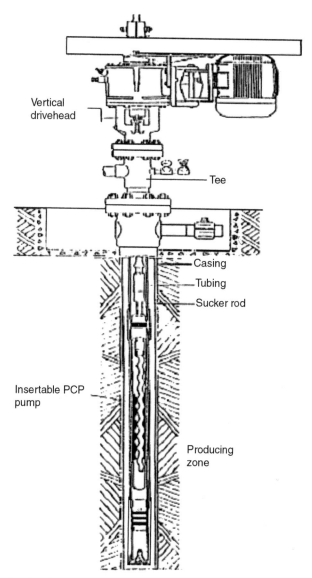

Fig. 10.5—Schematic of an insertable PCP. (Courtesy of Weatherford and Geriamia-Brazil.)

allow the PCP to turn at operational speeds in combination with a gearbox, but this system produces less output-starting torque.

Major PCP Advantages. PCPs have the following major advantages.

• The pumping system can be run into deviated and horizontal wells.

• The pump handles solids well, but the coating of the rotor will erode over time.

• The pump handles highly viscous fluids in a production well with a looser rotor/stator fit.

• Several of the components are off-the-shelf ESP components for the ESPCP.

• The production rates can be varied with the use of a variable-speed controller with an inexpensive downhole-pressure sensor.

• For appropriate conditions, the PCP can operate with a power efficiency exceeding other artificial lift methods.

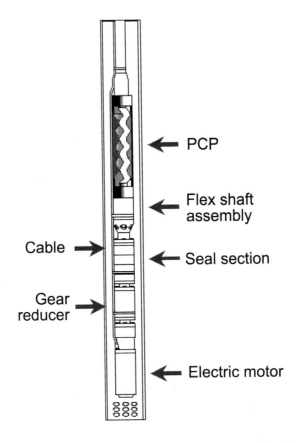

Fig. 10.6—Schematic of ESPCP system. (Courtesy of Centrilift.)

• The PCP can be set in a straight section of a deviated well.

• Use of an ESPCP eliminates the rotating rods and eliminates problems with rods rotating in a deviated well.

Major PCP Disadvantages. PCPs have the following disadvantages.

• The stator material will have an upper temperature limit and may be subject to H_2S and other chemical deterioration.

• Frequent stops and starts of the PCP pumps often can cause several operating problems.

• Although it will not gas lock, best efficiency occurs when gas is scparated.

• If the unit pumps off the well or gas flows continuously though the pump for a short period, the stator will likely be permanently damaged from overheating caused by gas compression.

• The gearbox in an ESPCP is another source of failure if wellbore fluids or solids leak inside it or if excessive wear occurs.

Progressive Cavity Pump Summary. For a low-pressure well with solids and/or heavy oil at a depth of less than approximately 6,000 ft and if the well temperature is not high (75 to 150°F typical, approximately 250°F or higher maximum), a PCP should be evaluated. Even if problems do not exist, a PCP might be a good choice to take advantage of its good power efficiency. If the application is offshore, or if pulling the well is very expensive and the well is most likely deviated, ESPCP should be considered so that rod/tubing wear is not excessive.

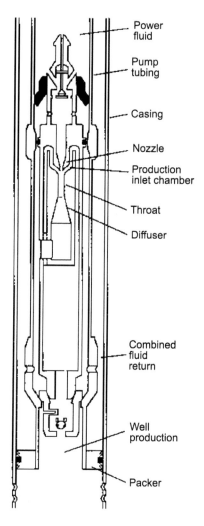

Power fluid

Pump tubing

Casing

Nozzle

Production inlet chamber

Throat

Diffuser

Combined fluid return

Well production

Packer

Fig. 10.7—Schematic of a hydraulic jet pump. (Courtesy of Weatherford.)

There is an ESPCP option that allows wire lining out a failed pump from the well while leaving the seal section, gearbox, motor, and cable installed for continued use.

10.5.4 Hydraulic Pumping. There are two primary kinds of hydraulic pumps: jet pumps and reciprocating positive-displacement pumps. **Fig. 10.7** shows a jet pump arrangement. For jet pumps, high-pressure power fluid is directed down the tubing to the nozzle where the pressure energy is converted to velocity head (kinetic energy). The high-velocity, low-pressure power fluid entrains the production fluid in the throat of the pump. A diffuser then reduces the velocity and increases the pressure to allow the commingled fluids to flow to the surface.

The positive-displacement pump consists of a reciprocating hydraulic engine directly coupled to a pump piston or pump plunger. **Fig. 10.8** shows a reciprocating hydraulically powered pump. Power fluid (oil or water) is directed down the tubing string to operate the engine. The pump piston or plunger draws fluid from the wellbore through a standing valve. Exhausted power fluid and production can be returned up a separate tubing string or up the casing.

Down stroke   Up stroke

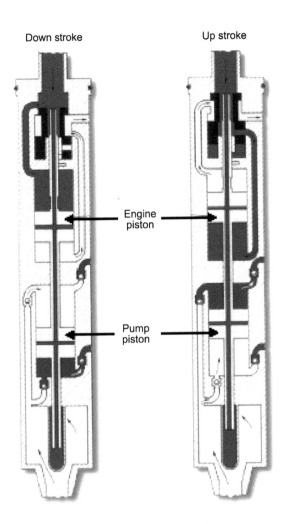

Engine
piston

Pump
piston

Fig. 10.8—Schematic of a reciprocating hydraulic pump. (Courtesy of Weatherford.)

When the power fluid and the production are combined, the system is an open power-fluid system. For a vented open power-fluid system, the production and power fluid typically are returned separately in a parallel tubing string with gas normally vented through the casing annulus to the surface. A nonvented casing installation requires a pump to handle the gas and production. The power fluid plus all reservoir fluids are produced up the annulus. Both completion types are used with positive-displacement pumps and with jet pumps. In fact, many bottomhole assemblies (BHAs) can accommodate jet or positive-displacement pumps interchangeably.

In a closed power-fluid arrangement, the power fluid is returned to the surface separately from produced fluids, requiring a separate tubing string. The use of a closed power fluid system is limited as a result of the added initial costs and clearance problems in small casing. Because the jet pump must commingle the power fluid and production, it cannot operate as a closed power-fluid pump.

The most outstanding feature of hydraulic pumps is the "free pump" system. **Fig. 10.9** shows a schematic of a free hydraulic pump. Fig. 10.9a shows a standing valve at the bottom

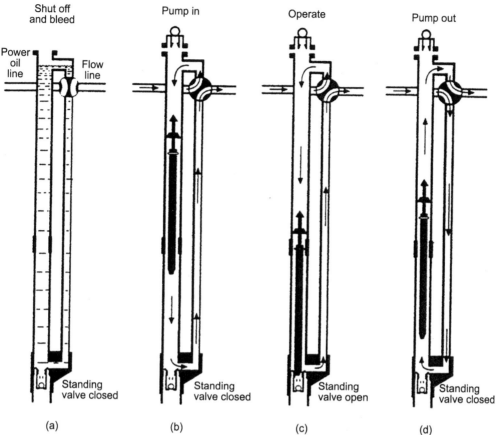

Fig. 10.9—Schematic showing the operation of a "free" hydraulic pump installation. (Courtesy of Weatherford.)

TABLE 10.1—CAPACITIES OF RECIPROCATING HYDRAULIC PUMPS		
Tubing Size (in.)	Working Fluid Level (ft)	Maximum Pump Displacement (B/D)
2⅜	6,000 to 17,000	1,311 to 381
2⅞	6,000 to 17,000	2,500 to 744
3½	6,000 to 15,000	4,015 to 1,357

of the tubing, and the tubing is filled with fluid. In Fig. 10.9b, a pump has been inserted in the tubing and power fluid is being circulated to the bottom. In Fig. 10.9c, the pump is on bottom and pumping. When the pump is in need of repair, fluid is circulated to the surface as shown in Fig. 10.9d. The positive-displacement pump, the jet pump, and the closed power-fluid system previously shown are all free pumps.

Surface facilities require a power-fluid storage and cleaning system and a pump. The most common cleaning systems are settling tanks located at the tank battery. Cyclone desanders sometimes are used in addition to settling tanks. In the last 40 years, wellsite power plants, which

TABLE 10.2—CAPACITIES OF JET-FREE PUMPS	
Tubing Size (in.)	Production (B/D)
2⅜	3,000
2⅞	6,000
3½	10,000

are separators located at the well with cyclone desanders to remove solids from the power fluid, have become popular.

Surface pumps are most commonly triplex plunger pumps. Other types are quintiplex plunger pumps, multistage centrifugal pumps, and "canned" ESPs. The surface pressure required is usually in the 1,500 to 4,000 psi range. It is important to specify 100% continuous duty for the power-fluid pump at the required rate and pressure. Low volume (< 10,000 B/D), high-pressure installations (> 2,500 psi) typically use plunger-type pumps.

Table 10.1 shows approximate maximum capacities and lift capabilities for positive-displacement pumps. In some cases, two pumps have been installed in one tubing string. Seal collars in the BHA hydraulically connect the pumps in parallel; thus, maximum displacement values are doubled.

A relationship between capacity and lift is not practical for jet pumps because of the many variables and the complex relationships among them. To keep fluid velocities below 50 ft/sec in suction and discharge passages, the maximum production rates vs. tubing size for jet-free pumps are approximated in **Table 10.2**.

Fixed-type jet pumps (those too large to fit inside the tubing) have been made with capacities of 17,000 B/D, and even larger pumps are possible. Maximum lifting depth for jet pumps is approximately 8,000 to 9,000 ft if surface power-fluid pressure is limited to approximately 3,500 psi for water power fluid and approximately 4,000 psi with oil power fluid, considering the operating life of a triplex pump. The maximum capacities can be obtained only to approximately 5,000 to 6,000 ft. These jet pump figures are only guidelines. The maximum capacities listed are for high-volume jet pumps that require BHAs that are incapable of accommodating piston pumps.

Hydraulic Pumping Advantages. Hydraulic pumping has the following advantages.

• Being able to circulate the pump in and out of the well is the most obvious and significant feature of hydraulic pumps. It is especially attractive on offshore platforms, remote locations, and populated and agricultural areas.

• Positive-displacement pumps are capable of pumping depths to 17,000 ft and deeper. Working fluid levels for jet pumps are limited to approximately 9,000 ft.

• By changing the power-fluid rate to the pumps, production can be varied from 10 to 100% of pump capacity. The optimum speed range is 20 to 85% of rated speed. Operating life will be significantly reduced if the pump is operated above the maximum-rated speed.

• Deviated wells typically present few problems to hydraulic free pumps. Jet pumps can even be used in through flowline installations.

• Jet pumps, with hardened nozzle throats, can produce sand and other solids.

• There are methods in which positive-displacement pumps can handle viscous oils very well. The power fluid can be heated, or it can have diluents added to further aid lifting the oil to the surface.

• Corrosion inhibitors can be injected into the power fluid for corrosion control. Added fresh water can solve salt-buildup problems.

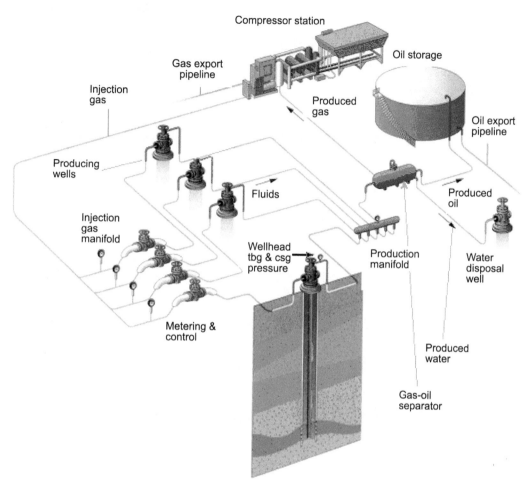

Fig. 10.10—Schematic of a gas lift system. (Courtesy of Schlumberger.)

Hydraulic Pumping Disadvantages. Hydraulic pumping has the following disadvantages.

• Removing solids from the power fluid is very important for positive-displacement pumps. Solids in the power fluid also affect surface-plunger pumps. Jet pumps, on the other hand, are very tolerant of poor power-fluid quality.

• Positive-displacement pumps, on average, have a shorter time between repairs than jet, sucker rod, and ESPs. Mostly, this is a function of the quality of power fluid but, on average, the positive-displacement pumps are operating from greater depths and at higher strokes per minute than for a beam pump system. Jet pumps, on the other hand, have a very long pump life between repairs without solids or if not subjected to cavitation. Jet pumps typically have lower efficiency and higher energy costs.

• Positive-displacement pumps can pump from a low BHP (< 100 psi) in the absence of gas interference and other problems. Jet pumps cannot pump from such low intake pressures, especially when less than the cavitation pressure. Jet pumps require approximately 1,000 psi BHP when set at 10,000 ft and approximately 500 psi when set at 5,000 ft.

• Positive-displacement pumps generally require more maintenance than jet pumps and other types of artificial lift because pump speed must be monitored daily and not allowed to

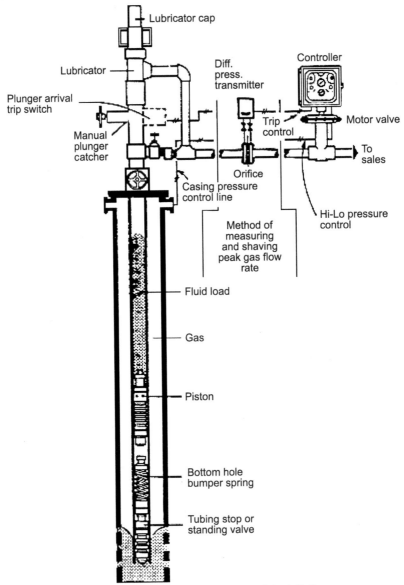

Fig. 10.11—Schematic of a plunger lift installation.

become excessive. Power-fluid-cleaning systems require frequent checking to keep them operating at their optimum effectiveness. Also, well testing is more difficult.

When should a jet be used, and when should a positive-displacement hydraulic pump be used? One possible answer is to use jet pumps if the flowing (pumping) BHP is large enough because the pressure drawdown capability for the jet system is inferior to that of the reciprocating pump. Other factors enter in as well as those mentioned previously. Jet pumps typically have low pump-repair costs but have high energy-consumption expenses because of low pump efficiencies, usually less than 35%. However, for both systems, a higher pump-failure rate can be very acceptable if a free system is present and the pumps can be retrieved quickly (less than 30 minutes typically) without pulling the tubing.

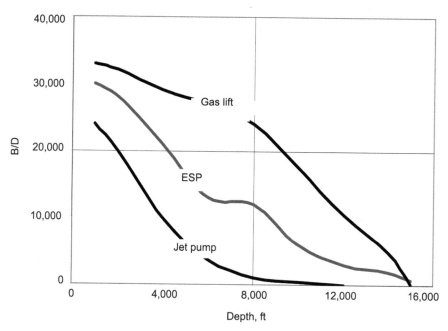

Fig. 10.12—Approximate depth-rate capabilities of artificial lift systems that can deliver high rates (after Weatherford[8]).

10.5.5 Gas Lift. Gas lift is used extensively around the world and dominates production in the U.S. Gulf Coast. Most of these wells are on continuous-flow gas lift. This section addresses the following issues: Why choose gas lift?; Where should continuous flow be used?; and When should intermittent lift be selected?

The principle of gas lift is that gas injected into the tubing reduces the density of the fluids in the tubing, and the bubbles have a "scrubbing" action on the liquids. Both factors act to lower the flowing BHP at the bottom of the tubing. Care must be exercised not to inject excess gas, or friction will begin to negate the desirable effects of injecting gas into the tubing.

Continuous-Flow Gas Lift. **Fig. 10.10** shows a schematic of a gas-lift system. Continuous-flow gas lift is recommended for high-volume and high-static BHP wells in which major pumping problems could occur with other artificial lift methods. It is an excellent application for offshore formations that have a strong waterdrive, or in waterflood reservoirs with good PIs and high gas/oil ratios (GORs). When high-pressure gas is available without compression or when gas cost is low, gas lift is especially attractive. Continuous-flow gas lift supplements the produced gas with additional gas injection to lower the intake pressure to the tubing, resulting in lower formation pressure as well.

A reliable, adequate supply of good quality high-pressure lift gas is mandatory. This supply is necessary throughout the producing life of the well if gas lift is to be maintained effectively. In many fields, the produced gas declines as water cut increases, requiring some outside source of gas. The gas-lift pressure typically is fixed during the initial phase of the facility design. Ideally, the system should be designed to lift from just above the producing zone. Wells may produce erratically or not at all when the lift supply stops or pressure fluctuates radically. Poor gas quality will impair or even stop production if it contains corrosives or excessive liquids that can cut valves or fill low spots in delivery lines. The basic requirement for gas must be met, or gas lift is not a viable lift method.

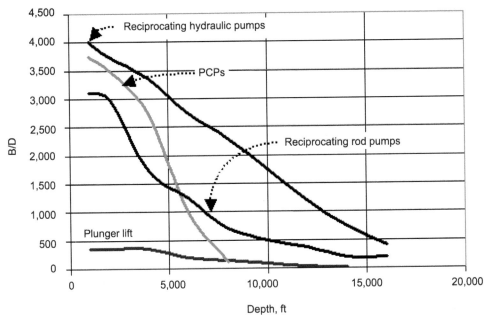

Fig. 10.13—Approximate depth-rate capabilities of lower rate artificial lift systems (after Weatherford[8]).

Continuous-flow gas lift imposes a relatively high backpressure on the reservoir compared with pumping methods; therefore, production rates are reduced. Also, power efficiency is not good compared with some artificial lift methods, and the poor efficiency significantly increases both initial capital cost for compression and operating energy costs.

Gas Lift Advantages. Gas lift has the following advantages.

• Gas lift is the best artificial lift method for handling sand or solid materials. Many wells produce some sand even if sand control is installed. The produced sand causes few mechanical problem in the gas-lift system; whereas, only a little sand plays havoc with other pumping methods, except the PCP type of pump.

• Deviated or crooked holes can be lifted easily with gas lift. This is especially important for offshore platform wells that are usually drilled directionally.

• Gas lift permits the concurrent use of wireline equipment, and such downhole equipment is easily and economically serviced. This feature allows for routine repairs through the tubing.

• The normal gas-lift design leaves the tubing fully open. This permits the use of BHP surveys, sand sounding and bailing, production logging, cutting, paraffin, etc.

• High-formation GORs are very helpful for gas-lift systems but hinder other artificial lift systems. Produced gas means less injection gas is required; whereas, in all other pumping methods, pumped gas reduces volumetric pumping efficiency drastically.

• Gas lift is flexible. A wide range of volumes and lift depths can be achieved with essentially the same well equipment. In some cases, switching to annular flow also can be easily accomplished to handle exceedingly high volumes.

• A central gas-lift system easily can be used to service many wells or operate an entire field. Centralization usually lowers total capital cost and permits easier well control and testing.

• A gas-lift system is not obtrusive; it has a low profile. The surface well equipment is the same as for flowing wells except for injection-gas metering. The low profile is usually an advantage in urban environments.

TABLE 10.3—RELATIVE ADVANTAGES OF ARTIFICIAL LIFT SYSTEMS[10]

Rod Pumping	Hydraulic Piston Pumping	Electric Submersible Pumping	Gas Lift
Relatively simple system design.	Not so depth limited—can lift large volumes from great depths.	Can lift extremely high volumes; 20,000 B/D (19 078 m³/d) in shallow wells with large casing.	Can handle large volume of solids with minor problems.
Units easily changed to other wells with minimum cost.	500 B/D (79.49 m³/d) from 15,000 ft (4572 m); have been installed to 18,000 ft (5486.4 m).	Currently lifting ± 120,000 B/D (19 068 m³/d) from water supply wells in Middle East with 600 hp (448 kW) units; 720 hp (537 kW) available; 1,000 hp (746 kW) under development.	Handles large volume in high-PI wells (continuous lift); 50,000 B/D (7949.37 m³/d).
Efficient, simple, and easy for field people to operate.	Crooked holes present minimal problems.		Fairly flexible—convertible from continuous to intermittent to chamber or plunger lift as well declines.
Applicable to slimholes and multiple completions.	Unobtrusive in urban locations.	Unobtrusive in urban locations.	Unobtrusive in urban locations.
Can pump a well down to very low pressure (depth and rate dependent).	Power source can be remotely located.	Simple to operate.	Power source can be remotely located.
System usually is naturally vented for gas separation and fluid level soundings.	Analyzable.	Easy to install downhole-pressure sensor for telemetering pressure to surface by cable.	Easy to obtain downhole pressures and gradients.
Flexible—can match displacement rate to well capability as well declines.	Flexible—usually can match displacement to well's capability as well declines.	Crooked holes present no problem.	Lifting gassy wells is no problem.
Analyzable.	Can use gas or electricity as power source.	Applicable offshore.	Sometimes serviceable with wireline unit.
Can lift high-temperature and viscous oils.	Downhole pumps can be circulated out in free systems.	Corrosion and scale treatment easy to perform.	Crooked holes present no problem.
Can use gas or electricity as power source.	Can pump a well down to fairly low pressure.	Availability of different sizes.	Corrosion is not usually as adverse.
Corrosion and scale treatments easy to perform.	Applicable to multiple completions.	Lifting cost for high volumes generally very low.	Applicable offshore.
Applicable to pumpoff control if electrified.	Applicable offshore.		
Availability of different sizes.	Closed system will combat corrosion.		
Hollow sucker rods are available for slimhole completions and ease of inhibitor treatment.	Easy to pump in cycles by time clock.		
Has pumps with double valving that pump on both upstroke and downstroke.	Adjustable gear box for triplex offers more flexibility.		
	Mixing power fluid with waxy or viscous crudes can reduce viscosity.		

• Well subsurface equipment is relatively inexpensive. Repair and maintenance expenses of subsurface equipment normally are low. The equipment is easily pulled and repaired or replaced. Also, major well workovers occur infrequently.

• Installation of gas lift is compatible with subsurface safety valves and other surface equipment. The use of a surface-controlled subsurface safety valve with a ¼-in. control line allows easy shut in of the well.

• Gas lift can still perform fairly well even when only poor data are available when the design is made. This is fortunate because the spacing design usually must be made before the well is completed and tested.

TABLE 10.3—RELATIVE ADVANTAGES OF ARTIFICIAL LIFT SYSTEMS[10] (continued)

Hydraulic Jet Pump	Plunger Lift	Progressive Cavity Pumps
Retrievable without pulling tubing.	Retrievable without pulling tubing.	Some types are retrievable with rods.
Has no moving parts.	Very inexpensive installation.	Moderate cost.
No problems in deviated or crooked holes.	Automatically keeps tubing clean of paraffin and scale.	Low profile.
Unobtrusive in urban locations.	Applicable for high GOR wells.	Can use downhole electric motors that handle sand and viscous fluid well.
Applicable offshore.	Can be used with intermittent gas lift.	High electrical efficiency.
Can use water as a power source.	Can be used to unload liquid from gas wells.	
Power fluid does not have to be as clean as for hydraulic piston pumping.		
Corrosion scale emulsion treatment easy to perform.		
Power source can be remotely located and can handle high volumes to 30,000 B/D (4769.62 m³/d).		

Gas Lift Disadvantages. Gas lift has the following disadvantages.

• Relatively high backpressure may seriously restrict production in continuous gas lift. This problem becomes more significant with increasing depths and declining static BHPs. Thus, a 10,000-ft well with a static BHP of 1,000 psi and a PI of 1.0 bpd/psi would be difficult to lift with the standard continuous-flow gas-lift system. However, there are special schemes available for such wells.

• Gas lift is relatively inefficient, often resulting in large capital investments and high energy-operating costs. Compressors are relatively expensive and often require long delivery times. The compressor takes up space and weight when used on offshore platforms. Also, the cost of the distribution systems onshore may be significant. Increased gas use also may increase the size of necessary flowline and separators.

• Adequate gas supply is needed throughout life of project. If the field runs out of gas, or if gas becomes too expensive, it may be necessary to switch to another artificial lift method. In addition, there must be enough gas for easy startups.

• Operation and maintenance of compressors can be expensive. Skilled operators and good compressor mechanics are required for reliable operation. Compressor downtime should be minimal (< 3%).

• There is increased difficulty when lifting low gravity (less than 15°API) crude because of greater friction, gas fingering, and liquid fallback. The cooling effect of gas expansion may further aggravate this problem. Also, the cooling effect will compound any paraffin problem.

• Good data are required to make a good design. If not available, operations may have to continue with an inefficient design that does not produce the well to capacity.

Potential gas-lift operational problems that must be resolved include freezing and hydrate problems in injection gas lines, corrosive injection gas, severe paraffin problems, fluctuating suction and discharge pressures, and wireline problems. Other problems that must be resolved are changing well conditions, especially declines in BHP and PI; deep high-volume lift; and valve interference (multipointing). Additionally, dual gas lift is difficult to operate and frequently results in poor lift efficiency. Finally, emulsions forming in the tubing, which may be accelerated when gas enters opposing the tubing flow, also must be resolved.

TABLE 10.4—RELATIVE DISADVANTAGES OF ARTIFICIAL LIFT SYSTEMS[10]

Rod Pumping	Hydraulic Piston Pumping	Electric Submersible Pumping	Gas Lift
Crooked holes present a friction problem.	Power oil systems are a fire hazard.	Not applicable to multiple compilations.	Lift gas is not always available.
High solids production is troublesome.	Large oil inventory required in power oil system, which detracts from profitability.	Only applicable with electric power.	Not efficient in lifting small fields or one-well leases.
Gassy wells usually lower volumetric efficiency.	High solids production is troublesome.	High voltages (1,000 V) are necessary.	Difficult to lift emulsions and viscous crudes.
Is depth limited, primarily because of rod capability.	Operating costs are sometimes higher.	Impractical in shallow, low-volume wells.	Gas freezing and hydrate problems.
Obtrusive in urban locations.	Usually susceptible to gas interference; usually not vented.	Expensive to change equipment to match declining well capability.	Problems with dirty surface lines.
Heavy and bulky in offshore operations.	Vented installations are more expensive because of extra tubing required.	Cable causes problems in handling tubulars.	Some difficulty in analyzing properly without engineering supervision.
Susceptible to paraffin problems.	Treating for scale below packer is difficult.	Cables deteriorate in high temperatures.	Cannot effectively produce deep wells to abandonment.
Tubing cannot be internally coated for corrosion.	Not easy for field personnel to troubleshoot.	System is depth limited, 10,000 ft (3048.0 m), because of cable cost and inability to install enough power downhole (depends on casing size).	Requires makeup gas in rotative systems.
H^2S limits depth at which a large-volume pump can be set.	Difficult to obtain valid well tests in low-volume wells.	Gas and solids production are troublesome.	Casing must withstand lift pressure.
Limitation of downhole pump design in small diameter casing.	Requires two strings of tubing for some installations.	Not easily analyzable unless good engineering know-how.	Safety problem with high-pressure gas.
	Problems in treating power water, where used.	Lack of production rate flexibility.	
	Safety problem for high surface pressure power oil.	Casing size limitation.	
	Loss of power oil in surface equipment failure.	Cannot be set below fluid entry without a shroud to route fluid by the motor. Shroud also allows corrosion inhibitor to protect outside of motor.	
		More downtime when problems are encountered because of the entire unit being downhole.	

10.5.6 Intermittent Gas Lift. The intermittent gas-lift method typically is used on wells that produce low volumes of fluid (approximately < 150 to 200 B/D), although some systems produce up to 500 B/D. Wells in which intermittent lift is recommended normally have the characteristics of high PI and low BHP or low PI with high BHP. Intermittent gas lift can be used to replace continuous gas lift on wells that have depleted to low rates or used when gas wells have depleted to low rates and are hindered by liquid loading.

If an adequate, good quality, low-cost gas supply is available for lifting fluids from a relatively shallow, high GOR, low PI, or low BHP well with a bad dogleg that produces some

Hydraulic Jet Pump	Plunger Lift	Progressive Cavity Pumps
Relatively inefficient lift method.	May not take well to depletion; therefore, eventually requires another lift method.	Elastomers in stator swell in some well fluids.
Requires at least 20% submergence to approach best lift efficiency.	Good for low-rate, normally less than 200 B/D (31.8 m/d) wells only.	Pumps off control is difficult.
Design of system is more complex.	Requires more engineering supervision to adjust properly.	Lose efficiency with depth.
Pump may cavitate under certain conditions.	Danger exists in plunger reaching too high a velocity and causing surface damage.	Rotating rods wear tubing; windup and afterspin of rods increase with depth.
Very sensitive to change in backpressure.	Communication between tubing and casing required for good operation unless used in conjunction with gas lift.	
The producing of free gas through the pump causes reduction in ability to handle liquids.		
Power oil systems are fire hazards.		
High surface power-fluid pressures are required.		

TABLE 10.4—RELATIVE DISADVANTAGES OF ARTIFICIAL LIFT SYSTEMS[10] (continued)

sand, then intermittent gas lift would be an excellent choice. Intermittent gas lift has many of the same advantages/disadvantages as continuous-flow gas lift, and the major factors to be considered are similar. Only the differences are highlighted in the following discussion. If plunger lift can be used instead of only intermittent lift, the efficiency will be higher. This difference could determine the success or failure of the system.

Intermittent Gas Lift Advantages. Intermittent gas lift has the following advantages.

• Intermittent gas lift typically has a significantly lower producing BHP than continuous gas-lift methods.

• It has the ability to handle low volumes of fluid with relatively low production BHPs.

Intermittent Gas Lift Disadvantages. Intermittent gas lift has the following disadvantages.

• Intermittent gas lift is limited to low volume wells. For example, an 8,000-ft well with 2-in. nominal tubing can seldom be produced at rates of more than 200 B/D with an average producing pressure much below 250 psig.

• The average producing pressure of a conventional intermittent lift system is still relatively high when compared with rod pumping; however, the producing BHP can be reduced by use of chambers. Chambers are particularly suited to high PI, low BHP wells.

• The power efficiency is low. Typically, more gas is used per barrel of produced fluid than with constant flow gas lift. Also, the fallback of a fraction of liquid slugs being lifted by gas flow increases with depth and water cut, making the lift system even more inefficient. However, liquid fallback can be reduced by the use of plungers, where applicable.

• Fluctuations in rate and BHP can be detrimental to wells with sand control. The produced sand may plug the tubing or standing valve. Also, pressure fluctuations in surface facilities cause gas- and fluid-handling problems.

• Intermittent gas lift typically requires frequent adjustments. The lease operator must alter the injection rate and time period routinely to increase the production and keep the lift gas requirement relatively low.

Gas lift has numerous strengths that can make it the best choice of artificial lift; however, there are limitations and potential problems. One has a choice of the use of either continuous flow for high volume wells or intermittent for low volume wells; there is little difficulty in

TABLE 10.5—ARTIFICIAL LIFT: DESIGN CONSIDERATIONS AND OVERALL COMPARISONS[11]

Lift Systems	Capital Cost Details	Downhole Equipment	Operating Efficiency (hydraulic horsepower/ input horsepower)
Rod Pump	Low to moderate. Increases as depth and unit size increases.	Reasonably good rod design and operating practices needed. Data bank of failures beneficial. Good selection, operating, and repair practices needed for rods and pumps.	Excellent total system efficiency. With full pump fillage, efficiency typically 45 to 60%.
PCP	Low, but increases as depth and pump rate increases.	Good design and operating practices needed. May have problems with selection of appropriate stator elastomer.	Excellent. May exceed rod pumps for ideal cases. Typical system efficiency of 40 to 70%.
ESP	Relatively low capital cost if electric power available. Costs increase as horsepower increases.	Requires proper cable in addition to motor, pumps, seals, etc. Good design plus good operating practices essential.	Good for high-rate wells but decreases significantly for <1,000 BFPD. Typically, total system efficiency is approximately 50% for high-rate well but for <1,000 BPD, efficiency typically is <40%. Efficiency can be as high as 60% for large ID equipment.
Hydraulic Reciprocating	Varies, but often competitive with rod pumps. Multiple well, central systems reduces cost per well but are more complicated.	Proper pump sizing and operating practices are essential. Requires two conductors (power fluid and returns). Single tubing string on packer and casing annulus most common. Clean power fluid is essential.	Fair to good. Usually not as good as rod pumping because of GLR, friction, and pump wear. Typical efficiencies run in the 30 to 40% range with GLR >100; may be 40 to 50% if lower GLR.
Hydraulic Jet	Competitive with rod pump. Relatively low cost over 1,500 BFPD. Cost increases with higher horsepower.	Requires computer design programs for sizing. Tolerant of moderate solids in power fluid. No moving parts in pump; long service life; simple repair procedures to run and retrieve pump downhole.	Fair to poor. Maximum efficiency for ideal case is 30%. Heavily influenced by power fluid plus production gradient. Typical operating efficiencies of 10 to 30%.
Gas Lift	Well gas lift equipment cost low but compression cost may be high. Central compression system reduces overall cost per well.	Good valve design and spacing essential. Moderate cost for well equipment (valve and mandrels). Typically less than 10 valves needed. Choice of wireline retrievable or conventional valves.	Fair. Increases for wells that require small injection GLRs. Low for wells requiring high GLRs. Typically 20%, but range from 5 to 30%.
Intermittent Gas Lift	Same as continuous-flow gas lift.	Unload to bottom with gas lift valves. Consider chamber for high PI and low BHP wells.	Poor. Normally requires a high injection gas volume/barrel fluid. Typical lift efficiency is 5 to 10%. Improved with plungers.
Plunger	Very low if no compressor required.	Operating practices have to be tailored to each well for optimization. Some problem with sticking plungers.	Excellent for flowing wells. No input energy required because it uses the energy of the well.

switching from one to the other. In addition, gas lift can be used to kick off wells, unload water from gas wells, or backflow injection wells. Gas lift deserves serious consideration as a

TABLE 10.5—ARTIFICIAL LIFT: DESIGN CONSIDERATIONS AND OVERALL COMPARISONS[11] (continued)

Lift Systems	Flexibility of Systems	Miscellaneous Problems	Operating Costs
Rod Pump	Excellent. Can alter strokes per minute, stroke length, plunger size, and run time to control production rate.	Stuffing box leakage may be messy and a potential hazard. (Antipollution stuffing boxes are available.)	Low for shallow to medium depth (<7,000 ft) land location with low production (<400 BFPD).
PCP	Fair. Can alter strokes per minute. Hydraulic unit provides additional flexibility but added costs.	May have limited service in some areas. Because it is a newer method, field knowledge and experience limited.	Potentially low, but short run life on stator or rotor frequently reported.
ESP	Poor for fixed speed. Requires careful design. Variable speed drive provides better flexibility.	Requires a highly reliable electric power system. System very sensitive to changes downhole or in fluid properties.	Varies. If high horsepower, high energy costs. High pulling costs result from short run life especially in offshore operation. Repair costs often high.
Hydraulic Reciprocating	Good to excellent. Can vary power-fluid rate; thus, strokes per minute of downhole pump. Numerous pump sizes and pump-to-engine ratios adapt to production and depth requirements.	Power-fluid solids control essential. 15 ppm of 15 μm particle size maximum to avoid excessive engine wear. Must add surfactant to a water power fluid for lubricity. High-pressure power-oil leakage may be hazardous. Triplex plunger leakage control required. Fluid system requires added tubing string.	Often higher than rod pumps even for free system. Short run life increases total operating costs.
Hydraulic Jet	Good to excellent. Power-fluid rate and pressure adjusts the production rate and lift capacity from no flow to full design capacity of installed pump. Selection of throat and nozzle sizes extends range of volume and capacity.	More tolerant of power-fluid solids; 200 ppm of 25 μm particle acceptable. Diluents may be added, if required. Power water, either fresh, produced, or seawater, is acceptable.	Higher power cost because of horsepower requirement. Low pump maintenance cost with properly sized throat and nozzle for long run life.
Gas Lift	Excellent. Gas-injection rate varied to change rates. Tubing needs to be sized correctly.	A highly reliable compressor with 95+% run time required. Gas must be properly dehydrated to avoid gas freezing.	Well costs low. Compression cost varies depending on fuel cost and compressor maintenance.
Intermittent Gas Lift	Good. Must adjust injection time and cycles frequently.	Labor intensive to keep fine tuned; otherwise, poor performance. Maintaining steady gas flow often causes injection-gas problems.	Same as continuous-flow gas lift.
Plunger	Good for low-volume wells. Can adjust injection time and frequency.	Plunger hang up and sticking is a major problem.	Usually very low unless plunger problem.

means of artificial lift; however, it is not energy efficient and continuous gas lift does not achieve a low BHP at the formation, compared with well operating pumping systems.

TABLE 10.5—ARTIFICIAL LIFT: DESIGN CONSIDERATIONS AND OVERALL COMPARISONS[11] (continued)

Lift Systems	System Reliability	Salvage Value	System Total
Rod Pump	Excellent. Run time efficiency >95% if good rod practices followed.	Excellent. Easily moved and good market for used equipment.	Straightforward and basic procedures to design, install, and operate following API specs and RPs. Each well is an individual system.
PCP	Good. Normally over pumping and lack of experience decrease run time.	Fair/poor. Easily moved and some current market for used equipment.	Simple to install and operate. Each well an individual system.
ESP	Varies. Excellent for ideal lift cases; poor for problem areas (very sensitive to operating temperatures and electrical malfunctions).	Fair. Some trade-in value. Poor open-market values.	Fairly simple to design but requires good rate data. System not forgiving. Requires excellent operating practices. Follow API RPs in design, testing, and operation. Each well is an individual producer with a common electric system.
Hydraulic Reciprocating	Good with a correctly designed and operated system. Wellsite power-fluid system minimizes power oil or water problems. Problems or changing well conditions reduce downhole pump reliability. Frequent downtime results from power oil problems, injection pressure, pump maintenance problems, and failure of downhole pumps.	Fair. Some trade-in value. Fair market for triplex pump. Good value for wellsite system that can be easily moved well to well.	Simple manual or computer design well application. Operating procedures easily learned. Free pump retrieved for servicing. Individual well unit flexible but extra cost. Requires attention. Central plant more complex; usually result in test and treatment problems.
Hydraulic Jet	Good with proper throat and nozzle sizing for operating conditions. Must avoid operating in cavitation range of jet pump throat; related to pump intake pressure. More problems if pressures >4,000 psig.	Good. Easily moved well to well. Fair; some trade-in value. Fair market for triplex pump.	Available computer design program for application design. Basic operating procedures for downhole pump and wellsite unit. Free pump easily retrieved for on-site repair/replacement. Downhole jet often requires trial and error to arrive at best/optimum jet.
Gas Lift	Excellent if compression system properly designed and maintained.	Fair. Some market for good used compressors and mandrels/valves.	An adequate volume, high pressure, dry, noncorrosive, and clean gas supply source is needed throughout the entire life. System approach needed. Low backpressure beneficial. Good data needed for valve design and spacing. API specs and design/operating RPs should be followed.
Intermittent Gas Lift	Excellent if there is an adequate supply of injection gas and an adequate low-pressure storage volume for injection gas.	Same as continuous flow gas lift.	Same as continuous-flow gas lift.
Plunger	Good if well production stable.	Fair. Some trade-in value. Poor open-market value.	Individual well or system. Simple to design, install, and operate.

TABLE 10.5—ARTIFICIAL LIFT: DESIGN CONSIDERATIONS AND OVERALL COMPARISONS[11] (continued)

Lift Systems	Usage/Outlook
Rod Pump	Excellent. Used on approximately 85% of U.S. artificial lift wells. The normal standard artificial lift method.
PCP	Limited to relative shallow wells with low rates. Used on less than 0.5% of U.S. lifted wells. Primarily gas well dewatering.
ESP	An excellent high-rate artificial lift system. Best suited for <200°F and >1,000 BFPD rates. Most often used on high water-cut wells. Used on approximately 5% of U.S. lifted wells.
Hydraulic Reciprocating	Often used as a default artificial lift well system. Good for flexible operation; wide rate range to relatively deep, high-volume, high-temperature, deviated, oil wells. Used on <5% of U.S. lifted wells.
Hydraulic Jet	Good for higher volume wells requiring flexible operation, wide depth range, high temperature, high corrosion, high GOR, significant sand production. Used on <1% of U.S. lifted wells. Sometimes used to test wells that will not flow offshore.
Gas Lift	Good, flexible, high-rate artificial lift system for wells with high bottomhole pressures. Most like a flowing well. Used on approximately 10% of U.S. lifted wells, mostly offshore.
Intermittent Gas Lift	Often used as a default artificial lift method in lieu of rod pumps. Also, a default for low-pressure wells on continuous gas lift. Used on <1% of U.S. wells.
Plunger	Essentially a low liquid rate, high GLR lift method. Can be used for extending flow life or improving efficiency. Ample gas volume and/or pressure needed for successful operation. Used on <1% of U.S. wells.

10.5.7 Other Lift Methods. Plunger lift commonly is used to remove liquids from gas wells or produce relatively low volume, high GOR oil wells. Plunger lift is important and, in its most efficient form, will operate with only the energy from the well. **Fig. 10.11** shows a schematic of a plunger lift installation. A free-traveling plunger and produced-liquid slug is cyclically brought to the surface of the well from stored gas pressure in the casing-tubing annulus and from the formation. In the off cycle, the plunger falls and pressure builds again in the well. A new two-piece plunger (cylinder with ball underneath) can lift fluids when the components are together, but both components are designed to fall when separate. Use of this plunger allows a shut-in portion of the operational cycle that is only a few seconds long, resulting in more production for many wells.

There is a chamber pump that relies on gas pressure to periodically empty the chamber and force the fluids to the surface, which is essentially a gas-powered pump. There are variations

TABLE 10.6—ARTIFICIAL LIFT: NORMAL OPERATING CONSIDERATIONS[11]			
Lift Systems	Casing Size Limits*	Depth Limits	Intake Capabilities**
Rod Pump	Problems only in high-rate wells requiring large plunger pumps. Small casing sizes (4.5 and 5.5 in.) may limit free gas separation.	Good. Rod or structure may limit rate at depth. Effectively, approximately 150 B/D at 15,000 ft. 100 to 11,000 ft typical; 16,000 ft maximum.	Excellent. <25 psi provided adequate displacement and gas venting. Typically approximately 50 to 100 psig.
PCP	Normally no problem for 4.5-in. casing and larger; but gas separation may be limited.	Poor. Limited to relatively shallow depths, possibly 5,000 ft. 2,000 to 4,500 ft typical; 6,000 ft true value depth (tvd) maximum.	Good. <100 psi provided adequate displacement and gas venting.
ESP	Casing size will limit use of large motors and pumps. Avoid 4.5-in. casing and smaller. Reduced performance inside 5.5-in. casing, depending on depth and rate.	Usually limited to motor horsepower or temperature. Practical depth approximately 10,000 ft. 1,000 to 10,000 ft tvd typical; 15,000 ft tvd maximum.	Fair if little free gas (i.e., p_p >250 psi). Poor if $\Phi=666(V_g/V_l)/p_p$ >1.0. 5% gas at low pressures can cause problems.
Hydraulic Reciprocating	Larger casing required for parallel free or closed systems. Small casing (4.5 and 5.5 in.) may result in excessive friction losses and limits producing rate.	Excellent. Limited by power-fluid pressure (5,000 psi) or horsepower. Low-volume/high-lift pump operating at depths to 17,000 ft. 7,500 to 10,000 ft tvd typical; 17,000 ft maximum.	Fair. Not as good as rod pumping. p_p <100 psig usually results in frequent pump repairs. Free gas reduces displacement efficiency and service life.
Hydraulic Jet	Small casing size limits producing rate at acceptable pressure drop level. Larger completion casing may be required if dual strings run.	Excellent. Similar limits as reciprocating pump. 5,000 to 10,000 ft tvd typical; 15,000 to 20,000 ft tvd maximum.	Poor to fair. >350 psig to 5,000 ft with low GLR. Typical design target is 25% submergence.
Gas Lift	The use of 4.5-and 5.5-in. casing with 2-in. nominal tubing normally limits rates to <1,000 B/D. For rates >5,000 B/D larger (>7-in.) casing and ≥ 4.5-in. tubing needed.	Controlled by system injection pressure and both gas and fluid rate. Typically, for 1,000 B/D with 2.5-in. tubing, a 1,440 psi lift system, and a 1,000 GLR, has an injection depth <10,000 ft; 15,000 ft maximum.	Poor. Restricted by the gradient of the gas lifted fluid. Typically moderate rate is limited to approximately 150 psi per 1,000 ft of injected depth. Thus, the backpressure on 10,000-ft well may be >1,500 psig.
Intermittent Gas Lift	Small casing (4.5 and 5.5 in.) normally is not a problem for this relatively low-volume-type lift.	Usually limited by fallback; few wells >10,000 ft.	Fair when used without chambers. p_p >250 psi for 10,000 ft well. Good when used with chamber. p_p <250 psi feasible at 10,000 ft.
Plunger	Small casing suitable for this low-volume-type lift.	8,000 ft tvd typical; 19,000 ft tvd maximum.	Good. Bottomhole pressures <150 psi at 10,000 ft for low rate, high GLR wells.

*Restricts tubing size. ** Ability to pump with low pressures at pump intake.

of gas lift and intermittent lift, such as chamber lift. Not all possible variations of artificial lift can be discussed; however, the principles presented apply to the selection of all methods that might be considered.

	TABLE 10.6—ARTIFICIAL LIFT: NORMAL OPERATING CONSIDERATIONS[11] (continued)		
Lift Systems	Noise Level	Obtrusiveness	Prime Mover Flexibility
Rod Pump	Fair. Moderately high for urban areas.	Size and operation are drawbacks in populated and farming areas.	Good. Both engines and motors can be used easily. (Motors more reliable and flexible.)
PCP	Good. Surface prime mover only noise.	Good. Low-profile surface equipment.	Good. Both engines and motors can be used.
ESP	Excellent. Very low noise. Often preferred in urban areas if production rate high.	Good. Low profile but requires transformer bank.	Fair. Requires a good power source without spikes or interruptions. Higher voltages can reduce losses.
Hydraulic Reciprocating	Good. Well noise low. Wellsite power-fluid units can be sound-proofed.	Fair to good. Wellhead equipment low profile. Requires surface treating and high-pressure pumping equipment. Free pump can be retrieved into lubricator to avoid oil spillage.	Excellent. Prime mover can be electric motor, gas, or diesel-fired engines or motors.
Hydraulic Jet	Same as hydraulic reciprocating pump.	Same as hydraulic reciprocating pump.	Same as hydraulic reciprocating pump.
Gas Lift	Low at well but noisy at compressor.	Good low profile, but must provide for compressor. Safety precautions must be taken for high-pressure gas lines.	Good. Engines, turbines, or motors can be used for compression.
Intermittent Gas Lift	Same as continuous flow.	Same as continuous flow.	Same as continuous flow.
Plunger	Low at well.	Good.	None required.

10.6 Selection Methods

10.6.1 Selection by Consideration of Depth/Rate System Capabilities. This section discusses various selection techniques. Some of the following discussion is after material from Refs. 5 and 6.

One simple selection or elimination method is the use of charts that show the range of depth and rate in which particular lift types can function. One example is a chart from Ref. 7. **Figs. 10.12 and 10.13** are slightly altered versions of information from Ref. 8 and are probably more accurate because they are more recent. Minimums for method applications are not shown in the charts from Ref. 8. The charts are approximate for initial selection possibilities, as any simplified charts such as these would be. Particular well conditions, such as high viscosity or sand production, may lead to the selection of a lift method that is not initially indicated by the charts. Specific designs are recommended for specific well conditions to more accurately determine the rates possible from given depths.

The depth-rate charts show how hydraulic systems can pump from the greatest depths because of the U-tube balancing of produced fluid pressures with the hydraulic fluid pressure. Gas lift is somewhat depth limited, primarily from compressor pressures required, but has a wide range of production capacity. Beam pump produces more from shallower depths and less

TABLE 10.6—ARTIFICIAL LIFT: NORMAL OPERATING CONSIDERATIONS[11] (continued)			
Lift Systems	Surveillance	Relative Ease of Well Testing	Time Cycle and Pump Off
Rod Pump	Excellent. Can be easily analyzed on the basis of well test, fluid levels, etc. Improved analysis by use of dynamometers and computers.	Good. Well testing simple with few problems with the use of standard available equipment and procedures.	Excellent if well can be pumped off.
PCP	Fair. Analysis based on production and fluid levels only. Dynamometers and pump off controls not possible to use.	Good. Well testing simple with few problems.	Poor. Avoid shutdown in high viscosity/sand producers.
ESP	Fair. Electrical checks but special equipment needed otherwise.	Good. Simple with few problems. High water cut and high-rate wells may require a free water knockout.	Poor. Soft start and improved seal/protectors recommended.
Hydraulic Reciprocating	Good/fair. Downhole pump performance can be analyzed from surface power-fluid rate and pressure, strokes per minute, and producing rate. Pressure recorder can be run and retrieved on free pump.	Fair. Well testing with standard individual well units present few problems. Well testing with a central system more complex; requires accurate power-fluid measurement.	Poor. Possible with electric drive wellsite unit but fair risk of pump restart problem. Usually controlled only by displacement checks; pumpoff control not currently developed.
Hydraulic Jet	Same as hydraulic reciprocating pump.	Same as hydraulic reciprocating pump. Three-stage production test can be conducted by adjusting production step rates, pressured recorder in place to monitor intake pressure. Current IPR development possible.	Poor. Does not appear applicable because of intake pressure requirement higher than pump off.
Gas Lift	Good/excellent. Can be analyzed easily. BHP and production log surveys easily obtained. Optimization and computer control being attempted.	Fair. Well testing complicated by injection gas volume/rate.	Not applicable to continuous-flow gas lift.
Intermittent Gas Lift	Fair. Complicated by standing valve and fallback.	Poor. Well testing complicated by injection gas volume/rate. Measurement of both input and outflow gas a problem. Intermittent flow can cause operating problems with separators, treaters, and tanks.	Poor. Cycle must be periodically adjusted. Labor intensive.
Plunger	Good depending on good well tests and well pressure chart.	Well testing simple with few problems.	Not applicable.

TABLE 10.7—ARTIFICIAL LIFT: SPECIAL PROBLEMS AND CONSIDERATIONS[11]

Lift Systems	Corrosion/Scale Handling Ability	Crooked/Deviated Holes	Duals Applications
Rod Pump	Good to excellent. Batch-treating inhibitor down annulus feasible.	Fair. Increased load and wear problems. High-angle deviated holes (>70°) and horizontal wells are being produced. Some success in pumping 15°/100-ft dogleg severity with use of rod guides. 0 to 20° typical; 0 to 90°, <15°/100 maximum.	Fair. Parallel 2x2-in. low-rate duals feasible inside 7-in. casing. Duals inside 5.5-in. casing currently not in favor; potential gas problem from lower zone. Increased mechanical problems. Duals result in producing one zone below packer.
PCP	Good. Batch-treating inhibitor down annulus feasible.	Poor to fair. Increased load and wear problems. Currently, very few known installations.	No known installations.
ESP	Fair. Batch-treating inhibitor only to intake unless shroud is used.	Good. Few problems. Limited experience in horizontal wells. Requires long radius wellbore bends to get through. 10° typical; 0 to 90° <10°/100 build angle maximum; however, must set in section 0 to 2° maximum deviation.	No known installations. Larger casing required. Possible run and pull problems.
Hydraulic Reciprocating	Good/excellent. Batch or continuous treating inhibitor circulated downhole with power fluid for effective control. Good on corrosion for standard materials; excellent for use with optional corrosion-resistant materials.	Excellent; if tubing can be run in the well, the pump will pass through the tubing. Free pump retrieved without pulling tubing. Operates in horizontal wells. Through-flow line use feasible.	Fair. Three strings nonvented application have been made with complete isolation of production and power fluid from each zone. Limited to low GLR and moderate rates.
Hydraulic Jet	Good/excellent. Inhibitor with power fluid mixes with produced fluid at entry of jet pump throat. Batch treat down annulus.	Excellent. Short jet pump can pass through doglegs up to 24°/100 ft in 2⅜-in. tubing. Same conditions as reciprocating pump. 0 to 20° typical; 0 to 90° <24°/100 build angle maximum.	Same as reciprocating except can handle higher GLR with sufficient surface horsepower.
Gas Lift	Good. Inhibitor in the injection gas and or batch inhibiting down tubing feasible. Steps must be taken to avoid corrosion in injection gas lines.	Excellent. Few wireline problems up to 70° deviation for wireline retrievable valves. 0 to 50° typical; 70° maximum.	Fair. Dual gas lift common but good operating of dual lift complicated and inefficient resulting in reduced rates. Parallel 2x2-in. tubing inside 7-in. casing and 3x3 in. inside 9⅝-in. casing feasible.
Intermittent Gas Lift	Same as continuous flow.	Same as continuous flow.	Same as continuous flow.
Plunger	Fair. Normal production cycle must be interrupted to batch treat the well.	Excellent.	No known installations.

TABLE 10.7—ARTIFICIAL LIFT: SPECIAL PROBLEMS AND CONSIDERATIONS[11] (continued)			
Lift Systems	Gas-Handling Ability	Offshore Application	Paraffin-Handling Capability
Rod Pump	Good if can vent and use gas anchor with proper designed pump. Poor if must pump (>50%) free gas.	Poor. Must design for unit size, weight, and pulling units space. Air balance is lightest unit.	Good/excellent. Hot water/oil treating and/or use of scrapers possible. However, these increase operating costs.
PCP	Poor if pump must handle free gas.	Poor. May have application. However, pulling unit needed.	Fair. Tubing may need treatment. Rod scrapers not possible to use.
ESP	Poor for free gas (i.e., >5% through pump). Poor if $\Phi=666(V_g/V_l)/p_p >1.0$. Rotary gas separators helpful if solids not produced.	Good. Must provide electrical power and service pulling unit.	Fair. Hot water/oil treatments, mechanical cutting, batch inhibition possible.
Hydraulic Reciprocating	Good/fair. Concentric fixed pump or parallel free permits gas venting with suitable downhole gas separator below pump intake. Casing free pump limited to low GLR.	Fair. Pump runs and operates well in highly deviated wells. Requires deck space for power fluid pumps and preferably wellsite-type power-fluid system to avoid increased production-treating capacity. Power water may be used in a closed power fluid system. Power oil a potential fire/safety problem.	Good/excellent. Heated power water/oil circulates heat to downhole pump to minimize buildup. Hot water/oil treatments, mechanical cutting, inhibition possible. Soluble plugs can be run if done frequently enough. For free pump system, pumps can be surfaced on a schedule.
Hydraulic Jet	Similar to reciprocating except jet can handle higher GLR. Free gas reduces efficiency but helps lift. Vent free gas is possible. Use a gas anchor.	Good. Produced water or seawater may be used as power fluid with wellsite-type system or power-fluid separation before production-treating system.	Same as reciprocating pump.
Gas Lift	Excellent. Produced gas reduces need for injection gas.	Excellent. Most common method if adequate gas.	Good. Mechanical cutting sometimes required. Injection gas may aggravate an existing problem.
Intermittent Gas Lift	Same as continuous flow.	Poor in wells needing sand control. Use of standing valve risky. Heading causes operating problems.	Same as continuous flow.
Plunger	Excellent.	Excellent for correct application.	Excellent. Cuts paraffin and removes small scale deposits.

from deeper depths because of increasing rod weight and stretch as depth increases. ESPs are depth limited because of burst limitations on housings and energy considerations for long cables but can produce large production rates. Plunger lift is for low liquid rates, although some wells can produce more than 300 B/D. Plunger lift is not particularly depth limited because of the increased energy storage in the casing annulus as depth increases. Along with advantage/disadvantage lists introducing the artificial lift methods, the depth-rate charts are tools for artificial lift selection or quick elimination of possibilities.

TABLE 10.7—ARTIFICIAL LIFT: SPECIAL PROBLEMS AND CONSIDERATIONS[11] (continued)

Lift Systems	Slimhole Completions*	Solids/Sand-Handling Ability	Temperature Limitations
Rod Pump	Feasible for low rates (<100 B/D) and low GOR (<250).	Fair for low viscosity (<10 cp) production. Improved performance for high (>200 cp) viscosity cases. May be able to handle up to 0.1% sand.	Excellent. Currently used in thermal operations (550°F).
PCP	Feasible if low rates, low GORs, and shallow depths but no known installations.	Excellent. Up to 50% sand with high viscosity (>200 cp) crude. Decreases to 10% sand for water.	Fair. Limited to stator elastomer. At present, maximum below approximately 250°F; 75 to 150°F typical.
ESP	No known installations.	Poor. Requires <100 to 200 ppm solids for standard construction. 200 to 2,000 ppm as special bushings, stage materials, coatings, and thrust bearings added. The maximum amount might be 5,000 ppm, but sharpness and angularity of grains is important.	Limited to <250°F for standard and <400°F for special motors and cable. 100 to 275°F typical.
Hydraulic Reciprocating	Possible but may have high friction losses or gas problems. Has been used when moderate production rates and low GLR.	Poor. Requires <10 ppm solids power fluids for good run life. Also produced fluids must have low solids (<200 ppm of 15 μm particles) for reasonable life. Freshwater injection into power stream may solve salt buildup in pumps.	Excellent. Standard materials to 325°F. 100 to 250°F typical. Operating to 400 to 500°F feasible with special materials.
Hydraulic Jet	Same as reciprocating pump except may handle higher GLR.	Fair/good. Jet pumps are operating with 3% sand in produced fluid. Power fluid to jet pump can tolerate 200 ppm of 25 μm particle size. Freshwater treatment for salt buildup possible.	Excellent. 100 to 250°F typical. Possible to operate to 500 to 600°F with special materials.
Gas Lift	Feasible but can be troublesome and inefficient.	Excellent. Limit is inflow and surface problems. Typical limit is 0.1% sand for inflow and outflow problems.	Excellent. Need to know temperatures to design bellows-charged valves. 100 to 250°F typical; maximum of 350 to 400°F.
Intermittent Gas Lift	Same as continuous flow.	Fair. Standing valve may cause problems.	Same as continuous flow.
Plunger	Good. Similar to casing lift but must have adequate formation gas.	Sand can stick plunger. Plunger wipes tubing clean. Brush plunger usually used for small amount of sand presence.	Excellent.

*2⅞-in. production casing string.

10.6.2 Selection by Advantages and Disadvantages. Although previous sections detailed the major artificial lift systems, more detailed listings of advantages and disadvantages are available from various sources. Ref. 9 contains a brief summary of advantages, disadvantages, and selection criteria for various artificial lift systems presented by experts in a forum discussion.

TABLE 10.7—ARTIFICIAL LIFT: SPECIAL PROBLEMS AND CONSIDERATIONS[11] (continued)			
Lift Systems	High-Viscosity Fluid-Handling Capability	High-Volume Lift Capability	Low-Volume Lift Capability
Rod Pump	Good for up to <200 cp viscosity fluids and low rates (400 B/D). Diluent, downhole stuffing box or other methods needed for higher rates.	Fair. Restricted to shallow depths with the use of large plungers. Maximum rate approximately 4,000 BFPD from 1,000 ft and 1,000 BFPD from 5,000 ft	Excellent. Most commonly used method for wells producing <100 BFPD.
PCP	Excellent for high-viscosity fluids provided no stator/rotator problems.	Poor. Restricted to relatively small rates. Possibly 2,000 BFPD from 2,000 ft and 200 BFPD from 5,000 ft. 4,500 B/D maximum at shallow depths.	Excellent for <100 BFPD shallow wells.
ESP	Fair. Limited to as high as 1000 cp. Depends on economics. (~>7 to 9°API). Increases horsepower and reduces head. Potential solution is to use "core flow" with 20% water.	Excellent. Limited by needed horsepower and can be restricted by casing size. In 5.5 in. casing can produce 4,000 BFPD from 4,000 ft with 240 horsepower. Tandem motors increase horsepower and operating costs. 200 to 20,000 B/D typical; approximately 30,000 B/D maximum. 52,000 B/D, shallow, 10.25 in. equipment has been done.	Generally poor. Lower efficiencies and high operating costs <400 BFPD.
Hydraulic Reciprocating	Good. >8°API production with <500 cp possible. Power fluids can be used to dilute low gravity production.	Good. Limited by tubulars and horsepower. Typically 3,000 BFPD from 4,000 ft and 1,000 BFPD from 10,000 ft with 3,500 psi system. 50 to 500 B/D typical; 4,000 B/D maximum.	Fair. Not as good as rod pumping. Typically 100 to 300 BFPD from 4,000 to 10,000 ft >75 BFPD from 12,000 ft possible.
Hydraulic Jet	Good/excellent. >6° API production with <800 cp possible. Power oil of >24°API and <50 cp or water power-fluid reduces friction losses.	Excellent. Up to 15,000 BFPD with adequate flowing bottom home pressure, tubular size, and horsepower. 300 to 1,000 B/D typical; >15,000 B/D maximum.	Fair. >200 BFPD from 4,000 ft.
Gas Lift	Fair. Few problems for >15° API or below 20 cp viscosity. Excellent for high watercut lift even with high viscosity oil.	Excellent. Restricted by tubing size and injection gas rate and depth. With 4 in. nominal tubing rates of 5,000 B/D from 10,000 feasible with 1,440 psi injection gas and GLR of 1000.	Fair. Limited by heading and slippage. Avoid unstable flow range. Typically lower limit is 200 BFPD for 2 in. tubing without heading; 400 B/D for 2.5 in. and 700 B/D for 3 in. tubing.
Intermittent Gas Lift	Same as continuous flow.	Poor. Limited by cycle volume and number of possible injection cycles. Typically approximately 200 BFPD from 10,000 ft with p_p <250 psi.	Good. Limited by efficiency and economic limit. Typically ½ to 4 barrels per cycle with up to 48 cycles per day.
Plunger	Normally not applicable.	Poor. Limited by number of cycles. Possibly 200 BFPD from 10,000 ft. 1 to 5 B/D typical; 200 to 300 B/D maximum.	Excellent for 1 to 2 BFPD with high GLR.

TABLE 10.8—DATA FOR EXAMPLE 10.1	
Vertical depth to perforations, ft	6,000
Separator pressure, psig	100
Surface temperature, °F	100
Casing size (OD), in.	7
Tubing size (OD) for gas lift, in.	3.5
Tubing size for other methods, in.	2.875
Water cut, %*	50
Oil gravity, API	30
Gas specific gravity	0.7
Water gravity**	1.03
Produced GOR (starting and ending), scf/bbl	400
Bubblepoint at equilibrium, psig	2,000
Static reservoir pressure, psig	2,000
Productivity index, B/D/psi	1
Economic Data[†]	
Fixed costs, $/month	300
Fluid disposal, $/bbl water	0.35
Electricity, $/kW-hr	.05
Oil revenue, $/bbl oil	20
Gas revenue, $/Mscf gas	2.00
Inflation rate, %/year	3
Discount rate for present value, %/year	8
Oil revenue increase, %/year	1
Fixed oil period, year	1
Royalty, %	12.5
Energy cost, $/kW-hr	0.10

*Initial value but increases with time to maintain an oil production rate of 1,000 B/D;
** >1.0 with salt content;
[†]Costs and economic variables would be the same for all artificial lift methods.

Tables 10.3 and 10.4[10] provide a useful summary of the advantages and disadvantages of the various artificial lift systems. Some were discussed previously when introducing each system.

Ref. 11 provides the most extensive and useful listing of the various advantages and disadvantages of lift systems under a broad range of categories. Some of the information is open to interpretation, but, in general, it is the best list of artificial lift advantages and disadvantages available at this time. The information in the tables from Ref. 11 is a very useful tool for artificial lift selection.

Tables 10.5 through 10.7 present the information in the selection tables from Ref. 11. Some of the details in the tables have been updated, but the majority of the work is from the original authors. These tables are used for a preliminary look at some operation details and capabilities for artificial lift. Much of the selection process can be accomplished with depth-rate charts[7,8] and this extensive set of tables of artificial lift capabilities.[11] Very severe conditions and special conditions can require further study. Also, a quantitative economic assessment is not possible with the charts and tables.

10.6.3 Selection by Expert Programs. "Expert" programs, or computerized artificial lift selection programs, are more advanced than a simple list of advantages and disadvantages and depth-

TABLE 10.9—LIFT METHOD COSTS

	Beam	Hydraulic	Gas Lift	ESP
Target rate, B/D	1,000	1,000	1,000	1,000
Initial installation, $	141,000	173,000	239,000	105,000
Energy efficiency, %	58	16	15	48
Direct operating expenses (fixed), $/month	600	700	600	600
Direct operating expenses per BFPD, $/month	0.50	0.50	1.00	0.50
Pull and repair, $/month	200	100	100	250

TABLE 10.10—RESULTS OF EXAMPLE 10.1

Method	Cumulative PVP (million $)	Time At Which Maximum Cumulative PVP Occurs (years)
ESP	4.32	~11
Gas Lift	3.85	~7
Hydraulic Pump	4.08	~10
Rod Pump	4.35	~11

rate charts. These programs include rules and logic that branch to select the best artificial lift system as a function of user input of well and operating conditions. Refs. 12 through 14 deal with expert systems for the selection of artificial lift systems.

Ref. 12 describes an expert system with selection criteria on sucker rod, hydraulic pump, ESP, progressive pump, continuous gas lift, intermittent gas lift, intermittent gas lift with plunger, constant slug injection gas lift, chamber gas lift, and conventional plunger lift. The program contains three modules. Module 1 is an expert module that includes a knowledge base structured from human expertise, theoretical written knowledge, and rule-of-thumb calculations. It ranks the methods and also issues warnings, some of which may rule out high-ranked methods. Module 2 incorporates simulation design and facility-component specification programs for all artificial lift methods considered. It contains a suite of design methods with advice to follow from Module 1. Module 3 is an economics evaluation module that includes a cost database and cost-analysis programs to calculate lift profitability. It uses the designs and expected production rate to calculate profitability with evaluation parameters such as NPV and rate of return. Module 3 also includes investment costs and repair and maintenance costs.

The rules in Ref. 12 take the form of "if (condition), then (type of process)." For each artificial lift method, a suitability coefficient (SC) from –1 to +1 is defined for the given condition, where SC = –1 eliminates the process from further consideration, and SC = +1 indicates a process well suited to the given condition. For example, "if (Pump Temperature > 275°F), then (ESP) –1" defines a rule that eliminates ESPs if the pump temperature exceeds 275°F. Rules such as this require constant updating because equipment capabilities change with time.

Intermediate values can be used to refine the system, and methods are presented for combining the coefficients into a single coefficient. The program can combine the suitability coefficients into one value for overall evaluation. Ref. 12 also gives other details for knowledge representation and technical and economic evaluation.

Ref. 13 describes an artificial lift program that decides, from the user's input, which system among gas lift, hydraulic, sucker rod, or ESP pumping systems is best for the particular condi-

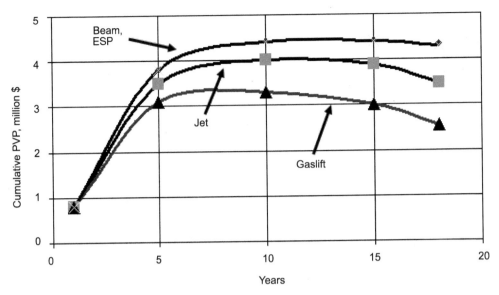

Fig. 10.14—Results of PVP analysis for Example 10.1.

tions. Problems—such as sand, paraffin, crooked hole, corrosion, small casing, flexibility, and scale—are used with the stored knowledge base and user input to allow the program to rank the most appropriate artificial lift method for the particular conditions.

Ref. 14 describes another encompassing expert system. It describes the optimum pumping-unit search program, which consists of a knowledge base containing the complete set of specific information on the domain of expertise, an inference engine with the data and heuristics of the knowledge base to solve the problem, and interactive modules enabling very simple use of the expert system. Another interesting feature[14] is the presentation of economical data for annual costs to be incurred by various artificial lift systems. The costs are presented in bar graphs that show how the component costs would occur above the wellhead or subsurface. For instance, much of the possible recurring costs for ESPs can be from the subsurface; whereas, for gas lift, other than wireline work, larger repair and servicing costs associated with compressors would be taken care of on the surface.

10.6.4 Selection by Net-Present-Value Comparison. A more thorough selection technique depends on the lifetime economics of the available artificial lift methods. The economics, in turn, depend on the failure rates of the system components, fuel costs, maintenance costs, inflation rates, anticipated revenue from produced oil and gas, and other factors that may vary from system to system. Refs. 15 through 17 are example studies that follow economically guided selection techniques. Refs. 18 through 26 discuss artificial lift in general, the efficiency of lift methods, selection techniques, and limitations on various artificial lift systems.

Economic Analysis of Artificial Lift Selection. The methods considered are ESP, gas lift, hydraulic pump, and rod pump. An enhanced method of analysis similar to the NPV comparison method is available from Ref. 17.

To use the NPV comparison method, the user must have a good idea of the associated costs for each system. This requires that the user evaluate each system carefully for the particular well and be aware of the advantages and disadvantages of each method and any additional equipment (i.e., additional costs) that may be required. Because energy costs are part of the

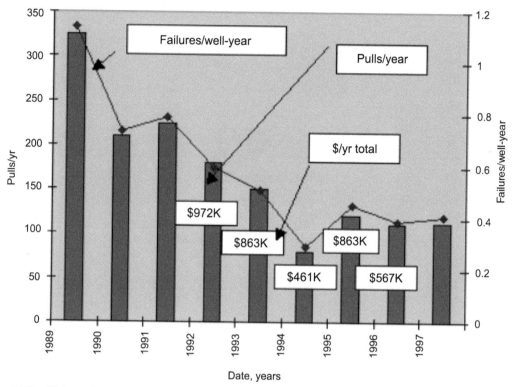

Fig. 10.15—History of typical beam pump operation: failures per year with approximate associated costs for a group of 532 wells.

NPV analysis, a design for each feasible method must be determined before running the economic analysis to better determine the efficiency of a particular installation. These factors force the consideration of all the applicable artificial lift methods to generate the necessary information for the NPV analysis.

Example 10.1 Consider a vertical well with the characteristics given in **Table 10.8**. To calculate the expected life of the well, reasonable reservoir production estimates must be supplied. For this example, assume that all artificial lift methods (ESP, gas lift, beam pump, and hydraulics) will be considered and initially will produce at the rate of 1,000 B/D with 50% water cut and 400 GOR. After a 1-year constant rate period, oil production is assumed to decline by 20% per year. The overall rate (oil+water+gas) will remain constant. The water cut will increase after the first year. The rate of 10 BOPD is selected as the end of the evaluation period, but the economic limit will be reached long before this rate occurs.

Table 10.9 contains the values needed for the NPV analysis that are specific to each lift method. The sources of all these values are typical of each of the methods. The direct operating expenses could be manpower to visit and monitor wells, site maintenance, overhead charged to field, etc. The direct operating expenses per barrel could be water disposal charges, injection of corrosion inhibitor or scale treatments, etc. The average pulling and repair charges are average charges for pulling because of failed or worn equipment. An analog field, if available, can be a source of such data.

Typical Beam Pump Failures

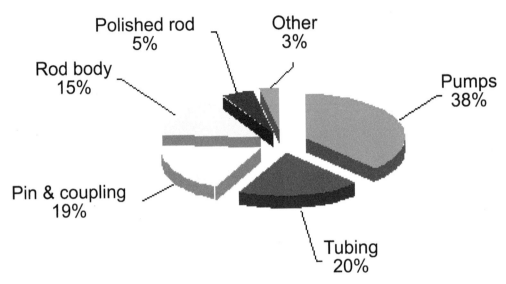

Fig. 10.16—A typical distribution of failures among the beam-pump system components.

The actual initial production rate may differ for each method, but for comparison and to illustrate concepts, an initial total rate of 1,000 B/D for each method is assumed. In this case, it is possible to accomplish this rate with all the methods considered. Different rates possibly would require different production facilities and different initial costs. Thus, each method should be optimized and the associated required costs included in the economic analysis.

Solution. **Fig. 10.14** plots the summary of the cumulative PVP income. The maximum in each curve occurs at the time the project should be ended, because beyond that, the project would be operating at a loss. The maximum PVP for each lift method examined is indicated in Fig. 10.14, and the results are tabulated in **Table 10.10**.

Again, the results depend on the particular cost-related data for each method. For this case, however, the rod pump or ESP would be the most economical method. Because rod pump and ESP are approximately the same economically, the decision then would fall on vendor availability, service expected, where equipment can be warehoused, and other factors. Gas lift and jet hydraulic pump would not be recommended for this case according to the results obtained. Different field conditions could easily change the lift system selected.

10.7 Sample Run-Life Information

As Example 10.1 shows, one of the factors to consider in artificial lift selection is the failure rates for the various artificial lift systems or the individual components of the systems. **Fig. 10.15** shows failure rates from a group of 532 beam-pumped wells over several years. The costs for downhole lift replacement and servicing are shown.

Fig. 10.16 shows a breakdown of the major causes for failure of the beam pump systems that went into the accumulation of the failure-rate data in Fig. 10.15. If a lift selection study is needed, field data from a field of similar conditions would be very helpful in evaluating beam pumping as a candidate and in comparing beam pump with other artificial lift methods. A breakdown of failing components for any lift method is a good evaluation tool.

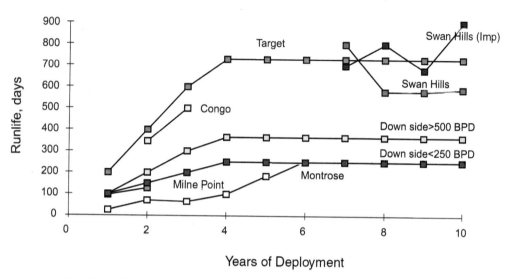

Fig. 10.17—Failure data from a number of field locations and target values.[26]

Fig. 10.17 shows ESP run lives for various fields. These data were collected and presented in Ref. 17 for a study of artificial lift feasibility and methods to use in a Siberian location. Targets and downside potentials were established for this study as shown in Fig. 10.17.

Refs. 5 and 6 include various run-life information and selection criteria. Swan Hills (Alberta), Milne Point (Alaska), the Amoco Congo field, the THUMS East Wilmington field, the Amoco North Sea field, and the Montrose field were used to help predict run lives for the Priobskoye field in Siberia. Ref. 17 contains additional information on the conditions in these fields. Fig. 10.17 shows the "learning curve" aspect of these field developments. The initial learning curve is very costly, showing the time required to come from low run lives before failures up to reasonable operational lives for the ESP installations. This learning curve can be eliminated with careful planning, reference to previous projects, and implementation of early good practices in the development.

From Ref. 6, **Table 10.11** shows downhole hydraulic pump lives for a collection of fields. Ref. 6 presents the conditions for these fields. The average life of the pumps is approximately 114 days. Target, downside, and industry data is summarized for the downhole hydraulic pumps. No data are presented for gas-lift-system costs and failures expected. Initial compressor costs are high, but after installation, most of the expense is wireline work unless a major compressor fix or addition is needed. Cost examples for other systems are not shown here.

The data shown are for particular fields and may or may not be indicative of what might be undertaken in the future. Again, the run lives to failure data cases for the various artificial lift systems presented are example cases and are not intended for general use.

10.8 Conclusions

This chapter presents information on the various methods available for the selection of the best artificial lift system for given field conditions. The discussion presents selection methods covering depth-rate feasibility maps; tables of advantages and disadvantages; expert system programs

TABLE 10.11—SUMMARY OF HYDRAULIC PUMP LIFE FOR VARIOUS FIELDS[6]

Operator	Depth (ft)	Production (B/D)	Power System	Pump Run Life (days)	Comments
Citronell Unit Operator, north of Mobile, Alabama	10,000 to 11,000	300 to 400	Triplex, oil system; 3,000 psi injected; several wells on one pump.	49	Use Kevlar spring-loaded plungers and liners.
Texaco Barre Field, Alabama	15,000	100 to 450	Triplex oil system; 1,800 to 2,400 BOPD at 3,900 psi.	75	Like soft-pack triplex.
Unocal Wyoming Woodland Unit	10,500	15 to 50	Triplex, oil; vortex to clean oil.	165	Single string systems; pressure annulus to bring pump up; takes approximately 1,000 psi to move pump up.
MWJ Baum/Sanders, New Mexico	10,000	75	Triplex, 3,000 to 3,500 psi; no trouble.	90	Reciprocating pumps, corrosion treated BHAs; 1-in. vent string; production up casing; injection down tubing (2⅜); recommends individual power supply.
Marathon Cody Unit, Wyoming	7,500	475	Triplex, uses water and oil for power fluid; vortex cleanup; 4 speed transmission	180 (min)	Likes now with experience. Slower pumps (< 45 strokes per minute) may run 3 yrs; pump repair costs of $1,500 to 2,000; for frac cleanup the fill; well with liquids, circulate, and filter with vortex unit at surface; single string-monitor tub press for pump off; trying variable speed drill; 200 to 300 psi on casing brings up pump.
Unocal Huntington Beach, California	4,000	295	First triplex with oil; now ESP with water; some 3,000 psi; some 2,000 psi.		Uses three strings (main and two side strings); free-pump installations; power water not mixed with production; BHAs 3 yrs; side strings leak, pull only one string if side string; few hours to pull side string; 4 hrs to round trip new pump; ESPs need less maintenance, more energy to run; triplex needs more maintenance, less energy to run.
Unocal Cook Inlet, Alaska	7,500 (measured depth)	105 (average)	Triplex and ESP; oil system tank only separation; no vortex cleanup; 3,550 psi generated; 60 hz ESPs gears on triplex.	180+	Likes hydraulic better than ESPs. Use reciprocating and jet pumps; 2½ hrs to replace pumps; tubing tripped not more than 3 to 4 yrs; two strings, open annulus; check fluid level with echometer; runs two strings simultaneously.

Average Pump Run Life, days

114.5

containing feasibility, technical, and economic programs; and economic analysis methods such as present-value analysis.

Because the present-value method requires designs to meet target rates, the user is somewhat forced to evaluate harsh conditions, etc., during the course of the design. The user must then add gas separators, sand control, or whatever is necessary to meet target rates before the NPV analysis is performed. By necessity, various feasibility criteria must be considered; therefore, even if all data required for a complete economic analysis are not available, going through the analysis forces the user to consider or make best estimates of critical parameters, pointing to a better selection process.

Although some fairly complete expert systems for selection exist, their use is not widespread at this time. This may be a result of the constant updating required or because other types of selection processes that use experienced personnel may work as well or better. The lack of use also may be a result of the general lack of experience with these tools and a lack of understanding about the results that may be obtained from their use.

Nomenclature

$\bar{p}$ = average reservoir pressure, m/Lt², psi

p_b = bubblepoint pressure, m/Lt², psi

p_p = pump intake pressure, m/Lt², psi

V_g = gas volume, L³, ft³

V_l = liquid volume at intake conditions, L³, ft³

s = skin (not rate dependent), dimensionless

Φ = dimensionless term to indicate gas problems at ESP intake

References

1. Vogel, J.V.: "Inflow Performance Relationship for Solution-Gas Drive Wells," *JPT* (January 1968) 83.
2. Babu, D.K. and Odeh, A.S.: "Productivity of a Horizontal Well," *SPERE* (November 1989) 417.
3. Bennett, P.: "Artificial Lift Concepts and Timing," *Petroleum Engineer* (May 1980) 144.
4. "ABB Automation Technology Products Presentation," ABB USA, Norwalk, Connecticut (December 2001).
5. Lea, J.F. and Patterson, J.: "Selection Considerations for Artificial Lift," presented at the 1997 Artificial Lift Equipment Forum, Dubai.
6. Lea, J.F. and Nickens, H.V.: "Selection of Artificial Lift," paper SPE 52157 presented at the 1999 SPE Mid-Continent Operations Symposium, Oklahoma City, Oklahoma, 28–31 March.
7. Blais, R.: "Artificial Lift Methods," poster, PennWell Publishing Co., Tulsa (1986).
8. "5 Steps to Artificial Lift Optimization," commercial presentation, Weatherford Artificial Lift Systems, Houston (May 2000).
9. Neely, A.B. *et al.*: "Selection of Artificial Lift Method," paper SPE 10337 presented at the 1982 SPE Annual Technical Conference and Exhibition, New Orleans, 26–29 September.
10. Brown, K.E.: "Overview of Artificial Lift Systems," *JPT* (October 1982) 2384.
11. Clegg, J.D., Bucaram, S.M., and Hein, N.W. Jr.: "Recommendations and Comparisons for Selecting Artificial-Lift Methods," *JPT* (December 1993) 1128.
12. Espin, D.A., Gasbarri, S., and Chacin, J.E.: "Expert System for Selection of Optimum Artificial Lift Method," paper SPE 26967 presented at the 1994 SPE Latin American and Caribbean Petroleum Engineering Conference, Buenos Aires, Argentina, 27–29 April.
13. Heinze, L.R., Thornsberry, K., and Wit, L.D.: "AL: An Expert System for Selecting the Optimal Pumping Method," paper SPE 18872 presented at the 1989 SPE Production Operations Symposium, Oklahoma City, Oklahoma, 13–14 March.
14. Valentin, E.P. and Hoffman, F.C.: "OPUS: An Expert Adviser for Artificial Lift," paper SPE 18184 presented at the 1988 SPE Annual Technical Conference and Exhibition, Houston, 2–5 October.

15. Etherton, J.H. and Thornton, P.: "A Case Study of the Selection Procedure for Artificial Lift in a High Capacity Reservoir," presented at the 1988 Annual Meeting of the Southwestern Petroleum Short Course, Lubbock, Texas, 20–21 April.

16. Smith, G.L.: "Lease Operational Study—Gas Lift vs. Submersible Pump Lift—G.H. Arledge 'C' Lease, Scurry County, Texas," paper SPE 6852 presented at the 1977 SPE Annual Technical Conference and Exhibition, Denver, 9–12 October.

17. Kol, H. and Lea, J.F.: "Selection of the Most Effective Artificial Lift System for the Priobskoye Field," 1992 SPE ESP Workshop, Houston, 26–28 April.

18. Clegg, J.D.: "Artificial Lift Efficiency Depends on Design," *American Oil & Gas Reporter* (June 1991).

19. Lea, J.F.: "Artificial Lift—Operating at Lower Cost," SPE Distinguished Lecturer Presentation, 1994–95.

20. Clegg, J.D.: "Artificial Lift: Producing at High Rates," SPE Distinguished Lecturer Presentation, 1992–93.

21. Johnson, L.D.: "Selection of Artificial Lift for a Permian Basin Waterflood," presented at the 1968 Annual Meeting of the Southwestern Petroleum Short Course, Lubbock, Texas.

22. Clegg, J.D.: "Improved Sucker Rod Pumping Design Calculations," presented at the 1988 Annual Meeting of the Southwestern Petroleum Short Course, Lubbock, Texas, 20–21 April.

23. Clegg, J.D.: "Another Look at Gas Anchors," presented at the 1989 Annual Meeting of the Southwestern Petroleum Short Course, Lubbock, Texas, 19–20 April.

24. Clegg, J.D.: "Rod Pumping Selection and Design," presented at the 1991 Annual Meeting of the Southwestern Petroleum Short Course, Lubbock, Texas, 17–18 April.

25. Duke, S.E.: "Artificial Lift—Which Method Best Fits Your Needs," presented at the 1981 Annual Meeting of the Southwestern Petroleum Short Course, Lubbock, Texas, 23–24 April.

26. Bucaram, S.M. and Yeary, B.J.: "A Data-Gathering System To Optimize Producing Operations: A 14-Year Overview," *JPT* (April 1987) 457.

General References

Allis, D.H. and Capps, W.M.: "Submersible Pumping—Long Beach Unit of East Wilmington Field: A 17-Year Review," *JPT* (August 1984) 1321.

Beadle, G., Harlan, J., and Brown, K.E.: "Evaluation of Surface Back-Pressure for Continuous- and Intermittent-Flow Gas Lift," *JPT* (March 1963) 243.

Beauregard, E. and Ferguson, P.L.: "Introduction to Plunger Lift: Applications, Advantages, and Limitations," presented at the 1981 Annual Meeting of the Southwestern Petroleum Short Course, Lubbock, Texas, 23–24 April.

Beauregard, E. and Morrow, S.: "New and Unusual Application for Plunger Lift System," paper SPE 18868 presented at the 1989 SPE Production Operations Symposium, Oklahoma City, Oklahoma, 13–14 March.

Blann, J.R. and Williams, J.D.: "Determining the Most Profitable Gas Injection Pressure for a Gas Lift Installation," *JPT* (August 1984) 1305.

Blann, J.R., Jacobson, L. and Faber, C.: "Production Optimization in the Provincia Field, Colombia," *SPEPE* (February 1989) 9.

Boone, D.M. and Clegg, J.D.: *Petroleum Engineering Software,* Integrity Consulting, Parker, Colorado.

Bull. 11L2, Catalog of Analog Computer Dynamometer Cards, API, Washington, DC (1999).

Bull. 11L5, Electric Motor Performance Date Request Form, API, Washington, DC (1990).

Brown, K.E.: *The Technology of Artificial Lift,* Petroleum Publishing Co., Tulsa (1980).

Christ, F.C. and Petrie, H.L.: "Obtaining Low Bottomhole Pressures in Deep Wells With Hydraulic Jet Pumps," *SPEPE* (August 1989) 290.

Clegg, J.D.: "High-Rate Artificial Lift," *JPT* (March 1988) 277.

Coberly, C.J.: *Theory and Application of Hydraulic Pumping Installations*, Kobe Inc., Huntington Park, California (1961).

Corteville, J.C. *et al.*: "Research on Jet Pumps for Single and Multiphase Pumping of Crudes," paper SPE 16923 presented at the 1987 SPE Annual Technical Conference and Exhibition, Dallas, 27–30 September.

DeMoss, E.E. and Tiemann, W.D.: "Gas Lift Increases High-Volume Production From Claymore Field," *JPT* (April 1982) 696.

Divine, D.L.: "A Variable Speed Submersible Pumping System," paper SPE 8241 presented at the 1979 SPE Annual Technical Conference and Exhibition, Las Vegas, 23–26 September.

Ferguson, P.L. and Beauregard, E.: "How to Tell if Plunger Lift Will Work in Your Well," *World Oil* (August 1985) 33.

Focht, F.T.: "Selecting Gas Lift Equipment for High Rate Wells," *World Oil* (January 1981) 165.

Foley, W.L. and Svinos, J.G.: "Expert Adviser Program for Rod Pumping," *JPT* (April 1989) 394.

Foss, D.L. and Gaul, R.B.: "Plunger Lift Performance Criteria With Operating Experience—Ventura Ave. Field," *Drilling and Production Practices,* API (1965) 124.

Gas Lift Manual, Vocational Training Series, API, Dallas (1991).

Gault, R.H.: "Designing a Sucker-Rod Pumping System for Maximum Efficiency," *SPEPE* (November 1987) 284.

Gaymard, B. *et al.*: "The Progressing Cavity Pump in Europe: Results and New Developments," paper presented at the 1988 Offshore Southeast Asia Conference, Singapore, 2–5 February.

Gibbs, S.G.: "A General Method for Predicting Rod Pumping System Performance," paper SPE 6850 presented at the 1977 SPE Annual Technical Conference and Exhibition, Denver, 9–12 October.

Gibbs, S.G.: "Predicting the Behavior of Sucker-Rod Pumping Systems," *JPT* (July 1963) 769; *Trans.*, AIME, **228.**

Gibbs, S.G.: "A Review of Methods for Design and Analysis of Rod Pumping Installations," *JPT* (December 1982) 2931.

Gipson, F.W. and Swain, H.W.: "The Beam Pumping Design Chain," *Proc.,* Annual Meeting of Southwestern Petroleum Short Course, Lubbock, Texas (1984) 296–383.

Gosline, J.E. and O'Brien, M.P.: "The Water Jet Pump," *U. of California Publications in Engineering,* U. of California Press (1942) **3**, No. 3, 167.

Gray, H.E.: "Kinematics of Oil-Well Pumping Units," *Drilling & Production Practice*, API (1963) 156.

Grupping, A.W., Coppes, J.L.R., and Groot, J.G.: "Fundamentals of Oil Well Jet Pumping," *SPEPE* (February 1988) 9.

Hollis, R.G.: "Deep Hydraulic Pumping—Reno Field," *JPT* (November 1966) 1395.

Jiao, B., Blais, R.N., and Schmidt, Z.: "Efficiency and Pressure Recovery in Hydraulic Jet Pumping of Two-Phase Gas/Liquid Mixtures," *SPEPE* (November 1990) 345.

Juch, A.H. and Watson, R.J.: "New Concepts in Sucker-Rod Pump Design," *JPT* (March 1969) 342; *Trans., AIME,* **246.**

Kanu, E.P., Mach, J. and Brown, K.E.: "Economic Approach to Oil Production and Gas Allocation in Continuous Gas Lift," *JPT* (October 1981) 1887.

Kramer, M.J.C., Martin, J.D., and Neely, A.B.: "On-site Analysis of Sucker Rod Pumping Wells," paper SPE 11037 presented at the 1982 SPE Annual Technical Conference and Exhibition, New Orleans, 26–29 September.

Lea, J.F.: "Dynamic Analysis of Plunger Lift Operations," *JPT* (November 1982) 2617.

Lea, J.F.: "Plunger Lift Versus Velocity Strings," *J. of Energy Resources Technology* (December 1999) 234.

Lea, J.F. and Bearden, J.L.: "Effect of Gaseous Fluids on Submersible Pump Performance," *JPT* (December 1982) 2922.

Lea, J.F. and Bearden, J.L.: "Gas Separator Performance for Submersible Pump Operations," *JPT* (June 1982) 1327.

Lea, J.F. and Bowen, J.F.: "Dynamic Measurements of Beam-Pump Parameters," *SPEPE* (February 1992) 113.

Lea, J.F. and Wilson, B.L.: "The Role of Power Cost in Selection of an Artificial Lift System," *Proc.*, 1990 SPE ESP Workshop, Houston, April.

LeBeaux, J.M. and Sudduth, L.F.: "Theoretical and Practical Aspects of Free Piston Operation," *JPT* (September 1955) 33.

Lubinski, A. and Blenkarn, K.A.: "Buckling of Tubing in Pumping Wells, Its Effects and Means for Controlling It," *JPT* (March 1957) 73; *Trans.*, AIME, **210.**

McCoy, C.D. and Ross, K.: "Plunger Lift and Economic Alternative to Sucker-Rod Pumps," *Proc.*, Southwestern Petroleum Short Course, Lubbock, Texas (1992) 337.

McMurry, E.D.: "Use of the Automatic Free Piston in Oil Well Production Problems," *JPT* (June 1953) 165.

"Metallic Materials for Sucker-Rod Pumps for Corrosive Oilfield Environments," MR0176-2000, NACE, Houston (2000).

Mower, L.N. *et al.*: "Defining the Characteristics and Performance of Gas-Lift Plungers," paper SPE 14344 presented at the 1985 SPE Annual Technical Conference and Exhibition, Las Vegas, 22–25 September.

Neely, A.B. and Tolbert, H.O: "Experience with Pumpoff Control in the Permian Basin," *JPT* (May 1988) 645.

Neely, A.B., Montgomery, J.W., and Vogel, J.V.: "A Field Test and Analytical Study of Intermittent Gas Lift," *SPEJ* (October 1974) 502.

Neely, A.B. and Patterson, M.M.: "Soft Start of Submersible Pumped Oil Wells," *JPT* (April 1984) 653.

Nelson, C.C.: "The Jet Free Pump-Proper Application Through Computer Calculated Operating Charts," *Proc.*, Southwestern Petroleum Short Course, Lubbock, Texas (1975).

Nolen, K.B. and Gibbs, S. G.: "Subsurface Hydraulic Pumping Diagnostic Techniques," paper SPE 4540 presented at the 1973 SPE Annual Meeting, Las Vegas, 30 September–3 October.

Petrie, H.L. *et al.*: "Jet Pumping Oil Wells," *World Oil* (December 1986) 35.

Powers, M.L.: "The Depth Constraint of Electric Submersible Pumps," paper SPE 24835 presented at the 1992 SPE Annual Technical Conference and Exhibition, Washington, DC, 4–7 October.

Reddin, J.D., Sherman, T.A.G., and Blann, J.R.: "Optimizing Gas-Lift Systems," paper SPE 5150 presented at the 1974 SPE Annual Meeting, Houston, 6–9 October.

RP 11AR, Care and Use of Subsurface Pumps, API, Washington, DC (2000).

RP 11BR, Care and Handling of Sucker Rods, API, Washington, DC (1991).

RP 11ER, Guarding of Pumping Units, API, Washington, DC (1991).

RP 11G, Installation and Lubrication of Pumping Units, API, Washington, DC (1994).

RP 11L, Recommended Practice for Design Calculations for Sucker Rod Pumping Systems (Conventional Units), API, Washington, DC (1988).

RP 11V5, Operation, Maintenance, and Troubleshooting of Gas Lift Installations, API, Washington, DC (1999).

RP 11V6, Design of Continuous Flow Gas Lift Installations Using Injection Pressure Operated Valves, API, Washington, DC (1999).

RP 11V7, Recommended Practice for Repair, Testing, and Setting Gas Lift Valves, API, Washington, DC (1999).

Saveth, K.J. and Klein, S.T.: "The Progressing Cavity Pump: Principle and Capabilities," paper SPE 18873 presented at the 1989 SPE Production Operations Symposium, Oklahoma City, Oklahoma, 13–14 March.

Schmidt, Z. and Doty, D.R.: "System Analysis for Sucker-Rod Pumping," *SPEPE* (May 1989) 125.

Simmons, W.E.: "Optimizing Continuous Flow Gas Lift Wells," *Petroleum Engineer Magazine* (August 1972) 46.

Simmons, W.E.: "Optimizing Continuous Flow Gas Lift Wells," *Petroleum Engineer Magazine* (September 1972) 68.

Spec. 1B, Oilfield V-Belting, API, Washington, DC (1995).

Spec. 11AX, Subsurface Sucker Rod Pumps and Fittings, Washington, DC (2001).

Spec. 11B, Sucker Rods, API, Washington, DC (1998).

Spec. 11C, Reinforced Plastic Sucker Rods, API, Washington, DC (1991).

Spec. 11E, Pumping Units, API, Washington, DC (1994).

Spec. 11V1, Gas Lift Valves, Orifices, Reverse Flow Valves and Dummy Valves, API, Washington, DC (1995).

Stewart, R.E.: "The Effects of Power Supply Integrity on Electrical Submersible Pumping Systems," paper SPE 9038 presented at the 1980 SPE Rocky Mountain Regional Meeting, Casper, Wyoming, 14–16 May.

Swaim, H.W. and Hein, N.W.: "Surface Dynamometer Card Interpretation: A Beam-Pumping Problem-Solving Tool," *Proc.,* Southwestern Petroleum Short Course, Lubbock, Texas (1987).

Tjondrodiputro, B. *et al.*: "Hydraulic Jet Pumping in a Remote Location," *World Oil* (November 1983) 51.

Tjondrodiputro, B. *et al.*: "Hydraulic Jet Pumping in a Remote Location," *World Oil* (December 1983) 109.

Tjondrodiputro, B. *et al.*: "Hydraulic Jet Pumping in a Remote Location," *World Oil* (January 1984) 101.

Tripp, H.A.: "Mechanical Performance of Fiberglass Sucker-Rod Strings," *SPEPE* (August 1988) 346.

Walker, M.: "Intermittent Injection of Gas in Gas Lift Installations," *Trans.,* AIME (1929) **82,** 151.

Weighhill, G.T.: "ESP Selection and Operating Strategy at Wytch Farm," presented at the 1992 European ESP Workshop, Aberdeen, 12 February.

White, G. *et al.*: "An Analytical Concept of the Static and Dynamic Parameters of Intermittent Gas Lift," *JPT* (March 1963) 301.

Wilson, P.M.: "Introduction to Hydraulic Pumping," Kobe Inc., Huntington Park, California (1976).

Wilson, P.M.: "Jet Pump—A Progress Review on Two Years of Field Performance," *Proc.,* Southwestern Petroleum Short Course, Lubbock, Texas (1973).

Winkler, H.W. and Smith, S.S.: *Camco Gas Lift Manual,* Camco Inc., Houston.

SI Metric Conversion Factors

acre	$\times$ 4.046 856	E + 03	= m^2
°API	141.5/(131.5+°API)		= g/cm^3
bbl	$\times$ 1.589 873	E – 01	= m^3
ft	$\times$ 3.048*	E – 01	= m
ft^3	$\times$ 2.831 685	E – 01	= m^3
°F	$\times$ (°F – 32)/1.8		= °C

hp	× 7.460 43	E − 01	= kW
in.	× 2.54*	E + 00	= cm
psi	× 6.894 757	E + 00	= kPa

*Conversion factor is exact.

Chapter 11
Sucker-Rod Lift
Norman W. Hein, Jr., ConocoPhillips*

11.1 Introduction

This chapter discusses the specific artificial-lift technique known as beam pumping, or the sucker-rod-lift method. Many books, technical articles, and industry standards have been published on the sucker-rod lift method and related technology.[1-7] This chapter is a complete revision of previous editions of the *Petroleum Engineering Handbook*,[6] but it combines the prior three relevant chapters that covered downhole rod pumps and sucker rods, along with pumping units and prime movers. Additionally, the other components of a sucker-rod pumping installation are discussed, including applicable engineering and operating information. The complete operating system should be understood and addressed to properly design, install, and operate this or any other type of artificial-lift system. Thus, this chapter uses the Gipson and Swaim "Beam Pump Design Chain" as a foundation and builds on this design philosophy by using relevant, published technology and the latest industry practices.[5-7]

11.1.1 Beam-Pumping Systems.
Beam pumping, or the sucker-rod lift method, is the oldest and most widely used type of artificial lift for most wells. A sucker-rod pumping system is made up of several components, some of which operate aboveground and other parts of which operate underground, down in the well. The surface-pumping unit, which drives the underground pump, consists of a prime mover (usually an electric motor) and, normally, a beam fixed to a pivotal post. The post is called a Sampson post, and the beam is normally called a walking beam. **Fig. 11.1** presents a detailed schematic of a typical beam-pump installation.

This system allows the beam to rock back and forth, moving the downhole components up and down in the process. The entire surface system is run by a prime mover, V-belt drives, and a gearbox with a crank mechanism on it. When this type of system is used, it is usually called a beam-pump installation. However, other types of surface-pumping units can be used, including hydraulically actuated units (with and without some type of counterbalancing system), or even tall-tower systems that use a chain or belt to allow long strokes and slow pumping speeds. The more-generic name of sucker-rod lift, or sucker-rod pumping, should be used to refer to all types of reciprocating rod-lift methods.

---

* Retired; now with Oil & Gas Optimization Specialists, Ltd.

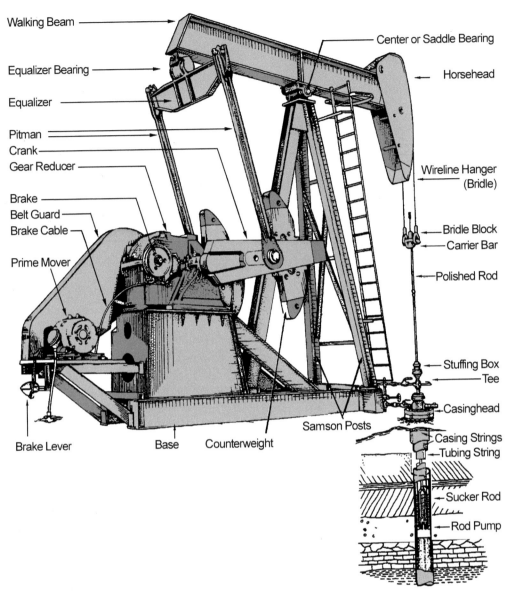

Fig. 11.1—Schematic of conventional pumping unit with major components of the sucker-rod-lift system.

   Linked rods attached to an underground pump are connected to the surface unit. The linked rods are normally called sucker rods and are usually long steel rods, from ⅝ to more than 1 or 1¼ in. in diameter. The steel rods are normally screwed together in 25- or 30-ft lengths; however, rods could be welded into one piece that would become a continuous length from the surface to the downhole pump. The steel sucker rods typically fit inside the tubing and are stroked up and down by the surface-pumping unit. This activates the downhole, positive-displacement pump at the bottom of the well. Each time the rods and pumps are stroked, a volume of produced fluid is lifted through the sucker-rod tubing annulus and discharged at the surface.

TABLE 11.1—ADVANTAGES AND DISADVANTAGES OF THE SUCKER-ROD
ARTIFICIAL-LIFT METHOD

Advantages	Disadvantages
Easy for personnel to operate to pump oil, water, and/or gas	Pulling unit needed to service downhole equipment
Mechanically simple	May cause solids formation such as paraffin and scale deposits
Will operate with a wide range of well-producing characteristics	Gassy wells usually lower volumetric efficiency and requires some type of downhole separation
Surface unit may be changed to other wells with minimum cost	Downhole pump may become gas locked
Method applicable to slimhole and multiple completions	Crooked holes present a problem and may require special operating equipment
Can pump a well down to very low pressure	Solids production from the well is a problem
System usually is naturally vented for gas-separation and fluid-level soundings	Surface system is noticeable and bulky in on-land and offshore operations
Method is flexible to match pump-displacement rate to well capability as well volumes decline	Downhole-pump design selection in small-diameter casing
High-temperature and viscous fluids can be lifted	Special requirements needed to install in some irrigated fields
Gas or electricity can be used as a power source	Surface stuffing-box leaks can cause pollution
Easy to perform corrosion and scale treatments if annulus is available	
Can analyze methods and has a wide operations knowledge base	
Can apply varying degrees of automation	

11.1.2 Selecting The Sucker-Rod Pumping Method. Many factors must be considered when determining the most appropriate lift system for a particular well. The chapter on Artificial Lift Selection in this volume of this *Handbook* presents a discussion of the normally available artificial-lift techniques, their advantages and disadvantages, and the selection of a method for a well installation.

Because of its long history of successfully lifting well fluids, the sucker-rod lift method is normally considered the first choice for most onshore, and even some offshore, installations all over the world. This method is limited by the size of the casing, tubing, and downhole pump; the strength and size of the various rods; and the speed with which they can be reciprocated. Under favorable conditions, approximately 150 BFPD can be lifted from greater than 14,000 ft, while more than 3,000 BFPD can be lifted from less than 2,000 ft.[8,9] Some of the major advantages and disadvantages of this lift technique are shown in **Table 11.1.**

11.2 The Producing Reservoir

Understanding the makeup of the producing reservoir, its pressure, and the changes that occur in it are important to attain maximum production. Because reservoir conditions change as fluids are produced, ongoing measurement of the reservoir conditions is necessary. The main considerations in measuring and understanding the reservoir are the types and volumes of reservoir fluids being produced, their pressures in both the reservoir and at the wellbore or pump intake, and the effects these fluids have as they pass through the producing system.

The relationship between the reservoir-fluid inflow and the produced-fluid outflow is extremely important for any artificial-lift method. This should be monitored and controlled so

that any excessive damage to the lift equipment is avoided while profitably obtaining the maximum amount of fluids. Undesirable effects result when the producing equipment's capacity is not properly balanced with reservoir-fluid inflow. These effects include the following:
- Loss or deferment of production.
- Excessive producing costs.
- Premature equipment failure.
- Ineffective use of energy.
- Increased operating expenses.

A variety of well tests and measurements may be used to determine production rates for oil-, gas-, and water-supply wells and to observe the status of the reservoir. Each test reveals certain information about the well and the reservoir being tested. The main reservoir considerations are determining bottomhole pressure and the inflow relationship of the fluids with changing reservoir and pump-intake pressure.

11.2.1 Bottomhole-Pressure Determination. Bottomhole-pressure-measuring equipment (pressure bombs) makes it possible to determine reservoir and tubing intake pressures within the desired range of accuracy. When this test is conducted at scheduled intervals, valuable information about the decline or depletion of the reservoir from which the well is producing can be obtained. However, it is difficult to obtain either bottomhole reservoir or operating pressures while the rod-pump system is installed and operating.

Calculations of the bottomhole pressures can be obtained by using instruments that detect the fluid level in the casing/tubing annulus. The simplest instrument is a fluid-level sounder with a strip chart. Bottomhole pressures can be estimated from the gravity of the fluids (i.e., oil, water, and gas), the volumes produced, and the fluid level. If producing and shut-in conditions are known, then approximate producing and shut-in reservoir pressures can be determined.

The key to accurate bottomhole-pressure determination in any pumping well is the ability to predict the gradient of the fluid in the casing/tubing annulus. In 1955, W.E. Gilbert* developed an iterative calculation procedure on the effect of gas bubbling up a static fluid column. This can be used in a trial-and-error method to determine a gradient correction factor (F) to determine the pressure at the desired depth in the presence of gas production. If the term $Q/(aP)^{0.4}$ is greater than 0.25, this method should be used with caution because this is an indication that liquid flow up the annulus may occur. Also, the crude pressure/volume/temperature (PVT) characteristics alter the results. The Gilbert curve and a calculation example are presented in "The Beam Pump Design Chain."[7]

Currently, the same fluid-level sounder equipment can be interfaced with a computer to determine the downhole pressures more easily.[10,11] However, there still needs to be verification of the fluid-level indication to ensure that "false" or incorrect annulus fluid levels are not recorded. Additionally, the fluid gravities and produced volumes must be accurate and reflect actual conditions.

Knowing the reservoir and pump-intake pressures during static and operating conditions will allow a determination of the well's production capacity. This is required to optimize the artificial-lift equipment and properly size the equipment that is installed. The well productivity under varying production conditions must then be known.

11.2.2 Inflow Performance Relationship (IPR). One of the most critical decisions in an artificial-lift system is the selection and design of equipment appropriate for the volume of fluid the reservoir produces. Other chapters of this *Handbook* detail the productivity index and IPR of fluids with changes in reservoir pressure. Because most fluid produced by an artificial-lift

---
* Unpublished internal report: "Curve Annulus Gradient Correction for Gas Bubbling Through Static Liquid Column," Shell Oil Co.

method is not single phase, it is not in a steady-state condition. Also, because most pumping operations occur after the fluid is below the bubblepoint pressure, the IPR method is usually considered. This technique takes into account various fluid phases and flow rates. It was originally devised by Vogel[12] and described by Eickmeier.[13] Each revision increased the accuracy of estimating flow rates from a well.

In the design of an artificial-lift system, it is necessary not only to predict production of the various fluids during existing conditions and reservoir pressure, but also to make a second type of prediction: future pressure performance. This can be accomplished with the IPR method and multiple, or a family of, IPR curves. Furthermore, the family of curves can be used to predict estimates of fluid production increases if the reservoir is repressurized from waterflooding or other secondary or tertiary methods.

Producing rates can be estimated within the desired range of accuracy using the IPR technique with two stabilized producing rates and corresponding stabilized producing pressures. This makes it possible to use the IPR without needing to shut in the well and lose production to obtain shut-in information. Obtaining a bottomhole pressure equal to 10% of the shut-in reservoir pressure is recommended for determining maximum production rates for sucker-rod lifted wells. At this pressure, the maximum well productivity will be 97% of the well's theoretical maximum production rate. However, the maximum lift-design rate should, in most cases, be slightly higher to permit some downtime and decreased pump efficiency.

11.2.3 Gas Production. In any artificial-lift system, the volume of gas produced should be considered in designing the system and in analyzing the operation after the system has been installed. A complete analysis requires knowing the volume of gas in solution, the volume of free gas, the formation volume factors, and whether gas is produced through the pump or is vented. If PVT analyses of reservoir fluids are available, they are the most accurate and easiest to use as a source of solution gas/oil ratio (GOR), formation volume factors, etc. The next best source is an analysis from a nearby similar reservoir.

A means of estimating PVT data is contained in *Volumetric and Phase Behavior of Oil Field Hydrocarbon Systems*.[14] With the produced GOR, gas gravity, oil gravity, and reservoir temperature, the following can be estimated using the instructions included on each chart:
  • Chart 1: The formation volume factor for the gas plus the liquid phases.
  • Chart 2: The bubblepoint pressure.
  • Chart 3: The formation volume factor of the bubblepoint liquid.

11.2.4 Gas Venting. When pumping through tubing in the absence of a production packer, free gas, which breaks out of the oil, should be vented up from the casing/tubing annulus. However, when it is necessary to produce from beneath a production packer, a vent string can be installed. The possibility of needing a vent string should be considered when planning casing sizes for a new well.

Both the size of the vent string and the location of its bottom, with respect to the location of the pump intake and producing perforations, will influence the string's effectiveness in removing free gas. The string's diameter should be designed to allow the production of the anticipated free-gas volume with a pressure drop no greater than the desired producing bottomhole pressure minus the surface backpressure. If the required pressure drop is greater than this, a portion of the free gas will have to go through the pump. **Fig. 11.2** is an indication of the effect of vent-string size on the pressure drop through it. Care should be taken if small-diameter tubing is used, because it may not allow all the gas to flow up the vent or may simply load up and prevent most gas flow.

11.2.5 Effect of Gas on Pump Performance. Gas that remains in solution when the liquid enters the pump increases the volume of total fluid through the pump compared to the liquid

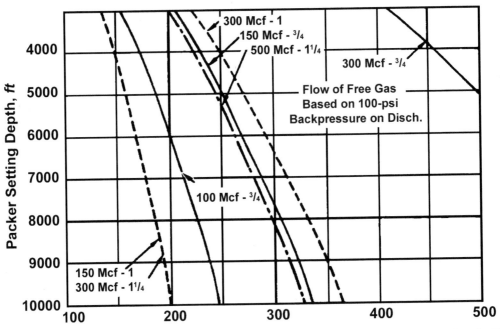

Fig. 11.2—Gas-flow-volume (Mcf) limitations for various-sized vent strings set at various packer depths (ft).

measured at the surface by the formation volume factor at pump-intake conditions. The gas also decreases the density of the fluid and, thus, the head or pressure to be pumped against in the tubing. Free gas that enters the pump must be compressed to a pressure equivalent to the head required to lift the fluid. This free gas will reduce the volume of both the produced liquid that enters the pump and the liquid measured at the surface. Any time the pump does not compress the free gas to a pressure greater than that exerted on the pump by the fluid column in the producing string, production ceases and the pump is said to be "gas locked." This condition can exist in both plunger and centrifugal pumps.

11.2.6 Intake Pressure. Intake pressure is the pressure in the annulus opposite the point at which the fluid enters the pump. If the pump-intake pressure is increased by increasing the pump submergence, the free-gas volume decreases because the fluid retains more gas in solution. Reducing the pressure drop in the pump-suction piping also reduces the free gas to be produced. The pump intake should not be deeper than is necessary to maintain the desired intake pressure. A pump intake that is too deep results in unnecessary investment and increased operating costs.

Fig. 11.3 is a graph of the liquid produced as a percent of the displacement of a plunger pump plotted against the pump-intake pressure for a typical reservoir.[15] If the pressure is greater than the bubblepoint (Point A to B), the volumetric efficiency remains nearly constant. If all the gas can be vented rather than passed through the pump, the volumetric efficiency will increase as the formation volume factor decreases (Point B to C). If all the gas must be pumped, the volumetric efficiency decreases as the intake pressure drops to less than the bubblepoint (Point B to F). The lines B–D and B–E indicate the volumetric efficiency with a partial venting of gas as its presence declines. Note that the efficiency declines to a minimum at less than the bubblepoint and with further pressure reduction, starts to increase. A general conclusion is that to obtain better efficiencies, the pump-intake pressure should be maintained

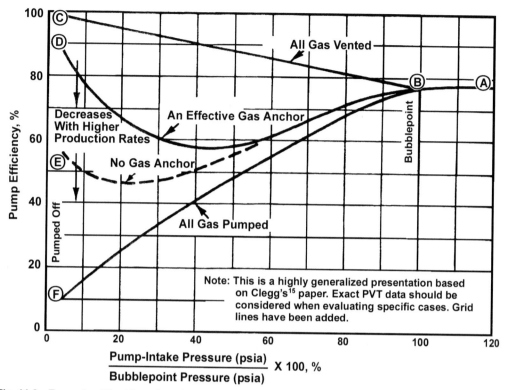

Fig. 11.3—Example of liquid produced as a percentage of plunger-pump displacement for various pump-intake pressures and the effect of gas on efficiency.

at or greater than the bubblepoint, or decreased to as low as possible to take advantage of the increased separation efficiencies at the low-pressure end. However, this considers only pump efficiency and not maximum production rate.

Gas bubbles entrained in the produced liquid(s) tend to rise because of the difference in the liquid and gas densities. The rate of bubble rise depends on the size of the bubbles and the physical properties of the fluid. The size of the bubbles increases as the pressure decreases. At low pump-intake pressures, the rate of gas-bubble rise in low-viscosity fluids will approximate 0.5 ft/sec, assuming a 400-μm bubble rise in water. The increase in bubble size and rate of rise as the pressure decreases causes the reversal in curves B–D and B–E in Fig. 11.3.

11.2.7 Downhole Gas Separators and Anchors. Downhole gas separators are used in gassy wells to increase the volume of free gas removed from the liquids before reaching the pump. However, they are not 100% effective in separating the gas. In sucker-rod-pumped wells, these separators are normally called "gas anchors." Gas anchors are usually designed and built in the field; **Fig. 11.4** contains schematic drawings of six common types. The most commonly used are the "natural" gas anchor (A) and the "poor boy" gas anchor (C). Typically, there are two major components for these gas-anchor assemblies, the mud anchor run on the bottom of the tubing string and the dip tube or strainer nipple run on the bottom of the pump.

The largest downhole gravity separator is normally the casing/tubing annulus. This area provides a maximum down passage for liquid and up-flow area for gas. This allows the oil (and water) to move relatively slowly, typically, downward from the perforations to the pump, and permits the gas to separate and flow upward. For this reason, a natural gas anchor should be used whenever practical because it takes advantage of the entire casing internal cross-sectional

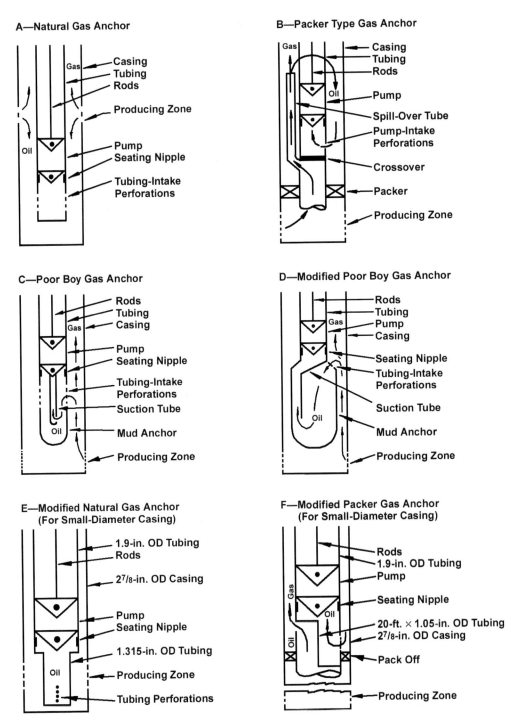

Fig. 11.4—Schematics of the six most common types of downhole gas separators (anchors).

area. This type of separator typically should be placed approximately 15 ft below the lowest most-active well perforations. However, if there is insufficient distance in the well to place the pump intake below the perforations, then the pump intake should be placed approximately 15 ft above the top-most perforation and a poor boy separator should be properly designed and installed.

There are limitations on how much gas can be handled by the downhole separator. If more gas is produced than can be handled by the separator, the gas will not separate completely. The downhole pump must then handle the excess gas. If the wells exceed these theoretical gas rates, then pump volumetric efficiency decreases, liquid production decreases, energy is wasted, and operating costs rise. The situation worsens if excessive gas enters the pump and there is insufficient compression ratio to pump all the fluids, resulting in a gas-locked pump. When this occurs, operating costs for this well increase dramatically because when there is no production, there is no revenue. However, a properly designed and spaced pump should not gas lock if the well is not pumped off.

Example calculations of the gas capacity of various casing/tubing annuli vs. different intake pressures have been presented in Ref. 9. This reference also discusses the types of downhole separators and emphasizes the need to run a natural gas-anchor assembly whenever possible.[9] Detailed discussions on design of the different types of separators, the arrangement of components, and example calculations for sizing components are presented by Gipson and Swaim.[7] Improved gas separators with decentralized intakes have been introduced.[16,17] This design aids in separation efficiency because it increases the local distance from the casing's inner diameter (ID) to the mud anchor, which results in an increased separation area. However, as with all specialty devices, the need to run this new design should be demonstrated by ensuring that the appropriate, standard systems have been properly installed and operated.

11.2.8 Fishing. It is often recommended that the outside diameter (OD) of the gas anchors' steel mud anchor be less than the ID of the largest overshot or wash pipe that can be run in the well casing. This limits the gas-anchor separation capacity that can be secured in wells with small casings. Reinforced plastic mud anchors that can be drilled up, or steel designs that can be recovered with spears, should be considered when mud anchor OD must approach casing-drift diameter. This design would then be considered the "modified poor boy." Agreement should be obtained from the field before installation to ensure acceptance of the possible problems when trying to pull this type of installation.

11.3 Downhole Sucker-Rod Pumps

11.3.1 Major Components. There are seven major components for downhole rod pumps: standing and traveling valves, plunger, barrel, seating assembly, pull tube or valve rod (for insert pump), and the fittings that hold the assembled pump together. The most common of these components and the final types of assembled pumps are covered by American Petroleum Inst. (API) *Specification 11AX*.[18]

11.3.2 Types of Pumps. API recognizes two main types of pumps: rod and tubing. Rod pumps also are called insert pumps because they are run (inserted) in the production tubing. Tubing pumps are so named because the working barrel of this pump is coupled with the production-tubing string.

There is a wide range of plunger (or pump-bore) sizes standardized by the industry. The API pump-bore sizes that are currently available range from $1\frac{1}{16}$ to $3\frac{3}{4}$ in. in diameter. This $1\frac{1}{16}$-in. size has been added back in the latest edition of the standard. Additionally, a new barrel type has been accepted in the latest API *Spec. 11AX*. This is the "X-type" barrel. It has a thin-walled barrel configuration for threads on either end of the heavy-walled barrel and is available for metal plungers only. This type of pump does not require the extension couplings normally needed for heavy-walled barrel pumps. Thus, this pump reduces the burst or collapse

TABLE 11.2—API *SPEC. 11AX*[18] LETTER DESIGNATION FOR THE VARIOUS TYPES OF STANDARD PUMPS

| | API Letter Designation | | | |
| | Metal Plunger Pumps | | Soft-Packed Plunger Pumps | |
Pump Type	Heavy-Wall Barrel	Thin-Wall Barrel	Heavy-Wall Barrel	Thin-Wall Barrel
Rod pumps				
Stationary barrel, top anchor	RHA	RWA	—	
Stationary barrel, bottom anchor	RHB	RWB	—	RSA
Stationary barrel, bottom anchor	RXB	—	—	RSB
Traveling barrel, bottom anchor	RHT	RWT	—	RST
Tubing pumps	TH	—	TP	—

concerns of the thin-walled extension couplings and allows deeper producing depths to be attained.

11.3.3 API Pumps and Nomenclature. While there are only two main types of pumps standardized by API, there are four different types of rod pumps. These are classified by the type of barrel (standing or traveling) and where the pump is anchored (top or bottom). **Table 11.2** shows the letter designations for the various types of rod and tubing pumps that are available for different barrel thicknesses and either metal or soft-packed plungers.

The complete pump designation of an API pump adds dimensional diameters and lengths to the letter designations. This has been modified in the latest revision to incorporate all approved sizes and barrel types along with separating the extensions into the top and bottom lengths, if required. The complete API designation includes the following:

- Nominal tubing size (from 1.9- to 4.5-in. OD).
- Basic bore diameter (from 1.0625 to 3.75 in.).
- Type of pump (rod or tubing).
- Type of barrel (heavy, thin, or X type).
- Seating-assembly location (top or bottom).
- Type of seating assembly (cup or mechanical).
- Barrel length (ft).
- Nominal plunger length (in.).
- Length (in.) of upper extension (if required).
- Length (in.) of lower extension (if required).

Fig. 11.5 shows the API nomenclature for pumps covered by API *Spec. 11AX*. For example, a 1¼-in. bore-rod-type pump with a 10-ft heavy-walled barrel, a 2-ft upper extension, a 2-ft lower extension, a 4-ft plunger, and a bottom-cup-type seating assembly that will be used in 2⅜-in. tubing would be designated as 20-125-RHBC-10-4-2-2.

It is important to know that the users of API pumps need to provide, along with the pump nomenclature, the following ordering information: barrel and plunger material, plunger clearance (or fit tolerance), and valve (ball and seat) and fittings material. The materials normally available for each of these components also are now included in the latest edition of API *Spec. 11AX.*

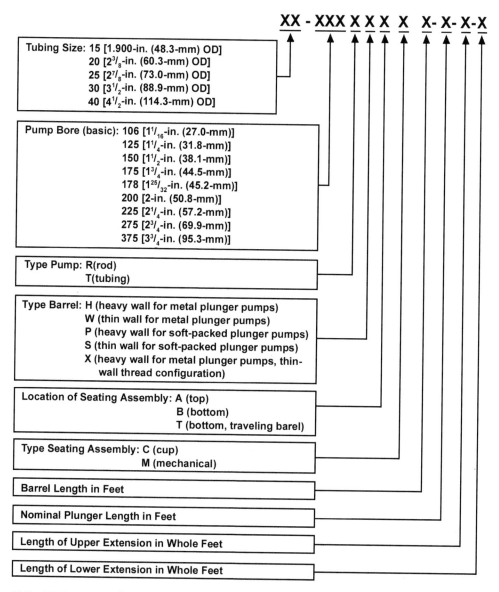

Fig. 11.5—API *Spec. 11AX*[18] description requirements for standardized pumps and the available options for the various components.

11.3.4 Non-API and Specialty Pumps. The types of pumps, sizes, and component materials that are included in the API standards are based on the best industry practices that meet the widespread industry needs. While API standardizes the majority of pumps and components that are used in sucker-rod lift, there are special parts and pumps that have been developed by manufacturers to try to solve specific pumping problems. This specialty equipment should be considered when best industry practices and standardized components have proved unacceptable. However, the manufacturer of these components should create all parts to the same quality level required in API *Spec. 11AX*.

Useful specialty pumps include the following:

• Casing pump for production without tubing.

• Pumps with two plungers that act in series to increase displacement.
• High-compression plunger assembly or pump for handling gas-interference problems.
• Three-tube pump for handling fines or solids.
• Pumps with a shorter barrel than normally recommended, so that the plunger completely wipes solids free of the barrel and prevents sticking.

Additionally, there are special pump components, such as valve rods, valves, and tubing drains, that are sometimes beneficial in situations in which the capabilities of normal API pumps and components have been exceeded. The manufacturer of special, non-API pumps and components should be contacted to determine the working capabilities and limitations of any of these specialty components. However, these items should be selected with care and used only after the best production effort has been thoroughly tested with standard components.

11.3.5 Materials Selection. The most recent API *Spec. 11AX* was modified to add not only new sizes and types of pumps with new quality, inspection, and tolerance requirements, but also standardized, widely used pump-component materials. **Table 11.3** presents the various material descriptions, their API identification symbol, surface condition, base core hardness, base material, and base-material minimum yield strength for plated barrels, as shown in API Table A of *Spec. 11AX*. Similar tables in *Spec. 11AX* (B through I) are incorporated for case-hardened barrels, nonhardened barrels, balls and seats, cages, pull tubes, valve rods, fittings, seating cups, spray-metal plungers, and plated plungers. These changes have incorporated the prior information in API *RP 11AR*[19] and the Natl. Assn. of Corrosion Engineers (NACE) *MR 01-76*[20] for materials to be used in most production environments.

11.3.6 Allowable Setting Depth. In the early 1990s, an industry task group analyzed the stresses that react on a downhole rod pump. This was required to determine if there were recommended allowable loads that could be subjected to rod pumps of different types, sizes, and metallurgy. This group developed the burst, collapse, and axial-loading equations to determine these limits and the associated maximum recommended setting depth for sucker-rod lift pumps,[21] published in API *RP 11AR*[19]; an example of the recommended setting depth of this standard is presented in **Table 11.4**. The depth limitation and stresses on the downhole pump barrel and components should be considered when selecting the size, type, and metallurgy for a downhole pump.

11.3.7 Slippage Past Plungers. The slippage or leakage past a plunger on a closely fitted sucker-rod pump is an important factor in properly designing and operating a well. The previous edition of the *Petroleum Engineering Handbook* discusses the main factors that affect leakage. Eq. 1 in Chap. 8 on sucker-rod pumps[6] can be rewritten, combining constants, as the following equation:

$$Q = (1{,}540{,}000 \times D \times p \times L_p \times C^3)/(\mu *), \quad\dots\dots\dots\dots\dots\dots\dots\dots\dots (11.1)$$

in which Q = slippage or leakage loss, in.^{3}/min; D = plunger diameter, in.; P = differential pressure across plunger, psi; C = diametrical clearance between plunger and barrel, in.; μ = absolute viscosity of fluid, cp; and L_p = plunger length, in.

The importance of plunger leakage is demonstrated in the example in the previous edition of the *Handbook* that shows for a 0.003-in. clearance, a 2¼-in.-diameter pump with a 48-in.-long plunger operating with a pressure differential of 2,000 psi at 15 strokes per minute (spm) and a 48-in. stroke length. Tight clearances (less than 0.003 in.) may cause producing problems, whereas loose clearances (greater than 0.008 in.) may result in excessive leakage by the pump. Good field-pump records are essential to make good pump recommendations.

TABLE 11.3—API *SPEC. 11AX*[18] TABLE 1: MATERIALS, DESIGNATION, AND PROPERTIES REQUIREMENTS FOR PLATED BARRELS

Identification Symbol	Description	Inside Surface Condition	Base Curve Hardness	Base Material	Base Material Minimum Yield Strength (ksi)
A1	Chrome plate on steel	0.0003-in. (0.76-mm) minimum thickness, 900 to 1160 HV_{100}	55 to 62 HRA	UNS G10XX0 steel	60
A2	Chrome plate on brass	0.0003-in. (0.76-mm) minimum thickness, 900 to 1160 HV_{100}	80 to 100 HRB	Inhibited admiralty brass	50
A3	Chrome plate on 4/6 chrome steel	0.0003-in. (0.76-mm) minimum thickness, 900 to 1160 HV_{100}	55 to 62 HRA	UNS S50100 steel, 4 to 6% alloy	70
A4	Chrome plate on Nickel/Copper alloy	0.0003-in. (0.76-mm) minimum thickness, 900 to 1160 HV_{100}	55 to 62 HRA	Nickel/Copper alloy	55
A5	Chrome plate on low-alloy steel	0.0003-in. (0.76-mm) minimum thickness, 900 to 1160 HV_{100}	55 to 62 HRA	UNS G10XX0 low-alloy steel	60
A6	Heavy chrome plate on steel	0.0003-in. (0.76-mm) minimum thickness, 900 to 1160 HV_{100}	55 to 62 HRA	UNS G10XX0 steel	60
E1	Nickel carbide composite on steel	0.0013-in. (0.033-mm) minimum thickness	55 to 62 HRA	UNS G10XX0 steel	60
E2	Nickel carbide composite on low-alloy steel	0.0013-in. (0.033-mm) minimum thickness	55 to 62 HRA	UNS G10XX0 low-alloy steel	50
E3	Nickel carbide composite on brass	0.0013-in. (0.033-mm) minimum thickness	80 to 100 HRB	Inhibited admiralty brass	50
E4	Nickel carbide composite on steel	0.0013-in. (0.033-mm) minimum thickness	55 to 62 HRA	UNS G10XX0 steel	60
E5	Nickel carbide composite on 4/6 chrome	0.0013-in. (0.033-mm) minimum thickness	55 to 62 HRA	UNS S50100 steel, 4 to 6% chrome	70

Note: HRA=Rockwell hardness A scale, HRB=Rockwell hardness B scale, UNS=Unified numbering system, and HV_{100}=Vickers Hardness, 100-kg load.

11.3.8 Compression Ratio. Increasing the "compression ratio" of a plunger pump may reduce the effects of free gas and help prevent gas locking. The compression ratio is the volume of the pump chamber at the start of the downstroke divided by the volume at the end of the stroke. This ratio is fixed by the manufacturer on the basis of the design of the rod pump's components and the fit of the plunger to the pump barrel. Varying the sucker-rod pump compo-

TABLE 11.4—API *RP11AR*[19] SETTING-DEPTH RECOMMENDATIONS FOR THE VARIOUS TYPES AND SIZES OF API STANDARD PUMPS FOR TWO STANDARD METALLURGIES

Bore Size	1.25	1.50	1.75	2.00	2.25	2.50	2.75
Material: Low-carbon steel—Su=80 ksi, S =32 ksi, and Sy=60 ksi							
RWA, RSA	6,394	5,520	—	3,732	—	3,183	—
RWB, RSB, and RWT	16,936	14,705	—	9,727	—	6,362	—
RHA	8,321	8,818	6,749	—	4,876	—	—
RHB, RHT	27,148	24,249	21,897	—	19,323	—	6,262
TH, TP	—	—	10,019	—	7,763	—	6,262
TH, TP (TPRD THD)	—	—	8,187	—	7,047	—	5,726
Extension couplings							
With RHA	7,568	6,118	4,706	—	3,824	—	—
With RHB	25,728	28,714	20,708	—	17,294	—	—
Material: Admiralty Brass—Su=75 ksi, S =25 ksi, and Sy = 60 ksi							
RWA, RSA	4,989	4,306	—	2,911	—	2,482	—
RWB, RSB, and RWT	16,936	14,704	—	9,727	—	6,362	—
RHA	6,490	6,878	5,264	—	3,802	—	—
RHB, RHT	27,148	28,714	21,897	—	18,323	—	—
TH, TP	—	—	7,815	—	6,062	—	4,809
TH, TP (TPRD THD)	—	—	6,386	—	5,496	—	4,466
Extension CPLGS*							
With RHA	5,913	4,780	3,675	—	2,986	—	—
With RHB	25,728	24,249	20,708	—	17,294	—	—

*The limiting setting depth should be that of the specific RHA or RHB that the extension coupling is used with.
Su=ultimate tensile strength, ksi=1000 lbm/psi; S=endurance limit, ksi=1000 lbm/in.; and Sy=yield strength, ksi.

nents and close spacing will alter the compression ratio; however, some of these components are not standardized by the API *Spec. 11AX*. This can increase waste space in the pump, resulting in a decreased compression ratio. The importance of the compression ratio and associated waste space may prevent a new pump from being able to pump down a well.[22] This work by McCafferty is further discussed in Ref. 9, which also presents different pump manufacturers' normal compression ratios for similar pump types.

11.3.9 Selection of Subsurface Rod Pumps. Pumps for sucker-rod lifted wells should be selected on the basis of numerous variables that are provided by the well, the operating conditions, and the life of the pump. The main variables to consider are as follows:
- Well depth.
- Bottomhole temperature.
- Fluid viscosity.
- Amount and size of particulates in the produced fluids.
- Produced-fluids corrosivity.
- Required production rate vs. pump capacity.
- Fluid-specific gravity.
- Casing/tubing size.
- Well-completion type.
- Gas/liquid ratio (GLR).
- Pump-intake pressure vs. fluid bubblepoint.

• Spare/surplus pumps and components.
• New purchase and repair costs.

These variables influence the stresses on the pump, type of pump used, component metallurgy, pump size, internal-fit tolerance, and ability to handle solids/gas. Discussing these parameters with the pump manufacturer and local pump shop should help determine the proper pump to ensure acceptable pump life.

11.3.10 Pump Sizing. There are two aspects to consider when sizing the downhole pump for an installation. The first is that the pump capacity should be related to the well capacity. The pump displacement is determined on the basis of the pumping speed, unit stroke length, and plunger diameter. This general equation is

$$P_D = 0.1166 \times S \times N \times D^2, \quad\text{..}\quad (11.2)$$

in which P_D = pump displacement, BFPD; 0.1166 = a volumetric conversion; S = stroke length, in.; N = pumping speed, spm; and D = diameter of the pump plunger, in.

The stroke length should be the expected downhole stroke or plunger stroke (S_p) that is calculated from a sucker-rod string calculation or sizing computer program. However, the surface stroke length may be considered an approximation of the maximum capacity for a given pumping situation.

The recommended relationship of pump displacement to well capacity (W_C), as discussed in Ref. 9, is as follows:

$$(W_C / 0.85) \leq P_D \leq (W_C / 0.65). \quad\text{...}\quad (11.3)$$

Thus, for a well that produces 100 BFPD, the various pumping parameters should be selected to provide a pump displacement of between 118 and 154 BFPD. Because the pump displacement is greater than the well capacity, the system will require some type of well control to prevent constant operation and overpumping of the well. This increased capacity accommodates pump wear and loss of efficiency with time. As this occurs, system control should be adjusted to continue producing as required, without overpumping by running the pump more often. It should be considered that as the pump diameter increases, the efficiency of the system increases. However, this also increases the load on the rod string and the peak torque for the pumping unit. Thus, reasonable selection of these pumping parameters should be considered that results in extended run time.

The second aspect of pump sizing, once the pump diameter is selected, is ensuring that the downhole pump is properly built. The main component that needs to be sized is the barrel length, which should be long enough to accommodate the plunger length, the downhole stroke length, all fittings, and a rounding factor.

The minimum plunger length recommended is normally 3 ft. It is recommended that the length of the plunger is increased 1 ft/1,000 ft of well depth, up to a 6-ft maximum length. Plunger lengths longer than 6 ft have not shown to be an advantageous, while specialty pumps may have a plunger shorter than 3 ft.

When determining the barrel length, normally the maximum pumping-unit stroke length is considered to allow pump displacement to be increased with the existing downhole pump without pulling the downhole pumping equipment to change the capacity. However, this extra length and the pump-displacement option increase the price of the pump. Thus, the downhole S_p length should be considered the stroke measurement to use in the barrel-length calculation.

The types of fittings and their respective lengths depend on the type of pump being used. Normally, 12 to 18 in. covers the length range for various pump types.

The final factor in determining the barrel length is a rounding factor. Once the previous factors are added together, the length-of-barrel calculation is normally increased to the next available whole-foot standard length for a pump according to API *Spec. 11AX.*[18] Using the surface stroke length vs. the downhole S_p length, and designating this length as the rounding factor, may provide sufficient barrel length to accommodate the spacing length some operators or pump shops suggest.

This spacing factor is normally a minimum of 24 in. for wells up to 4,000 ft deep, then increases 6 in. in length per 1,000 ft of increased well depth. These rules are recommended for all steel sucker-rod strings. When fiber-reinforced plastic (FRP) rods are used, additional increased spacing may be required because of the increased "stretch" or elongation of the rod string under the load. The FRP-rod manufacturer should have, or have access to, a sucker-rod-string design program that will estimate the increased plunger travel. This length then should be used in the barrel-length determination. Thus, for a 5,000-ft-deep well, with a required 74-in. surface stroke, a 48-in.-long plunger with a steel rod string and a designated 2⅞ × 1½-in. RHB pump, the displacement length must be greater than 152 in. to permit adequate spacing. A standard 12-ft barrel with 1-ft top and bottom extension couplings should be considered.

11.3.11 Pump Operating Problems and Solutions. There are four common ways subsurface rod pumps are abused. These problems may also be applicable to other downhole pumps, and thus, these related solutions probably are applicable to other artificial-lift techniques. The four common abuses follow:

- Overpumping the well.
- Gas interference.
- Pump hitting up or down.
- Trash entering the pump.

Because the recommended pump-displacement design is for the pump to have greater capacity than the well, an overpumping condition may occur if the well is not properly controlled. An overpumping condition is indicated when there is a fluid pound more than one-quarter of the way down on the downstroke because of insufficient fluid in the well to charge or fill the downhole pump. This condition may be seen on the surface if the pound is very severe, but the best way to detect this is with the use of a dynamometer. Other indications of overpumping are if the pump volumetric efficiency is less than 70% or if a downhole fluid-level survey shows that the normal operating fluid level is at or very near the pump intake. Overpumping may cause mechanical damage to the pump or cause damage uphole to the rod/tubing because of increased buckling and wear. Properly setting a well controller will help reduce severe overpumping.

Indications of gas interference include low volumetric efficiency, while the fluid-level survey shows apparent, adequate pump submergence and a polish rod that is excessively hot to the touch. A dynamometer survey, when combined with the precalculated well loads for the applicable design conditions, may indicate gas pound, gas lock, or inconsistency with the assumed conditions. The gas-interference condition may be remedied by increasing the pump compression ratio, if possible. This may be as simple as respacing the pump as the fluid level decreases in the well annuli or changing the stroke length for the pump downhole, or it may require pulling the pump and altering its design. The compression ratio of the replacement pump should be determined to ensure adequate lift capabilities. Additionally, a pump with tighter fit tolerance/waste space, smaller pump diameter, increased stroke length, adequate downhole separation, and properly designed pump gas anchor should be considered along with properly placing the pump intake above or below the perforations, as previously discussed. Finally, if these normal solutions do not resolve the problem, then special pumps or specialty components may be considered.

A pump component hitting on the up- or downstroke is indicated by an instantaneous load change and can be shown with a load-capable dynamometer. This condition normally occurs because of inadequate pump spacing as the fluid level pumps down or because the pump has inadequate compression ratio/excessive waste space for the seating depth for the designed pumping parameters. While severely "tapping," or "tagging," the pump may be heard, felt, or seen, the smashed pump components obtained during a pump teardown will show the damage this condition causes. This condition may also be magnified for tubing that does not have an anchor, or if the anchor is not properly set. Other conditions that may cause this problem include if the pump-intake piping is plugged or not properly designed, if the pump has inadequate compression ratio, if the polished-rod clamp is not sufficiently tightened, and/or if the pump barrel is not properly sized.

The last normal operating problem is caused by solids entering the pump. There are many reasons for these particulates. The particulates may be caused by well conditions such as producing the fracturing sand back into the wellbore, very fine powder from the formation, iron sulfide scale from the downhole equipment because of inadequate corrosion inhibition, iron sulfide or other scales from the formation because of incompatible fluids, or from overpumping the well. Solutions include using different types of pumps designed to handle fines and solids, such as three-tube pumps or soft-packed plungers, and using harder materials or coatings for the pump components. Filters or downhole, wire-wrapped screens have been used with limited success until they plug. In the past, tighter fit tolerances (< 0.003 in.) for the plunger-barrel annuli have been considered; however, recent work done in both the laboratory and the field, has shown the benefit of increasing these tolerances to greater than 0.005 in. when solids are a problem.[23] This work has resulted in the variable-slippage pump that would be useful for conditions in which solids are present in the produced fluids and gas interference is also a problem.[24]

11.3.12 Pump Shop, Repair, and Audit. The pump manufacturer typically machines or obtains subcontract pump components for future assembly of the pump by a pump shop. The shop, the knowledge of the design, selection of pump types, and associated component metallurgies become critical to long well life and a decreased failure frequency. API *RP 11AR*[19] provides useful information on pump types, component and metallurgy selection, pump-setting-depth calculation, and pump assembly/teardown.

While the pump manufacturers usually produce their pump components with an acceptable quality program (such as ISO *9001*[25] or API *Spec. Q1*[26]), most pump shops are not covered under these rigorous plans. Thus, it becomes critical to have the pump shop and its employees audited by qualified personnel to ensure that training, workmanship, safety, and environmental considerations are adequate. On the basis of many shop audits, assembly and teardown observations, requirements and recommendations in API standards, and performance quality requirements, a checklist that should be used as a first step in obtaining an acceptable pump shop has been developed and published.[27] Once the audit is performed and the checklist completed, the findings should be discussed with the appropriate pump-shop personnel and a time line developed detailing when changes to resolve any problem areas will be made.

11.4 Sucker Rods

11.4.1 Steel Sucker Rods. API *Spec. 11B*[28] provides the industry requirements for sucker rods and some related sucker-rod lift equipment. The three main grades of steel rods follow:
• Grade C rods that have minimum and maximum tensile strengths of 90,000 and 115,000 psi, respectively.
• Grade K rods that have a minimum tensile strength of 90,000 psi and a maximum strength of 115,000 psi. These rods are made with 1.65 to 2.00% nickel and are, therefore, more expensive than Grade C rods, but may have improved corrosion-related properties.

• Grade D rods that have a minimum tensile strength of 115,000 psi and a maximum strength of 140,000 psi. Three types of this grade are covered by *Spec. 11B:* plain-carbon, alloy, and special-alloy steels.

Spec. 11B allows for rod lengths of 25 or 30 ft and pony rods in six lengths (i.e., 20, 44, 68, 92, 116, and 140 in. measured from contact face of pin shoulder to contact face of pin shoulder). The acceptable rod diameter goes from ⅝ to 1⅛ in. in ⅛-in. increments. The most common rods in use will meet API specifications and will probably be in 25-ft lengths. The most important selection requirement is that the pulling rig can accommodate single-, double-, or triple-length rod segments.

The API does not specify the minimum yield strength for sucker rods. Where the yield strength of a rod string is necessary in calculations, it is recommended that if the manufacturer is not known, a minimum yield of 60,000 psi for Grade C and K and of 100,000 psi for Grade D should be used. If the manufacturer and rod type are known, the actual yield-strength values may be used. For good operating practices, the minimum yield strength should not be exceeded.

API *RP 11BR*[29] provides industry recommendations on the selection and use of API-grade rods.

11.4.2 Pony Rods. Pony rods are sucker rods shorter than 25 ft, and they vary in length. They are most commonly placed adjacent to the polished rod at the top of the rod string, on top of the downhole pump for handling purposes, and on top of the polished rod with appropriate couplings to prevent the string from falling downhole if the polished-rod clamp slips. Old pony rods normally should not be used in the load-carrying part of a new rod strings. Thus, when placing the rod string with new suckers, new pony rods should be used.

11.4.3 FRP Sucker Rods. FRP sucker rods may be used instead of metal under certain conditions. These rods are normally made from protruded fiberglass. They also are standardized in size and performance by API *Spec. 11B.* Reviewing this standard shows that temperature, load reversals, and fatigue life have a bigger effect on FRP rods than on steel rods. It is important to keep the following in mind when screening a well for FRP-rod use:

• FRP-rod bodies will not corrode, but the rest of the steel components, including the fiberglass pin connectors and couplings, the steel rods making up the rest of the string, the pump, tubing, casing, flowlines, etc., still have to be protected if producing a corrosive fluid. Thus, fiberglass rods should not be used alone to prevent rod-string corrosion or system failures or to eliminate the need for an effective corrosion-inhibition program.

• FRP rods should be considered when the pumping-unit gear-reducer torque or structure rating exceed design limitation and need to be decreased. Reducing the weight of the sucker-rod string reduces the torque measured at the polished rod. However, if the well is expected to produce long term, it may be more cost effective to upsize the pumping unit.

• It should be determined if it will be possible to stroke the subsurface pump plunger because of the increased elasticity and effect on S_p.

• If the well deviation is very large at any point, the increased friction may cause buckling and compressive stresses on the sucker rods. Increased buckling is very damaging to FRP rods; thus, these probably should not be run in deviated wells.

• Allowing fluid or gas pounding may produce damaging compressive forces in the FRP rods; thus, maximum drawdown is not possible.

Currently, there is no recognized formula for calculating overtravel when a mixed FRP and steel rod string is used. An attempt was made by an API task group to try modifying API *RP 11L*[30] to include a FRP-rod-string analysis, but this was not accepted by the industry. A study of several FRP string-design analyses indicate that rod-string overtravel may be approximately equal to the following:

$$3.1(S \times N^2)/70,500(L_{PSD}/1,000)^2, \dots\dots\dots\dots\dots\dots\dots\dots\dots \quad (11.4)$$

where S = stroke length, in.; N = pumping speed, spm; and L_{PSD} = seating nipple/pump depth, ft. This overtravel approximately equals twice the expected value when using steel sucker-rod strings.

11.4.4 Non-API Sucker Rods. Non-API sucker rods generally fall into two groups: one contains rods with a higher strength than API Grade D, and the other contains rods made of alloys that are less susceptible to corrosion or that have received a special heat treatment.

The high-strength group is generally harder and higher strength than Grade D and may be more susceptible to hydrogen embrittlement and notch effects that may then decrease run life.

Those rods that have a special heat treatment or are made of special alloys are normally premium-priced items. Thus, a full economic analysis should be conducted and good operating records obtained to determine if use of these rods is cost effective.

Flexible Strand. Approximately 40 years ago, a top steel manufacturer experimented with the use of plastic-coated wire cable instead of sucker rods. This cable was a continuous strand that required special pulling equipment. Sufficient sinker bars or a special pull-down pump had to be used to keep any compressive force from acting on the strand. The connectors used at the pump or at the top of the sinker bars were the weakest portion of the flexible strand. If any of the strands furnished the weight that was required to help open the traveling valve, the strands immediately above the sinker bars failed in short order because of the compressive forces. This type of rod string was less expensive than a normal API steel string and was found useful for unloading gas wells. The biggest disadvantages that restricted the use of this type of string were lack of service-company support and the inability to make field repairs.

Continuous Solid Rod (COROD).* The advantage of this rod is its ability to pull the entire rod string in one piece with a special pulling unit. These rods are available in either round or elliptical configurations and vary in size from $^{12}\!/_{16}$- to $^{18}\!/_{16}$-in. diameter. The disadvantages include the need for a special wheeled pulling rig, and the two different pulling units are required to service the well if the tubing has to be pulled. There is some concern that the COROD's heat treatment is not consistent throughout its length. This is especially problematic if field welds are made and the rods are used in an inadequately protected corrosive environment.

A continuous strand of composite materials, called "ribbon rods," was developed and field tested.[31] This type of special rod contained carbon composite with a polymer wrap. Despite having high strength and a small cross-sectional area, it was expensive and ran into field support problems similar to those of flexible strands and CORODs.

"Electra" Sucker Rods. Another type of non-API sucker rod is the Electra (EL)** rod. These currently are available only in ¾-, ⅞-, and 1-in. diameters. They should be selected for wells in which operating stresses do not exceed 50,000 psi. These rods have a special heat treatment that should put the surface in a compressive set. Thus, they could be used in a hydrogen sulfide (H_2S) environment in which the strength of Grade C rods is exceeded. These rods have been effectively used to produce approximately 150 BFPD from a depth of approximately 14,500 ft.

High-Strength, Low-Alloy Rods. A number of manufacturers have developed higher-strength steel rods to compete with other specialty rods. These rods take advantage of the newer alloys and heat-treating procedures currently available and are based on American Iron and Steel Inst. (AISI) 8630- or 4130-type steels, which have high tensile strengths. The tensile strength is generally greater than 140,000 psi, while the yield strength is generally greater than

---

* COROD is a product of Weatherford Intl. Ltd., Houston.
** EL is a trademark of Weatherford Intl. Ltd., Houston.

100,000 psi; therefore, these rods could not be classified as API Grade D. The fine-grain heat treatment done on these alloys theoretically should provide increased fatigue life. However, this rod type may be more notch-sensitive and may require better handling and corrosion protection than normal API-type rods.

As with any specialty equipment, good field testing and records for several years in which good handling and operating practices were followed are required to prove the benefit for any of these non-API rods.

11.4.5 Criteria for Rod-String Design. *Rod Stress.* In a noncorrosive environment, the endurance limit of steel is primarily determined by the maximum stress, the range of stresses, and the number of stress reversals. This is often illustrated by the use of a Goodman diagram, as discussed in API *RP 11BR*.[29] Derating, or service, factors also are discussed to allow potential decreasing of the load range for different service/corrosive environments. If the environment is corrosive and not properly treated, the sucker rods and their associated downhole equipment life is minimal. In such cases, corrosion-fatigue failures occur frequently in the rod string.

Effectively inhibited systems may be considered noncorrosive, which would limit the surface pitting of the steel rods or components. However, in the presence of H_2S and a corrosive environment, steel may become susceptible to hydrogen embrittlement/sulfide-stress cracking. Steels that have a Rockwell C hardness greater than ≈ 23 (Brinell hardness number 237) are susceptible to embrittlement. The harder the steel is, the more susceptible it becomes. API Grade C sucker rods normally have a Rockwell C hardness < 23, while API Grade D sucker rods normally have a Rockwell C hardness > 23. Thus, API Grade D rods should be used with caution in the presence of hydrogen sulfide. Chemical inhibition may not prevent embrittlement. This results in a significantly decreased run life.

Stress raisers cause areas of concentrated stresses and may be caused by a number of things. Corrosion pits are one type of stress raiser. Stress raisers may be notches caused by improper handling, tool cuts, bending, and subsequent cold straightening, for example, and may also result from the manner in which the threads are formed on the rod pin (i.e., cutting vs. the now-required cold rolling). Corrosion pits may have rounded or notched shape; notch-shaped pits are more serious and are more likely to occur in Grade D rods than in Grade C rods.

API *RP 11BR* recommends using the modified Goodman diagram for determining the allowable stress on API steel-grade sucker rods, while API *Spec. 11B*[28] covers FRP rods. Manufacturers of non-API rods should specify the rod's allowable stress. An allowable load or stress curve should be developed to discern during the design of a rod string if it is overloaded, and adjustments should be made to prevent this. Recent discussions have promoted a hyperbolic relationship for allowable load using the Gerber parabola, rather than a straightline relationship.[32] This loading criterion, coupled with cleaner steels and better-quality sucker-rod manufacturing, should enable higher allowable loads to be applied to the rod strings, provided that good sucker-rod handling practices are followed. Rod strings that are considered "overloaded" by more than 20%, according to the straightline method, have been successfully run in the Permian Basin fields in the U.S.A. and provided adequate run time. Additionally, Ref. 30 discusses the need to reduce the allowable load or stress on used rods. Recommendations are presented for derating based on the class of the inspected rod, according to the inspection-criteria classes in API *RP 11BR*.

Rod-String Selection. The primary factors affecting the selection and sizing of rods and the rod system are as follows:
- Size of pump and tubing.
- Liquid viscosity and pourpoint.
- Kind of corrosion [e.g., H_2S, carbon dioxide (CO_2), or saltwater].

- Conditions for unseating the downhole pump.
- Pump setting depth.
- Production rate.
- Sand, paraffin, salt crystals, scale, foam, and GLR.

These factors should be considered when manual (according to API *RP 11L*[30]) or computer design calculations are performed to size the rod string and the related production equipment for a specific well.

11.4.6 Size Designation. Sucker-rod strings may be composed of a single size or may be tapered, typically to include rods of two and three sizes. Using four or more sizes of rods in a taper is not normally recommended. The primary factor determining the proportion of each size of rod in the rod string is the size of the pump. However, typically only one grade of rod is used in the string to avoid mixing during running and pulling operations.

API *RP 11L* contains recommended rod-string design data. The first column of Table I in this reference contains the rod-string size designation. The first number in the column refers to the largest rod size in the string, while the second number refers to the smallest rod size in the string, both representing the size in eighths of an inch. An example rod number of 76 is a two-way taper of $\frac{7}{8}$- and $\frac{6}{8}$-in. rods. Rod number 86 is a three-way taper of $\frac{8}{8}$-, $\frac{7}{8}$-, and $\frac{6}{8}$-in. rods.

11.4.7 Pump Unseating. Rod strings should be designed to enable the operator to unseat the pump without yielding any rod in the rod string. The diameter of the pump plunger determines the fluid load lifted during the pumping cycle. However, the ID of the seating nipple determines the fluid load that must be lifted to unseat the pump. Friction in the pump holddown plus sediments in the pump-tubing annulus increases the required pump-unseating force. However, a high tubing-casing-annulus fluid level decreases the load on the rod string when attempting to unseat a pump. Normally, the pulling-rig weight indicators are not accurate enough to use as the only tool to prohibit yielding the sucker rods. The rod string's stretch in Table 4.1, Column 4, of API *RP 11L*, gives elastic constants (E_r) for sucker rods that can be used to indicate rod load.

The top rod in the bottom section normally has the highest stress in the string because it has the smallest cross-sectional area. This is because it has to support the weight of the rest of the small-diameter rod load, the pump and the very large fluid load on the gross seating nipple area. The weak point in the string is this rod. A free-body diagram can be used to determine the loads acting on this rod; an allowable unseating load or stretch can then be determined so that the rods are not yielded or damaged when trying to unseat the pump.

11.4.8 To Taper or Not To Taper a Rod String. Tapered rod strings that use different segments of different-sized rods are commonly used to save unnecessary weight and to distribute the loading on long strings of rods used in deep wells. The proper design will decrease the stress on the rods above the bottom section. This allows pumps to be run deeper than would be possible if just one size of rod was run. Tapered rod strings can be operated at a higher pumping speed (N) than straight rod strings. This may reduce the required pumping-unit gearbox size and increase rod stretch because stretch is proportional to rod-string weight. Thus, more production may be possible from the well with a tapered string than a straight string using the same-diameter pump.

Ideally, a rod string should be a continuous taper from top to bottom. This is impractical, not only because of the manufacturing difficulties involved, but also because the lower rods must have sufficient stiffness to support the entire string in the tubing if failures occur high up in the string. For this reason, 75 to 85 strings are not normally recommended because, if the rod string parts high in the well, close to the surface, the $\frac{5}{8}$-in. rods may be permanently damaged when the upper rods fall on them. Coupled sucker rods come in diameter variations of $\frac{1}{8}$

in. With the introduction of the continuous sucker rod, the opportunity for a greater number of tapers is possible because these rods may be manufactured in size variations of $\frac{1}{16}$ in. or even smaller.

The primary factor in determining the proportion of each size of rod in the rod string is the size of the pump. Columns 6 through 11 in Table D.1 of API *RP 11L* contain the percentages of the various sizes to be placed in a tapered rod string with various pump sizes. Before 1977, percentages were calculated so that the unit stress on the top rod of each section from the weight of the rods in air plus the weight of the produced fluids on the gross plunger area is equal. This is calculated as a static load. Work done by API and Shell in 1977 resulted in the percentages shown in API *RP 11L*. This work used the dynamic effects on the rod's upstroke and downstroke, along with assumed pumping speeds for varying stroke lengths. Currently, most operators and rod manufacturers have proprietary rod-string design programs that include these data.

One of the earliest means used for designing tapered sucker-rod strings is in the *Sucker Rod Handbook*.[33] This design is based upon equal stress in the top of each size of rod, assuming a static condition and pumping water (specific gravity = 1.0) with the well pumped off. Buoyancy of the rod string is not taken into account. The recommendations in API *RP 11L3*[34] are based on the same assumptions. However, continued work suggested adopting a "modified-stress" approach in which the stress from the dynamic loads at the top of each size of rod is equalized.[35,36] Computer programs are available to perform the calculations on this complex process of assessing stress for various rod-string designs.

11.4.9 Rod Couplings. API *Spec. 11B*[28] contains requirements for the rod couplings, as well as the rods, and recommends minimum tubing sizes. The current edition provides for two classes of couplings: Class T (through hardened coupling) has a Rockwell C hardness range of minimum 16 and maximum 23, and Class SM (surface hardened) has a minimum Rockwell C surface hardness of 50. This hardness is normally accomplished by the spray-metal process. Care should be taken when recommending the SM couplings, even though they have longer wear life than T couplings. Because of the increased hardness and lower coefficient of friction, if properly surface treated, coupling-on-tubing wear is transferred from the rods—which are easy and less expensive to replace—to the softer tubing, which is more expensive to replace. Thus, while the SM couplings help to increase rod-string life, the tubing life may be decreased. API *Spec. 11B* also standardizes "full-sized" coupling in both grades and a "slimhole" coupling in Class T. Tables 4.1 and 4.2 from API *Spec. 11B* shows recommendations for the minimum tubing sizes for the various couplings.

Slimhole couplings for $\frac{5}{8}$- to 1-in. rods can be run and fished in one-size-smaller tubing than the respective full-sized coupling. This enables operators to run 1-in. rods in $2\frac{7}{8}$-in.-OD tubing and $\frac{7}{8}$-in. rods in $2\frac{3}{8}$-in.-OD tubing. This coupling type, however, decreases the coupling area available for supporting the pumping loads. Thus, slimhole couplings are not as strong as the full size. Original work by Gipson and Swaim[5] recommended derating these couplings on the basis of the assumption that the 1-in. slimhole coupling has an acceptable minimum decreased area. Further work by Hermanson[37] using the area relationships and allowable strength of the different grades of steel rods resulted in different derating factors, shown in **Table 11.5**. Additionally, these have been accepted by the industry and included in API *RP 11BR*.[29] Note that the use of $\frac{7}{8}$-in. slimhole couplings results in the highest derating factor for all rod strengths and sizes.

11.4.10 Sucker-Rod Maintenance. Well equipment, including sucker rods, must be in good working condition. The sucker-rod string is often highly stressed and usually fails because of the repeated load reversals. Corrosion, scale, and paraffin deposits may accelerate such failures. Tubing and rods will wear because of the reciprocating movement in the well caused by pound-

TABLE 11.5—API *RP1 BR*[19] RECOMMENDED DERATING FACTORS FOR STANDARD SLIMHOLE COUPLINGS BASED ON SIZE AND ROD GRADE

API Rod Size (in.)	API Rod Grade		
	K	C	D
⅝	—	0.97	0.77
¾	—	—	0.86
⅞	0.93	0.88	0.69
1	—	—	0.89

ing fluid, buckling because of unanchored tubing, and/or bad wellbore deviation that allows contact.

Sucker-rod strings are lifting a great deal of weight every cycle. They are under stress on both the downstroke and the upstroke. Combining this with the normally corrosive environmental conditions of water, H_2S, CO_2, etc. may mean that one of the greatest expenses of a producing beam-pump system is replacing the sucker rods. Carrying out the various procedures described in this section can greatly reduce operating costs and make production more efficient and economical.

Care and Handling of Sucker Rods. Proper running, handling, and makeup procedures should be followed to secure maximum service from a rod string. API *RP 11BR* contains the practices recommended by the industry.

Torque measurement has been discredited as a sucker-rod-connection makeup method. When the threads are properly lubricated, an estimated 10% of the applied torque turns the coupling relative to the pin, and 90% of the torque is consumed by friction. Any variation in lubricants or in the surface finish of the threads or mating surfaces drastically changes these percentages, indicating that torque could never be a precision makeup method for sucker rods.

API *RP 11BR* recommends circumferential displacement (CD) for making up sucker-rod joints, and it should also be used for calibrating power tongs. To make up a sucker-rod joint using CD, the pin and coupling threads should be cleaned and lubricated with a lubricant that has passed the NACE *MR-01-74* screening test.[38] This test states that an acceptable lubricant will allow the lubricated pin to be made up hand tight, then fully made up and broken out 10 times without galling the threads. A hand-tight position is attained when full shoulder abutment is made and a 0.002-in.-thick feeler gauge cannot enter into this interface between the rod and coupling face. The coupling should then be turned by the amount specified in API *RP11BR* or by the rod manufacturer, relative to the pin. The manufacturer of specialty or non-API rods should be consulted for their recommended CD values and makeup procedures.

Rod-String Equipment Failure. The downhole production strings may fail for a variety of reasons, some of which have been discussed previously. Steward[39] and Moore[40] discuss reasons for common sucker-rod string failures and provide discussion and pictures of the failures. Additionally, Hermanson[37] provides discussion and photographs of different rod failures. The following is a summary of the normal rod-string equipment and typical reasons for failure:

• Polished rods.
 - Not in center of tee throughout pumping cycle.
 - Smaller than recommended by API.
 - Top of carrier bar not horizontal.
 - Crooked—not vertical—wellhead.
 - Crooked hole near surface, with pony rods below the polished rod.
 - Corrosion.

- Abrasion.
- Excessive heat.
- No lubrication.
- Packing too tight.
• Pony rods (rod subs).
  - Old subs used with new rod string.
  - Improper API-grade rod.
  - Sub directly below polished rod.
• Rod couplings (boxes).
  - Slimhole couplings used.
  - Hammered-on boxes.
  - Insufficient circumferential displacement.
  - Dirty or improperly cleaned threads.
  - Improper or no lubricant (should be a properly screened inhibitor, not tubing or drillpipe dope).
  - End face not perpendicular to the threads.
  - Oxygen in system.
  - Couplings made from free-machining steels.
• Rod pins.
  - Old-style, nonundercut pins.
  - Incorrect circumferential displacement.
  - Box and pin not made up, but broken out and remade on new C and K rods.
  - Box shoulder and pin shoulder not parallel.
• Rod upsets.
  - Worn elevators.
  - Rod bent while tailing out or in.
  - Rods corkscrewed above the pump during normal pumping.
  - Rods corkscrewed after parting.
  - Vibrations.
  - Manufacturer's marks.
  - Running too fast in the hole.
• Rod body.
  - Inadequate/ineffective corrosion inhibition.
  - Hydrogen embrittlement.
  - Overload.
  - Nicks.
  - Service time exceeds fatigue life.
  - Rough surface.
  - Yield strength exceeded while attempting to unseat pump.
  - Defective material.
  - Oxygen allowed in the pumping system.
  - Bends.
• Valve rod (stationary barrel pump).
  - Pump not centralized in tubing.
  - Improper material.
  - Plunger too short and pump not centralized.
  - Crooked hole at pump setting depth.
  - Pounding fluid.
• Pull tube (traveling barrel pump).
  - Pump not centralized in tubing.

- Pull tube buckling on downstroke.
- Improper material.
- Pump set too deep for pull-tube length.
- Pounding fluid.

11.4.11 String Replacement. Replacing a rod string one rod at a time is not normally a good operating practice; thus, the economic life of a rod string needs to be considered if rods start to fail. Typically, the rod-string section will be replaced after two or three failures, while the entire rod string may be replaced after three or four failures. However, the reasons for failures need to be investigated and the root cause for this failure must be determined to extend the rod life in the future.

An SPE paper by Powers[41] considers the factors that enter into the decision about when to replace the entire rod string after sustaining the calculated number of failures. Usually, wells of the same type in a field can be grouped together and the necessary calculations do not have to be performed for each well. Sufficient calculations need to be done to assess the economic impact for all wells in a field.

11.5 Miscellaneous Subsurface Equipment

11.5.1 Tubing. The chapter on tubing selection, design, and installation from this *Handbook* provides detailed information on the design, selection, and use of tubing for production wells. As related to most sucker-rod-lifted wells, the standard weight of external-upset-end, API tubing[42] should be used because of the increased wall thickness in the threaded ends. Thus, if there is rod coupling-on-tubing wear, more life and fewer leaks will be realized than if nonupset API tubing is used. Using API Grade J55 tubing, consider full-body normalizing after upsetting to prevent "ringworm corrosion" in the heat-affected upset region when the tubing is placed in corrosive (H_2S or CO_2) service. If the production application is noncorrosive, then this extra heat treatment may not be required.

Tables 4.1 and 4.2 from API *Spec. 11B*[28] include minimum tubing size for each size of full-sized and slimhole rod couplings. There should be sufficient clearance between the tubing and the rod box for fishing tools.

The yield strength of the tubing must be sufficient to support the weight of the tubing in air, the weight of the rods and of the fluid in the tubing, plus an overpull allowance that will allow the tubing to be pulled. Normally, API Grade J55 is acceptable for most rod-pumped wells to a depth of approximately 9,500 ft. However, with greater well depths and higher production rates, API Grade N80 or L80 (if H_2S is present) and, in some cases, P110 should be considered.

It is recommended that API tubulars be drifted to ensure equipment can be run without problems.

Thread dope must be used on API tubing threads to keep the joints from leaking, but it does not have an infinite life. If collar- or tubing-connection leaks begin to appear in tubing strings, it may be necessary to remove all collars (if applicable), clean the threads on the tubing and the collar or upset connection, and apply new thread dope. Additionally, tubing that has been in storage should at least be visually inspected, and the threads cleaned and freshly doped, following API recommendations, before running.

Most wells will be able to use normal torque makeup requirements for tubing. A guideline for appropriate makeup of oil-country tubular goods is found in API *RP 5 C1*.[43] This *RP* also includes care and handling along with running casing and tubing information.

Hydraulic testing of tubulars in the well will determine only whether, under that circumstance, the tubing and couplings are leak free. Once the well is put back on pump, rod-on-tubing wear may reduce the wall thickness, causing a split. Additionally, hydrotesting itself

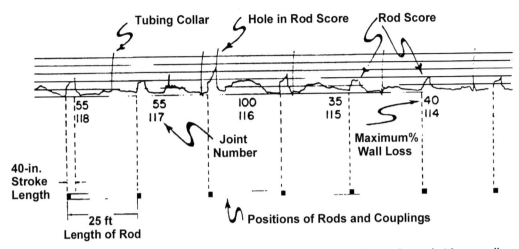

Fig. 11.6—Example of downhole tubing caliper survey showing wear at the sucker-rod-string couplings and secondary tubing wear between couplings because of sucker-rod buckling and associated metal contact.

may provide sufficient pressure to fail a worn tubular that may have had acceptable pressure retention to handle the pumping pressures. Thus, if tubing wear is a problem, downhole tubing-caliper surveys or surface tubular inspection should be done to separate unacceptably worn tubing before it leaks. **Fig. 11.6** presents an example of a downhole tubing-caliper survey.[44] It should be noted that the major wear is approximately midway between rod couplings because of rod buckling from pounding fluid. The chart also shows that there was wear caused by the couplings themselves contacting and wearing the tubing.

New developments have been made in using internally plastic-lined tubing in rod-pumped wells. Such tubing has been beneficial in preventing erosion at the pump discharge and/or wear along the inside of the tubing.[45] One west Texas operator dramatically reduced the field failure frequency from 0.42 to less than 0.25 in the Howard Glasscock field[46,47] by running full and partial strings and, in many cases, just a few joints of this poly-lined tubing on the bottom of the tubing string. Monitoring of these lined tubing joints should continue to ensure that the liner does not wear or degrade with time.

The failure frequency is a dimensionless number found by dividing the total downhole well failures by the total number of producing wells in a field. This failure frequency can be further described by dividing the number of sucker-rod, tubing, or pump failures in a year by the total number of sucker-rod-lifted wells to determine which equipment is causing the most failures in the field. Similar calculations can be done for other lift methods that are used in the field.

11.5.2 Tubing-Anchor Catchers (TACs). Tubing anchors are used to prevent movement of the tubing during the pumping cycle. **Fig. 11.7** shows an example of the recommended mechanical-type TAC for rod-pumped wells. During pump operation, part of the fluid load is transferred from the tubing to the sucker rods, alternately. This causes the tubing to elongate on the downstroke when it supports the fluid load and to shorten when the rods carry the fluid load on the upstroke. This action shortens the effective plunger stroke and decreases the pump displacement. This load transfer also causes helical buckling in the bottom portion of the tubing string, which, in turn, causes additional rod-on-tubing wear. The recommended TAC has two-way slips; these prevent parted tubing from falling in addition to preventing movement during the pumping cycle.

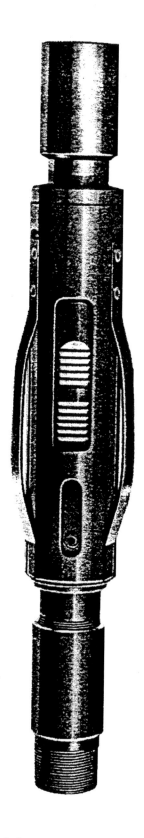

Fig. 11.7—Schematic of typical TAC showing upward- and downward-opposed hardened slips.

Tubing anchors are normally placed within 30 to 100 ft above the pump's seating nipple. The tubing is set in the surface hanger with tension equal to the sum of the tensions required to overcome the stretch because of load transfer, helical buckling, the anticipated temperature change between producing the shut-in conditions, and the change in fluid level. A calculation procedure from the manufacturer should be followed to properly set the TAC "total stretch," rather than pounds of pull from the rig. Further consideration should be given for adequate settings, if the downhole pump diameter exceeds the tubing diameter, as in the case of over-sized tubing pumps (sometimes called casing pumps). When this occurs, the normal applied stretch or load for the tubing has shown to be inadequate, requiring increased stretch-setting inches.

This equipment can be difficult to remove; thus, care should be taken using a TAC in wells having scale, heavy paraffin, sand production, and/or bad casing. The TAC release method should be considered before this equipment is installed.

Several of the tubing anchors available have shear pins to release the slips if the normal releasing mechanism fails. Varying the material type and number of shear pins can vary the amount of necessary pull; this is called the "shear-out value." The tubing must have sufficient yield strength to support the weight of the tubing in air, the weight of the rods, and the weight of the fluid in the tubing as well as to shear the pins left in the tubing anchor. These factors will limit the pumping depth to which a TAC can be used. However, the running depth can be increased with stronger tubing and/or tapered tubing strings and with the required minimum strength and number of shear pins. Care should be used to ensure that the design shear out or production loads do not exceed the tubing-grade yield strength. If this possibility exists, the tubing should be cut rather than pulled apart.

11.5.3 Tubing Rotators. Tubing rotators may be used to spread tubing wear because of rods and/or rod couplings around the entire diameter instead of being concentrated in one spot. They may be used in conjunction with rod rotators to even out the wear on both the tubing and rod coupling.

Tubing rotators come in more than one size. The manufacturer should be consulted when selecting these items to ensure the rotators purchased are sufficiently strong for the particular job. In most cases, the use of a TAC, coupled with rod centralizer and possibly a rod rotator, will prevent sufficient wear such that a tubing rotator is not required.

11.5.4 Sinker Bars. A sinker (or heavy-weight) bar is normally a special steel bar or large-diameter sucker rod placed directly above the downhole pump. Such bars may be used polished rods or a rod specifically standardized by API *Spec. 11B.*

During the pumping cycle, these bars help to open the traveling valve because a portion of the pressure required to open the valve on the downstroke must be obtained from the weight of the sucker-rod string pushing down on the top of the plunger. This places the lower portion of the rod string in reduced tension. Rod buckling will result unless properly sized and centralized sinker bars are used immediately above the pump to provide the additional needed weight. Sucker-rod buckling will cause excessive rod- and/or coupling-on-tubing wear above the pump. The buckling at the bottom of the rod string also may cause premature valve-rod or pull-tube failures. Overall, there are a number of advantages for using sinker bars in a sucker-rod string, which may include the following:

- Keeps tension on the sucker-rod string.
- Increases the minimum polished-rod load.
- Decreases polished-rod horsepower (HP).
- Decreases low tubing leaks.
- Decreases valve-rod or pull-tube pump failures if caused by buckling or bending.
- Increased production.

TABLE 11.6—RECOMMENDED SBF FOR VARIOUS SIZES OF TRAVELING AND STATIONARY BARREL PUMPS		
Plunger Size (in.)	Traveling Barrel SBF (in.^{2})	Stationary Barrel SBF (in.^{2})
1.06	—	0.30
1.25	0.20	0.30
1.50	0.30	0.40
1.75	—	0.45
2.00	0.45	0.50
2.25	—	0.55
2.50	0.60	0.60
2.75	—	0.70
3.75	—	1.4

• Overall decrease in operating costs.

There also are disadvantages from using sinker bars, including the following:

• Creates added mechanical problems when the production equipment is allowed to pound fluid more than one-quarter of the way down on the downstroke.

• Increases operating expense if purpose-manufactured rods are purchased.

• Inadequate coupling makeup and pounding fluid can cause the connection to unscrew, if polished rods are used.

The theoretical sinker-bar weight required in a rod string depends on the specific gravity of the produced fluids, the size and type of downhole pump, the associated valve-seat contact area, and the depth of the well. There are differing thoughts on the minimum amount of sinker bars required. Some operating companies and sinker-bar manufacturers use a weight equal to the buoyant weight of the rod string in the produced fluid. Others use only 20% of the well depth or no sinker bars—only a few sucker-rod centralizers or guides near the bottom. Some operating companies use a sinker-bar factor (SBF) for the various types of pumps. Gipson and Swaim developed the SBF for stationary barrel pumps in the "Beam Pumping Fundamentals" (April 1969) and published them in Ref. 7. Traveling-barrel pumps normally have a traveling valve one size larger than stationary barrel pumps; thus, these SBFs need to be increased.

The SBF process is to determine the theoretical weight of sinker bars in the produced fluids. Then, 20% of this theoretical weight is the recommended starting point for the actual weight or length of sinker bars used to replace the lowest rods in a rod string. This was recommended because sinker bars act dynamically to help valve action and to help keep the rods in tension. Once sinker bars are run, an optimization to increase the number of bars or weight can be conducted. However, there is a minimum point of benefit at which adding more sinker bars will not provide the useful dynamic effects. When this occurs, the extra bars or weight will be detrimental to rod-string loading.

An SBF summary for the theoretical weight for the various-diameter stationary and traveling barrel pumps is presented in **Table 11.6**. With these values, the recommended starting sinker-bar weight is as follows:

$$SBW_{(20\%)} = SBF \times 0.433 \times L \times G \times 0.20. \dots\dots\dots\dots\dots\dots\dots (11.5)$$

The resulting sinker-bar weight to install is as follows:

$$SBW_{(\text{in fluid})} = SBW_{(20\%)} / (1 - 0.128 \times G), \quad\quad\quad (11.6)$$

where L_{PSD} = seating nipple depth, ft, and G = specific gravity of the combined fluid in the tubing.[7]

11.5.5 Rod Centralizers. Sucker-rod centralizers also may be called paraffin scrapers or rod guides. They keep the rods and couplings away from the tubing to decrease wear. However, special mechanical paraffin scrapers have been developed to also aid in keeping paraffin off the tubing and most of the sucker-rod length.

Rod centralizers with full-bore-fluted centralizers should be placed on or between the pump-handling pony rod, the sinker bars used above the pump, and the first two sucker rods above the sinker bars. Rod centralizers in these locations help stabilize the pump and valve rod and prevent valve-rod bending or breakage. When a tubing anchor is not used, rod centralizers will reduce tubing wear because of tubing helical buckling on the upstroke. Rod centralizers also may be used in crooked holes in which there are areas of concentrated tubing wear.

11.5.6 Sucker-Rod-Guide Placement. When setting rod guides, it is necessary to determine the correct spacing when the tubing anchor is set several hundred feet above the seating nipple or when a TAC is not run. It is recommended as a starting point to use the Lubinski curve to determine guide spacing; **Fig. 11.8** provides the minimum guide-spacing curves for 2- and 2½-in. tubing.

The formulas for determining the distance that unanchored tubing will buckle above the seating nipple are as follows:

- For 2⅜-in.-OD API tubing, buckling distance = $F_0 / 4.1$ ft, $\quad\quad$ (11.7)

- For 2⅞-in.-OD API tubing, buckling distance = $F_0 / 5.7$ ft, $\quad\quad$ (11.8)

- For 3½-in.-OD API tubing, buckling distance = $F_0 / 8.1$ ft, $\quad\quad$ (11.9)

where $F_0 = 0.34 \times G \times D^2 \times H$, which is the fluid load on the gross plunger area, G = specific gravity of the mixed fluid in the tubing string, D = pump-plunger diameter, and H = pump-seating depth in ft.

Example. As an example problem, solve the following:

Given: tubing = 2⅞-in. OD API, D = 1.50 in. (pump plunger diameter), $L = H$ = 8,000 ft (pump-seating-nipple depth and assumed pumped-off fluid level), and G = 1.03 (specific gravity of the liquid in the tubing). A TAC is to be set at 7,450 ft, which is 15 ft above the top casing perforation.

Find: (a) the buckling distance and (b) the recommended spacing for sucker-rod guides.

Solution.

1. buckling distance = F_0 / 5.7 = [0.34 × 1.03 × (1.5) × 8,000] / 5.7 = 6,304 / 5.7 = 1,106 ft.

2. Fig. 11.8 indicates that when the neutral point is 1,106 ft above the seating nipple, the first guides should be approximately 15 ft apart, or approximately two guides are recommended per 25-ft-long sucker rod in 2⅞-in. OD.

In summary, there will be 8,000 – 7,450 = 550 ft from the seating nipple to the anchor. The anchor will be 1,106 – 550 = 556 ft below the neutral point. Fig. 11.8 indicates that guides should not be less than 25 ft apart until approximately 380 ft below the neutral point;

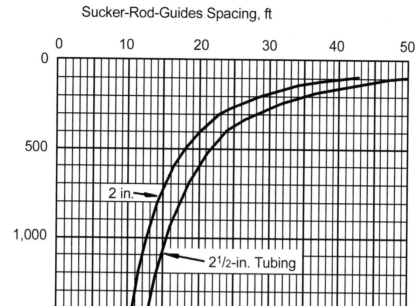

Fig. 11.8—Minimum recommended number of rod guides per rod that may buckle for normal sucker-rod-lift production tubing.

therefore, it is recommended that two guides be placed on each 25-ft-long sucker rod, between the seating nipple at 8,000 ft and the TAC at 7,450 ft. This is the minimum number of guides per rod.

If continued rod and/or coupling-on-tubing wear is a problem, more centralizers should be considered. Wellbore deviation is one of the biggest problems for sucker-rod-lifted wells. If the deviation is 0 to 3°/100 ft, there should be no pumping problem. A deviation of 3 to 5°/100 ft is a bearable problem, and it usually can be handled by properly locating the rod guides. A deviation greater than 5°/100 ft is a definite problem. An increased number of guides per rod, tubing anchors, and/or special roller rod guides may be necessary within the local deviation region.

11.5.7 Rod-Centralizer Types and Materials. There are two main types of sucker-rod centralizers: field installable or molded on. The field-installable guides can be hammered on, twisted on, or (with two pieces) slid together on the rod. Usually, these field-installable guides do not grip the rod area very well; thus, they do not stay where they are required. However, guide manufacturers continue to develop these field installable guides to increase their holding power. A word of caution is necessary, especially with the field-installable guides, to make sure the rods are slowly run in or out of the well to decide if a wellhead running guide is necessary.

Molded-on rod guides are the recommended type, especially for new sucker rods, if continued rod coupling/tubing wear is a problem. This type of guide is also recommended if the well is allowed to pound fluid or if the well-servicing contractor is not properly trained to run rods with field-installable guides.

There are varieties of materials that can be used for rod centralizers, including steel paraffin scrapers. However, most guides and scrapers are elastomers, including rubber, nylon, isobutyl, Ryton PPS (polyphenylene sulfide),* a nylon composite, and a high-density polyethylene. Guide manufacturers continue to develop new guide materials that will provide the needed centralizing capabilities, rod-gripping strength, long wear life, and ability to function in increasingly hostile downhole environments. All these materials have chemical compatibility, temperature, and applied-stress limitations. The manufacturer should be consulted for their recommended service limitations.

11.5.8 Paraffin Scrapers. Mechanical scrapers fastened to the rod string through the zone of paraffin deposition (normally near the surface) have been used to keep the tubing and most of the rod bodies free of paraffin. Paraffin-scraper systems have proved to be effective in reducing, if not eliminating, hot-oiling or watering treatments in both Canada and in the U.S. Additionally, a Canadian operator has shown that, along with the mechanical scraper system, internal plastic tubing coating has been beneficial in preventing paraffin buildup.[48] However, it is recommended that paraffin scrapers be used only when necessary.

11.6 Sucker-Rod Pumping Units

Many devices are connected to the downhole sucker-rod equipment through the polished rod on the surface that imparts the reciprocating motion to the rod string and pump. In the history of sucker-rod pumping, a standalone, surface-pumping unit has become the proven technology. Many pumping-unit types are commercially available. Those most widely used have a walking beam as the horizontal load-bearing element and a sampson post that vertically supports the beam. These terminologies and configurations were adapted from the cable-tool drilling rigs used to drill early oil wells and developed into the conventional pumping unit.

API has standardized the design, terminology, and many components used for pumping units in API *Spec. 11E*.[49] ISO accepted the use of this standard as a base to fast track the publication of ISO *Standard 10431*.[50] Currently, these are comparable standards and cover the two main components making up a pumping unit: the gear reducer and the structure. They are standardized separately because the gear-reducer manufacturer may be separate from the structural manufacturer, who would be responsible for the assembly.

11.6.1 Unit Designation. A pumping unit results when the gear reducer and the structure are combined together. These units have a size rating that describes the unit's capacities with the

---

* Ryton PPS is a registered trademark of Chevron Phillips Chemical Co., The Woodlands, Texas.

TABLE 11.7—NORMALLY AVAILABLE RANGES OF PUMPING-UNIT
SIZES FOR THE VARIOUS STANDARD-UNIT GEOMETRIES

Geometry	Minimum	Maximum
Beam-balanced conventional	6.4-28.12	80-76-64
Crank-balanced conventional	25D-53-30	1824D-305-240
Air balanced	114D-173-64	2560D-470-240
Mark II	114D-143-64	1824D-427-216
Reverse Mark	228D-147-74	1824D-427-192

reducer rating, maximum structural capacity, and the maximum stroke length. The reducer number is the maximum torque rating in lbf-in. divided by 1,000. The structure number is the maximum load normally on the beam in lbf divided by 100, while the maximum stroke length is in inches. This results in a three-number hyphenated description that ranges from 6.4-21-24 to 3,648-470-300 for the 77 possible standardized units. These describe the smallest unit with a 6,400-lbf-in. reducer, a 2,100-lbf structure capacity, and 24-in. stroke to the largest unit with a 3,648,000-lbf-in. reducer, 47,000-lbf structure, and 300-in. stroke. However, not all of these unit sizes are available from all manufacturers in all the possible structural geometries.

The commercially available units are further described by adding the structural type or geometry and possibly the type of gear reducer [single (no letter) or double (D)]. Normally,

- B is for a beam-balanced conventional unit.
- C is for a conventional crank-balanced unit.
- A is for an air-balanced unit.
- M is for a Mark II* unit.
- RM is for Reverse Mark* unit.

An example designation for a conventional, crank-balanced pumping unit with a 456,000-lbf-in. double-reduction-gear reducer, a 30,500-lbf structure, and a maximum stroke length of 168 in. would be C456D-305-168.

Manufacturers should be contacted for their normal availability, special designs, sizes, and types of units they sell. However, **Table 11.7** shows the minimum and maximum size ranges commercially available from a large U.S. manufacturer.[51]

11.6.2 Gear Reducer. There are 18 gear-reducer sizes currently included in API *Spec. 11E.*[49] The size range is from 6.4- to 3,648- or 6,400- to 3,648,000-lbf-in. capacity. **Table 11.8** presents the various sizes and capacities of available API gear reducers. When these gear reducers are put in their operating enclosure and attached to a pumping-unit structure, then this equipment is normally called a gearbox. Pumping units typically use single- or double-reduction gearing, with an approximate 30:1 speed reduction from the prime-mover to the pumping speed.

The standards also include chain reducers that use sprockets and chains for transmitting the prime-mover speed through the structure to the rod string. These are available as single-, double-, and triple-reduction drives. While this is still a possible reducer design, they are limited in capacity and are not normally used.

11.6.3 Gear Ratings for Speed and Life. Sucker-rod pumping units can be operated over a range of pumping speeds. It has been recognized that there is a need for a nominal pumping

---

* Mark II and Reverse Mark are registered trademarks of Lufkin Industries Inc., Lufkin, Texas.

TABLE 11.8—API *SPEC. 11E*[49] STANDARDIZED SIZES AND RELATED GEAR-REDUCER PEAK-TORQUE RATING

Size	Peak Torque Rating (lbf-in.)
6.4	6,400
10	10,000
16	16,000
25	25,000
40	40,000
57	57,000
80	80,000
114	114,000
160	160,000
228	228,000
320	320,000
456	456,000
640	640,000
912	912,000
1280	1,280,000
1824	1,824,000
2560	2,560,000
3648	3,648,000

TABLE 11.9—API *SPEC. 11E*[49] MAXIMUM RATED SPEEDS FOR VARIOUS-SIZED GEAR REDUCERS

spm (N_o)	Peak-Torque Rating (lbf-in.)
16	456,000
16	640,000
15	912,000
14	1,280,000
13	1,842,000
11	2,560,000 and larger

speed to rate the various gear reducers. Originally, the industry adopted a nominal speed of 20 spm. This assumed that the up and down stroke of a unit forms one complete stroke cycle.

In 1981, API *Spec. 11E* was revised and reduced the rating speed for the 456- and larger-sized reducers, as shown in **Table 11.9**. The reduced speed setting was done because it was not practical to expect larger gearboxes to operate at 20 spm with longer stroke lengths and larger-sized structures. In actuality, industrial applications with these similar-sized reducers can be operated from 580 to 1,750 rpm. American Gear Manufacturer's Association (AGMA) *Standard 422.03,*[52] which is the basis for API *Spec. 11E,* limits the speed of the reducer to either the pitch-line velocity of any stage to 5,000 ft/min and/or the speed of any shaft to less than 3,600 rpm.

It should be noted that none of the industry standards from API, ISO, or AGMA[53] address a required reducer life; however, the operating rule of thumb is an expected 20 to 25 years of life. This assumes the gearbox is not overloaded or abused and is properly maintained. One pumping unit manufacturer has developed a graph (shown in **Fig. 11.9**) depicting the effect on

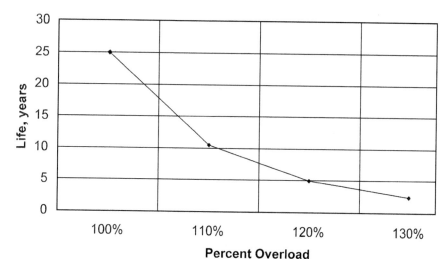
Fig. 11.9—Effect of overloading pumping-unit gear reducers on expected life.

gearbox life from overloading the gearbox capacity.* This shows that, while current API designed and manufactured reducers may be overloaded without catastrophic failure, depending on the amount of overload, the expected life should be reduced.

AGMA *Standard 2001-C95*[53] provides a way to calculate tooth stress that should provide satisfactory operation for a reasonable time. If the existing calculations are used and worked backwards to calculate the life of an acceptable design, then a reducer life of more than 4×10^8 cycles should be expected at the rated torque load. This would result in a life—assuming a constant 10-spm pumping-unit speed for every day of the year—of more than 76 years. However, this still assumes proper gear-reducer installation, operation, and maintenance.

11.6.4 Standard Structures. The industry standards for pumping units have developed minimum requirements for the design and manufacture of the various structured components—the beams, shafting, hanger, brakes, horsehead, cranks, and bearings. The four main standard pumping-unit structural geometries covered by API *Spec. 11E* are as follows:

- Rear-mounted geometry, Class I lever systems with crank counterbalance.
- Front-mounted geometry, Class III lever systems with crank counterbalance.
- Front-mounted geometry, Class III lever systems with air counterbalance.
- Rear-mounted geometry, Class I lever systems with phased-crank counterbalance.

These standardized structures are more widely known by the respective designations: conventional, Mark II, air balanced, and Reverse Mark. There are variations of these geometries, such as for slant wells or as low profile for overhead irrigated fields. Additionally, there are special geometries or structures that are based on hydraulics, pneumatics, or belts. Because these structures are not covered by industry standards, it is recommended that these special units are designed properly, manufactured to industry quality standards, and installed and operated according to the manufacturer's recommendations.

11.6.5 Unit Selection. There have been many publications about the advantages, disadvantages, and selection of the various standard geometries and the specialty pumping units, including the following:

- Theoretical development of torque factors and pumping unit "kinematics."[2,4,30,49,54]

---

* Personal communication with C. Hunt, Lufkin Industries Inc., Lufkin, Texas (2002).

- Description of geometries, applications, and efficiencies for standard units.[1–11,55–71]
- Specialty hydraulic, strand, pneumatic, and long-stroke pumping units.[1–5,11,72–89]

The following paragraph provides a brief summary and comparison of the four standard pumping units.

The conventional unit is probably the unit used most often. It is simple to install, has the widest range of sizes available, usually has lower operating costs than other units, needs no hoisting equipment or rigid supports for changing stroke length, and can run faster in wells in which free fall limits pumping speed. The maximum pumping speed for the conventional unit in an average well is estimated at 70% of the maximum free fall of rods in air. This compares with 63% for air-balanced units and 56% for Mark II units. The free-fall speed is defined for the conventional unit by the following formula:

$$\text{spm} = 0.7(60,000/S \text{ in in.})^{0.5} \dots\dots\dots\dots\dots\dots\dots\dots\dots\dots\dots\dots\dots \text{(11.10)}$$

The free-fall speed is reduced by 10 and 20% for the air-balanced and Mark II units, respectively. This means that in a well with average friction and a 100-in. polished-rod stroke, the rods will fall a maximum of 17.15 spm with a conventional unit, 15.43 spm with an air-balanced unit, and 13.72 spm for the Mark II. However, there should be no separation between the carrier bar of the unit and the polished-rod clamp during the downstroke. These speeds would be further reduced in wells with increased friction from composite-ring-type plungers, deviated holes, particulates sticking the downhole pump, and/or very viscous crude. Furthermore, the conventional unit's geometry allows either clockwise or counterclockwise rotation. This may be beneficial for gear teeth that are damaged in one direction from poor operation or maintenance and may enable rotating in the opposite direction. This would extend the life of the gearbox.

Air-balanced units use a leverage system different from conventional units. The use of compressed air instead of heavy, cast-iron counterweights allows more-accurate fingertip control of the counterbalance, which can be adjusted without stopping the unit. With no counterweights, the unit weighs much less than a comparably sized conventional unit. It also has a lighter substructure and a slightly lighter beam. Thus, there are several advantages to its compact size and light weight, especially for portable test units and for use on offshore platforms. It also uses more degrees of crank travel to complete the first one-half of the upstroke, which tends to decrease the peak load. This is a slight advantage if rod fatigue is a problem. However, there are increased maintenance problems or concerns, especially with leakage past the piston, which may make it difficult to maintain the proper air pressure. Additionally, the leakage also may cause an oil spray and resulting environmental consideration. Further, water condensation in the air system may cause damage if it is allowed to freeze, unless proper antifreeze is used.

The Mark II unit has an equalizer bearing between the Samson post and the well load. The equalizer bearing is located ahead or to the well side of the centerline of the slow-speed shaft. This is different from the air-balanced unit in which the equalizer bearing is directly over the slow-speed shaft. The equalizer bearing location results in an upstroke of approximately 195° and a downstroke of 165°. This makes a slower upstroke with 20% less acceleration, which results in reduced peak polished-rod load. The slower upstroke also allows more time for viscous fluids to fill the pump barrel and can increase the pump's volumetric efficiency, but this requires the unit to operate only in the counterclockwise rotation.

While comparably sized Mark II units are heavier and more expensive than conventional units, the claimed torque reductions may make it possible to use a Mark II unit one size smaller than required for a conventional unit. However, these units should not be used when high pumping speeds or undertravel-type dynamometer cards are anticipated and/or there are crooked or deviated wells. When an undertravel card or a card that showed neither undertravel nor overtravel is developed, the conventional or Reverse Mark unit has a better-suited permissible-load diagram.

The Reverse Mark unit is classified as a rear-mounted geometry, Class I lever system with phased-crank counterbalance. The phased cranks improve load-lifting capabilities; thus, like the Mark II, this unit may enable a one-size-smaller gear reducer than a conventional unit. However, this rule of thumb needs to be tempered by the actual pumping parameters and resulting dynamometer-card shape. Furthermore, the phase crank also makes this a unidirectional unit.

The other specialty units have their own advantages and disadvantages that may be considered if the standard units are not capable of meeting production-design requirements. Regardless of which unit is selected, a full-cycle economic consideration should be conducted to compare the costs for purchase, installation, maintenance, operation, repairs, failure frequency, and resale value. These parameters should all be considered, along with the capability of producing the required fluid volume from the required well depth, to decide which unit would be best for a particular well.

11.6.6 Sizing. There have been a variety of methods for determining the required reducer size for a pumping unit, including the "approximate method," "engineering analysis," and kinematics.[2,4–7,30,49,64] Today, most engineers/operators who select the pumping unit will rely on the output from a rod-string-design program that calculates the peak torque at the polished rod. These are based on the API *RP 11L*[30] method and the extension to wave equations that allow geometries other than the conventional unit to be considered. Because these calculations provide peak torques at the polished rod, the torque has to be transmitted through the structure and its bearings to the gearbox. However, because these bearings are not 100% efficient, Gipson and Swaim[7] developed curves for selecting the gearbox to account for these inefficiencies; **Fig. 11.10** shows the loss of efficiency curves for both new and used units. Typically, this requires a gearbox approximately 10 or 20% larger in capacity than the peak torque calculated at the polished rod for new or used units, respectively. Once the design's peak-torque capacity is determined, then the closest available, but higher-rated, reducer should be selected. The beam should be selected on the basis of the calculated peak polished-rod load from the rod-string-design program. Finally, the unit stroke length should be selected on the basis of the required pump capacity with a 10 to 20% production cushion.

Specialty pumping units and the required reducer, structural capacity, and the desired stroke length should be discussed with the manufacturer to guarantee unit performance.

11.6.7 Installation, Operation, and Maintenance of Pump Units. Many publications have been issued on the installation, operation, maintenance, and lubrication of pumping units.[5,6,90–101] These papers have been incorporated into API *RP 11G1*[102] to reflect the minimum recommended practices considered for installation, operation, and lubrication of the pumping unit. Additionally, manufacturers of the units may have their own documents and recommended procedures for installation, operation, and maintenance that should be followed.

11.6.8 Guards. Properly guarding a pumping unit is of critical importance. The industry standard, American National Standard Institute (ANSI)/API *RP 11ER*,[103] should be followed when guarding the pumping unit, V-belts, sheaves, flywheels, cranks, counterweights, and moving parts on pumping units. Major pumping-unit manufacturers are also excellent sources of guidance on guarding and can usually supply guards that will meet specific regulatory requirements.

11.7 Prime Movers

11.7.1 Introduction. The prime mover (PM) rotates the gear-reducer gears through a V-belt drive. The two most common PMs are electric motors and internal-combustion (IC) engines.

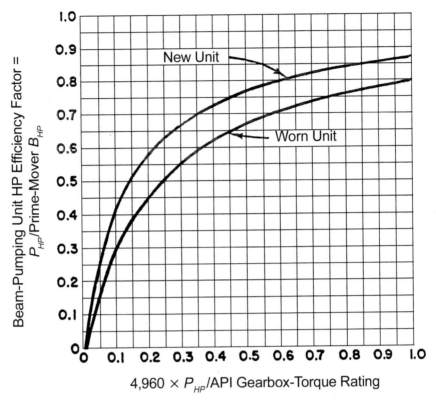

Fig. 11.10—Derating recommendations for standardized pumping-unit gear reducers based on sucker-rod-string predictions and available or selected gearbox.

The decision concerning which to use depends on a variety of considerations, which includes the following:

- Availability of the power source (electricity or combustible fluid).
- HP required to pump the well.
- Efficiency of the system.
- Ability to control the PM to match the on/off potential operation of the pumping unit.
- Availability of field and/or service personnel capable of maintaining and repairing the equipment.
- Condition of the gas (sweet or sour) or availability now and in the future of the gas or liquids (i.e., propane or diesel) if an IC engine is used.
- Current and future expected cost for the power source.
- Anticipated full-cycle total cost (including initial capital, operating, maintenance, downtime, and repairs) for the duration of the well.

These considerations, as well as other factors, have been discussed in numerous publications.[1-6,104-107]

11.7.2 Engines. There are three common types of gas engines used for beam pumping units: two-cycle, slow-speed engine; four-cycle, slow-speed engine; and four-cycle, high-speed engine. The characteristics of these engines are summarized here, and the detailed comparisons and field experiences have been published elsewhere.[108,109]

Two-cycle, slow-speed engine (less than 750 rpm):

- A minimum number of moving parts.

• Rugged, heavy-duty construction.

• A heavy flywheel that provides comparatively uniform crankshaft rotation on the cyclic loading of a pumping unit.

• Requires a minimum amount of maintenance.

• Can be overhauled on location.

• Requires a heavy foundation.

• Higher cost per HP than for high-speed engines.

• Weight per HP is higher than for high-speed engines.

• Can usually run only on natural gas or liquefied petroleum gas (LPG).

• May have either one or two cylinders.

• Fuel-injection system should be used when HP is greater than 40.

Four-cycle, slow-speed engine:

• Widely used.

• Relatively few moving parts.

• Uniform crankshaft speed because of a large flywheel.

• Can operate on governor control to compensate for load changes.

• Will operate on either natural gas or LPG.

• Repairs can usually be made without removing the engine from the pumping unit.

• Cost and weight per HP is greater than for high-speed engines.

• Limited engine sizes.

• Usually has a single horizontal cylinder.

Four-cycle, high-speed engines (greater than 750 rpm):

• Best suited for portable test installations vs. permanent installations.

• Lower initial cost.

• Lower weight per HP.

• Wide speed and power range.

• Operates on a variety of fuels.

• Large speed variations occur during pumping cycle because of a small flywheel effect.

• Operates on a fixed throttle with the governor mechanism acting only as an overspeed device.

• Has relatively short life because of the fast moving parts and the close tolerances required.

• Requires frequent oil changes.

• Requires frequent maintenance.

• Major repairs require that the engine be removed from the pumping unit.

API *Spec. 7B-11C*[110] contains standard test and operating procedures that are used by manufacturers to determine the ratings of engines for oilfield service. These test data should be requested and furnished to the purchaser from the manufacturer. The data should include the manufacturer's curves showing the torque, maximum brake HP, and the rated-brake HP vs. engine speed. These are important to know the speed range in which the engine would be able to operate.

A general guide for installation and maintenance of gas engines is API *RP 7C-11F*,[111] which covers all three types of engines and includes a troubleshooting section. This practice should be used as a starting point for engines unless the specific manufacturer's operating manual details otherwise. Additionally, there are a number of published papers on installation, care, operation, and lubrication of engines as prime movers for pumping units.[112–118]

Gas-engine performance needs to be derated for altitude and temperature. The API *Spec. 7B-11C* for IC engines recommends the following:

• Deduct 3% of the standard brake HP for each 1,000-ft rise in altitude above sea level.

• Deduct 1% of the standard brake HP for each 10° rise in temperature greater than 60°F or add 1% for each drop in degree, if temperature is less than 60°F.

- Deduct 20% if the engine is continuously operated.

One of the biggest drawbacks of using IC engines is being able to automatically control their operation. There have been a few publications on automatic controllers, but these typically have had limited field use with no long-term production performance recorded.[119,120]

11.7.3 Electric Motors. Once it has been determined that an electric motor is needed vs. a gas engine, there are several things to consider, including design standard, unit efficiency, cyclic-load factor, and motor enclosure. These factors are discussed later in this chapter. Additionally, there have been a number of papers written on the use of electric motors for sucker-rod-lifted wells.[1,2,4–6,104,121,122] Detailed discussions with example problems for sizing motors, along with discussion of electrical-power distribution systems for multiple-well installations, are presented in previous editions of the *Petroleum Production Handbook* and the *Petroleum Engineering Handbook*.[5,6]

11.7.4 Common Motors. The electric motor most commonly used for beam-pumping installations is an alternating-current (AC), three-phase, squirrel-cage induction motor. These motors are used for the following reasons:

- Suitability for the load requirements.
- Low initial cost.
- Availability.
- Service dependability in the field.

If three-phase power is not available, single-phase motors up to 5 HP can be used. This motor is larger and more expensive than the three-phase motor of the same HP. The amount of motor voltage (V) needed depends on V on the distribution system, distance to the transformers, and motor size.

A general guide of motor size vs. V is 115 or 230 V for single-phase motors; 115, 230, 460, or 575 V for polyphase motors up to 50 HP; and 460, 575, or 796 V for polyphase motors 50 to 200 HP. Motors for pumping units come in a variety of common sizes: 1, 1.5, 2, 3, 5, 7.5, 10, 15, 20, 25, 30, 40, 50, 60, 75, 100, and 125 HP.

11.7.5 Natl. Electrical Manufacturers Assn. (NEMA) Design Standards. Motors can be purchased in six standard synchronous speeds, with the 1,200-rpm motor being the most commonly used in oilwell pumping. Multiple-HP-rated motors that may be either dual- or triple-rated are sometimes used for oilwell pumping; the triple-rated is more common. Changing one of these motors from one HP rating to another requires changing leads in the motor housing, which in turn changes the motor's internal wiring system. Any capacitors, fuses, or overload relays in the circuit will also require evaluation and possible revision at the same time to make sure it agrees with the new voltage/current requirements.

NEMA presents five general design standards that provide for varying combinations of starting current, starting torque, and slip. The most commonly recommended electric motor for pumping units is a 1,200-rpm NEMA Design D. It has a normal starting current, a high starting torque (272% or more of full-load torque), and a high slip (5 to 8%). Because Design D specifications are not drawn as closely as they are for other designs, manufacturers have developed several designs with variations in slip that still fall within Design D specifications.

The other NEMA designs (A, B, C, and F) are not used as often. However, there have been publications concerning when NEMA C and/or B designs could be considered, especially with variable-speed drives.[123]

11.7.6 Power Factors. A power factor determines the amount of line current drawn by the motor. A high power factor is desirable because it is important in reducing line losses and minimizing power costs. A lower power factor means that the unit is not operating as efficiently as it should. Oversized motors tend to have low power factors. Typically, a NEMA D has a power factor of 0.87 when fully loaded, but decreases to 0.76 at half load. Usually, units must operate at a power factor of greater than 0.80 to avoid penalties from the power companies; thus, optimization of the pumping unit's size and motor needs to be considered as the well-fluid volume changes.

Using capacitors can increase power factors. To determine if and how much capacitance is needed, determine the power factor of an installation upon initial startup and then decide if a correction is justified. If a pumping-unit motor has a low power factor, a capacitor can be placed between the motor and disconnect. Because of the possibility of electrical shock, only qualified personnel should make this connection. Remember that changing producing conditions might require that the power factor be checked and that the motor-overload relays be resized if the capacitor is on the load side of the overload relays.

11.7.7 Cyclic-Load Factor. When a motor is used for a cyclic load, such as oilwell pumping, it will be thermally loaded more than the same average load applied on a steady-state basis. HP ratings of electrical motors depend on how much the temperature increases in the motor under load. A motor functioning cyclically must be derated from its full-load nameplate rating.

A motor's true performance and rating on a cyclic-load application cannot be determined by the use of normal indicating- or recording-type instruments. Motor heating is a function of the thermal current or root-mean-square (RMS) current, which is the square root of the mean of the squares of currents of definite time intervals. This may be more easily determined with an RMS or the thermal-type ammeter, which records RMS current corresponding to the true heating or "thermal" HP load on the motor. This current will always be higher than the average input current. The ratio of the average HP output to the "thermal HP output" corresponding to the RMS line current is called the motor derating factor and is always less than one. Its inverse is the cyclic-load factor, which is always greater than one. An average motor derating factor for NEMA Design C motors is 0.65; an average motor derating factor for NEMA Design D motors is 0.75.

11.7.8 Motor Enclosures. There are four basic types of motor enclosures: drip-proof guarded, splashproof guarded, totally enclosed fan cooled (TEFC), and explosion proof. "Guarded" refers to screens used over air intakes to prevent the entrance of rodents or other foreign items. The TEFC enclosure provides the maximum protection for the interior of the motor. The drip-proof motor should prove adequate for most pumping-unit installations in which the motor is elevated. This type of construction is built with a closed front-end bell to eliminate the entry of horizontal rain, sleet, or snow into the motor. The splashproof motor affords somewhat more protection against splashing liquids than does the drip-proof one. The preferred enclosure sets the motor on or close to the base; the explosion-proof enclosure will seldom be required. Motor-high mounts on pumping units have also been useful in protecting the motor from sand or snow.

11.7.9 Motor Insulation. NEMA has established the insulation classes and the maximum total temperatures applicable to these classes for insulations used in motor winding. For normal service life, the temperature of the motor windings should not exceed the maximum allowable temperature for that particular insulation type. Class A insulation has a maximum total temperature of 105°C, Class B = 130°C, Class F = 155°C, and Class H = 185°C. Generally, the more the motor enclosure restricts the flow of outside cooling air, the higher the temperature rise will be, and in all probability, the higher the winding temperature. This temperature increase has to be incorporated into the decision regarding which insulation class is required.

The service life of an AC induction motor is determined by the bearing life, the insulation life, and routine maintenance/inspection. Temperature rise is important because studies have indicated that for every 8°C rise above the temperature values stated, the insulation life is cut approximately in half.

11.7.10 Motor Slip. Slip is the difference between motor synchronous speed and speed under load, usually expressed in percent of synchronous speed. Synchronous speed is the theoretical, no-load speed of the motor. Slip characteristics are very important because they will determine how much HP can be converted to torque to start the gearbox gears turning. A high-slip motor permits the kinetic energy of the system to assist in carrying the peak-torque demands. A low-slip motor will respond to the instantaneous demand; in other words, the high-slip motor slows down more under peak torque demands than the low-slip motor. The result is that the high-slip motor will require lower peak currents than the low-slip motor. How high the motor slip should be for pumping installations is debatable; however, Howell and Hogwood stated, "A slip greater than 7 to 8% offers no additional advantages from the overall pumping efficiency standpoint."[104] On the basis of this information and the slip characteristics of the various designs, the Design D motor with a 5 to 8% slip is recommended for most sucker-rod installations.

11.7.11 Ultrahigh-Slip (UHS) Motors. Higher-slip motors are available from some manufacturers; one has claimed to have slip characteristics up to 35 to 40%, also claiming that using their UHS motor would result in lower loading on the sucker rods, lower electric-current peaks, and reduced power use.[123–126] However, to obtain the mechanical advantage, these systems have to be set up in the high-slip mode. When this is done, the increased slip normally decreases the operating speed and may result in a decrease in production when compared to a NEMA D installation.

11.7.12 Motor Controls. Motor controls are housed in a weatherproof, NEMA Type 3 enclosure with special explosion-proof enclosures available. All control units should contain the following:
- Fused manual disconnect.
- Hand on/off/automatic selection switch.
- Lightning arrester system.

Circuit breakers are sometimes used instead of fuses. The fused manual disconnect acts as a line-disconnect switch at the entrance to the control box. A fused disconnect may be located on a pole upstream of the motor starter; the lightning arrester is connected to the incoming line terminals, just ahead of the fused-manual disconnect and must be properly grounded. Depending on the inherent protection built into the motor, the control box may contain an overload relay, an undervoltage relay, and/or a sequence-restart timer.

11.7.13 Grounding Systems. The electrical equipment must be properly grounded. Good grounding procedures are essential to personnel safety and good equipment operation. It is recommended that reference be made to the Natl. Electrical Code and the Natl. Electrical Safety Code to ensure safe grounding is met. Particular attention should be given to the connection of the ground wire to the well casing. The connection should be located where it will not be disturbed during well-servicing operations and should be mechanically secure. Periodic (yearly is recommended as a minimum) continuity measurements should be made with a volt-/ohmmeter between "a new clean spot" (not where the ground wire is terminated) on the well casing and new spot on each piece of grounded equipment. The resistance measured between any piece of equipment and the casing should not exceed 1 ohm. The resistance measured between the pumping-unit ground system and another nearby moisture ground should not exceed 5 Ω. However, these measurements should to be checked with current circulating through the system to determine if the ground is good.

11.7.14 Beam-Pump HP. There are seven HP values that should be considered in the proper design and operation of sucker-rod-pumped wells; these are hydraulic, friction, polished-rod, gear-reducer, V-belt drive, brake, and indicated.

Hydraulic HP (H_{HP}) is the theoretical amount of work or power required to lift a quantity of fluid from a specified depth. This is a theoretical power requirement because it is assumed that there is no pump slippage and no gas breakout. The H_{HP}, thus, is the minimum work expected to lift the fluid to the surface and can be found with the following equations:

$$H_{HP} = [Q(\text{BFPD}) \times 350(\text{lbf}/\text{bbl}) \times G \times H(\text{ft})]$$
$$/ \{33,000[(\text{lbf-ft})/(\text{HP-min})] \times 440(\text{min}/\text{D})\} \dots\dots\dots\dots\dots\dots\dots\dots\dots (11.11)$$

or

$$H_{HP} = [(F_o(\text{lbf}) \times S_p(\text{in.}) \times N(\text{spm})] / \left\{12(\text{in.}/\text{ft}) \times 33,000[(\text{lbf-ft})/(\text{HP-min})]\right\} \dots\dots (11.12)$$

Friction HP (F_{HP}) is the amount of work required to overcome the rubbing-contact forces developed when trying to lift the fluid to the surface. This friction can be caused by a number of sources including plunger-on-barrel friction; rod- and/or coupling-on-tubing wear; sand, scale, and/or corrosion products hindering pump action, rods, and couplings moving through the fluid; fluid moving up the tubing; normal and excessive stuffing-box friction; and liquid and gas flowing through the flowline and battery facilities. F_{HP}, thus, is dependent on factors such as how straight and deep the well is, the fluid viscosity, the pumping speed, and the tubing/rod buckling. In most situations, unless we know all of these factors, we do not know what F_{HP} is. However, for design purposes, API *RP11L* calculations assume the friction effects, which show up in the peak and minimum polished-rod loads and in the calculation of polished-rod HP (P_{HP}).

P_{HP} is the amount of work required to artificially lift the fluid to the stock tank. It is the sum of H_{HP} plus F_{HP}. For design purposes, API *RP11L* assumes these values are related to F_o/SK_r and N/N_o, where K_r is the load necessary to stretch the rod string 1 in., and N_o is the natural frequency of a straight rod string. If a surface dynamometer card is available, the P_{HP} can be measured because the area of the card is the work done at the polished rod to lift the fluid to the surface. The formula for calculating P_{HP} follows:

$$P_{HP} = [\text{card area} \times \text{dynamometer constant} \times S(\text{in.}) \times N(\text{spm})]$$
$$/(\text{card length} \times 12 \times 33,000) . \dots\dots\dots\dots\dots\dots\dots\dots\dots\dots\dots (11.13)$$

Gear-reducer HP (G_{HP}) is a value used to find the efficiency of the unit (i.e., how much the gear reducer is loaded, compared to required peak torque). G_{HP} can be calculated by the following:

$$G_{HP} = (\text{gearbox-torque rating})/4,960. \dots\dots\dots\dots\dots\dots\dots\dots\dots (11.14)$$

V-belt-drive HP (V_{HP}) is the maximum power required by the V-belts to be transmitted to the gear reducer. API *Spec. 1B*[127] states that the V_{HP} for a beam-pumping unit is as follows:

$$V_{HP} = [\text{peak crankshaft torque (lbf-in.)} \times N(\text{spm})]/70,000. \dots\dots\dots\dots (11.15)$$

Brake HP (B_{HP}) is the power required by the prime mover to turn the sheave that makes the reducer's gears turn and starts the cranks going around. This power must accommodate the inefficiencies of all components involved in getting the cranks to turn to transmit the power to the polished rod. B_{HP} can be found with Gipson and Swaim[7] recommendations by the following equation:

$$B_{HP} = P_{HP} / (\text{efficiency factor}) . \dots\dots\dots (11.16)$$

The efficiency factor is found from a graph by taking G_{HP} divided by API gearbox-torque rating and then intersecting either a worn- or new-unit efficiency curve. This efficiency factor is applied to the P_{HP} to convert it to B_{HP} at the prime mover and is required to offset power losses caused by friction in the surface equipment. Fig. 11.10 is a recommended curve to find the HP efficiency factor.

Additionally, a minimum estimate for this HP by NEMA for Design D and C motors is as follows:

$$B_{HP} = [Q(\text{BFPD}) \times L(\text{ft})] / (\text{derating factor}) . \dots\dots (11.17)$$

This derating factor is 56,000 or 45,000 for D or C motors, respectively.

Indicated HP (I_{HP}) is the power required by the prime mover to meet the B_{HP} requirements and determines the size of motor that needs to be ordered. It is found through the following equation:

$$I_{HP} = (B_{HP} / \text{derating factor}) . \dots\dots\dots (11.18)$$

This derating factor accommodates continuous operation and thermal effects. The derating factors for electric motors are 0.75 and 0.65 for NEMA D and C, respectively. The derating factor for a gas engine is dependent on the type of engine and service, rotational speed, elevation, and ambient temperature. The effects of these parameters are discussed in API *Spec. 7B-11C*,[110] paragraphs 2.11 and 2.13. A rule-of-thumb estimate for an engine's derating factor is as follows:

$$\text{Derating factor} = 0.80 + \{[\text{elevation (ft)} \times 0.03] / 1,000 \text{ ft}\}$$
$$+ \{[\text{temperature (°F)} - 85°F] \times [0.01 / 10°F] . \dots\dots (11.19)$$

11.7.15 HP Problem-Solving Example. Given the previous HP definitions, along with the information and calculations in API *RP11L* (p.7), find all seven HPs:
- $H_{HP} = [175 \text{ (BFPD)} \times 350 \text{ (lbf/bbl)} \times 0.9 \times 4,500 \text{ (ft)}] / (33,000 \times 1,440) = 5.2$ HP.
- $P_{HP} = $ line 26 = 8.5 HP.
- $F_{HP} = P_{HP} - H_{HP} = 8.5{-}5.2 = 3.3$ HP.
- $G_{HP} = $ line 25/4,960 = 133,793/4,960 $^-$ 26.9 HP.
- Assuming a 160,000-lbf-in. unit is ordered to accommodate a calculated 133,793-lbf-in. peak torque, and using Fig. 11.10, find the efficiency factor of 0.86: $V_{HP} = (133,793 \times 16) / 70,000 = 35.6$ HP.
- $B_{HP} = (P_{HP} / \text{efficiency factor})$, where the efficiency factor is found by $G_{HP} / $ reducer rating = $(8.5 \times 4,960) / 160,000 = 0.2635$. With Fig. 11.10, the efficiency factor is 0.64. Thus, $B_{HP} = (8.5 / 0.64) = 13.28$ HP.
- Assuming a NEMA D motor, $I_{HP} = (B_{HP} / \text{derating factor}) = 13.28/0.75 = 17.7$ HP.

Therefore, a 20-HP motor should be purchased. However, a 15-HP motor may work, but certain aspects are not known, including actual counterbalance divided by optimum counterbalance, flowline pressure, and actual friction effects. Thermal current (amps) can be measured to determine how much motor capacity is actually being used once the unit and motor are installed. The actual motor size could then be refined for other units in the area.

11.7.16 Sheaves and V-Belt Drives. Prime movers—whether with a gas engine or an electric motor—run at a speed of 300 to 1,200 rpm. This speed must be reduced to the required pumping-unit speed of 2 to 25 spm. This is accomplished with sheaves, V-belt drives, and gear reducers. A sheave is a grooved pulley, and its primary purpose is to change the speed between the prime mover and the gearbox. The belt—usually a V-belt —is a flexible band connecting and passing around each of the two sheaves. Its purpose is to transmit power from the sheave on the prime mover to the sheave on the pumping unit. It is important to understand the basics of sheaves and V-belt to know how to select a sheave for a certain pumping speed and to determine the number of V-belt needed.

11.7.17 Sheave Basics. Sheaves come in different widths and have from 1 to 12 grooves. They are selected on the basis of the pitch diameter (PD) relative to how many spm the unit will pump. New beam-pumping units can be purchased with different-sized sheaves on the reducer. Sheaves can also be purchased to accept different V-belt cross sections. A pumping-unit sheave should be selected that will allow as much speed variation (up and down) from the design speed as is practical without violating API *Spec. 1B*[127] rules. Most unit sheaves will have grooves for more belts than are actually needed because most units seldom, if ever, operate at maximum HP. The maximum V_{HP} is shown in Eq. 11.15. Only the grooves closest to the prime mover and the gear reducer should be filled, and only enough belts to transmit the V_{HP} should be installed because of the following considerations:
  • The tension in the excessive belts, which will be further from the equipment than the required belts, will place unnecessary loads on the bearings.
  • Wider sheaves than necessary and extra belts increase investment costs.
  • It takes more energy to flex the extra belts around the sheaves, which increases operating costs.
   Pumping-unit manufacturers usually list all unit-sheave sizes in their catalogs. Motor sheaves are available with various PDs and numbers of belt grooves. Table A.1 in API *Spec. 1B* contains commonly available sheaves. Because of availability, motor sheaves should be selected from those listed in the top portion of the table.

11.7.18 V-Belt Basics. A V-belt has a trapezoidal cross section that is made to run in sheaves with grooves that have a corresponding shape. It is the workhorse of the industry, available from virtually every V-belt distributor, and it is adaptable to practically any drive. It was designed to wedge in the pulley, thereby multiplying the frictional force produced by the tension; this, in turn, reduces the belt tension required for an equivalent torque. Remember, the purpose of the belt is to transmit power from the sheave on the prime mover to the sheave on the pumping unit. Therefore, the number and size of the belts needed depend on the amount of power to be transmitted.
   Reinforcing cords normally made of rayon, nylon, or other polymer materials provide the load-carrying capability of a V-belt. The cords are usually embedded in a soft rubber matrix called a cushion section. The balance of the belt is made of harder rubber, and the entire section is usually enclosed (i.e., wrapped) in an abrasion-resistant jacket or cover.
   As the belt bends around a sheave, the bending-neutral axis is the only portion that does not change the circumferential length. This line (which does not change length) is called the pitch line and determines the "effective" radius of the pulley, which in turn, determines the torque and speed ratios. The position of this line as it curves around the pulley forms a pitch circle with a pitch diameter.

TABLE 11.10—API *SPEC 1B* TABLE A1 SHOWING AVAILABLE RANGES OF SHEAVES, SIZES, AND MAXIMUM GROOVES FOR VARIOUS STANDARD V-BELT SECTION SIZES

1	2	3	4	5	6	7	8	9	10	11	12	13
Combination A-B Section				B Section			C Section			D Section		
Diameter				Diameter			Diameter			Diameter		
Outside	Pitch Using A Section	Pitch Using B Section	Grooves	Outside	Pitch	Grooves	Outside	Pitch	Grooves	Outside	Pitch	Grooves
3.75	3.0	--	1 thru 6	20.35	20.0	2 thru 6,8,10	7.4	7.0	2 thru 6	12.6	12.0	4 thru 6, 8,10,12
3.95	3.2	--	1 thru 6				7.9	7.5	2 thru 6	13.6	13.0	4 thru 6, 8,10,12
4.15	3.4	--	1 thru 6	25.35	25.0	2 thru 6,8,10						
4.35	3.6	--	1 thru 6				8.4	8.0	2 thru 6 8,10	14.1	13.5	4 thru 6, 8,10,12
4.55	3.8	--	1 thru 6	30.35	30.0	2 thru 6,8,10						
4.75	4.0	--	1 thru 6				8.9	8.5	2 thru 6, 8,10	14.6	14.0	4 thru 6, 8,10,12
4.95	4.2	--	1 thru 6	38.35	38.0	2 thru 6,8,10						
5.15	4.4	4.8	1 thru 6				9.4	9.0	2 thru 6, 8,10,12	15.1	14.5	4 thru 6, 8,10,12
5.35	4.6	5.0	1 thru 6									
5.55	4.8	5.2	1 thru 6				9.9	9.5	2 thru 6, 8,10,12	15.6	15.0	4 thru 6, 8,10,12
5.75	5.0	5.4	1 thru 6									
5.95	5.2	5.6	1 thru 6				10.4	10.0	2 thru 6, 8,10,12	16.1	15.5	4 thru 6, 8,10,12
6.15	5.4	5.8	1 thru 6									
6.35	5.6	6.0	1 thru 6				10.9	10.5	2 thru 6, 8,10,12	16.6	16.0	4 thru 6, 8,10,12
6.55	5.8	6.2	1 thru 6									
6.75	6.0	6.4	1 thru 6				11.4	11.0	2 thru 6, 8,10,12	18.6	18.0	4 thru 6, 8,10,12
6.95	6.2	6.6	1 thru 6									
7.15	6.4	6.8	1 thru 6				12.4	12.0	2 thru 6, 8,10,12	20.6	20.0	4 thru 6, 8,10,12
7.75	7.0	7.4	1 thru 6				13.4	13.0	2 thru 6, 8,10,12	22.6	22.0	4 thru 6, 8,10,12
8.95	8.2	8.6	1 thru 6				14.4	14.0	2 thru 6, 8,10,12	27.6	27.0	4 thru 6, 8,10,12
9.75	9.0	9.4	1 thru 6				16.4	16.0	2 thru 6, 8,10,12	33.6	33.0	4 thru 6, 8,10,12
11.35	10.6	11.0	1 thru 6				18.4	18.0	2 thru 6, 8,10,12	40.6	40.0	4 thru 6, 8,10,12
12.75	12.0	12.4	1 thru 6				20.4	20.0	2 thru 6, 8,10,12	48.6	48.0	5,6,8,10,12
15.75	15.0	15.4	1 thru 6				24.4	24.0	2 thru 6, 8,10,12	58.6	58.0	5,6,8,10,12
18.75	18.0	18.4	1 thru 6				27.4	27.0	2 thru 6, 8			
							30.4	30.0	2 thru 6, 8,10,12			
							36.4	36.0	3 thru 6, 8,10,12			
							44.4	44.0	3 thru 6, 8,10,12			
							50.4	50.0	3 thru 6, 8,10,12			

NOTE: This information is shown here as an aid to the drive designer. It does not constitute a rigid standard, and is not intended to preclude future additions or deletions of sheave sizes.

Classical V-belts are made in five standard cross sections designated by the letters A (the smallest cross section), B, C, D, and E (the largest cross section). The HP that a belt is able to transmit falls off rapidly as the sheave size diminishes. **Table 11.10** lists the minimum PDs recommended by API for the various belt sections. Smaller-PD sheaves are not recommended because of decreased HP, reduced transfer efficiency, shorter belt life, and less economical drive. **Fig. 11.11** shows the HP capacity a single belt can transmit for a selected small-diameter sheave for the various belt cross sections.

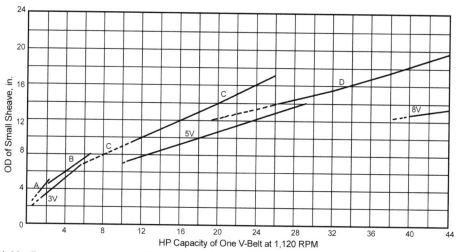

Fig. 11.11—Recommended transmitted HP per single belt for selected-OD sheave size and V-belt cross-section type.

11.7.19 Other Types of Belts. There are other types of belts (i.e., flat, narrow, and synchronous belts, as well as other variations of the V-belt). For example, narrow multi-V-belts (power bands) were developed because the maximum load capacity for a given width of belt required the use of a narrow section. This provided the maximum support of the tensile cords by joining the belts together. V-ribbed belts provide complete support with only a modest compromise in terms of additional tension.

11.7.20 Selecting a Sheave. The first step in designing the V-belt drive for a pumping unit consists of selecting a sheave for the unit and the prime mover. To do this, the desired pumping speed (N), along with the speed (in rpm) of the prime mover and gear ratio, must be known. If the other parameters are known, this equation can be rearranged to determine any required factor:

$$(N \times \text{unit gear ratio} \times \text{pumping-unit sheave size})$$
$$= (\text{prime-mover speed} \times \text{motor sheave size}) . \dots\dots\dots\dots\dots\dots\dots\dots (11.20)$$

The largest motor sheave in this group will provide for the greatest reduction in pumping speed for future operations merely by changing motor sheaves.

11.7.21 Double Reduction With Electric Motor. A double-reduction unit run by an electric motor will require a speed reduction through the V-belt drive of approximately 2:1 at fast pumping speeds. At slow speeds, the ratio will be 6:1. When two belt sections are offered for the unit sheave, the smaller belt section will allow the use of a smaller motor sheave and a lower pumping speed. In most cases, the smaller belt section, with one of the two largest-unit sheaves, will offer the greatest flexibility.

11.7.22 Double Reduction With Gas Engine. A double-reduction unit run by a slow-speed gas engine will require a speed reduction of 1:1 at a fast pumping speed; at a slow pumping speed, the ratio will be 3:1. In these cases, speed reductions (which may be anticipated through the drive) should be checked with the proposed unit and prime mover. If little or no speed reduction will ever be required through the V-belt drive, one of the two smaller-unit sheaves

TABLE 11.11—SUMMARY OF CALCULATED PUMPING SPEEDS FROM EQ. 11.20			
Given Gear-Reducer Sheave PD (in.)	Speed (spm) With 9.0-in. PD Prime-Mover Sheave	Speed (spm) With 16.0-in. PD Prime-Mover Sheave	Comments/Remarks
20	17.6	31.3	Both speeds too high
24	14.6	26.0	Both speeds too high
30	11.7	20.8	Maximum speed too high
36	9.8	17.4	Maximum speed too high, but acceptable
38	9.3	16.4	Maximum speed too high, but acceptable

will enable the use of a smaller (and less-expensive) prime-mover sheave. The larger belt section could also be used and may require fewer belts.

11.7.23 Determining the Required Number of Belts. The first step in determining the number of belts required is to calculate the V_{HP}. When the peak torque is known, this is the preferred method of calculating the design HP. When the peak torque is not known, a service correction of 1.6 is recommended.

The remainder of the calculation can be performed by following the procedure in Section 4 of API *Spec. 1B,* starting with Paragraph 4.5 (page 11). A complete design requires that the distance between the centers of the driver and driven sheaves be known. The basic steps are given in API *Spec. 1B.* An example calculation is presented here.

Example. As an example problem, select the optimum gear-reducer sheave for a C-160D-173-86 pumping unit that will be operated with the reducer fully loaded.

Given: gear-reducer sheaves available from the pumping-unit manufacturer's catalog: 20-, 24-, 30-, 36-, and 38-in. PD-3C. Assume that the prime mover's average rpm = 1,120. The smallest C-section motor sheave that should be considered = 9 in. PD (i.e., 9.4-in. OD in Table 3.1 of API *Spec. 1B*). The largest sheave that should be considered to keep the design PD velocity at less than 5,000 ft/min = 16-in. PD (calculations indicate a 17-in. PD, but page 32 of API *Spec. 1B* indicates that 17-in. PD C-section sheaves are not generally available; economics should discourage engineers and others from recommending sheaves not listed). The liquid to be pumped has a viscosity of approximately 1 cp. The pumping-unit gear ratio is 28.67. The maximum speed with an 86-in. stroke should result in an acceleration factor of 0.3, in which the maximum spm $\leq (0.3 \times 70,500/86)^{0.5} \leq 15.7$. The minimum speed with an 86-in. stroke should result in an acceleration factor ≤ 0.225, in which the minimum spm $\leq (0.225 \times 70,500/86)^{0.5} \leq 13.6$.

Find: the optimum gear-reducer sheave and the number of C-section belts required, assuming the reducer is fully loaded and is operated at the maximum and minimum speed dictated by the sheave selected.

Solution 1: solving for pumping speeds from Eq. 11.20 = [prime-mover speed (rpm) × prime-mover-sheave PD]/[(gear-reducer sheave PD) × (1/pumping-unit gear ratio)]. For example, 1,120 × 9/20 × 1/28.67 = 17.1. The rest of the speeds can be calculated similarly for the different available gear-reducer sheaves, and the smallest or largest prime-mover sheaves. The summary of these calculations is shown in **Table 11.11.**

The table shows that the 38-in. PD-4C gear-reducer sheave should be selected; however, the 36-in. gearbox sheave is acceptable.

Solution 2:

1. V_{HP} at 9 spm = 160,000 × 9/70,000 = 20.6.

2. HP that can be transmitted with one C-section belt and with a 9-in.-PD prime-mover sheave (as shown in Fig. 11.11) = 11.

3. Number of belts required = 20.6/11 = 2 belts.

4. V_{HP} at 16 spm = 160,000 × 16/70,000 = 36.6

5. HP that can be transmitted with one C-section belt and with a 16-in.-PD prime-mover sheave (as shown in Fig. 11.11) = 25.

6. Number of belts required = 36.6/25 = 2 belts.

Note that neither calculation justifies filling all the grooves in the gear-reducer sheave. No justification is known for using more belts than is indicated by API *Spec. 1B*.

11.8 Miscellaneous Surface Equipment

11.8.1 Polished Rods. A polished rod is the top-most rod in a rod string. These rods come in various lengths and sizes. Polished rods are made of various materials, including carbon steel, stainless steel, and monel. It is usually more economical to use corrosion-resistant polished-rod liners on carbon-steel polished rods than to use corrosion-resistant polished rods. Polished rods must be properly aligned in relation to the pumping tee. Poor alignment will result in decreased life of the stuffing-box packing and possible failure of the polished rod. Furthermore, if the polished rod does not travel straight up and down during the pumping cycle, liners may not be practical. For situations in which the pumping unit is not properly set and/or the wellhead is crooked, a full-length sucker rod should be installed between the polished rod and the top of the string's pony rods. This will decrease crooked wellhead-induced polished-rod failures and increase packing life. The polished rod must have a coupling and a sub on top. This is required in case the rod slips because the polished-rod clamp is not sufficiently tight. The coupling keeps it from falling through the stuffing box. The subrod helps retrieve the polished rod and helps prevent moisture from getting into the coupling.

Section 12 of API *Spec. 11B* discusses polished rods and polished-rod liners. Table 12.1 in API *Spec. 11B* recommends polished-rod size vs. the size of the top rod in the rod string. API polished-rod lengths are 8, 11, 16, and 22 ft. Upset ends can be furnished on 1⅛-, 1¼-, and 1½-in. polished rods and are recommended for heavy loads. Upset ends have sucker-rod connections that are superior to the pipe-thread connections on nonupset polished rods. This type of connection decreases stress concentration and results in improved fatigue life. The surface finish on polished rods is specified in Section 12 API *Spec. 11B*. Although the range of surface finish is 10 to 20 micro-inches, roughness average scale (R_A), it is recommended that a 16-micro-inch-R_A finish be specified because, if the finish is too smooth, it may be difficult for the clamps to work properly and a too-rough finish reduces polished-rod packing life.

11.8.2 Polished-Rod Clamps. Polished-rod clamps are fitted on the polished rod and come in several designs. Clamps for the light loads may have only one bolt, whereas clamps for heavier loads will have two bolts. The clamp manufacturer specifies the torque required to tighten the clamps, which is also discussed in both API *Spec. 11B* and API *RP 11BR*.[29] They also specify the forces that will cause clamps to slip on polished rods in API *Spec. 11B*. This is based on the assumption that the OD of the polished rod will be approximately equal to the OD the manufacturers assumed when they designed and built the clamp. The clamp must be the right size for the polished rod (no homemade bushings) and be strong enough to support the maximum well load. Open-end, box-end, or socket wrenches should be used on the clamp nuts and bolts. Pipe wrenches cut the nuts and make it hazardous for those who must loosen the clamp in the future. Be careful of foreign material in the clamp or on the polished rod. If the polished rod and clamp are not properly cleaned, the clamp may slip. Clamps that do not have a load-bearing surface perpendicular to the polished rod can also bend the polished rod. The following are some maintenance tips to keep in mind when working with the clamps:

• Use the clamp manufacturer's recommended torque for tightening the bolts. Do not over-tighten polished-rod clamps—it may be the start of polished-rod failure. API *Spec. 11B* requires that a properly attached clamp may not cause an indentation of more than 0.010 in.

• The polished rod's clamp area and the inside area of the clamp should be cleaned before installation.

• Do not allow the use of pipe wrenches on polished-rod bolt nuts. Replace all pipe-wrench-cut nuts.

• Do not put clamps on polished-rod liners.

• Do not clamp on the sprayed-metal part of polished rods.

11.8.3 Stuffing Boxes. A stuffing box is a device attached to the pumping tee that seals fluids in the tubing by forming a tight seal with the polished rod and diverting the produced fluids out of the pumping tee into the flowline. Packing for stuffing boxes is made from a variety of different materials. Local experience is the best guide in selecting the appropriate packing material to use.

Stuffing boxes may have one or two sets of packing elements. In a stuffing box with two sets of packing, the lower set is left relaxed and inoperative during normal operations. When it becomes necessary to replace the upper set of packing, the unit is shut down, and the lower set of packing is tightened against the rod, which enables the upper-packing element to be safely replaced with pressure on the tubing. After replacing the upper element, the lower-packing element must be backed off before starting the unit. This method not only retains the tubing pressure and decreases pollution, but also keeps low-pressure gas out of the face of the person doing the work.

There are stuffing boxes made with attached oil containers to keep the polished rod lubricated on wells that pump off, have high water cuts, or are in a semiflowing gas-heading condition. The proper method for handling the pumpoff condition is adjusting the pump capacity with time clocks, stroke lengths, stroke, speed, or pumpoff controllers. Maintaining a surface backpressure on the tubing may be beneficial on wells that are in a semiflowing gas-heading condition. Both conditions should be corrected to decrease polished-rod and stuffing-box wear and to increase overall pumping efficiency.

11.8.4 Rod Rotators. Rod rotators must be used with certain types of mechanical paraffin scrapers. Rod rotators may also be used when rod-coupling wear is a problem. The rotation of the rods spreads the wear around the entire surface of the coupling instead of allowing it to be concentrated on one small area. Rotation does not solve the problem, but it does make the coupling or centralizer last longer. Rotators need to be selected properly and are dependent on the well load.

11.8.5 Pumping Tees. API *Spec. 11B* covers design and rating of pumping tees. The major requirement for tees and stuffing boxes are that they be properly installed. In addition, the threads need to be clean and in line with the tubing when it is screwed on.

11.8.6 Check Valves. A check valve is a valve that permits flow in only one direction. If the gas or liquid flow starts to reverse, the valve automatically closes and prevents reverse flow. A check valve should be placed between the casing head and flowline to prevent backflow from the flowline into the casing annulus. An oversized check valve will chatter and destroy the seat seal prematurely; an undersized check valve will hold too much backpressure on the casing.

11.8.7 Surface Valves. The casing/tubing annulus should be equipped with a wing valve that will allow the casing pressure and the fluid level to be monitored. This valve also can be used to introduce to the well corrosion inhibitors, hot oil, water, etc. It should be bull-plugged closed when not in use. Introducing liquids into the annulus at a higher rate than the annulus self-venting rate drives the producing-liquid level to less than the pump intake, which starves the pump and causes premature pump failure. Self-venting can occur if the equivalent annulus diameter $\geq 0.92 \times Q^{0.4}$, where Q is the pumping rate in gal/min. Wing valves allow the installation of a pressure gauge so that casing pressure can be measured. This is important to check because, if the casing pressure is greater than ½ the pump-intake pressure, the flowline is probably too small or partially blocked.

Another type of surface valve that could be used is a backpressure valve. This valve is normally installed in the flowline, upstream from the casing-annulus gas-piping tie in and is typically used to keep the tubing from unloading when the well still has high bottomhole pressure (when the well alternates between flowing and pumping, this situation is called "flumping"). The optimum backpressure to prevent flumping would be equal to or just greater than the pump-intake pressure. It should be noted that backpressure on the tubing can cause paraffin deposits in the tubing to come loose, flow up the tubing, and block the backpressure valve, or may cause the stuffing-box packing to blow out; thus, the tubing and rods should be cleaned before applying backpressure.

11.9 Design Calculations

There has been a long history of work trying to model or design sucker-rod strings. This includes the original work from Slonneger[128] and Mills[129] on vibration effects of rod strings. Fatigue of rods also was considered in 1940.[130] These effects helped develop the Slonneger, Mills,[131] and Langer[132] formulas for rod loads. A detailed discussion and development of these formulas is provided by Zaba.[1]

Zaba[2] detailed the next refinement of sucker-rod loading, which was the organization of the Sucker Rod Pumping Research Inc. in 1954, and the development of an analog computer model to simulate the elastic behavior of rod strings. This method was provided to the industry in the 1960s, and the design results were developed into the hand-calculation and graphical method in API *RP 11L*.[30]

Companies used this graphical chart and calculation method for many years, with some refinements and changes to the practice, to account for tapered-rod strings and rod percentages, that provide equal loading in each section of a string. The development of the wave equation for sucker-rod lift by S.G. Gibbs[133] in 1961 was a major step forward because its use permitted design or analysis for all types of units and rod strings. The advent of the personal computer and its continued developments of power and speed allowed more developments of rod-string simulators, including extending the API simulator using a next-order wave equation, pumping units different than conventional ones, mixed-steel and fiberglass-rod strings, frictional effects of the fluid and wellbore deviation, and current models that address very viscous fluids and 3D horizontal wells.[61,133–151] Regardless of what method or program is used to predict loads, once the equipment is installed and the well has stable production and fluid levels, it is recommended that a dynamometer survey be run with a load-capable dynamometer attached to the polished rod. The predicted loads should be compared to the actual loads and the associated fluid production. Adjustments to the predictions should be made for future troubleshooting and any further design changes.

While these models have improved, they still address only the loads on the selected grade of rods and the string design, the size of downhole pump, and the type and size of the pumping unit. However, for a complete design of a beam-pump installation, all the equipment discussed in the preceding sections needs to be addressed, as well as the data provided from a rod-string design program, which at minimum, include the following:

• Where the pump is set and the associated downhole separator design.
• Type of pump, along with its design and metallurgy.
• Sinker-bar use and design, if required.
• Tubing size and grade.
• TAC use, position, and setting.
• Polished-rod size.
• Polished-rod clamp size.
• Type and size of prime mover.
• Sheave and V-belt design.

Gipson and Swaim did an excellent job of summarizing a sucker-rod lift-system design in The Beam Pump Design Chain[7] with the API *RP 11L* approach. This recommended practice should be consulted for continued discussion of this equipment, along with a review of a sample problem and a recommended solution. In summary, use the design procedure presented in API *RP 11L* or a suitable wave equation. Several commercial wave-equation computer programs are available that many operators have successfully used.

11.10 Automation and Pumping Control

"Automation" means different things to different people and becomes a problem when the term triggers concern from the field about personnel reduction. Thus, sucker-rod-lift automation may not always be considered good if not properly applied. However, there needs to be monitoring and control equipment on an installation to enhance proper operation, monitoring, failure reduction or prevention, and troubleshooting/problem solving.

At minimum, a sucker-rod-lift installation should have vibration switches on the unit to shut it down if there is a high part in the rod string that will cause overloading of the gearbox or damage to the unit foundation. There should be a pressure gauge (or a connection for a pressure gauge to allow temporary installation) on the flowline-pumping T, downstream of the check valve that monitors the flowline pressure. There should also be some type of pump-cycle controller. This may be from a simple time clock to a more sophisticated pumpoff or rod-pump controller.

A number of papers have been published that address automation of sucker-rod-lift or beam-pump automation and control.[152-165] There is also a reference on practical automation for mature fields.[166] If a high degree of automation is considered, then a very important side consideration is keeping this electrical equipment working, especially during electrical storms; thus, proper lightning protection and grounding should be considered.[104,167,168,169]

A study made several years ago indicated that at least one-half of the pumping wells surveyed had a subsurface pump installed that was too large.[*] The results of such installations were devastating fluid pounds when wells were overpumped, resulting in short run times and increased failure frequency. Because of the cost to pull and replace a pump, typically other parts of the sucker-rod-lift system were changed to compensate for the oversized pump. Too many times, the too-large pump is a result of habit or of not optimizing when the well capacity has changed.

It is still possible to live with the too-large pump until the correct size can be installed. Some interim measures are to reduce the pump displacement by reducing the strokes per minute, shortening the stroke, and decreasing backpressure on the tubing/casing annulus, there-

---

* Conoco unpublished internal report.

by decreasing formation backpressure, allowing more fluid inflow, and reducing the pumping time.

Probably the most common type of well control or automation is time clocking, which consists of pumping a portion of a 15-minute period. Percentage timers and pumpoff controls are used in modern time-clocking work. The purpose of time clocking is to adjust the pump capacity to the well capacity.

Pumpoff controllers have been developed over the years to be standalone monitors, to provide rod-string load and polished-rod position and related dynamometer cards, and to be installed with communication links to allow remote monitoring and control of the installation. Current advancements in computers along with electrical end devices allow sophisticated control of individual installations and/or a whole field. If new pumping installations are planned, these types of controllers/automation should be considered. It becomes more difficult to justify a retrofit to a long-time producing field, but this may be considered depending on access to the field, variable well inflow, and/or reduction in operating costs by reducing well failures. Many papers on pumpoff or rod-pump controllers, different theories concerning their operation, and controller installation and operation have been published.[170–181] These should be reviewed to determine if or when a controller may be advantageous to install.

11.11 Troubleshooting Sucker-Rod-Lift Installations

Once a sucker-rod-lift system is installed on a well, the continued monitoring and optimization of pumping parameters begins. Obtaining monthly well tests on the fluid production from the well and a fluid/pump submergence level is recommended to ensure that the well capacity is within the recommended pump-capacity range, the well does not have excess capacity or equipment needs to be changed because of excessively high fluid levels, and that excessive pumping of the well is not occurring.

Although current rod-string-design models, simulators, and programs are fairly accurate, they still need individual-well calibration to ensure that the design assumptions are correct for the actual well conditions. Additionally, to know what is different and why, the six main well loads need to be recorded from the predictive design. These loads need to be compared to the actual well loads with known fluid-level, well-test, and pumping parameters. Gipson and Swaim[7] have described these six basic loads and their relationship to a surface dynamometer card.

Many papers have been published on dynamometers and their use on sucker-rod-lifted wells.[182–191] Some of these provide discussion of surface loads and surface dynamometer cards, while the latest trend is to discuss downhole dynamometer cards (or pump cards). While obtaining actual downhole loads that these dynagraphs recorded, there has been recent work on developing and field-testing a downhole dynamometer.[192–194]

While these measurements investigate the sucker-rod-string loads, the other components of the lift system also should be investigated, including the pumping unit and gearbox. As previously discussed, there are only two techniques to check if a pumping unit is overloaded[9]: conducting a torque analysis or comparing the permissible-load diagram (PLD) for the pumping unit to the loads from the surface dynamometer card. The torque-analysis technique has been demonstrated by Gipson and Swaim,[195] and Takacs,[196] Gault,[197] and Teel[198] have discussed PLDs or envelopes. Chastain discussed examples of PLD use for properly counterbalancing a pumping unit.[199]

Failures of sucker-rod-lift components have been discussed in countless papers. The use of current data processing and root-cause analysis of these failures has been the recent industry trend to assist in reducing failures.[200,201] Additionally, the Artificial Lift Energy Optimization Consortium (ALEOC) program in west Texas has been useful for operators to compare the failure frequency of their sucker-rod-lift components, wells, and fields with other operators to find areas of improvement.[202] One final new trend developing for this lift method is a total well-management concept that integrates the well capacity/pump submergence and rod-string and pumping-unit loads with power demands. This may prove the best practice for optimizing, troubleshooting, and reducing failures along with reducing associated lifting costs.

Nomenclature

a = casing/tubing annulus area, in.^{2}

B_{HP} = brake horsepower

C = diametrical clearance between plunger and barrel, in.

D = plunger diameter, in.

E_r = elastic constant rods, in./lbf

F = gradient correction factor

F_{HP} = friction horsepower

F_o = differential fluid load on the full pump-plunger cross-sectional area, lbf

F_o/SK_r = dimensionless sucker-rod stretch load (fluid load on full plunger area divided by load necessary to stretch the total-rod string to an amount equal to the polished-rod stroke length)

G = specific gravity of the combined fluid in the tubing

G_{HP} = gear-reducer horsepower

H = pump seating depth, ft

H_{HP} = hydraulic horsepower

I_{HP} = indicated horsepower

P_{HP} = polished-rod horsepower

V_{HP} = V-belt drive horsepower

K_r = the load necessary to stretch the rod string 1 in.

L = pump-seating nipple depth, ft

L_p = plunger length, in.

L_{PSD} = seating nipple/pump depth, ft

N = pumping-unit speed, spm

N_o = the natural frequency of a straight rod string, spm

p = differential pressure across plunger, psi

P_D = pump displacement, BLPD

P = producing pressure, psia

Q = slippage or leakage loss, in.^{3}/min

$Q/aP^{0.4}$ = parameter from Gilbert used to determine gradient correction factor, where Q is gas flow rate, Mscf/D; a is the casing-tubing cross-sectional area, in.^{2}; and p is the producing pressure, psia

R_A = roughness average

S = surface stroke length, in.

S_p = downhole pump-plunger stroke length, in.

W_C = well production capacity, BFPD

μ = absolute viscosity of fluid, cp

References

1. Zaba, J.: "Oil Well Pumping Methods: A Reference Manual for Production Men," *Oil and Gas J.* (July 1943).
2. Zaba, J.: *Modern Oil Well Pumping,* Petroleum Publishing Co., Tulsa (1962).
3. Donnelly, R.W.: *Oil and Gas Production: Beam Pumping,* PETEX, U. of Texas, Dallas (1986).
4. Saber, T.: *Modern Sucker Rod Pumping,* PennWell Books, Tulsa (1993).

5. *Petroleum Production Handbook,* T.C. Frick (ed.), SPE, Dallas (1962) **1.**

6. *Petroleum Engineering Handbook,* H.B. Bradley (ed.), SPE, Richardson, Texas (1987).

7. Gipson, F.W. and Swaim, H.W.: "The Beam Pumping Design Chain," paper presented at the 1988 Southwestern Petroleum Short Course, Lubbock, Texas, 23–25 April.

8. Clegg, J.D.: "High Rate Artificial Lift," *JPT* (March 1988) 277.

9. Hein, N.W. Jr.: "Beam-Pumping Operation: Problem Solving and Technology Advancements," *JPT* (April 1996) 330.

10. McCoy, J.N. *et al.:* "Acoustic Static Bottomhole Pressures," paper SPE 13810 presented at the 1985 SPE Production Operations Symposium, Oklahoma City, Oklahoma, 10–12 March.

11. McCoy, J.N., Podio, A.L., and Becker, D.: "Pressure Transient Digital Data Acquisition and Analysis From Acoustic Echometric Surveys in Pumping Wells," paper SPE 23980 presented at the 1992 SPE Permian Basin Oil and Gas Recovery Conference, Midland, Texas, 16–20 March.

12. Vogel, J.V.: "Inflow Performance Relationships for Solution-Gas Drive Wells," *JPT* (January 1968) 83; *Trans.,* AIME, **243.**

13. Eickmeier, J.R., "How to Accurately Predict Future Well Productivities," *World Oil* (May 1968) 99.

14. Standing, M.B.: *Volumetric and Phase Behavior of Oil Field Hydrocarbon Systems,* Reinhold Publishing Corp., New York City (1952).

15. Clegg, J.D.: "Understanding and Combating Gas Interference in Pumping Wells," *Oil & Gas J.* (29 April 1963).

16. Podio, A.L. *et al.:* "Field and Laboratory Testing of a Decentralized Continuous Flow Gas Anchor," presented at the 1995 Annual Technical Meeting of the Petroleum Soc. of CIM, 14–17 May.

17. McCoy, J.N. and Podio, A.L.: "Improved Downhole Gas Separators," paper 11 presented at the 1998 Southwestern Petroleum Short Course, Lubbock, Texas, 7–8 April.

18. *Spec. 11AX, Subsurface Sucker Rod Pumps and Fittings,* eleventh edition, API, Washington, DC (June 2001).

19. *RP 11AR, Recommended Practices for Care and Use of Subsurface Pumps,* fourth edition, API, Washington, DC (June 2000).

20. *MR01-76, Metallic Materials for Sucker Rod Pumps for Hydrogen Sulfide Environments,* Natl. Assn. of Corrosion Engineers (NACE), Houston.

21. Hein, N.W. Jr. and Loudermilk, M.R.: "Review of New API Pump Setting Depth Recommendations," paper SPE 24836 presented at the 1992 SPE Annual Technical Conference and Exhibition, Washington, DC, 4–7 October.

22. McCafferty, J.F.: "Importance of Compression Ratio Calculation in Designing Sucker Rod Pump Installations," paper SPE 25418 presented at the 1993 SPE Production Operation Symposium, Oklahoma City, Oklahoma, 21–23 March.

23. Patterson, J. *et al.:* "Fluid Slippage in Down-Hole Rod-Drawn Oil Well Pumps," paper 16 presented at the 2000 Southwestern Petroleum Short Course, Lubbock, Texas 12–13 April.

24. Williams, B.J.: "Summary of Testing of Variable Slippage Pump (VSP) for Gas Locking Conditions in Down-Hole Sucker Rod Pump," paper 22 presented at the 2001 Southwestern Petroleum Short Course, Lubbock, Texas, 24–25 April.

25. "Quality Systems—Model for Quality Assurance in Design, Development, Production, Installations, Servicing," *ISO 9001,* Intl. Organization for Standardization (ISO), Geneva, Switzerland (1987).

26. *Spec. Q1, Specification for Quality Programs for the Petroleum and Natural Gas Industry,* sixth edition, API, Washington, DC (March 1999).

27. Hein, N.W. Jr. and Thomas, S.: "Rod Pump Shop Audits and Performance Requirements," paper 6 presented at the 2000 Southwestern Petroleum Short Course, Lubbock, Texas, 12–13 April.

28. *Spec. 11B, Specification for Sucker Rods,* 26th edition, API, Washington, DC (January 1998).

29. *RP 11BR, Recommended Practice for Care and Handling of Sucker Rods,* eighth edition, ANSI/API, Washington, DC (October 1989, Supplement 1 July 1991).

30. *RP 11L, Recommended Practice for Design Calculations for Sucker Rod Pumping Systems,* fourth edition, API, Washington DC (June 1988, Errata 1 October 1988).

31. Hensley, H.N. *et al.:* "Ribbon Rod Development for Beam Pumping Applications," paper 05 presented at the 1994 Southwestern Petroleum Short Course, Lubbock, Texas, 20–21 April.

32. Hein, N.W. Jr. and Hermanson, D.E.: "A New Look at Sucker Rod Fatigue Life," paper SPE 26558 presented at the 1993 SPE Annual Technical Conference and Exhibition, Houston, 3–6 October.
33. *Sucker Rod Handbook,* Bethlehem Steel Co., Bethlehem, Pennsylvania (1953).
34. *Bull. 11L3, Sucker Rod Pumping System Design Book,* first edition, API, Washington, DC (May 1970).
35. Neely, A.B.: "Sucker Rod String Design," *Petroleum Engineer* (March 1976) 58.
36. Gault, R.H.: "Rod Stresses from RP11L Calculations," paper 25 presented at the 1990 Southwestern Petroleum Short Course, Lubbock, Texas, 18–19 April.
37. Hermanson, D.E.: "Sucker Rods," *Petroleum Engineering Handbook,* H.B. Bradley (ed.), SPE, Richardson, Texas (1987) Chap. 9.
38. *MR 01–74, Recommendations for Selecting Inhibitors for Use as Sucker Rod Thread Lubricants,* NACE, Houston (2001).
39. Steward, W.B.: "Sucker Rod Failures," *Oil & Gas J.* (4 April 1984).
40. Moore, K.H.: "Stop Sucker Rod Failures to Save Money," *Petroleum Engineer Intl.* (July 1981).
41. Powers, M.L.: "Optimization of Sucker Rod Replacement," paper SPE 3470 presented at the 1971 SPE Annual Meeting, New Orleans, 3–6 October.
42. *Spec. 5CT, Specification for Casing and Tubing,* sixth edition, API, Washington, DC (November 1998).
43. *RP 5C1, Recommended Practice for Care and Use of Casing and Tubing,* 18th edition, API, Washington, DC (May 1999).
44. Lincicone, E.A.: "Reduced Tubing Failures in Rod Pumped Wells Utilizing Downhole Caliper Surveys," *Petroleum Engineer Intl.* (July 1980) 34.
45. Sirgo, E.C., Gibson, E.D., and Jackson, W.E.: "Polyethylene Lined Tubing in Rod Pumped Wells," paper SPE 39815 presented at the 1998 SPE Permian Basin Oil and Gas Recovery Conference, Midland, Texas, 23–26 March.
46. Hickman, J.: "Polylined Tubing Reduces Downhole Failures," *World Oil* (January 2003) 51.
47. Bowerman, J. *et al.:* "Seven+ Years Review of Poly-lined Production Tubing in the Howard Glasscock Field," paper presented at the 2006 Southwestern Petroleum Short Course, Lubbock, Texas, 20–26 April.
48. Hanson, D.G.: "Pembina Cardium Beam Pumping Equipment—Case Histories," paper 83-34-42 presented at the 1983 Annual Technical Meeting of Petroleum Soc. of CIM, 10–13 May.
49. *Spec. 11E, Specification for Pumping Units,* 17th edition, API, Washington, DC (November 1994/ Reaffirmed January 2000).
50. *Spec. 10431, Specification for Petroleum and Natural Gas Industries—Pumping Units,* ISO (1993).
51. *Oilfield Products Group General Catalog,* Lufkin Industries Inc., Lufkin, Texas (2001).
52. AGMA *422.03, Practice for Helical and Herringbone Speed Reducers for Oilfield Pumping Units,* American Gear Manufacturers Assn., Alexandria, Virginia (1998).
53. AGMA *2001-C95, Fundamental Rating Factors and Calculation Method for Involute, Spur and Helical Gear Teeth,* American Gear Manufacturers Assn., Alexandria, Virginia (2001).
54. Svinos, J.G.: "Exact Kinematic Analysis of Pumping Units," paper SPE 12201 presented at the 1983 SPE Annual Technical Conference and Exhibition, San Francisco, 5–8 October.
55. Watson, J.: "Comparing Class I and Class III Varying Pumping Unit Geometries," paper 030 presented at the 1983 Southwestern Petroleum Short Course, Lubbock, Texas, 27–28 April.
56. Evans, C.E.: "What Type of Beam Pumping Unit Would You Use?" paper 015 presented at the 1961 Annual West Texas Oil Lifting Short Course, Lubbock, Texas, 20–21 April.
57. Keiner, C.J.: "API Pumping Units," paper 024 presented at the 1962 Annual West Texas Oil Lifting Short Course, Lubbock, Texas, 12–13 April.
58. Kilgore, J.J., Tripp, H.A., and Hunt, C.L. Jr.: "Walking Beam Pumping Unit System Efficiency Measurements," paper SPE 22788 presented at the 1991 SPE Annual Technical Conference and Exhibition, Dallas, 6–9 October.
59. Byrd, J.P. and Jackson, B.C.: "Field Testing a Front-Mounted Mechanical Oilfield Pumping Unit," paper SPE 382 presented at the 1962 SPE Rocky Mountain Joint Regional Meeting, Billings, Montana, 24–25 May.
60. Byrd, J.P.: "High Volume Pumping with Sucker Rods," *JPT* (December 1968) 1355.

61. Nolen, K.B.: "Deep High Volume Rod Pumping," paper SPE 2633 presented at the 1964 SPE Annual Meeting, Denver, 28 September–1 October.
62. Gipson, F.W.: "Maximum Capacity of Beam Pumping Equipment and High Strength Steel Sucker Rods," paper 026 presented at the 1990 Southwestern Petroleum Short Course, Lubbock, Texas, 18–19 April.
63. Gault, R.H.: "Pumping Unit Geometry," paper 002 presented at the 1961 Annual West Texas Oil Lifting Short Course, Lubbock, Texas, 20–21 April.
64. Byrd, J.P.: "The Effectiveness of a Special Class III Lever System Applied to Sucker Rod Pumping," paper 009 presented at the 1970 Southwestern Petroleum Short Course, Lubbock, Texas, 16–17 April.
65. Richards, C.: "Application of Air Balance Pumping Units," paper 019 presented at the 1956 Annual West Texas Oil Lifting Short Course, Lubbock, Texas, 15–16 April.
66. Byrd, J. P.: "History, Background and Rationale of the Mark II Beam Type Oil Field Pumping Unit," paper 024 presented at the 1990 Southwestern Petroleum Short Course, Lubbock, Texas, 18–19 April.
67. Byrd, J.P.: "Recent Advances in Beam Type Unit Designs," paper 001 presented at the 1962 Annual West Texas Oil Lifting Short Course, Lubbock, Texas, 12–13 April.
68. Slaughter, E. Jr.: "Pitfalls of Pumping Unit Selection and Application," paper 001 presented at the 1962 Annual West Texas Oil Lifting Short Course, Lubbock, Texas, 19–20 April.
69. Byrd, J.P.: "Rating the Effectiveness of Beam and Sucker Rod Pumping Modes," paper 021 presented at the 1989 Southwestern Petroleum Short Course, Lubbock, Texas, 19–20 April.
70. Lekia, S.D.L. and Day, J.J.: "An Improved Technique for the Evaluation of Performance Characteristics and Optimum Selection of Sucker-Rod Pumping Well Systems," paper SPE 18548 presented at the 1988 SPE Eastern Regional Meeting, Charleston, West Virginia, 1–4 November.
71. Juch, A.H. and Watson, R.J.: "New Concepts in Sucker-Rod Pumping Design," *JPT* (March 1969) 342; *Trans.*, AIME, **246.**
72. Lietzow, C.H.: "The Long Stroke Hydraulic Pumping Unit," paper 008 presented at the 1956 Annual West Texas Oil Lifting Short Course, Lubbock, Texas, 15–16 April.
73. Joy, R.F.: "Flexible Pumping Strand," paper 011 presented at the 1969 Southwestern Petroleum Short Course, Lubbock, Texas, 17–18 April.
74. Lietzow, C.H.: "Hydraulic Pumping—New Developments," paper 035 presented at the 1957 Annual West Texas Oil Lifting Short Course, Lubbock, Texas, 17–18 April.
75. Metters, E.W.: "A New Concept in Pumping Unit Technology," SPE 3193 presented at the 1970 SPE Hobbs Petroleum Technology Symposium, Hobbs, New Mexico, 29–30 October.
76. Ewing, R.D.: "Long Stroke Pumping Unit," paper SPE 3186 presented at the 1970 SPE California Regional Meeting, Santa Barbara, California, 28–30 October.
77. Nickell, R.L.: "Dewatering Gas Wells with Pneumatic Pumping Equipment," paper 18 presented at the 1973 Southwestern Petroleum Short Course, Lubbock, Texas, 26–27 April.
78. Smith, L.A.: "Sucker Rod Pumping with Pneumatic Surface Units," paper 033 presented at the 1975 Southwestern Petroleum Short Course, Lubbock, Texas, 17–18 April.
79. Brinlee, L.D.: "Operating Experience With The Alpha 1 Pumping Unit: A New Alternative in Artificial Lift," paper SPE 8240 presented at the 1979 SPE Annual Technical Conference and Exhibition, Las Vegas, Nevada, 23–26 September.
80. Hollenbeck, A.L.: "An Alternative Approach to High Volume, a Long Stroke Pumper," paper SPE 9216 presented at the 1980 SPE Annual Technical Conference and Exhibition, Dallas, 21–24 September.
81. Jesperson, P.J., Laidlaw, R.N., and Scott, R.J.: "The HEP (Hydraulic, Electronic, Pneumatic) Pumping Unit: Performance Characteristics, Potential Applications, and Field Trial Results," paper SPE 10250 presented at the 1981 SPE Annual Technical Conference and Exhibition, San Antonio, Texas, 4–7 October.
82. Mourlevat, J.J. and Morrow, T.B.: "Recently Developed Long Stroke Pumping Unit Incorporates Novel Flexibility for a Wide Variety of Applications," paper SPE 11338 presented at the 1982 SPE Production Technology Symposium, Hobbs, New Mexico, 8–9 November.
83. Tart, H.C.: "Operating and Performing Experience with Computer Controlled Long Stroke Rod Pumping Systems," paper 29 presented at the 1983 Southwestern Petroleum Short Course, Lubbock, Texas, 27–28 April.

84. Pickford, K.H. and Morris, B.J.: "Hydraulic Rod Pumping Units in Offshore Artificial-Lift Applications," *SPEPE* (May 1989) 131.

85. Hicks, A.W. and Jackson, A.: "Improved Design for Slow Long Stroke Pumping Units," paper 22 presented at the 1991 Southwestern Petroleum Short Course, Lubbock, Texas, 17–18 April.

86. Adair, R.L. and Dillingham, D.C.: "Ultra Long Stroke Pumping System Reduces Mechanical Failures, Lowers Lifting Cost While Increasing Production," paper 001 presented at the 1995 Southwestern Petroleum Short Course, Lubbock, Texas, 14–15 April.

87. Zhiqi, Z. *et al.*: "Hydraulic Pumping Units for Offshore Platform," paper SPE 64507 presented at the 2000 SPE Asia Pacific Oil and Gas Conference and Exhibition, Brisbane, Australia, 16–18 October.

88. McConnell, D. and Holden, D.R.: "Long Stroke Pumping Systems in Deep Well Applications—Field Study," paper SPE 68791 presented at the 2001 SPE Western Regional Meeting, Bakersfield, California, 26–30 March.

89. McCoy, J.N., Podio, A.L., and Rowlan, L.: "Rotaflex Efficiency and Balancing," paper SPE 67275 presented at the 2001 SPE Production and Operations Symposium, Oklahoma City, Oklahoma, 24–27 March.

90. Leitzow, C.H.: "Care and Maintenance of Long Stroke Hydraulic Pumping Units," paper 020 presented at the 1984 Southwestern Petroleum Short Course, Lubbock, Texas, 24–26 April.

91. McLane, C. Jr.: "Operation, Care and Maintenance of Pumping Units," paper 010 presented at the 1954 Annual West Texas Oil Lifting Short Course, Lubbock, Texas, 13–14 April.

92. Richards, C.: "Maintenance of Beam Type Pumping Units," paper 020 presented at the 1955 Annual West Texas Oil Lifting Short Course, Lubbock, Texas, 14–15 April.

93. Amerman, J.: "Foundation and Installation of Beam Type Pumping Units," paper 032 presented at the 1952 Annual West Texas Oil Lifting Short Course, Lubbock, Texas, 13–14 April.

94. Van Sant, R.W. Jr.: "Pumping Unit Lubrication," paper 018 presented at the 1954 Annual West Texas Oil Lifting Short Course, Lubbock, Texas, 13–14 April.

95. Pickens, J.: "Operation, Care and Maintenance of Beam Pumping Units," paper 013 presented at the 1957 Annual West Texas Oil Lifting Short Course, Lubbock, Texas, 11–12 April.

96. Amerman, J.: "Causes and Curse of Pumping Unit Reducer Troubles," paper 006 presented at the 1958 Annual West Texas Oil Lifting Short Course, Lubbock, Texas, 17–18 April.

97. Griffin, F.: "Installation and Care of Pumping Units," paper 24 presented at the 1959 Annual West Texas Oil Lifting Short Course, Lubbock, Texas, 23–24 April.

98. Elliot, B.: "Effect of Abuse and Misapplication of Pumping Unit Gears," paper 02 presented at the 1962 Annual West Texas Oil Lifting Short Course, Lubbock, Texas, 12–13 April.

99. Bullard, B.D.: "Preventative Maintenance for Beam Pumping Equipment," paper 32 presented at the 1976 Southwestern Petroleum Short Course, Lubbock, Texas 22–23 April.

100. Griffin, F.D.: "Maintenance of Pumping Units," paper 022 presented at the 1977 Southwestern Petroleum Short Course, Lubbock, Texas, 21–22 April.

101. Miceli, L.D. and Huff, M.D.: "Pumping Unit Preventative Maintenance," paper 024 presented at the 1988 Southwestern Petroleum Short Course, Lubbock, Texas, 20–21 April.

102. *RP 11G, Recommended Practices for Installation and Lubrication of Pumping Units,* fourth edition, API, Washington, DC (November 1994).

103. *RP 11ER, Recommended Practices for Guarding of Pumping Units,* second edition, API, Washington, DC (January 1990).

104. Howell, J.K. and Hogwood, E.E.: *Electrified Oil Production,* PennWell Books, Tulsa (1981).

105. Hood, J.T.: "Selection and Application of Prime Movers for Oil Well Pumping," paper 022 presented at the 1956 Annual West Texas Oil Lifting Short Course, Lubbock, Texas, 15–16 April.

106. Owen, R.K.: "Economics of Prime Movers for Oil Lifting," paper 010 presented at the 1958 Annual West Texas Oil Lifting Short Course, Lubbock, Texas, 17–18 April.

107. Drake, R.W. Jr.: "Selection of Prime Movers," paper 007 presented at the 1963 Annual West Texas Oil Lifting Short Course, Lubbock, Texas, 18–19 April.

108. Rehborg, H.E.: "Slow Speed Pumping Engines for Oil Pumps," paper 015 presented at the 1956 Annual West Texas Oil Lifting Short Course, Lubbock, Texas, 15–16 April.

109. Hood, J.J.: "A Comparison of Slow and High Speed Engines for Oil Fields," paper 010 presented at the 1957 Annual West Texas Oil Lifting Short Course, Lubbock, Texas, 11–12 April.

110. *Spec. 7B-11C, Specification for Internal–Combustion Reciprocating Engines,* ninth edition, API, Washington, DC (November 1994, Reaffirmed January 2000).

111. *RP 7C-11F, Recommended Practice for Installation, Maintenance and Operation of Internal-Combustion Engines,* fifth edition, API, Washington, DC (November 1994, Reaffirmed January 2000).

112. Hood, J.T.: "Operation and Maintenance of Mechanical Prime Movers," paper 009 presented at the 1954 Annual West Texas Oil Lifting Short Course, Lubbock, Texas, 13–14 April.

113. Freeman, W.F.: "Maintenance of Low Speed Gas Engines," paper 023 presented at the 1955 Annual West Texas Oil Lifting Short Course, Lubbock, Texas, 14–15 April.

114. McConnell, L.A.: "Care and Operation of Multi-Cylinder Engines," paper 017 presented at the 1957 Annual West Texas Oil Lifting Short Course, Lubbock, Texas, 11–12 April.

115. Jenkins, W.L.: "Care and Operation of High Speed Pumping Engines," paper 012 presented at the 1958 Annual West Texas Oil Lifting Short Course, Lubbock, Texas, 17–18 April.

116. Hiltpold, M.W.: "Care and Operation of Multi Cylinder Engines," paper 014 presented at the 1958 Annual West Texas Oil Lifting Short Course, Lubbock, Texas, 17–18 April.

117. Foringer, D.E.: "Engine Lubrication Oil Performance," paper 040 presented at the 1962 Annual West Texas Oil Lifting Short Course, Lubbock, Texas, 12–13 April.

118. Roden, D.: "Maintenance and Operation of Multi Cylinder Engines," paper 063 presented at the 1960 Annual West Texas Oil Lifting Short Course, Lubbock, Texas, 21–22 April.

119. Armstrong, J.R.: "Automatic Operation of Gas Engines," paper 015 presented at the 1980 Southwestern Petroleum Short Course, Lubbock, Texas, 17–18 April.

120. Millo, S.F. Jr. and Millo, D.: "Pump Off Control for Gas Engine Driven Pumping Units," paper 018 presented at the 1996 Southwestern Petroleum Short Course, Lubbock, Texas, 17–18 April.

121. Howell, J.K.: "Electric Motors and Their Rating for Sucker Rod Pumping," paper 011 presented at the 1958 Annual West Texas Oil Lifting Short Course, Lubbock, Texas, 17–18 April.

122. *Spec. 11L6, Specification for Electric Motor Prime Movers for Beam Pumping Unit Service,* first edition, API, Washington, DC (June 1993, Supplement November 1996).

123. Vineyard, T.D., Humphries, T.W., and Devine, D.L.: "A Dynamic New Concept in Beam Pumping—Adjustable Speed Pumping," paper 027 presented at the 1992 Southwestern Petroleum Short Course, Lubbock, Texas, 22–23 April.

124. Chastain, J.: "How to Pump More for Less with Extra High Slip Motors," *Oil & Gas J.* (March 1968) 62.

125. Simon, D.J.: "Design Considerations for the Application of UHS Motors in Beam Pumping Systems," paper 020 presented at the 1973 Southwestern Petroleum Short Course, Lubbock, Texas, 26–27 April.

126. Justice, M.W.: "Optimizing Pumping with HHS Motors," paper 024 presented at the 1986 Southwestern Petroleum Short Course, Lubbock, Texas, 23–24 April.

127. *Spec. 1B, Specification for Oil-Field V-Belting,* sixth edition, API, Washington, DC (January 1955, Reaffirmed January 2000).

128. Slonneger, J.C.: "Vibration Problems in Oil Wells," API *Drilling and Production Practices,* API, Washington, DC (1937) 179.

129. Mills, K.N.: "Effects of Rod Vibration on Dynamometer Cards," *Oil Weekly* (June 1940) 23.

130. Dale, D.H. and Johnson, D.O.: "Laboratory and Field Endurance Values of Sucker Rod Materials," API *Drilling and Production Practices,* API, Dallas (1940).

131. Mills, K.N.: "Factors Influencing Well Loads Combined in a New Formula," *Petroleum Engineering J.* (April 1939) 37.

132. Langer, B.F. and Ianbergg, E.H.: "Calculation of Load and Stroke in Oil Well Pumping Rods," *Oil & Gas J.* (1942).

133. Gibbs, S.G.: "Predicting the Behavior of Sucker Rod Pumping Systems," *JPT* (July 1963) 769; *Trans.,* AIME, **228.**

134. Gibbs, S.G.: "A General Method for Predicting Rod Pumping System Performance," paper SPE 6850 presented at the 1977 SPE Annual Technical Conference and Exhibition, Denver, 9–12 October.

135. Gibbs, S.G.: "A Review of Methods for Design and Analysis of Rod Pumping Installations," *JPT* (December 1982) 2931; *Trans.,* AIME, **273.**

136. Doty, D.R. and Schmidt, Z.: "An Improved Model for Sucker Rod Pumping," *SPEJ* (February 1983) 33.

137. Clegg, J.D.: "Rod Pump Design Using Personal Computers," paper 021 presented at the 1986 Southwestern Petroleum Short Course, Lubbock, Texas, 23–24 April.

138. Clegg, J.D.: "Improved Sucker Rod Pumping Design Calculations," paper 019 presented at the 1988 Southwestern Petroleum Short Course, Lubbock, Texas, 20–21 April.

139. Schmidt, Z. and Doty, D.R.: "System Analysis for Sucker-Rod Pumping," *SPEPE* (May 1989) 125.

140. Brunings, C.A. and Castillo, V.: "BOMEC: A New Artificial-Lift Design Method for Producing Heavy Crudes," paper SPE 19716 presented at the 1989 SPE Annual Technical Conference and Exhibition, San Antonio, Texas, 8–11 October.

141. Lekia, S.D.L and Evans, R.D.: "A Coupled Rod and Fluid Dynamic Model for Predicting the Behavior of Sucker-Rod Pumping Systems—Part 1: Model Theory and Solution Methodology," *SPEPF* (February 1989) 26.

142. Lekia, S.D. and Evans, R.D.: "A Coupled Rod and Fluid Dynamic Model for Predicting the Behavior of Sucker-Rod Pumping Systems—Part 2: Parametric Study and Demonstration of Model Capabilities," *SPEPF* (February 1995) 34.

143. Lukasiewicz, S.A.: "Dynamic Behavior of Sucker Rod String in the Inclined Well," paper SPE 21665 presented at the 1991 SPE Production Operations Symposium, Oklahoma City, Oklahoma, 7–9 April.

144. Gibbs, S.G.: "Design and Diagnosis of Deviated Rod-Pumped Water," *JPT* (July 1992); *Trans.,* AIME, **293.**

145. Cortines, J.M. and Hollabaugh, G.S.: "Sucker-Rod Lift in Horizontal Wells in Pearsall Field, Texas," paper SPE 24764 presented at the 1992 SPE Annual Technical Conference and Exhibition, Washington, DC, 4–7 October.

146. Laine, R.E.: "Conceptual Sucker-Rod Design: An Unsolved Problem," paper 25419 presented at the 1993 SPE Production Operations Symposium, Oklahoma City, Oklahoma, 21–23 March.

147. Xu, J.: "A New Approach to the Analysis of Deviated Rod-Pumped Wells," paper SPE 28697 presented at the 1994 SPE International Petroleum Conference and Exhibition of Mexico, Veracruz, Mexico, 10–13 October.

148. Jennings, J.W.: "QRod, A Practical Beam Pumping Design Program," paper 006 presented at the 1994 SPE Southwestern Petroleum Short Course, Lubbock, Texas, 20–21 April.

149. Gibbs, S.G.: "Assumption of the API Rod Pumping Design Method as Related to Practical Applications and Wave Equation Techniques," paper SPE 27988 presented at the 1994 SPE U. of Tulsa Centennial Petroleum Engineering Symposium, Tulsa, 29–31 August.

150. Cullen, R.P. and Mansure, A.J.: "Fluid Dynamics in Sucker Rod Pumps," paper 003 presented at the 1999 Southwestern Petroleum Short Course, Lubbock, Texas, 21–22 April.

151. Xu, J. *et al.:* "A Comprehensive Rod-Pumping Model and Its Applications to Vertical and Deviated Wells," paper SPE 52215 presented at the 1999 SPE Mid-Continent Operations Symposium, Oklahoma City, Oklahoma, 28–31 March.

152. Shore, R.A.: "The Kern River SCAN Automation System—Sample, Control and Alarm Network," paper SPE 4173 presented at the 1972 SPE California Regional Meeting, Bakersfield, California, 8–10 November.

153. Wadlington, W.H.: "How Amoco Approached Automation in West Texas," paper SPE 4684 presented at the 1973 SPE Annual Meeting, Las Vegas, Nevada, 30 September–3 October.

154. Egan, J.D.: "Oil Field Automotive—Ten Years' Experience," paper 041 presented at the 1976 Southwestern Petroleum Short Course, Lubbock, Texas, 22–23 April.

155. Irby, R.E.: "Wellsite Management and Control of Rod Pumped Wells," paper 023 presented at the 1977 Southwestern Petroleum Short Course, Lubbock, Texas, 21–22 April.

156. Jentsch, W.A. Jr. and Marrs, R.D.: "Computerized Automation of Oilfield Production Operations: An Extensive 5-Year Study into the Costs and Benefits," *SPEPE* (August 1988) 229.

157. Svinos, J.G.: "Application of Expert System Technology to the Design of Rod Pumping Systems," paper 033 presented at the 1990 Southwestern Petroleum Short Course, Lubbock, Texas, 18–19 April.

158. Luppens, J.C.: "Practical Automation for Mature Producing Areas," *SPECA* (April 1995) 44.

159. Outomuro, M.V.: "Using Automation for Optimizing Production Fields," paper SPE 29534 presented at the 1995 SPE Production Operations Symposium, Oklahoma City, Oklahoma, 2–4 April.

160. Findley, C.P. II, Herring, R.B., and Pike, J.S.: "Automation in Cyclical Rate Primary Reservoirs Significantly Reduces Beam Pumping Failures," paper 012 presented at the 1996 Southwestern Petroleum Short Course, Lubbock, Texas, 17–18 April.

161. Westerman, G.W.: "Automated Well Head Management," paper 034 presented at the 1997 Southwestern Petroleum Short Course, Lubbock, Texas, 2–3 April.

162. Ray, L.: "Using Integrated Software for Fall Field Automation and Analysis," paper 016 presented at the 1998 Southwestern Petroleum Short Course, Lubbock, Texas, 8–9 April.

163. Vásquez, M. and Fernandes, J.: "Rod-Pumping Optimization Through Surface or Downhole Parameter Estimation and Simulation," paper SPE 52214 presented at the 1999 SPE Mid-Continent Operations Symposium, Oklahoma City, Oklahoma, 28–31 March.

164. Fernandes, J. and Lestra, A.: "Experiences on Heavy and Extra-Heavy Crude Rod Pumping Automation Applications Using Thermal and Dilution Techniques," paper SPE 69900 presented at the 2001 SPE International Thermal Operations and Heavy Oil Symposium, Porlamar, Margarita Island, Venezuela, 12–14 March.

165. Sengul, M. and Bekkousha, M.A.: "Applied Production Optimization: I—Field," paper SPE 77608 presented at the 2002 SPE Annual Technical Conference and Exhibition, San Antonio, Texas, 29 September–2 October.

166. Cerqueira, J.F. et al.: "Development of an Intelligent Distributed Management System for Automated Wells (SPGA)," paper SPE 77609 presented at the 2002 SPE Annual Technical Conference and Exhibition, San Antonio, Texas, 29 September–2 October.

167. Brinner, T.R. and Atkins, J.D.: "Oilfield Grounding," paper 44 presented at the 2002 Southwestern Petroleum Short Course, Lubbock, Texas, 24–25 April.

168. Skinner, D.R.: "Lightning Protection for an Oilfield Automatic and Instrumentation System," JPT (November 1977) 1405.

169. Lapis, T.: "Sucker-Rod Pumping Unit Lightning Protection," paper 21 presented at the 2002 Southwestern Petroleum Short Course, Lubbock, Texas, 24–25 April.

170. Hudgins, T.A. and McKee, F.E.: "Pump-Off Control—The Average Motor Current Method," paper 032 presented at the 1975 Southwestern Petroleum Short Course, Lubbock, Texas, 17–18 April.

171. Westerman, G.W.: "Successful Application of Pump-Off Controllers," paper SPE 6853 presented at the 1977 SPE Annual Technical Conference and Exhibition, Denver, 9–12 October.

172. Hunter, J.D. et al.: "Denver Unit Well Surveillance and Pump-Off Control Systems," JPT (September 1978) 1319.

173. Neely, A.B.: "Computer Pump Off Control of Sucker Rod Pumped Wells—Denver Unit, Wasson Field, Gaines and Yoakum Counties, Texas," paper 017 presented at the 1979 Southwestern Petroleum Short Course, Lubbock, Texas, 19–20 April.

174. Amezcua, J.D.: "Comparative Analysis of Pump-off Control Systems for Field Applications," paper SPE 9362 presented at the 1980 SPE Annual Technical Conference and Exhibition, Dallas, 21–24 September.

175. Neely, A.B. and Tolbert, H.O.: "Experience with Pump-off Control in the Permian Basin," JPT (May 1988) 645.

176. Guffey, C.G., Rogers, J.D., and Hester, L.R.: "Beam Pump Control Today," paper 024 presented at the 1989 Southwestern Petroleum Short Course, Lubbock, Texas, 19–20 April.

177. Blackford, T.A., Dunn, J.R., and Joseok, R.: "Benefits of Improving Pump-Off Control for Beam Pumped Producing Wells," paper 020 presented at the 1991 Southwestern Petroleum Short Course, Lubbock, Texas, 17–18 April.

178. Echel, A.C., Abels, H.P., and Merritt, R.A.: "Testing and Practically Applying Pump-Off Controllers in a Waterflood," paper SPE 29636 presented at the 1995 SPE Western Regional Meeting, Bakersfield, California, 8–10 March.

179. Gill, R.A., Soza, R.L., and Ott, R.E.: "Using Pump-Off Controllers (P.O.C.) to Their Fullest," paper 007 presented at the 1997 Southwestern Petroleum Short Course, Lubbock, Texas, 2–3 April.

180. Lindsay, A.B.: "Applying Pump Off Controllers to Marginal Producers," paper 009 presented at the 1998 Southwestern Petroleum Short Course, Lubbock, Texas, 8–9 April.
181. McCoy, J.N., Podio, A.L., and Becker, D.: "Timer Control of Beam Pump Run Time Reduces Operating Expenses," paper 009 presented at the 1999 Southwestern Petroleum Short Course, Lubbock, Texas, 21–22 April.
182. Chastain, J.: "Diagnosis of Pumping Well Equipment Troubles by the Use of a Dynamometer," paper 019 presented at the 1954 Annual West Texas Oil Lifting Short Course, Lubbock, Texas, 13–14 April.
183. Fagg, L.W.: "Dynamometer Fundamentals as Applied to Water Flood Operations," paper 035 presented at the 1956 Annual West Texas Oil Lifting Short Course, Lubbock, Texas, 15–16 April.
184. Merryman, C.J. and Lawrence, D.L.: "Dynamometer Testing for Analyzing the Pumping Well Problem," paper 041 presented at the 1958 Annual West Texas Oil Lifting Short Course, Lubbock, Texas, 17–18 April.
185. Lawrence, D.L. and Merryman, C.J.: "Dynamometer Lease Studies," paper 004 presented at the 1959 Annual West Texas Oil Lifting Short Course, Lubbock, Texas, 23–24 April.
186. Slonneger, J.C.: *Dynagraph Analysis of Sucker Rod Pumping,* Gulf Publishing, Houston (1961).
187. Gibbs, S.G. and Neely, A.B.: "Computer Diagnosis of Downhole Conditions in Sucker Rod Pumping Wells," *JPT* (January 1966) 91; *Trans.,* AIME, **237.**
188. Hudgins, T.A.: "Use and Applications of Dynamometer for Surface and Downhole Analysis," paper 026 presented at the 1981 Southwestern Petroleum Short Course, Lubbock, Texas, 23–24 April.
189. Houang, A.B. *et al.:* "Pattern Recognition Applied to Dynamometer Cards for Sucker Rod Diagnosis," paper 023 presented at the 1991 Southwestern Petroleum Short Course, Lubbock, Texas, 17–18 April.
190. McCoy, J.N., Jennings, J.W., and Podio, A.L.: "A Polished Rod Transducer for Quick and Easy Dynagraphs," paper 003 presented at the 1992 Southwestern Petroleum Short Course, Lubbock, Texas, 22–23 April.
191. Swaim, H.W. and Hein, N.W. Jr.: *Surface Dynamometer Card Interpretation: A Beam Pumping Problem Solving Tool,* presented at the 1987 Southwestern Petroleum Short Course, Lubbock, Texas, 22–23 April.
192. Albert, C.D.: "Downhole Dynamometer Tool," paper 001 presented at the 1994 Southwestern Petroleum Short Course, Lubbock, Texas, 20–21 April.
193. Soza, R.L.: "Review of Downhole Dynamometer Testing," paper SPE 35217 presented at the 1996 SPE Permian Basin Oil and Gas Recovery Conference, Midland, Texas, 27–29 March.
194. Waggoner, J.R. and Mansure, A.J.: "Development of the Downhole Dynamometer Database," *SPEPF* (February 2000) 3.
195. Gipson, F.W. and Swaim, H.W.: "Beam Pumping Fundamentals," presented at the 1969 Southwestern Petroleum Short Course, Lubbock, Texas, 19–20 April.
196. Takacs, G.: "Torque Analysis of Pumping Units Using Dynamometer Cards," paper 028 presented at the 1989 Southwestern Petroleum Short Course, Lubbock, Texas, 19–20 April.
197. Gault, R.H.: "Envelopes for Pumping Units," paper 017 presented at the 1991 Southwestern Petroleum Short Course, Lubbock, Texas, 21–22 April.
198. Teel, L.: "Permissible Load Envelopes for Beam Pumping Units," paper 029 presented at the 1991 Southwestern Petroleum Short Course, Lubbock, Texas, 17–18 April.
199. Chastain, J.: "Use of Lead/Lag to Reduce Torque on Pumping Units," *Oil & Gas J.* (October 1976) 38.
200. Junkins, E.D. Jr.: "Pumping Well Failure Analysis Using Electronic Data Processing Techniques," paper 015 presented at the 1971 Southwestern Petroleum Short Course, Lubbock, Texas, 15–16 April.
201. Gantz, K. and Disney, V.: "Guide to Well Failure Root Cause Analysis in Sour Beam Pumping Service," paper 005 presented at the 1997 Southwestern Petroleum Short Course, Lubbock, Texas, 2–3 April.
202. Rahman, M.M. and Heinze, L.R.: "Development of ALEOC Beam Pumping Failure Data Base," paper 017 presented at the 2000 Southwestern Petroleum Short Course, Lubbock, Texas, 12–13 April.

SI Metric Conversion Factors

bbl	×	1.589 873	E–01	= m^3
cp	×	1.0*	E–03	= Pa·s
ft	×	3.048*	E–01	= m
ft^3	×	2.831 685	E–01	= m^3
ft/min	×	5.080*	E–03	= m/sec
ft/sec	×	3.048*	E–01	= m/sec
°F		(°F – 32)/1.8		= °C
gal/min	×	2.271 247	E–01	= m^3/h
hp	×	7.460 43	E–01	= kW
in.	×	2.54*	E+00	= cm
in.^{2}	×	6.451 6*	E+00	= cm^2
in.^{3}	×	1.638 706	E+01	= cm^3
in.^{3}/min	×	2.731 177	E–07	= m^3/sec
lbf	×	4.448 222	E+00	= N
lbf-in.	×	1.129 848	E–01	= N·m
lbm	×	4.535 924	E–01	= kg
psi	×	6.894 757	E+00	= kPa

*Conversion factor is exact.

Chapter 12
Gas Lift

Herald W. Winkler, Texas Tech U. and **Jack R. Blann,** Consultant (Retired, Exxon Production Research Co.)

12.1 Introduction

12.1.1 Description of Gas Lift. Gas lift is a method of artificial lift that uses an external source of high-pressure gas for supplementing formation gas to lift the well fluids. There are two basic types of gas lift in use today—continuous and intermittent flow.

Continuous-Flow Gas Lift. The vast majority of gas lift wells are produced by continuous flow, which is very similar to natural flow. In continuous-flow gas lift, the formation gas is supplemented with additional high-pressure gas from an outside source. Gas is injected continuously into the production conduit at a maximum depth that depends upon the injection-gas pressure and well depth. The injection gas mixes with the produced well fluid and decreases the density and, subsequently, the flowing pressure gradient of the mixture from the point of gas injection to the surface. The decreased flowing pressure gradient reduces the flowing bottomhole pressure below the static bottomhole pressure thereby creating a pressure differential that allows the fluid to flow into the wellbore. **Fig. 12.1** illustrates this principal.

Intermittent-Flow Gas Lift. As the name implies, intermittent flow is the periodic displacement of liquid from the tubing by the injection of high-pressure gas. The action is similar to that observed when a bullet is fired from a gun. (See **Fig. 12.2.**) The liquid slug that has accumulated in the tubing represents the bullet. When the trigger is pulled (gas lift valve opens), high-pressure injection gas enters the chamber (tubing) and rapidly expands. This action forces the liquid slug (shaded in Fig. 12.2) from the tubing in the same way that expanding gas forces the bullet from the gun. The disadvantage of intermittent-flow gas lift is the "on/off" need for high-pressure gas, which presents a gas-handling problem at the surface and causes surging in the flowing bottomhole pressure that cannot be tolerated in many wells producing sand. Because of the intermittent production of the well, intermittent-flow gas lift is not capable of producing at as high a rate as continuous-flow gas lift. Intermittent flow should not be considered unless the flowing bottomhole pressure is low, and the well is gas lifting from the bottom valve.

Applications. Gas lift is particularly applicable for lifting fluids in wells that have a significant amount of gas produced with the crude. Gas compressors are nearly always installed to gather the produced gas and, with only minor changes, can be designed to supply the high

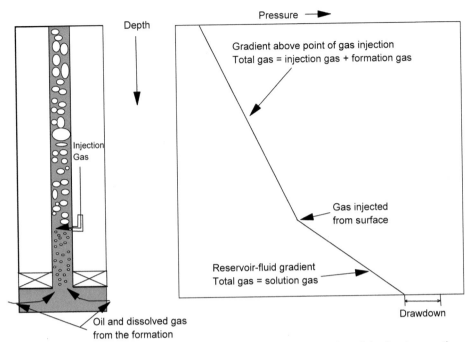

Fig. 12.1—Flowing pressure gradient traverses above and below the depth of gas injection in a continuous-flow gas lift well.

injection-gas pressure for the gas lift system. The injected gas only supplements the formation gas and may amount to only a small percentage of the total produced-gas volume. Most continuous-flow wells can be depleted by gas lift because reservoir-pressure maintenance programs are implemented in most major oil fields and many reservoirs have waterdrives.

Advantages of Gas Lift. The flexibility of gas lift, in terms of production rates and depth of lift, can seldom be matched by other methods of artificial lift if adequate injection-gas pressure and volume are available. Gas lift is one of the most forgiving forms of artificial lift because a poorly designed installation will normally gas lift some fluid. The mandrel depths for many gas lift installations with retrievable-valve mandrels are calculated with minimal well information.

Highly deviated wells that produce sand and have high formation-gas/liquid ratios are excellent candidates for gas lift when artificial lift is needed. Many gas lift installations are designed to increase the daily production from flowing wells. No other method is as ideally suited for through-flowline ocean-floor completions as a gas lift system. Wireline-retrievable gas lift valves can be replaced without killing a well or pulling the tubing.

The gas lift valve is a simple device with few moving parts, and sand-laden well fluids do not have to pass through the valve to be lifted. The individual-well downhole equipment is relatively inexpensive. The surface equipment for injection-gas control is simple and requires little maintenance and practically no space for installation. Typically, the reported high overall reliability and lower operating costs for a gas lift system are superior to other methods of lift.

Limitations of Gas Lift. The primary limitation for gas lift operations is the lack of formation gas or an injection-gas source. Wide well spacing and lack of space for compressors on offshore platforms may also limit the application of gas lift. Poor compressor maintenance can increase compressor downtime and add to the cost of gas lift gas, especially with small field units. Compressors are expensive and must be properly maintained. Generally, gas lift is not as

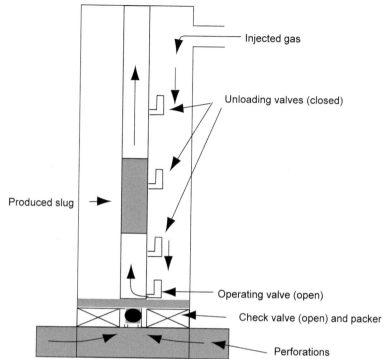

Fig. 12.2—Injection-gas cycle for gas lifting a liquid slug in an intermittent gas lift well.

suitable as some other systems for single-well installations and widely spaced wells. The use of wet gas without dehydration reduces the reliability of gas lift operations.

12.2 Designing a Gas Lift System

12.2.1 Timing. Ideally, an artificial-lift system should be chosen and designed during the initial planning phase of an oil field. However, in the haste to get a field on production, artificial lift may not be considered until after other production facilities are designed and installed. It is difficult to choose and install the optimum artificial-lift system after the surface production facilities have been installed. This is especially true in the case of gas lift.

12.2.2 Factors Having an Effect on the Design of a Gas Lift System. Most production equipment affects the design of a gas lift system, so it is best to design the gas lift system concurrently with the design of surface facilities. The entire purpose of a gas lift system is to reduce the bottomhole flowing pressure of the well. Anything that restricts or prevents this from occurring will have an impact on the system and must be considered in the design.

Field Layout and Well Design. Consideration of gas lift operations should be a prime factor in sizing the hole for the desired oilwell tubulars. This is particularly true in offshore wells where all of the downhole gas lift equipment, except the valves, is installed during the initial completion. In on-shore fields, gas lift affects the size and location of gathering lines and production stations. Artificial lift should be considered before a casing program is designed. Casing programs should allow the maximum production rate expected from the well without restrictions. Skimping on casing size can ultimately cost lost production that is many times greater than any savings from smaller pipe and hole size. The same is true in flowline size and length. Production stations should be relatively near the producing wells. In most cases, increasing the size of the flowline does not compensate for the backpressure generated by the added

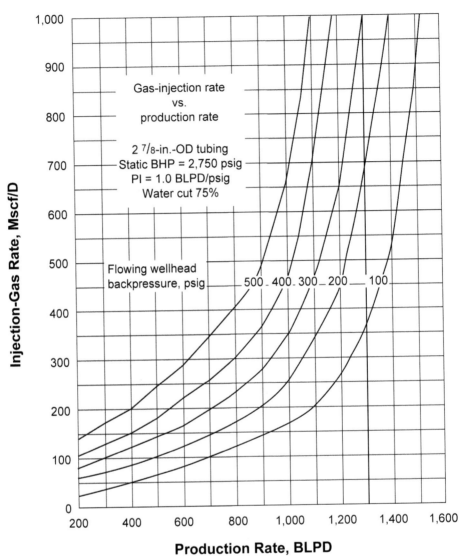

Fig. 12.3—Effect of wellhead backpressure on daily production rates and injection-gas requirements.[2]

pipe length. Any item of production equipment that increases backpressure at the wellhead, whether it be wellhead chokes, small flowlines, undersized gathering manifolds and separators, or high compressor suction pressure, seriously impacts the operation of a gas lift system. **Fig. 12.3** illustrates the effect of backpressure on injection-gas requirement and fluid production in a 6,900-ft gas lift well.[1]

Injection-Gas Pressure. Choosing a proper injection-gas pressure is critical in a gas lift system design.[2] Several factors may affect the choice of an injection-gas pressure. However, one primary factor stands out above all others. To obtain the maximum benefit from the injected gas, it must be injected as near the producing interval as possible. The injection-gas pressure at depth must be greater than the flowing producing pressure at the same depth. Any compromise with this principle will result in less pressure drawdown and a less efficient operation. High volumes of gas injected in the upper part of the fluid column will not have the same

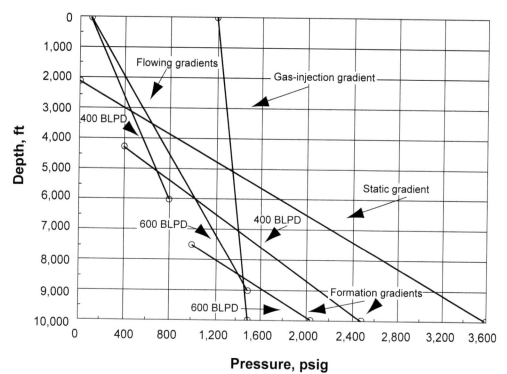

Fig. 12.4—Construction of an equilibrium curve.

effect as a much smaller volume of gas injected near the producing formation depth because the fluid density is reduced only above the point of gas injection.

The equilibrium curve[1] illustrates the effect of injection-gas depth on a particular well. The equilibrium curve is established by determining the intersection of the formation-fluid pressure gradient below the depth of gas injection with the produced gas lift gradient above the depth of gas injection for various producing liquid rates (See **Fig. 12.4**). In Fig. 12.4, the intersections of the flowing formation-fluid pressure-gradient traverses for a 400-B/D rate and a 600-B/D rate with the flowing total (formation plus injection gas) -pressure-gradient traverses above the point of gas injection to the surface for both rates are shown. If intersections are established for a large number of rates, as are shown in **Fig. 12.5**, the points can be connected and will form what is referred to as an equilibrium curve. When injection-gas pressure traverses are drawn from the surface, it is possible to determine the maximum gas lift rate from the well for various surface injection-gas pressures. Referring again to Fig. 12.5, a 1,200-psig surface injection-gas pressure would gas lift this well at a rate slightly above 600 B/D.

Less downhole equipment may be required when higher injection-gas pressures are used (see **Fig. 12.6**). The higher injection-gas pressure provides a greater pressure differential between the injected-gas pressure and the flowing tubing pressure; thereby, allowing a greater spacing between valves. Thus, fewer mandrels and valves are required to reach the maximum injection-gas depth. Note that in Fig. 12.6, the 800-psig design reaches only the depth of 4,817 ft and requires seven gas lift valves. In comparison, the 1,400-psig design uses only four gas lift valves to reach the full depth of the well at 8,000 ft. The maximum pressure drawdown at the formation with the 800-psig injection gas is only 210 psi (2,200 to 1,990) compared to 1,010 psi (2,200 to 1,190) when 1,400-psig injection gas is used.

Major Factors That Have an Effect on Choosing the Most Economical Injection-Gas Pressure. Only the basic conditions that must be met to ensure the most efficient injection-gas pressure

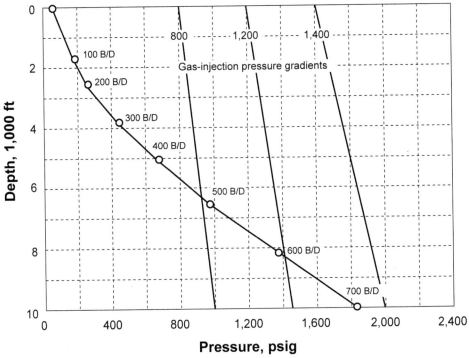

Fig. 12.5—Complete equilibrium curve for specific well conditions.

to maintain operating pressure for a given well have been discussed. A variety of other factors can affect the selection of the most efficient surface injection-gas pressure. These may include such things as the pressure/volume/temperature (PVT) properties of the crude, water cut of the producing stream, density of the injected gas, wellhead backpressure, pressure rating of the equipment, and design of the well facility.

Calculating the Effect of Injection-Gas Pressures on Surface Production Facilities. The selection and design of compression equipment and related facilities must be closely considered in gas lift systems because of the high initial cost of compressor horsepower and the fact that this cost usually represents a major portion of the entire project cost. In most instances, the injection-gas pressure required at the wellhead determines the discharge pressure of the compressor. Higher injection-gas pressures increase the discharge pressure requirement of the compressor, which is translated into a related increase in the compressor horsepower required for a given volume of gas. However, if the gas lift system is designed properly, the related decrease in gas volume requirements will result in an improvement in overall operating efficiency.

Gas Volume. The total injection gas required for a continuous-flow gas lift well may be determined by well-performance prediction techniques. Well-performance calculations are discussed later in this chapter, but they are typically obtained by simultaneously solving the well inflow and well outflow equations. Well inflow, or fluid flow from the reservoir, can be simulated by either the straight line pressure drawdown (*PI*) or the inflow performance relationship (IPR) methods.[3] Likewise, well outflow, or fluid flow from the reservoir to the surface, is typically predicted by empirical correlations such as those presented by Poettmann and Carpenter,[4] Orkiszewski,[5] Duns and Ros,[6] Hagedorn and Brown,[7] Beggs and Brill,[8] and others. Once typical gas volume requirements for individual wells are determined, totals for the entire field can be calculated.

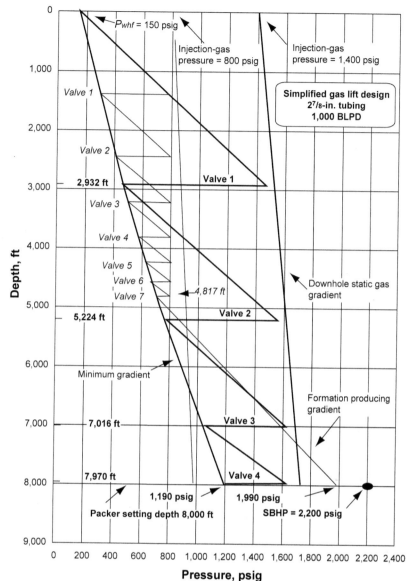

Fig. 12.6—A graphical design for a continuous-flow gas lift installation based on 800-psig injection-gas pressure (light lines) overlaying a design for 1,400-psig injection-gas pressure.

12.3 Compressor Horsepower

12.3.1 Gas Lift Systems. Figs. 12.7 and 12.8 show the amount of injection gas and compression brake horsepower per well, respectively, required to obtain identical producing rates using several different surface injection-gas pressures. As expected, compression horsepower decreases as injection-gas pressure increases for a given daily liquid rate, until the injection-gas pressure reaches maximum injection depth. An injection-gas pressure greater than that required to inject at maximum depth requires additional compression without additional production.

In the example shown in Figs. 12.7 and 12.8, a significant decrease in horsepower requirements is possible by employing an injection-gas pressure of 2,000 psig (ANSI Class 900 pipe)

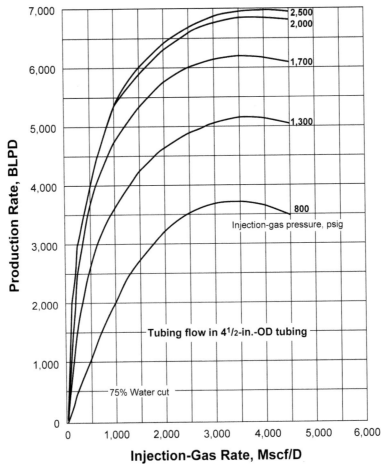

Fig. 12.7—Effect of injection-gas pressure on daily production and injection-gas rates.

rather than one of 1,440 psig (ANSI Class 600 pipe) or lower. For these conditions, the compression horsepower requirements represent the minimum for each producing rate when an injection-gas pressure of approximately 2,000 psig is used. Unlike an injection-gas pressure of 2,500 psig, 2,000-psig pressure allows the use of ANSI Class 900 piping (2,160-psig working pressure) in the distribution system.

Most high-pressure gas lift systems are designed to recirculate the lift gas. The low-pressure gas from the production separator is compressed and reinjected into the well to lift the fluids from the well. This closed loop, as illustrated in **Fig. 12.9** is referred to as a closed rotative gas lift system. Continuous-flow gas lift operations are preferable with a closed rotative system. Intermittent gas lift operations are particularly difficult to regulate and operate efficiently in small closed systems having limited gas-storage capacities.

12.3.2 Gas Distribution and Control. The control and distribution of injection gas to a gas lift well is as important as the control and distribution of electric power is to a pumping well. The distribution system must be large enough so that very little pressure is lost between the compressor and the wellhead. This is usually best accomplished with a main distribution line that circles a producing area and is connected to distribution manifolds located at each production station. Manifolds of this type were first used in the vast gas lift systems of Lake

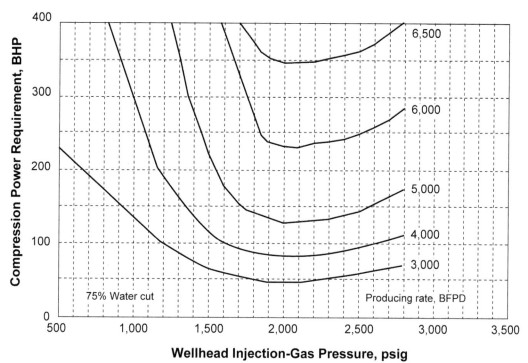

Fig. 12.8—Effect of injection-gas pressure on compressor horsepower and daily production rate.

Maracaibo. They proved so successful for centralizing the control of injection gas that their use spread to many areas of the world. The distribution manifold consists of a control valve, gas meter, and distribution line to each well. Such a system is illustrated in **Fig. 12.10.**[9]

Gas Compression and Dehydration. In the early days of gas lift, most injection gas for the gas lift wells came from large gas-processing facilities. This ensured a good constant source of dry gas to lift the wells. However, as more gas was gathered and processed, the processing plants became larger and were located further from the oil-production facilities. This resulted in the widespread use of field compressors to compress gas gathered in the field before it was sent to the processing facilities. The field compressors tended to be smaller, high-speed, skid mounted, reciprocal units that could be moved and quickly installed wherever required.

The use of the field compressors made gas lift easily accessible in any field where sufficient gas was available from a local source. This brought about many closed-cycle gas lift systems where gas was separated from the produced crude, gathered and sent to compressors, and then after compression, returned to the wells for reinjection as gas lift gas or sold.

Both the centrifugal and reciprocating compressors are used in production facilities. However, because of their flexibility under changing conditions and applicability to small volumes, reciprocating compressors are used far more often than centrifugal compressors in gas lift operations.

Gas Dehydration. Because most injection gas for gas lift is now compressed in the field, dehydration of the gas has become an important part of a successful gas lift operation. Natural gas may contain substantial amounts of water vapor because of the presence of connate water in the reservoir. The ability of a gas to hold water in the vapor phase is dependent upon the pressure and temperature of the gas. As a gas is cooled, its ability to hold water in the vapor phase is reduced. The water dewpoint of a gas is defined as the temperature under a given pressure at which water initially begins to condense from an all-vapor system. Water vapor

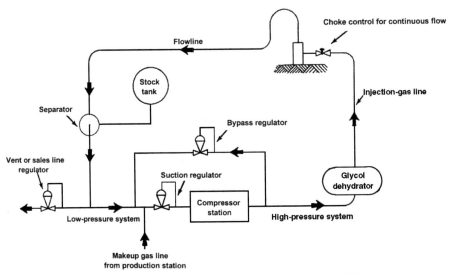

Fig. 12.9—Simplified flow diagram of a closed rotative gas lift system.

should be removed from lift gas to prevent the formation of liquids in the distribution system. Liquids can cause the formation of hydrates, which are solid compounds resembling dirty ice that is caused by the reaction of natural gas with water. Hydrates consist of approximately 10% hydrocarbons and 90% water. These hydrates may pack solidly in gas distribution systems causing blocked valves, lines, and orifices. In distribution systems that contain acid gas fractions (CO_2 and H_2S), liquids can also greatly accelerate the corrosion of the gas-handling facilities, as well as the well casing and tubing.

Gas dehydration removes the source of the problem and is preferred over methanol injection or line heaters. Dehydration can be accomplished by either absorption or adsorption processes. The absorption process involves the passing of the gas stream through a liquid desiccant that has a strong affinity for water. In the adsorption process, gas flows through a bed of granular solids called solid desiccants. The most widely used dehydration system in oilfield and gas lift operations is the absorption-type process. The desiccant used in these systems is usually a solution of one of the glycols; generally, diethylene glycol (DEG) or triethylene glycol (TEG) is used. The method of operation is the same for both systems.

12.3.3 Surface Production Facilities. The location of surface production facilities can greatly impact the efficiency of a gas lift operation. Production stations that provide liquid and gas separation along with other gathering facilities should be located as near the wells as practical. Every effort should be made to minimize the length of multiphase flowlines. In some cases, substations with a minimum of facilities can be employed to shorten the length of the multiphase flowlines.

12.3.4 Gas Lift Equipment. Downhole gas lift equipment consists mainly of the gas lift valves and the mandrels in which the valves are placed. The American Petroleum Inst. (API) *Spec. 11V1* covers the manufacture of gas lift valves and mandrels.[10]

Tubing- and Wireline-Retrievable Equipment. The early gas lift valves were the conventional tubing-retrievable type, in which the tubing mandrel that held the gas lift valve and reverse check valve was part of the tubing string. It was necessary to pull the tubing to replace a conventional gas lift valve. The first selectively wireline-retrievable gas lift valve and mandrel were introduced around 1950. The wireline-retrievable-valve mandrel was designed with a pock-

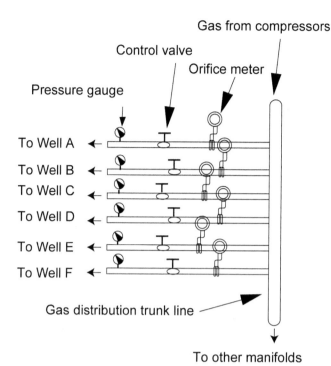

Fig. 12.10—Injection-gas manifold for controlling and measuring gas to individual wells.[4]

et receiver within the mandrel. A gas lift valve could be removed or installed by wireline operations without pulling the tubing. The primary wireline device for locating the mandrel pocket and selectively removing or installing a gas lift valve is a kickover tool. The mandrel is called a sidepocket mandrel because the pocket is offset from the centerline of the tubing. Most sidepocket-type retrievable-valve mandrels have a full-bore inside diameter (ID) equal to the tubing ID. These mandrels permit normal wireline operations, such as pressure surveys. This wireline-retrievable system for gas lift valves revolutionized the application of gas lift for inaccessible wells. The newer generation of retrievable-valve mandrels uses orienting devices to ensure successful wireline operation in highly deviated wells. A description of such equipment can be found in API *Spec. 11V1*.[10]

The operating principles for a given type of tubing-retrievable or wireline-retrievable gas lift valve are the same. Although the performance characteristics may vary between the same type of tubing- and wireline-retrievable valve, the installation design calculations outlined in this chapter do not change. The choice between tubing- and wireline-retrievable equipment depends primarily on the costs associated with pulling the tubing and whether a workover fluid may damage the deliverability of a well.

With the increased cost of pulling the tubing in today's field operations, wireline-retrievable equipment is now used in most new wells and particularly in offshore and inaccessible wells. A wireline-retrievable gas lift valve and mandrel are illustrated in **Fig. 12.11**, while a tubing-retrievable valve and mandrel are shown in **Fig. 12.12**.[10]

Open and Closed Installations. Most tubing flow gas lift installations include a packer to stabilize the fluid level in the casing annulus and prevent injection gas from blowing around the lower end of the tubing in wells with a low flowing bottomhole pressure. A closed gas lift installation implies that the installation includes a packer and a standing valve. An installation without a standing valve may be referred to as semiclosed, and this is widely used for continuous-

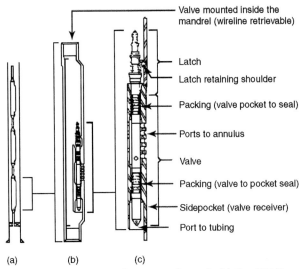

Fig. 12.11—Wireline-retrievable gas lift valve and mandrel (after API *Spec. 11 V1*).[10]

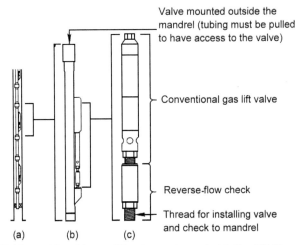

Fig. 12.12—Tubing-retrievable gas lift valve and mandrel (after API *Spec. 11 V1*).[10]

flow operations. An installation without a packer or standing valve is called an open installation. An open installation is seldom recommended.

A packer is required for gas lifting low-bottomhole-pressure wells to isolate the injection gas in the casing annulus and to control the gas volume per cycle for intermittent-lift operations. Intermittent gas lift operations require a packer and possibly a standing valve. Although most illustrations of an intermittent gas lift installation show a standing valve, many actual installations do not include this valve. If the permeability of the well is very low, the need for a standing valve is optional. The advantages of a packer are particularly important for gas lift installations in an area where the injection-gas-line pressure varies or the injection-gas supply is interrupted periodically. If the installation does not include a packer, the well must be unloaded after each shutdown. More damage to gas lift valves can occur during unloading operations than during any other time in the life of a gas lift installation. If the injection-gas-line pressure varies, the working fluid level changes. The result is a liquid washing action through all valves below the working fluid level, and this continuing fluid transfer can eventually fluid-cut the seat assemblies of some gas lift valves. A packer stabilizes the working fluid level and eliminates the need for unloading fluids in the annulus after a shutdown.

Considerations for Selecting the Proper Installation and Equipment. If a well can be gas lifted by continuous flow, this form of gas lift should be used to ensure a constant injection-gas circulation rate within the closed rotative gas lift system. Continuous flow reduces pressure surges in the bottomhole flowing pressure, flowline, and the low- and high-pressure surface facilities that are associated with intermittent gas lift operations. Overdesign rather than underdesign of a gas lift installation is recommended when the well data are questionable. The gas lift equipment in the wells is the least expensive portion of a closed rotative gas lift system. The larger-outside-diameter (OD) gas lift valve should be selected for lifting most wells if casing size permits. The superior injection-gas volumetric throughput performance for the 1.5-in.-OD gas lift valve, as compared to the 1-in.-OD valve, is an important consideration for gas lift installations with a high injection-gas requirement. The smaller diameter 1-in.-OD valve is designed to be used in small-casing-diameter wells. Structurally, the 1-in.-OD valve is not as strong as the 1.5-in.-OD valve. Its bellows size is much smaller, which results in an increase in the ratio of port area to bellows area. This increase in port-to-bellows area ratio and higher bellows-assembly load rate can increase the number of gas lift valves and the injection-gas pressure required to lift deep wells.

The gas lift design techniques presented in this chapter include several factors to compensate for errors in well information and provide for an injection-gas pressure increase to stroke the gas lift valves. If an installation is properly designed, all gas lift valves above an operating valve should be closed, and all valves below should be open. The installation methods presented here are based on this premise. Gas lift valve operation is discussed in detail because it is difficult to design or analyze a gas lift installation properly without understanding the mechanical operation of a gas lift valve.

A large-bore seating nipple, which is designed to receive a lock, is recommended for most gas lift installations. This seating nipple should be installed at the lower end of the tubing and, if feasible, below the packer. Applications for a seating nipple include installation of a standing valve for testing the tubing or for intermittent gas lift operation and a means to secure and to pack off a bottomhole-pressure gauge for conducting pressure-transient tests. The lock should have an equalizing valve if the tubing is to be blanked off. The pressure across the lock can be equalized before the lock is disengaged from the nipple to prevent the wireline tool string from being blown up the hole.

12.4 Gas Fundamentals

Only the gas fundamentals essential to the design and analysis of gas lift installations and operations are discussed in this section. The more important gas calculations related to gas lift wells and systems can be divided into these topics: (1) gas pressure at depth, (2) temperature effect on the confined nitrogen-charged bellows pressure, (3) volumetric gas throughput of a choke or gas lift valve port, and (4) gas volume stored within a conduit.

The fundamental gas equations are based on pressure in pounds per square inch absolute (psia), temperature in degrees Rankine (°R), and volume or capacity in cubic feet (ft³). An exception is pressure difference in pounds per square inch (psi), which may be a difference in gauge or absolute units because the calculated pressure difference is the same. Generally, field measurements of pressure are in gauge readings; therefore, the volumetric gas throughput and gas-pressure-at-depth charts are in units of psig. The gas lift valve equations and calculations for bellows-charge and operating pressures in this chapter use gauge pressure.

12.4.1 Gas Pressure at Depth. Prediction of injection-gas pressure at depth is essential for proper gas lift installation design and for analyzing or troubleshooting gas lift operations. Most gas-pressure-at-depth calculations are based on a static gas column. Pressure loss, because of friction from the flow of injection gas through a typical casing/tubing annulus, is negligible. The gas velocity in the annulus is considered negligible because the cross-sectional area of the annulus is so much larger than the port area of a gas lift valve. The maximum gas flow rate is limited by the valve port size. Only in annular flow, where the flow areas are reversed and large volumes of gas may be injected down a small tubing string, does pressure loss because of velocity become a concern. Eq. 12.1 is used for predicting the static bottomhole injection-gas pressures.

$$P_{ioD} = P_{io}[e]^{\left(\dfrac{\gamma_g(D)}{53.34(\overline{T})\overline{z}}\right)}, \quad\text{...}\quad (12.1)$$

where

P_{io} = injection-gas pressure at surface, psia,
P_{ioD} = injection-gas pressure at depth, psia,
e = Napierian logarithm base = 2.718...,
γ_g = gas specific gravity (air = 1.0), dimensionless,
D = true vertical depth of gas column, ft,
$\overline{T}$ = average gas-column temperature, °R,

and

$\overline{z}$ = compressibility factor based on gas-column average pressure $\overline{P}$ and temperature $\overline{T}$, dimensionless.

The depth used in the equation is the true vertical depth of the gas column. Because the gas compressibility factor is a function of the average pressure and temperature, the solution to this equation requires several iterations. Generally, the average pressure and temperature are assumed to be the arithmetic mean of the wellhead and bottomhole values. This assumption is reasonable because the increase in well temperature with depth tends to result in a relatively constant gas density with depth. A straight-line traverse will approximate an actual static injection-gas pressure-at-depth traverse and is used for the design of most gas lift installations.

12.4.2 Temperature Effect on the Confined Nitrogen-Charged Bellows Pressure. There are many more bellows-charged than spring-loaded gas lift valves in service. Most of the bellows-charged valves have nitrogen gas in the dome and bellows. Because it is impractical to set each gas lift valve at its operating well temperature, the test-rack opening or closing pressure is set at a standard base temperature. Most manufacturers set their bellows-charged gas lift valves with the nitrogen-gas charge in the bellows at 60°F. Nitrogen was selected as the charge gas because: (1) the compressibility factors for nitrogen at various pressures and temperatures are known, (2) nitrogen is noncorrosive and safe to handle, (3) nitrogen is readily available throughout the world, and (4) nitrogen is inexpensive. The temperature correction factors for nitrogen can be obtained from tables such as the one shown in **Table 12.1.**[2] Table 12.1 is calculated for a specific condition of temperature and pressure (nitrogen-charged bellows pressure of 1,000 psig at 60°F) and is based on the work of Winkler and Eads.[11] An equation for calculating the temperature correction factor, C_T, at other conditions of temperature and pressure is shown at the bottom of the table. However, for most gas lift designs, unless pressures are considerably higher than 1,000 psig, Table 12.1 gives sufficient accuracy. C_T is used to calculate the nitrogen-charged bellows pressure at 60°F for a given valve operating or unloading temperature at valve depth in a well.

$$P_b = C_T(P_{bvD}), \quad\text{...}\quad (12.2)$$

where

C_T = temperature correction factor for nitrogen from P_{bvD} at T_{vuD} to P_b at 60°F, dimensionless,

P_b = nitrogen-charged bellows pressure at 60°F, psig, and

P_{bvD} = nitrogen-charged bellows pressure at valve temperature, psig.

If a more accurate calculation of C_T is required, the alternative solution shown in Example Problem 1b may be used.

An Alternative Solution for Calculating Nitrogen-Charged Bellows Pressure at 60°F. If the C_T from Table 12.1 is used to calculate the nitrogen-charged bellows pressure at the test-rack valve setting temperature for gas lift valves in a high-injection-gas-pressure system, the possible error in the test-rack opening pressures may prevent successful gas lift operations. If the operating injection-gas-line pressure exceeds a range of 1,200 to 1,500 psig, the following correlation, based on the work of Winkler and Eads[11], is recommended for calculating the gas lift valve nitrogen-charged bellows pressure in psig at the setting test-rack opening temperature of 60°F.

$$P_b = \left[\frac{-B + \sqrt{(B)^2 - 4(A)(C)}}{2(A)} \right] - P_{atm}, \quad \dots\dots\dots\dots\dots\dots\dots\dots (12.3)$$

where

$P = P_b + P_{atm}$ and $T = T_{vD} - 60$

If P_b is less than 1,250 psia:

$A = 3.054\text{E} - 07\ (T)$, $B = 1 + 0.001934(T)$ and $C = -0.00226\ (T - P)$.

If P_b is greater than 1,250 psia:

$A = 1.84\text{E} - 07\ (T)$, $B = 1 + 0.002298\ (T)$ and $C = -0.267\ (T - P)$.

When Eq. 12.3 is used to calculate P_b, Eq. 12.4 is used to calculate C_T:

$$C_T = \frac{P_b}{P_{bvD}} \quad . \quad \dots\dots\dots\dots\dots\dots\dots\dots\dots\dots\dots\dots (12.4)$$

Example Problem 1a. A 1.5-in.-OD gas lift valve with a ¼-in.-ID port ($A_p/A_b = 0.064$ from **Table 12.2**), nitrogen-charged bellows pressure at well temperature $P_{bvD} = 800$ psig at 142°F. Calculate P_{vo} using Table 12.1 and Eqs. 12.2 and 12.15:

1. Determine C_T from Table 12.1: $C_T = 0.845$ for $T_{vD} = 142°F$.
2. Using Eq. 12.2, solve for P_b: $P_b = 0.845(800) = 676$ psig at 60°F.
3. Using Eq. 12.15, calculate the test-rack opening pressure, P_{vo}:

$$P_{vo} = \frac{676}{1 - 0.064} = 722 \text{ psig at } 60°F.$$

When Eq. 12.3 is used to calculate P_b: $P = 814.7$, $T = 82$, $A = 2.50428\text{E} - 05$, $B = 1.158588$, $C = -814.8853$, and $P_b = 678.3$ psig at 60°F. Using Eq. 12.15 to calculate P_{vo} and Eq. 12.4 to calculate C_T:

$$P_{vo} = \frac{678.3}{(1 - 0.064)} = 725 \text{ psig at } 60°F, \quad \text{and } C_T = \frac{678.3}{800} = 0.848.$$

TABLE 12.1—TEMPERATURE FACTOR, C_T, FOR NITROGEN BASED ON 60°F AND P_b = 1,000 PSIG[2]

°F	C_T	°F	C_T	°F	(C_T)	°F	C_T	°F	C_T	°F	C_T
61	0.998	101	0.916	141	0.847	181	0.787	221	0.735	261	0.690
62	0.996	102	0.914	142	0.845	182	0.786	222	0.734	262	0.689
63	0.993	103	0.912	143	0.843	183	0.784	223	0.733	263	0.688
64	0.991	104	0.910	144	0.842	184	0.783	224	0.732	264	0.687
65	0.989	105	0.909	145	0.840	185	0.781	225	0.730	265	0.686
66	0.987	106	0.907	146	0.839	186	0.780	226	0.729	266	0.685
67	0.985	107	0.905	147	0.837	187	0.779	227	0.728	267	0.683
68	0.982	108	0.903	148	0.836	188	0.777	228	0.727	268	0.682
69	0.980	109	0.901	149	0.834	189	0.776	229	0.726	269	0.681
70	0.978	110	0.899	150	0.832	190	0.775	230	0.724	270	0.680
71	0.976	111	0.898	151	0.831	191	0.773	231	0.723	271	0.679
72	0.974	112	0.896	152	0.829	192	0.772	232	0.722	272	0.678
73	0.972	113	0.894	153	0.828	193	0.771	233	0.721	273	0.677
74	0.970	114	0.892	154	0.826	194	0.769	234	0.720	274	0.676
75	0.968	115	0.890	155	0.825	195	0.768	235	0.719	275	0.675
76	0.965	116	0.889	156	0.823	196	0.767	236	0.717	276	0.674
77	0.963	117	0.887	157	0.822	197	0.765	237	0.716	277	0.673
78	0.961	118	0.885	158	0.820	198	0.764	238	0.715	278	0.672
79	0.959	119	0.883	159	0.819	199	0.763	239	0.714	279	0.671
80	0.957	120	0.882	160	0.817	200	0.761	240	0.713	280	0.670
81	0.955	121	0.880	161	0.816	201	0.760	241	0.712	281	0.669
82	0.953	122	0.878	162	0.814	202	0.759	242	0.711	282	0.668
83	0.951	123	0.876	163	0.813	203	0.758	243	0.710	283	0.667
84	0.949	124	0.875	164	0.811	204	0.756	244	0.708	284	0.666
85	0.947	125	0.873	165	0.810	205	0.755	245	0.707	285	0.665
86	0.945	126	0.871	166	0.808	206	0.754	246	0.706	286	0.664
87	0.943	127	0.870	167	0.807	207	0.753	247	0.705	287	0.663
88	0.941	128	0.868	168	0.805	208	0.751	248	0.704	288	0.662
89	0.939	129	0.866	169	0.804	209	0.750	249	0.703	289	0.661
90	0.937	130	0.865	170	0.803	210	0.749	250	0.702	290	0.660
91	0.935	131	0.863	171	0.801	211	0.747	251	0.701	291	0.659
92	0.933	132	0.861	172	0.800	212	0.746	252	0.700	292	0.658
93	0.931	133	0.860	173	0.798	213	0.745	253	0.698	293	0.657
94	0.929	134	0.858	174	0.797	214	0.744	254	0.697	294	0.656
95	0.927	135	0.856	175	0.795	215	0.743	255	0.696	295	0.655
96	0.925	136	0.855	176	0.794	216	0.741	256	0.695	296	0.654
97	0.924	137	0.853	177	0.793	217	0.740	257	0.694	297	0.654
98	0.922	138	0.851	178	0.791	218	0.739	258	0.693	298	0.653
99	0.920	139	0.850	179	0.790	219	0.738	259	0.692	299	0.652
100	0.918	140	0.848	180	0.788	220	0.736	260	0.691	300	0.651

$C_T = 1/\left[1.0 + \left(°F - 60\right) \times M/P_b\right]$, for P_b < 1,238 psia.

$M = 3.054 \times P_b^2/10,000,000 + 1.934 \times P_b/1,000 - 2.26/1,000$

for P_b greater than 1,238 psia,

$M = 1.840 \times P_b^2/10,000,000 + 2.298 \times P_b/1,000 - 0.267$.

C_T = Temperature correction factor for nitrogen gas.

T_v = Temperature at valve, °F.

P_b = Bellows-charged dome pressure at 60°F, psig.

TABLE 12.2—VALVE SPECIFICATIONS FOR STEM WITH BALL AND SHARP-EDGED SEAT

Port Size (ID), in.	Area of Port, A_p–in.^{2}	A_p/A_b	$1-A_p/A_b$	Production Pressure Factor, F_p	Full-Open Stem Travel*, in.
\multicolumn{6}{c}{1-in.-OD Gas Lift Valves With A_b = 0.31 in.^{2}}
1/8	0.0123	0.040	0.960	0.041	0.0440
3/16	0.0276	0.089	0.911	0.098	0.0714
1/4	0.0491	0.158	0.842	0.188	0.1002
5/16	0.0767	0.247	0.763	0.329	0.1302
3/8	0.1104	0.356	0.644	0.553	0.1610
\multicolumn{6}{c}{1½-in.-OD Gas Lift Valves With A_b = 0.77 in.^{2}}
3/16	0.0276	0.036	0.964	0.037	0.0714
1/4	0.0491	0.064	0.936	0.068	0.1002
5/16	0.0767	0.100	0.900	0.111	0.1302
3/8	0.1104	0.143	0.857	0.167	0.1610
7/16	0.1503	0.195	0.805	0.243	0.1925
1/2	0.1963	0.255	0.745	0.342	0.2246

*Full-open stem travel is on the basis of a stem-ball OD that is 1/16 in. larger than the port ID.

The difference between using Eq. 12.3 or Table 12.1 for calculating P_{vo} is only 3 psi.

Example Problem 1b. A 1.5-in.-OD gas lift valve with a ¼-in. ID port (A_p/A_b = 0.064 from Table 12.2), nitrogen-charged bellows pressure at well temperature P_{bvD} = 2,228 psig at 200°F. Calculate P_{vo} using Table 12.1 and Eqs. 12.2 and 12.15:
1. Determine C_T from Table 12.1 for T_{vD} = 200°F: C_T = 0.761.
2. Using Eq. 12.3, solve for P_b: P_b = 0.761(2,228) = 1,695.5 psig at 60°F.
3. Using Eq. 12.15, calculate the test-rack opening pressure, P_{vo}:

$$P_{vo} = \frac{1,695.5}{(1-0.064)} = 1,811 \text{ psig at } 60°F.$$

Using Eq. 12.3 to calculate P_{bvD}: P = 2,242.7 and T = 140.
A = 2.576E – 05, B = 1.32172, C = –2,280.1, and P_b = 1,656 psig at 60°F.
Using Eq. 12.15 to calculate P_{vo} and Eq. 12.4 to calculate C_T:

$$P_{vo} = \frac{1,656}{(1-0.064)} = 1,769 \text{ psig at } 60°F, \text{ and } C_T = \frac{1,656}{2,228} = 0.743.$$

For the high-injection-gas-pressure system, note that the calculated test-rack opening pressure is higher using the C_T from Table 12.1 to correct the nitrogen-charged bellows pressure from valve temperature in the well to the setting temperature of 60°F. The above data represent an actual 1,800-psig injection-gas system for gas lifting deep wells in Alaska. The operator had difficulty unloading and gas lifting these wells because the set test-rack opening pressures of the gas lift valves were too high.

12.4.3 Volumetric Gas Throughput of an Orifice or Choke. The volumetric gas throughput of an orifice or choke is calculated on the basis of an equation for flow through a converging nozzle. This equation is complex and lengthy for noncritical flow. For this reason, gas passage charts are widely used for estimating the volumetric gas flow rate. A widely used equation for calculating the gas flow rate through an orifice, choke, or full-open valve port was published by Thornhill-Craver.[12]

$$q_{gsc} = \frac{155.5 \ C_d \ (A) \ P_1 \sqrt{2 \ (g) \left(\frac{k}{k-1}\right)\left[(F_{du})^{2/k} - (F_{du})^{(k+1)/k}\right]}}{\sqrt{\gamma_g (T_1)}}, \quad \ldots\ldots\ldots\ldots\ldots (12.5)$$

where

q_{gsc} = gas-flow rate at standard conditions (14.7 psia and 60°F), Mscf/D,
C_d = discharge coefficient (determined experimentally), dimensionless,
A = area of orifice or choke open to gas flow, in.^{2},
P_1 = gas pressure upstream of an orifice or choke, psia,
P_2 = gas pressure downstream of an orifice or choke, psia,
g = acceleration because of gravity, ft/sec^2,
k = ratio of specific heats (C_p/C_v), dimensionless,
T_1 = upstream gas temperature, °R,
F_{du} = pressure ratio, P_2/P_1, consistent absolute units,

and

$$F_{cf} = \left(\frac{2}{k-1}\right)^{\frac{k}{k-1}} \text{critical-flow pressure ratio, dimensionless.}$$

If $F_{du} \leq F_{cf}$, then $F_{du} = F_{cf}$ (critical flow).

The gas-compressibility factor is not included in Eq. 12.5; therefore, most published gas passage charts do not include a gas-compressibility factor correction. Since the compressibility factor would enter the equation as a square root term in the denominator, the chart values will be lower than actual values for most injection-gas gravities and pressures. One type of choke capacity chart is illustrated in **Figs. 12.13 and 12.14.** The advantages of this type of display are the number of orifice sizes on a single chart for a full range of upstream and downstream pressures and that an orifice size can be determined for a given gas rate throughput and the given upstream and downstream pressures. The gas throughput capacity of the different orifice sizes is based standard conditions of 14.65 psia and 60°F for a gas gravity of 0.65 and an orifice discharge coefficient of 0.865.

Because gas flow in a gas lift installation occurs at the gas temperature at valve depth, a correction for temperature improves the prediction for the volumetric gas rate. If the actual gravity differs from 0.65, a second correction should be applied. An approximate correction for gas passage can be calculated using Eq.12.6.

$$C_{gT} = 0.0544\sqrt{\gamma_g \ (T_{gD})}, \quad \ldots\ldots\ldots\ldots\ldots\ldots\ldots\ldots\ldots (12.6)$$

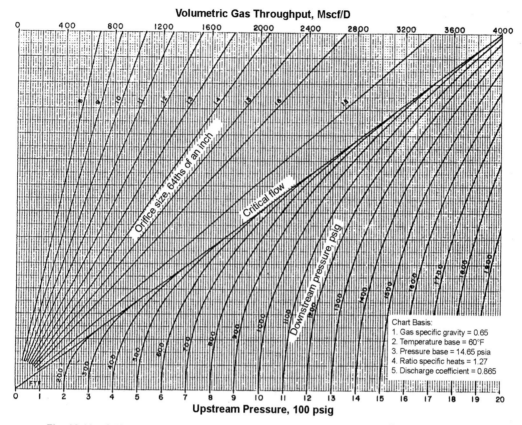

Volumetric Gas Throughput, Mscf/D

Upstream Pressure, 100 psig

Chart Basis:
1. Gas specific gravity = 0.65
2. Temperature base = 60°F
3. Pressure base = 14.65 psia
4. Ratio specific heats = 1.27
5. Discharge coefficient = 0.865

Fig. 12.13—Orifice or choke daily injection-gas throughput rates for 8$\frac{18}{64}$-in.-ID orifices.

and

$$q_{ga} = \frac{q_{gc}}{C_{gT}}, \dots\dots\dots\dots\dots\dots\dots\dots\dots\dots\dots\dots\dots (12.7)$$

where

C_{gT} = approximate gas gravity and temperature correction factor for choke charts, dimensionless,

T_{gD} = gas temperature at valve depth, °R,

q_{ga} = actual volumetric gas rate, Mscf/D, and

q_{gc} = chart volumetric gas rate, Mscf/D.

Although many gas lift manuals will include gas capacity charts for most typical orifice and choke sizes, numerous charts are unnecessary. The gas capacity for an orifice or choke size can be calculated from a known gas capacity for a given choke size because the calculated volumetric gas throughput rate is directly proportional to the area open to flow for the same gas properties and discharge coefficient.

$$q_{g2} = q_{g1}\left(\frac{d_2}{d_1}\right)^2, \dots\dots\dots\dots\dots\dots\dots\dots\dots\dots\dots\dots (12.8)$$

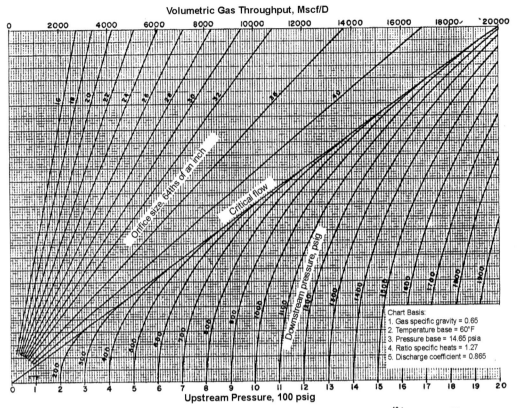

Fig. 12.14—Orifice or choke daily injection-gas throughput rates for 16^{40}⁄$_{64}$-in.-ID orifices.

where

q_{g1} = known volumetric gas rate, Mscf/D,
d_1 = orifice or choke ID for known volumetric gas rate, in.,
q_{g2} = unknown volumetric gas rate, Mscf/D, and
d_2 = orifice or choke ID for unknown volumetric gas rate, in.
If d_1 and d_2 are fractions, then the denominator of both terms must be the same.

Example Problem 2. Given:
• Injection-gas specific gravity (air = 1.0), γ_g = 0.7
• Orifice check valve choke size = ¼-in. ID.
• Injection-gas pressure at valve depth (upstream pressure, P_1), P_{ioD} = 1,100 psig.
• Flowing-production pressure at valve depth (downstream pressure, P_2), P_{pfD} = 900 psig.
• Injection-gas temperature at valve depth (T_1), T_{gD} = 140°F.
• Determine the actual volumetric gas throughput of the orifice-check valve:

q_{gc} = 1,200 Mscf/D for ¼-in.-ID orifice from Fig. 12.13 (chart value).

$$C_{gT} = 0.0544\sqrt{0.7(140 + 460)} = 1.115, \text{ and } q_{ga} = \frac{1,200}{1.115} = 1,076 \text{ Mscf/D (actual gas rate)}.$$

Calculate volumetric gas throughput of a ½-in.-ID orifice on the basis of the capacity of a ¼-in.-ID orifice and compare the calculated and chart values (1,200 Mscf/D from Fig. 12.13 for ¼-in.-ID orifice),

$$q_{gc} = 1,200 \left(\frac{32/64}{16/64} \right)^2 = 1,200 \left(\frac{32}{16} \right)^2 = 4,800 \ \text{Mscf/D for } \ \frac{1}{2}\text{-in.-ID orifice, and}$$

q_{gc} = 4,800 Mscf/D for ½-in.-ID orifice from **Fig. 12.14.**

There have been misleading references in the literature to the validity of the Thornhill-Craver equation related to gas lift installation design and operation. It is not the equation that is in error. The assumption that a gas lift valve is fully open for all injection-gas throughput calculations is incorrect in most instances. An unloading or operating gas lift valve is seldom fully open. The Thornhill-Craver equation would yield a reasonably accurate injection-gas rate through an operating valve if the actual equivalent port area open to injection-gas flow and the correct discharge coefficient were used in the equation.

12.4.4 Gas Volume Stored Within a Conduit. Typical applications for gas volume calculations are given next.

1. The volume of injection gas required to fill the production conduit and to displace a liquid slug to the surface for intermittent gas lift operations.

2. The volume of injection gas available, or removed, from a casing annulus on the basis of a change in the casing pressure during an intermittent injection-gas cycle (particularly important for design calculations using choke control of the injection gas).

3. The capacity calculations for storage, or retention, of the injection gas in the low- and high-pressure systems in a closed, rotative gas lift system.

The gas capacity and volume calculations are based on an equation of state for real gases.

$$P(V) = z(n)R(T), \ \dots\dots\dots\dots\dots\dots\dots\dots\dots\dots\dots\dots\dots\dots \ (12.9)$$

where

P = pressure, psia,
V = volume or capacity, ft³,
z = compressibility factor based on P and T, dimensionless,
n = number of pound-moles, lbm mol,
R = universal gas constant = $\dfrac{10.73 \ \text{psia-ft}^3}{\text{lbm mol-°R}}$, and
T = gas temperature, °R.

The volume of gas required to fill a conduit can be calculated with Eq. 12.10.

$$V_{gsc} = V_c \left[\frac{\overline{P}\left(T_{sc} \right)}{\overline{z}\left(P_{sc} \right) \overline{T}} \right], \ \dots\dots\dots\dots\dots\dots\dots\dots\dots\dots\dots\dots \ (12.10)$$

where

V_{gsc} = volume of gas at standard conditions, scf,
V_c = physical capacity of conduit, ft³,
$\overline{P}$ = average gas-column pressure, psia,
P_{sc} = standard pressure base, psia,
$\overline{T}$ = average gas-column temperature, °R,

T_{sc} = standard temperature base, °R, and
$\bar{z}$ = compressibility factor based on average pressure, $\bar{P}$, and average temperature, $\bar{T}$, dimensionless.

Also, the volume of gas can be calculated by solving for the number of pound-moles in Eq. 12.9 and by converting the pound-moles to standard cubic feet using Avogadro's principle which states that 1 lbm-mole of any gas occupies approximately 379 scf at 14.7 psia and 60°F. Average values for pressure and temperature based on surface and bottomhole values and the corresponding compressibility factor must be used in the equation for inclined conduits.

A gas volume equation for pressure difference can be written as

$$V_{gsc} = \frac{V_c(T_{sc})}{\bar{T}(P_{sc})}\left(\frac{\bar{P}_1}{\bar{z}_1} - \frac{\bar{P}_2}{\bar{z}_2}\right), \dots\dots\dots\dots\dots\dots\dots\dots\dots (12.11)$$

where subscripts 1 and 2 refer to the high and the low average pressure and the corresponding compressibility factor, respectively, and the average gas temperature does not change. If the conduit is horizontal, average pressures and temperature are the surface values in Eqs. 12.10 and 12.11. The average temperature of a gas column in the casing is assumed to be the same at the instant a gas lift valve opens or closes. Eq. 12.11 may be simplified by using one compressibility factor for an average of the average pressures. This assumption is particularly applicable for very little change at high pressure.

Approximate estimations and questionable field data do not warrant detailed calculations. The approximate volume of gas required for a given change in pressure within a conduit can be calculated with Eq. 12.12.

$$V_{gx} = V_c\left(\frac{\bar{P}_1 - \bar{P}_2}{P_{sc}}\right), \dots\dots\dots\dots\dots\dots\dots\dots\dots (12.12)$$

where
V_{gx} is the approximate gas volume at standard conditions, scf.
The ratio of the standard to the average temperature, which is less than unity in most cases, tends to offset the reciprocal of the compressibility factor that is greater than unity. This compensation decreases the error from not including several variables in the approximate equation.

12.5 Gas Lift Equipment

12.5.1 Introduction. The advent of the unbalanced, single-element, bellows-charged gas lift valve (as illustrated in **Fig. 12.15**) revolutionized gas lift application and installation design methods. Before the bellows-charged gas lift valve, there were differential valves and numerous types of unique devices used for gas lifting wells. These devices, or valves, were operated by rotating or vertically moving the tubing and by means of a sinker bar on a wireline.

Single-element implies that the gas lift valve consists of a bellows and dome assembly, a stem with a tip that generally is a carbide ball, and a metal seat housed in a valve body that is attached to a mandrel in the tubing string. This is illustrated in Fig. 12.15. The original patent for this type of gas lift valve was filed in 1940 by W.R. King. Currently, the unbalanced, single-element nitrogen-charged, bellows valve remains the most widely used type of gas lift valve for gas lifting wells. The original King valve had most of the protective design features of the present gas lift valves. The bellows was protected from high hydrostatic fluid pressure by a gasket that sealed the bellows chamber from well fluids after full stem travel. A small orifice

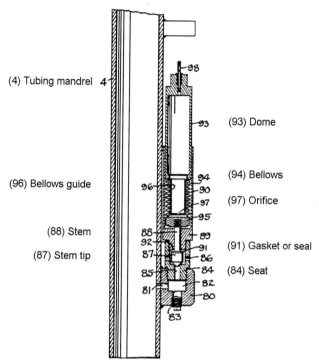

(4) Tubing mandrel

(96) Bellows guide

(88) Stem

(87) Stem tip

(93) Dome

(94) Bellows

(97) Orifice

(91) Gasket or seal

(84) Seat

Fig. 12.15—Original King unbalanced, single-element, bellows-charged gas lift valve on a tubing-installed mandrel (U.S. Patent No. 2,339,487).

was drilled in a bellows guide tube. The orifice was designed to be an anti-chatter mechanism, and the bellows guide provided bellows support.

12.5.2 Purposes of Gas Lift Valves and Reverse Checks. The gas lift valve is the heart of most gas lift installations and the predictable performance of this valve is essential for successful gas lift design and operations. The gas lift valve performs several functions in a typical gas lift installation.

The primary function of a string of gas lift valves is to unload a well with the available injection-gas pressure to a maximum depth of lift that fully uses the energy of expansion of the injection gas for the available injection-gas pressure. Gas lift valves provide the flexibility for a varying depth of gas injection as a result of a changing flowing bottomhole pressure, water cut, daily production rate, and well deliverability.

Gas lift valves provide the means to control the injection-gas volume per cycle in an intermittent gas lift operation. The operating gas lift valve in an intermittent gas lift installation prevents an excessive injection-gas pressure bleed down following an injection-gas cycle.

When wet gas must be used for gas lifting with an orifice-check operating valve, freezing may occur across the surface control valve because of a low flowing bottomhole pressure. This condition can sometimes be eliminated by replacing the orifice-check valve with an injection-pressure-operated gas lift valve. This allows the pressure drop to be taken across the operating gas lift valve at depth where freezing will not occur.

The reverse check in a gas lift valve is especially important if any valves are located below the working fluid level. The check prevents backflow from the tubing into the casing, which is particularly important if the well produces sand and has a packer.

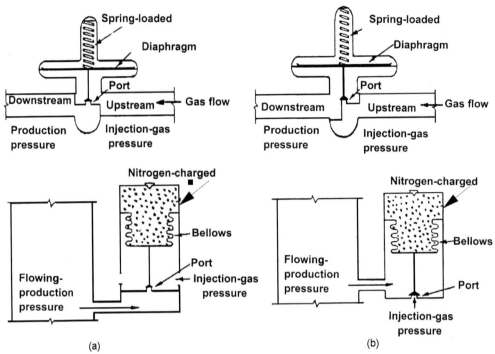

Fig. 12.16—Analogy of unbalanced, single-element, bellows-charged gas lift valves to unbalanced back-pressure and downstream-pressure regulators.

12.6 Gas Lift Valve Mechanics

12.6.1 Unbalanced, Single-Element Gas Lift Valves. The unbalanced, single-element gas lift valve is essentially an unbalanced pressure regulator. The analogy between these two devices is apparent in **Fig. 12.16**, where (a) injection-pressure-operated gas lift valve and backpressure regulator responds to injection-gas pressure and upstream pressure, respectively, and (b) production-pressure-(fluid)-operated gas lift valve and downstream-pressure regulator respond to flowing production pressure and downstream pressure, respectively. The closing force for a gas lift valve can be a gas pressure charge in the bellows exerted over the effective bellows area or a spring force, or a combination of both. The closing force for the regulator or gas lift valve can be adjusted to maintain a desired backpressure for injection-pressure operation. The regulator or valve remains closed until this set closing force is exceeded.

Generally, the major initial opening force for a gas lift valve is the pressure exerted over the effective bellows area minus the port area, and the lesser opening force is the pressure acting over the port area. In like manner, the major opening pressure for a pressure regulator is applied over an area equal to the diaphragm area minus the port area. The effect of the unbalanced opening force is far less for most unbalanced backpressure and pressure-reducing regulators than for gas lift valves. The reason is that the ratio of the port area to the total effective bellows area of a gas lift valve is much greater than the ratio of the port area to the total diaphragm area for most regulators. The operating principle remains identical for the gas lift valve and regulator, but the pressure applied over the port area has greater effect on the initial opening pressure of most gas lift valves.

12.6.2 Pilot-Operated Gas Lift Valves.

There are numerous special application gas lift valves available. The operation of many of these unique valves can be analyzed using the static force-balance equations for the unbalanced, single-element, gas lift valve. The many different types of gas lift valves and the variation in calculations are not discussed in this section because of their limited application. However, one special-purpose valve of particular importance is the pilot-operated gas lift valve.

The pilot-operated gas lift valve in **Fig. 12.17** has operating characteristics that are ideally suited for chamber installations and deep intermittent gas lift operations with low injection-gas operating pressure and small tubing in large casing. The pilot valve offers a very large main port with controlled spread and a predictable constant closing pressure. Spread is defined as the difference between the initial valve opening and closing pressures. This type of valve functions properly on time cycle or choke control of the injection gas. The pilot section operates in the same manner as a single-element gas lift valve with a small choke located downstream of the valve seat. The production pressure at valve depth is exerted over the ball/seat contact area of the pilot section as an initial opening force. When the pilot section begins to open, an increase in pressure occurs between the pilot valve seat and the main valve piston. This increase in pressure above the piston results in compression of the spring under the piston, and the main valve snaps open. An exceedingly high, instantaneous, injection-gas rate enters the tubing through the large main valve port. As the injection-gas pressure in the casing decreases from gas passage through the large main port, the pilot section begins to close. The pressure downstream of the pilot port remains approximately equal to the injection-gas pressure until the pilot port area open to injection-gas flow becomes less than the bleed-hole area in the main valve piston. When the pressure across the piston approaches equalization, the spring returns the main valve to its seat.

The closing pressure of a pilot valve is considered predictable because it is approximately equal to the theoretical closing pressure of an unbalanced, single-element gas lift valve. The pressure upstream and downstream of the pilot port is approximately equal at the instant the pilot section closes. Selecting the proper pilot port size controls the spread of a pilot valve. The high injection-gas throughput capacity of the large main valve port is unaffected by the pilot port size.

12.6.3 Valve Specifications Including Full-Open Stem Travel.

Manufacturers publish gas lift valve specifications for their valves. Some manufacturers assume a sharp-edged seat for the ball/seat contact, and others arbitrarily add a small increase to the port ID to account for a slight bevel for the ball-seat contact. Because most manufacturers use the same sources for their supply of bellows, the effective bellows areas are considered the same. The generic gas lift valve specifications in Table 12.2 are representative of many actual unbalanced, single-element, gas lift valves. The theoretical fully open stem travel is not included in the valve specifications published by most manufacturers.

The stem travel required to fully open an unbalanced, single-element gas lift valve increases with port size, as illustrated in **Fig. 12.18**. The curves were calculated for gas lift valves with a square, sharp-edged seat and a ball on the stem that is $\frac{1}{16}$-in. larger in OD than the bore diameter of the port. The calculated equivalent port area, before a valve is fully open, is based on the lateral surface area of the frustum of a right circular cone. The major area of the frustum is the ball/seat contact area, which remains constant. The minor area decreases with an increase in stem travel as the ball moves away from its seat.

Actual gas lift valve injection-gas rate throughput performance is seldom mentioned in published gas lift installation design literature. Gas lift valves with the larger ports may, or may not, fully open and have the predicted injection-gas capacity for gas lifting high-rate wells through large tubing or the casing annulus.

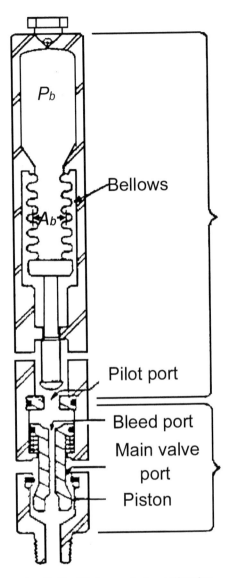

P_b

Bellows

A_b

Pilot port

Bleed port
Main valve
port
Piston

Fig. 12.17—Pilot-operated gas lift valve.

12.6.4 Gas Lift Valve Port Configurations. The port geometry and the maximum valve-stem travel affect the volumetric injection-gas throughput rate of a gas lift valve. Most gas lift valves have a polished carbide ball that is silver soldered to the valve stem. The valve seat can have a sharp-edged port or a taper. The chamfer may be very slight for breaking the seat line or may be of sufficient depth to assure that the ball remains in the taper for full-stem travel. A sharp-edged and a tapered seat with a 45° chamfer are illustrated in **Fig. 12.19**. Note that in (a) the sharp-edged seat has an effective A_p equal to the bore area through the seat and in (b) the tapered seat has a 45° chamber measured from the horizontal (90° included angle). The effective A_p in the A_p/A_b ratio is the ball/seat contact area and not the bore area through the seat. The example calculations in this section are based on the sharp-edged seat because the majority of gas lift valves in service have a sharp-edged seat or a very shallow chamfer for breaking

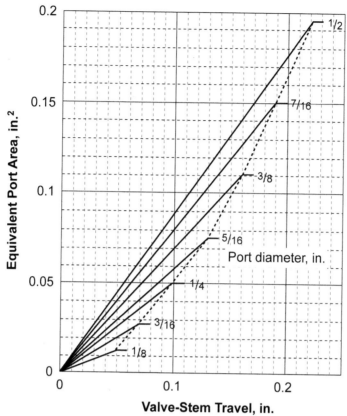

Fig. 12.18—Equivalent area of a gas lift valve port vs. stem travel based on the lateral surface area of the frustum of a right circular cone.

the seat line. The calculations are basically the same for a sharp-edged seat and a seat with a shallow taper. The calculations for an equivalent area open to the injection-gas flow differ for a seat with a deep chamfer. There has been no standard angle adopted for the taper of a gas lift valve seat. Certain manufacturers use the same tapered seat for different stem-ball sizes, and the bore area through the seat may be the same. The area of the port used in the port-to-bellows area ratio must be redefined for a tapered seat when the ball/seat contact area is larger than the bore area through the seat, as shown in Fig. 12.19b. The A_p/A_b ratio is the ball/seat contact area, not necessarily the bore area through the seat, divided by the effective bellows area.

The specifications for the gas lift valve depend upon the ball size and the angle of the chamfer for valves with a port configuration similar to Fig.12.19b. The selection of an angle for the taper, ball size, and the bore area through the seat can result in a ball/seat contact at the base of the taper. For this geometry, the bore area of the port would be used in the A_p/A_b term. The maximum stem travel in many gas lift valves with a deep taper is restricted to prevent the ball from pulling out of the taper, and the valve always remains in the throttling mode. A throttling mode implies that the generated area open to flow for the injection gas is less than the bore area through the valve seat. Certain types of gas lift valves with a deep tapered seat are designed to operate only in the throttling mode for continuous-flow application.

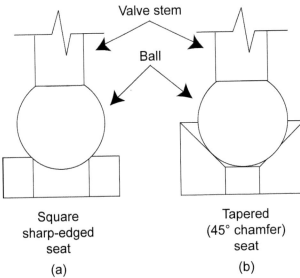

Fig. 12.19—Square sharp-edged- and tapered-seat gas lift valve port configurations.

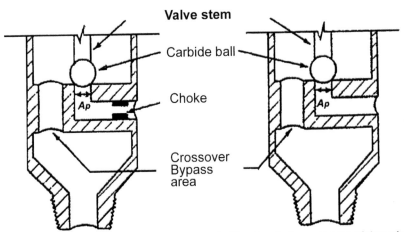

Fig. 12.20—Schematic of crossover seats with and without a choke upstream of the valve port.

12.6.5 Crossover Seats. Several types of gas lift valves have a crossover seat for a particular application. The crossover seat is designed to direct the downstream pressure into the valve body where the pressure is exerted over the effective bellows area less the ball/seat contact area. The upstream pressure is applied to the ball/seat contact area. The crossover seat in **Fig. 12.20** is a schematic illustrating the principle of a crossover seat. A choke upstream of the port controls the maximum injection-gas rate and aids in keeping downstream pressure applied over the bellows area after the valve opens. An actual crossover seat has a group of bypass openings or a milled area around the main port. The total bypass area must significantly exceed the port area to ensure that a valve with a crossover seat will close.

An example of the need for a crossover seat is a production-pressure-operated gas lift valve installed in an injection-pressure-operated gas lift valve mandrel. Another application is a casing (annulus) -flow gas lift valve in a tubing-flow mandrel. In both examples, the gas lift valve is modified, rather than the mandrel. An example is a wireline-retrievable gas lift valve mandrel with pockets designed for injection-pressure-operated gas lift valves and tubing flow that has been installed in a well. The operator desires production-pressure operation. The solution is production-pressure-operated gas lift valves with a crossover seat.

Gas lift valves with a crossover seat are not recommended if the proper mandrels can be installed to eliminate the need for a crossover seat. The maximum port size is limited for valves with a crossover seat. This limitation can be very serious in wells requiring high injection-gas rates. Another problem with a crossover seat is the possibility of partial plugging of the crossover bypass area. The physical bypass area should be at least 100% greater than the valve port area because the bypass openings usually are smaller and more likely to plug than a valve port that can be opened and closed. The production-pressure-operated gas lift valve does not close at the design closing pressure when the crossover area results in a significant pressure loss. The pressure exerted over the bellows area is between the flowing-production and injection-gas pressures rather than at the lower flowing-production pressure.

Many production-pressure-operated gas lift valves with crossover seats can be choked up-stream of the ball/seat contact area. The same port size may be used in all valves, and the volumetric injection-gas throughput, for the upper unloading gas lift valves, is limited by a choke size that is smaller than the port area. The small inlet chokes tend to reduce the valve closing-pressure problem associated with production-pressure operation.

12.6.6 Bellows Protection. All reputable manufacturers of gas lift valves have provided bel-lows protection in the design of their valves. A bellows should be protected from a high pressure differential between the bellows-charge and the wellbore pressures and from the possi-bility of a resonance condition that can result in high-frequency valve stem chatter. The bellows-charge pressure is atmospheric pressure for most spring-loaded valves. The maximum pressure differential across the valve bellows occurs in most installations during initial unloading opera-tions when the lower gas lift valves are subjected to exceedingly high hydrostatic-load-fluid pressures in deep wells.

Gas lift valve bellows are protected from high hydrostatic pressures by several methods: (1) hydraulically preformed bellows by a high pressure differential, with or without, support rings within the bellows convolutions, (2) a confined liquid seal in the bellows with full stem travel, and (3) isolation of bellows from outside pressure with full stem travel. The primary purpose of these methods for protecting the bellows is to prevent a permanent change in the radii of the convolutions after installation in a well, which in turn, can change the operating pressure of a gas lift valve.

The possibility of a valve-stem chatter condition is not predictable. The evidence of valve-stem chatter is a bellows failure and a dished-out seat if the valve seat is not manufactured from an extremely hard material. Many gas lift valves have some form of dampening mecha-nism, and the majority of these devices operate hydraulically. The bellows are partially filled with a liquid, generally a high-viscosity silicone fluid. A restricted liquid-flow rate within the bellows or a fluid-shear dampening mechanism prevents valve-stem chatter.

12.6.7 Stabilization of Test-Rack Opening Pressures. One of the most important procedures for preparing gas lift valves for installation in a gas lift well is the stabilization of the operat-ing pressure. The test-rack set opening or closing pressure of an unbalanced, single-element, nitrogen-charged or spring-loaded bellows gas lift valve should be stabilized before installation in a well. Many operators and manufacturers call the process "aging." The purpose of this pro-cedure is to prevent the set operating pressure of a valve from changing after being run in a well. Another term for valve operating pressure changes is valve set pressure "scrambling," which may prevent a gas lift well from unloading, cause inefficient multipoint gas injection, or may cause an unpredictable variation in operating valve depth.

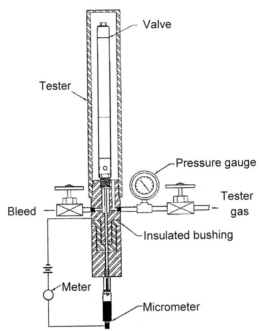

Fig. 12.21—Typical gas lift valve probe-test fixture (after API *Spec. 11 V1*).[10]

After setting the test-rack opening or closing pressure, the gas lift valve is placed in a high-pressure vessel filled with water. The valve is fully stroked several times by alternately increasing and decreasing the pressure of the water confined in the vessel. The exact procedure varies among manufacturers. Typically, the maximum pressure ranges between 3,000 and 5,000 psig, and the minimum number of cycles is between 5 and 10. The valve is removed from the high-pressure vessel, and the test-rack opening pressure is rechecked at the base setting temperature. If the opening pressure varies more than a specified few psi, the valve must be reset and the procedure repeated until the test-rack opening or closing pressure stabilizes. Also, the process identifies valve bellows and bellows weld failures.

12.6.8 Bellows-Assembly Load Rate. Bellows-assembly load rate is defined as: the psi increase exerted over the bellows area per linear unit travel of the valve stem. The controlled pressure is applied over the entire effective bellows area, and the valve-stem travel is measured by means of a depth micrometer. A typical gas lift valve probe tester is shown in **Fig. 12.21**.[10] The bellows-assembly load rate is the slope of the pressure vs. stem travel best-fit straight line in the linear portion of the curve in **Fig. 12.22**.[10]

The best-fit straight line represents an average between the stem travel measured for increasing and decreasing probe-tester pressures. The increase in nitrogen-charged dome pressure with stem travel is negligible, as compared with the load rate of a bellows-assembly in most bellows-charged gas lift valves. The load rate of a bellows assembly, which is analogous to the load rate of a helical spring, is far greater than the effect of the increase in dome pressure resulting from the decrease in dome capacity for the stem travel required to open a typical gas lift valve.

The measured bellows-assembly load rate is not identical for all gas lift valves with the same size bellows. The typical three-ply, seamless Monel bellows that is used in many 1.5-in.-OD gas lift valves has a reported effective bellows area of 0.77 in.[2]. The typical bellows-assembly load rate for a valve with a nitrogen-charged bellows ranges from 400 to 600 psi/in. in the linear portion of the curve for a valve with a test-rack opening pressure between 600

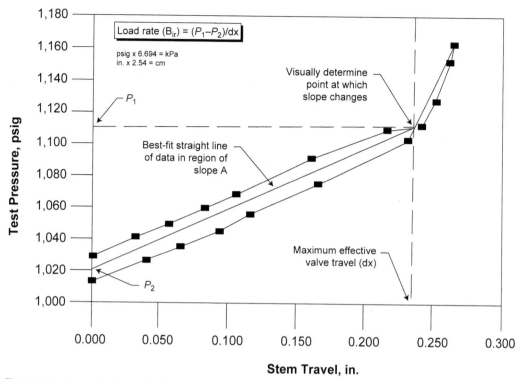

Fig. 12.22—Determination of bellows-assembly load rate and maximum linear valve-stem travel (after API Spec. 11 V1).[10]

and 1,200 psig. The three-ply, seamless Monel bellows in the 1-in.-OD valve has a reported effective area of 0.31 in.[2] and a bellows-assembly load-rate range of 1,200 to 2,200 psi/in. for a valve with a nitrogen-charged bellows and a test-rack opening pressure between 600 and 1,200 psig. The bellows-assembly load rate for a spring-loaded 1-in.-OD valve can range from near 2,000 to more than 3,500 psi/in. It is similar to the load rate of a spring. The load rate of a spring depends on the wire size, material, and number of free coils. The purpose in noting the magnitude of the bellows-assembly load rate for typical gas lift valves is to emphasize the fact that an unbalanced, single-element, gas lift valve will not "snap" open. An increase in injection-gas pressure, or in flowing-production pressure, or a combination of an increase in both pressures, is necessary to stroke the valve stem. The larger-OD gas lift valves should be selected for installations requiring high injection-gas rates because the smaller valves do not have the same gas throughput rate performance as the larger-OD valve with the same port size. Valves with the smaller bellows assembly are not recommended for low-pressure injection-gas systems that may be used to gas lift shallow wells. The low closing force and bellows stiffness can result in leaking valve seats because of poor ball/seat seating characteristics at low injection-gas valve opening pressures.

12.6.9 Static Force-Balance Equations for Unbalanced, Single-Element, Bellows-Charged Gas Lift Valves. Most gas lift equipment manufacturers test-rack set valve opening pressures are based on 60°F for nitrogen-charged gas lift valves. The valve is submerged in a 60°F water bath to ensure a constant nitrogen temperature in the bellows of each valve during the test-rack setting procedure. The initial test-rack opening pressure is measured with the tester pressure applied over the effective bellows area less the ball/seat contact area while atmospheric pressure (0 psig) is exerted over the ball/seat contact area. The valve actually is closed and begins to open from an opening force that is slightly greater than the closing force. The tester gas rate through the valve seat is very low. Although most gas lift valves are set with an initial opening pressure, certain types of valves with high production-pressure factors and valves with unique construction may be set at test-rack closing pressures.

The test-rack closing pressure is obtained by bleeding the tester gas from the downstream side of a gas lift valve. This theoretical closing pressure is noted when the downstream pressure continues to decrease and the upstream pressures remain constant. The upstream and downstream pressures are equal momentarily at the instant a gas lift valve closes. An accurate closing pressure is more difficult to observe than an initial opening pressure and can be affected by the rate of decrease in the tester pressure during bleedoff of the tester gas. An encapsulating tester with gas capacity rather than a ring-type tester is recommended so that any small leaks in the tester piping will not prevent observation of the true gas lift valve closing pressure. The pressure should be bled off of the downstream side of the valve through a very small orifice.

The equations for initial valve opening pressure in a tester and in a well, and a tester closing pressure, are based on static force-balance equations. These equations also apply to spring-loaded gas lift valves. The spring-load effect replaces the bellows-charge pressure of the valve as the closing force. Several manufacturers with spring-loaded gas lift valves report a test-rack closing pressure. The spring is adjusted until the force exerted by the spring is equal to the desired test-rack closing pressure. A base-temperature correction does not apply to the opening- or closing-pressure calculations of spring-loaded gas lift valves. If the total closing force for a gas lift valve is a combination of a bellows-charge pressure and a spring load, the spring-load effect must be subtracted from the total closing force to obtain the bellows-charged-pressure portion of this closing force before calculating the bellows charge pressure from well to tester base temperature.

The following equations for the initial gas lift valve opening pressures in a tester and in a well are derived for a bellows-charged injection-pressure-operated gas lift valve because most gas lift installations are gas lifted with this type of valve In **Fig. 12.23**, (a) shows the determination of the test-rack opening pressure, P_{vo}, by flowing supply gas at a low rate into a ring type tester with atmospheric pressure applied to the port area and in (b) the test-rack closing pressure, P_{vct}, is obtained by opening the gas lift valve, closing the supply valve, and slowly bleeding off the encapsulating tester pressure downstream of the port. In (c), the initial valve opening pressure in a well, P_{oD}, is based on the injection-gas and flowing-production pressures at valve depth. The injection-gas and flowing-production pressures are interchanged for production-pressure-operated (fluid-operated) gas lift valves.

Initial Valve Opening Pressure in a Tester at 60°F (Fig. 12.23a). Closing force = opening force.

$$P_b\left(A_b\right) = P_{vo}\left(A_b - A_p\right) . \quad\text{...} (12.13)$$

$$P_b = P_{vo}\left(1 - A_p / A_b\right) . \quad\text{...} (12.14)$$

$$P_{vo} = \frac{P_b}{\left(1 - A_p / A_b\right)} . \quad\text{...} (12.15)$$

Valve Closing Pressure in a Tester at 60°F (Fig. 12.23b). Closing force = opening forces.

$$P_b\left(A_b\right) = P_{vct}\left(A_b - A_p\right) + P_{vct}\left(A_p\right) . \quad\text{...........................} (12.16)$$

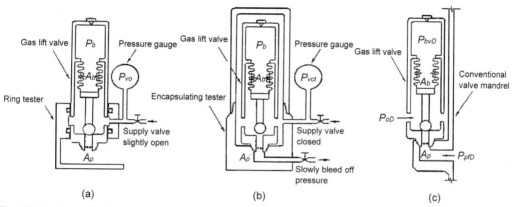

Fig. 12.23—Illustration for nomenclature used in static force-balance equations for gas lift valves in testers and a well.

$$P_b\left(A_b\right) = P_{vct}\left(A_b\right), \quad \text{if } P_{ot} = P_{vct}. \quad\text{...} \quad (12.17)$$

$$P_b = P_{vct}, \quad \text{if } P_{ot} = P_{vct}. \quad\text{...} \quad (12.18)$$

Initial Opening Pressure in a Well (Fig. 12.23c). Closing force = opening forces.

$$P_{bvD(n)}\left(A_b\right) = P_{oD(n)}\left(A_b - A_p\right) + P_{pfD(n)}\left(A_p\right). \quad\text{...............................} \quad (12.19)$$

$$P_{bvD(n)} = P_{oD(n)}\left(1 - A_p / A_b\right) + P_{pfD(n)}\left(A_p / A_b\right). \quad\text{...............................} \quad (12.20)$$

Solving for the Injection-Gas Initial Valve Opening Pressure in a Well.

$$P_{oD(n)} = \frac{P_{bvD(n)}}{\left(1 - A_p / A_b\right)} - P_{pfD(n)}\left(\frac{A_p / A_b}{1 - A_p / A_b}\right). \quad\text{..............................} \quad (12.21)$$

$$P_{oD(n)} = P_{voD(n)} - P_{pfD(n)}\left(F_p\right). \quad\text{..} \quad (12.22)$$

$$P_{oD(n)} = \frac{P_{vo(n)}}{C_T} - P_{pe(n)}. \quad\text{...} \quad (12.23)$$

Additional Related Valve Mechanics Equations.

$$F_p = \frac{A_p / A_b}{\left(1 - A_p / A_b\right)} = \frac{A_p}{A_b - A_p}, \quad\text{..} \quad (12.24)$$

$$P_{voD(n)} = \frac{P_{bvD(n)}}{\left(1 - A_p / A_b\right)}, \quad\text{...} \quad (12.25)$$

$$P_{voD(n)} = \frac{P_{vo(n)}}{F_T}, \quad \text{...} \quad (12.26)$$

$$P_{pe(n)} = F_p\left[P_{pfD(n)}\right], \quad \text{...} \quad (12.27)$$

and

$$\Delta P_{pe(n)} = F_p\left\{\left[P_{pfD(n)}\right]\text{max} - \left[P_{pfD(n)}\right]\text{min}\right\}, \quad \text{.........................} \quad (12.28)$$

where

A_b = total effective bellows area, in.^{2},

A_p = valve port area (ball/seat line contact area for sharp-edged seat), in.^{2},

C_T = temperature correction factor for nitrogen from P_{bvD} at T_{vuD} to P_b at 60°F, dimensionless,

F_p = production-pressure factor, dimensionless,

n = valve location designation (n = 1 for top valve),

P_b = nitrogen-charged bellows pressure at 60°F, psig,

P_{bvD} = nitrogen-charged bellows pressure at valve temperature, psig,

P_o = surface initial valve opening pressure, psig,

P_{oD} = initial gas lift valve opening pressure at valve depth, psig,

P_{ot} = tester pressure upstream of gas lift valve port, psig,

P_{pe} = production-pressure effect, psi,

P_{pfD} = flowing-production pressure at valve depth, psig,

P_{pft} = tester pressure downstream of gas lift valve port, psig,

P_{vct} = test-rack valve closing pressure at 60°F if $P_{pft} = P_{ot}$ at instant valve closes, psig,

P_{voD} = initial gas lift valve opening pressure at valve depth if $P_{pfD} = 0$, psig,

and

ΔP_{pe} = variation in production-pressure effect, psi.

12.6.10 Initial Opening and Closing Pressures of an Unbalanced, Single-Element Gas Lift Valve. An understanding of the relationship between the initial opening and closing pressures of an unbalanced, single-element gas lift valve is important for calculating gas lift installation designs and analyzing gas lift operations. An unbalanced, single-element, gas lift valve does not have a constant closing pressure as noted in many publications, and the valve does not "snap" fully open at the initial injection-gas opening pressure. This type of gas lift valve initially opens and closes at the same injection-gas pressure if the flowing-production pressure and valve temperature remain constant. In like manner, an unbalanced backpressure regulator opens and closes at the same upstream pressure if the downstream pressure remains constant.

Fig. 12.24 shows a plot of the initial injection-gas opening pressure vs. the flowing-production pressure curves for both a ¼-in.- and ½-in.-ID sharp-edged port in a 1.5-in.-OD gas lift valve having an effective bellows area of 0.77 in.^{2}. Most manufacturers use this bellows size in the 1.5-in.-OD gas lift valve.

The closing force for an unbalanced, single-element gas lift valve is assumed to remain constant for this analysis. The gas lift valve is actually closed on the line that represents a balance between the opening and closing forces in Fig. 12.24. The valve begins to open above the line and is closed below the line. The valve can be opened by increasing the injection-gas pressure with a constant flowing-production pressure, increasing both the injection-gas and flowing-production pressures simultaneously, and increasing the flowing-production pressure with a constant injection-gas pressure.

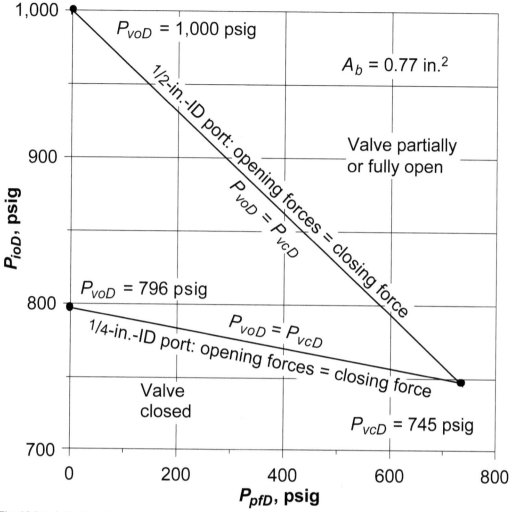

Fig. 12.24—Initial injection-gas opening pressure vs. production pressure for 1.5-in.-OD, unbalanced, single-element, gas lift valves with a 0.77-in.² effective bellows area and a ¼-in.-ID and a ½-in.-ID sharp-edged seats.

12.7 Production-Pressure Factor and Valve Spread

The production-pressure factor, F_p, is a relationship based on the effective bellows and ball/seat-contact areas for an unbalanced gas lift valve. Unbalanced implies that the flowing-production pressure is exerted over the entire ball/seat contact area as a portion of the initial opening force for a valve. In terms of gas lift valve operation, the production-pressure factor is the ratio of the incremental difference in the initial injection-gas opening pressures to a difference in the corresponding flowing-production pressures. If the flowing-production pressure increases, the initial injection-gas opening pressure decreases, and vice versa. The production-pressure factor can be obtained from the slope of the force-balance lines in Fig. 12.24 or can be calculated from the specifications for the valve.

Valve spread is defined as the difference between the initial injection-gas opening and the injection-gas closing pressures of a gas lift valve. The valve spread is zero for a constant flowing-production pressure because a valve initially opens and closes at the same injection-gas pressure. The valve spread observed in intermittent gas lift operations results from a large port and the change in the flowing-production pressure at the depth of the operating gas lift valve during an injection-gas cycle. The production pressure at valve depth approaches the injection-gas pressure beneath a liquid slug during gas injection, thus decreasing the valve closing pressure, which results in a spread between the initial opening and closing pressures of the operating valve. This can be a very important consideration for a chamber-lift installation where the initial opening pressure of the operating gas lift valve is high because of low tubing pressure. The operating gas lift valve is located above the chamber, and the tubing pressure, at valve depth exerted over the ball/seat contact area when the valve initially opens, is very low. The tubing pressure may approach the injection-gas pressure at the time the valve closes, thus resulting in a low closing pressure.

12.7.1 Injection-Gas Volumetric Throughput Rates for a Fixed Choke Compared to Unbalanced, Single-Element Gas Lift Valves. The difference in the injection-gas rate throughput performance of unbalanced, single-element, injection-pressure-operated gas lift valves and a fixed-size choke is illustrated in **Fig. 12.25.** The flowing-production pressure is a constant 500 psig. The gas lift valves have an injection-gas initial opening pressure of 1,000 psig. As soon as the injection-gas pressure exceeds 500 psig, injection gas enters the production conduit through the ¼-in.-ID choke. The injection-pressure-operated gas lift valves are backpressure regulators and metering devices because of the bellows-assembly load rate. These valves prevent injection-gas entry into production conduit until the injection-gas pressure exceeds the 1,000-psig set pressure. The difference in the injection-gas throughput performance of these two gas lift valves with the same ¼-in.-ID sharp-edged port is from the bellow-assembly load rates. A greater injection-gas pressure increase is required to stroke the valve stem of the valve with the higher load rate.

The effective area of the bellows, the bellows-assembly load rate, the stem/seat configuration, and the linear valve-stem travel control the injection-gas throughput performance of a gas lift valve. The 1-in.-OD valve with a 0.31-in.^{2} bellows area has the higher load rate of 1,800 psi/in., and the 1.5-in.-OD valve with a 0.77-in.^{2} bellows area has the lower load rate of 400 psi/in.

12.8 Dynamic Gas Lift Valve Performance
The importance of gas lift valve performance in the design of a gas lift installation is primarily dependent upon the maximum required injection-gas rates through the gas lift valves to unload and gas lift a well. Dynamic testing of gas lift valves indicated a noticeable difference in the performance of the 1-in.- and 1.5-in.-OD gas lift valves. Although both OD of these gas lift valves had the same port size, the 1.5-in.-OD valve with the larger bellows had a much higher injection-gas throughput rate for the same increase in the injection-gas pressure above the initial valve opening pressure. For this reason, the larger-OD gas lift valve with a 0.77-in.^{2} bellows area is recommended for gas lifting high-rate wells with large tubing.

In recent years, there has been considerable interest in the actual injection-gas throughput rates of gas lift valves. API *RP 11V2*[13] presents the recommended methods for testing gas lift valves. A single-element unbalanced gas lift valve has two fundamental characteristics that are determined from a probe test. The procedure for performing the probe test is outlined in *RP 11V2*. These characteristics are the bellows-assembly load rate or spring rate and the approximate effective linear travel of the valve stem. The required valve-stem travel to ensure a fully open port increases with the valve port size, as shown in Fig. 12.18, for gas lift valves with square, sharp-edged seats. If the maximum linear stem travel is less than required for a fully open port area, the injection-gas throughput will be less than the gas rate through an orifice with an area equal to the port area.

Gas lift design and operation can be divided into two categories on the basis of the primary opening force. If a valve is opened primarily by an increase in the injection-gas pressure in the casing, the valve is called an injection-pressure-operated gas lift valve. A production-pressure-

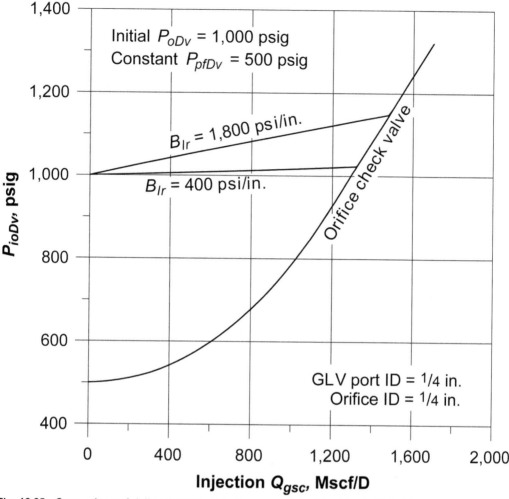

Fig. 12.25—Comparison of daily injection rates through a ¼-in.-ID orifice to ¼-in.-ID-port gas lift valves with a B_{lr} of 400 and 1,800 psi/in.

operated valve is opened primarily by an increase in the flowing-production pressure in the tubing at valve depth.

The typical standardized bellows sizes are 0.31 in.² for 1-in.-OD gas lift valves and 0.77 in.² for the 1.5-in.-OD valve. There are other sizes of bellows and smaller-OD gas lift valves for special clearance applications that will not be included in this section. The OD of a gas lift valve does not ensure the bellows size. The 1.5-in.-OD gas lift valve may have a smaller bellows. The published specifications for a valve indicate the bellows size.

A gas lift valve should be tested in the exact same manner as it is operated in a well. Typical port sizes for 1-in.-OD gas lift valves are ⅛-, ³⁄₁₆-, ¼-, ⁵⁄₁₆-, and ⅜-in. ID. Port sizes of ³⁄₁₆-, ¼-, ⁵⁄₁₆-, ⅜-, ⁷⁄₁₆-, and ½-in. ID are available for 1.5-in.-OD gas lift valves (See Table 12.2.). These injection-pressure-operated valves are opened by an increase in the injection-gas pressure being applied over a major portion of the effective bellows area. It is impractical to attempt to open these valves by increasing the flowing-production pressure that acts on a much smaller area. Theoretically, a several hundred or thousand psi increase is required to fully stroke these valves by only increasing the flowing-production pressure.

Operators should recognize the possibility of limited injection-gas passage of gas lift valves for gas lifting high-rate wells through large tubing or casing annulus. An injection-gas through-put rate based on a fully open port size should not be assumed for the larger port sizes in many unbalanced, single-element gas lift valves. For the maximum actual range in the injection-gas pressure during typical gas lift unloading operations, the equivalent port area open for the injection-gas flow is less than an area based on the reported port size for gas lift valves with a large port area relative to the effective bellows area. Assuming that a 1-in. OD gas lift valve with a large port has the valve stem travel to fully open, the necessary increases in the injection-gas pressure to stroke the valve stem for this required travel may approach, or exceed, 200 psi for a constant flowing-production pressure. Maximum valve-stem travel may also be limited by manufacturing tolerances running in the same direction, a mechanical stop, or by the bellows stacking before a fully open port is achieved.

12.9 Design of Gas Lift Installations

12.9.1 Continuous Flow. Continuous-flow gas lift is analogous to natural flow, but there are generally two distinct flowing-pressure traverses. The traverse below the point of gas injection includes only formation gas; whereas, the traverse above the point of gas injection includes both the formation and injection gases. These two distinct flowing-pressure traverses and their corresponding gas/liquid ratios (GLR) are illustrated in Fig. 12.1.

There are numerous gas lift installation design methods offered in the literature. Several installation designs require unique valve construction or gas lift-valve injection-gas throughput performance. Only two design techniques are illustrated in this section: (1) a design based on a constant decrease in the operating injection-gas pressure for each succeeding lower valve (this design is essentially the same as the API gas lift design technique in *RP 11V6*[14]), and (2) an alternative design for wells requiring high injection-gas rates. The API design can be used on the majority of wells in the United States. However, when high-volume lift and high injection-gas rates are required, gas lift valve performance should be considered in the design. Both of these techniques use the simple single-element-type, unbalanced, gas lift valve with a nitrogen-charged bellows. This type of valve is the most widely used in the industry and is available from all major gas lift equipment manufacturers.

Gas lift installation design calculations are divided into two parts. The first part is the determination of the gas lift valve depths, and the second part is the calculation of the test-rack opening pressures of the gas lift valves. The opening pressures are calculated after the valve depths because the operating injection-gas and flowing-production pressures and temperatures during unloading are based on these valve depths.

The primary objective of this section is to outline in detail installation design methods for calculating the valve depths and the test-rack opening pressures of the gas lift valves that will unload a well to a maximum depth of lift for the available injection-gas volume and pressure. The unloading operations, as illustrated by the two-pen pressure recorder chart in **Fig. 12.26**, should be automatic. The static-load-fluid level was near the surface in the casing and tubing before initial unloading began. The wellhead pressure remains relatively constant during U-tubing operations before injection gas enters the tubing for the first time through the top gas lift valve. A surge in wellhead tubing pressure and a decrease in the injection-gas casing pressure occur as the depth of gas injection transfers to each lower gas lift valve. As each lower gas lift valve is uncovered, the valve immediately above closes, and the point of gas injection transfers from the upper to the lower valve. All gas lift valves above an operating valve should be closed and the valves below should be open in a properly designed gas lift installation.

12.9.2 Description of Unloading Operations for Continuous-Flow Gas Lift. The depths of the unloading gas lift valves are calculated to unload the kill (load) fluid to the design depth of

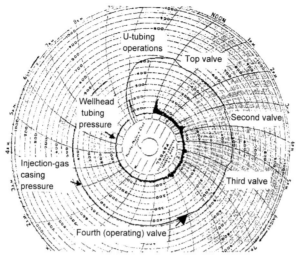

Fig. 12.26—Two-pen pressure-recorder chart illustrating continuous-flow gas lift unloading operations with choke control of the injection gas.

the operating valve with the injection-gas pressure and gas volume available at the wellsite. As the injection gas is initially injected into the casing annulus, the injection-gas pressure downstream of the control device on the injection-gas line increases as the load-fluid level in the casing annulus is lowered during U-tubing of the load fluid. The load fluid is transferred into the tubing through the open gas lift valves in a well with a packer, or through the open gas lift valves and lower end of the tubing in a well without a packer. Initial gas lift operations begin after the first gas lift valve is uncovered and injection gas enters the tubing at this top-valve depth.

The pressures in the casing and tubing are essentially equal at the instant a gas lift valve is uncovered. Immediately after injection gas begins to enter the tubing through the next lower gas lift valve, the injection-gas pressure in the casing begins to decrease because the newly uncovered gas lift valve is set to remain open at a lower injection-gas pressure than the unloading valve above. Less and less injection gas enters the tubing through the upper unloading valve. The injection-gas rate through the newly uncovered valve increases until the injection-gas pressure in the casing decreases to the closing pressure of the upper unloading valve. The depth of gas-injection transfer is complete when all injection gas is entering the tubing through the lower valve and all upper gas lift valves are closed. The principles of continuous-flow operation are illustrated by a pressure/depth diagram shown in **Fig. 12.27.**

As injection gas enters the tubing through a newly uncovered valve, the flowing-production pressure decreases. The injection-gas pressure in the casing begins to increase from a decreasing opening force from a lower flowing-production pressure at the valve depth and the need for stroking the valve stem to increase the injection-gas rate into the tubing for uncovering the next lower valve. The increase in the injection-gas pressure above the initial valve opening pressure at valve depth for passing the injection-gas rate to establish the flowing-production transfer pressure must be determined. This maximum injection-gas pressure required to stroke the valve stem sufficiently to pass the injection-gas rate necessary to transfer the depth of gas injection to the next lower valve depends on the gas lift valve performance. The valve port ID, bellow-assembly load rate, and linear stem travel control the gas lift valve performance. The design maximum injection-gas pressure for establishing the flowing-production transfer pressure from a lower valve during unloading should not result in reopening any of the upper gas

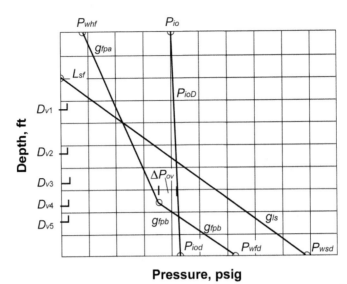

Fig. 12.27—Principles of continuous-flow operation illustrated by a pressure/depth diagram. The datum depth (D_d) for the static bottomhole pressure (P_{wsd}) is the lower end of the production conduit.

lift valves. In Fig. 12.27, the injection gas is entering the production conduit through the fourth gas lift valve and the three upper unloading gas lift valves are closed. Although the bottom gas lift valve is open, no injection gas can enter this valve at depth D_5 because the flowing-production pressure exceeds the injection-gas pressure at this depth. The flowing-pressure-at-depth traverse gradient, g_{pfa}, above the operating gas lift valve depth, D_{ov}, includes the injection- plus the formation-gas production, and the flowing-pressure-at-depth traverse gradient, g_{pfb}, below D_{ov} contains only formation-gas production.

12.9.3 Initial Installation Design Considerations. Continuous-flow installation designs vary depending on whether complete and precise well data are known. Reliable inflow well performance and an accurate multiphase-flow correlation are required to establish the approximate point of gas injection in deep wells. When the well data are limited or questionable, the exact point of gas injection cannot be calculated accurately in many wells. If there is insufficient injection-gas pressure to reach the bottom of the well, a desired depth of gas injection may not be possible. If there is no change in injection-gas pressure or well conditions, the point of gas injection should remain at the maximum depth for the life of the gas lift installation.

Retrievable gas lift valve mandrels are installed (usually with dummy valves in place) in many wells before little, if any, well-production information is available. The engineer must locate these mandrels in wells before gas lift is required. The design considerations are similar for wells with a changing point of gas injection. In general, many gas lift installations are in this category, in which accurate well data are unknown or limited and the point of gas injection is unknown and/or changing as the reservoir is depleted.

12.10 Installation Design Methods
The two installation design methods given in this chapter can be classified as: (1) the decreasing injection-gas pressure design in API[14], and (2) a variation of the decreasing injection-gas pressure design that considers valve performance at each station.[15] Valves with small production-pressure factors, F_p, are recommended for the decreasing injection-gas pressure installation design method. Valves with a small F_p (under 0.2) are sensitive primarily to a change in the injection-gas pressure. A decrease in the surface operating injection-gas pressure for each lower

gas lift valve is essential to ensure the closure of upper unloading valves after gas injection has been established through a lower operating valve. This design is particularly applicable when the available injection-gas pressure is high relative to the required depth of lift and an additional incremental decrease in injection-gas pressure can be added between valves.

If gas lift valves with large ports are required to pass sufficient gas rates for unloading and lifting a well, the design that incorporates valve performance should be used. Generally, if the operating valve is not near the packer, the calculated point of gas injection will be bracketed by installing at least one valve below the calculated operating valve depth in the event there is a slight error in the well information or a change in well conditions.

12.10.1 Assumptions and Safety Factors in the Simplified Continuous-Flow Installation Design Methods Without Consideration of Gas Lift Valve Performance.

Safety factors are used for continuous-flow gas lift installation design with unbalanced, single-element, gas lift valves when the load rate and the gas throughput performance of the valve are not considered in the calculations. The initial gas lift valve opening pressures are based on the static force-balance equations. Safety factors allow the injection-gas and/or the flowing-production pressure to increase at valve depth, which is needed to properly stroke the valve stem and provide the equivalent port area required to pass the injection-gas rate necessary for unloading and gas lifting most wells. The following safety factors compensate for the fact that most operators set the gas lift valves to the nearest tubing joint. The actual depth of the gas lift valve is usually within 15 ft of the calculated depth.

1. The operating injection-gas pressure used for the installation design calculations should be the average and not the maximum injection-gas pressure available at the wellsite for most wells. In special cases, a kick-off pressure can be used.

2. The unloading daily production rate is assumed equal to the design daily production rate. Generally, the actual unloading daily production rate may be less than the design production rate and can be controlled at the surface by the injection-gas rate.

3. No formation gas is produced during the unloading operations. The total gas/liquid ratio is based on the daily injection-gas rate available for unloading the well.

4. The flowing-pressure-at-depth traverses above the unloading gas lift valves are assumed to be straight lines for the design calculations.

5. The unloading flowing-temperature-at-depth traverse is assumed to be a straight rather than a curved line between an assigned unloading flowing wellhead temperature, T_{whu}, and the bottomhole temperature, T_{wsd}.

The design surface unloading flowing temperature generally is assumed to be lower than the final, operating temperature. A final flowing temperature that is slightly higher than the design temperature increases the initial opening pressure of a bellows-charged gas lift valve and aids in keeping the upper valves closed while lifting from a lower gas lift valve.

1. An assigned valve-spacing pressure differential, ΔP_{sD}, of 20 to 60 psi across a valve for unloading is used by many gas lift design engineers. As a result, the actual minimum flowing-production pressure required to uncover the next lower unloading gas lift valve is greater by the assigned ΔP_{sD}.

2. The flowing-pressure traverse below the point of gas injection for locating the valve depths is normally assumed to be the static-load-fluid gradient. Once formation production occurs, the actual flowing pressure gradient decreases in most wells.

12.10.2 An Orifice-Check Valve for the Operating Gas Lift Valve in Continuous-Flow Installations.

An orifice being used for gas lifting a well should include a reverse-flow check valve. The check disk, or dart, should be closed by gravity or spring loaded. In a well with a packer, the check portion should remain closed to prevent debris from accumulating on top of the packer when this valve is below the working fluid level and is not the operating valve. An inlet screen is recommended for orifice-check valves with a small choke to prevent possible plugging. The individual openings in the inlet screen should be smaller than the choke in the orifice-check valve.

A properly designed continuous-flow gas lift installation with an orifice-check valve does not have a higher injection-gas requirement than the same well with an injection-pressure-operated gas lift valve. The injection-gas rate for lifting a well is controlled by the metering device on the injection-gas line at the surface. An orifice-check valve rather than a more expensive and complicated pressure-operated gas lift valve should be considered for the bottom valve in most continuous-flow installations.

Advantages of an Orifice-Check Valve. The orifice-check valve is the simplest of all types of operating valves and has a very low possibility of malfunction. It can be used as a "flag" because of the change in the surface injection-gas pressure downstream of the control valve when the orifice-check valve is uncovered and becomes the point of gas injection. **Fig. 12.28** illustrates an unloading operation using an orifice-check valve on bottom. The heading flowing wellhead tubing pressure is the result of the opening and closing of the unloading gas lift valves because of a $^{24}/_{64}$-in. choke in the flowline and a frictional drag mechanism in the valve to prevent stem shatter. After the orifice-check valve is uncovered at approximately 3:00 a.m., there is no heading. The operating injection-gas pressure decrease is the result of low reservoir deliverability and not the gas lift system. A properly sized orifice-check valve can prevent severe heading or surging in a continuous-flow gas lift installation by ensuring a constant orifice size. No injection-gas pressure increase is required to stroke an orifice-check valve, and the orifice size is always known because it is equal to the choke size in the valve. The orifice-check valve is always open and passes gas as long as injection-gas pressure at valve depth exceeds the flowing-production pressure at the same depth. A properly sized orifice is required to control the injection-gas volume for gas lifting some wells. One application is gas lifting one zone of a dual gas lift installation with a common injection-gas source in the casing annulus. A design pressure differential of at least 100 to 200 psi across the orifice is necessary to ensure a reasonably accurate gas-passage prediction.

Disadvantages of the Orifice-Check Valve. If the injection-gas-line pressure is high, relative to the flowing-production pressure at the orifice-check valve depth, freezing can occur at the surface if wet gas is used. The weak wells with an orifice-check operating valve will continue to consume injection gas at lower injection-gas-line pressure than stronger wells with higher flowing-production pressures at the depth of the operating orifice-check valve.

A hole in the tubing or a leaking packer is indistinguishable from an orifice-check valve during a normal, uninterrupted, continuous-flow gas lift operation. An orifice-check valve generally is not recommended for a small closed rotative gas lift system when costly makeup gas is required to charge the system after a shutdown. A properly set injection-pressure-operated gas lift valve closes after a slight decrease in the injection-gas pressure and prevents the unnecessary loss of injection gas from the casing annulus and the small high-pressure system.

12.10.3 Depth of the Top Gas Lift Valve. The top gas lift valve should be located at the maximum depth that permits U-tubing the load fluid from this depth with the available injection-gas pressure. If the well is loaded to the surface with a kill fluid, the depth of the top valve can be calculated with one of the following equations.

$$D_{v1} = \frac{P_{ko} - P_{whu}}{g_{ls}}, \quad \text{..} (12.29)$$

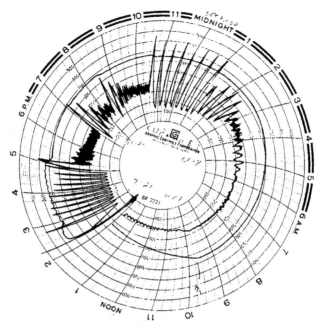

Fig. 12.28—Two-pen pressure-recording unloading chart from a continuous-flow gas lift installation with an orifice-check valve on bottom.

$$D_{v1} = \frac{P_{ko} - P_{whu}}{\left(g_{ls} - g_{gio}\right)}, \quad\text{...} (12.30)$$

or

$$D_{v1} = \frac{P_{ko} - P_{whu} - \Delta P_{sD}}{\left(g_{ls} - g_{gio}\right)}, \quad\text{...} (12.31)$$

where
D_{v1} = depth of top valve, ft,
P_{ko} = surface kick-off or average field injection-gas pressure (optional), psig,
P_{whu} = surface wellhead U-tubing (unloading) pressure, psig,
ΔP_{sD} = assigned spacing pressure differential at valve depth, psi,
g_{ls} = static load (kill)-fluid pressure gradient, psi/ft,
and
g_{gio} = injection-gas pressure-at-depth gradient, psi/ft.

Eq. 12.29 does not include the increase in the injection-gas pressure to the valve depth, D_{v1}. This equation is widely used because of a safety factor from neglecting this increase in gas pressure with depth. Eq. 12.30 yields the same depth as a graphical solution without any pressure drop across the top gas lift valve at the instant this valve is uncovered. In other words, the top valve is not uncovered if the actual kick-off injection-gas pressure is less than the design value or if the U-tubing wellhead pressure is higher than assumed. Eq. 12.31 includes injection-gas column weight and an assigned pressure differential at the instant the top valve is uncovered.

The surface U-tubing wellhead pressure is less than the flowing wellhead pressure for most installations. The difference between these two pressures increases for longer flowlines and higher production rates. The wellhead U-tubing pressure is approximately equal to the separator or production-header pressure because the rate of load fluid transfer is very low during the U-tubing operation and no injection gas can enter the flowline until the top gas lift valve is uncovered. Gas lift operations do not begin until injection gas enters the production conduit through the top valve. Flowing wellhead pressure should be used to locate the depths of the remaining gas lift valves.

A load-fluid traverse based on g_{ls} can be drawn from the wellhead U-tubing pressure to the intersection of the kick-off injection-gas pressure-at-depth curve (P_{koD} traverse) on a pressure/depth plot. The top valve may be located at this intersection, which is the same depth as calculated with Eq. 12.30. An arbitrary pressure drop across the top gas lift valve can be assumed in conjunction with the graphical method, and this technique is the same as Eq. 12.31. If no gas pressure increase with depth is assumed, this method becomes similar to the calculation of D_{v1} with Eq. 12.29. For simplicity, Eq. 12.28 is often used for top-valve spacing calculations.

12.10.4 Multiphase-Flow Correlations and Flowing-Pressure-at-Depth Gradient Curves. Accurate flowing-pressure-at-depth predictions are essential for good continuous-flow gas lift installation design and analysis. When computer programs for gas lift installation design and analysis are unavailable for daily routine calculations, the gas lift designers must rely on published gradient curves to determine flowing pressures at depth. Many oil-producing companies have their own multiphase-flow correlations and publish in-house gradient curves. Gradient curves are available from the gas lift manufacturers and are published in books that can be purchased. Where possible, use field data to verify the accuracy of the computer program calculations and gradient curves. It is not the purpose of this chapter to compare the various multiphase-flow correlations or published gradient curves.

The widely accepted multiphase-flow correlations and mechanistic models are based on pseudo-steady state flow without serious heading through a clean production conduit with an unrestricted cross-sectional area. Accurate pressures cannot be obtained from gradient curves based on these correlations if the conduit is partially plugged with paraffin or scale. Emulsions also can prevent the application of these correlations and gradient curves. The applicability of a particular correlation or set of gradient curves for a given well can be established only by comparing a measured flowing pressure to a pressure at depth determined from the correlation or gradient curves. The measured production data must be accurate and repeatable before discounting the multiphase-flow correlations or gradient curves.

A set of typical gradient curves is given in **Fig. 12.29**. These gradient curves are used in the example installation design calculations in Example Problem 4. GLR and not gas/oil ratio (GOR) is used for these installation design calculations.

Most gradient curves display GLR rather than GOR. For this reason, the first step in the application of gradient curves is to convert GOR to GLR, if only GOR is reported and the well produces water. The GLR can be calculated for a given GOR and water cut with Eq. 12.32.

$$R_{glf} = f_o\left(R_{go}\right), \qquad\qquad\qquad\qquad\qquad\qquad (12.32)$$

where
R_{glf} = formation gas/liquid ratio, scf/STB,
f_o = oil cut $(1 - f_w)$, fraction,
and
R_{go} = gas/oil ratio, scf/STB.

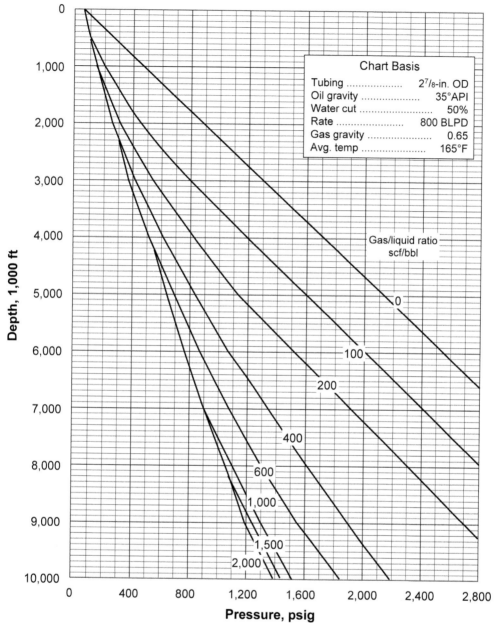

Fig. 12.29—Flowing pressure at depth gradient curves for 800 B/D with a 50% water cut through 2⅞-in.-OD tubing.

Example Problem 3. Given:
- R_{go} = 500 scf/STB
- Water cut f_w = 0.60 (60%)

Calculate the formation GLR:

R_{glf} = (1 − 0.6) 500 = 200 scf/STB.

When gradient curves are used, the depth is a relative depth and may be shifted, whereas pressure is never shifted. If a flowing-pressure-at-depth traverse is being traced, the pressures on the pressure/depth plot must always overlie the same pressures on the gradient curves. For deviated wells where friction is small, use true vertical depths rather than measured depths in a graphical design.

12.10.5 Flowing Temperature at Depth. The accurate prediction of the flowing-production fluid temperature at valve depth is important in the design and analysis of many gas lift installations with nitrogen-charged gas lift valves. The temperature of a wireline-retrievable valve is assumed to be the same as the temperature of the flowing fluids at the valve depth. A retrievable gas lift valve is located in a mandrel pocket inside the tubing and is in contact with the production from the well. The temperature of a conventional valve is between the flowing fluid temperature and the geothermal temperature for the well but is normally closer to the flowing fluid temperature because steel has higher thermal conductivity than gas.

Kirkpatrick[16] published one of the most widely used flowing-temperature-gradient correlations in 1959. The family of flowing-temperature-gradient curves in **Fig. 12.30** is based on data from high-water-cut wells being produced by gas lift through 2⅞-in.-OD tubing over a wide range of production rates. Although the correlation does not include several important parameters, such as GLR and fluid properties, the estimated surface temperature and temperatures at depth have proved to be reasonably accurate for many gas lift operations. Sagar *et al.*[17] published another flowing-temperature correlation. This empirical method for calculating flowing-temperature profiles is far more rigorous and is based on well data from several areas. The calculation procedure can be programmed easily for predicting surface flowing temperatures in vertical and inclined wells. However, the best approach, when possible, is to measure the temperature-at-depth traverse in the actual gas lift well.

12.10.6 Continuous-Flow Installation Design Based on a Constant Decrease in the Operating Injection-Gas Pressure for Each Succeeding Lower Gas Lift Valve (API Design Technique). This installation design method is based on all gas lift valves having the same port size and a constant decrease in the operating injection-gas pressure for each succeeding lower gas lift valve. The gas lift valve selection must be based on a port size that allows the injection-gas throughput required for unloading and gas lifting the well. This installation design method is recommended for gas lift valves with a small production-pressure factor. When the ratio of the port area to the bellows area is low, the decrease in the injection-gas pressure between gas lift valves, based on the additional tubing-effect pressure for the top valve, is not excessive. The effect of bellows-assembly load rate on the performance of the gas lift valves is not considered in the installation design calculations. Safety factors included in these design calculations should allow sufficient increase in the operating injection-gas pressure, which is necessary to provide the valve-stem travel for adequate injection-gas passage through each successively lower unloading gas lift valve without excessive interference from upper valves.

Selection of a constant injection-gas pressure decrease, or drop, in the surface operating-injection-gas pressure for each succeeding lower gas lift valve should not be arbitrary, as proposed in some design methods. The pressure decrease should be based on the gas lift valve specifications to minimize the possibility of upper valves remaining open while lifting from a lower valve. The additional tubing-effect pressure for the top gas lift valve is a logical choice for this decrease in the operating injection-gas pressure between valves. Closing or reopening of an injection-pressure-operated gas lift valve is partially controlled by the production-pressure effect, which is equal to the production-pressure factor for the valve multiplied by the difference flowing-production pressure at the top valve depth.

The flowing-production pressure at an unloading-valve depth changes from the transfer pressure, $(P_{pfD})_{min}$, to a higher flowing-production pressure after the next lower valve becomes the operating valve. The additional tubing-effect pressure is the difference between $(P_{pfD})_{min}$ and

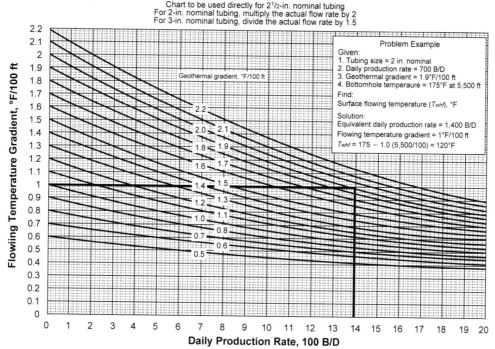

Chart to be used directly for 2½-in. nominal tubing
For 2-in. nominal tubing, multiply the actual flow rate by 2
For 3-in. nominal tubing, divide the actual flow rate by 1.5

Problem Example
Given:
1. Tubing size = 2 in. nominal
2. Daily production rate = 700 B/D
3. Geothermal gradient = 1.9°F/100 ft
4. Bottomhole temperaure = 175°F at 5,500 ft
Find:
Surface flowing temperature (T_{whf}), °F
Solution:
Equivalent daily production rate = 1,400 B/D
Flowing temperature gradient = 1°F/100 ft
T_{whf} = 175 − 1.0 (5,500/100) = 120°F

Fig. 12.30—Flowing-fluid-temperature gradients in the production conduit for different flow rates and geothermal gradients.

the maximum flowing-production pressure, at the unloading valve depth, $(P_{pfD})_{max}$, after the point of gas injection has transferred to this next lower valve. As the unloading gas lift valve depths increase, the distance between valves and the difference between $(P_{pfD})_{min}$ and $(P_{pfD})_{max}$ decrease. Although the additional tubing-effect pressure decreases for lower valves, the injection-gas requirement for unloading increases with depth. An increased stem travel, or stroke, is usually needed for the lower valves to generate the larger equivalent port area necessary for the higher injection-gas requirements with the lower pressure differentials that occur across these deeper valves. A constant decrease in the operating injection-gas pressure equal to the additional tubing-effect pressure for the top valve allows a greater increase in the injection gas above initial opening pressure for lower gas lift valves.

Another application for this simplified design method depends on the relationship between the available injection-gas pressure and the flowing-production pressure at the maximum depth of lift. When the injection-gas pressure significantly exceeds this flowing-production pressure, an arbitrary decrease in the injection-gas pressure, ΔP_{io}, can be added to the additional production-pressure effect for the top valve for calculating the spacing and the initial opening pressures of the unloading gas lift valves. The total decrease in the injection-gas pressure is distributed equal-ly between each successively lower unloading gas lift valve rather than having a sizable injection-pressure drop across the operating gas lift or orifice-check valve. This procedure reduces the possibility of multipoint gas injection through upper unloading gas lift valves by ensuring that these valves remain closed after the point of gas injection has transferred to the next lower gas lift valve.

Determination of Valve Depths. Because this final injection-gas pressure is unknown until the installation is designed, a pressure difference of at least 100 to 200 psi between the unload-ing P_{ioD} and P_{pfD} traverses is assumed for locating the deepest-valve depth. This assumption of

$(P_{ioD} - P_{pfD} = 100$ to 200 psi) should ensure calculation of the operating valve depth. The static bottomhole pressure, P_{wsd}, and temperature, T_{wsd}, generally are referenced to the same depth, which is the lower end of the production conduit, D_d. The steps for establishing the gas lift valve depths follow.

1. Calculate the maximum unloading GLR based on the maximum injection-gas rate available for unloading and the maximum daily design total fluid rate.

$$R_{glu} = \frac{q_{giu}}{q_{lt}}, \quad\dotfill (12.33)$$

where

q_{giu} = maximum unloading injection-gas rate, Mscf/D,
q_{lt} = total liquid (oil + water) daily production rate, B/D,
R_{gl} = maximum unloading GLR, scf/STB,

and

R_{glu} = maximum unloading GLR, scf/STB.

2. Calculate with a multiphase-flow computer program or determine from an appropriate gradient curve the unloading flowing-production pressure at the lower end of the production conduit, P_{pfd} at D_d, based on the installation design R_{gl} and q_{lt}.

3. Calculate the unloading flowing-pressure-at-depth gradient above the point of gas injection, g_{pf}, by subtracting the wellhead U-tubing (unloading) wellhead pressure, P_{whu}, from the flowing-production pressure, P_{pfd} at D_d, and dividing by the reference datum depth, D_d.

$$g_{pfa} = \frac{(P_{pfD} - P_{whu})}{D_d}. \quad\dotfill (12.34)$$

The traverse above the point of gas injection will actually be a curved line representing a fluid density that typically becomes increasingly less dense as it travels toward the surface. An exception to this is the case of high GLRs at low pressures where the pressure traverse may reverse slope near the surface. However, a straight line is used because it will be easier to calculate the flowing-production pressure at valve depth, P_{pfD}, than with an actual curved flowing-pressure-at-depth traverse. This assumption normally will give a slightly more conservative design.

4. Calculate the static injection-gas pressure at the lower end of the production conduit, P_{iod} at D_d, using Eq. 12.1 and the static injection-gas pressure-at-depth gradient, g_{gio}, by subtracting the surface injection-gas pressure, P_{io}, from P_{iod} at D_d and dividing by the reference datum depth, D_d.

$$g_{gio} = \frac{(P_{iod} - P_{io})}{D_d}. \quad\dotfill (12.35)$$

5. Calculate the unloading gas lift valve temperature-at-depth gradient, g_{Tvu}, by assuming a straight line and subtracting the surface unloading flowing wellhead temperature, T_{whu}, from the bottomhole temperature, T_{wsd} at D_d, and dividing by the reference datum depth, D_d.

$$g_{Tvu} = \frac{(T_{wsd} - T_{whu})}{D_d}. \quad\dotfill (12.36)$$

6. Calculate the depth of the top gas lift valve, D_{vl}, on the basis of the surface kick-off or average field injection-gas pressure, P_{ko}, static-load fluid gradient, g_{ls}, and the wellhead U-tubing unloading pressure, P_{whu}, with either Eqs. 12.29, 12.30, or 12.31. Eq. 12.31 is used in this example. The flowing wellhead pressure, P_{whf}, and the wellhead unloading U-tubing pressure, P_{whu}, are considered equal in the API Design.

7. Calculate the minimum flowing-production pressure, $(P_{pfD1})_{min}$, the injection-gas pressure, P_{ioD1}, and the unloading gas lift valve temperature, T_{vuD1}, at the top valve depth by multiplying the appropriate gradient by the valve depth, D_{vl}, and adding to the appropriate surface values (where $n = 1$ for top valve):

$$\left[P_{pfD(n)} \right]_{min} = P_{whu} + g_{pfa}\left[D_{v(n)} \right] . \quad\text{..} (12.37)$$

$$P_{ioD(n)} = P_{io} + g_{gio}\left[D_{v(n)} \right] . \quad\text{..................................} (12.38)$$

$$T_{vuD(n)} = T_{whu} + g_{Tvu}\left[D_{v(n)} \right] . \quad\text{..................................} (12.39)$$

8. Calculate the depth of the second gas lift valve, D_{v2}, where $n = 2$, on the basis of the assigned minimum decrease in surface injection-gas pressure, Δp_{io}, for spacing the gas lift valves and the P_{ioD} traverse. A valve-spacing differential of approximately 20 to 30 psi will usually be sufficient for most 1.5-in.-OD gas lift valves. However, 1-in.-OD valves with large ports may require a higher Δp_{io}. This can be checked by calculating the additional production-pressure effect, ΔP_{pe1}, using Eq. 12.49 after the valve depths are calculated for the assigned Δp_{io}. The distance between valves and valve depth are calculated as follows:

$$\left[P_{pfD(n-1)} \right]_{min} + g_{ls}\left(D_{bv} \right) = \left[P_{ioD(n-1)} - (n-1)\Delta P_{io} \right] - \Delta P_{sD} + g_{gio}\left(D_{bv} \right) . \quad\text{........} (12.40)$$

Solve for D_{bv}.

$$D_{bv} = \frac{P_{ioD(n-1)} - \left[(n-1)\Delta P_{io} \right] - \left[P_{pfD(n-1)} \right]_{min} - \Delta P_{sD}}{\left(g_{ls} - g_{gio} \right)} , \quad\text{....................} (12.41)$$

and

$$D_{v(n)} = D_{v(n-1)} + D_{bv} . \quad\text{..................................} (12.42)$$

The decrease in surface injection-gas pressure for calculating D_{v2} is ΔP_{io}, and for D_{v3} is 2 (ΔP_{io}), and for D_{v4} is 3 (ΔP_{io}), and this procedure continues for each successively lower valve.

Repeat calculations in Step 7 at second valve depth by calculating $(P_{pfD2})_{min}$, P_{ioD2}, and T_{vuD2} with Eqs. 12.37, 12.38, and 12.39.

Repeat calculations in Step 8 for D_{bv} and D_{v3} with Eqs. 12.41 and 12.42.

Repeat Steps 7 and 8 until the maximum desired valve depth, $D_{v(max)}$, is attained. When the calculated distance between gas lift valves, D_{bv}, is less than an assigned minimum distance between valves, $D_{bv(min)}$, use $D_{bv(min)}$.

12.10.7 Gas Lift Valve Port Sizing and Test-Rack Opening Pressure Calculations. The port size selection is based on the maximum depth of lift and the final operating injection-gas pressure for spacing the deepest valve. The port size and the test-rack setting pressures of the gas lift valves are calculated as follows:

1. Determine the port size for the type of gas lift valves to be installed in the installation on the basis of the unloading and operating injection-gas requirements. Correct the injection-gas rate for the actual gas gravity and temperature at each valve depth with Eq. 12.6. Determine from Fig. 12.13 the port ID needed to pass the required injection-gas rate with the pressure differential available at the operating valve. When an orifice-check valve is selected for the bottom valve, the upstream injection-gas pressure, P_1, should be equal to or less than the injection-gas initial valve opening pressure of the last unloading valve, corrected to the depth of the orifice-check valve. The pressure differential across the orifice-check valve is the difference between P_1 and the downstream flowing-production pressure, P_2, at the valve depth.

2. Record the gas lift valve specifications, which include the effective bellows area, A_b, port area, A_p, (A_p/A_b), $(1 - A_p/A_b)$, and the production-pressure factor, F_p.

3. Calculate the injection-gas initial opening pressure at depth of the top gas lift valve, P_{oD1}.

$$P_{oD1} = P_{ioD1}, \quad\dots\dots\dots\dots\dots\dots\dots\dots\dots\dots\dots\dots\dots\dots\dots\dots\dots\dots\dots\dots (12.43)$$

where

P_{ioD1} = injection-gas pressure at valve depth, psig, and

P_{oD1} = injection-gas initial gas lift valve opening pressure at valve depth, psig.

4. Calculate the test-rack set opening pressure of the first valve ($n = 1$), P_{vo1}, with Eqs. 12.44 and 12.45 or 12.46.

$$P_{bvD(n)} = P_{oD(n)}(1 - A_p/A_b) + \left[P_{pfD(n)}\right]_{\min}\left(A_p/A_b\right), \quad\dots\dots\dots\dots\dots\dots (12.44)$$

$$P_{vo(n)} = \frac{C_{T(n)}\left(P_{bvD(n)}\right)}{\left(1 - A_p/A_b\right)}, \quad\dots\dots\dots\dots\dots\dots\dots\dots\dots\dots\dots\dots\dots\dots\dots (12.45)$$

or

$$P_{vo(n)} = C_{T(n)}\left\{F_p\left[P_{pfD(n)}\right] + P_{oD(n)}\right\}, \quad\dots\dots\dots\dots\dots\dots\dots\dots\dots\dots (12.46)$$

where

C_T = temperature correction factor for nitrogen from P_{bvD} to P_b at 60°F, dimensionless,

P_{bvD} = nitrogen-charged bellows pressure at valve temperature, psig,

$(P_{pfD})_{\min}$ = minimum flowing-production pressure at valve depth, psig,

and

P_{vo} = test-rack valve opening pressure at 60°F, psig.

Some designers prefer Eq. 12.46, which does not require calculation of P_{bvD} and gives the same result.

5. Calculate the injection-gas initial opening pressure of the second gas lift valve at depth ($n = 2$) with Eq. 12.47.

$$P_{oD(n)} = P_{ioD(n)} - (n - 1)\Delta P_{io} . \quad\dots\dots\dots\dots\dots\dots\dots\dots\dots\dots\dots\dots (12.47)$$

6. Calculate the maximum flowing-production pressure opposite the top unloading valve immediately after the point of gas injection has transferred to the second (lower) valve, $(P_{pfD1})_{\max}$. $(P_{pfD1})_{\max}$ is shown graphically in **Fig. 12.31** and can be calculated with Eq. 12.48.

$$(P_{pfD1})_{max} = P_{whf} + D_{v1}\left(\frac{P_{oD2} - P_{whf}}{D_{v2}}\right). \quad\text{.................................... (12.48)}$$

7. Determine if the assumed decrease in surface injection-gas pressure, ΔP_{io}, is sufficient for the required gas lift valve port size by calculating the additional production-pressure effect, ΔP_{pe1}, at the top valve:

$$\Delta P_{pe1} = F_p\left[(P_{pfD1})_{max} - (P_{pfD1})_{min}\right]. \quad\text{.................................... (12.49)}$$

If ΔP_{pe1} is less than or equal to the assumed ΔP_{io}, proceed with the design. If ΔP_{pe1} is greater than the assumed ΔP_{io}, then set $\Delta P_{io} = \Delta P_{pe1}$ and recalculate the spacing design. This is a conservative approach, and many operators use actual operating experience to determine which ΔP_{io} to use.

Repeat Steps 3 and 4 calculations for the second gas lift valve.

Repeat Steps 3, 4, and 5 calculations for remaining gas lift valves. If the operating valve is an orifice-check valve, determine the orifice ID for lifting the well on the basis of the calculated upstream and downstream pressures, P_1 and P_2.

Example Problem 4. Well information for continuous-flow installation design (API Design Technique).

- Tubing size = 2⅞-in. OD.
- Tubing length, D_d = 6,000 ft.
- Maximum valve depth, $D_{v(max)}$ = 5,970 ft.
- Static bottomhole pressure at D_d, P_{wsd} = 1,800 psig at 6,000 ft.
- Daily production rate = 800 STB/D.
- Water cut = 50% (f_w = 0.50).
- Formation GOR = 500 scf/STB.
- Oil gravity = 35°API.
- Gas gravity, γ_g = 0.65.
- Produced-water specific gravity, γ_w = 1.08.
- Bottomhole temperature, T_{wsd} = 170°F at 6,000 ft.
- Design unloading wellhead temperature, T_{whf} = 100°F.
- Load-fluid pressure gradient, g_{ls} = 0.46 psi/ft.
- U-tubing wellhead pressure, P_{whu} = 100 psig.
- Flowing wellhead pressure, P_{whf} = 100 psig.
- Static fluid level = 0 ft (well loaded with kill fluid).
- Surface kick-off injection-gas pressure, P_{ko} = 1,000 psig.
- Surface operating injection-gas pressure, P_{io} = 1,000 psig.
- Maximum unloading injection-gas rate, q_{giu} = 800 Mscf/D.
- Operating daily injection-gas rate, q_{gi} = 500 Mscf/D.
- Wellhead injection-gas temperature, T_{gio} = 100°F.
- Assigned valve-spacing pressure differential at valve depth, ΔP_{sD} = 50 psi.
- Test-rack valve setting temperature, T_{vo} = 60°F.
- Assigned minimum decrease in surface operating injection-gas pressure between valves, ΔP_{io} = 20 psi.
- Minimum distance between valves, $D_{bv(min)}$ = 150 ft.
- Gas lift valves: 1.5-in.-OD nitrogen-charged with A_b = 0.77 in.^{2} and sharp-edged seat.

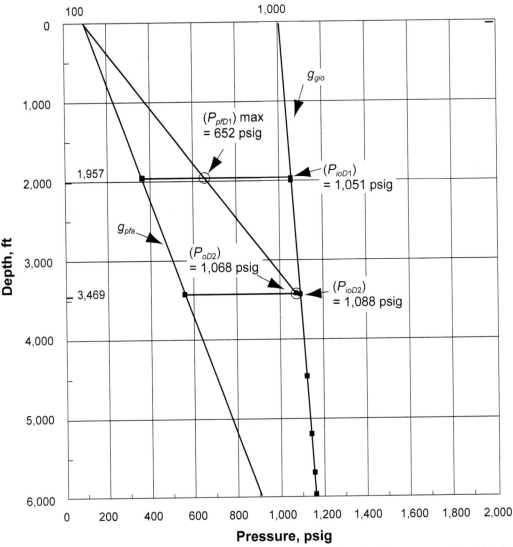

Fig. 12.31—Pressure/depth graphical determination of the additional production-pressure effect for the top gas lift valve in a continuous-flow gas lift installation designed with a constant decrease in operating injection-gas pressure between valves.

Solution—Calculation of Valve Depths. The pressure traverses used to establish the gas lift valve depths are drawn on pressure/depth worksheets in **Figs. 12.31 and 12.32.**

1. Calculate maximum injection GLR with Eq. 12.33.

$$R_{glu} = \frac{800,000 \ \text{scf/D}}{800 \ \text{STB/D}} = 1,000 \ \text{scf/STB} \ .$$

2. Determine the flowing-production pressure P_{pfd} at D_d from the appropriate gradient curves in Fig. 12.29 for 800 B/D and 1,000 scf/STB:

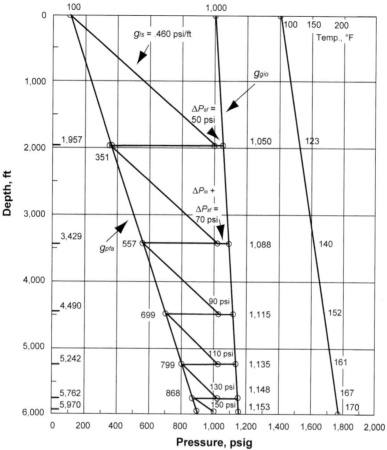

Fig. 12.32—Graphical representation of a continuous-flow gas lift installation design with nitrogen-charged gas lift valves based on a constant decrease in the operating injection-gas pressure for each successively deeper valve.

Actual Depth, ft	Chart Depth, ft	Pressure, psig
0	725	100
6,000	6,725	900

P_{pfd} = 900 psig at 6,000 ft, where P_{pfd} is the flowing-production pressure at the lower end of the production conduit, D_d.

3. Calculate g_{pfa} with Eq. 12.34.

$$g_{pfa} = \frac{(900 - 100)}{6,000} = 0.1333 \ \text{psi/ft}.$$

4. Calculate the operating injection-gas pressure at the lower end of the production conduit using Eq. 12.1 and g_{gio} with Eq. 12.35.

P_{iod} = 1,154 psig at 6,000 ft (calculated).

$$g_{gio} = \frac{(1,154 - 1,000)}{6,000} = 0.0257 \text{ psi/ft}.$$

Because the difference between P_{pfd} and P_{iod}, ($P_{iod} - P_{pfd} = 1,154 - 900 = 254$ psi), exceeds 200 psi, the maximum valve depth of 5,970 ft can be attained.

5. Calculate the unloading gas lift valve temperature at depth gradient with Eq. 12.36.

$$g_{Tvu} = \frac{(170 - 100)}{6,000} = 0.0117°F/ft.$$

6. Calculate the depth of the top gas lift valve with Eq. 12.31.

$$D_{v1} = \frac{1,000 - 100 - 50}{(0.46 - 0.0257)} = 1,957 \text{ ft}.$$

7. Calculate the minimum flowing-production pressure, $(P_{pfD1})_{min}$, injection-gas pressure, P_{ioD1}, and the unloading flowing temperature, T_{vuD1} at D_{v1} of 1,957 ft with Eqs. 12.37 through 12.39.

$(P_{pfD1})_{min} = 100 + 0.1333 (1,957) = 361$ psig.
$P_{ioD1} = 1,000 + 0.0257 (1,957) = 1,050$ psig.
$T_{vuD1} = 100 + 0.0117 (1,957) = 123°F.$

8. Calculate D_{bv} for depth of second valve, D_{v2}, where $\Delta P_{ioD2} = 20$ psi, using Eqs. 12.41 and 12.42:

$$D_{bv} = \frac{1,050 - 0 - 361 - 50}{(0.46 - 0.0257)} = 1,472 \text{ ft and } D_{v2} = 1,957 + 1,472 = 3,429 \text{ ft}.$$

Repeat Step 7: Calculate $(P_{pfD2})_{min}$, P_{ioD2}, and T_{vuD2} at valve depth $D_{v2} = 3,429$ ft.
$(P_{pfD2})_{min} = 557$ psig, $P_{ioD2} = 1,088$ psig, and $T_{vuD2} = 140°F.$
Repeat Step 8: Calculate depth of third valve, D_{v3}, where $\Delta P_{ioD3} = 40$ psi.
$D_{bv} = 1,061$ ft and $D_{v3} = 4,490$ ft.
Repeat Step 7: Calculate $(P_{pfD3})_{min}$, P_{ioD3}, and T_{vuD3} at valve depth $D_{v3} = 4,490$ ft.
$(P_{pfD3})_{min} = 699$ psig, $P_{ioD3} = 1,115$ psig, and $T_{vuD3} = 152°F.$
Repeat Step 8: Calculate depth of fourth valve, D_{v4}, where $\Delta P_{ioD4} = 60$ psi.
$D_{bv} = 752$ ft and $D_{v4} = 5,242$ ft.
Repeat Step 7: Calculate $(P_{pfD4})_{min}$, P_{ioD4}, and T_{vuD4} at valve depth $D_{v4} = 5,242$ ft.
$(P_{pfD4})_{min} = 799$ psig, $P_{ioD4} = 1,135$ psig, $T_{vuD4} = 161°F.$
Repeat Step 8: Calculate depth of fifth valve, D_{v5}, where $\Delta P_{ioD3} = 80$ psi.
$D_{bv} = 520$ ft and $D_{v5} = 5,762$ ft.
Repeat Step 7: Calculate $(P_{pfD5})_{min}$, P_{ioD5}, and T_{vuD5} at valve depth $D_{v5} = 5,762$ ft.
$(P_{pfD5})_{min} = 868$ psig, $P_{ioD5} = 1,148$ psig, and $T_{vuD5} = 167°F.$

The calculated valve spacing for the sixth valve, D_{v6}, would exceed the maximum valve depth, $D_{v(max)}$, of 5,970 ft. Because an orifice-check valve will be placed in the bottom wireline-retrievable valve mandrel, no test-rack valve setting information is required. This completes the valve spacing calculations. A graphical representation of the valve installation design is shown in Fig. 12.32.

Solution—Determination of Gas Lift Valve Port Size and Calculation of Test-Rack Opening Pressures. The gas lift valves port ID and test-rack opening pressure calculations are given next.

1. Determine the port size required for the gas lift unloading valves and the operating orifice-check valve orifice ID. The upstream injection-gas pressure, P_1, is based on P_{oD5} of the last unloading valve using Eq. 12.47 corrected to the orifice-check valve depth of 5,970 ft.

$P_1 = 1,068 + 0.0257 (5,970 - 5,762) = 1,073$ psig at 5,970 ft.

The downstream flowing-production pressure, P_2, is equal to the minimum flowing-production pressure at 5,970 ft with Eq. 12.37.

$P_2 = 100 + 0.1333 (5,970) = 896$ psig at 5,970 ft.

$\Delta P_{ov} = 1,073 - 896 = 177$ psi across the orifice-check valve.

From Fig. 12.13, the required equivalent orifice size is near $^{14}\!/_{64}$ in.; therefore, the next largest gas lift valve port ID is ¼ in. This size is sufficient for all of the upper unloading valves because they have a higher injection-gas operating pressure and a greater differential pressure between P_{ioD} and $(P_{pfD})_{min}$. An equivalent orifice size of $^{12}\!/_{64}$ in. to $^{13}\!/_{64}$ in. is required to pass the operating injection-gas rate of 500 Mscf/D.

2. Record the valve specifications for a 1.5-in.-OD gas lift valve having a ¼-in.-ID port with a sharp-edged seat where $A_b = 0.77$ in.^{2} from Table 12.2.

$(A_p/A_b) = 0.064$, $(1 - A_p/A_b) = 0.936$, and $F_p = 0.068$.

3. Calculate P_{oD1} with Eq. 12.43: $P_{oD1} = 1,050$ psig at 1,957 ft.

4. Calculate P_{bvD1} with Eq. 12.44 for $C_{T1} = 0.876$ (Calculated with Eq. 12.3 for $T_{vuD1} = 123°F$).

$$P_{bvD1} = 1,050(0.936) + 361(0.064) = 1,006 \text{ psig at } 123°F .$$

5. Calculate P_{vo1} with Eq. 12.45: $P_{vo1} = \dfrac{0.876(1,006)}{0.936} = 942$ psig at 60°F.

6. Calculate P_{oD2} with Eq. 12.47: $P_{oD2} = 1,088 - 20 = 1,068$ psig at 3,429 ft.

7. Calculate $(P_{pfD1})_{max}$ with Eq. 12.48:

$$\left(P_{pfD1}\right)_{max} = 100 + 1,957\left(\frac{1,068 - 100}{3,429}\right) = 652 \text{ psig at } 1,957 \text{ ft} .$$

8. Calculate ΔP_{pe1} with Eq. 12.49: $\Delta P_{pe1} = 0.068 (652 - 361) = 20$ psi.

Because the ΔP_{pe1} of 20 psi is the same as the assumed ΔP_{io} of 20 psi for spacing, a pressure differential of 20 psi can be used for setting the valves. Note that if 1-in.-OD valves had been used in this design, $F_p = 0.188$ for a ¼-in.-ID port and ΔP_{pe1} would be 55 psi.

Repeat Steps 6, 4, and 5 for remaining gas lift valves:

$P_{oD2} = 1,035$ psig at 3,429 ft, $P_{bvD2} = 1,035$ psig, $C_{T2} = 0.847$ for $T_{vuD2} = 140°F$, and $P_{vo2} = 937$ psig.

$P_{oD3} = 1,075$ psig at 4,490 ft, $P_{bvD3} = 1,051$ psig, $C_{T3} = 0.828$ for $T_{vuD3} = 152°F$, and $P_{vo3} = 929$ psig.

$P_{oD4} = 1,075$ psig at 5,242 ft, $P_{bvD4} = 1,057$ psig, $C_{T4} = 0.815$ for $T_{vuD4} = 161°F$, and $P_{vo4} = 919$ psig.

$P_{oD5} = 1,068$ psig at 5,762 ft, $P_{bvD5} = 1,055$ psig, $C_{T5} = 0.805$ for $T_{vuD5} = 167°F$, and $P_{vo5} = 907$ psig.

An orifice-check valve is recommended for the sixth valve at 5,962 ft. The orifice ID should be ¼ in. to pass sufficient gas to gas lift the well. A tabulation form for these calculations is given in **Table 12.3**.

12.10.8 Continuous-Flow Installation Design When Injection-Gas Pressure is High, Relative to Depth of Lift. An additional incremental decrease in the injection-gas pressure can be added

TABLE 12.3—TABULATION OF GAS LIFT DESIGN CALCULATION

Valve Number	D, ft	P_{ioD}, psig	P_{oD}, psig	$(P_{pfD})_{min.}$, psig	P_{bvD}, psig	T_{vD}, °F	C_T	$P_{vo,}$ psig
1	1,957	1,050	1,050	361	1,006	123	0.876	942
2	3,429	1,088	1,068	557	1,035	140	0.847	937
3	4,490	1,115	1,075	699	1,051	152	0.828	929
4	5,242	1,135	1,075	799	1,057	161	0.814	919
5	5,762	1,148	1,068	868	1,055	167	0.805	907
6	5,970	1,153		896	An orifice check valve is used.			

Valve description: 1½-in.-OD gas lift valve. Valve specifications taken from Table 12.2. $A_b = 0.77$ in.², port ID = ¼ in., $A_p = 0.049$ in., $A_p/A_b = 0.064$, and $(1 - A_p/A_b) = 0.936$. $F_p = (A_p/A_b)/(1 - A_p/A_b) = .0684$.

to the calculated decrease to ensure unloading a gas lift installation when the injection-gas pressure is high, relative to the required depth of lift. The flowing-production pressure at the depth of lift limits the maximum injection-gas pressure that can be used in terms of contributing to the lift process. The higher available injection-gas pressure cannot be utilized in this installation. An excessive injection-gas pressure drop across the operating valve represents an inefficient energy loss. Distributing the decrease in the injection-gas pressure between each successively lower unloading gas lift valve prevents multipoint gas injection through upper gas lift valves after the point of gas injection transfers to a lower valve. In other words, the gas lift installation can be unloaded without valve interference, and the unloading process is apparent from the injection-gas pressure recording at the surface. A high available injection-gas pressure, relative to the depth of lift, may exist in areas where both shallow and deep wells are being gas lifted with injection gas from the same system. The flowing-production pressure in the shallow wells limits the injection-gas pressure that can be used to gas lift these wells.

12.10.9 High Rate Continuous-Flow Installation Design.[15] The application of the injection-gas rate throughput performance for injection-pressure-operated gas lift valves is illustrated in the high daily liquid rate continuous-flow installation design. The importance of valve performance data for high daily injection-gas rates is shown, and their unimportance for low-injection-gas-rate installation designs is illustrated. Valve performance data is of no value in selection of the top two unloading gas lift valves in this installation. For these two upper valves, an assumed reasonable decrease in the surface injection-gas pressure of 20 psi for each valve ensures unloading the well and these upper valves remaining closed while lifting from a lower valve. When the required daily injection-gas rate increases for lifting from the third and fourth gas lift valves, valve performance information becomes very important. A pressure-vs.-depth plot for this continuous-flow installation is shown in **Fig. 12.33.**

Although the flowing-production transfer-pressure-traverse method for locating the depths of the valves may require an additional valve, or valves, in some installations, this design method has several advantages in wells requiring a high daily injection-gas rate for unloading. Because the injection-gas requirement to uncover the next lower valve is reduced, smaller valve ports can be used and the increase in the injection-gas pressure to stroke the valve stem is less. The unloading operations are faster because of the lesser difference in injection-gas requirement between unloading valves. This fact is of more importance after an injection-gas supply interruption when several wells must be unloaded and the total-system available daily injection-gas volume is limited. The chance of heading and surging with a smaller port is reduced because a change in flowing-production pressure has a lesser affect on the valve-stem position. Bubble-tight seats are easier to achieve with small ports.

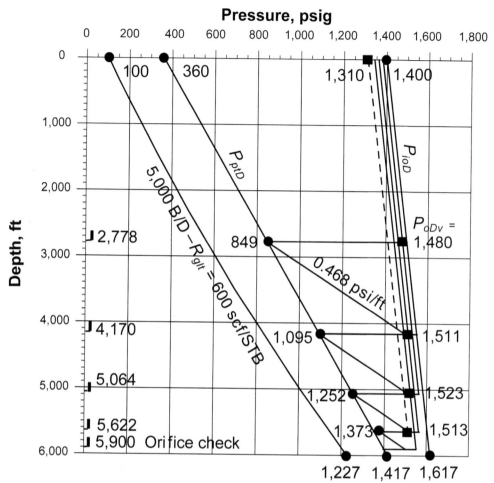

Fig. 12.33—Pressure/depth graphical design for a continuous-flow gas lift installation requiring high injection-gas rates for unloading and final gas lift operation.

The surface origin and final downhole termination pressures for the flowing-production transfer-pressure traverse are arbitrary. The 20% in this example for locating the surface transfer-pressure traverse is widely used. The unloading injection-gas requirements for uncovering each lower valve increase as that percentage decreases and decrease as that percentages increases. The flowing-production transfer pressure at datum depth should be at least 100 to 200 psi less than the available design operating injection-gas pressure at the same depth. This flowing-production transfer pressure at datum depth should also be less than the flowing-production pressure at the same depth based on the design daily production rate and maximum total GLR.

The multiphase-fluid-flow correlation selected for these calculations can significantly affect the results. Several assumptions for calculating the depths of the unloading valves are very conservative in this example (e.g., assuming a load-fluid pressure gradient below an unloading valve after significant bottomhole-pressure drawdown and the assigned valve spacing pressure differential of 50 psi at the next lower valve depth). These design calculations provide a comprehensive understanding of the overall well unloading process and operations. The installation designer can modify the assumptions on the basis of the availability and accuracy of the known well information.

A lower-than-the-design daily liquid-production rate is assigned for spacing the unloading valves until the flowing-bottomhole-pressure drawdown results in a calculated daily production rate that exceeds the assigned rate. Typical assigned unloading daily liquid rates would be 200 to 400 B/D for 2⅜-in.-OD tubing and 400 to 600 B/D for 2⅞-in.-OD tubing. When the calculated flowing-bottomhole-pressure drawdown results in a higher than the assigned unloading daily liquid production rate for the flowing-production transfer pressure at the depth of the operating unloading valve, this higher rate is used for spacing the next lower unloading valve. A 1,000-B/D unloading rate is assigned for unloading valves before a higher liquid rate occurs from a flowing-bottomhole-pressure drawdown in this high-productivity well with large tubing. The assigned design flowing-wellhead temperature of 120°F is between the ambient surface temperature and the flowing-well fluids temperature at the design daily production rate from the well.

Simplified Mathematical Gas Lift Valve Performance Model. Because performance equations for specific gas lift valves are not available from gas lift valve manufacturers, a simplified gas lift valve performance computer model was used to illustrate the calculations in this paper. The model is based on static force-balance equations and several simplifying assumptions. This computer model describes qualitatively the injection-gas rate throughput of unbalanced, single-element gas lift valves using the Thornhill-Craver[12] equation (Eq. 12.5).

For this computer model, the gas lift valve has a square sharp-edged seat and the stem tip is a carbide ball with a $\frac{1}{16}$-in. larger OD than the bore ID of the valve seat. The equivalent port area for a partially open valve is defined by the lateral surface area of the frustum of a right circular cone. The frustum area is generated between the surface of the ball and the valve seatline as the valve stem moves away from its seat. The bellows-assembly load rate is assumed to be linear for the stem travel required to attain a given equivalent port area, and there is no increase in nitrogen-charged bellows pressure during this stem travel. The flow restriction and the pressure loss, resulting from a check-valve assembly, are not included in the gas lift valve model calculations. The same gas gravity, ratio of specific heats, and discharge coefficient are used for all calculations.

There are many unknown dynamic quantities in terms of actual areas and pressures acting on these areas as the gas-flow rate through a valve changes with valve-stem travel. For the valve performance calculations with a partially open port, the injection-gas pressure is assumed to act over the effective bellows area minus the port ball/seat contact area. Regardless of the valve-stem position, the flowing-production pressure is applied over the entire port ball/seat contact area. These assumptions should result in the calculated injection-gas rate being less than the actual rate. As the ball on the valve stem moves away from its seat during an increase in injection-gas pressure, the two areas over which the opening pressures are applied will change. The bellows area exposed to the injection-gas pressure increases and the flowing-production pressure approaches the injection-gas pressure downstream of the port as the equivalent port area increases in the variable-orifice throttling mode. This pressure is difficult to define accurately because of the varying pressure loss as the equivalent port area changes with valve-stem travel.

Although several of the assumptions for the mathematical valve model are known to be approximate, the predicted performance illustrates, with reasonable accuracy, the manner in which an unbalanced, injection-pressure-operated, single-element gas lift valve operates in a well. The valve performance curves, in the continuous-flow installation design, were calculated using the computer model in Appendix A. The coefficient for Eq. A-9 in Appendix A is based on the Thornhill-Craver coefficient of 155.5, a gas gravity of 0.65, ratio of specific heats of 1.26, discharge coefficient of 0.865, and acceleration caused by gravity of 32.174.

Determination of Valve Depths. The procedure for referencing the static bottomhole pressure, P_{wsd}, and temperature, T_{wsd}, to the lower end of the production conduit, D_d, is the same as for the previous lower-injection-gas-rate continuous-flow installation design in Example Problem 4.

1. Determine the static operating injection-gas pressure at the lower end of the production conduit, P_{iod}, with Eq. 12.1 and calculate the static operating injection-gas pressure at depth gradient, g_{gio}, with Eq. 12.35. The same operating injection-gas pressure at depth gradient, g_{gio}, is used for all calculations regardless of the surface injection-gas pressure. This is not a recommended procedure; particularly, for high injection-gas pressures in deep wells. The injection-gas pressures at depth should be calculated on the basis of the actual surface pressures, gas properties, and temperature. The constant g_{gio} was used in the following installation design to simplify the calculations.

2. Calculate the gas lift valve unloading temperature-at-depth gradient, g_{Tvu}, with Eq. 12.36 on the basis of the assigned unloading flowing-wellhead temperature, T_{whu}, and the static bottomhole temperature, T_{wsd}, in the well. The assigned unloading flowing-wellhead temperature should be between the ambient surface temperature and the flowing-well fluids temperature at the design maximum daily production rate from the well.

3. Calculate the surface flowing-production transfer pressure, P_{pt}, on the basis of the assigned flowing-production transfer-pressure valve-spacing factor at the surface, f_{pt}. The assigned f_{pt} will generally range between 0.15 and 0.25 (15 to 25%).

$$P_{pt} = P_{whf} + f_{pt}\left(P_{io} - P_{whf}\right). \qquad (12.50)$$

4. Calculate the flowing-production transfer pressure at the lower end of the production conduit, P_{ptd}, and the flowing-production transfer pressure at depth gradient, g_{pt}. The recommended minimum pressure difference, ΔP_{ptd}, between the flowing-production transfer pressure at the lower end of the production conduit, P_{ptd}, and the operating injection-gas pressure at the same depth, P_{iod}, should be at least 100 to 200 psi or greater and can be based on operating experience in the area.

$$\Delta P_{ptd} = P_{iod} - P_{ptd}. \qquad (12.51)$$

$$g_{pt} = \frac{\left(P_{ptd} - P_{pt}\right)}{D_d}. \qquad (12.52)$$

5. Determine from the appropriate set of gradient curves, or calculate using a reliable multiphase-flow computer program, the flowing-production pressure at the lower end of the production conduit, P_{pfd} at D_d, on the basis of the maximum operating total GLR, R_{glt} (operating daily injection-gas plus formation-produced gas rates), and the installation design total daily liquid rate (oil + water), q_{lt}.

$$R_{gli} = \frac{q_{gi}}{q_{lt}}. \qquad (12.53)$$

$$R_{glt} = R_{glf} + R_{gli}. \qquad (12.54)$$

The P_{pfd} calculation (or determination from gradient curves) determines if the tubing size restricts the maximum design daily production rate and whether a higher injection-gas pressure is recommended. If P_{pfd} is less than P_{ptd}, the tubing size does not appear to restrict the design production rate, and the available injection-gas-line pressure appears to be adequate. The final maximum daily production rate will be controlled by the productivity of the well. If P_{pfd} is greater than P_{ptd}, a higher operating injection-gas pressure is necessary to achieve the assigned maximum depth of lift for this design method.

6. Determine the depth of the top gas lift valve, D_{v1}. The top unloading valve depth is calculated using Eqs. 12.29, 12.30, or 12.31 on the basis of the terms defined for the equation or can be located graphically.

7. Calculate the flowing-production transfer pressure, $P_{ptD(n)}$, the operating injection-gas pressure, $P_{ioD(n)}$, and the unloading valve temperature, $T_{vuD(n)}$, at the gas lift valve depth, $D_{v(n)}$.

$$P_{ptD(n)} = P_{pt} + g_{pt}\left[D_{v(n)}\right]. \quad\text{(12.55)}$$

8. Calculate the flowing bottomhole pressure, $P_{wfd(n)}$, while lifting from the gas lift valve at depth, $D_{v(n)}$, based on the flowing-production transfer pressure, $P_{ptD(n)}$, and the static load (kill) fluid pressure gradient, g_{ls}, to determine whether the calculated daily liquid rate, $q_{lc(n)}$, based on Productivity Index, PI, exceeds the assigned unloading daily liquid rate, $q_{lu(n)}$.

$$P_{wfd(n)} = P_{ptD(n)} + g_{ls}\left[D_d - D_{v(n)}\right]. \quad\text{(12.56)}$$

If $P_{wfd(n)} < P_{wsd}$, calculate $q_{lc(n)}$.

$$q_{lc(n)} = PI\left[P_{wsd} - P_{wfd(n)}\right]. \quad\text{(12.57)}$$

The static load (kill)-fluid pressure at depth gradient is recommended for calculating the valve depths after flowing-bottomhole-pressure drawdown. The time required to recover all load (kill) fluid that entered the reservoir during workover is unknown. It may require days, or weeks, before normal formation-fluids production returns. When reservoir fluids begin to re-enter the wellbore, the flowing-pressure-at-depth gradient below an operating unloading valve will normally decrease and formation free-gas production will reduce the injection-gas requirement.

9. Calculate the daily injection-gas rates, $q_{gi(n)}$, on the basis of the assigned unloading or calculated daily producing liquid rate in Step 8 if $q_{lc(n)} > q_{lu(n)}$. Assume injection-gas/liquid ratios, $R_{gli(n)}$, that result in flowing-production pressures, $P_{pfD(n)}$, at the valve depth, $D_{v(n)}$, that bracket the flowing-production transfer pressure, $P_{ptD(n)}$. Values of $P_{pfD(n)}$ for varying R_{dlt} can be calculated or determined from gradient curves. Then calculate the $q_{gi(n)}$ for the $P_{ptD(n)}$ after the assumed R_{dlt} equals the calculated R_{dlt}.

10. Calculate the increase in the injection-gas pressure, $\Delta P_{ioc(n)}$, above injection-gas initial valve opening pressure, $P_{oD(n)}$, for the valve to pass the required daily injection-gas rate, $q_{gi(n)}$, to establish the $P_{ptD(n)}$ in Step 9 on the basis of the valve port ID, bellows-assembly spring rate, $B_{sr} = B_{lr} (A_b)$ in Appendix A, the $P_{oD(n)}$ and the $P_{ptD(n)}$. The injection-gas rate through a gas lift valve for an assumed $P_{ioD(n)}$ greater than $P_{oD(n)}$ is calculated with the equations in Appendix A. Similar to Step 9, the increase in the injection-gas pressure, $P_{ioD(n)}$, above $P_{oD(n)}$ to attain the $q_{gi(n)}$ in Step 7 can be determined graphically or calculated using a curve-fitting routine. The calculated increase in the injection-gas pressure, $\Delta P_{ioc(n)}$, is equal to the difference between the $P_{ioD(n)}$ that results in the required $q_{gi(n)}$ and the $P_{oD(n)}$ of the valve.

11. Compare the assigned minimum surface injection-gas pressure decrease between valves, ΔP_{ioa}, (represents the assigned minimum surface design injection-gas pressure increase above $P_{oD(n)}$ for stroking a valve) to the calculated injection-gas pressure increase in Step 10. If the calculated surface injection-gas pressure increase in Step 10, $\Delta P_{ioc(n)}$, is less than ΔP_{ioa}, use this assigned injection-gas pressure decrease, ΔP_{ioa} ($\Delta P_{io(n)} = \Delta P_{ioa}$). Then calculate the sum of the

$\Delta P_{io(n)}$ values, $\Sigma\Delta P_{io(n)}$, required for calculation of the injection-gas initial gas lift valve opening pressure at depth of the next lower valve, $P_{oD(n)}$. The $\Sigma\Delta P_{io(n)}$ equals zero for the top gas lift valve in Eq. 12.58.

12. Calculate the depth of the next lower valve, $D_{v(n+1)}$, below the operating unloading valve with a load (kill)-fluid g_{ls} traverse (no formation production fluids) below the valve. The top and the second valve depths, D_{v1} and D_{v2}, respectively, are based on the assigned surface operating injection-gas pressure, P_{io}. The following equation is used for calculating the depths of the second and lower valves until the assigned maximum valve depth or minimum distance between valves is reached.

$$D_{bv} = \frac{\left\{P_{ioD(n)} - \left[\Sigma\Delta P_{io(n-1)} - \Delta P_{io1}\right] - P_{ptD(n)} - \Delta P_{sD}\right\}}{\left(g_{ls} - g_{gio}\right)} \quad\text{.......................} \quad (12.58)$$

$$D_{v(n+1)} = D_{v(n)} + D_{bv} . \quad\text{...................................} \quad (12.59)$$

If $D_{v(n+1)}$ exceeds $D_{v(max)}$, $D_{v(n+1)} = D_{v(max)}$, and $P_{ptD(n)}$ is calculated with Eqs. 12.60 and 12.61.

$$D_{bv} = D_{v(max)} - D_{v(n)}, \quad\text{...................................} \quad (12.60)$$

and

$$P_{ptD(n)} = P_{ioD(n)} - \Sigma\Delta P_{io(n-1)} + D_{bv}\left(g_{ls}\right) - \Delta P_{sD} . \quad\text{...........................} \quad (12.61)$$

Orifice-Check Valve Calculations. The deepest (bottom) operating valve of choice in many continuous-flow installations is an orifice-check valve. Because an orifice-check valve is always fully open, there are no dynamic valve performance calculations required. The published orifice or choke equations or charts are used to select the proper orifice or gas lift valve seat ID and determine the injection-gas rate throughput. Orifice-check valve calculations for the bottom valve are outlined in detail in the following high-rate continuous-flow installation design in Example Problem 5.

Example Problem 5: High-Rate Continuous-Flow Installation Design Calculations. Well data for installation design using unbalanced, nitrogen-charged, injection-pressure-operated gas lift valves for unloading.
- Tubing size = 4½ -in. OD (ID = 3.958 in.), and length = 6,000 ft.
- Casing size = 8⅝-in. OD, 44 lbm/ft (ID = 7.725 in.).
- Datum depth for bottomhole pressures and temperature, D_d = 6,000 ft.
- Bottomhole temperature at D_d, T_{wsd} = 170°F.
- Shut-in (static) bottomhole pressure at D_d, P_{wsd} = 2,000 psig.
- Maximum depth for bottom valve, $D_{v(max)}$ = 5,900 ft.
- Productivity index (gross liquid), PI = 6.3 B/D/psi.
- Oil gravity = 35°API $(\gamma_o = 0.850)$.
- Gas specific gravity (air = 1.0), and γ_g = 0.65.
- Water specific gravity, γ_w = 1.08.
- Water fraction, f_w = 0.50 (50%).
- Formation GOR, R_{go} = 400 scf/STB.

- Formation GLR, R_{glf} = 200 scf/STB.
- Assigned minimum daily unloading production rate, q_{lu} = 1,000 B/D
- Design total (oil + water) daily production rate, q_{lt} = 5,000 B/D.
- Wellhead U-tubing unloading pressure, P_{whu} = 100 psig.
- Surface flowing wellhead pressure, P_{whf} = 100 psig.
- Static load (kill)-fluid pressure gradient, g_{ls} = 0.468 psi/ft.
- Unloading wellhead temperature, T_{whu} = 120°F (basis for calculation of P_{vo}).
- Wellhead injection-gas temperature, T_{gio} = 120°F.
- Surface kick-off injection-gas pressure, P_{ko} = 1,400 psig (at wellsite).
- Surface operating injection-gas pressure, P_{io} = 1,400 psig (at wellsite).
- Assigned daily injection-gas rate, q_{gi} = 2,000 Mscf/D.
- Minimum assigned surface injection-gas pressure decrease between valves, ΔP_{io} = 20 psi.
(Represents minimum surface injection-gas pressure increase for stroking gas lift valve).
- Valve spacing design line percent factor at surface = 20% (f_{pt} = 0.20).
- Minimum transfer-production-pressure difference ($P_{iod} - P_{ptd}$) at D_d, ΔP_{ptd} = 200 psi.
- Valve-spacing pressure differential at valve depth, ΔP_{sD} = 50 psi.
- Minimum distance between valves $D_{bv(min)}$ = 400 ft.
- Gas lift valve test-rack setting temperature, T_{vo} = 60°F.
- Gas lift valves: 1.5-in.-OD wireline-retrievable, unbalanced, single-element, nitrogen-charged bellows with A_b = 0.77 in.^{2}, B_{lr} = 600 psi/in., and square sharp-edged seat.

Solution—Calculation of Valve Depths.

1. P_{iod} = 1,617 psig at 6,000 ft (Eq. 12.1), and $g_{gio} = \dfrac{(1,617 - 1,400)}{6,000} = 0.03617$ psi/ft.

2. $g_{Tvu} = \dfrac{(170 - 120)}{6,000} = 0.008333$ °F/ft.

3. P_{pt} = 100 + 0.20 (1,400 − 100) = 360 psig at wellhead.

4. P_{ptd} = 1,617 − 200 = 1,417 psig at 6,000 ft, and $g_{pt} = \dfrac{(1,417 - 360)}{6,000} = 0.1762$ psi/ft.

5. $R_{glf} = \dfrac{2,000,000}{5,000} = 400$ scf/STB, and R_{glt} = 200 + 400 = 600 scf/STB.

P_{pfd} = 1,227 psig at 6,000 ft for 5,000 B/D, and R_{glt} = 600 scf/STB (R_{gli} + R_{glf}) using the Ros multiphase-flow correlation. Because P_{pfd} is less than P_{ptd} by 390 psi (1,617 − 1,227), the tubing size does not appear to restrict the design production rate and the available injection-gas-line pressure seems adequate. The final maximum daily production rate will be controlled by the reservoir productivity of this well.

Top Valve Depth Calculations.

6. $D_{v1} = \dfrac{(1,400 - 100)}{0.468} = 2,778$ ft (Eq.12.29).

7. P_{ptD1} = 360 + 0.1762 (2,778) − 849 psig at 2,778 ft.
P_{ioD1} = 1,400 + 0.03617 (2,778) = 1,500 psig at 2,778 ft.
T_{vuD1} = 120 + 0.008333 (2,778) = 143°F at 2,778 ft.

8. P_{wfd1} = 849 + 0.468 (6,000 − 2,778) = 2,357 psig at 6,000 ft for g_{ls} traverse below D_{v1}.
Because $P_{wfd1} > P_{wsd}$, there is no flowing-bottomhole-pressure drawdown.

9. Refer to **Table 12.4** with values of P_{pfD1} and q_{gi1} for assumed varying total-injection GLRs, $R_{glt} = R_{gli}$, and to the intersection of P_{ptD1} = 849 psig with the tubing performance curve in **Fig. 12.34**, where q_{gi1} = 104 Mscf/D.

10. Refer to Table 12.4 with values of P_{ioD1} vs. q_{gi1} based on equations in Appendix A and the intersection of the gas lift valve performance curve in Fig. 12.34 with q_{gi1} = 104 Mscf/D, where P_{ioD1} = 1,484 psig.

TABLE 12.4—FLOWING-PRODUCTION PRESSURE AND PERFORMANCE DATA FOR GAS LIFT VALVE AT 2,778 FT IN FIG. 12.34				
Tubing Performance 4 1/2-in. OD, 1,000 B/D			Gas Lift Valve Performance 1/4-in.-ID Port, B_{lr} = 600 psi/in.	
R_{glt}, scf/STB	q_{gi},* Mscf/D	P_{pfD}, psig	P_{ioD}, psig	q_{gi}, Mscf/D
85	85	938	1,480	0
90	90	914	1,481	28
95	95	890	1,482	56
100	100	867	1,483	84
05	105	846	1,484	113

*Because R_{glt} = R_{gli}, q_{gi} 1= R_{glt} (in Mscf/D for 1,000 B/D).

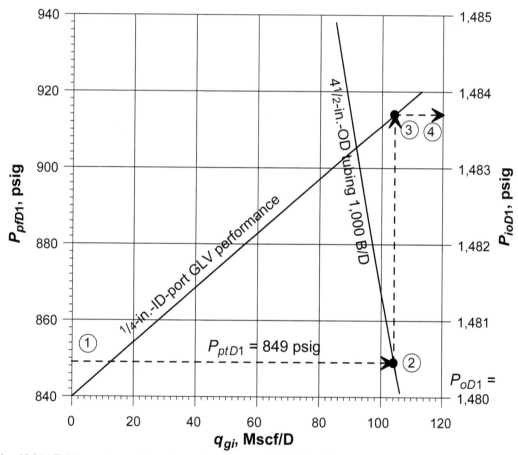

Fig. 12.34—Tubing and gas lift valve performance at 2,778 ft with only load fluid and no formation production.

11. Because P_{oD1} = 1,480 psig, ΔP_{ioc1} = 1,484 − 1,480 = 4 psi, which is less than the 20-psi minimum assigned surface pressure increase required to stroke the valve.

ΔP_{ioc1} < ΔP_{ioa}, ΔP_{io1} = ΔP_{ioa} = 20 psi and $\Sigma \Delta P_{io1}$ = 20 psi for calculation of P_{oD1}.

**TABLE 12.5—FLOWING-PRODUCTION PRESSURE
AND PERFORMANCE DATA FOR GAS LIFT
VALVE AT 4,170 FT IN FIG. 12.35**

Tubing Performance 4¹/₂-in. OD, 1,000 B/D			Gas Lift Valve Performance ¹/₄-in.-ID Port, B_{lr} = 600 psi/in.	
R_{glt}, scf/STB	q_{gli},* Mscf/D	P_{pfD}, psig	P_{ioD}, psig	q_{gi}, Mscf/D
155	155	1,146	1,511	0
160	160	1,128	1,514	79
165	165	1,108	1,516	133
170	170	1,089	1,518	187
175	175	1,073	1,520	241

*Because R_{glt} = R_{gli}, q_{gi} = R_{glt} (in Mscf/D for 1,000 B/D).

Second Valve Depth Calculations.

12. $D_{bv} = \dfrac{[1,500 - (20-20) - 849 - 50]}{(0.468 - 0.03617)} = 1,392$ ft and $D_{v2} = 2,778 + 1,392 = 4,170$ ft.

7. For D_{v2} = 4,170 ft: P_{ptD2} = 1,095 psig, P_{ioD2} = 1,551 psig, and T_{vuD2} = 155°F.

8. P_{wfD2} = 1,951 psig at 6,000 ft and q_{lc} = 309 BPD.
Because $q_{lc} < q_{lu}$, use q_{lu} = 1,000 BPD.

9. Refer to **Table 12.5** with values of P_{pfD2} and q_{gi2} for assumed varying total-injection GLRs, R_{glt}. The P_{ptD2} of 1,095 psig intersects the tubing performance curve in **Fig. 12.35** at q_{gi2} = 168 Mscf/D.

10. Refer to Table 12.5 with values of P_{ioD2} and q_{gi2} based on equations in Appendix A and the intersection of the gas lift valve performance curve in Figure 12.35 with q_{gi2} = 168 Mscf/D where P_{ioD2} = 1,518 psig.

11. Because P_{oD2} = 1,511 psig, ΔP_{ioc2} = 1,518 – 1,511 = 7 psi:
$\Delta P_{ioc2} < \Delta P_{ioa}$, $\Delta P_{io2} = \Delta P_{ioa}$ = 20 psi and $\Sigma \Delta P_{io2}$ = 40 psi for calculation of P_{oD2}.

Third Valve Depth Calculations.

12. $D_{bv} = \dfrac{[1,551 - (40-20) - 1,095 - 50]}{(0.468 - 0.03617)} = 894$ ft, and $D_{v3} = 4,170 + 894 = 5,064$ ft.

7. For D_{v3} = 5,064 ft: P_{ptD3} = 1,252 psig, P_{ioD3} = 1,583 psig, and T_{vuD3} = 162°F.

8. P_{wfd3} = 1,252 + 0.468 (6,000 – 5,064) = 1,690 psig at 6,000 ft and q_{lc} = 6.3 (2,000 – 1,690) = 1,953 B/D.

9. Refer to **Table 12.6** with values of P_{pfD3} and q_{gi3} for varying assumed total-injection GLRs, R_{glt}. The P_{ptD3} of 1,252 psig intersects the tubing performance curve in **Fig. 12.36** at q_{gi3} = 430 Mscf/D.

10. Refer to Table 12.6 with values of P_{ioD3} and q_{gi3} based on equations in Appendix A and the intersection of the gas lift valve performance curve in Fig. 12.36, with q_{gi3} = 430 Mscf/D where P_{ioD3} = 1,538 psig.

11. Because P_{oD3} = 1,523 psig, ΔP_{ioc3} = 1,538 – 1,523 = 15 psi:
$\Delta P_{ioc3} < \Delta P_{ioa}$, $\Delta P_{io3} = \Delta P_{ioa}$ = 20 psi and $\Sigma \Delta P_{io3}$ = 60 psi for calculation of P_{oD3}.

Fourth Valve Depth Calculations.

12. $D_{bv} = \dfrac{[1,583 - (60-20) - 1,252 - 50]}{(0.468 - 0.03617)} = 558$ ft and $D_{v4} = 5,064 + 558 = 5,622$ ft.

7. For D_{v4} = 5,622 ft: The calculated D_{bv} for the fifth valve results in D_{v5} exceeding the maximum valve depth of 5,900 ft. Refer to the fifth valve depth calculations in Step 12 where

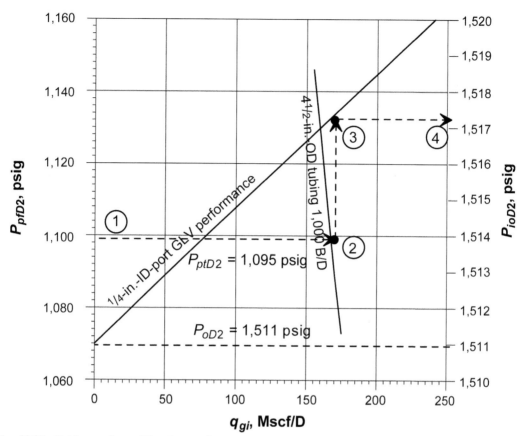

Fig. 12.35—Tubing and gas lift valve performance at 4,170 ft with only load fluid and no formation production.

the D_{bv} = 278 ft (5,900 – 5,622). The transfer P_{ptD4} is based on the actual D_{bv} of 278 ft and calculated with the following equation.

$$P_{ptD4} = P_{ioD4} - \Sigma\Delta P_{io3} + D_{bv}(g_{gio}) - D_{bv}(g_{ls}) - \Delta P_{sD}.$$
$$P_{ptD4} = 1,603 - 60 + 278\,(0.03617) - 278\,(0.468) - 50 = 1,373 \text{ psig.}$$
$$P_{ioD4} = 1,603 \text{ psig and } T_{vuD4} = 167°F.$$

8. P_{wfd4} = 1,373 + 0.468 (6,000 – 5,622) = 1,550 psig at 6,000 ft.
q_{lc4} = 6.3 (2,000 – 1,550) = 2,835 B/D for g_{ls}-traverse below D_{v4}.
9. Refer to **Table 12.7** with values of P_{pfD4} and q_{gi4} for varying assumed total-injection GLRs, R_{gli}, and to the intersection of P_{ptD4} = 1,373 psig with the tubing performance curve in **Fig. 12.37**, where q_{gi4} = 730 Mscf/D.
10. Refer to Table 12.7 with values of P_{ioD4} and q_{gi4} based on equations in Appendix A and the intersection of the gas lift valve performance curve in Fig. 12.37 with q_{gi4} = 730 Mscf/D where P_{ioD4} = 1,543 psig.
11. Because P_{oD4} = 1,513 psig, ΔP_{ioc4} = 1,543 – 1,513 = 30 psi
$\Delta P_{ioc4} > \Delta P_{io}$, $\Delta P_{io4} = \Delta P_{ioc4}$ = 30 psi and $\Sigma\Delta P_{io4}$ = 90 psi for calculation of P_{oD4}.

**TABLE 12.6—FLOWING-PRODUCTION PRESSURE
AND PERFORMANCE DATA FOR GAS LIFT
VALVE AT 5,064 FT IN FIG. 12.36**

Tubing Performance 4½-in. OD, 1,953 B/D			Gas Lift Valve Performance ⅜-in.-ID Port, B_{tr} = 600 psi/in.	
R_{glt}, scf/STB	q_{gi},* Mscf/D	P_{pfD}, psig	P_{ioD}, psig	q_{gi}, Mscf/D
205	400	1,305	1,523	0
210	410	1,287	1,525	54
215	420	1,270	1,530	193
220	430	1,253	1,535	338
225	439	1,237	1,540	488

*Because $R_{glt} = R_{gli}$, $q_{gi} = \dfrac{1{,}953\left(R_{glt}\right)}{1{,}000}$ (in Mscf/D).

Fifth Valve Depth Calculations.

12. $D_{bv} = \dfrac{[1{,}603 - (90 - 20) - 1{,}350 - 50]}{(0.468 - 0.03617)} = 308$ ft, and $D_{v5} = 5{,}622 + 308 = 5{,}930$ ft exceeds given maximum valve depth of 5,900 ft; therefore, $D_{v5} = D_{v(max)} = 5{,}900$ ft and $D_{bv} = 278$ ft (5,900 – 5,622).

7. $T_{vuD5} = 120 + 0.008333\,(5{,}900) = 169°F$ at 5,900 ft for injection-gas rate calculations.

An orifice-check valve with a ⁵⁄₁₆-in.-ID port is installed in the bottom wireline-retrievable gas lift valve mandrel at 5,900 ft. An orifice-check valve is fully open at all times. The three-parameter graphical solution in **Fig. 12.38** includes two curves that are a function of P_{pfD5}.

The daily liquid production rates curve is based on the well *PI*, P_{wfd}, and P_{wsd} ($P_{wfd} = P_{pfD5}$ + 34 psi for the approximate increase in pressure between 5,900 and 6,000 ft). An increase in the q_{gi} (higher R_{glt}) decreases the P_{pfD5} and increases the calculated q_{lc} for the given *PI* and P_{wsd}. For a constant assigned q_{gia}, different values of q_l are assumed and the R_{glt} and corresponding P_{pfD5} are calculated (or P_{pfD5} is determined from gradient curves) for each q_l. The assumed q_l is compared to the calculated q_{lc} based on the *PI* and P_{wsd}. This procedure is repeated until the calculated q_{lc} is equal to the assumed q_l for the total assigned q_{gia}. Refer to **Table 12.8.**

In the above calculations, a P_{pfD5} is calculated for each assumed q_{gia} that is less than and a q_{gia} equal to the assigned maximum of 2,000 Mscf/D. The injection-gas requirements curve is a plot of the assumed q_{gia} vs. the calculated P_{pfD5}.

The maximum assigned q_{gia} of 2,000 Mscf/D intersects the injection-gas requirements curve at P_{pfD5} = 1,190 psig. The calculated P_{ioD5} is 1,393 psig at 5,900 ft (upstream pressure) for the maximum assigned q_{gia} of 2,000 Mscf/D through a ⁵⁄₁₆-in.-ID orifice with a P_{pfD5} of 1,190 psig downstream pressure and an upstream T_{gD5} of 169°F. The P_{io5} at the surface is 1,180 psig for a P_{ioD5} of 1,393 psig at 5,900 ft. The upstream surface injection-gas pressure for 2,000 Mscf/D should not exceed a surface injection-gas pressure that would reopen any of the upper unloading valves. The calculated minimum P_{io} to reopen the deepest unloading valve is 1,310 psig at the surface (injection-gas available line pressure, $P_{io} - \Sigma\Delta P_{io} = 1{,}400 - 90$) and is 1,523 psig at 5,900 ft. Because the calculated upstream choke pressure of 1,393 psig is considerably less than 1,523 psig, there will be no unloading valve interference when the orifice-check valve becomes the operating valve, and the change in surface injection-gas pressure will be readily apparent after the depth of gas injection has transferred to the orifice-check valve.

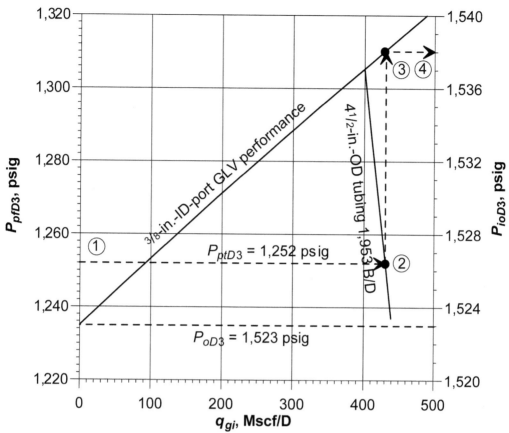

Fig. 12.36—Tubing and gas lift valve performance at 5,064 ft with load fluid and no formation gas production.

Calculation of Test-Rack Opening Pressures of the Gas Lift Valves. The following calculations apply to injection-pressure-operated, unbalanced, single-element, nitrogen-charged bellows gas lift valves with a square, sharp-edged seat.

1. Calculate the injection-gas initial valve opening pressure at valve depth, $P_{oD(n)}$, on the basis of the available installation design injection-gas pressure at depth, $P_{ioD(n)}$.

$$P_{oD(n)} = P_{ioD(n)} - \sum \Delta P_{io(n)} . \qquad (12.62)$$

2. The nitrogen-charged bellows pressure is calculated at the unloading valve temperature at depth, T_{vuD}, in the well using Eq. 12.63.

$$P_{bvD(n)} = P_{oD(n)}\left(1 - A_p/A_b\right) + P_{ptD(n)}\left(A_p/A_b\right) . \qquad (12.63)$$

3. Calculate the temperature correction factor for nitrogen, C_T, using Eq. 12.3 or determine C_T from Table 12.1.

4. Calculate the nitrogen-charged bellows pressure at a test-rack setting temperature of 60°F.

$$P_{b(n)} = C_{T(n)}\left[P_{bvD(n)}\right] . \qquad (12.64)$$

**TABLE 12.7—FLOWING-PRODUCTION PRESSURE
AND PERFORMANCE DATA FOR GAS LIFT
VALVE AT 5,622 FT IN FIG. 12.37**

Tubing Performance 4^1/$_2$-in. OD, 2,835 B/D			Gas Lift Valve Performance ^{1}/$_2$-in.-ID Port, B_{lr} = 600 psi/in.	
R_{glt}, scf/STB	q_{gi},* Mscf/D	P_{pfD}, psig	P_{ioD}, psig	q_{gi}, Mscf/D
245	695	1,407	1,513	0
250	709	1,392	1,520	152
255	723	1,377	1,530	381
260	737	1,362	1,540	655
265	751	1,347	1,550	940

* Because $R_{glt} = R_{gli}$, $q_{gi} = \dfrac{2,835(R_{glt})}{1,000}$ (for Mscf/D).

5. Calculate the test-rack opening pressure at 60°F using Eq. 12.45 or Eq. 12.65.

$$P_{vo(n)} = \frac{P_{b(n)}}{\left(1 - A_p / A_b\right)} \quad \dots \dots \dots \dots \text{(12.65)}$$

Solution—Calculation of Test-Rack Opening Pressures.
Top Valve Calculations (¼-in.-ID Port). 1. $P_{oD1} = P_{ioD1} - \sum \Delta P_{io1} = 1,500 - 20 = 1,480$ psig at 2,778 ft.
2. and 3. $P_{bvD1} = 0.936 (1,480) + (0.064)849 = 1,440$ psig at 143°F, and $C_{T1} = 0.8378$ (calculated).
4. and 5. $P_{b1} = 0.8378 (1,440) = 1,206$ psig at 60°F, and

$$P_{vo1} = \frac{1,206}{0.936} = 1,288 \text{ psig at } 60°F.$$

Second Valve Calculations (¼-in.-ID Port). 1. $P_{oD2} = 1,551 - 40 = 1,511$ psig at 4,170 ft.
2. and 3. $P_{bvD2} = (0.936) 1,511 + (0.064) 1,095 = 1,484$ psig at 155°F, and $C_{T2} = 0.8184$ (calculated).
4. and 5. $P_{b2} = (0.8184) 1,484 = 1,215$ psig at 60°F, and

$$P_{vo2} = \frac{1,215}{0.936} = 1,298 \text{ psig at } 60°F.$$

Third Valve Calculations (⅜-in.-ID Port). 1. $P_{oD3} = 1,583 - 60 = 1,523$ psig at 5,064 ft.
2. and 3. $P_{bvD3} = 0.857 (1,523) + 0.143 (1,252) = 1,484$ psig at 162°F, and $C_{T3} = 0.8079$ (calculated).
4. and 5. $P_{b3} = 0.8079 (1,484) = 1,199$ psig at 60°F, and

$$P_{vo3} = \frac{1,199}{0.857} = 1,399 \text{ psig at } 60°F.$$

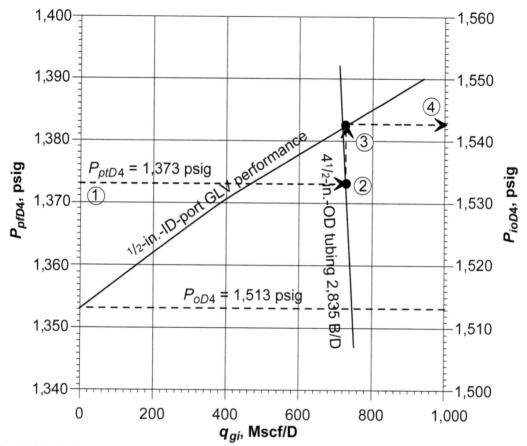

Fig. 12.37—Tubing and gas lift valve performance at 5,622 ft with load fluid and no formation gas production.

Fourth Valve Calculations (½-in.-ID Port). 1. $P_{oD4} = 1,603 - 90 = 1,513$ psig at 5,622 ft.

2. and 3. $P_{bvD4} = 0.745\,(1,513) + 0.255\,(1,373) = 1,477$ psig at 167°F, and $C_{T4} = 0.8007$ (calculated).

4. and 5. $P_{b4} = 0.8007\,(1,477) = 1,183$ psig at 60°F, and

$$P_{vo4} = \frac{1,183}{0.745} = 1,588 \text{ psig at } 60°F.$$

A summary of the installation design calculations is shown in **Table 12.9**. The significant increase in $P_{vo(n)}$ with depth is the result of the larger-ID port sizes required for the unloading gas lift valve Numbers 3 and 4.

12.10.10 Casing-Annulus-Flow Installation Design. The design calculations for an annular-flow installation are similar to those for a continuous-flow installation through the tubing. Intermittent gas lift is not recommended for annular flow. Because the gross liquid production is generally thousands of barrels per day, selecting valve port ID sizes for adequate gas passage is very important for annular-flow installations. Actual gas lift valve performance, based on port ID, maximum linear stem travel, and bellows-assembly load rate, is an important factor

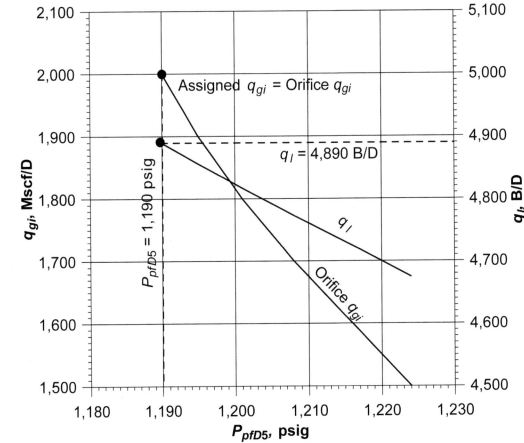

Fig. 12.38—Predicted daily production rate for a ⁵⁄₁₆-in.-ID orifice in a 1.5-in.-OD orifice-check valve at 5,900 ft.

in the design calculations for annular-flow installations because of the high injection-gas requirements. The increase in the injection-gas pressure to overcome the bellows-assembly load rate and to attain the needed equivalent port area for a required injection-gas throughput should be considered.

Selection of the proper size of gas-injection tubing string that will deliver the required daily injection-gas requirement for unloading and operating is absolutely essential. An initial assumption can be an injection-gas tubing size that will deliver the maximum daily injection-gas requirement with no pressure loss (i.e., the increase in the injection-gas pressure with depth, as a result of gas-column density, is offset by the flowing frictional pressure loss). This should be the smallest nominal tubing size considered for the injection-gas string. Charts for static injection-gas pressure at depth cannot be used for the valve spacing calculations.

The Cullender and Smith[18] correlation is recommended for calculating the pressure loss in the injection-gas tubing string. This method for calculating the flowing injection-gas pressure at depth was derived for a producing gas well and not for gas injection. The only difference in the calculations is the friction term for gas being injected rather than being produced. The sign for the friction term changes (i.e., the friction term becomes negative in the Cullender and Smith equation for gas injection).

TABLE 12.8—DATA FOR GRAPH OF 5/16-IN.-ID ORIFICE IN ORIFICE CHECK VALVE AT 5,900 FT IN FIG. 12.38

P_{pfD5}, psig	q_l,* B/D	q_{gi}, Mscf/D
1,224	4,675	1,500
1,216	4,725	1,600
1,208	4,773	1,700
1,201	4,817	1,800
1,195	4,856	1,900
1,190	4,890	2,000

*Based on P_{wsd} = 2,000 psig, PI = 6.3 B/D/psi, and 34-psi increase in pressure between 5,900 and 6,000 ft.

TABLE 12.9—INJECTION-GAS VALVE SPACING, INITIAL VALVE OPENING, VALVE-STEM STROKING (ΔP_{io}), AND GAS LIFT VALVE TEST-RACK OPENING PRESSURES

(1) Valve No., (n)	(2) Port ID, in.	(3) $D_{v(n)}$, ft	(4) $T_{gD(n)}$, = T_{vD} °F	(5) $P_{ptD(n)}$, psig	(6) Surface $P_{io(n)}$[1], psig	(7) Depth $P_{ioD(n)}$, psig	(8) Stroking $\Delta P_{io(n)}$, psi	(9) Initial $P_{o(n)}$, psig	(10) Initial $P_{oD(n)}$, psig	(11) $P_{vo(n)}$[2], 60 °F, psig
1	0.25	2,778	143	849	1,400	1,500	20	1,380	1,480	1,288
2	0.25	4,170	155	1,095	1,400	1,551	20	1,360	1,511	1,298
3	0.375	5,064	162	1,252	1,380	1,583	20	1,340	1,523	1,399
4	0.50	5,622	167	1,373	1,360	1,603	30	1,310	1,513	1,588
5	0.3125	5,900	169			Orifice-Check Valve				

[1] P_{io} = 1,400 psig available injection-gas line pressure at surface.
[2] $P_{vo(n)}$ was calculated using the equations for $C_{T(n)}$ rather than $C_{T(n)}$ values from Table 12.1.

Wireline-retrievable gas lift valve mandrels that accommodate standard injection-pressure-operated valves for annular flow are available (**Fig. 12.39**). When these mandrels are used, the valves are run and set in the pocket in exactly the same manner as for tubular flow. However, the mandrel configuration is such that the injection gas enters the side of the pocket from inside the tubing. This allows injection gas to pass through the valve and exit the pocket into the casing annulus rather than into the tubing. Annular-flow mandrels should be used for annular flow wherever possible because they allow full gas passage through the valve without the restriction imposed by cross-over seats. Also, gas is injected from the bottom rather than the side of the mandrel. This provides a much safer installation from an erosion standpoint than the installation using valves with crossover seats in which gas is injected from the side of the pocket into the wall of the casing.

Where mandrels for tubing flow are already installed and are not feasible to replace, valves with crossover seats must be installed. In such installations, the check disk in the reverse-flow checks valve seats in the opposite direction for casing flow as compared to a tubing flow installation and allows gas passage from the injection-gas tubing to the casing annulus. In the wireline-retrievable valve tubing flow series mandrel, the valve for casing flow is similar to a production-pressure-operated valve, except the integral check valve is reversed for injection-gas flow from tubing to casing.

Because nitrogen-charged bellows gas lift valves have a lower bellows-assembly load rate than a spring-loaded valve, bellows-charged valves are recommended for high injection-gas volumetric throughput, as required for most annular-flow installations. Fortunately, the valve

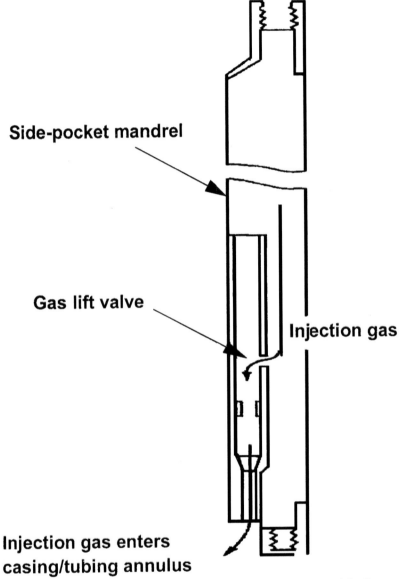

Side-pocket mandrel

Gas lift valve

Injection gas

Injection gas enters casing/tubing annulus

Fig. 12.39—The mandrel pocket configuration differs for annular flow because injection gas enters the pocket from the tubing rather than the casing.

temperature at depth is not difficult to predict accurately in high-volume wells. The flowing surface temperature is near the bottomhole flowing temperature; therefore, the operating temperature of all valves in a high-volume, annular-flow gas lift installation is approximately the same. An important caution is to never use the surface injection-gas temperature to estimate the valve temperature at depth. The injection gas will begin to approach the flowing-fluid temperature within a few hundred feet of the surface. The flowing wellhead temperature of the fluid production should be used to establish the unloading valve temperatures at depth. This same consideration is applicable to the Cullender and Smith injection-gas pressure-at-depth calculations.

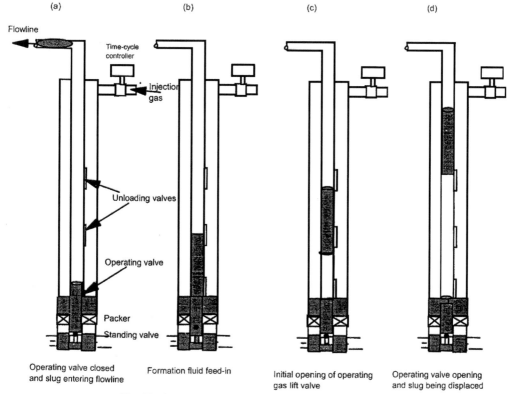

Fig. 12.40—Intermittent-flow gas lift cycle of operation.

12.11 Intermittent-Flow Gas Lift

12.11.1 Introduction. Intermittent-flow gas lift is applicable to low-productivity wells and to low- and high-productivity wells with low reservoir pressure. Chamber installations may be beneficial to gas lift the low-flowing-bottomhole-pressure wells, particularly those wells with a high productivity index.

As the name implies, the reservoir fluid is produced intermittently by displacing liquid slugs with high-pressure injection gas, as illustrated in **Fig. 12.40**. Either an electronic or clock-driven time-cycle controller, or an adjustable or fixed choke, controls the flow of injection gas. Not all gas lift valves operate on choke control. The number of intermittent-flow gas lift installations on time-cycle control far exceeds the number of choke-controlled installations.

12.11.2 Disadvantages of Intermittent-Flow Gas Lift. Intermittent-flow gas lift has several disadvantages compared to continuous-flow operations. If the desired production can be gas lifted by continuous flow, this method is preferable. It is difficult to handle the high instantaneous gas volumes properly in the low- and high-pressure sides of a closed rotative gas lift system. Choke control of the injection gas into a well eliminates the removal of injection-gas volume at high instantaneous rates from the high-pressure system. However, it does not solve the problem of the large gas volume beneath the slug that enters the low-pressure system following displacement of the liquid slug to the surface. Gas volume storage requires pressure difference and physical capacity. The difference between the compressor discharge pressure and the operating injection-gas casing pressures normally exceeds the difference between the separator and compressor suction pressures. For this reason, retaining the needed injection-gas volume in the low-pressure side of a small, closed rotative gas lift system can be difficult unless the injection-gas cycles are staggered properly. Staggering of the injection-gas cycles is less precise on choke control than with a time-cycle controller. The electronic timers have improved the accuracy of controlled gas injection, whereby the injection cycles can be scheduled to prevent more than one well receiving injection gas at the same time. Therefore, total injection plus formation gas can be scheduled to enter the low-pressure system at a more constant rate with accurate time cycle than with choke control of the injection gas.

Severe surging in the flowing bottomhole pressure can present a serious production problem in unconsolidated-sand wells where sand production cannot be controlled. Sand bridging can plug off production and result in sand cleanout costs. Pressure surges in a chamber installation may be far more severe than in a regular intermittent-flow installation. A wireline release type of lock with an equalizing valve is recommended for the standing valve in a chamber to prevent the standing valve from being blown out of its seating nipple following blowdown after an injection-gas cycle. Some companies have resorted to increasing the operating injection-gas pressures to lift near total depth by continuous flow rather than intermittent flow wells that produce sand.

The total energy in the formation and injection gas is not fully used with intermittent-flow gas lift. The high-pressure gas under the slug is spent in the flowline and does not contribute to the lift process. This is one reason for using continuous-flow operations for a high-GLR well if possible. Plunger lift may be the best method for lifting certain high-GLR wells.

The injection-gas requirements are usually higher for intermittent-flow than for continuous-flow gas lift operations. The tubing capacity beneath the slug must be filled with injection gas to displace the liquid slug to the surface. The tubing under the liquid slug cannot be one-half or two-thirds filled with high-pressure gas. For this reason, the gas requirements for intermittent lift of low-GLR wells that do not partially flow can be estimated with reasonable accuracy. Unfortunately, articles have been published that imply that a well, or group of wells, is being intermittent lifted with a certain type of gas lift valve that results in an injection-gas requirement of only a fraction of the gas volume needed to fill the tubing beneath the liquid slug. Although gas orifice meter charts are published to illustrate these claims, the truth is, these wells are partially flowing. Only minimal agitation and displacement of the liquid slug is required to lift these wells. Most of the energy needed to lift the well is being furnished by the formation and not the gas lift system. Intermittent-flow gas lift is much more labor intensive than continuous flow. In intermittent-flow gas lift, the operator should frequently adjust the injection time and cycle frequency to maintain an efficient operation.

The injection-gas requirements for intermittent-flow and continuous-flow gas lift should be compared before eliminating continuous-flow operations. With the advent of several reliable multiphase-flow correlations, the predictable range of continuous flow has been extended to much lower daily production rates. A careful investigation of the proper production conduit size for lifting a well by continuous flow may permit this type of gas lift in place of intermittent-flow gas lift.

12.11.3 Types of Intermittent-Flow Gas Lift Installations. Intermittent-flow gas lift should be used only for tubing flow. Most installations have a packer and may include a standing valve in the tubing. If a well produces sand, a standing valve is recommended only if it is essential. A seating nipple should be installed at the lower end of the tubing string in intermittent-flow installations where a standing valve may be needed.

The working fluid level in a well should result in a minimum starting slug length that provides a production pressure at the depth of the operating gas lift valve equal to 50 to 60% of the operating injection-gas pressure at the same depth. If this is not possible, a chamber or plunger installation should be considered. In a chamber installation, the calculated depths of the unloading gas lift valves are the same as for a regular intermittent-lift installation. The chamber design converts a few feet of fluid, standing above the formation, into many feet of fluid in the tubing above the chamber. This entire liquid column is transferred into the tubing above the standing valve before injection gas enters the production conduit. The standing valve is required for efficient chamber operation to ensure U-tubing all fluid from the chamber into the tubing rather than allowing fluid to be pushed into the formation.

If a chamber installation is not installed in a low-bottomhole-pressure well, a plunger downhole stop and bumper spring can be set by wireline immediately above the operating gas lift valve. The plunger reduces the injection-gas slippage through the small liquid slug and decreases the liquid fallback. Smaller starting liquid slugs can be gas lifted more efficiently with the plunger acting as a sealing interface between the liquid slug and injection gas.

12.11.4 Prediction of Daily Production Rates. Two basic factors control the maximum production from a high-rate intermittent-flow gas lift installation: (1) the total liquid production reaching the surface per cycle and (2) the maximum number of injection-gas cycles per day. An intermittent gas lift installation should be designed to maximize the liquid recovery per cycle on low- and high-capacity wells. All restrictions in and near the wellhead should be eliminated. For this reason, streamlined wellheads are recommended. If the wellhead cannot be streamlined, all unnecessary ells and tees should be removed to reduce the number of bends between the tubing and flowline. If the velocity of the liquid slug is reduced before the entire column of liquid can be displaced into the horizontal flowline, additional injection-gas breakthrough, or gas slippage, will occur and decrease the liquid recovery per cycle. Performance of the operating gas lift valve, or valves, is important for efficient liquid-slug displacement. The operating gas lift valve should have a large port that opens quickly to ensure ample injection-gas volumetric throughput for efficiently displacing the liquid slug. Even though a large port is used, the valve spread (the difference between initial valve opening and closing pressure) should be kept relatively low to prevent excessive gas usage. This is especially true where large volumes of gas are stored in wells with small tubing and large casing.

The gas lift valve should not open slowly and meter a small injection-gas rate into the production conduit, which tends to aerate and percolate through the liquid slug rather than displace the slug. Rapid increase in the injection-gas casing pressure, after a time-cycle controller opens, improves the gas lift valve performance and ensures a more efficient displacement of a liquid slug in a time-cycle-operated intermittent-lift installation. Ample injection-gas volume must be available at the wellsite from the high-pressure injection-gas system. If the line pressure in the high-pressure system decreases to the casing pressure immediately after the time-cycle controller opens, poor valve action is the fault of the high-pressure system and not the gas lift installation in the well.

The size and length of the flowline can significantly affect the maximum cycle frequency. A flowline should always be at least equal to, or one size larger than, the tubing. The maximum number of injection-gas cycles per day is controlled by the time required for the wellhead pressure to return to the separator or production-header pressure after a slug surfaces. Reducing the separator pressure increases the starting slug length for the same flowing bottomhole pressure but does not solve the problem of decrease in wellhead pressure after the slug surfaces. When comparing or predicting the maximum production from two relatively high-capacity wells on intermittent gas lift, the size and length of the flowlines must be considered. If one installation requires 45 minutes and another 10 minutes for the wellhead pressure to approach the production-header pressure after a slug surfaces, the difference in maximum production (assuming that both wells have the same deliverability) is not the result of the gas lift installation in the well but of the surface facilities.

One definition of liquid fallback is the difference between the starting-liquid-slug volume, or length, and the produced slug volume, or length. The purpose of a properly designed intermittent gas lift installation is to recover a large portion of the starting slug. An important parameter that can be observed is the average slug velocity. The operating gas lift valve normally opens in less than 30 seconds after the time-cycle controller opens in most intermittent-lift installations. An approximate slug velocity can be estimated by assuming the valve opens 15 seconds after the controller opens and recording the time elapsed from this instance until the slug surfaces. In most installations, the depth of the operating gas lift valve is known or can be estimated from an acoustical fluid-level survey. If the average liquid-slug velocity is not near or exceeding 1,000 ft/min, the liquid fallback may be excessive. A slug velocity less than 800 ft/min can result in excessive fallback.

The maximum number of injection-gas cycles per day can be estimated for many wells by assuming 2 to 3 min/1,000 ft of lift for typical wells. The actual time can be less for installations on a production platform without flowlines and much longer for intermittent installations with small-ID and/or long flowlines, such as a well with 2⅞-in.-OD tubing and a 2-in. flowline that is 2 miles in length. Also, emulsions and other unique well problems can decrease the maximum number of injection cycles per day and the recoverable liquid production per cycle.

12.11.5 Injection-Gas Requirement for Intermittent Lift. Multiphase-flow correlations are not applicable for the prediction of the gas requirement to lift a well by intermittent gas lift. Intermittent lift is the displacement of a liquid slug by high-pressure gas. The injection-gas requirement is not based on reducing the density of the fluid column. It is based instead upon the volume of gas needed to fill the tubing between the bottom of the slug when it reaches the surface and the depth of the deepest gas lift valve that opens during an injection-gas cycle. The injection-gas pressure and volume following the liquid slug at the instant this slug surfaces are spent in the flowline.

In intermittent lift, the energy in the formation gas does little to assist in lifting most wells. One method for calculating the injection-gas requirement is to assume the produced slug to be a continuous liquid column without any after-flow production in the tail gas. The theoretical pressure under this liquid slug at the instant the slug surfaced is approximately the wellhead production pressure plus the length of the produced slug multiplied by the liquid gradient. The actual average pressure in the tubing under a liquid slug is more than this pressure based on the solid slug length and a dry-gas gradient. This results from the injection-gas penetration of the slug during the lift process and the frictional losses that occur. An average injection-gas pressure in the tubing equal to the theoretical pressure under the produced liquid slug plus the surface closing pressure of the operating gas lift valve divided by two is a realistic assumption on the basis of numerous bottomhole-pressure measurements in intermittent-flow gas lift installations.

The total volume of injection gas per cycle depends on the average pressure in the tubing under the slug and the physical capacity of the tubing. When the depth of lift is several thousand feet, compared to an equivalent produced slug length of only a few hundred feet, the length of the slug may be subtracted from the tubing length above the operating valve for calculating the capacity of tubing filled with injection gas each cycle. This assumption implies that the rate of decrease in the pressure of the expanding injection-gas volume beneath the liquid slug is less than the rate of decrease in the pressure exerted by the slug length remaining in the tubing as the upper portion of the slug enters the flowline.

12.11.6 Comparison of Time-Cycle to Choke Control of the Injection Gas. The advantage of choke-controlled injection-gas volume for an intermittent-flow gas lift installation is the fact that a low volumetric injection-gas rate is required from the high-pressure system into the well. Several conditions must be met before choke control of the injection gas can be used successfully. The gas lift valve must be suited for choke-control operation, and the casing annulus must provide adequate storage capacity for the injection-gas volume needed to displace the slug. Clean, dry gas is extremely important in choke control, and low-capacity wells are more

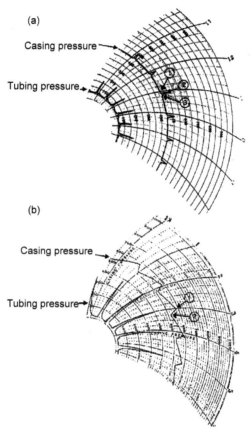

Fig. 12.41—Two-pen pressure-recording charts from intermittent gas lift installations with time-cycle and choke control of the injection gas.

difficult to choke control because of the small surface injection-gas choke size required for the low daily injection-gas rate needed to lift the well. A pressure-reducing regulator to maintain a constant maximum valve opening casing pressure between valve operating cycles may be necessary to permit the use of a larger-sized choke in the injection-gas line. Other limitations of choke control of the injection gas include a reduction in the maximum liquid slug size that can be lifted each cycle and the maximum number of injection-gas cycles per day. Time-cycle control of the injection gas should be considered for high-rate intermittent-lift operations. Two-pen pressure recorder charts, shown in **Fig. 12.41**, illustrate time-cycle and choke-control operations. Fig. 12.41a is time-cycle control where: (1) time-cycle controller opens, (2) time-cycle controller closes, and (3) gas lift valve closes. Fig. 12.41b is choke control of the injection gas where (1) gas lift valve opens and (2) gas lift valve closes. The difference in the maximum recorder tubing pressure for the time-cycle and choke-controlled installations results from different bourdon-tube ranges in the two pressure recorders. The pressure range for tubing pressure for time-cycle control is 0 to 1,000 psig, and it is 0 to 500 psig for the choke-control chart.

Most intermittent-flow gas lift installations use time-cycle-operated controllers on the injection-gas line because of the many advantages of time-cycle over choke control of the injection gas. Rugged unbalanced, single-element, nitrogen-charged bellows gas lift valves with large ports can be used. Much larger liquid slugs can be lifted with time-cycle control because injection gas in the annulus can be supplemented with gas from the high-pressure injection-gas system during each injection-gas cycle.

12.11.7 Intermittent-Flow Gas Lift Installation Design Methods. There are many published methods and variations in these methods for designing intermittent-flow gas lift installations. These methods can be divided into one type of design that is based on a production rate and another design that can be described as a percentage-load technique. Intermittent pressure gradient spacing factors are used for installation designs based on an assumed daily production rate. Production rate is not a consideration for a percent-load design method. The procedures for calculating a percent-load installation vary between gas lift manufacturers and between operators who have introduced slight variations in these calculations. The gas lift valve depths in most designs can be calculated or determined graphically. Regardless of the method used, the design should ensure unloading and operation from the deepest gas lift valve.

12.11.8 Gas Lift Valves for Intermittent Lift. Most operating valves used for intermittent lift are the unbalanced, single-element, bellows-charged valve with a large port. The majority of intermittent-lift designs require an operating gas lift valve with a large production-pressure factor. Single-element, spring-loaded gas lift valves are not recommended for intermittent lift because of the higher bellows-assembly load rate from the additional load rate of the spring. The operating gas lift valve should tend to "snap" open and provide a large port size for injection-gas throughput so that the liquid slug can be displaced efficiently with minimal injection-gas slippage and liquid fallback. Time-cycle control of the injection gas is recommended for inter-mittent-lift installations using unbalanced, single-element gas lift valves. These valves may or may not operate on choke control of the injection gas.

There are gas lift valves that have been designed for choke-controlled intermittent gas lift operation. These valves have a large port for gas passage and may be designed to operate on either time-cycle or choke control of the injection gas. Several types of gas lift valves are de-signed for only choke-control operation. A properly selected pilot-operated gas lift valve as the operating valve, functions in most wells on time cycle or choke control. It is extremely impor-tant to select the proper pilot port size based on the relationship between the capacity of the casing annulus and tubing if choke control of the injection gas is required. Choke control may be mandatory because of limited gas storage capacity in the high-pressure surface facilities.

12.11.9 Intermittent Pressure-Gradient Spacing Factor. The intermittent pressure-gradient spacing factor is similar to a flowing-pressure gradient above the point of gas injection in a continuous-flow installation. This factor increases with daily production rate for a given size of tubing. These intermittent spacing factors account for the following conditions: (1) liquid fall-back from injection-gas penetration of the displaced liquid slug while the slug is in the tubing, (2) fluid transfer from the casing annulus to the tubing during unloading operations, (3) fluid production after flowing-bottomhole-pressure drawdown occurs, and (4) increase in tubing pres-sure with depth in deep wells with a high surface wellhead tubing pressure.

The fluid level in the tubing immediately after an injection-gas cycle is not at the operating valve depth. There is always an accumulation of liquid fallback because of gas slippage through the liquid slug during displacement. Consequently, the minimum flowing-production pressure between injection-gas cycles is greater than a gas pressure at operating valve depth based on the surface wellhead tubing pressure.

The intermittent pressure-gradient spacing factors, F_s, given in **Fig. 12.42**, were published many years before flowing-pressure-gradient curves were available for continuous-flow installa-tion designs. The same unloading pressure gradients were used for intermittent-lift and continu-ous-flow installation design. These data were compiled from a limited number of flowing-pressure surveys from low GLR, high-water-cut wells with 2⅜-in.- and 2⅞-in.-OD tubing. Other tubing sizes were added to Fig. 12.42 at a later date. One of several important parame-ters missing from this correlation is depth. The only two correlating parameters in Fig. 12.42 are the production rate and conduit size. The rate of injection-gas penetration velocity into the

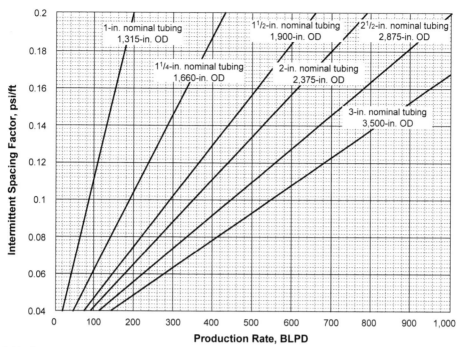

Fig. 12.42—Intermittent pressure-gradient spacing factors for varying daily production rates and different tubing sizes.

slug is reported to be relatively constant for a given fluid. Therefore, the liquid fallback increases with the depth of lift because the liquid slug requires more time to reach the surface in deeper wells. These published intermittent spacing factors may be too low for deep intermittent lift and too high for shallow lift.

12.11.10 Selection of Surface Closing Pressure of Gas Lift Valves. The surface closing pressure of an operating gas lift valve is the minimum surface injection-gas pressure between gas injections if there are no leaks in the producing string, which includes wellhead, tubing, and gas lift valves. The maximum surface injection-gas pressure occurs at the instant the time-cycle controller closes in time-cycle control, or when the operating gas lift valve opens on choke control. The available operating injection-gas-line pressure at the wellsite must exceed the maximum surface casing pressure during an injection-gas cycle. For this reason, an assumed gas lift valve surface closing pressure of 15% less than the available injection-gas-line pressure at the wellsite is recommended for line pressures between 700 and 1,000 psig. This is the same as assuming a surface closing pressure equal to 85% of the available injection-gas-line pressure. A minimum 100-psi difference between the injection-gas line and the gas lift valve surface closing pressure is suggested for lower injection-gas pressures and a maximum of 200 psi for higher pressures. The maximum surface casing pressure during an injection-gas cycle for intermittent-lift operations is usually 8 to 10% higher than the surface closing pressure of the operating gas lift valve. This assumption can be used for approximate injection-gas requirement calculations in typical tubing/casing combinations such as 2⅜-in.-OD tubing in 5½-in.-OD casing and 2⅞-in.-OD tubing in 7-in.-OD casing.

When a time-cycle controller on the injection-gas line opens, pressure upstream of the controller decreases. To have an injection-gas volume stored in the high-pressure injection-gas lines, there must be a pressure difference in addition to the capacity of the high-pressure system. If the difference between the injection-gas-line pressure and the surface closing pressure of the operating gas lift valve is insufficient, the casing pressure will not increase at a rate necessary to ensure rapid opening of an unbalanced, single-element, gas lift valve after the controller opens. A near instant increase in casing pressure after the controller opens improves the gas throughput performance of a single-element valve and decreases the liquid fallback. To ensure fast opening of the operating gas lift valve, it is better to design an intermittent installation with a pressure difference between the injection-gas line and valve closing pressure that is slightly excessive rather than insufficient.

12.11.11 Selection of Valve Port Size. Many gas lift designers disagree on port sizing for intermittent-flow unloading valves. One school of thought maintains that because most intermittent-flow installations are a natural progression from continuous flow, the same mandrel spacing for continuous flow can be used for intermittent flow. In such instances, small ports can be used in the unloading valves and a large-ported valve placed on bottom for the operating valve. This would also hold true for the spacing factor method of locating the unloading valves. On the other hand, another school of thought maintains that the constant surface closing and percent-load intermittent gas lift installation designs require unbalanced, single-element, gas lift valves with large ports relative to the effective bellows area. The design principle is based on the production-pressure effect. This is the tubing-production pressure from the liquid column above the valve at depth immediately before valve opening multiplied by the production-pressure factor for the valve. The valve with the highest tubing-production pressure that is less than the injection-gas pressure at valve depth is the deepest operating gas lift valve in the installation. There is no reason to decrease the surface closing pressure for each successively lower unloading gas lift valve for valves with high-production-pressure factors. The point of gas injection transfers automatically from an upper to the next lower valve after the production pressure at the lower-valve depth becomes less than the injection-gas pressure at the same depth. This same design technique can be used for pilot-operated gas lift valves used on bottom for the operating valve. The calculations for pilot valves apply to the pilot section of the valve.

When the design technique employing large ported valves for unloading is used, there may be variations in the port size or surface closing pressure of the bottom gas lift valve. If the casing size is large relative to the tubing size, such as with 2⅜-in.-OD tubing in 7-in.-OD casing, a smaller-ported gas lift valve may be used for the bottom valve. The 1.5-in.-OD unloading gas lift valves may have a ⁷⁄₁₆- or ½-in.-ID port and the bottom valve a ⅜-in.-ID port to reduce the valve spread (i.e., the difference between the initial opening and closing pressures of the operating valve). This consideration is important for installations in wells with an anticipated low flowing bottomhole pressure. The design surface closing pressure can be the same as the assumed closing pressure for the unloading gas lift valves with larger ports. Another variation in the installation design is to decrease the surface closing pressure of the bottom gas lift valve. The purpose of decreasing the closing pressure of the bottom valve is to provide a visible change in operating injection-gas pressure when the well is unloaded to this valve depth. This procedure is referred to as "flagging" the bottom valve, and a typical decrease in surface closing pressure is 20 to 30 psi.

12.11.12 Intermittent Gas Lift Installation Design Based on Valves With a Large Port, Constant Surface Closing Pressure, and an Intermittent-Spacing-Factor Pressure Gradient With Depth. There are two advantages to a properly designed constant-surface-closing-pressure installation design: (1) no decrease in operating injection-gas pressure with depth of lift is required (particularly important in deep wells with low available injection-gas pressure) and (2) the depth of lift is always the deepest valve depth where the maximum production pressure in the tubing is less than the injection-gas pressure at the same depth.

Because intermittent-flow gas lift is normally used only when lifting from near total depth of a well, it is important to know which valve is the operating valve at any given time. One disadvantage of the constant-surface-closing-pressure design method is the difficulty of establishing the depth of the operating valve from the surface operating injection-gas pressure because the operating pressure does not decrease with each successively lower valve. Determining the fluid level acoustically or recording the time for a liquid slug to surface are two methods for establishing the approximate depth of lift. A liquid-slug velocity of approximately 1,000 ft/min can be assumed for most installations. Decreasing the surface closing pressure of the bottom valve is another method used by some operators to indicate that a well has unloaded to and is operating from the deepest valve. A decrease in the surface-closing pressure of the operating gas lift valve should be considered if a plunger is being installed in an intermittent-lift installation. Intermittent installations with a low *PI* should operate from the maximum possible depth of lift. This design technique uses an intermittent-spacing-factor pressure gradient based on the tubing size and design gas lift production rate from the well. This pressure gradient is used for locating all unloading valves in the well.

12.11.13 Determination of the Gas Lift Valve Depths. The bottomhole pressures, P_{wsd} and P_{wfd}, and bottomhole temperature, T_{wsd}, are generally referenced to the same datum depth, D_d, which is usually the lower end of the production conduit. The steps for establishing the gas lift valve depths on a pressure/depth plot are the same as used in a continuous-flow design, except that the intermittent spacing factor represents the unloading flowing-pressure gradient above the depth of gas injection. The steps for establishing the gas lift valve depths are discussed next.

1. Determine the intermittent spacing factor, F_s, for the design daily production rate and tubing size from Fig. 12.42. Using the intermittent spacing factor as the unloading pressure gradient above the depth of gas injection, g_{pfa}, calculate the unloading flowing-production pressure at the lower end of the production conduit, P_{pfd}.

2. Plot the minimum wellhead pressure between gas injections, P_{wh}, and the P_{pfd} on the pressure/depth graph in **Fig. 12.43** and connect these two pressures with a straight line. This represents the minimum unloading flowing-tubing-pressure-at-depth $(P_{pfD})_{min}$ traverse above the depth of gas injection.

3. Add a temperature scale to the pressure/depth graph and plot the surface unloading-wellhead temperature, T_{whu}, and the bottomhole temperature, T_{wsd}, at D_d. Draw the unloading gas lift valve temperature at depth (T_{vuD}) traverse by assuming a straight-line traverse between T_{whu} and T_{wsd}. Calculate the unloading gas lift valve temperature at depth gradient, g_{Tvu}, using Eq. 12.36.

4. Calculate a surface closing pressure for the gas lift valves, P_{vc}, with Eq. 12.66, and calculate the valve closing pressure, P_{vcd}, at D_d, with Eq. 12.1. Draw a straight line between P_{vc} at the surface and, P_{vcd}, at D_d, which represents the valve closing pressure at depth, P_{vcD}-traverse, and calculate the valve closing gas pressure at depth gradient, g_{gvc}, with Eq. 12.67.

$$P_{vc} = 0.85 \ P_{io} \cdot \ \dots\dots\dots\dots\dots\dots\dots\dots\dots\dots\dots\dots \ (12.66)$$

$$g_{gvc} = \frac{\left(P_{vcd} - P_{vc}\right)}{D_d} \cdot \ \dots\dots\dots\dots\dots\dots\dots\dots\dots\dots \ (12.67)$$

5. Calculate the depth of the top gas lift valve, D_{v1}, on the basis of the available injection-gas-line pressure, P_{io}, load-fluid pressure gradient, g_{ls}, and the wellhead U-tubing pressure, P_{whu}, with either Eq. 12.29, 12.30, or 12.31.

6. Draw a horizontal line on the pressure/depth plot at depth D_{v1} between the $(P_{pfD})_{min}$ and T_{vuD} traverses, which includes P_{vcD1}, and record $(P_{pfD1})_{min}$, P_{vcD1}, and T_{vD1}, or calculate these pressures and temperature using the appropriate gradients and depth D_{v1}.

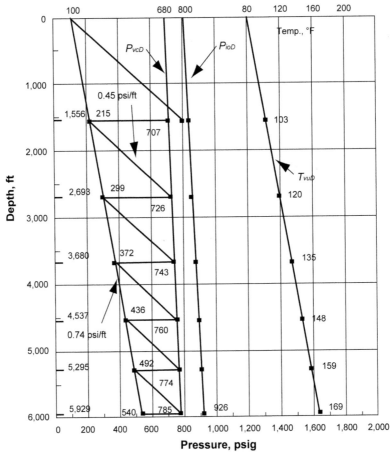

Fig. 12.43—Intermittent-flow gas lift installation design based on a constant valve surface closing pressure and a single intermittent spacing-factor gradient.

7. Locate the second gas lift valve depth graphically by drawing the static-load-fluid traverse, g_{ls}, below the depth of the top gas lift valve with the traverse originating at the minimum unloading flowing tubing pressure, $(P_{pfD1})_{min}$, and extend this traverse to the valve closing pressure at depth (P_{vcD}) traverse The spacing between valves may be solved mathematically.

$$\left[P_{pfD(n)}\right]_{min} + g_{ls}\left(D_{bv}\right) = P_{vcD(n)} + g_{gvc}\left(D_{bv}\right). \quad\text{.......................} (12.68)$$

Solving for D_{bv},

$$D_{bv} = \frac{\left\{P_{vcD(n)} - \left[P_{pfD(n)}\right]_{min}\right\}}{\left(g_{ls} - g_{gvc}\right)}. \quad\text{...........................} (12.69)$$

8. Repeat Step 6 at depth D_{v2}.

9. Locate the depth of the third gas lift valve, D_{v3}, graphically or mathematically, and record the pressures and valve temperature at D_{v3} as outlined in Steps 7 and 8. Repeat Steps 7 and 8 until the maximum desired gas lift valve depth is attained or the calculated distance

TABLE 12.10—CALCULATION OF THE TEST-RACK SET OPENING PRESSURE OF 1/2-IN.-OD GAS LIFT VALVES WITH 1/2-IN.-ID PORT (A_P/A_B = 0.255) ON THE BASIS OF A CONSTANT SURFACE CLOSING PRESSURE OF 680 PSIG

Valve, n	D_v, ft	D_{bv}, ft	P_{pfD}, psig	P_{bvD} = P_{vcD}, psig	T_{vuD}, °F	C_T	P_{vo}, psig
1	1,556	1,137	215	707	103	0.914	868
2	2,693	987	299	726	120	0.884	862
3	3,680	857	372	743	135	0.860	857
4	4,537	744	436	758	148	0.839	854
5	5,281	647	491	771	159	0.823	851
6	5,928		539	762	169	0.809	829*

*An additional pressure drop of 20 psi in P_{vo} is taken at the bottom valve to flag the surface injection-gas operating pressure when lifting from this valve.

between valves is less than the assigned minimum distance between valves. The minimum distance is used for calculating the remaining valve depths until the maximum valve depth is reached.

12.11.14 Calculation of the Test-Rack Set Opening Pressures of the Gas Lift Valves. A tabulation form for these calculations is illustrated in **Table 12.10**. The bellows-charged pressure at the valve unloading temperature, P_{bvD}, is calculated.

$$P_{bvD(n)} = P_{vcD(n)} \cdot \quad\text{.. (12.70)}$$

For Eq. 12.70 to be valid, the flowing-production pressure at valve depth is assumed equal to the injection-gas pressure at the same depth when the valve closes. This assumption is reasonable for the deeper gas lift valves with large ports. The pressure in the tubing approaches the injection-gas pressure at valve depth immediately before the valve closes. Eq. 12.70 does not accurately describe the closing pressure for the upper one or two valves as the point of gas injection transfers to the next lower valve. The pressure downstream of the valve port can be significantly less than the injection-gas pressure at the instant the upper one or two valves close. These upper valves will have a higher closing pressure.

The unloading valve temperature at the depth of the valve can be estimated from a T_{vuD} traverse on the pressure/depth plot or calculated with Eq. 12.39. The test-rack opening pressure is calculated with Eq. 12.45 for a tester setting temperature of 60°F using $C_{T(n)}$ from Table 1 or calculated with Eq. 3.

The design given in Example Problem 6 is based on valves with a constant surface closing pressure and uses large-ported unloading valves. The design uses a single intermittent spacing-factor gradient for the spacing calculations. Unloading valves are spaced from the surface because of the possibility that the fluid level may be high after a workover. As discussed earlier, this is only one of many design techniques. Many designers prefer to use small-port valves for an unloading design similar to continuous flow.

Example Problem 6. Intermittent gas lift well data for installation design calculations:
- Tubing size = 2⅞-in. OD.
- Tubing length, D_d = 6,000 ft.

- Maximum valve depth, $D_{v(max)}$ = 5,950 ft.
- Static bottomhole well pressure at depth D_d, P_{wsd} = 1,600 psig at 6,000 ft.
- Bottomhole well temperature at D_d, T_{wsd} = 170°F at 6,000 ft.
- Design daily production rate, q_{lt} = 300 B/D.
- Design unloading wellhead temperature, T_{vuD} = 80°F.
- Static-load-fluid pressure gradient, g_{ls} = 0.45 psi/ft.
- U-tubing wellhead pressure, P_{whu} = 100 psig.
- Minimum wellhead pressure between injection-gas cycles, P_{wh} = 100 psig.
- Specific gravity of injection gas, γ_g = 0.65.
- Injection-gas wellhead temperature, T_{gio} = 80°F.
- Surface injection-gas-line pressure, P_{io} = 800 psig.
- Minimum distance between gas lift valves, $D_{bv(min)}$ = 350 ft.
- Test-rack valve setting temperature, T_{vo} = 60°F.
- Gas lift valves: 1.5-in.-OD with nitrogen-charged bellows A_b = 0.77 in.^{2} and ½-in.-ID port with sharp-edged seat.

Determination of Valve Depths. The traverses for the pressures and temperatures used for calculating the gas lift installation design are drawn on a pressure/depth plot in Fig. 12.43.

1. $g_{pfa} = F_s$ = 0.074 psi/ft from Fig. 12.42 for a rate of 300 B/D through 2⅞-in.tubing, and P_{pfd} = 100 + 0.074 (6,000) = 100 + 444 = 544 psig at 6,000 ft.

2. Draw the $(P_{pfD})_{min}$ traverse.

3. Draw the T_{vuD} traverse and $g_{Tvu} = \dfrac{(170-80)}{6,000} = 0.015°F/ft$.

4. P_{vc} = 0.85 (800) = 680 psig at surface, and P_{vcD} = 783 psig at 6,000 ft. (Eq. 12.1).

5. $g_{gvc} = \dfrac{(783-680)}{6,000} = 0.0172$ psi/ft, and draw the P_{vcD} traverse.

First Gas Lift Valve Depth Calculations. 5. $D_{v1} = \dfrac{800-100}{0.45} = 1,556$ ft. (Eq. 12.29 is the conservative approach).

6. $(P_{pfD1})_{min}$ = 100 + 0.074 (1,556) = 215 psig at 1,556 ft.
P_{vcD1} = 680 + 0.0172 (1,556) = 707 psig, and T_{vuD1} = 80 + 0.015 (1,556) = 103°F at 1,556 ft.

Second Gas Lift Valve Depth Calculations. 7. $D_{bv} = \dfrac{(707-215)}{(0.45-0.0172)} = 1,137$ ft, and D_{v2} = 1,556 + 1,137 = 2,693 ft.

8. $(P_{pfD2})_{min}$ = 299 psig, P_{vcD2} = 726 psig, and T_{vuD2} = 120°F at 2,693 ft.

Third Gas Lift Valve Depth Calculations. 7. $D_{bv} = \dfrac{(726-299)}{(0.45-0.0172)} = 987$ ft, and D_{v3} = 2,693 + 987 = 3,680 ft.

8. $(P_{pfD3})_{min}$ = 372 psig, P_{vcD3} = 743 psig, and T_{vuD3} = 135°F at 3,680 ft.

Fourth Gas Lift Valve Depth Calculations. 7. $D_{bv} = \dfrac{(743-372)}{(0.45-0.0172)} = 857$ ft, and D_{v4} = 3,680 + 857 = 4,537 ft.

8. $(P_{pfD4})_{min}$ = 436 psig, P_{vcD4} = 758 psig, and T_{vuD4} = 148°F at 4,537 ft.

Repeat Steps 7 and 8 until the maximum desired gas lift valve depth is attained or the calculated distance between gas lift valves is less than an assigned minimum distance between valves. If the desired maximum valve depth had not been reached, assume the minimum distance between valves until the maximum valve depth is reached. The minimum distance between valves of 350 ft was not used in the design of this installation because the maximum calculated valve depth of 5,928 ft was reached before the calculated distance between valves was less than 350 ft.

12.11.15 Calculation of the Test-Rack Set Opening Pressures of the Gas Lift Valves. A tabulation form for these calculations is given in Table 12.10. The bellows-charged pressure at the valve unloading temperature, P_{bvD} at T_{vuD}, is calculated with Eq. 12.60. The temperature correction factor, C_T, is calculated with Eq. 12.3 rather than read from Table 12.1.

1. For the first valve at D_{v1} using Eq. 12.70: $P_{bvD1} = P_{vcD1} = 707$ psig at 103°F.
2. Calculated $C_{T(1)} = 0.914$ with Eq. 12.3.
3. With Eq. 12.45, calculate the test-rack opening pressure, P_{vo1}, of the valve at D_{v1}:

$$P_{vol} = \frac{0.914(707)}{0.745} = 868 \ \text{psig} \ .$$

Repeat Steps 1 to 3 for the remaining valves. An additional pressure drop of 20 psi in P_{vcD} may be taken at the last (bottom) valve to flag it and ensure that the upper valves do not reopen.

The calculated test-rack opening pressure of Valve 6 in Table 12.10 is based on a ½-in. ID port. A valve with the same surface closing pressure and a ⅜-in ID port can be run as the bottom valve to reduce the spread for a lower than predicted flowing bottomhole pressure. The test-rack opening pressure for a valve with a ⅜-in. ID port $(1 - A_p/A_b = 0.857)$ would be 754 psig.

12.11.16 Gas Lift Chambers.[19,20] Chamber lift is a form of intermittent-flow gas lift. The chamber installation design determines the success of this type of gas lift operation. There are three primary reasons for selecting a chamber lift to gas lift a well:

1. To lower the depth of gas injection in a low-flowing-bottomhole-pressure well with a long perforated interval or open hole.
2. To fully use an available injection-gas pressure that significantly exceeds the flowing bottomhole pressure in terms of the pressure resulting from the starting slug length.
3. To attain the lowest possible average flowing bottomhole pressure by reducing the fluid-head backpressure against the formation for a given liquid feed-in volume.

Although there are numerous variations in the physical design of a chamber, the two fundamental types are the two-packer and the insert bottle type for collecting the well fluids. Both types are shown in **Fig. 12.44.** The two-packer chamber utilizes the casing annulus for accumulation of the well fluids. The insert type of chamber is usually fabricated from the largest pipe that can be safely run inside of the casing or open hole. Chamber location and size relative to the working fluid level, the injection- and formation-gas venting, the injection-gas rate through the chamber-operating gas lift valve for lifting the slug, and properly using the chamber-lift principle can be the difference between efficient and inefficient chamber-lift operations.

Chamber-Lift Principle. The chamber-lift principle implies that the injection gas initially contacts the top of the liquid column in the chamber and displaces this liquid into the tubing above the chamber before injection gas enters the lower end of the dip tube. The dip tube is assumed to be filled with liquid at the beginning of an injection-gas cycle; that is, the top of the chamber is located at the working fluid level. The accumulated liquid in the chamber annulus is U-tubed into the tubing above the chamber before injection gas entry into the lower end of the dip tube. Chamber-lift operation prevents water accumulation in the production conduit because the water is U-tubed first from the chamber, followed by the oil, and then by the injection gas.

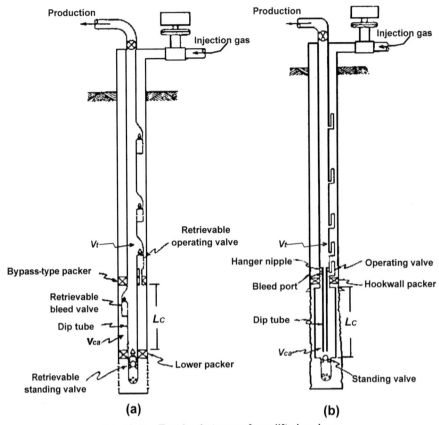

Fig. 12.44—Two basic types of gas lift chambers.

Design Considerations and Chamber Length. The chamber length should be calculated on the basis of an injection-gas pressure that is 60 to 75% of the initial opening pressure of the chamber-operating gas lift valve to ensure adequate pressure differential across the liquid column at the instant the injection gas enters the lower end of the dip tube. Actual operations have shown higher chamber-lift efficiency when the chamber length is based on an injection-gas pressure that is at least 60 to75% of the opening pressure of the chamber-operating gas lift valve. An adequate pressure differential across the liquid slug is necessary to ensure maximum liquid recovery with a minimum of injection-gas breakthrough during displacement to the surface.

$$P_{ioDc} = 0.6 \text{ to } 0.75\left(P_{oDov}\right), \quad \text{..} \quad (12.71)$$

$$F_{at} = \frac{V_{ca}}{V_t}, \quad \text{...} \quad (12.72)$$

and

$$L_c = \frac{\left(P_{ioDc} - P_{tDc}\right)}{\left[g_{lc}\left(F_{at} + 1\right)\right]}, \quad \text{...................................} \quad (12.73)$$

where

P_{ioDc} = injection-gas pressure at depth for calculating chamber length, psig,

P_{oDov} = injection-gas initial opening pressure of the chamber-operating gas lift valve at depth, psig,

L_c = chamber length, ft,

P_{tDc} = tubing pressure at chamber depth based on P_{wh} when chamber-operating gas lift valve opens, psig,

g_{lc} = average pressure gradient for liquid production in chamber, psi/ft,

F_{at} = ratio of physical capacities per foot of chamber annulus/tubing above chamber, dimensionless,

V_{ca} = capacity per foot of casing or chamber annulus, ft³/ft,

and

V_t = capacity per foot of tubing above chamber, ft³/ft.

The actual chamber length is the distance from the top of the chamber to the lower end of the dip tube. The chamber-length equation is based on three assumptions: (1) the top of the chamber is located at the working fluid level between injection-gas cycles, (2) the dip tube is full when the chamber-operating gas lift valve opens, and (3) the physical size of the chamber and dip tube do not change over the entire chamber length. The chamber-length equation must be modified for other geometries and assumptions.

Example Problem 7: Two-Packer Chamber-Length Calculations. The following data are given for a two-packer chamber at 6,000 ft (top packer):

• Casing size = 7-in. OD, 26 lbm/ft.
• Tubing and dip tube size = 2⅞-in. OD.
• P_{oDov} = 800 psig at 6,000 ft.
• g_{lc} = 0.40 psi/ft.
• P_{tDc} = 100 psig at 6,000 ft.
• V_{ca} = 0.1697 ft³/ft.
• V_t = 0.0325 ft³/ft.

Calculate the approximate chamber length using Eqs. 12.71 through 12.73.

$$P_{io}D_c = 0.70(800) = 560 \text{ psig at 6,000 ft}, \quad F_{at} = \frac{0.1697}{0.0325} = 5.22,$$

and

$$L_c = \frac{(560 - 100)}{[0.40(5.22 + 1)]} = 185 \text{ ft.}$$

Unloading Valve Depths. The unloading valve spacing calculations for a chamber installation are the same as the valve depth calculations for an intermittent installation with the exception of the bottom unloading valve. The bottom unloading gas lift valve should be within a few joints of the chamber-operating valve because the depth of gas-injection for the chamber-operating valve is the lower end of the dip tube rather than the actual valve depth, and the fluid-slug length above the valve is based on the chamber annular capacity plus the dip-tube length. The initial opening pressure of a chamber-operating gas lift valve should be at least 50 psi lower than the initial opening pressure of the bottom unloading valve in most installations to ensure lifting from the chamber-operating valve. The tubing pressure at the top of a properly designed chamber that is located at the working fluid level will be near wellhead tubing pressure. The operating-chamber valve must have proper spread characteristics (difference between the operating valve initial opening and closing pressures in the well) to prevent excessive injection-gas usage per cycle. Pilot-operated gas lift valves are widely used as the chamber-operating valve because a large port is available with controlled spread characteristics.

There can be a significant pressure differential across the standing valve immediately after the liquid slug surfaces and blowdown occurs. A mechanical-locking-type standing valve is recommended to prevent the standing valve from being blown out of its seating nipple from this pressure differential.

Importance of Chamber-Bleed Valve. An important consideration is the design and operation of the chamber-bleed valve for venting free gas in the upper section of the chamber after an injection-gas cycle. Most of the free gas is injection gas trapped above the increasing fluid level in the chamber during fill-up. A liquid seal at the lower end of the dip tube occurs soon after a liquid slug surfaces and the injection-gas velocity in the tubing begins to decrease. The liquid seal results from liquid fallback accumulating in the lower end of the dip tube and chamber. Injection-gas from the previous chamber U-tubing cycle is trapped in the chamber annulus above the lower end of the dip tube. The trapped injection gas from the previous injection-gas cycle must be vented from the chamber annulus before the chamber can fill with liquid. If the injection gas is not vented, the trapped injection gas will reduce the liquid production entering the chamber. Without venting the trapped injection gas, a portion of the production entering the chamber increases the length of the liquid column in the tubing. If a significant volume of the reservoir-liquid production fills the tubing above the chamber, the major benefit of an accumulation chamber is nullified in terms of lowering the liquid-column backpressure against the formation. Differential valves have been used as chamber-bleed valves. The differential valve must be properly set with choke sizes that ensure closure immediately after the chamber-operating gas lift valve opens.

Description of Chamber-Lift Injection-Gas Cycle. A complete injection-gas cycle of operation for chamber lift is described for stabilized operation after unloading. Stabilized production infers that the well has unloaded the kill fluid, all production is from the reservoir, and the production per injection-gas cycle remains approximately the same.

When the chamber-operating valve opens, the standing valve closes. The liquid column in the chamber annulus is U-tubed into the dip tube and tubing above the chamber to form the starting-liquid-slug length. A portion of the starting liquid slug is displaced to the surface by the injection gas. Not all of a starting liquid slug reaches the surface because of injection-gas breakthrough and resulting liquid fallback during displacement.

While the standing valve is closed and the liquid slug is surfacing, the reservoir fluid feed-in continues to enter the wellbore. Formation production enters the casing annulus between the chamber OD and casing ID of an insert chamber or below the bottom packer of a two-packer chamber installation. Reservoir production cannot enter the chamber while the standing valve is closed. All free gas, including the formation and trapped injection gas, is vented into the tubing through the chamber bleed valve in a properly designed two-packer installation. The formation-gas production in the annular area between the insert chamber OD and casing ID beneath the packer should be vented into the tubing above the chamber to prevent a significant decrease in the maximum daily production from a high-*PI*, low-flowing-bottomhole-pressure well.

Free-Gas Problems With Insert Chambers.[21] Gas separation occurs beneath the packer in the annulus between the insert chamber OD and casing ID. The formation free gas accumulates above the liquid level in this annulus. This trapped formation free gas is compressed by the new production entering the wellbore. The additional formation free-gas production is added to the trapped free gas beneath the packer as the formation free gas separates from the liquid production. This trapped free gas under the packer restricts the total volume of produced-liquid accumulation in the casing-ID/insert-chamber-OD annulus below the packer.

After a liquid slug surfaces, the injection gas in the tubing exhausts into the flowline, and the flowing bottomhole pressure in the chamber decreases. The standing valve opens when the pressure in the chamber is less than the reservoir pressure beneath the standing valve. The liquid in the casing/chamber annulus below the gas/liquid level flows into the chamber first. Liquid is followed by the trapped formation free gas from the casing/chamber annulus until the annulus and chamber pressures are equal at the depth of the standing valve. The casing/chamber annulus between the packer and standing valve depth is totally filled with formation free gas and no liquid at the equalized minimum flowing bottomhole pressure between injection-gas cycles.

The injection-gas cycle frequency depends on the well deliverability. When maximum cycle frequency is required, the next injection-gas cycle begins as soon as the tubing wellhead pressure approaches the production-header (separator) pressure. Time-cycle control of the injection-gas cycle is required to ensure maximum cycle frequency. A very short time after beginning the surface injection-gas cycle, the chamber-operating valve opens and the standing valve closes. Because of the high injection-gas cycle frequency, most of the well production enters the wellbore while the standing valve is closed and the liquid slug is surfacing. As a result, nearly all of the liquid entering the chamber is the liquid accumulation in the casing/chamber annulus before the standing valve opens. Very little production enters the chamber directly from the reservoir because the standing valve is open for a much shorter length of time than it is closed at maximum injection-gas cycle frequency. The solution to this problem is to vent the free gas in the casing/chamber annulus beneath the packer into the tubing above the chamber. The separated formation gas would not be trapped in this annular space. The casing opposite the insert chamber annulus could fill with liquid if the free gas was vented into the tubing above the chamber. When the standing valve opens after a slug surfaces and the pressure in the chamber decreases, mostly liquid rather than free gas enters the chamber when free gas is vented from below the packer.

If a well is producing less than 10 to 20 B/D and is requiring less than 6 or 12 injection-gas cycles per 24 hours, the free gas in the casing annulus is not a serious a problem. Most of the reservoir-fluid production enters the wellbore while the standing valve is open during the long time interval between injection-gas cycles. The free-gas volume above the liquid level in the chamber annulus has sufficient time to flow into the dip tube through a small orifice or bleed valve. One reason that inefficient insert chamber operations in a high-injection-gas-cycle frequency, gassy well is not addressed in the literature is the fact that most low-cost insert-chamber installations use a hookwall packer and hanger nipple, as illustrated in Fig. 12.44a. This is the type of insert chamber that is run in low-rate, "stripper-type" wells.

There may be little benefit from an insert-chamber installation in a gassy well with a high-frequency injection-gas cycle if the design does not provide a means to vent the trapped free gas below the packer as shown in **Fig. 12.45**. Improved chamber-lift operations can be expected by installing a gravity-closed or spring-loaded gas lift valve check below the packer. A tubing-retrievable conventional gas lift mandrel and check valve is run upside down between the packer and top of the insert chamber in **Fig. 12.46**. Wireline- instead of tubing-retrievable equipment can be used. Adding a screen to the check-valve inlet is recommended to prevent trash in the well fluids from entering and preventing the check dart from closing. The check valve adds very little cost to this type of chamber installation. Because liquid, rather than trapped formation gas, is in contact with the formation in the casing annulus, better reservoir-liquid feed-in between injection-gas cycles should occur. Only the trapped formation free and injection gas in the chamber must vent through the chamber-bleed valve.

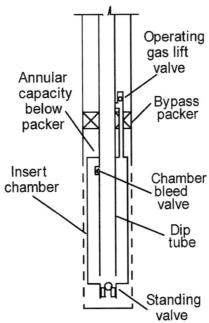

Fig. 12.45—Bypass-packer insert-chamber installation without venting free gas below packer.

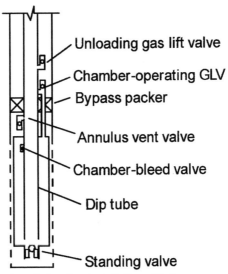

Fig. 12.46—Bypass-packer insert-chamber installation with free-gas vent valve below packer.

12.11.17 Plunger Application for Intermittent Gas Lift. An important consideration related to intermittent gas lift operations is the injection-gas breakthrough and resulting loss of the liquid production per cycle from the injection gas penetrating the liquid slug during the time required to displace this slug to the surface. The produced-liquid slug can be a small fraction of the starting slug size because of injection-gas breakthrough. The losses are greater when the injection-gas pressure is low and the required depth of lift is near total depth in a deep well. For example, a 12,000-ft well with a bottomhole flowing pressure of 300 psig and an available

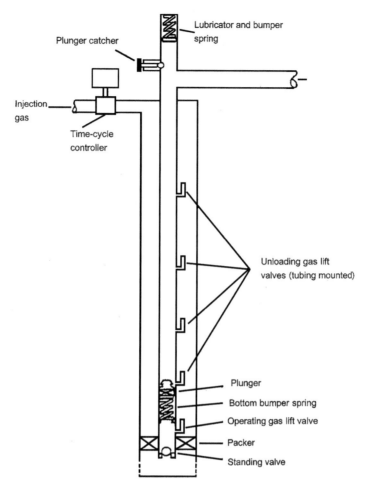

Fig. 12.47—Plunger in an intermittent gas lift installation.

injection-gas pressure of only 450 psig can be gas lifted intermittently with the proper plunger. The well could not be gas lifted successfully from this depth without a plunger.

A typical plunger installation for intermittent gas lift operation is shown in **Fig. 12.47**. A plunger can be expected to decrease the injection-gas requirement for an intermittent gas lift installation from 30 to 70% depending on plunger construction, the depth of lift, injection-gas pressure, and adjustment of the injection-gas volume to the well before the plunger is installed.

There is little if any liquid-slug recovery by intermittent gas lift from very deep wells with low injection-gas pressure unless a plunger is installed. The plunger provides a solid interface between the starting liquid slug and the displacing injection gas. The plunger practically eliminates liquid fallback as a result of gas penetrating the liquid slug. The increase in liquid recovery and the decrease in the injection-gas requirement per cycle from installing a plunger are minimal in an intermittent gas lift installation with small liquid slugs being lifted at an exceedingly high slug velocity in shallow wells. Another advantage of a plunger is that it reduces paraffin in a well with a paraffin problem. Plungers are installed in some wells for the sole purpose of keeping the tubing free of paraffin deposition.

A plunger can be installed in an existing tubing-retrievable conventional gas lift valve installation by wireline without pulling the tubing if there are no tight spots in the tubing. A standing valve and a bottomhole collar lock or a stop with a bumper spring can be installed with wireline tools. A standing valve normally is recommended but not required in wells with a low permeability. The bottomhole bumper spring is located immediately above the operating gas lift valve, and a standing valve is stationed below the valve. The remaining equipment is on the surface and includes a lubricator with a bumper spring and a plunger catcher mechanism. A plunger-arrival detector to shut in the tubing is not needed for an intermittent gas lift installation because the tubing is not shut in between injection-gas cycles.

A plunger ascent velocity of 800 to 1,000 ft/min is recommended for the most efficient lift. A plunger may stall or tend to stop and start at plunger velocities less than 350 to 400 ft/min. Plunger velocities in excess of 1,200 to 1,500 ft/min are not recommended because of possible damage to the plunger on arrival at the surface and an apparent tendency to bypass a thicker than normal liquid boundary on the tubing wall. Noting the times when a time-cycle controller opens and when the plunger arrives at the surface can approximate an average plunger velocity.

The addition of a plunger to an intermittent gas lift installation should be considered when (1) the available injection-gas pressure is low relative to the required depth of lift in a low-flowing-bottomhole-pressure well; (2) there is an excessive increase in wellhead tubing pressure as the liquid slug enters the flowline because of such factors as a small-ID flowline, excessive number of bends at the wellhead, and flowline choke; and (3) a paraffin-deposition problem exists. A plunger should increase the efficiency required of most intermittent gas lift installations. Because a plunger adds several moving parts, it can also increase the operating problems.

Well conditions that prohibit the use of a plunger are a bore opening through surface wellhead and tree valves that differs from the tubing ID; excessive well deviation, which prevents a plunger from descending to its bottomhole bumper spring; tight spots in the tubing; appreciable sand production; and high-rate intermittent gas lift operations. The fall time required for a plunger to descend to the bottom bumper spring could reduce the maximum production from a high-cycle-frequency intermittent gas lift installation.

Specially designed plungers are available for wells with side-pocket mandrels. Plungers have worked in wells with a deviation near 50°, but the maximum deviation for a plunger operation depends on the construction of the plunger. The manufacturers should be able to provide the information related to their plunger operation in a deviated well.

There are numerous types of plunger sealing elements, bypass valves, plunger weights and lengths, and other features that may have been developed for unique applications. Some plungers are particularly applicable for gas lift and other types are not. Select the proper plunger to match the well conditions and application for trouble-free service and efficient operation. Please refer to the chapter on Plunger Lift in this volume of the *Handbook*.

12.12 Operation of Gas Lift Installations

A recommended practice for operation, maintenance, and troubleshooting gas lift installations is given in API *RP 11V5*.[22]

12.12.1 Unloading Procedures and Proper Adjustment of Injection-Gas Rate.

The importance of properly unloading a gas lift installation cannot be overemphasized in terms of possible damage to gas lift valves and for attaining the optimum depth of lift. If a permanent meter tube is not installed in the injection-gas line to the well, provisions should be made for the installation of a portable meter tube before unloading and adjustment of the injection-gas rate to the well. Preferably, the meter tube and the orifice meter or flow computer should be located near the well's injection-gas control device so that the effect of changes in the adjustment of the injection-gas volume can be observed.

A two-pen pressure recorder should be installed before unloading all gas lift installations. The ranges of the pressure elements in the recorder should be checked before hookup. A typical recorder will have a 0- to 500- or 0- to 1,000-psig range element for the flowing wellhead production pressure and a 0- to 1,000- or 0- to 2,000-psig range element for the injection-gas pressure, depending on the kick-off and available operating injection-gas pressure at the wellsite. These pressure elements should be calibrated periodically with a dead eight tester to ensure accurate recordings.

Recommended Practices Before Unloading. If the injection-gas line is new, it should be blown clean of scale, welding slag, and the like, before being connected to a well. This precaution prevents damage and plugging of the surface control equipment and entry of debris with the injection gas into the casing annulus. Debris may cause serious operational problems to gas lift valves.

The surface facilities for a gas lift installation should be checked before the well is unloaded. This includes all valves between the wellhead and the battery, the separator gas capacity, and the stock-tank room. It is important to check the pop-off safety release valve for the gas gathering facilities if this is the first gas lift installation in the system.

Recommended Procedure for Unloading Gas Lift Installations. Preventing excessive pressure differentials across the gas lift valves during initial U-tubing operations minimizes the chance for equipment failure because of fluid and sand cutting. The following procedure avoids excessive pressure differential across the valves during the unloading operation. The permissible rate of increase in the injection-gas pressure downstream of the control device can be greater for an open installation without a packer than for an installation with a packer. Most of the load fluid from the casing annulus will be U-tubed through the lower end of the tubing in an open installation; whereas all the load fluid in the annulus must pass through the small ports of the gas lift valves in an installation with a packer. The initial U-tubing is the most critical operation during the unloading procedure. There is no reason to hurry the U-tubing of the load fluid to uncover the top gas lift valve. Because the tubing remains full of load fluid during the U-tubing operation, there is no drawdown in flowing bottomhole pressure. Gas lifting does not begin until the initial U-tubing is completed and injection gas enters the tubing through the top valve. The load-fluid production rate is controlled by the rate of increase in the injection-gas pressure, which in turn, depends on the injection-gas rate. Because most gas lift installations include a packer, the load fluid enters the tubing through the gas lift valves. If the load fluid contains sand and debris and full line injection-gas pressure is applied to the casing by opening a large valve on the injection-gas line, the gas lift valves may leak after the well is unloaded. An instantaneous pressure differential that is approximately equal to the full line injection-gas pressure occurs across every gas lift valve because the casing and tubing are full of load fluid. If sand or debris is in the load fluid, the resulting high fluid velocity through the small valve ports might fluid cut the seats. The following procedure is recommended for monitoring and controlling the unloading operations for all gas lift installations to prevent damage to the gas lift valves and surface facilities.

1. Install a two-pen pressure recorder that is accurate and in good working condition. The injection-gas pressure downstream of the gas-control device and the wellhead tubing pressure should always be recorded during the entire unloading operation.

2. If the well has been shut in and the tubing pressure exceeds the separator pressure, bleed down the tubing through a small flowline choke. Do not inject lift gas before or while the tubing is being bled down.

3. Remove all wellhead and flowline restrictions including a fixed or adjustable choke if the well does not flow after all load fluid has been produced. If the gas lift installation is in a new well, or a recompletion that could flow, a $^{24}\!/_{64}$- to $^{32}\!/_{64}$-in. flowline choke is recommended until the well has cleaned up and does not flow naturally. The selected range of the element for the flowing-wellhead-pressure pen in the two-pen recorder should be able to handle the maximum flowing wellhead pressure with a choke in the flowline.

4. Inject lift gas into the casing at a rate that does not allow more than a 50-psi increase in casing pressure per 10-minute interval. Continue until the casing pressure has reached at least 300 psig. Most companies use a standard choke size in the injection-gas line for U-tubing and initial unloading operations. A typical injection-gas choke size ranges from $\frac{6}{64}$ to $\frac{8}{64}$ in. for the U-tubing operation.

5. After the casing pressure has reached 300 to 500 psig, the injection-gas rate can be adjusted to allow a 100-psi increase per 10-minute interval until gas begins to circulate through the top gas lift valve (top valve is uncovered). After the top gas lift valve is uncovered and gas has been injected through this valve, a high pressure differential cannot occur across the lower gas lift valves. Any time the casing injection-gas pressure is increased above the opening pressure of the top valve, the valve will open and prevent a further increase in the injection-gas pressure. Gas lifting begins with injection gas entering the top valve.

6. If the gas lift installation does not unload to the bottom valve or the design operating gas lift valve depth, adjustment of the injection-gas rate to the well is required. An excessive or inadequate injection-gas rate can prevent unloading. This is particularly true for intermittent gas lift on time-cycle control where the maximum number of injection-gas cycles per day decreases with depth of lift. It may be necessary to decrease the number of injection-gas cycles per day and to increase the duration of gas injection as the point of gas injection transfers from an upper to a lower valve. Proper adjustment of the injection-gas volume to a well is not permanent for most installations. The injection-gas requirements change with well conditions; therefore, continuous monitoring of the injection-gas rate and the wellhead and injection-gas pressure is recommended to maintain efficient gas lift operations.

12.12.2 Depressing the Fluid Level ("Rocking" a Well). If the top gas lift valve cannot be uncovered with the available injection-gas pressure, the fluid level can be depressed when there is no standing valve in the tubing. The injection-gas pressure is applied simultaneously to the tubing and casing. Several hours may be required to depress the fluid level sufficiently in a "tight" low-permeability well. The tubing pressure is released rapidly, and the source of the major portion of the fluid entering the tubing is load fluid from the annulus. This procedure may be required several times to lower the fluid level in the casing annulus below the depth of the top gas lift valve.

High-production-pressure-factor valves in an intermittent gas lift installation or an installation with production-pressure-operated valves may cease to unload after the top valve has been uncovered. Gas lift valves with a high degree of tubing-pressure sensitivity may require a minimum production pressure at valve depth to open the valve with the available injection-gas pressure. This problem occurs more frequently with the top one or two gas lift valves and may be referred to as a "stymie" condition. The stymie condition can be corrected by applying an artificial increase in production pressure at valve depth by "rocking" the well. The valve cannot detect the difference between a liquid column and a pressure increase from partially equalizing the tubing and casing pressure with injection gas. If a well should stymie, the proper procedure for "rocking" the well follows.

First, with the wing valve on the flowline closed, inject lift gas into the tubing until the casing and tubing pressures indicate that the gas lift valve has opened. A small copper tubing or flexible high-pressure line can be used for this purpose. When a valve opens, the casing pressure begins to decrease and to equalize with the tubing pressure. The tubing pressure also should begin to increase at a faster rate with injection gas entering the tubing through the valve and surface connection.

Next, stop gas injection into the tubing and immediately open the wing valve to lift the liquid slug above the gas lift valve into the flowline as rapidly as possible. A flowline choke may be required to prevent venting injection gas through the separator relief valve. Some surface facilities are overloaded easily, and bleeding off the tubing must be controlled carefully.

Last, the rocking process may be required several times until a lower gas lift valve has been uncovered. As the depth of lift increases, the possibility of stymie decreases because of a higher minimum production pressure at the greater depth and the decrease in the distance between valves.

12.12.3 Controlling the Daily Production Rate From Continuous-Flow Installations. The daily production rate from a continuous-flow gas lift installation should be controlled by the injection-gas volumetric flow rate to the well. A flowline choke should not be used for this purpose. Excessive surface flowline backpressure increases the injection-gas requirement. Production-pressure-operated gas lift valves and injection-pressure-operated valves with a large production-pressure factor are particularly sensitive to high wellhead flowing pressure. Inefficient multipoint gas injection can result and prevent unloading an installation to the maximum depth of lift for the available operating injection-gas pressure when the flowing wellhead backpressure is excessive.

12.12.4 Adjustment of a Time-Cycle-Operated Controller for Intermittent-Flow Operations. When initially unloading an intermittent-flow gas lift installation, an excessive injection-gas-cycle frequency may prevent "working down" (unloading the gas lift installation beyond a certain depth). As the depth of lift increases, the maximum possible number of injection-gas cycles per day decreases and the volume of injection gas required per cycle increases. If the number of injection cycles per day becomes excessive and there is insufficient time between gas injections for the casing pressure to decrease to the closing pressure of an upper unloading gas lift valve, the unloading process will discontinue until the number of injection-gas cycles is reduced. Many installations require several adjustments of the time-cycle controller before the operating valve depth is reached.

The following procedure is recommended for final adjustment of a time-cycle-operated controller to minimize the injection-gas requirement when lifting from the operating gas lift valve:

1. Adjust the controller for a duration of gas injection that ensures an excessive volume of injection gas used per cycle (approximately 500 ft^3/bbl/1,000 ft of lift). For most systems 30 sec/1,000 ft of lift results in more gas being injected into the casing annulus than is actually needed.

2. Reduce the number of injection-gas cycles per day until the well will not lift from the final operating valve depth and/or the producing rate declines below the desired or maximum daily production rate.

3. Reset the controller for the number of injection-gas cycles per day immediately before the previous setting in Step 2. This establishes the proper injection-gas-cycle frequency.

4. Reduce the duration of gas injection per cycle until the producing rate decreases and then return to the previous setting and increase the duration of gas injection by 5 to 10 seconds for fluctuations in injection-gas-line pressure.

A time-cycle-operated controller on the injection-gas line can be adjusted as previously outlined, provided the line pressure remains relatively constant. If the line pressure varies significantly, the controller is adjusted to inject ample gas volume with minimum line pressure. When the line pressure is above the minimum pressure, excessive injection gas is used each cycle. One solution to this problem is a controller that opens on time and closes on a set increase in casing pressure. Several electronic timers are designed to operate in conjunction with pressure control.

12.13 Gas Lift for Unusual Environments

Gas lift is especially suited for application in unusual environments. This section discusses a few of these environments and how gas lift is used in the particular application.

12.13.1 Offshore Platforms. Gas lift is a widely used artificial-lift system in offshore installations and has performed exceptionally well. Most downhole gas lift equipment has few if any moving parts and requires little maintenance. What little maintenance that is required can normally be done with wireline equipment. For this reason, downhole gas lift equipment is much less costly to replace than other forms of downhole artificial-lift equipment. The required space, or "footprint," and weight of gas lift surface controls are minimal. Because produced gas from the offshore wells generally must be conserved, it can be compressed and provide a ready source of high-pressure gas for gas lift.

The process of gas lift from offshore platforms is slightly different from gas lift onshore. In many cases, the surface installations on offshore platforms are better designed than onshore installations. If designed properly, there will be very little pressure loss caused by restrictions or flowlines. The compressors for gas lift are located nearby, so the distribution of gas should be no problem. Because of the importance to the overall installation, gas compression and dehydration equipment is normally operated and maintained by people who are provided for this specific purpose.

Safety Devices. There are many more safety devices on offshore platforms than on onshore installations. High-/low-pressure shutoff devices are installed at the wellhead on both the injection-gas line and the flowline to automatically close in the well at the surface, should there be a radical change in either line's operating pressure.

Surface or downhole safety devices are a necessary part of any offshore well. With so much property and human life at stake on the platforms, it is an absolute necessity to prevent downhole or surface catastrophic failure. Safety valves are included on the production string of a gas lift well and may cause some restriction to flow. In the North Sea, governmental agencies also require a safety valve on the gas-injection side of gas lift wells. The reason is the possibility of the check valve on the gas lift valve failing, which would allow well fluids to flow into the casing. Restrictions from subsurface safety equipment may enter into the design of a gas lift installation.

12.13.2 Gas Lift Installations Drilled From Offshore Platforms. Wells drilled from offshore platforms have varying degrees of deviation that must be accounted for in predicting vertical multiphase flow. Most gas lift design programs can take this varying deviation into account. Wireline operators report little problems in setting valves in mandrels at deviations up to 60°. Motors have been developed to move tools downhole at high deviations and have been used in some instances. The gas lift retrievable-valve mandrels with orientation sleeves are designed to insure that the valve enters the pocket regardless of pocket orientation relative to the vertical.

12.13.3 Subsea Gas Lift Installations. Subsea installations increased dramatically in the last few years with the addition of producing areas in greater and greater water depths. Today, it is not unusual to find production from water depths over 6,000 ft with gas lift being the preferred production method in most of these completions. With extreme water depths, some form of artificial lift is usually required just to kick off the well and move the production from the seafloor to the surface.

Devices and equipment for carrying gas lift equipment into subsea wells were perfected at the onset of subsea technology. These include devices for carrying the valves and engines for driving the valve downhole through flowlines and other systems.[23] Although such tools are available, these operational techniques are not widely used. Most subsea gas lift today is done with high-pressure gas and a single orifice placed as deep as the pressure will permit. By using this approach, there is no gas lift equipment in the well that could fail or need replacing. In many deepwater installations, where the water depth itself adds considerable head that must be overcome to produce the well, gas injection is often through a single point at the wellhead or near the mudline.[24,25]

12.13.4 Heavy-Oil Production. Gas lift has been used to produce high-viscosity oil in many parts of the world. Heavy oil is being produced by gas lift in Venezuela. Diluent injection has been found to be very beneficial in producing all types of artificial-lift wells in eastern Venezuela. Diesel fuel is usually used as the diluent, and the injection of approximately 10% by volume lowers the specific gravity and increases the API gravity of the oil.[26]

Water can be used as a diluent as well as diesel fuel and has been proven effective to reduce backpressure in large pipelines. In most cases, water acts to reduce backpressure by adding a water ring around the viscous crude that reduces friction between the crude and the pipe wall. When this occurs, water becomes the wetting phase and the resulting friction is similar to that of water. However, unlike the diesel fluid which increases the value of the produced oil by lowering its viscosity, water adds another phase that must eventually be removed.

12.13.5 Gas Lift With Air, Nitrogen, and Carbon Dioxide. Typically, gas lift designs are based on natural gas as the injection gas. However, gas lift with natural gas did not begin in a big way until the 1920s. Early gas lift operations were conducted using air as the injection gas. Many of the early great oil fields such as Spindletop and Goose Creek were produced with air lift. Air has its disadvantages when used for gas lift because oxygen in the air causes serious corrosion, scale, and the possibility of combustion when it is mixed with well fluids. Air is still used in gas lift installations today but on a very limited scale.

Nitrogen and carbon dioxide offer good alternatives to natural gas for gas lift. Nitrogen can be used for gas lift because it is inert, relatively inexpensive, and noncorrosive. Quite often, nitrogen is available at high pressure near the producing facilities, where it is being used for various enhanced-oil-recovery and pressure-maintenance projects.[27]

Carbon dioxide is also readily available from miscible displacement projects and can be used for gas lift purposes. Natural gas containing 75% carbon dioxide was used for gas lift in two large fields in Argentina without noticeable problems.[28] In heavy-oil reservoirs, carbon dioxide is also very useful in decreasing the viscosity of the oil. Both nitrogen and carbon dioxide can be purchased at a price competitive with natural gas in many locations. The use of small nitrogen plants for gas lift of remote offshore and onshore locations has proved feasible under certain conditions.

Nomenclature

A = area of orifice or choke open to gas flow, in.^{2}

A_b = total effective bellows area, in.^{2}

A_p = valve port area (ball/seat-line contact area for sharp-edged seat), in.^{2}

B_{lr} = bellows-assembly load rate, psi/in.

B_{sr} = bellows-assembly spring rate, lbf/in.

C_d = discharge coefficient (determined experimentally), dimensionless

C_{gT} = approximate gas gravity and temperature correction factor for choke charts, dimensionless

C_T = temperature correction factor for nitrogen from P_{bvD} at T_{vuD} to P_b at 60°F, dimensionless

d_1 = orifice or choke ID for known volumetric gas rate, in.

d_2 = orifice or choke ID for unknown volumetric gas rate, in.

D = true vertical depth of gas column, ft

D_{bv} = distance between gas lift valves, ft

$D_{bv(min)}$ = minimum distance between gas lift valves, ft

D_d = reference datum depth (usually lower end of production conduit) for bottomhole temperature and pressures, ft

D_{ov} = depth of operating valve, ft

D_v = valve depth, ft

D_{v1} = depth of top valve, ft

$D_{v(max)}$ = maximum depth for bottom (deepest) valve, ft

e = Napierian logarithm base = 2.718...

f_o = oil cut, fraction

f_{pt} = valve spacing design line transfer-pressure factor at surface, fraction

f_w = water cut, fraction

F_{at} = ratio of capacities of chamber annulus/tubing above chamber, consistent units

F_{cf} = critical flow pressure ratio, dimensionless

F_{du} = pressure ratio P_2/P_1, consistent absolute units

F_p = production-pressure factor, dimensionless

F_s = intermittent pressure-gradient spacing factor, psi/ft

g = acceleration due to gravity, ft/sec^2

g_{pfa} = flowing pressure at depth gradient (traverse) above the depth of gas injection, psi/ft

g_{pfb} = flowing pressure at depth gradient (traverse) below the depth of gas injection, psi/ft

g_{gio} = static injection-gas pressure at depth gradient, psi/ft

g_{gvc} = gas lift valve closing pressure at depth gradient, °F/ft

g_{lc} = average pressure gradient for liquid production in chamber, psi/ft

g_{ls} = static load (kill)-fluid pressure gradient, psi/ft

g_{Tv} = unloading gas lift valve temperature at valve depth gradient, °F/ft

k = ratio of specific heats (C_p/C_v), dimensionless

L_c = chamber length, ft

n = number of pound-moles, lbm mol

n = valve location designation (top valve $n = 1$)

P = pressure, psig or psia

$\overline{P}$ = average gas pressure, psig

P_1 = gas pressure upstream of an orifice or choke, psia

P_2 = gas pressure downstream of an orifice or choke, psia

P_{atm} = atmospheric pressure, psia

P_b = nitrogen-charged bellows pressure at 60°F, psig

P_{bvD} = nitrogen-charged bellows pressure at valve temperature, psig

P_{bvs} = nitrogen-charged bellows pressure at T_{vs}, psig

P_{iDc} = tubing pressure at chamber depth when chamber-operating gas lift valve opens, psig

P_{iDov} = injection-gas pressure at chamber depth for calculating P_{vo} of chamber-operating gas lift valve, psig

P_{io} = injection-gas pressure at surface, psig or psia

P_{iod} = static injection-gas pressure at D_d, psig or psia

P_{ioD} = injection-gas pressure at depth (usually valve depth), psig or psia

P_{ioDc} = injection-gas pressure for calculating chamber length, psig

P_{ko} = surface kick-off or average field injection-gas pressure (optional), psig

P_{kod} = kickoff or average field injection-gas pressure at D_d, psig

P_{koD} = kickoff injection-gas pressure at depth, psig

P_o = surface injection-gas initial valve opening pressure of gas lift valve, psig

P_{oD} = injection-gas initial opening pressure of gas lift valve at valve depth, psig

P_{oDov} = injection-gas initial opening pressure of chamber-operating gas-valve at depth, psig

P_{ot} = tester pressure upstream of gas lift valve port, psig

P_{pe} = production-pressure effect, psi

P_{pfd} = flowing-production pressure at D_d based on design q_{lt} and R_{glu}, psig

P_{pfD} = flowing-production pressure at valve depth, psig

$(P_{pfD1})_{max}$ = maximum flowing-production pressure opposite an unloading valve immediately after the point of gas injection has transferred to the next lower valve, psig

$(P_{pfD})_{min}$ = minimum flowing-production pressure at valve depth, psig

P_{pft} = tester pressure downstream of gas lift valve port, psig

P_{pt} = surface valve-spacing transfer production pressure, psig

P_{ptd} = valve spacing transfer production pressure at D_d, psig

P_{ptD} = flowing-production transfer (spacing) pressure at valve depth, psig

P_{sc} = standard pressure base, psia

P_{tDc} = tubing pressure at chamber depth based on P_{wh} when chamber-operating valve opens, psig

P_{tDov} = tubing pressure at top of the chamber based on P_{wh}, psig

P_{vc} = valve closing pressure at surface, psig

P_{vcd} = valve closing pressure at D_d, psig

P_{vcD} = valve closing pressure at valve depth, psig

P_{vct} = test-rack valve closing pressure at 60°F if $P_{pft} = P_{ot}$ at instant valve closes, psig

P_{vctD} = gas lift valve closing pressure at valve depth if $P_{pfD} = P_{oD}$, psig

P_{vo} = test-rack valve opening pressure at 60°F, psig

P_{voD} = initial gas lift valve opening pressure at valve depth if $P_{pfD} = 0$, psig

P_{vos} = test-rack valve opening pressure at T_{vs}, psig

P_{wfd} = bottomhole flowing pressure at depth D_d, psig

P_{wh} = surface wellhead pressure, psig

P_{whf} = surface flowing wellhead pressure, psig

P_{whu} = wellhead U-tubing unloading pressure, psig

P_{wsd} = static bottomhole well pressure at depth D_d, psig

PI = productivity index, B/D/psi

ΔP_{aov} = assigned design operating pressure differential across operating valve, psi

ΔP_{io} = assigned minimum decrease in surface injection-gas pressure between valves, psi

ΔP_{ioa} = assigned minimum surface injection-gas pressure increase above P_{oD} for stroking valve, psi

ΔP_{ioc} = calculated surface injection-gas pressure increase above P_{oD} for stroking valve, psi

ΔP_{ov} = pressure differential across operating valve, psi

ΔP_{pe} = production-pressure effect, psi

ΔP_{ptd} = minimum transfer production-pressure difference ($P_{iod} - P_{ptd}$) at D_d, psi

ΔP_{sD} = assigned spacing pressure differential at valve depth, psi

q_{g1} = known daily volumetric gas rate, Mscf/D

q_{g2} = unknown daily volumetric gas rate, Mscf/D

q_{ga} = actual daily volumetric gas rate, Mscf/D

q_{gc} = chart daily volumetric gas rate, Mscf/D

q_{gi} = daily injection-gas rate, Mscf/D

q_{giu} = maximum unloading daily injection-gas rate, Mscf/D

q_{gsc} = daily gas-flow rate at standard conditions (14.7 psia and 60°F), Mscf/D

q_l = liquid (oil + water) daily production rate, B/D

q_{lt} = total liquid (oil + water) daily production rate, B/D

q_{lu} = assigned minimum daily unloading production rate, B/D

R = universal gas constant = 10.73, psia-ft^3/lbm-mol-°R

R_{gl} = gas/liquid ratio (GLR), scf/STB

R_{glf} = formation-gas/liquid ratio, scf/STB

R_{gli} = operating injected-gas/liquid ratio, scf/STB

R_{glu} = maximum unloading injection-gas/liquid ratio, scf/STB

R_{go} = formation gas/oil ratio (GOR), scf/STB

T = gas temperature, °F or °R

$\bar{T}$ = average gas-column temperature, °F or °R

T_1 = upstream gas temperature, °F or °R

T_{gD} = gas temperature at valve depth, °F or °R

T_{gio} = wellhead injection-gas temperature, °F

T_{sc} = standard temperature base, °F or °R

T_{vD} = valve temperature at depth, °F

T_{vo} = test-rack valve setting temperature of 60°F

T_{vs} = test-rack valve or tester setting temperature (other than 60°F), °F

T_{vuD} = unloading gas lift valve temperature at depth, °F

T_{wh} = surface wellhead temperature, °F

T_{whf} = flowing surface wellhead temperature, °F

T_{whu} = assigned unloading flowing surface wellhead temperature, °F

T_{wsd} = bottomhole well temperature at D_d, °F

V = volume or capacity, ft^3

V_c = physical capacity of conduit, ft^3

V_{ca} = capacity of casing or chamber annulus, ft^3

V_{gsc} = volume of gas at standard conditions (14.7 psia and 60°F), scf

V_{gx} = approximate gas volume at standard conditions (14.7 psia and 60°F), scf

V_t = capacity of tubing per foot above chamber, ft^3/ft

V_{ta} = capacity of tubing annulus per foot, ft^3/ft

z = compressibility factor based on P and T, dimensionless

$\bar{z}$ = compressibility factor based on gas-column average pressure $\bar{P}$ and temperature $\bar{T}$, dimensionless

γ_g = gas specific gravity (air = 1.0), dimensionless

γ_o = oil specific gravity, dimensionless

γ_w = water specific gravity, dimensionless

Subscripts

a = actual, annulus, assigned, or assumed
b = bellows, below, or between
c = capacity, critical, closing, calculated, or chamber
d = reference datum depth
D = depth
e = effect
f = flow, flowing, or formation
g = gas
i = injection
ko = kickoff
l = liquid
n = valve number
o = oil, opening, or operating
p = production, pressure, or port
s = static, shut-in, set, or spacing
sc = standard conditions
t = tubing, total, tester, or transfer
T = temperature
u = unloading or U-tubing
v = valve
w = well or water
wh = wellhead

References

1. Blann, J.R. and Williams, J.D.: "Determining the Most Profitable Gas Injection Pressure for A Gas Lift Installation," *JPT* (August 1984) 1305.
2. *Gas Lift, Book 6 of Vocational Training Series,* third edition, API, E&P Dept., Dallas (1994).
3. Vogel, J.V.: "Inflow Performance Relationships for Solution-Gas Drive Wells," *JPT* (January 1968) 83.
4. Poettmann, F.H. and Carpenter, P.G.: "The Multiphase Flow of Gas, Oil and Water Through Vertical Flow Strings," *Drilling & Prod. Prac.,* **257** (1952).
5. Orkiszewski, J.: "Predicting Two-Phase Pressure Drops in Vertical Pipe," *JPT* (June 1967) 829.
6. Duns, H. Jr. and Ros, N.C.J.: "Vertical Flow of Gas and Liquid Mixtures from Boreholes," *Proc.,* Sixth World Petroleum Congress, Frankfurt, Germany (1963) Sec. II, Paper 22-PG.
7. Hagedorn, A.R. and Brown, K.E.: "The Effect of Liquid Viscosity on Two-Phase Flow," *JPT* (February 1964) 203.
8. Beggs, H.D. and Brill, J.P.: "An Experimental Study of Two-Phase Flow in Inclined Pipes," *JPT* (May 1973) 607.
9. Blann, J.R.: *Gas Lift Optimization*, J&L Publishing, Houston (April 2001) Revision.
10. *Spec. 11V1, Specification for Gas Lift Equipment*, first edition, API, Washington, DC (1995).
11. Winkler, H.W. and Eads, P.T.: "Algorithm for More Accurately Predicting Nitrogen Charged Gas Lift Valve Operation at High Pressures and Temperatures," paper SPE 18871 presented at the 1989 SPE Production Operations Symposium, Oklahoma City, Oklahoma, 13–14 March.
12. Cook, H.L. and Dotterweich, F.H.: *Report on Calibration of Positive Flow Beans Manufactured by Thornhill-Craver Company, Inc.,* Houston (1946) 26.
13. *RP 11V2, Recommended Practice for Gas Lift Valve Performance Testing*, first edition, API, Washington, DC (1995).
14. *RP 11V6, Recommended Practice for Design of Continuous Flow Gas Lift Installations Using Injection Pressure Operated Valves*, second edition, API, Washington, DC (1999).

15. Winkler, H.W. and Eads, P.T.: "Applying the Basic Performance Concepts of Single-Element, Unbalanced Gas Lift Valves for Installation Design," *SPEPF* (August 1993) 211.
16. Kirkpatrick, C.V.: "Advances in Gas Lift Technology," *Drill. & Prod. Prac.* (March 1959) 24.
17. Sagar, R., Doty, D.R., and Schmidt, Z.: "Predicting Temperature Profiles in a Flowing Oil Well," *SPEPE* (November 1991) 441.
18. Cullender, M.H. and Smith, R.V.: "Practical Solution of Gas-Flow Equations for Wells and Pipelines with Large Temperature Gradients," *JPT* (December 1956) 281; *Trans.,* AIME, **207.**
19. Winkler, H.W. and Camp, G.F.: "Downhole Chambers Increase Gas Lift Efficiency—Part 1," *Pet. Eng. Intl.,* **28,** No. 9, B-87.
20. Winkler, H.W. and Camp, G.F.: "Downhole Chambers Increase Gas Lift Efficiency—Part 2," *Pet. Eng. Intl.,* **28,** No. 9, B-91.
21. Winkler, H.W.: "Re-Examine Insert Chamber-Lift for High Rate, Low Bottomhole Pressure, Gassy Wells," paper SPE 52120 presented at the 1999 SPE Mid-Continent Operations Symposium, Oklahoma City, Oklahoma, 28–31 March.
22. *RP 11V5, Recommended Practice for Operation, Maintenance and Troubleshooting of Gas Lift Installations,* first edition, API, Washington, DC (1995).
23. Arendt, H.P., Dines, C., and Heard, T.: "Pumpdown (TFL) Technology for Subsea Completions," *JPT* (October 1978) 1481.
24. Noonan, S. and Decker, K.: "Subsea Gas Lift Design and Analysis for Chevron's Subsea Developments," paper presented at the 2001 ASME/API Gas Lift Workshop, Houston, February 2001.
25. Stinson, R.: "Equipment Development for Gas Lift in Deepwater," paper presented at the 2001 ASME/API Gas Lift Workshop, Houston, February 2001.
26. Blann, J.R. *et al.:* "Advances in Heavy Oil Lifting in the Morichal Area of Venezuela," paper SPE 52211 presented at the 1999 SPE Mid-Continent Operations Symposium, Oklahoma City, Oklahoma, 29–31 March.
27. Dickens, R.J.: "High-Pressure Gas Lift For Deep, Sour Production," paper SPE 14347 presented at the 1985 SPE Annual Technical Conference and Exhibition, Las Vegas, Nevada, 22–25 September.
28. Blann, J.R. and Laville, G.M.: "Gas Lifting a Major Oil Field in Argentina With High CO_2 Content Associated Gas" paper SPE 30638 presented at the 1995 SPE Annual Technical Conference and Exhibition, Dallas, 22–25 October.

General References

Blann, J.R., Brown, J.S., and Dufresne, L.P.: "Improving Gas Lift Performance in a Large North African Oil Field," paper SPE 8408 presented at the 1979 SPE Annual Technical Conference and Exhibition, Las Vegas, Nevada, 23–26 September.

Brown, K.E. *et al: The Technology of Artificial Lift Methods,* The Petroleum Publishing Co., Tulsa (1980) Vol. 2a, 224–229.

Mower, L.N. *et al.:* "Defining the Characteristics and Performance of Gas Lift Plungers," paper SPE 14344 presented at the 1985 SPE Annual Technical Conference and Exhibition, Las Vegas, Nevada, 22–25 September.

Ros, N.C.J. and Gray, H.E.: "Shell Two-Phase Vertical Flow Computer Program MK 1X-H," proprietary paper (June 1964) Shell Development Co. E&P Research Div., a Division of Shell Oil Co., Houston.

RP11V7, Recommended Practice for Repair, Testing and Setting Gas Lift Valves, first edition, API, Washington, DC (1995).

Winkler, H.W. and Smith, S.S.: *Camco Gas Lift Manual,* Camco Inc., Houston (1962) A2-001.

Appendix A—Simplified Mathematical Gas Lift Valve Performance Model

A.1 Calculation of GLV Stem Movement.

$$M_{vs} = \frac{(P_{ioD} - P_{bvD}) \, A_b - (P_{ioD} - P_{ptD}) \, A_p}{B_{sr}}, \quad \text{...............} \text{(A-1)}$$

where

$$P_{bvD} = \frac{P_{vo} \, (A_b - A_p)}{A_b \, (C_T)}, \quad \text{...............} \text{(A-2)}$$

and

$$B_{sr} = A_b (B_{lr}). \quad \text{...............} \text{(A-3)}$$

A.2 Calculation of Equivalent Port Area Open to Gas Flow.

$$A_{pe} = \pi(r_{tf} + r_p)s, \quad \text{...............} \text{(A-4)}$$

where

$$C_1 = \sqrt{(r_b)^2 - (r_p)^2}, \quad \text{...............} \text{(A-5)}$$

$$C_2 = \sqrt{(r_p)^2 + (C_1 + M_{vs})^2}, \quad \text{...............} \text{(A-6)}$$

$$r_{tf} = \frac{r_p(r_b)}{C_2}, \quad \text{...............} \text{(A-7)}$$

and

$$s = C_2 - r_b. \quad \text{...............} \text{(A-8)}$$

If $A \, A_{pe} > A_p$, then $A_{pe} = A_p$ (fixed-ID orifice flow).

A.3 Calculation of Gas Rate Through A_{pe}.

$$q_{gsc} = \frac{2{,}946 \, (A_{pe}) \, (P_{ioD} + P_{atm})\sqrt{(R_{du})^{1.587} - (R_{du})^{1.794}}}{\sqrt{T_{gD} + 460}}, \quad \text{...............} \text{(A-9)}$$

where

$$R_{du} = \frac{\left(P_{ptD} + P_{atm}\right)}{\left(P_{ioD} + P_{atm}\right)} . \dots\dots\dots\dots\dots\dots\dots\dots\dots\dots\dots\dots\dots\dots\dots\dots\dots \text{(A-10)}$$

If $R_{du} < = 0.553$, then $R_{du} = 0.553$ (critical flow).

Nomenclature

A_b = effective area of bellows, in.^{2}

A_p = valve port area (ball/seat-line contact area for sharp-edged seat), in.^{2}

A_{pe} = valve port equivalent area open to gas flow, in.^{2}

B_{lr} = bellows-assembly load rate, psi/in.

B_{sr} = bellows-assembly spring rate, lbf/in.

C_T = temperature correction factor for nitrogen from P_{bvD} at T_{vuD} to P_b at 60°F, dimensionless

M_{vs} = movement of the gas lift valve stem, in.

P_{atm} = atmospheric pressure, psia

P_{bvD} = nitrogen-charged bellows pressure at valve temperature, psig

P_{ioD} = injection-gas pressure at valve depth, psig

P_{ptD} = flowing-production transfer pressure at valve depth, psig

P_{vo} = test-rack valve opening pressure at 60°F, psig

q_{gi} = daily injection-gas rate through gas lift valve, Mscf/D

r_b = radius of ball on gas lift valve stem, in.

r_p = radius of valve port (ball/seat-line contact for sharp-edged seat), in.

r_{tf} = top radius of frustum of right circular cone, in.

R_{du} = ratio of downstream pressure/upstream pressure, psia

s = slant height of frustum of right circular cone, in.

T_{giD} = injection-gas temperature at valve depth, °F

Chapter 13
Electrical Submersible Pumps
John Bearden, Centrilift, Baker Hughes Inc.

13.1 Introduction

13.1.1 What Is an Electrical Submersible Pump? The electrical submersible pump, typically called an ESP, is an efficient and reliable artificial-lift method for lifting moderate to high volumes of fluids from wellbores. These volumes range from a low of 150 B/D to as much as 150,000 B/D (24 to 24,600 m³/d). Variable-speed controllers can extend this range significantly, both on the high and low side. The ESP's main components include: a multistaged centrifugal pump, a three-phase induction motor, a seal-chamber section, a power cable, and surface controls. The components are normally tubing hung from the wellhead with the pump on top and the motor attached below. There are special applications in which this configuration is inverted. This chapter provides a general understanding of the ESP artificial-lift method. The topics covered include: the ESP system components and accessories, principles of operation, ESP system selection and performance calculations, installation and handling, and maintenance and troubleshooting. In addition, references are given to lead the reader to more-detailed operation and performance information.

13.2 History[1,2]

In 1911, 18-year-old Armais Arutunoff organized the Russian Electrical Dynamo of Arutunoff Co. in Ekaterinoslav, Russia, and invented the first electric motor that would operate in water. During World War I, Arutunoff combined his motor with a drill. It had limited use to drill horizontal holes between trenches so that explosives could be pushed through. In 1916, he redesigned a centrifugal pump to be coupled to his motor for dewatering mines and ships. In 1919, he immigrated to Berlin and changed the name of his company to REDA. In 1923, he immigrated to the United States and began looking for backers for his equipment. Initially, he approached Westinghouse but was turned down because their engineers thought it would not work because it was impossible under the laws of electronics.

In 1926, at the American Petroleum Institute (API) conference in Los Angeles, two parties joined together to start the ESP industry. Just before this conference, Arutunoff had joined forces with Samual VanWert, a sucker-rod salesman who saw the potential of the new device. Together, they initiated a prototype test in a Baldwin Hills oil well. The second party involved Clyde Alexander, a vice president of a 9-year-old Bartlesville, Oklahoma, oil company—

Phillips Oil Co. He was at the conference to look for ways of lifting oil from wells that also required producing large amounts of water. Arutunoff and Phillips signed a contract to field test the concept in the El Dorado field near Burns, Kansas. After a successful test, Bart Mfg. was organized. On 15 March 1930, Phillips sold his rights to Charley Brown, a Bart stockholder and executive in Marland Oil Co., and Arutunoff. This was the birth of REDA Pump Co. In 1969, REDA merged with TRW Inc., and in 1987, it was sold to Camco Intl., which merged with Schlumberger in 1998.

In 1957, a second company was established. This product line started at the Byron Jackson Pump facility in Vernon, California. Byron Jackson was a division of Borg Warner Corp. In 1959, the oilfield product line of Byron Jackson Pump was moved to Tulsa and quickly became known as a "BJ" pump. In 1979, it became Centrilift Inc., a subsidiary of Borg Warner Corp., and was moved to Claremore, Oklahoma, in 1980. Just after the relocation in 1980, Centrilift was sold to Hughes Tool Co. Then, in 1987, Hughes Tool and Baker Intl. merged to become Baker Hughes Inc.

In 1962, Goulds Pump Oil Field Submergible Division approached Franklin Electric to find a better motor for their oilfield-pump product. By 1967, they had designed a new product and had formed a joint venture company, Oil Dynamics Inc. (ODI). In 1997, ODI was sold to Baker Hughes Inc., and its product line was merged into Centrilift's.

The story behind the third company becomes a little more convoluted. In 1965, Hydrodynamics was formed as a part of Peerless Pump to develop an oilfield submersible product. After limited financial success, it was sold to FMC Corp. and renamed Oiline. In 1976, it was sold again, this time to Kobe, and became Kobe Oiline. Kobe was sold to Trico in 1983, but the Kobe Oiline product was spun off to Baker Intl., and it became Bakerlift Systems. Trico had also just purchased the Standard Pump water-well line from REDA. A side branch to this tree starts with the emergence of Western Technologies in 1978. It was sold to Dresser Industries and renamed WesTech in 1982. Then, in 1985, it was sold to Bakerlift Systems. When Baker Intl. and Hughes merged in 1987, the U.S. operation of Bakerlift was divested and sold to Trico, but Baker Hughes retained the international segment of the Bakerlift business. Trico's product line was made up of equipment from Kobe Oiline, Standard Pump, WesTech, and Bakerlift Systems. It was renamed Trico Sub Services. On another side branch, ESP Inc. was formed in 1983. Wood Group purchased it in 1990. Then, in 1992, Trico Sub Services was purchased by Wood Group and was merged into ESP Inc.

13.3 ESP System
The normal ESP system configuration is shown in **Fig. 13.1**. It shows a tubing-hung unit with the downhole components comprising of a multistage centrifugal pump with either an integral intake or separate, bolt-on intake; a seal-chamber section; and a three-phase induction motor, with or without a sensor package. The rest of the system includes a surface control package and a three-phase power cable running downhole to the motor. Because of the ESP's unique application requirement in deep, relatively small-bore casings, the equipment designer and manufacturer are required to maximize the lift of the pump and the power output of the motor as a function of the diameter and length of the unit. Therefore, the equipment is typically long and slender. The components are manufactured in varying lengths up to approximately 30 ft, and for certain applications, either the pump, seal, or motor can be multiple components connected in series.

Throughout their history, ESP systems have been used to pump a variety of fluids. Normally, the production fluids are crude oil and brine, but they may be called on to handle liquid petroleum products; disposal or injection fluids; and fluids containing free gas, some solids or contaminates, and CO_2 and H_2S gases or treatment chemicals. ESP systems are also environmentally esthetic because only the surface power control equipment and power cable run from the controller to the wellhead are visible. The controller can be provided in a weatherproof,

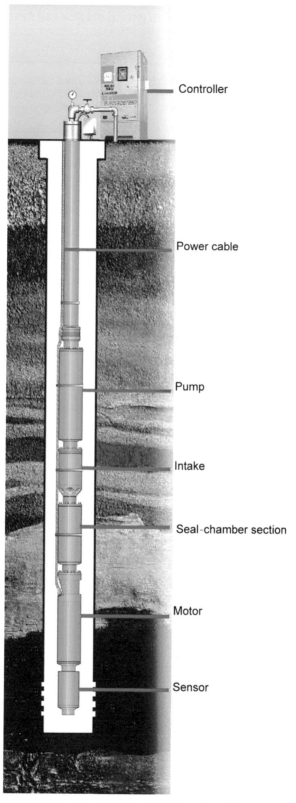

Fig. 13.1—ESP system configuration [after Centrilift Graphics, Claremore, Oklahoma (2003)].

TABLE 13.1—API RECOMMENDED PRACTICES FOR ESP SYSTEMS

Document Number	Document Title	Scope
RP11S	Recommended Practice for the Operation, Maintenance, and Troubleshooting of Electric Submersible Pumps	Covers all the major components that form the standard ESP pumping system—operation, maintenance, and troubleshooting. It is specifically prepared for installations in oil/water producing wells where the equipment is installed on tubing.
RP11S1	Recommended Practice for Electric Submersible Pump Teardown Report	Covers the recommended ESP teardown report form. It also includes equipment schematic drawings which may provide assistance in identifying equipment components.
RP11S2	Recommended Practice for Electric Submersible Pump Testing	Provides guidelines and procedures covering ESP pump performance testing intended to establish product consistency. It covers the acceptance testing of ESP pumps (sold as new) by the manufacturer, vendor, or user to the prescribed minimum specifications.
RP11S3	Recommended Practice for Electric Submersible Pump Installations	Covers the installation and replacement of all major components that form the typical, ESP system. Specifically, it covers installations in oil/gas operations where the equipment is installed on tubing. It does not cover equipment selection or application.
RP11S4	Recommended Practice for Sizing and Selection of Electric Submersible Pump Installations	Addresses the fundamental procedures for sizing and selecting ESPs and related equipment for various well conditions.
RP11S5	Recommended Practice for Application of Electric Submersible Cable Systems	Covers the materials and application of ESP cable systems.
RP11S6	Recommended Practice for Testing of Electric Submersible Pump Cable Systems	Covers the testing of ESP cable systems. It includes only the field testing category, not factory testing.
RP11S7	Recommended Practice for Application and Testing of Electric Submersible Pump Seal Chamber Sections	It contains tutorial, testing, and failure evaluation information. It provides a general understanding of the construction and functioning of seal-chamber sections and identification of well conditions, system requirements, and characteristics that influence component selection and application.
RP11S8	Recommended Practice for Electric Submersible Pump System Vibrations	Provides guidelines to establish consistency in control and analysis of ESP system vibration. It covers the vibration limits, testing, and analysis of ESP systems and subsystems.

outdoor version or an indoor version for placement in a building or container. The control equipment can be located within the minimum recommended distance from the wellhead or, if necessary, up to several miles away. API *RP11S3* provides the guidelines for the proper installation and handling of an ESP system.[3] All the API recommended practices for ESPs are listed in **Table 13.1**, some of which are discussed later in this chapter.

13.3.1 Centrifugal Pump. The ESP is a multistage centrifugal type. A cross section of a typical design is shown in **Fig. 13.2**. The pumps function is to add lift or transfer pressure to the fluid so that it will flow from the wellbore at the desired rate. It accomplishes this by imparting kinetic energy to the fluid by centrifugal force and then converting that to a potential energy in the form of pressure.

In order to optimize the lift and head that can be produced from various casing sizes, pumps are produced in several diameters for application in the most common casing sizes. **Table 13.2** lists some common unit diameters, flow ranges, and typical casing sizes in which they fit.

Functional Features. *Shaft.* The shaft is connected to the seal-chamber section and motor by a spline coupling. It transmits the rotary motion from the motor to the impellers of the pump stage. The shaft and impellers are keyed, and the key transmits the torque load to the impeller. As was mentioned earlier, the diameter of the shaft is minimized as much as possible because of the restrictions placed on the pump outside diameter. Therefore, there are usually several shaft material options available, depending on the maximum horsepower (HP) load and corrosion protection required.

Housing. The housing is the pressure-containing skin for the pump. It holds and aligns all the components of the pump. There are several material options available for different application environments. For additional corrosion protection, there are several coatings that can be applied.

Discharge Head/Tubing Connection. The discharge head provides a female threaded connection to the production tubing. There are usually several thread forms and sizes to select from.

Pump Base. Several different styles of intakes can be selected. They allow for entrance of the fluid into the bottom of the pump and direct it into the first stage. Integral intakes can be threaded directly into the bottom of the housing during the manufacturing assembly process, while others are separate components, which are bolted on to the bottom pump flange.

A standard intake has intake ports that allow fluid to enter the pump. It is used when the fluid is all liquid or has a very low free-gas content. The intake shown in Fig 13.2 would be a standard intake if the reverse-flow screen were omitted.

A reverse-flow intake is used when the free-gas content in the fluid is high enough to cause pump-performance problems. The pump in Fig. 13.2 is shown with a reverse-flow design. The produced fluid with free gas flows up the outside of the reverse-flow intake screen, makes a 180° turn to enter through the perforations or holes at the top of the screen, flows back down to the intake ports and then back up to the first pump stage. These reversals in direction allow for a natural separation of the lighter gases from the liquid. The separated gas travels up the casing annulus and is vented at the wellhead. Another style is shown in the right-hand graphic of **Fig. 13.3**, which has a longer reversing path than does the intake with the screen.

The next step in handling free gas with an ESP involves downhole mechanical separation devices such as separator intakes. These devices take the fluid that enters its intake ports, impart a centrifugal force to it, vent the lighter-density fluid back to the annulus, and transfer the heavier-density fluid to the first pump stage. The heavier-density fluid, which is routed to the pump, has been either fully or partially degassed. Two of these devices are shown in the left-hand and center graphics of Fig. 13.3. The first device is the vortex-type separator. The produced fluid, which has already undergone some natural annular separation, is drawn into the unit through the intake ports. These can be straight intake ports, as already mentioned, or a reverse-flow-intake style. The fluid is then boosted to the vortex generator by the positive-displacement inducer. The vortex generator is generally an axial-type impeller. It imparts a high-velocity rotation to the fluid. This causes the heavier fluids (liquids) to be slung to the outer area of the flow passageway and the lighter fluids (free-gas laden) to mingle around the inner area and the shaft. The fluid then enters a stationary flow-crossover piece. The crossover has

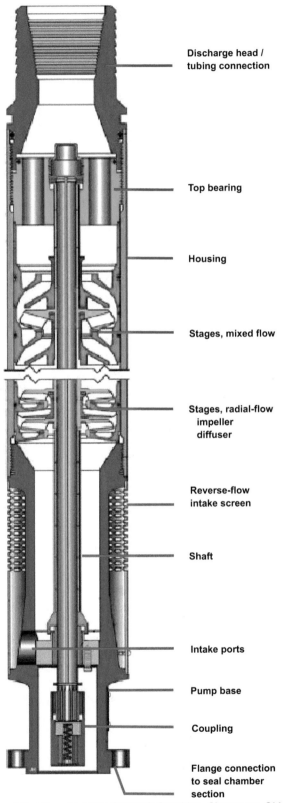

Discharge head /
tubing connection

Top bearing

Housing

Stages, mixed flow

Stages, radial-flow
   impeller
   diffuser

Reverse-flow
intake screen

Shaft

Intake ports

Pump base

Coupling

Flange connection
to seal chamber
section

Fig. 13.2—ESP centrifugal pump [after Centrilift Graphics, Claremore, Oklahoma (1990)].

TABLE 13.2—TYPICAL PUMP UNIT DIAMETERS AND FLOW RATES

Casing Size, in. (mm)	Pump Diameter, in. (cm)*	Flow Rate—Minimum, B/D (m³/d)**	Flow Rate—Maximum, B/D (m³/d)**
4 ½ (114.3)	3.38 (8.57)	550	3,100
5 ½ (139.7)	4.00 (10.16)	150	6,800
6 ⅝ (168.3)	5.13 (13.02)	750	12,000
7 (177.8)	5.38 (13.65)	900	18,400
7 ⅝ (193.7)	5.62 (14.29)	9,500	24,000
8 ⅝ (219.1)	6.75 (17.15)	5,000	46,000
10 ¾ (273.0)	8.75 (22.23)	10,300	32,200
13 ⅜ (339.8)	10.25 (26.04)	19,200	58,900

*This is the nominal diameter of the pump and not necessarily the maximum diameter of the ESP.
**These rates are based on the ESP operating at 60 Hz (3,500 rpm).

an outer annular passageway that takes the heavier-density fluids that enter it and directs them to the entrance of the pump. The lighter-density fluid that enters the inner annular passageway of the crossover is directed to the separator vents, where it exits to the casing annulus and flows up the wellbore.

The second device is a rotary centrifuge-type separator and is shown on the left in Fig. 13.3. It is similar in design to the vortex style, but it has a rotating chamber instead of the vortex generator. The chamber has several radial blades that are enclosed by an outer shroud or shell. The fluid that enters the chamber is centrifuged at very high g forces over the length of the chamber. Upon exiting the chamber, the fluid enters the flow crossover and follows the same processing as already described in the vortex style.

Flanged Connection to Seal-Chamber Section. The bottom flange of the pump bolts to the flange of the seal-chamber-section head. It maintains axial alignment of the shafts of the two units. It also allows the floating pump shaft to engage the end of the seal-chamber-section shaft so that the axial thrust produced by the pump is transferred to the thrust bearing in the seal-chamber section.

Stages. The stages of the pump are the components that impart a pressure rise to the fluid. The stage is made up of a rotating impeller and stationary diffuser. The stages are stacked in series to incrementally increase the pressure to that calculated for the desired flow rate. A graphic of the fluid flow path is illustrated in **Fig. 13.4**. The fluid flows into the impeller eye area and energy, in the form of velocity, is imparted to it as it is centrifuged radially outward in the impeller passageway. Once it exits the impeller, the fluid makes a turn and enters the diffuser passageway. As it passes through this passageway, the fluid is diffused, or the velocity is converted to a pressure. It then repeats the process upon entering the next impeller and diffuser set. This process continues until the fluid passes through all stages, and the design discharge pressure is reached. This pressure rise is often referred to as the total developed head (TDH) of the pump.

There are two styles of stages for the range of flow rates in which ESPs operate. The first is a radial stage. The impeller is shown in **Fig. 13.5** and the diffuser in **Fig 13.6**. Its geometry has the flow entering the impeller or diffuser parallel to the axis of the shaft and exiting perpendicular to the shaft, or in a "radial" direction. They are sometimes referred to as "pancake" or "mushroom" stages, respectively, because of the impellers' flat shape and the diffusers' mushroom-shaped downthrust pedestal. A cross-sectional schematic of a radial stage is shown in **Fig. 13.7**.

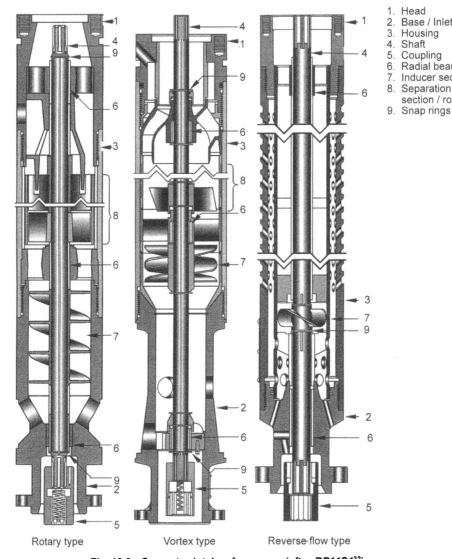

1. Head
2. Base / Inlet
3. Housing
4. Shaft
5. Coupling
6. Radial bearing
7. Inducer section
8. Separation section / rotor
9. Snap rings

Rotary type   Vortex type   Reverse-flow type

Fig. 13.3—Separator intakes for pumps (after *RP11S1*[32]).

The second is a mixed-flow stage; a typical impeller is shown in **Fig. 13.8**, and the diffuser is shown in **Fig. 13.9**. Its geometry has the flow exiting the impeller at an angle less than 90° to the shaft. A graphic of this flow path is shown in **Fig. 13.10**. Generally, this angle changes from near perpendicular to near axial, as the design flow rate of the stage increases for a particular-diameter unit. This relationship is shown in **Fig. 13.11**.

A key feature for both styles of stages is the method by which they carry their produced axial thrust. Usually, the pumps that are under a 6-in. diameter are built as "floater" stages. On these, the impellers are allowed to move axially on the pump shaft between the diffusers. Contrary to the name given to this configuration, the impellers never truly float. They typically run in a downthrust position, and at high flow rates, they may move into upthrust. To carry this thrust, each impeller has synthetic pads or washers that are mounted to the lower and upper

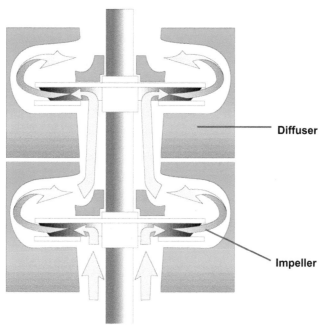

Fig. 13.4—Centrifugal-pump stage flow path [after Centrilift Graphics, Claremore, Oklahoma (1995)]

surfaces, as shown in the previous figures. These washers transfer the thrust load from the impeller through a liquid film to the smooth thrust pad of the stationary diffuser.

Three forces are involved in determining whether the impeller runs in downthrust or upthrust. The first is the downward force, and it is a result of a portion of the impeller discharge pressure acting on the area of the top impeller shroud. Two forces act in the upward direction. One is a result of a portion of the impeller discharge pressure acting against the bottom shroud of the impeller. The second is the force produced by the momentum of the fluid making its turn in the impeller passageway. A graphic description of the thrust forces on an impeller is shown in **Fig. 13.12**. Because the shaft is allowed to move axially and positions itself by contact with the seal-chamber section shaft, the fluid pressure causes a thrust load through the shaft to the seal thrust bearing. The thrust is the result of the force on the top end of the shaft (discharge pressure multiplied by the end area of the shaft) minus the force on the bottom end of the shaft (intake pressure multiplied by the end area of the shaft).

On 6-in. and larger pumps and on specially built smaller pumps, the impellers are usually fixed or locked to the shaft. These pumps are referred to as "fixed impeller" or "compression" pumps. In this configuration, all the thrust is transferred to the shaft and not to the diffuser. Therefore, the seal thrust bearing carries the load of all the impellers plus the shaft thrust. Particular care should be exercised in selecting the proper seal thrust bearing to match the fixed impeller pump conditions because these loads can be very high.

To maintain the optimum flow-path alignment between the impeller and its diffuser, the impeller is designed to maintain a downthrust position through its operating range. Usually, the impeller does not transfer into upthrust until its operating point is to the right of its maximum recommended point. Stage-specific thrust characteristics should be available from the manufacturers.

Performance Characteristics. The manufacturers state the performance of their pump stages on the basis one stage, 1.0 specific gravity (SG) water at 60- or 50-Hz power. A typical performance curve for a 4-in.-diameter radial-style pump, with a nominal best-efficiency perfor-

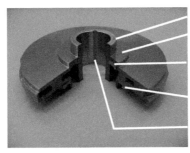

Hub

Upthrust pad

Downthrust
pad, hub

Downthrust
pad, eye

Shaft bore and
keyway

Impeller Top View

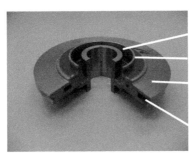

Impeller eye

Skirt

Bottom shroud

Flow passageway

Impeller Bottom View

Fig. 13.5—Radial-style impeller [after Centrilift Graphics, Claremore, Oklahoma (2003)].

mance flow of 650 B/D, is shown in **Fig. 13.13**. A mixed-flow style with a nominal flow rate of 6,000 B/D is shown in **Fig. 13.14**. In these graphs, the head, brake horsepower (BHP), and efficiency of the stage are plotted against flow rate on the x-axis. Head, flow rate, and BHP are based on test data, and efficiency is calculated on the basis of

$$\text{efficiency} = \eta_p = [Q \times \text{TDH} \times \text{SG}] / (C \times \text{BHP}), \quad \text{..................................} \quad (13.1)$$

where Q is given in gal/min, TDH is given in ft, and $C = 3,960$; or Q is given in m³/d, TDH = m, and $C = 6,750$.

The head/flow curve shows the head or lift, measured in feet or meters, which can be produced by one stage. Because head is independent of the fluid SG, the pump produces the same head on all fluids, except those that are viscous or have free gas entrained. If the lift is presented in terms of pressure, there will be a specific curve for each fluid, dependent upon its SG.

The dark (highlighted) area on the curve is the manufacturers recommended "operating range." It shows the range in which the pump can be reliably operated. The left edge of the area is the minimum operating point, and the right edge is the maximum operating point. The best efficiency point (BEP) is between these two points, and it is where the efficiency curve peaks. The shape of the head/flow curve and the thrust characteristic curve of that particular stage determines the minimum and maximum points. The minimum point is usually located where the head curve is still rising, prior to its flattening or dropping off and at an acceptable downthrust value for the thrust washer load-carrying capabilities. The location of the maximum point is based on maintaining the impeller at a performance balance based on consideration of the thrust value, head produced, and acceptable efficiency.

API *RP11S2* covers the acceptance testing of ESP pumps.[4] It also recommends the performance tolerance limits and describes the test procedure. One should pay particular attention to

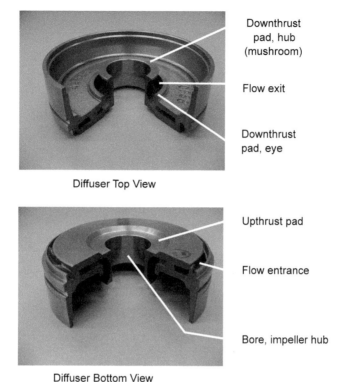

Diffuser Top View

Diffuser Bottom View

Fig. 13.6—Radial-style diffuser [after Centrilift Graphics, Claremore, Oklahoma (2003)].

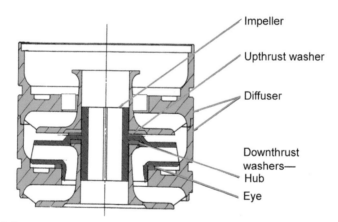

Fig. 13.7—Radial-stage cross section [after Centrilift Graphics, Claremore, Oklahoma (1990)].

the method of calculating the acceptable limits of the head/flow curve. A good layman's description of the method is given in Ref. 5. The limit is calculated by a combination of ± 5% head and ± 5% flow.

Several parameters are used to relate the characteristics of stages of different size, under dynamically similar conditions. They show that head (H) is a function of diameter (D) to the second power and also of rotating speed (N) to the second power. Flow (Q) is a function of diameter to the third power and also a direct function of rotating speed.

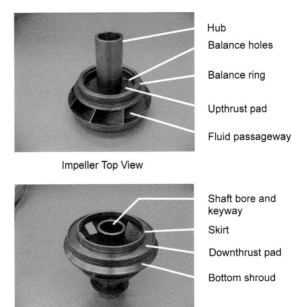

Impeller Top View

Impeller Bottom View

Fig. 13.8—Mixed-flow-style impeller [after Centrilift Graphics, Claremore, Oklahoma (2003)].

$$H_1 / H_2 = (D_1 / D_2)^2 = (N_1 / N_2)^2, \quad\quad\quad (13.2)$$

and

$$Q_1 / Q_2 = (D_1 / D_2)^3 = (N_1 / N_2) . \quad\quad\quad (13.3)$$

The BHP curve shows the power required to drive the stage. The power is lowest at shutoff or zero flow and increases with flow. The HP also follows the relationship that is given in Eq. 13.4 for different-sized pumps under dynamically similar conditions.

$$HP_1 / HP_2 = (D_1 / D_2)^5 = (N_1 / N_2)^3 . \quad\quad\quad (13.4)$$

Another performance-altering technique is to reduce the diameter of an impeller by trimming or cutting back its outside diameter. When this is done, the head, flow, and power are changed by the relationships shown in Eqs. 13.5 through 13.7.

$$H_1 / H_2 = (D_1 / D_2)^2, \quad\quad\quad (13.5)$$

$$Q_1 / Q_2 = D_1 / D_2, \quad\quad\quad (13.6)$$

and

$$HP_1 / HP_2 = (D_1 / D_2)^3 . \quad\quad\quad (13.7)$$

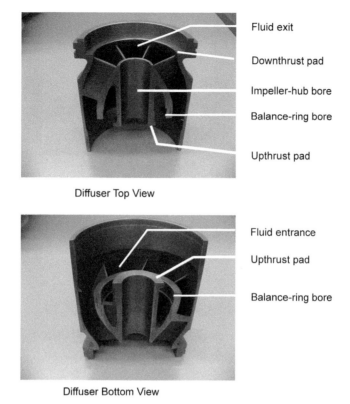

Diffuser Top View

Diffuser Bottom View

Fig. 13.9—Mixed-flow-style diffuser [after Centrilift Graphics, Claremore, Oklahoma (2003)].

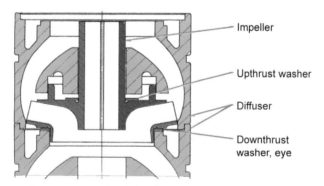

Fig. 13.10—Mixed-flow-stage cross section [after Centrilift Graphics, Claremore, Oklahoma (1990)].

For any particular-diameter-pump series, there is generally an overlap region between the radial and mixed-flow styles. A typical relationship of a family of similar-diameter stages is shown in **Fig. 13.15**. Notice that each style increases in efficiency as the flow rate increases, until the efficiency peaks and begins dropping off.

13.3.2 Seal-Chamber Section.[6] The component located below the lowest pump section and directly above the motor, in a standard ESP configuration, is the seal-chamber section (**Fig. 13.16**). API *RP11S7* gives a detailed description of the design and functioning of typical seal-

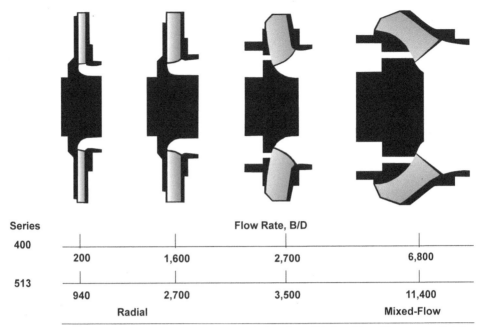

Series	Flow Rate, B/D			
400	200	1,600	2,700	6,800
513	940	2,700	3,500	11,400
	Radial			Mixed-Flow

Fig. 13.11—Centrifugal-pump stage design vs. flow rate [after Centrilift Graphics, Claremore, Oklahoma (1994)].

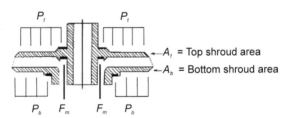

Fig. 13.12—Thrust forces on impellers (after Centrilift[41]).

chamber sections.[7] The following discussion repeats some of this information, but it is also intended to supplement the information contained in API *RP11S7*. The seal-chamber section is basically a set of protection chambers connected in series or, in some special cases, in parallel. This component has several functions that are critical to the operation and run-life of the ESP system, and the motor in particular.

• It protects the motor oil from contamination by the wellbore fluid. The motor is filled with a high-dielectric mineral or synthetic oil for electrical protection and lubrication. Well fluid migrating into the motor can potentially cause a premature electrical or mechanical failure through the reduction of the motor dielectric or lubricating properties.

• It allows for pressure equalization between the interior of the motor and the wellbore. Its design allows for a breathing or equalization method that compensates for pressure variances caused by the submergence pressure encountered during the installation from surface pressure to downhole static pressure and the thermal expansion and contraction of the motor oil because of motor heat rise during operation.

• It also absorbs the axial thrust produced by the pump and dissipates the heat that the thrust bearing generates.

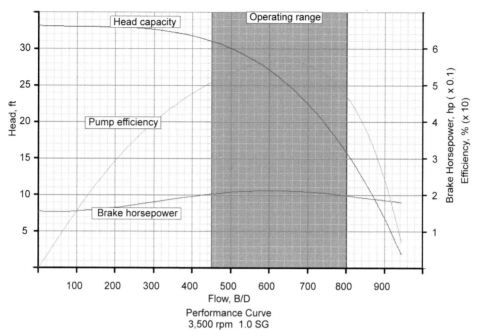

Fig. 13.13—Performance curve—650-B/D radial stage [after Centrilift Graphics, Claremore, Oklahoma (2003)].

Functional Features. *Shaft.* Usually, there are several shaft options available, and their selection is based on the fluid environment and the HP to be transmitted. Even though a majority of the shaft is exposed only to the clean, dielectric motor oil, the top end is exposed to the wellbore fluid. Therefore, the material must be an alloy that protects the integrity and function of the shaft. This could be the entire shaft or, at a minimum, the top section that is directly exposed to the wellbore fluid.

Labyrinth Protection Chambers. This chamber design features a direct fluid interface between the wellbore fluid and the motor oil. A typical design layout is shown in **Fig. 13.17**. It is commonly referred to as a "labyrinth"- or "U-tube"-style chamber. It is configured to have several concentric annular volumes that form a U-tube-type communication path for fluids coming in the top of the chamber to travel through to get to the exit point at the base of the chamber. This flow path is shown schematically in **Fig. 13.18**. In many mild applications, it is a very effective protection design. There are several application weaknesses that need to be considered. First, there is a direct fluid interface between the motor oil and the wellbore fluid in the top chamber. This allows the motor oil to be slowly wetted through a wicking action of the wellbore fluid, thereby, slowly degrading the dielectric strength of the motor oil. In some applications, high-density blocking fluids are used to retard or eliminate this motor oil. Second, gasses can permeate into the motor oil causing potential corrosion problems or burping and excessive loss of motor oil if there is a sudden decompression. Third, the labyrinth's effective volume decreases as the chamber is inclined. Therefore, they are not generally recommended at deviations greater than 30° from vertical.

Positive-Barrier Protection Chambers. This chamber incorporates a positive barrier between the wellbore fluid and the motor oil. The barrier is usually an elastomeric or rubber bag, which is also called a bladder. A typical design layout is shown in **Fig. 13.19**. The bag or bladder forms a seal between the motor oil inside the bag and the wellbore fluid between the bag and

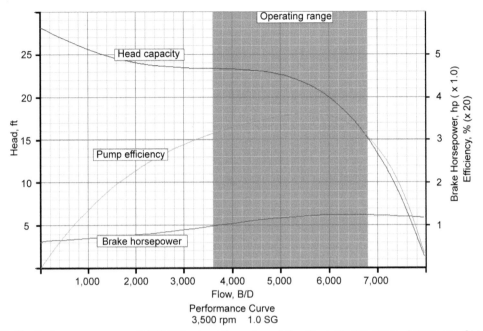

Fig. 13.14—Performance curve—6,000-B/D mixed-flow stage [after Centrilift Graphics, Oklahoma (2003)].

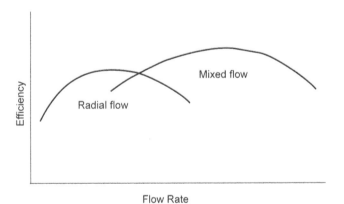

Fig. 13.15—Efficiency relationship of similar-diameter centrifugal-pump stages [after Centrilift Graphics, Claremore, Oklahoma (2003)].

seal-chamber section's housing. It also allows for pressure compensation by expanding and contracting in this annular area. The motor oil flow path is shown in **Fig. 13.20.** The barrier-style chamber is recommended for deviated-well applications. The bladder material should be resistant to the well fluids and any injected chemicals.

Mechanical Face Seals. A rotating mechanical face seal is generally located at the top of each protection chamber. A typical design is shown in **Fig. 13.21.** The rotating part of the face seal is sealed to the shaft by elastomeric bellows. The stationary part is sealed into the stationary component of the seal-chamber section. A spring preload force then keeps the rotating and stationary seal faces in contact. Once the unit starts rotating, a hydrodynamic fluid film is de-

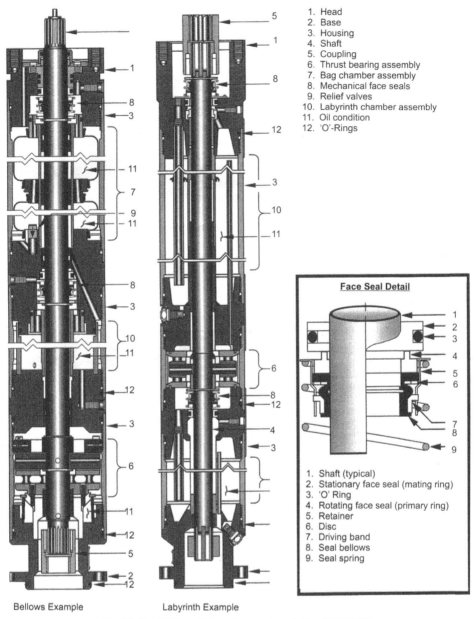

1. Head
2. Base
3. Housing
4. Shaft
5. Coupling
6. Thrust bearing assembly
7. Bag chamber assembly
8. Mechanical face seals
9. Relief valves
10. Labyrinth chamber assembly
11. Oil condition
12. 'O'-Rings

Face Seal Detail

1. Shaft (typical)
2. Stationary face seal (mating ring)
3. 'O' Ring
4. Rotating face seal (primary ring)
5. Retainer
6. Disc
7. Driving band
8. Seal bellows
9. Seal spring

Bellows Example   Labyrinth Example

Fig. 13.16—ESP seal-chamber section (after *RP11S1*[32]).

veloped on the face. This film then carries the load, prevents wellbore fluid from crossing the face by the pressure-differential setup, and cools the loaded face.

Axial Thrust Bearing. This bearing carries all of the axial thrust produced by the pump and seal-chamber section. Generally, sliding-shoe hydrodynamic types are used for this application because of their robustness and ability to function totally immersed in lubricating fluid. It is composed of two main components: a stationary pad and a rotating flat disk. The stationary part has pads finished to a very close flatness tolerance, connected to a base by a thin pedestal or flexible joint. The rotating disk is also finished to a very close flatness tolerance. Several

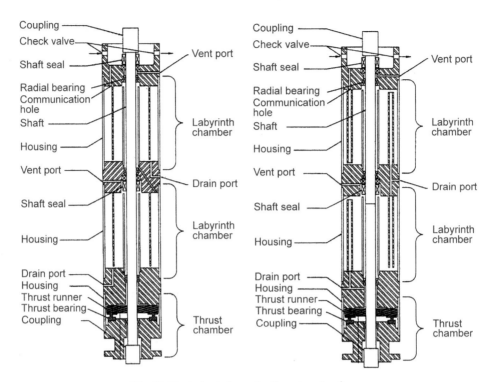

Fig. 13.17—Labyrinth-protection chamber.[6]

different bearing designs are shown in **Fig. 13.22.** They represent standard-style cast bearings for normal applications and machined bearings for intermediate- and high-load applications.

Performance Characteristics. When selecting the style and options of a seal-chamber section for an application, the user must consider the shaft torque, thrust-bearing load, volumetric motor oil expansion required, and the wellbore-fluid environment to which it will be subjected.

The shaft has to transmit, from the motor to the pump, the entire torque required by the equipment for its application. This not only includes the stabilized running torque but also the short-term torque spikes caused by unit startup and intermittent pump loads. Because the diameter of the shaft is constrained because of the maximum diameter of the unit, materials of differing mechanical properties must be used to provide different load capabilities. These materials must also provide protection from corrosive wellbore fluids.

The thrust-bearing performance is a function of the load that is transferred to it and the viscosity of its lubricating oil. The load transmitted from the pump can be calculated on the basis of the pump geometry and the TDH produced for the application. For "floater" pumps, the shaft load is always down and is equal to the cross-sectional area of the top of the shaft multiplied by the discharge pressure of the pump ($P_{discharge}$) minus the cross-sectional area of the bottom of the shaft multiplied by the pump intake pressure (PIP). For "fixed" impeller pumps, the load is equal to the shaft force, as just calculated, plus the summation of all the impeller thrust forces. The impeller thrust forces can be roughly calculated, as previously described in the pump-stage section, or obtained from the pump manufacturer.

The hydrodynamic thrust bearing depends on developing and maintaining a fluid film between the stationary pads and the rotating disk. This fluid film actually carries the load, not the running of the disk against the pads. In fact, if contact is made between the two components, heat is generated and rubbing can become severe enough to start bearing failure, even seizure.

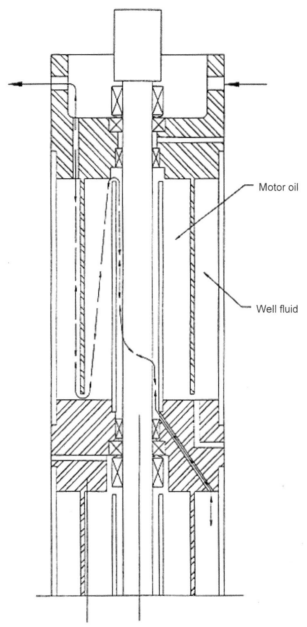

Motor oil

Well fluid

Fig. 13.18—Labyrinth-protection-chamber flow path.[6]

To maintain the proper film thickness, both the viscosity of the lubricating oil and the operating temperature of the thrust bearing are critical. Most manufacturers provide a range of lubricating oils, so the proper viscosity range can be provided at the estimated operating downhole temperature.

The seal-chamber section also adds HP load to the motor. It is usually a low value and significant only on lower-HP applications. Because each style of seal-chamber section has its own characteristics, the manufacturer should be consulted for these values.

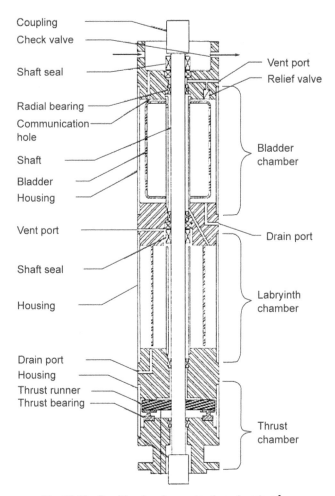

Coupling
Check valve
Shaft seal
Radial bearing
Communication hole
Shaft
Bladder
Housing
Vent port
Shaft seal
Housing
Drain port
Housing
Thrust runner
Thrust bearing

Vent port
Relief valve
Bladder chamber
Drain port
Labryinth chamber
Thrust chamber

Fig. 13.19—Positive-barrier protection chamber.[6]

The seal-chamber section also has to handle the volumetric expansion and contraction of the motor oil. This volume includes everything from the top of the seal-chamber section to the bottom of the motor. This expansion and contraction is a result of the changing temperatures and pressures the unit undergoes during operation. During installation, the unit goes from surface ambient conditions to wellbore setting-depth conditions. The impact of the increase in pressure does not have a significant impact on the volume occupied by the motor oil, as long as the unit is vented of air properly during filling. The temperature, on the other hand, causes the volume to change significantly. As the motor oil heats up during installation, it expands, and the volume that cannot be contained in the seal-chamber section, whether labyrinth or bag style, is vented from the top chamber into the wellbore annulus. When the ESP is started, it undergoes further temperature rise until it reaches its stabilized operating point. During this stabilization, it continues to vent any expanding volume of motor oil. Once it reaches a stabilized operation, the venting stops and the seal-chamber section and motor run at almost equal pressure with the wellbore. The next significant event is when the ESP shuts down. At this point, the motor oil temperature starts dropping from the operating temperature back down to

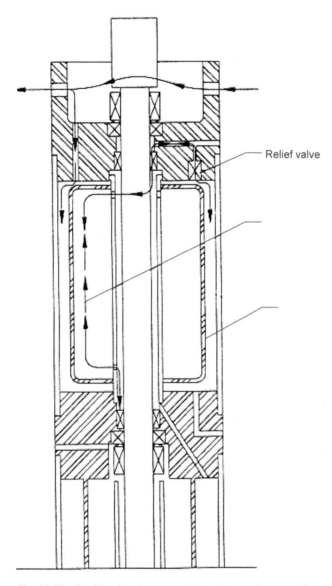

Fig. 13.20—Positive-barrier-protection-chamber flow path.[6]

the wellbore ambient. The pressure also increases from wellbore flowing to static. Once again, the temperature change has the largest impact and, in this case, on fluid contraction.

On a labyrinth style, well fluid is pulled back into the first chamber as the motor oil contracts back along its communication paths (Fig. 13.18). As long as the contraction volume does not exceed the volume of the first chamber, well fluid is contained in the first chamber. If the fluid contraction exceeds the chamber volume, well fluid is drawn into the second or lower chamber. With multiple thermal cycles, the well fluid can slowly be drawn towards the seal-chamber section thrust bearing and motor where it can be fatal or, at least, reduce the total run-life of the equipment. Because of the method of breathing, the labyrinth style is not recommended for well deviations greater than 30°. When the labyrinth chamber is tilted or

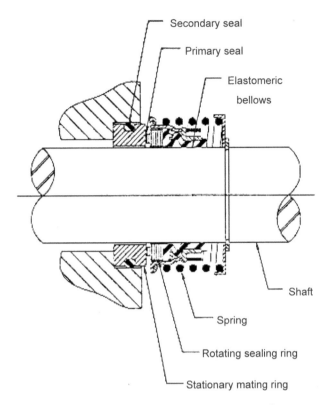

Fig. 13.21—Typical shaft mechanical face seal.[6]

inclined, the effective length of the labyrinth or U-tube communication path is shortened, effectively reducing the volume of the chamber.

The bag style, with its positive barrier, maintains a physical separation of the motor oil and wellbore fluid during expansion and contraction. Upon contraction, the cylindrical bag collapses around the center of the chamber, absorbing the contraction. Then, on a recycle or temperature increase, the bag expands to its original position before any motor oil venting is allowed. A more detailed explanation of these processes is found in the API *RP11S7* document.[7]

In recent years, many operators have begun to run multiple seal-chamber sections in series. This gains additional chambers or more protection between the well-fluid entry point and the motor. While this is true, it must be balanced with the fact that more motor oil fluid volume is also being added. More motor oil volume means more expansion and contraction. Because the first chamber volume is fixed, there is a better chance of operating over the capacity of this chamber. Therefore, the selection of which style seal-chamber section to use and how many to run is dependent upon the application. The proper selection is to choose the one in which the operational expansion cycle uses only a portion of the first chamber. In some very severe applications, seal-chamber sections with the first two bag chambers communicated in parallel instead of series have been used in an effort to handle the wellbore-fluid contraction volume.

13.3.3 Motor. The ESP motor is a two-pole, three-phase, squirrel cage, induction design.[8,9] A two-pole design means that it runs at 3,600-rpm synchronous speed at 60-Hz power or roughly 3,500-rpm actual operating speed. It operates on three-phase power at voltages as low as 230 and as high as 5,000, with amperages between 12 and 200. Generally, the length and diameter

Standard thrust bearing

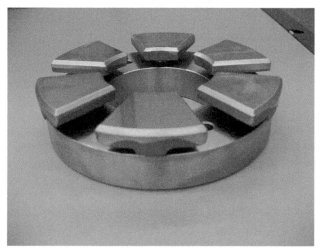

Intermediate-load thrust bearing

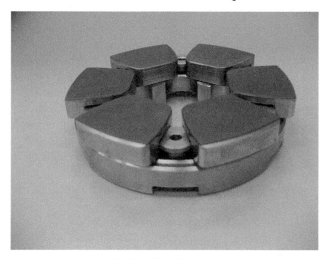

High-load thrust bearing

Fig. 13.22—Typical hydrodynamic thrust bearings [after Centrilift Graphics, Claremore, Oklahoma (2003)].

TABLE 13.3—TYPICAL MOTOR SIZES AND NOMINAL HORSEPOWER RANGES		
Motor Diameter, in. (cm)*	Horsepower Range**	Casing Size—Minimum, in. (mm)
3.75 (9.52)	8–195	4 ½ (114.3)
4.50–4.56 (1.43–11.58)	10–306	5 ½ (139.7)
5.40–5.44 (13.72–13.82)	18–750	6 ⅝ (168.3)
5.62 (14.29)	18–920	7 (177.8)
7.25 (18.42)	100–1,600	8 ⅝ (219.1)
7.38 (18.75)	200–1,020	8 ⅝ (219.1)

*This is the nominal diameter of the motor and not necessarily the maximum diameter of the ESP.
**These ratings are based on the ESP operating at 60 Hz (3,500 rpm).

determines the motors HP rating. Because the motor does not have the power cable running along its length, it can be manufactured in diameters slightly larger than the pumps and seal-chamber sections and still fit in the same casing bores. Typical diameters and rated HP ranges are shown in **Table 13.3**. A cross section of a motor is shown in **Fig. 13.23**.

Functional Features. *Wound Stator.* A wound stator comprises an unwound stator, electrical windings, and insulation and encapsulation systems. The unwound stator has thousands of electrical-grade steel laminations stacked in the housing and is compressed to hold them aligned and stationary. The laminations are die-punched with a center bore for the rotating components to fit into and 18 winding slots for the winding wire. Each slot is insulated with a very-high-dielectric-strength polyamide insulation material. This slot insulation provides winding-to-stator (turn-to-ground) electrical protection.

Insulated copper wire called "magnet" wire or "mag" wire is then wound into each slot to form three separate phase coils displaced at 120° intervals. The insulation on the mag wire provides wire-to-wire (turn-to-turn) electrical protection. Also, at the end of the lamination stack, where the coil has to make a 180° winding turn ("end turn"), insulation is placed between the first winding phase and the motor housing and then between each phase. This protects for phase-to-phase faults.

After the mag-wire winding and insulation is complete, the wound stator is then encapsulated with either a solid-fill epoxy or varnish coating. The encapsulation process fills the voids left in the slots and around the end-turn coils. This provides several important functions. First, it mechanically holds the windings to resist movement that causes wire-to-wire rubbing and possible damage to the wire's insulation. Second, it adds dielectric strength to the slot winding and end turns. Third, it significantly improves the overall thermal conductivity for better heat dissipation from the motor core through the slots to the motor housing skin. And last, it protects the winding from an attack by contaminates such as wellbore fluid. The last two are less significant for the varnish coating method. As its name implies, it is just a thin coating, mainly on the surfaces of the lamination slots and the mag wire, and has voids where motor lubricating oil accumulates, reducing both the thermal conductivity and the dielectric strength.

The length of the wound stator determines the number of rotors, which also determines the nameplate HP for a given-diameter motor. Within each given length or HP, there are numerous voltage/amperage combinations. Typically, there are various selections running from low voltage/high amperage to high voltage/low amperage. Voltages range from 440 to 4,000+, and amperages typically range from 15 to 150+ amps. The relationship of the HP, voltage, and amperage is

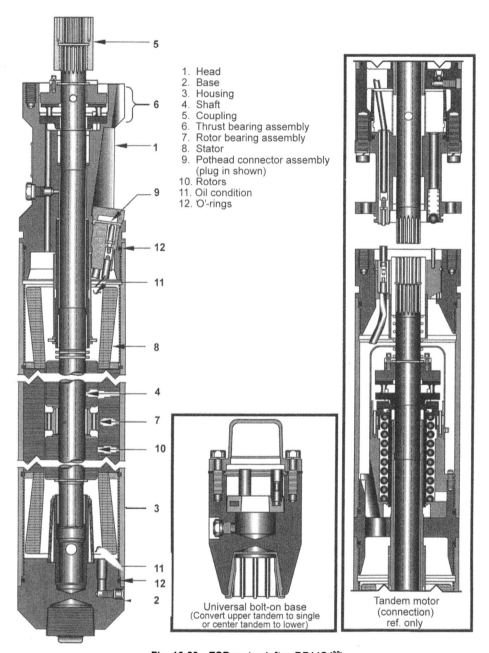

1. Head
2. Base
3. Housing
4. Shaft
5. Coupling
6. Thrust bearing assembly
7. Rotor bearing assembly
8. Stator
9. Pothead connector assembly (plug in shown)
10. Rotors
11. Oil condition
12. 'O'-rings

Universal bolt-on base
(Convert upper tandem to single
or center tandem to lower)

Tandem motor
(connection)
ref. only

Fig. 13.23—ESP motor (after *RP11S1*[32]).

$$HP_{output} = (V \times I \times 1.73 \times \text{power factor (PF)} \times \eta_m)/746. \quad\quad\quad (13.8)$$

Shaft. The shaft transmits the torque produced by the rotors, keeps all the rotating components aligned axially, and provides a path for the cooling and lubricating oil to the radial bearings and rotors. The shaft is generally tubular material, and the hollow core allows for the motor oil to communicate from the motor head and base areas to the hotter radial bearing and rotor areas. Because the shaft is completely immersed in clean oil, exotic corrosion-resistant materials are not required. Typically, the shaft material is alloyed carbon steel. Its straightness is also critical because of its close rotating clearances and high speed.

Rotor. Ideally, the rotor should be one continuous component that runs the length of the stator lamination bore. This would cause tremendous dynamic-instability problems because of the very large rotor length-to-diameter ratio. Therefore, the rotors are constructed in short segments with radial support bearings placed between them for dynamic stability. Rotors are constructed by stacking hundreds of thin, electrical-grade laminations between two metal end rings. Copper rotor bars are inserted into the lamination slots, the whole stack is compressed, and the rotor bar's ends are mechanically bonded to the end rings. This results in the "squirrel cage" rotor. The center bore of the rotor has an axial-keyway groove for engaging the axial key stock mounted on the motor shaft. This locks the rotor to the shaft for torque transmission but allows axial movement for thermal growth.

Radial Bearings. A sleeve-type-bearing system provides the alignment and radial support for the long shaft and rotor assembly. The sleeve part of the journal is keyed to the shaft and rotates with the shaft. The stationary part of the bearing has a bore in which the sleeve runs. It has an outside diameter (OD) that has a small clearance with the stator-lamination inside diameter. Also, the stator laminations at the bearing locations are made of nonmagnetic material to reduce the rotating magnetic field and the rotational forces tending to rotate the radial bearing. In some designs, an elastomer ring or locking key is located between the bearing OD and the stator inside diameter (ID) to prevent or retard any relative rotation. If rotation does occur, the bearing may start wearing into the stator until contact with the phase mag wires causes an electrical short.

Motor Head. The motor head contains the electrical termination for the connection of the three-phase windings to the electrical power cable. This connection is made in an insulated cavity either by a male/female plug-in design or a motor-wire to power-cable-wire splice. Also, a small thrust bearing is located in the head. It is designed to carry the weight of the shaft and rotor stack during startup and maintains the axial position of the rotors and radial bearings relative to the stator.

Performance Characteristics. The performance of a submersible motor is usually characterized by the manufacturer's performance curve. An example is shown in **Fig. 13.24**. The curve represents typical motor performance for a given motor diameter, based on the average of several tests. To get the curve data, a motor is loaded across a broad HP load range with a dynamometer. A detailed description of these tests is given in Ref. 10. Data collected include: three-phase voltage, amperage, kilowatts, speed or rpm, motor torque, motor temperature rise, and fluid velocity past the motor. The motor amperage, rpm, efficiency, and temperature rise are especially important for the proper application of any motor. Even though the motor temperature rise is measured during the dynamometer test, it is not generally plotted on the motor characteristic curve. This is because it is a critical parameter in the proper application of the motor, and its value is affected by several application conditions.

Amperage. The motor current is nearly linear with HP loading and is one of the easiest parameters to measure. Because of this, it is the most useful for determining the actual loading of the motor. On the basis of nameplate current rating of the motor and the amperage curve of the motor characteristics, an output HP can be determined. Calculate the percentage of nameplate amps in which the motor runs, and determine the percent of nameplate HP the motor is developing.

Revolutions per Minute (RPM). The rotational speed or RPM of the motor at its application load point is very important in determining the operating point or output of the pump. The pump-performance curve used in determining the head and flow output of the pump for its application is based on a pump-motor speed of 3,500 RPM. If the RPM varies from 3,500, the pump flow will vary with the ratio of the speed, and the flow rate will vary with the ratio of the

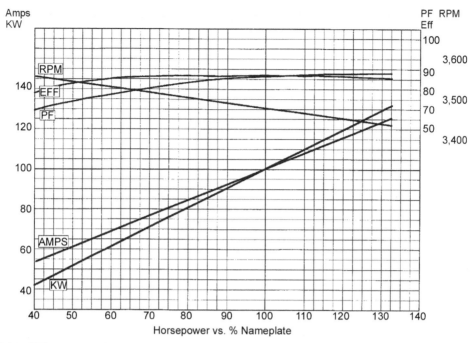

Fig. 13.24—ESP-motor performance curve—example [after Centrilift Graphics, Claremore, Oklahoma (1995)].

speed squared. (See Eqs. 13.1 and 13.2.) Once again, by knowing the percent of nameplate amps, the motor speed can be read from the motor characteristic curve. Even though this RPM change is usually small, it can still impact the final motor and pump operating point for a particular application. When the pump-performance point is modified, because of the motor RPM, the pump head and flow rate change; therefore, the load on the motor is changed. Determining the final pump operating point and motor loading point becomes an iterative process.

Efficiency. Because power costs are a major part of the overall expense of operating an ESP, the efficiency of the motor is an important factor. The efficiency curve for a submersible motor has a fairly flat peak through its normal operating range but starts dropping off significantly at less than 50% loading. Note that this efficiency curve is based on the nameplate voltage being maintained at the motor. If the surface power is not optimized, the voltage delivered to the motor can vary, and the efficiency drops off. **Fig. 13.25** shows the constant motor HP plotted as a function of current and voltage. It indicates that as the motor voltage is increased or decreased away from its nameplate rating, the current increases, resulting in a decrease in efficiency. Therefore, the ESP-motor operating efficiency can be optimized by adjusting the surface voltage and monitoring the motor amperage until the bottom of the current or amps curve is found.

Motor Temperature Rise. The temperature-rise data of the motor, where provided, are an indication of the average winding temperature rise above the ambient motor temperature. At test conditions, with water circulating by the motor at 1 ft/sec, submersible motors typically have rises of 50 to 100°F (10 to 38°C). Under wellbore-application conditions, the temperature rise is affected by various parameters, including: the velocity and thermal-conductivity characteristics of the production fluid flowing past the motor skin, API gravity of the crude, water cut, the percentage of free gas, fluid emulsions, fluid scaling tendencies, voltage imbalance at the motor terminals, and the use of a variable-speed drive. Typically, the industry guideline has

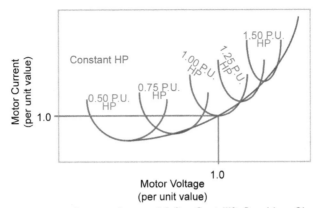

Fig. 13.25—Motor horsepower vs. voltage and current [after Centrilift Graphics, Claremore, Oklahoma (1985)].

been a 1-ft/sec flow by the motor, but there are many applications with velocities below this. The manufacturers have a method for calculating or estimating the impact of these parameters on the heat rise of their motors.

The rating of a motor or its nameplate HP is determined by its designer, on the basis of these same performance-test values.[11] Specifically, the designer is interested in the voltage, amperage, and HP ratings that provide the best motor performance for general operating conditions. Additionally, there are only three absolute limits that also influence the nameplate HP rating. These limits include mechanical, torque, and temperature.

Mechanical Limit. The mechanical constraints applied to the motor rating are determined by the maximum torsional-load capability of the design and materials. This limit is based on the mechanical strength properties and the geometry of the shaft.

Torque Limit. Here, the designer is looking at the maximum torque of the motor at rated voltage. For a particular motor design, a motor can produce only a given amount of torque for the volume of available active material. The active material is the material that contributes to producing magnetic flux. The maximum amount of torque a motor can produce is called breakdown or pullout torque. The breakdown torque of the motor is usually greater than 2.5 times the existing running torque, which poses no practical limit to the HP rating.

Changing the frequency of the electrical power can also vary the torque or HP rating of the motor. Generally, the motor's HP rating is based on either 50- or 60-Hz power. A fixed frequency motor has a specified full-load nameplate HP at the specified nameplate voltage, as stated earlier. This same torque can be achieved at other speeds by varying the voltage in proportion to the frequency. This maintains a constant magnetizing current and flux density, which provides a constant available torque. Therefore, the HP output rating of the motor is directly proportional to the frequency or speed (Eq. 13.9) because power rating is a function of torque (ft-lbf) multiplied by speed (Eq. 13.10).

$$HP_1 / HP_2 = Freq_1 / Freq_2 = N_1 / N_2, \quad\quad\quad (13.9)$$

and

$$HP_m = (T \times N) / 5{,}250. \quad\quad\quad (13.10)$$

Temperature Limit. For this limit, the designer is interested in the maximum temperature rating of the insulation system and the motor bearing lubrication system. The high-tech insulation used in today's ESP motors allows an insulation temperature rating in excess of 500°F (260°C). The limiting factor is the motor bearing system. Even though significant advances have been made in bearing design and motor oil formulations, the maximum recommended operating temperature of an ESP motor is around 400°F (205°C). There have been application incursions above this, but they have generally been made with experimental designs or in applications where a reduced ESP run-life has been accepted.

An important application point is that the proper motor oil lubricating viscosity must be maintained at the motor operating temperature. Therefore, the manufacturers provide and specify several grades of dielectric motor oils to cover the range of motor operating temperatures. Each type of oil has a minimum and maximum recommended motor operating temperature.

13.3.4 Power Cable. The ESP power cable transmits the required surface power to the ESP motor. Typically, it is banded or clamped to the production tubing from below the wellhead to the ESP unit because it is not designed to support its own weight. It is a specially constructed three-phase power cable designed specifically for downhole well environments. The cable design must be small in diameter, protected from mechanical abuse, and impervious to physical and electrical deterioration because of aggressive well environments. They are available in a wide range of conductor sizes or gauges. They can be manufactured in either round or flat configurations, using several different insulation and metal armor materials for different hostile well environments. Cross-sectional views of flat and round cable construction are shown in **Figs. 13.26 and 13.27.** There are two very good documents that fully describe the design, application, and testing of ESP submersible power cables—API *RP11S5* and *RP11S6*.[12,13] This section will repeat some of the basic information and add supplemental information.

Functional Features.[14] *Conductor.* Conductors are copper wires that can be either a single solid configuration or multiple smaller strands. Solid conductors offer more advantages than their stranded counterpart. They are smaller, easier to clean and splice, do not adsorb gases, have a smoother surface to the insulation, which reduces electrical stress, and they are less expensive. Stranded cable offers more mechanical flexibility, but this is usually not an overriding benefit. Also, unless the voids in the strand are filled, gases can migrate up or down the cable more easily.

The copper conductor is generally tinned or coated with a tin/lead alloy when it is insulated with polypropylene. In certain well environments, direct contact between copper and polypropylene can cause "copper poisoning" of the insulation, which reduces its electrical strength and degrades its physical properties. Synthetic-rubber insulation does not react with copper, so the vast majority of all rubber-insulated ESP cables are made with bare copper conductors.

Insulation. There are two basic types of insulation used in ESP cable: polypropylene and ethylene propylene diene monomer (EPDM) synthetic rubber. Polypropylene or "poly" is the lower-temperature-rated insulation, a tougher material than rubber, and generally more cost effective. The insulation temperature rating for poly is 205°F (96°C), but it can be increased to 225°F (107°C) with the addition of an extruded protective layer of lead.[15] Above these temperatures, a rubber insulation is always required. The EPDM is the insulation of choice for synthetic-rubber-insulation cables. The compounding of the rubber, with more than twenty other ingredients, allows for it to be designed to have low oil swell, fairly low elongation, and a high modulus. By contrast, the EPDM formulated for surface power cable is not suitable for downhole oilwell service because of its excessive swell characteristic. Most high-quality EPDM-based insulation is rated for conductor temperatures up to 450°F (232°C).[16]

Insulation Protective Layers. The EPDM-insulated conductors need protection from the oilwell environment because of swelling in the oil. To provide protection from the oil and to control swelling, different types of protective layers are applied over the insulation. Starting from the lowest level of protection to the highest, these layers are discussed next.

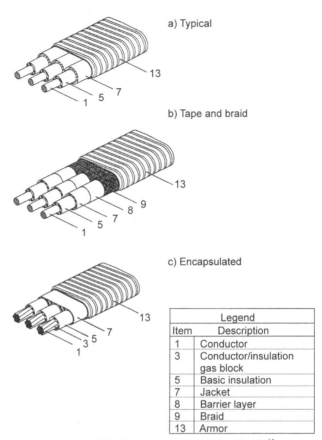

a) Typical

b) Tape and braid

c) Encapsulated

Legend	
Item	Description
1	Conductor
3	Conductor/insulation gas block
5	Basic insulation
7	Jacket
8	Barrier layer
9	Braid
13	Armor

Fig. 13.26—ESP flat power cable (after *RP11S5*[12]).

Tapes and Braids. Thin tapes of polyvinyl fluoride are wrapped over the EPDM-insulated single conductors. The limitation of the tape is that it has an overlap that allows oil to seep through. To make the tapes more effective, a 50% overlap can be used. To add some additional containment, braids can be put over the tape. Common braid materials are nylon and polyester, which have temperature limits in water of about 250°F (121°C). More expensive engineered filaments can be used to extend this temperature rating to 300 to 400°F (149 to 205°C).

Extruded Barrier. The next level of protection is a continuous extrusion of a high-temperature plastic layer over the insulation. The extruded barrier has no overlaps to let the oil contact the insulation. In addition, it increases the electrical strength of the insulation system. It also increases the chemical resistance of the cable, and in gassy wells, it regulates the rate of decompression of wellbore gases that have saturated into the insulation. Extruded barriers are made from fluoropolymers, such as polyvinylidene fluoride (PVDF) rated up to 320°F (160°C) and fluorinated ethylene propylene (FEP) (Teflon®) rated up to 400°F.

Lead Barrier. In wells that have a damaging amount of hydrogen sulfide gas, the copper conductors can be attacked and destroyed. To protect against this, a thin layer of lead is extruded over the insulation. For poly insulation, the lead increases the maximum operating temperature of the cable. For EPDM insulation, fabric tape or a braid is placed over the lead as a manufacturing aid to minimize distortion of the lead during armoring. This step is not required

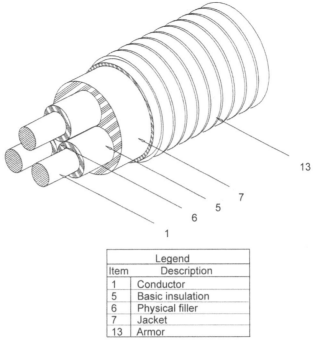

Legend	
Item	Description
1	Conductor
5	Basic insulation
6	Physical filler
7	Jacket
13	Armor

Fig. 13.27—ESP round power cable (after *RP11S5*[12]).

for poly, because it is harder and more difficult to distort during the armoring process. Generally, lead cables are manufactured in flat configurations but can be made in round configurations for added containment and protection.

Jacket. The jacket is designed to protect the insulation from physical damage. Also, in round cables, the jacket fills the space between the insulated conductors and the inside of the armor so that the armor can effectively contain the whole cable from oil and decompression swelling. Typical jacket materials include nitrile and EPDM rubber. Nitrile rubber has an operating temperature of 280°F (138°C) and is very resistant to oil swelling. As discussed in the insulation section, the EPDM rubber's properties can be varied by its compounding but is rated up to 400°F (205°C), and it swells in oil.

Armor. The metal armor that is wound around the three insulated conductors (flat cable) or the jacketed conductors (round cable) has a primary function of providing mechanical protection to the insulated conductors. On round cable, it has the added function of providing additional containment protection for oil swelling and gas decompression. The armor is usually made of mild galvanized steel, which is applicable to non- to mildly-corrosive wells. The galvanized armor is usually offered in several thicknesses, which increases the mechanical and corrosion protection. In more-corrosive applications, specialty metals are available, such as stainless steel and other alloys.

Flat Construction. The typical construction and geometry of the ESP flat power cable is shown in Fig. 13.26. It has the three insulated conductors laying parallel with armor wrapped around them, providing a lower profile when the clearance between the casing ID and production-tubing outside diameter (OD) is limited. Flat cable is not suitable for containing oil swell or gas decompression forces because of the interstices between the single conductors. If the insulation or jacket expands on a flat cable, it will deform the armor, bending it apart over its long axis and allowing the conductors to slide over one another. Insulation and jacket expansion can cause insulation splitting, leading to potential electrical failure. Flat cables, by virtue of their parallel conductor configuration, have an inherently induced imbalance. Flat-cable induced voltage and current imbalance is usually not a practical consideration in lengths less than 10,000 ft, unless the well is very hot and is pushing the thermal limits of the motor.

Round Construction. Round cable is superior to flat cable because it provides more protection to the conductors. Its typical construction and geometry are shown in Fig. 13.27. Round cable provides superior containment to the cable core, enabling it to better withstand decompression and oil swell forces without damage. Because pressure is naturally contained in a round shape and the space between the insulation and the inside of the cable armor is filled with jacket material, the cable armor acts to restrain and prevent any insulation expansion because of oil swell or gas-decompression expansion. Round cable is also naturally impedance balanced because of the equidistant spacing between the conductors. Therefore, there are no voltage or current imbalance issues affecting the motor.

Motor Lead Extension (MLE). The motor lead extension cable, also referred to as the motor flat, is a specially constructed, low-profile, flat cable. It is spliced to the lower end of the round or flat main power cable, banded to the side of the ESP pump and seal-chamber section, and has the male termination for plugging or splicing into the motor electrical connection. Because of its need for low profile, it requires compact construction. It generally has a thin layer of high-dielectric-strength polyamide material wrapped or bonded directly to the copper conductors. This allows for a thinner layer of insulation material, allowing for a lower profile. The MLE is generally selected on the basis of equipment: casing clearance and the voltage capacity requirement.

Performance Characteristics. The cable materials for the wellbore application should be selected from the guidelines already provided and by the cable manufacturer. These guidelines include:

• Insulation up to 205°F (96°C) uses polypropylene insulated cables. Over 205°F and up to 450°F (232°C), it utilizes synthetic rubber insulated cables.

• Gassy wellbores use a cable that provides protection from decompression damage. This is a construction that adds hoop strength to the insulation to contain the insulation from expanding and rupturing. Generally, tapes and braids, as well as extruded barriers, provide this protection.

• Hydrogen sulfide (H_2S)—generally lead barrier cables are used to protect the copper conductor from damage.

Once the proper cable materials have been determined for the wellbore environment, the only remaining variable is the conductor size. The conductor size can be optimized on the basis of motor voltage/amperage rating and the casing clearance. Because there are several motor voltage/amperage combinations available for the HP required for the application, the selection of the cable to match the motor can be based on either the surface switchgear and transformer available or the most favorable economic evaluation. The testing methods and acceptance criteria are discussed and provided in Ref. 17.

Cable Voltage Drop. Because of conductor resistance, there will be a voltage drop from the surface supply to the motor terminals. The voltage drop of a particular gauge cable can be determined from the cable voltage drop vs. the amperage graph shown in **Fig. 13.28**. This value is for a conductor temperature of 77°F (25°C) and a length of 1,000 ft. To determine the conductor temperature in its application, a power cable ampacity chart must be used. There is a separate curve for each conductor gauge and round or flat configuration. An ampacity plot for No. 2 American Wire Gauge (AWG) solid, round cable is shown in **Fig. 13.29**. In it, the various conductor temperatures are plotted against the current carried and the maximum well temperature. The temperature correction factor for the cable voltage drop can then be calculated with Eq. 13.11.

$$TCF_{cable} = 1 + 0.00214(T_{conductor} - 77), \quad \text{.......................................} \quad (13.11)$$

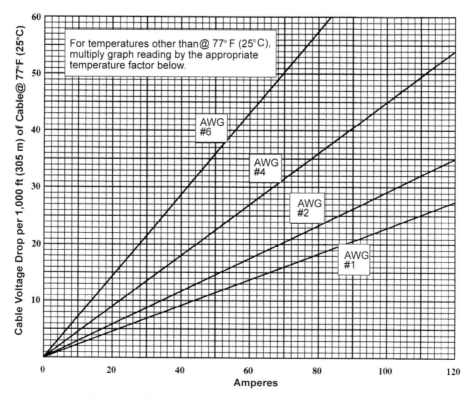

Fig. 13.28—ESP-power-cable voltage drop (after Centrilift[41]).

where TCF is the temperature correction factor for cable, and $T_{conductor}$ is the wellbore temperature at the ESP setting depth. This calculation provides a worst-case cable-voltage loss because it assumes that the entire cable conductor is at the same temperature. Computer sizing programs actually provide a closer estimation of the voltage drop because they consider the wellbore-temperature gradient from the wellhead to the ESP-setting depth and additional wellbore heating caused by the ESP-efficiency losses.

Once the voltage drop of the cable has been determined, the voltage available at the motor terminals can be calculated (surface supply voltage minus cable voltage drop). If the voltage delivered to the motor terminals is low compared to the motor nameplate voltage (typically < 50 to 60%), there could be motor starting issues. One should contact the motor manufacturer for application assistance in this case. If the motor HP and the cable length are known, the graphs, shown in **Fig. 13.30**, can be used for a quick approximation in the selection of motor voltage and cable size.

13.3.5 Motor Controllers. The surface controller provides power to the ESP motor and protects the downhole ESP components. There are three types of motor controllers used on ESP applications and all are generally specifically designed for application with ESPs. They include the switchboard, soft starter, and the variable speed controller. All units vary in design, physical size, and power ratings. They are offered in two versions: indoor, NEMA 1 and outdoor, NEMA 3. Normally, all utilize solid state circuitry to provide protection, as well as a means of control for the ESP system.

Motor controller designs vary in complexity from the very simple and basic to the very sophisticated, which offer numerous options to enhance the methods of control, protection, and

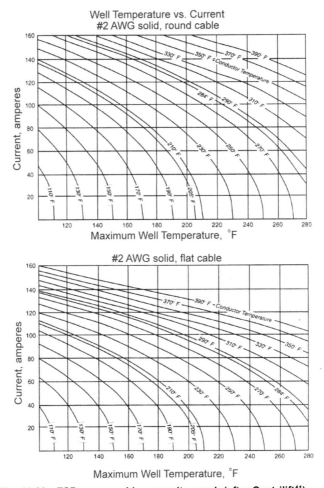

Fig. 13.29—ESP-power-cable ampacity graph (after Centrilift[41]).

monitoring of the ESP operation. The selection of the type of controller and optional features depends on the application, supporting economics, and the preferred method of control.

Fixed-Frequency Switchboard. The switchboard, fixed-speed controller, or across-the-line starter consists of a manual fused disconnect switch or circuit breaker, a motor starter, and a control power transformer. Because this controller is only a switch and does not modify the input voltage or current, it provides full-rated, instantaneous voltage to the downhole ESP system. The low inertia characteristics of the ESP allow for it to be at full rated speed within 0.200 seconds. During this starting process, the ESP motor can draw between 4 to 8 times its nameplate, or rated current, allowing it to produce several times its rated torque. This can cause excessive electrical and mechanical stresses on the ESP equipment in some situations. Normally, on deep-set systems with long lengths of power cable, the voltage drop, because of the cable, allows for a reduction in these stresses.

Functional Features. Disconnect Switch. The manual disconnect switch allows for the primary power to be shut off from the outside of the unit. It is also fused to provide circuit protection in case of power surges.

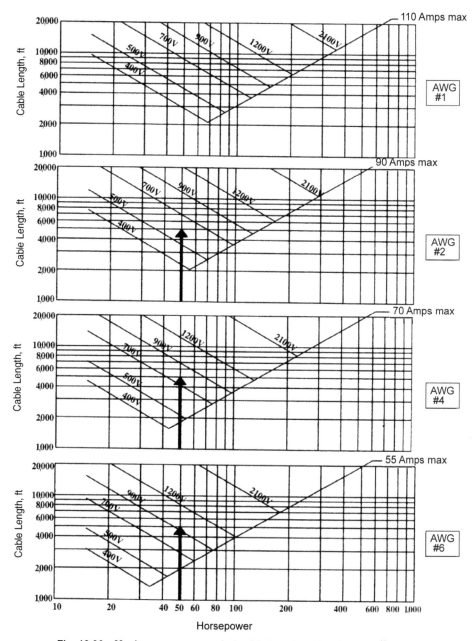

Fig. 13.30—Maximum recommended cable lengths (after Centrilift[41]).

Control Power Transformer (CPT). The CPT generally has multiple taps for selection of a range of output voltages. This allows a switchboard to be used within its rated range for different voltage- and amperage-rated motors.

Recording Ammeter. The recording ammeter historically has been a pen-type chart recorder that plots one leg of the three-phase current. Currently, there are digital monitoring systems available that monitor all three-phase currents. They also have capability to store the monitored data in memory and display these data in graphical format.

Control Module. These are solid-state devices that offer basic functions necessary to monitor and operate the ESP in a reliable manner. The unit examines the inputs from the CPT and other input signals and compares them with preprogrammed parameters entered by the operator. Some of the functions include overload and time-delayed underload protection, restart time delay, and protection for voltage or current imbalance. Additional external devices can be connected, which provide for downhole pump intake pressure protection, downhole motor temperature protection, surface tank high/low level controls, line pressure switches, and others.

Soft-Start Controllers. The soft starter is designed to reduce the high electrical and mechanical stresses that are associated with starting ESP systems. Typically, these are systems that are either on very short cables or are very high HP relative to their mechanical rating. The soft starter is similar to a standard switchboard, except that it is designed to drop the voltage to the motor during the initial startup phase. The drop-in voltage reduces the inrush current, thus "softening" the starting characteristic. These devices use either primary reactors or solid-state devices to control the amount of power delivered to the motor as it is coming up to speed. A soft starter typically extends the time for the motor to reach full speed from 0.200 seconds of the across the line switchboard to 0.500 seconds. After this startup period, the soft-start system switches off and the controller becomes a normal switchboard.

Most ESP design and application software programs evaluate the downhole system for these electrical and mechanical stresses and will advise as to whether a soft start is recommended. If a system is too soft, a motor could be damaged because of cogging or failure to reach starting speed.

Variable Speed Controllers.[18] A variable speed controller (VSC), also referred to as a variable speed drive, designed for use with ESP systems, was first used in the late 1970s. Since that time, the industry has seen a significant increase in their use. This increase has been a result of the benefits that variable speed ESP operations can bring to the artificial-lift application. With the benefits comes an increase in the complexity and cost of the total system. Therefore, to properly apply and receive the maximum benefit, the end user should understand both the potential benefits and cautions in using VSCs. Benefits include: a broadened application range of the ESP pump, optimal efficiency of the downhole system, maximum well production, electrical isolation of the downhole equipment from surface power disturbances, reduced starting stresses, production matched with surface processes, and maintenance improvements for operations in high free-gas applications. Cautions include: higher initial-capital cost, increased design complexity, interface with the electrical utility, additional motor heating, potential increase in voltage stresses, and possibly higher electrical cost.

One should appreciate and understand the potential for problems or damage to the downhole equipment if certain types of VSCs are not applied and operated correctly. Since the introduction of the first VSC, the design has been simplified and reliability increased. Also, the user understanding of the system and user friendliness of the VSC have been greatly increased. Both the benefits and cautions are discussed in more detail in Sec. 13.3.6.

VSCs used with ESPs should be designed for the specific requirements of the downhole ESP motor and pump. This is because of the unique design and characteristics of the downhole centrifugal pump and submersible motor as compared to their surface counterparts. Generally, the VSC is designed to provide a constant volts/hertz output through a broad range of frequency variations. The magnetic flux that is generated in the stator of the submersible motor and passes through the rotors is directly proportional to the voltage and inversely proportional to the frequency of the applied power. The result is a constant magnetic flux density in the motor. Because the output torque of the motor is proportional to the magnetic flux density, the motor is a constant-torque variable-speed device. Also, because of its low inertia characteristics and unique rotor design, it does not have the same high-operating-speed restrictions as a typical surface induction motor. Therefore, a VSC is typically applied to frequencies from 30 to 90

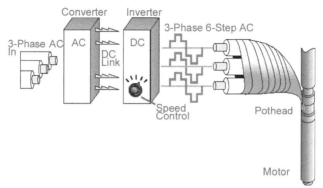

Fig. 13.31—VSC topology [after Centrilift Graphics, Claremore, Oklahoma (1994)].

Hz, with its minimum and maximum frequencies restricted only by the mechanical limitations of the downhole ESP equipment.

Functional Features. The fundamental building blocks of variable speed technology are an input rectifier or converter, a DC bus, and an output inverter, as shown in **Fig. 13.31**. In general, a converter is a piece of electrical equipment that changes electrical energy from one form to another. It may change the voltage and current magnitudes, change AC to DC or DC to AC, and change the frequency. VSCs applied to ESP equipment are AC to AC converters. They convert the input 460 volts, 60-Hz power (380 to 460 volts, 50 Hz) to output 40 to 480 volts, 10- to 120-Hz power.

Input Rectifier (Converter). This unit converts the input AC voltage and current to DC current and power. Current input rectifiers contain either diode bridges or silicon controlled rectifiers (SCRs). There are several types of input rectifiers, which are discussed next.

First, there is the three-phase full bridge rectifier. This most common rectifier in high-power electronics uses six devices, which are usually diodes or SCRs, to form the bridge. Two of the devices are connected to each of the incoming power phases. One device connects to the positive DC bus and the other to the negative bus. Each of these devices conducts during either the positive or negative half cycle of its respective phase. This means that we get two pulses on each incoming phase; thus, in total, it is a six-pulse converter. These converters are somewhat invariant and can cause input current total harmonic distortion (THD) levels of 25 to 35%.

Multipulse converter rectifiers are also used. They reduce input current harmonics in high-power electronic equipment. Most systems used today are multiple three-phase bridge rectifiers connected in parallel via phase or time-shifted power supplies. In multipulse systems, two pulses per phase are still achieved. Thus, the pulse number is always twice its input phase number. A phase-shifted power supply is accomplished by using a phase-shifting transformer. The transformer is connected to three-phase power and, through a vector combination of these three phases, develops the required number output phases. The most common multiphase system is a twelve-pulse bridge. It uses two six-pulse converters that are phase-shifted by 30 degrees. Normally, this converter can reduce the THD to a level of about 8%. Higher-pulse number converters further reduce the input current distortion levels. For example, an eighteen-pulse converter will produce less than 3% THD.

DC Bus. The DC bus of the VSC is composed of passive, noncontrolled devices. Typical elements include inductors, capacitors, and resistors. These devices form a damped low-pass filter to smooth the DC voltage and current that is provided from the input rectifier. Depending on the design of the VSC, the DC bus provides a smooth DC voltage or current source to the output inverter. Typically, in medium-horsepower VSC units, the DC bus is composed of multiple inductors, capacitors, and/or resistors to achieve the design voltage and current ratings. Some designs include only inductors; others have only capacitors and resistors, while some have all three. The selection of the design and size of the components determines the effect of the VSC's input current distortion and its overall performance.

Output Inverter. The output inverter converts the DC power provided by the DC bus to a variable-frequency, AC power. This inverter can be either a voltage or current source inverter. In a voltage source inverter, the output voltage waveform is controlled, and the load applied determines the output current waveform. The current source inverter is just the opposite. In it, the output current waveform is controlled, and the load applied determines the output voltage waveform. Most VSCs for ESP applications use the voltage source inverter.

Current Source Inverters. In a current source inverter, large inductors are used to supply a current source to the inverter. The current is normally controlled by an SCR. The current source inverter controls only the output frequency of the drive, while the input converter controls the current and voltage. The inverter may operate in six steps or with pulse-width-modulated (PWM) inverters.

Voltage Source Inverters. In a voltage source inverter, large banks of capacitors act as low impedance DC voltage sources for the inverter. The inverter changes the DC voltage by one of several switching methods. These methods generally fall into two categories: a variable voltage inverter (VVI) or constant voltage inverter (CVI). A VVI usually employs a controlled rectifier to control the DC bus voltage and, thereby, the output voltage of the inverter. In a CVI, the output is controlled by the method of switching.

Variable Voltage Inverters. VVI drives are most generally six step inverters. The unit consists of six switches, each turning on and off one time during every output cycle. The name comes from the fact that each cycle is divided into six 60° periods. During each period, there is a unique combination of power devices activated. This results in a phase-to-phase voltage waveform that has six identifiable "steps" to approximate a sine wave (**Fig. 13.32**). This is also referred to as a "quasisine wave" inverter. The inverter controls only the output frequency, and the electrical stresses on the power devices are significantly reduced over other output topologies.

Pulse-Width-Modulated Inverters. PWM inverters also consist of six switches, but they switch many times per output cycle to control both the output voltage and frequency. The voltage waveform is divided into many small time periods that range from several hundred to several thousand (**Fig. 13.33**). During each period, the instantaneous output voltage is approximated by a square wave at some duty cycle. A 100% duty cycle would represent full voltage, while 0% would represent zero voltage.

To generate a sine wave, these pulses start at zero width and build, sinusoidally, to 100% duty cycle at the 90° point on the waveform. Then, they would decrease in width sinusoidal to zero at the 180° point of the waveform. The output voltage level is the integral of these pulse widths of DC bus voltage height over any given cycle. This integration is performed by the inductance of the motor, and the resultant current waveform becomes more and more sinusoidal as more pulses are used. To vary the average voltage, each pulse width is multiplied by a scale factor (to get half the output voltage, each pulse must be one-half its original width).

The electrical stresses on the power devices of a PWM inverter are significantly higher than a six-step inverter. Each switching transition causes high losses in the power devices, occurring hundreds or thousands of times per cycle. Therefore, extra care must be taken to ensure that these electrical stresses are managed properly.

Control Module. This unit functions the same as explained in the switchboard section. When used with a VSC, the controller can be programmed to provide some speed adjustment depending on certain input conditions. If the input indicates the unit is approaching or is in a shut-down parameter range, the controller could send a signal to the VSC to change its frequen-

6 Step

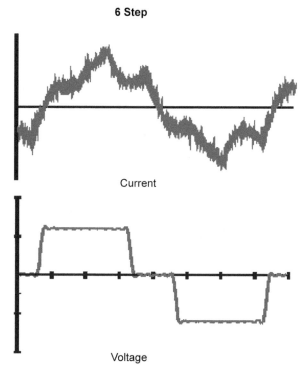

Fig. 13.32—Variable-voltage inverter waveform [after Centrilift Graphics, Claremore, Oklahoma (1998)].

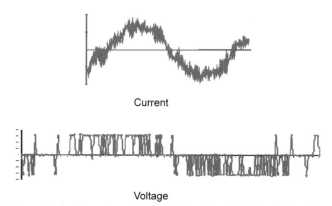

Fig. 13.33—Pulse-width-modulated-inverter waveform [after Centrilift Graphics, Claremore, Oklahoma (1998)].

cy, within its preprogrammed, allowable frequency range. If this specific parameter moved back into its preprogrammed operating range, the controller would maintain this VSC frequency until the next input parameter occurrence. In most cases, there is a preset time function for this adjustment to take effect; otherwise the unit would shut down.

13.3.6 Application Considerations. Because of the relationship of the performance of a centrifugal pump to its rotational speed (Eqs. 13.2 through 13.4), the VSC allows for wider flexibility of the downhole ESP system. The effect on pump operation is shown in **Fig. 13.34**. This is the same pump that is represented in the 60-Hz fixed-speed performance curve of Fig.

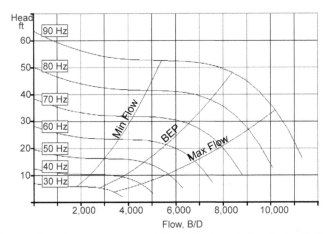

Fig. 13.34—Variable-speed performance curve—6,000-B/D stage [after Centrilift Graphics, Claremore, Oklahoma (2003)].

13.14. This allows the designer to select the flow rate and speed of the system on the initial design. For this pump stage, it can be operated between 1,800 B/D at 30 Hz (minimum recommended operating point) and 10,200 B/D at 90 Hz (maximum recommended operating point). The benefits of VSC usage are discussed next.

Broadened Application Range. On fixed-speed operation, a pump stage has a recommended minimum and maximum flow rate. Beyond these points, the pump can operate in a detrimental run-life or reliability area. By operating at reduced frequency, the minimum recommended operating point is reduced, and, at higher frequencies, the maximum operating point is increased. This allows the application of ESPs in low-productivity-index (PI) wells and higher flow rates to be obtained from small bore casings. It also allows a limited inventory of pumps to be applied over a broader flow range.

ESP Efficiency Optimization. Either when an ESP system is initially designed or after it is deployed, adjusting the frequency of the unit can maximize the total system efficiency. In light of wellbore PI uncertainties, this allows the operator some flexibility between the requirements of the initial design and the actual operating conditions of the equipment in the wellbore.

Maximize Well Production. If the well PI is greater than that for the original design, either through data error or changing wellbore parameters, the ESP operating point can be increased with a VSC. The HP rating of the motor limits the frequency increase. Remember, the HP load from the pump increases with the cube of the frequency ratio, and the HP capability of the motor increases directly to the speed ratio. Therefore, the designer must consider using an oversized motor if there is a potential need of higher flow rates.

Minimum Well Production. If the well PI is lower than that for the original design, the ESP operating point can be decreased with the VSC. The TDH of the pump is the limiting factor on the minimum VSC frequency. The produced head of the pump decreases with the square of the frequency ratio. Therefore, the designer must consider initially oversizing the pump lift, if there is a potential for reduced-frequency operation.

There may also be cases where the ESP is operated at reduced frequency to reduce stresses on the reservoir. This could prevent reservoir damage or control the influx of unconsolidated sand or frac materials because of sudden pressure differentials across the wellbore face.

ESP Electrical Isolation. In a fixed-speed ESP application, the downhole motor is connected directly to the power source via the switchboard contactor, with isolation only from the transformer and cable impedances. When a VSC is connected, automatic isolation occurs. The input converter and output inverter are decoupled or isolated by the DC bus. Also, high-energy transients open fuses or destroy solid-state semiconductor devices in the VSC instead of potentially damaging the electrical components (motor, cable, electrical penetrators downhole).

Matching Surface Processes. If the well has any surface processing constraints, the wellhead flow and/or pressure can be controlled by the operating frequency. This would include items such as tank level control and flowline pressure. Also, where multiple wells are manifolded together and a constant flow rate is desired, any drop off in the rate of one or more wells can be made up by an increase in speed to one or more wells.

Reduced Starting Stresses. With a VSC, maximum current starting levels can be controlled. At startup, the frequency to produce minimum starting torque can be used with a controlled ramp up to operational speeds and power settings. This produces the optimum soft start. With any added benefits and capabilities, there are also some cautions.

Increased Design Complexity. The ESP application design becomes much more complex with the use of a VSC and, in all practicality, requires the use of a design software program to do it properly.

Utility Interface. When using a VSC, it is desirable not to feedback problems to the utility-power system that could interact with other users on the system. The problems could include a poor input power factor or high-input current distortion (harmonics). A poor power factor leads to unnecessarily high-input current levels, thereby reducing the overall capacity to serve other loads. Input current distortion, which is injected into the power system, can reduce the life of other equipment connected to the system or cause electronic devices to malfunction. Ref. 18 gives a detailed description of the impact of VSCs on these two utility concerns—how each VSC topology measures up and the method to control or diminish the impact. The guidelines for the harmonic control of electrical power systems is provided in the Inst. of Electrical and Electronic Engineers (IEEE) *Stand. 519-1992.*[19]

ESP Interface. To fully achieve the benefits that a VSC can bring to an ESP application, care must be taken to understand its impact on the downhole system and minimize any potential damaging influences. Several concerns include: excessive motor heating, increased voltage stress, and maximization of motor torque performance.

Motor Heating. Excessive motor heat can impact the motors performance and, in the long term, its overall life. Operation of an ESP motor with a VSC causes additional heating from two main sources: increased winding losses because of higher current values and increased core losses because of high-frequency components. Because all drives provide a modified sine wave to the motor, it is distorted and contains other frequency components. Therefore, the total current values of VSC operation over across-the-line values are higher. This increased current level produces higher resistive losses in the motor windings, causing increased heat. Increased core losses, because of the changes in applied terminal voltage, also result in higher motor temperatures. When the motor core experiences changes in the applied terminal voltage, the magnetic dipoles must realign to the new magnetic field present. Every time this happens, the friction of the motion of the dipoles releases heat. Therefore, it is important to minimize the subcycle voltage fluctuations at the motor terminals, although testing has shown heat rise to be very small.

Increased Voltage Stress. Even though the VSC is a buffer to input power surges or spikes, their power inverters have the potential to generate higher peak voltages than those from a true sinusoidal voltage source. This is because inverters are inherently digital in nature rather than analog. Basically, the output can only change in discrete voltage steps and the transition from step to step happens very rapidly. When this power is applied to the complex impedance of a downhole ESP system, the natural response is a damped sine wave and the resultant ringing is a normal response. On a VVI drive, the ringing has time to decay to zero between each vertical edge of the waveform. On a PWM waveform, the vertical edge of the VSC output waveform can occur on top of the ringing of a previous vertical edge. Under the worst conditions, this effect can produce peak voltages in multiples of the original applied voltage, and they can occur many times per cycle. This impact can be reduced by the application of filters on the output side of the VSC and step-up transformer. Each PWM application should be reviewed for this potential condition, but, generally, the user should be concerned about high-voltage and -horsepower equipment and long lengths of cable.

Motor Torque. The ESP motor has the capability to deliver a large percentage of its full torque capability over a wide speed range. It is important to examine the VSC's capability to deliver the necessary current to achieve required torque levels. Any of the VSC types can be matched to the ESP motor when properly set up.

13.3.7 Accessories. There are components provided by the ESP manufacturers and other suppliers that provide additional mechanical and electrical protection, monitoring, or performance enhancements. Installation of such components on all wells may not be justified, but their use on key wells should be carefully considered. Several of these components are listed next.

Downhole Sensors. Because the ESP operates in a hostile and confined environment, monitoring how it operates is very difficult. Additionally, it is also difficult to find sensors and electronics that operate reliably and long term under the range of downhole conditions required. The ESP's reliability or run-life is directly related to the continual monitoring of its operating parameters and the wellbore conditions. Not only is this information critical to the run-life, but it is also important for the evaluation of the application design of the ESP system in the hole. This evaluation can provide guidance on possible operational changes that can be made to optimize the current system or the ESP design changes needed to optimize the application. If ESP systems were fully instrumented and continuous monitoring systems employed, improvements in run-life and operational performance would be improved significantly. But, to do this, the wellbore economics has to support it.

Sensors are available for mounting internally in the ESP components or externally as an attachment to the system. The signals from these sensors are communicated to the surface readout module by a separate instrument wire, "I"-wire, or by a signal imposed on one leg of the ESP power cable.

Typically, the standard ESP application only provides the opportunity to monitor surface parameters, such as three-phase amps and volts, wellhead pressure, and, to a limited extent, flow rate. Therefore, the protection and evaluation possibilities are reduced. Today, there are sensor packages available that provide measurement and monitoring of the following parameters.

Pump Intake or Casing Annulus Pressure. This information provides wellbore static pressure and the well flowing pressure at the production rate. If the measurement is sensitive enough, it can also provide excellent well drawdown information.

Internal Motor Temperature. This measurement is critical not only to the protection of the motor but also in selecting the correct motor HP rating and lubricating oil for the application. If a loaded motor is running close to its maximum temperature rating, some operational steps could be implemented to reduce its load and temperature. Also, the next unit in the hole could be derated or sized with a larger motor to run underloaded. Likewise, if the motor is running cool, there are future opportunities to install a smaller motor. Additionally, sudden temperature spikes or long-term gradual changes are an indication of changing equipment performance or wellbore conditions, which may need evaluation.

Pump Discharge Pressure. This parameter provides a reading on the discharge pressure of the pump. This reading and the pump intake pressure provide a measurement of the TDH of the pump. Comparing this value to the design TDH, hydraulic performance of the pump can be monitored and continually evaluated. Additionally, for gassy and/or viscous fluids, pump-performance correction factors can be established or verified for that particular wellbore condition.

Pump Discharge Temperature. This measurement provides the temperature of the discharge fluid from the pump. The production fluid is heated as a result of the heat rejected by the motor and pump inefficiencies. The fluid heat rise through the pump can be used to calculate the fluid volumetric increase and the viscosity change of the fluid. Once again, sudden spikes or longer-term changes can provide warnings of potential problems.

Downhole Flow Rate. Downhole flowmeters are available that provide flow-rate measurements from the pump discharge. This is an excellent tool, when compared to the surface flow rate, for evaluating ESP performance and warning of potential problems. Because surface flow rate is not generally continuously monitored, this can be a piece of information for enhanced ESP protection. In multiphase-fluid (gassy) applications, the selection and calibration of the flowmeter is important because of the difficulty in accurately measuring this fluid.

Equipment Vibration. There have been several applications that have used downhole vibration sensors. Unless there is a sudden step change in the measurement, this parameter is difficult to evaluate. There is a possibility that, with more case histories, this can become a good evaluation tool.

ESP Packers. Typically, ESP packers are used when there is a requirement or a need for it to be set above the ESP system (**Fig. 13.35**). Their use normally prevents venting free gas up the annulus, unless a vented packer is used. Packers can be shallow set or deep set, depending on design requirements or regulations. ESP packers have an electrical power cable feed-through feature added to the normal wellbore packer functions. A bore for an electrical feed-through mandrel is provided. Mating connectors are attached to the cable from the surface and another to the cable below the packer for connecting to the mandrel. This design allows for the maintenance of a pressure barrier, while still allowing for electrical power communication to the motor.

Packers are used with ESP systems when there is a need to isolate the annular area above the ESP and/or provide a positive barrier between the pressurized wellbore fluid and the area above the packer. Isolating the area above the packer is done to segregate two separate zones or prevent or reduce the rate of wellbore fluid corrosion damage to the casing. With a deep-set packer, operational precautions must be observed to prevent damage to the ESP system. With a deep-set packer, the volume contained between the packer and pump intake is usually small. Upon startup, the ESP can evacuate this volume quickly, causing a sudden drop from wellbore static to flowing pressure. This causes sudden decompression to the cable and internal volumes of the seal-chamber section and motor, especially if they have been saturated with solution gas. This decompression can cause expansion and insulation damage to the cable. If it is severe enough, it can result in extensive expulsion of motor oil from the seal-chamber section and motor, possibly rupturing elastomer seals and bags.

ESP Wellheads. The wellhead is designed to support the weight of the subsurface equipment and to maintain the surface annular control of the well. It is selected on the basis of casing and tubing size, maximum recommended load, surface pressure, and the power cable pass-through requirements. There are two cable pass-through designs. The first uses the compression of elastomer grommets around the power cable jacket to provide a low-pressure seal. It is used in many areas where the well has a zero to low gas/oil ratio (GOR). In areas where the annular pressure can be high or where safety requires a positive pressure barrier, the electrical feed-through mandrel design is used. A feed-through mandrel mounts in a cavity of the wellhead, sealing the annular pressure and providing electrical connection points above and below the wellhead. Mating electrical connectors (pigtails) are spliced to the upper end of the downhole power cable and to the surface power cable.

Centralizers/Protectorilizers. Centralizers are sometimes used when the ESP is installed in a deviated wellbore or into a tapered-string casing. Its function, when used in a deviated wellbore, is to be a contact point with the casing and allow the ESP unit to have some standoff clearance. They are typically located at the bottom of the ESP unit and, in some cases, at points along its length or at the discharge tubing. They have to be constructed so as not to

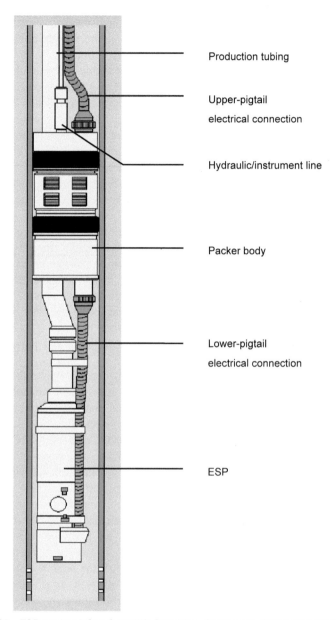

Production tubing

Upper-pigtail
electrical connection

Hydraulic/instrument line

Packer body

Lower-pigtail
electrical connection

ESP

Fig. 13.35—ESP packer [after Centrilift Graphics, Claremore, Oklahoma (2003)].

restrict the flow by the motor and to the pump intake. Generally, they are designed with at least three radial fins attached to either tubing, for the top and bottom unit or to metal straps, which can be attached around the ESP body. Centralizers are also used when an ESP is deployed into a tapered-string casing. Its function is to help guide the unit into and through the casing step to reduce the chance of mechanical damage. It is normally a finned configuration with the bottom end tapered or bull nosed.

Protectorilizers are used to protect the power cable, MLE, and any small hydraulic or electrical communication line from mechanical damage in deviated or restricted-clearance casing. Along the ESP unit, they are normally attached at the unit's flanged connection points and either cradle or cover the MLE and communication lines, so they become the rub points. Protectorilizers are clamped or strapped onto the production tubing for the same purpose. They are usually at the coupling points and midjoint. They also provide axial support to the power cable and replace the cable bands.

Check/Drain Tubing Valves. A check valve is used in the production tubing string, generally two to three joints above the pump discharge, to maintain a full column of fluid above the pump. This may be desired to eliminate the time it takes to raise the fluid from its static fluid level to the surface ("pump-up time") or the protective shutdown time for fluid fallback. Normally, each time an ESP cycles off, the fluid falls back from the surface to its static fluid level. On restart, it again has to lift the fluid from its static point to the surface. Holding the fluid in the tubing can eliminate this. Also, when the fluid is falling back, it causes the de-energized pump to spin backwards. If power is applied during this period, damage to the ESP could result. Generally, a backspin sensor or restart timer is used on the motor controller for premature restart protection.

The use of a check valve should be reviewed in gassy or high-GOR wells and wells that produce significant solids. In a gassy well, when the unit shuts down, a gas cap can form under the check valve and be held there by the fluid column above the check. If the gas cap volume is large enough to extend down to or below the pump intake, the pump will be immediately gas locked and unable to pick up a prime. When there are solids (especially sand) entrained in the production fluid and the ESP is shut down, the solids fall back in the production tubing and settle either on the check valve or into the pump discharge. This could either plug the tubing above the check valve or the pump. Therefore, the use of a check valve in fluids with solids should be reviewed.

Motor Shroud/Recirculation Systems. Shrouds, as shown in **Fig. 13.36**, are used to redirect the flow of production fluid around the ESP system. The shroud assembly is made up of a jacket (a length of casing or pipe), a hanging clamp and sealing retainer for the top, and a centralizer for the bottom. The jacket dimensions are selected on the basis of shroud location relative to the production source and the function of the shroud. But, at a minimum, the shroud should extend to below the bottom of the motor. The shroud ID has to allow for the insertion of the ESP with flow clearance to allow for proper cooling velocities without choking or excessive pressure drop to the flow. The shroud OD must have sufficient clearance with the casing ID to assure reliable deployment and proper flow from the well perforations to the pump intake. Fluid pressure drop in this annular area, similar to the shroud-to-ESP annular area, can be significant enough to impact the pump intake conditions.

The most commonly used shroud configuration is shown in the left graphic of the same figure. In this configuration, the ESP is set below perforations and the shroud directs the production flow down and back up by the motor for cooling. Otherwise, the fluid would be pulled down to the pump intake, leaving the motor in stagnate fluid with heat rise concerns. The purpose of setting below perforations is to increase the production rate for the same pump intake pressure or to serve as a simple reverse-flow gas-separation system. In the gas-separation application, the configuration depends on the free gas flowing from the perforations taking the path of least resistance—up the open casing annulus, instead of down to the bottom of the shroud. One caution, in this configuration, is not to use a gas-separation intake on the pump. The vented free gas from the separation intake would recycle to the bottom of the shroud, increasing the free-gas ratio to the pump and decreasing the cooling of the motor.

This configuration is not recommended for setting above perforations in an application with free gas. But where the ESP and casing annular area is large, creating too low a cooling flow, a shroud can be used to increase the production-fluid cooling velocity. For those special cases of setting above perforations and the problem of free gas, an inverted shroud (right graphic in the figure) has proved successful in separating free gas from the fluid that is directed back down to the pump intake.

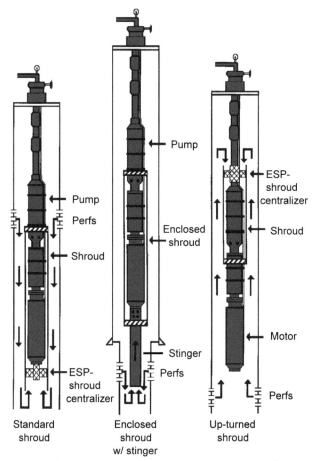

Fig. 13.36—ESP-motor shroud systems (after Centrilift[9]).

In wells that have a diameter restriction because of tapered casing, liners, or screens, a stinger can be attached to the bottom of the shroud to position the intake below perforations and down into the restriction. A stinger is a section of tubing, usually smaller in diameter than the shroud, which is attached to the bottom of the shroud and provides fluid communication from the wellbore to the interior of the shroud. This configuration is shown in the center graphic of the figure. The pressure drop through the stinger must be calculated to check for possible choking of the pump and also for an increase in the free gas liberated, causing gas interference issues with the pump and cooling issues with the motor.

Screens and Filters. Screens and filters are used with ESP systems to prohibit the flow of large solids into the pump intake. In one configuration (shown on the intake of Fig. 13.2), a mesh screen or perforated metal sheet is wrapped or mounted over the pump intake ports. The mesh or perforation size has to be small enough not to allow the passage of large particles, but large enough not to cause a flow restriction. The size of particle that must be screened is a function of the flow-passageway clearances through the pump. If a shroud is used, a screen can be used to cover the open intake area at the bottom of the shroud.

Filters have also been used on ESP applications. The simplest method is to use a motor shroud with a stinger, shown in the center graphic of Fig. 13.36. The stinger is sealed at the end, perorated along its length, and a filter element or gravel pack is inserted into or around the stinger. The production fluid then has to pass through the stinger filter prior to entering the pump intake.

Several cautions must be mentioned if screens or filters are used. The open area of the screen must be several times larger than that of the open area of the pump intake ports. This allows for proper flow without choking when, not if, the screen starts building up debris and plugging. This is also the case with the filters. Also, remember that the separated debris has to go somewhere and that is generally in the rathole below the ESP. The rathole must be large enough to hold the amount of debris expected over a period of time. This is because if it starts building up on the ESP, it can cause motor heat problems, eventual complete plugging of the intake ports, and difficulty in pulling the unit. Plugged screens and filters may cause severe pump and motor problems, if not designed and applied correctly.

Y-Tool or Bypass. The Y-tool allows for treating or working below the ESP through a bypass. A configuration of the system is shown in **Fig. 13.37**. The "Y" is somewhat of a misnomer because it is just an offset layout. The bypass tube is on axial centerline with the production tubing string. This allows the work string to have a straight shot through and out the bypass tube from the production tube. Typical sizes for these bypass tubes are 1.995 to 2.441 in. (50.67 to 62.00 mm) ID. The ESP is connected to the offset path of the crossover head and hangs parallel to the bypass tube. Clamps secure the ESP and bypass tube together. During normal operation of the ESP, the bypass is sealed off with a blanking plug seated in a landing nipple, set just below the Y-tool head or by a flapper valve in the cross-over head. The blanking plug can be set and retrieved with wireline or coiled tubing. Y-tool systems are provided and best suited for 7-in. and larger casing applications.

13.3.8 Optional ESP Configurations. What has been described up to this point is the standard ESP configuration. It has the pump, seal-chamber section, and motor attached to the production tubing, in this order from top down. In some wellbore completions and unique ESP applications, the arrangement and configuration of the system is modified. Some of these applications are listed next.

Inverted Bottom-Intake ESP. An inverted-unit configuration has the motor on top, attached to the tubing string; seal-chamber section underneath the motor; and the pump on bottom (**Fig. 13.38**). For a bottom-intake design, the production fluid is drawn in the intake ports located at the very bottom of the ESP system and discharged out of ports located just below the connection to the seal-chamber section. Because the discharged production fluid cannot flow through the seal-chamber section and motor, it has to exit into the casing or liner annulus and flow past these units. Once above the motor, it can continue flowing up the annulus or be ported back into the production tubing string. Additionally, the casing annulus communication flow path, between the intake and discharge ports, has to be sealed to prevent recirculation. Generally, the intake is stung into the casing packer to seal this path. This configuration is typically used for applications in which the intake needs to be located as low as possible, cavern or mine applications, annular flow designs, coiled tubing with internal power cable, or cable-deployed ESP systems.

The ESP design has to be modified from the standard unit design. In this application, the seal-chamber section and motor have to equalize with the high-pressure discharge conditions. This requires that all the sealing and breathing paths be able to handle the sudden high-pressure, high-velocity startup and shutdown surges.

Inverted Bottom-Discharge ESP. This design is configured the same as the inverted bottom-intake ESP system with the exception that the pump stages are inverted to pump down (**Fig. 13.39**). Once again, the intake and discharge fluid communication path in the casing annulus has to be closed. Generally, the pump discharge, on the bottom of the ESP assembly, is stung into an isolation packer. The wellbore production fluid is transferred from above this packer to

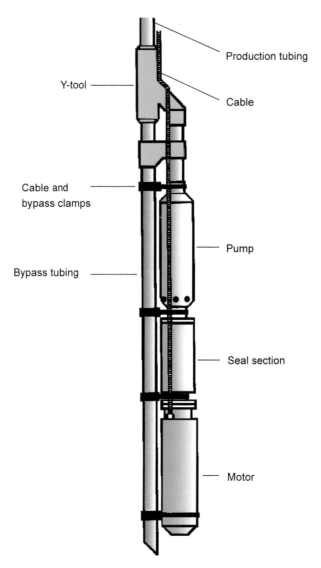

Fig. 13.37—Y-tool (after Centrilift[9]).

below under high enough pressure to inject into the lower formation. This configuration is typi-cally used for injection of water into a disposal zone.

Special designs that incorporate downhole hydrocyclone separators have been used to sepa-rate some of the water from the wellbore fluid (**Fig. 13.40**). In this case, the reduced-water-content oil is pumped to the surface, and a significant portion of the deoiled water is injected into a disposal zone.

Dual ESP. A dual-ESP configuration is one in which two or more ESP systems are in-stalled concurrently in the same wellbore. One configuration uses a Y-tool with the first ESP attached, as described in the previous Y-tool section, and a second ESP system attached to the bottom of the bypass tube or to another Y-tool bypass head (**Fig. 13.41**). For a triple system, another Y-tool is attached to the bottom of the first bypass tube, allowing for a third unit to be incorporated. Each ESP system requires its own cable and control system.

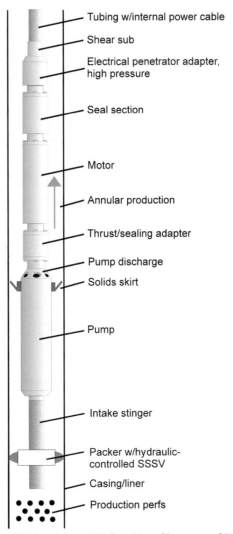

- Tubing w/internal power cable
- Shear sub
- Electrical penetrator adapter, high pressure
- Seal section
- Motor
- Annular production
- Thrust/sealing adapter
- Pump discharge
- Solids skirt
- Pump
- Intake stinger
- Packer w/hydraulic-controlled SSSV
- Casing/liner
- Production perfs

Fig. 13.38—Inverted ESP [after Centrilift Graphics, Claremore, Oklahoma (1994)].

A second configuration has the first ESP system connected to the production tubing with a sealed shroud or can around the entire unit (**Fig. 13.42**). The next ESP system is attached to the bottom of the first unit's shroud. In this configuration, the lower unit's discharge feeds the upper unit's intake so as to set up stepped fluid pressurization.

Parallel Production. A Y-tool, dual ESP system can be used for high-flow-rate applications in which the required HP is too great for one unit or it is desirable to split the total HP requirement into two or more segments. In this case, all the units are operating and discharging into the production tubing at a common pressure, with the total flow rate being a summation of the flow of each individual unit.

Series Production. A dual-ESP system can also be used for high total-developed-head requirements. This is where the lift requirement or pressure increase across the pump is beyond the equipment design limitations. By connecting the ESP systems in series, large pressure increases can be achieved for the desired flow rate while staying within each individual unit's HP and burst-pressure limitations (Fig. 13.42).

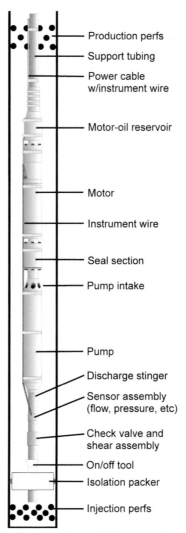

	Production perfs
	Support tubing
	Power cable w/instrument wire
	Motor-oil reservoir
	Motor
	Instrument wire
	Seal section
	Pump intake
	Pump
	Discharge stinger
	Sensor assembly (flow, pressure, etc)
	Check valve and shear assembly
	On/off tool
	Isolation packer
	Injection perfs

Fig. 13.39—Bottom-discharge ESP [after Centrilift Graphics, Claremore, Oklahoma (1994)].

Backup Unit. This concept also utilizes the Y-tool configuration, but only one ESP system operates at a time. The other units are held in backup until the operating unit either fails or is shutdown voluntarily. To prevent recirculation flow through the nonoperating unit, a plug has to be set in the Y-tool flow path. These systems are used in high-cost workover areas to reduce the total number of interventions and operating costs.

Booster ESP. The ESP can also be used as a pressure boost system for surface applications. They can handle a wide variety of fluid conditions and do not have the pressure pulsation attribute associated with positive-displacement-type pumps.

Canned System. This configuration is basically an ESP installed in a shallow well or can (**Fig. 13.43**). The low-pressure fluid is fed into the can annulus, and the ESP boosts the pressure. It is used primarily for flowline or pipeline pressure boost and for fluid disposal or injection purposes.

Surface Horizontal System. This configuration utilizes an ESP centrifugal pump driven by a surface electric motor, engine drive, or other primary mover. It is generally mounted on a skid

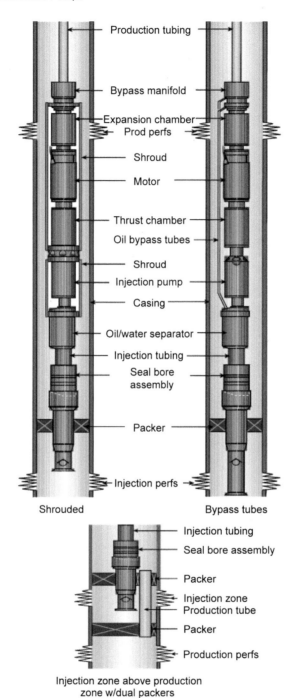

Fig. 13.40—Downhole oil/water-separation system [after Centrilift Graphics, Claremore, Oklahoma (1998)].

for stability and alignment (**Fig. 13.44**). It can provide a nonpulsating flow and a wide flow range with the use of a variable-speed drive.

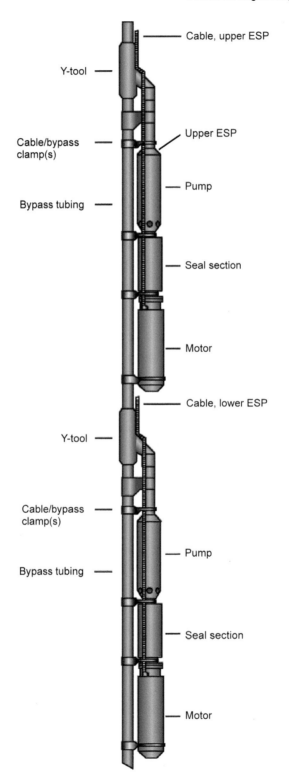

Fig. 13.41—Dual ESP's Y-tool [after Centrilift Graphics, Claremore, Oklahoma (2003)].

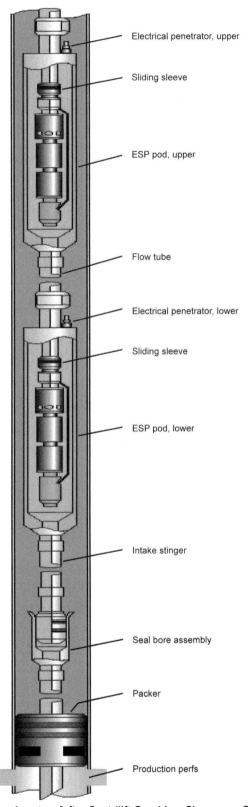

Fig. 13.42—Dual ESP's pod system [after Centrilift Graphics, Claremore, Oklahoma (2003)].

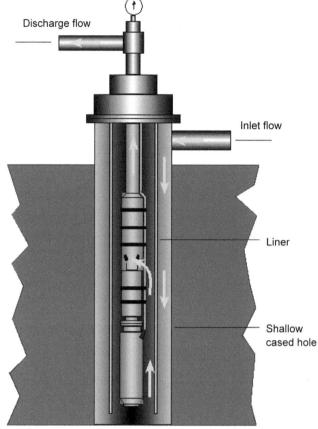

Fig. 13.43—Canned pump [after Centrilift Graphics, Claremore, Oklahoma (2004)].

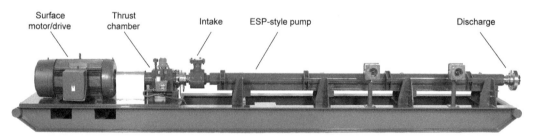

Fig. 13.44—Surface horizontal pump [after Centrilift Graphics, Claremore, Oklahoma (2003)].

Pipeline-Insert System. In this configuration, the ESP is inserted into a parallel section of piping. Fluid can then either flow directly through the pipeline or can be valved to bypass through the pump leg section for pressure boosting.

Through-Tubing-Conveyed ESP. In applications where pump wear and intervention costs are a major concern, a through-tubing-deployed pump is an option. The configuration is shown in **Fig. 13.45**. The motor and seal-chamber section are deployed on the bottom of a tubing string. The power cable is connected to the motor and deployed with the tubing, locating and protecting it in the casing/tubing annulus. The pump section is then deployed by a work string,

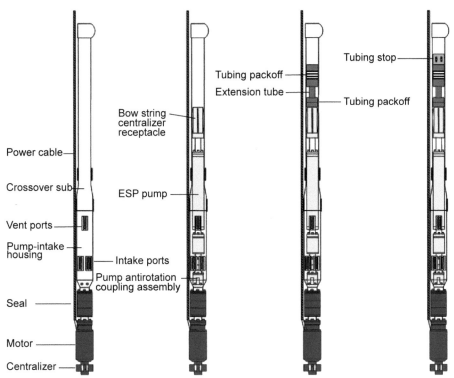

Fig. 13.45—Through-tubing-conveyed ESP system [after Centrilift Graphics, Claremore, Oklahoma (2000)].

typically wireline or coiled tubing, and latched onto the seal-chamber section. Thereafter, workovers, because of pump issues, can be done at a lower expense with wireline or coiled-tubing rigs, instead of regular jointed-tubing workover rigs.

13.3.9 Harsh-Environment Options. ESPs are typically thrust into more difficult and harsh wellbore environments as production conditions change. Harsh or severe conditions include multiphase fluids or high GOR wells, fluids with abrasive particles, viscous fluids, high-temperature wellbores, corrosive fluids, and scale and asphaltenes. With this movement, the demands on the equipment design functions, materials, and operational processes increase. The run-life of the entire system can be affected if proper designs for these applications are not used.

Multiphase Flow.[20–25] The presence of free gas in the produced fluid does affect the performance of the ESP pump. Generally, a pump is designed to handle incompressible fluids (liquids), and a compressor is designed to handle compressible fluids (gases). The performance or efficiency of both will suffer if they are required to handle a multiphase fluid (liquid and free gas). Typically, as the amount of free gas to total volume of the pumped fluid increases, the pump-stage head and flow both deteriorate.[20]

Performance Variables. The amount of free gas that an ESP pump can handle is a function of the following variables: pump-stage geometry, operating point of the pump stage, control by a fixed-speed or variable-speed drive, pump-intake flowing pressure, and wellbore geometry.

Pump-Stage Geometry. The gas handling capability of a centrifugal pump stage increases with flow rate or stage specific speed—a nondimensional design parameter. In other words, as the stage style moves from radial to mixed flow (Fig. 13.11), the gas-handling capability increases.

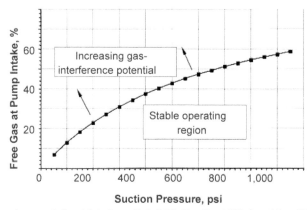

Fig. 13.46—Modified Turpin correlation (data from Ref. 24) [after Centrilift Graphics, Claremore, Oklahoma (1995)].

Pump Operating Point. The most stable operating region for a pump stage on gassy fluid is from the maximum recommended flow rate back to its BEP. As the flow rate moves from the BEP toward the minimum recommended operating point, the potential for gas interference affecting pump performance is increased.

VSC Operation. The VSC allows for some additional flexibility and reduction in unit shutdowns that are related to pump gas locking. Tests have shown that the pump gas-handling capability increases slightly with increasing speed. If the pump load decreases and the motor amps drop, indicating an initiation of gas lock, the VSC can be programmed to speed up for a short period to attempt to clear the gas-lock situation. If it clears and the load picks back up, the VSC would then return to its set operating frequency. If it does not clear, the unit would then shut down on an underload situation and restart on the time out delay.

Pump-Intake Pressure. The gas handling capability of the pump is very sensitive to pump-intake pressure. An empirical correlation[24] for the relationship of the amount of free gas a pump can handle and the fluids flowing pressure was established from numerous tests on a variety of pump stages. A graphical representation of this correlation is shown in **Fig. 13.46**. The area under the curve represents stable operation, and the area above indicates potential gas-interference and -locking regions.

Wellbore Geometry. The natural and mechanical separation of free gas from the flowing fluid is a function of the wellbore geometry. The annular area between the casing and the ESP unit and the fluid flow rate determines the flowing fluid velocity. The natural annular gas separation decreases as the velocity increases. Also, whether the casing is horizontal, inclined, or vertical determines the flow regime of the multiphase fluid and influences its natural separation characteristics. The efficiency of annular separation is still unknown, and additional research must be done in this area.

Optimal ESP Configurations for Gas Handling. Optimal ESP configurations for gassy applications are listed next. Depending on the severity of the application, they can be used individually or in multiple combinations.

Tapered Pumps. Tapered pumps utilize several different sets of pump stages in the same pump housing or pump string. Generally, the first section of stages is mixed-flow style because they can handle a higher percentage of free gas. As the gassy fluid is pressurized through each of these first stages, the total fluid volume decreases because of the compression of the free gas. When the flow rate nears the BEP flow rate of these stages, a second set of stages is selected. Generally, a good design can be accomplished with two or three sets of stages in the taper.

Mechanical Separation. The vortex and rotary separation intake components, which were discussed in the pump section, are used here to add centrifugal separation to the gassy fluid that enters the intake section. Because there are so many variables that affect their effectiveness or efficiency, the manufacturers should be contacted for separation efficiency values or guidelines. These units can also be used in tandem to accomplish series separation.

Motor Shrouds. Not only can motor shrouds be used to raise the velocity of the production fluid by the motor for increased cooling, they can also be used to assist with annular separation of the free gas in the produced fluid. The different styles and their uses were discussed in the section on motor shrouds and recirculation systems.

Recirculation Pump. In a completion scheme where there is insufficient clearance to run a shrouded unit below perforations, a recirculation pump can be used. A recirculation pump bleeds a small portion of the pumped fluid off and circulates it down below the motor by a small-diameter hydraulic tube. This establishes a small flow in the rathole where the motor is set. By properly designing the bleed flow, cooling flow by the motor can be maintained. Since the perforations are above the unit and pump intake, natural annular gas separation can be maximized.

Although there are guidelines from the manufacturers for ESP configurations for gassy applications, the area still remains somewhat of a black art. Since there are so many variables that affect an ESP's ability to perform in a gassy application, the best method is for the operator to select what they feel is the best solution, based on prior field experience or the manufacturer's guidelines. Once the equipment is operational, field tests on each wellbore can be conducted to test that specific ESP configuration under those specific wellbore conditions.

Abrasive Slurries.[26,27] The standard ESP pump does not tolerate abrasive particles in the pump fluid. The amount of tolerance is directly related to the aggressiveness of the solids or sand. The aggressiveness is a function of the percentage of the solid substance that is harder than the material of the pump components, the size and shape of the particles, and the concentration of solids in the fluid. The most aggressive solids are those with a high solids concentration (> 1% by weight), a large percentage of the solids sample being quartz (harder than the base stage and bearing material), a majority of the sample under a 100-mesh sieve size (able to get into the bearing and sealing areas easier and faster), or quartz grain shapes that are angular or barbed. On the other extreme, there are cases where very round, smooth, soft sands are relatively benign to the operation of the pump.

Performance Impact of Abrasives. There are three types of wear that impact the pump stage and its performance. They are listed next and prioritized in order of importance or impact.

Radial Wear. As the slurry wears the radial-support bushing system of the pump, it loses its lateral stability. This allows the rotating parts to start interfering with the stationary parts. Vibration increases, and it starts impacting the top of the seal section where the first mechanical shaft face seal is located. Once vibration and radial movement start to influence the face seal, leakage starts across the sealing face. This initiates a path for the well fluid to progress toward the motor.

Downthrust Wear. On the floating-style stages, the abrasive slurry migrates into the downthrust bearing pad area of the pump stage. The stationary diffuser thrust pad starts boring into the impeller thrust washer area. Once it breaks through the lower shroud of the impeller, the impeller loses part of its work to recirculation flow. As the diffuser pad bores further into the impeller passageway, it also blocks a portion of the impeller flow path, thus restricting the remaining flow.

Erosion Wear. As with any abrasive-slurry flow along a twisting path, erosion wear takes place. Although it is not usually associated with the failure of the pump, it is a potential failure mode and a concern, especially when modifications have been made to the pump to address the radial and downthrust wear modes. Erosion wear not only damages the stage pieces, it also wears any surface with which it comes into contact. Severe cases have resulted in the wear perforating the pump or production-tubing walls and dropping units in the well.

Optional ESP Configurations for Abrasives. Depending on the severity of the application, the following design options can be used individually or in combination.

Compression Pumps. For many years, this was the answer for abrasive applications. In a compression or "fixed-impeller" pump, the impellers are fixed to the shaft or stacked hub to hub so there is no axial movement. With all the impellers fixed relative to the shaft, the whole impeller stack can be raised slightly so that it does not run into contact with the downthrust or upthrust pads on the diffuser. This pump design eliminates the downthrust wear mode. When it is used in conjunction with hardened journal bearings, it also addresses radial wear problems. There are several issues with compression pumps. First, they are very difficult to assemble properly. Because an ESP pump is a very long, multistaged assembly, it is very difficult to locate all of the impellers and still have the needed minimum shaft axial movement. Also, now, the thrust of each impeller is transferred to the shaft and is added to the normal shaft thrust produced by the discharge pressure on the top area of the shaft. The thrust bearing in the seal-chamber section is required to carry this additional thrust. Additionally, as the sealing areas of the pump stage wear, the downthrust also increases. Therefore, the selection of the proper thrust bearing is critical, and the anticipated thrust must be calculated on the basis of the maximum thrust seen from worn stages.

Thrust and Radial Protection. In this modification, the base material in the radial and downthrust areas of the stage is replaced with inserts of hardened materials. The materials are usually tungsten or silicon carbides, or ceramics. This results in a pump with both radial and downthrust protection but is built in a floater style.

Erosion Protection. Currently, this area is under development, but some coatings, heat treatments, surface hardening, and hard-material liners have had limited-to-moderate success.

Generally, the abrasive production fluid does not impact the motor and seal-chamber section. There could be minor erosion worries because of the flow velocities of the production fluid by the outside surfaces of both units. Also, if the top shaft's mechanical face seal in the seal-chamber section is exposed and operates in the production fluid, hardened stationary and rotating seal faces are recommended.

Viscous Crude and Emulsions. ESPs are also used to lift viscous fluids, commonly referred to as heavy and extra-heavy crudes. Viscosity is defined as the resistance of a fluid to movement as a result of internal friction. Resistance causes additional internal losses in a centrifugal pump. The increases in internal losses of a centrifugal pump affect each performance parameter.

Performance Impact of Fluid Viscosity. Effect on Flow Capacity. Flow capacity of a given pump stage diminishes rapidly with a relatively small increase in viscosity. The rate of correction tends to moderate as viscosity continues to increase. The amount of correction is also dependent on stage geometry, and the decrease in capacity is more exaggerated for radial flow stages.

Effect on Head. The total dynamic head at the BEP diminishes on a moderate curve as viscosity increases. It is affected to a lesser extent than flow capacity. The head at zero flow remains relatively constant. **Fig. 13.47** shows various head vs. flow-rate curves for an ESP pump stage rated for about 2,100 B/D on water.

Effect on Horsepower. BHP increases rapidly with increasing viscosity but tends to level off because of diminishing flow rate and total dynamic head (**Fig. 13.48**).

Effect on Efficiency. Efficiency decreases in proportion to the changes in flow capacity, TDH, and HP, in terms of Eq. 13.1 (**Fig. 13.49**).

There are several published methods for estimating the effect of viscosity on the head, flow rate, and BHP of a centrifugal pump. These "standard" correction factors are usually not accurate for the specific small-diameter, multistage design of ESP pumps. Therefore, most manufac-

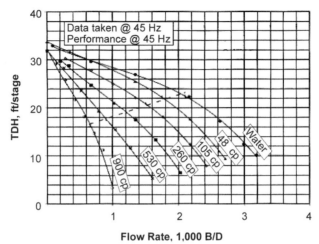

Fig. 13.47—Pump-head performance vs. fluid viscosity [after Centrilift Graphics, Claremore, Oklahoma (2003)].

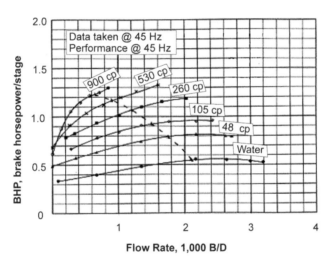

Fig. 13.48—Pump-horsepower performance vs. fluid viscosity [after Centrilift Graphics, Claremore, Oklahoma (2003)].

turers have established corrections through testing for each pump stage type in their product line. These correction factors are based on dead-oil viscosity values for the fluid at pump-intake conditions. When applying these corrections to the pump, the following should also be considered.

Effects of Gas. When gas saturates into the crude, it reduces the viscosity of the fluid. Some amount of gas is helpful in reducing fluid viscosity, but an excessive amount of free gas is disruptive to well fluid production. Gas tends to migrate out of highly-viscous fluid slowly. Therefore, a higher percentage of gas tends to pass through the pump with the produced well fluid. In an application with gas, the designer must be aware of two viscosity values. The first is the dead-oil viscosity. This is the viscosity of the crude at dead or completely degassed conditions. The other is the live-oil viscosity. It is the apparent viscosity of the gas-saturated crude and the viscosity that affects the pump performance in a well with gas. There are several dead-

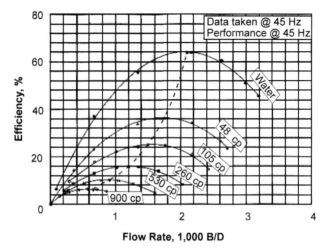

Fig. 13.49—Pump-efficiency performance vs. fluid viscosity [after Centrilift Graphics, Claremore, Oklahoma (2003)].

oil and saturated-oil viscosity correlations that can be used during the design process. The correlation selection should be based on modeling of the actual wellbore performance.

Effects of Temperature. Temperature has a dramatic effect on the viscosity of the crude oil. Therefore, it is critical to the ESP design process that the fluid temperature in the wellbore at the pump setting depth is known. This determines the fluid viscosity and pump-performance correction factors at the first pump stage. Additionally, the inefficiency of the pump results in additional heat loss to the fluid and surrounding wellbore. This incremental elevation in temperature from stage to stage through the pump moderates the impact of the fluid viscosity on the total pump performance. Therefore, the designer should, at a minimum, use an average viscosity for the fluid through the pump for sizing applications. A more accurate method is to calculate the performance on a stage-by-stage basis, using the fluid input conditions to each stage. Most design software programs use this method.

Effects of Water. With the incursion of water or brine into the wellbore, the viscosity of the oil/water mixture can increase, sometimes dramatically when emulsions occur. The shear forces on the fluid mixture, as it flows through the formation, perforations, or centrifugal pump, can cause an emulsion. Because thousands of molecular structures with different chemical and physical properties exist in crude oils, it is virtually impossible to predict viscosity characteristics on the basis of oil and water cuts. A default viscosity correction factor for emulsions, referenced in many petroleum engineering textbooks and references, has been used for many years with questionable results.[28] The correction factor is shown graphically in **Fig. 13.50**. The curve provides for a progressive increase in the viscosity multiplier, up to 15, as the water cut increases. It then drops to 1, indicating the emulsion has inverted or become water-wetted. Use of this correction factor in viscous applications has indicated that it is too severe. Recent work has shown that because of the complexity of emulsion characteristics, it is best to run carefully controlled baseline laboratory tests on reservoir crude and brine samples to develop an emulsion correction curve.[29]

ESP Options for Fluid Viscosity. Several options are available for improving the performance of the ESP pump when applied to viscous crudes.

Dilution. Some success has been achieved with diluent injection. In this process, a lighter crude or refined product, such as diesel, is injected from the surface via a separate hydraulic line to a point below the ESP or directly into the pump intake. This effectively cuts the viscos-

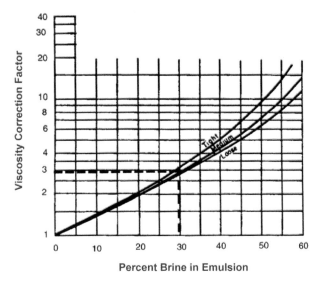

Fig. 13.50—Viscosity correction factor for emulsion.

ity of the wellbore fluids. The amount of injected diluent depends on the desired final mixture viscosity. This type of viscosity reduction also reduces the surface flowline losses, which reduces the required wellhead pressure or the need for diluent injection at the wellhead. Using a diluent fluid is an effective, but expensive, approach.

Temperature Increase. The temperature of the reservoir or near-wellbore area can be artificially raised to make the viscous crude more mobile. The most successful method for adding heat has been through steam injection or soaking, although trials have been made with resistive, induction, and microwave technologies. This reduces the viscosity of the crude, but it also raises concerns in high-temperature operations.

Chemical Injection. Viscosity-reduction and emulsion-breaking chemicals can be injected from the surface by hydraulic injection lines. This impacts the fluids in the annulus and through the pump but not very far back into the reservoir.

Water Injection. When emulsions are encountered through a certain water-cut range, additional water can be injected to increase the water cut of the produced fluid, moving it out of the high-viscosity correction area. Field trials on this concept were conducted in the mid-1980s and were successful in reducing the fluid viscosity and increasing the ESP performance.

High Temperature. Another trend has been the application of ESPs into higher-temperature reservoirs. Typically, these are reservoirs that are either deeper or artificially heated. Standard ESP systems are commonly applied to well ambient temperatures of 250°F (121°C). Even with a velocity greater than 1 ft/sec, the temperature rise above ambient conditions will be about 50°F (10°C) for water and 90°F (32°C) for oil—higher if fluids contain gas.

Systems that have minor modifications or optional features are applied in ambient temperatures up to 350°F (177°C). Additional research and field testing is being done on systems that operate in ambient temperatures above 350°F. For these units, the motor and seal-chamber section have the most significant design changes. The design areas of concern in the motor include the insulation system, mechanical bearing system, and the internal lubrication and cooling system. The seal-chamber section modifications include the mechanical journal and thrust bearing systems, internal lubricating system, and, in positive-barrier styles, the elastomeric bag. Also, the selection of a power cable rated for elevated temperature service is critical.

Since the early 1990s, the focus on the application of submersible motors in high-temperature wells has not been entirely on the ambient wellbore temperature, but rather the internal operating temperature of the motor. This is because, even in what would be considered a relatively cool well, a misapplied design can possibly operate at dangerously high internal operating temperatures. Most of the ESP application software programs calculate the expected motor operating temperatures, or the manufacturer can be contacted to provide this information. The calculation of the motor operating temperature involves many variables, which were mentioned in the previous motor-heat-rise section. Historically, this calculation has been made at the stabilized design operating point of the motor. Recently, new computerized programs have allowed the ESP system operating conditions to be dynamically modeled from the static startup condition to the stabilized-flow operating point. This has allowed the designer to identify potentially dangerous transient operating conditions and to provide for options to eliminate or reduce their impact.

If the operator is operating an ESP at elevated motor operating conditions, it is suggested that a downhole motor-temperature monitoring system be run. This monitor provides warning of any high-temperature excursions of the downhole system so that remedial action is taken before potential catastrophic damage occurs.

Corrosion. The application expansion of ESPs into more corrosive wells has required the industry to provide enhanced corrosion-protection options. In the early years, the normal protection scheme for mild-corrosion applications was the use of protective coatings. These were either epoxy paint, babbit spray, or stainless-steel/high-alloy metal flame spray. Each of these has the disadvantage of the potential for mechanical damage during the installation handling process and deployment through the casing. The need for a higher-level corrosion-resistant ESP was first recognized with the application of units into carbon dioxide (CO_2) enhanced-recovery reservoirs in the late 1970s. From this need, the first-generation corrosion-resistant ESP unit was developed. Current units use high-chromium alloys in the components exposed to the wellbore fluids.

Another source of corrosion is hydrogen sulfide, H_2S. The H_2S mainly attacks copper-based alloys of the pump, seal-chamber section, and cable. This type of corrosion can be controlled by replacing the copper-based alloy components with suitable materials or by isolating them from exposure to the well fluid and gases. When CO_2, H_2S, and hot brine are combined, unpredictable corrosion results may appear. With small changes in the concentration of CO_2 and/or H_2S and temperature, corrosion could even vary significantly from well to well within the same reservoir.

Another corrosion mechanism that has been around the oil field for years, but has been misunderstood or misdiagnosed, is microbiologically influenced or induced corrosion.[30] It is caused by sulfate-reducing bacteria, as well as other forms of anaerobic and aerobic bacteria. The four common types found in oil wells and affecting ESPs are anaerobic sulfate-reducing bacteria (SRB), anaerobic acid-producing bacteria, aerobic acid-producing bacteria, and slime-forming bacteria. The SRB and anaerobic/aerobic acid-producing bacteria species attach themselves to the surface of the ESP components and cause direct and indirect corrosion and severe pitting. The slime-forming species can cause some minor corrosion but is noted more for downhole formation and equipment plugging.

Scale and Asphaltenes. If the well has scaling or asphaltene-forming tendencies, these can be detrimental to the performance and run-life of the total ESP system. Because of the characteristics of the ESP system, there are pressure and temperature changes, which provide a mechanism for scales to form or precipitate out of solution. Typically, scales cause two problems. They plug the flow passageways of the pump stages, reducing or stopping the flow entirely. They also adhere to the outside surfaces of the motor and seal-chamber section, reducing the heat-transfer rate, causing both units to run hotter. Asphaltenes generally only cause plugging of the pump stages. Both problems can be reduced, but not totally eliminated, by applying synthetic coatings to the surfaces affected or by using a downhole inhibitor-chemical treatment.

13.3.10 Installation and Handling. Although there can be many factors that influence or directly affect the run-life of an ESP system, proper installation and handling procedures are critical. The recommended installation and handling procedures are detailed in API *RP11S3*.[3] In addition to these, manufacturers should be contacted for specific recommendations on their equipment.

13.3.11 Maintenance and Troubleshooting. Operating, maintenance, and troubleshooting recommendations are covered in API *RP11S*.[31] Additionally, much can be learned from the disassembly of the ESP components after they are pulled from the well. This is true whether they are in reusable condition or have been through a catastrophic failure. The equipment and the wellbore always indicate items that can be changed or improved. API *RP11S1* provides guidelines on the disassembly of ESP components and the evaluation of the findings.[32] Also, each ESP manufacturer has recommendations and guidelines on this topic.

Ref. 33 provides a practical checklist for optimizing the life of an ESP system. It covers all the critical or sensitive steps, from the design and manufacture to the operational procedures. There have been several papers written that deal with literature on ESP application problems and solutions.[34-37] These papers summarize and categorize ESP reference literature by a number of different application or problem topics. They are an excellent bibliography set for troubleshooting application-related problems or issues.

13.4 ESP System Selection and Performance Calculations

The sizing and selection procedure is from a published nine-step design procedure.[38] The overview provides a step-by-step process for evaluating and selecting the proper ESP equipment for a particular application. This is a manual procedure used to illustrate the ESP design steps. While it is accurate for simple water and light-crude designs, there are commercially available ESP design software programs that give accurate designs for wells with high GORs, viscous crudes, high temperature, and/or operation on VSCs.

This nine-step procedure helps one design the appropriate submersible pumping system for a particular well. Each of the nine steps is explained in the sections that follow, including gas calculations and variable-speed operations. The nine steps are listed next.

• Step One: Basic Data—Collect and analyze all the well data that will be used in the design.

• Step Two: Production Capacity—Determine the well productivity at the desired pump setting depth, or determine the pump setting depth at the desired production rate.

• Step Three: Gas Calculations—Calculate the fluid volumes, including gas at the pump-intake conditions.

• Step Four: TDH—Determine the pump discharge requirement.

• Step Five: Pump Type—For a given capacity and TDH, select the pump type that will have the highest efficiency for the desired flow rate.

• Step Six: Optimum Size of Components—Select the optimum size of pump, motor, and seal section, and check equipment limitations.

• Step Seven: Electric Cable—Select the correct type and size of cable.

• Step Eight: Accessory and Optional Equipment—Select the motor controller, transformer, tubing head, and optional equipment.

• Step Nine: The Variable-Speed Pumping System—For additional operational flexibility, select the variable-speed submersible pumping system.

13.4.1 Step 1: Basic Data. The design of a submersible pumping unit, under most conditions, is not a difficult task, especially if reliable data are available. Although, if the information, especially that pertaining to the well's capacity, is poor, the design will usually be marginal. Bad data often result in a misapplied pump and costly operation. A misapplied pump may operate outside the recommended range, overload or underload the motor, or draw down the well at a rapid rate that may result in formation damage. On the other extreme, the pump may not be large enough to provide the desired production rate.

Too often, data from other wells in the same field or in a nearby area are used, assuming that wells from the same producing horizon have similar characteristics. Unfortunately, for the engineer sizing the submersible installations, oil wells are much like fingerprints (i.e., no two are quite alike).

The actual selection procedure can vary significantly depending on the well-fluid properties. The three major types of ESP applications are wells with single-phase flow of oil and/or water, wells with multiphase flow of liquids and gas (especially high free-gas rates), and wells producing highly-viscous fluids typically much greater than 10 cp. A list of required data is outlined next.

• Well Data: Casing or liner size, weight, grade; tubing size, weight, grade type and thread, plus condition; pump setting depth (measured and vertical); perforated or openhole interval; well plugback total depth (measured and vertical).

• Production Data: Wellhead tubing pressure; wellhead casing pressure; present production rate; producing fluid level and/or pump-intake pressure at datum point; static fluid level and/or static bottomhole pressure at datum point; datum point; bottomhole temperature; desired production rate (target); GOR; and water cut.

• Well-Fluid Conditions: Specific gravity of water; oil °API or specific gravity; specific gravity of gas; bubblepoint pressure of gas; viscosity of oil (dead); and other available pressure/volume/temperature (PVT) data.

• Power Sources: Available primary voltage, frequency, and power source capabilities.

• Possible Production Problems: Sand, scale deposition, corrosion, paraffin/asphaltenes, emulsion, gas, high reservoir temperature.

13.4.2 Step Two: Production Capacity. The following is a simplification of procedures for predicting well performance. This discussion assumes little or no well skin. A damaged wellbore or other factors affects the well flow performance.

Productivity Index. When the well flowing pressure (P_{wf}) is greater than bubblepoint pressure (P_b), the fluid flow is single-phase flow, and the inflow performance relationship is a straight line with slope J, as given by the PI.

$$\text{PI} = J = Q/(P_r - P_{wf}) \ . \ \text{...} \ (13.12)$$

Inflow Performance Relationship. If P_{wf} is less than P_b, resulting in multiphase flow in the reservoir, the inflow-performance-relationship (IPR) method should be used. The relationship is given by Eq. 13.13.

$$Q_{o\text{max}} = Q_o/[1 - 0.2(P_{wf}/P_r) - 0.8(P_{wf}/P_r)^2] \ . \ \text{..............................} \ (13.13)$$

This relationship was first used by Gilbert[39] and further developed by Vogel.[40] Vogel developed a dimensionless reference curve that can be used to determine the IPR curve for a particular well. Others have developed variations of the IPR equation. (See the chapter on inflow and outflow in this section of the *Handbook*).

13.4.3 Step Three: Gas Calculations. The presence of free gas at the pump intake and in the discharge tubing makes the process of equipment selection much more complicated and voluminous. As the fluid (liquid/gas mixture) flows through the pump stages from the intake to the discharge and through the discharge tubing, the pressure and, consequently, fluid properties (such as volume, density, etc.) are undergoing continuous change. Also, the presence of free gas in the discharge tubing may create a significant "gas lift" effect and considerably reduce the required discharge pressure or TDH of the pump.

Ideally, a well is produced with a submergence pressure above the bubblepoint pressure to keep gases in solution at the pump intake. This is typically not feasible, so the gases must be either handled by the pump or separated from the other fluids prior to the pump intake.

It is essential to determine the effect of the gas on the fluid volume to select the proper pump and any auxiliary equipment. The following calculations yield the approximate percent free gas by volume.

If the solution GOR (R_s), the gas volume factor (B_g), and the formation volume factor (B_o) are not available from reservoir data, they must be calculated, and there are a number of multiphase correlations to select from. The correlation selected will affect the design, so select the one that best matches the conditions. Standings correlations for solution GOR and formation volume factor are shown next.

Solution GOR.

$$ R_s = SG_g[(P_b/18) \times (10^{0.0125 \times °API}/10^{0.00091 \times T_F})]^{1.2048} \quad \dots\dots\dots (13.14) $$

Or, in metric,

$$ R_s = 0.1342 \ SG_g[P_b \times (10^{0.0125 \times °API}/10^{0.00091(1.8T_C + 32)})]^{1.2048} \quad \dots\dots (13.15) $$

Note: pump-intake pressure should be substituted for bubblepoint pressure when calculating pump-intake conditions.

Gas Volume Factor. The gas volume factor, B_g, is expressed in reservoir scf/bbl gas (m³/m³).

$$ B_g = 5.04 \ (ZT_R/P) \ . \quad \dots\dots\dots\dots (13.16) $$

Or, in metric,

$$ B_g = 0.00377 \ (ZT_K/P) \ . \quad \dots\dots\dots\dots (13.17) $$

Formation Volume Factor. The formation volume factor, B_o, represents the increased volume that a barrel of oil occupies in the formation as compared to the stock-tank barrel of oil (STBO).

$$ B_o = 0.972 + 0.000147F^{1.175}, \quad \dots\dots\dots\dots (13.18) $$

where

$$ F = R_s(SG_g/SG_o)^{0.5} + 1.25T_F \ . \quad \dots\dots\dots (13.19) $$

Or, in metric,

$$B_o = 0.072 + 0.000147 \left[5.61 \ R_s \ (SG_g / SG_o)^{0.5} + 1.25 \ (1.8 T_C + 32) \right]^{1.175} . \ \text{..........} \quad (13.20)$$

Also, see chapters in the General Engineering section of this *Handbook*.

Total Volume of Fluids. When these three variables: R_s, B_o, and B_g are known, the volumes of oil, water, and free gas can be determined and percentages of each calculated. The total volume of gas (both free and in solution) can be determined as

$$\text{total gas} = (\text{producing GOR} \times \text{BOPD}) / 1{,}000 = \text{Mcf}$$

$$= \text{producing GOR} \times \text{m}^3 / \text{d} = \text{m}^3 . \ \text{...} \quad (13.21)$$

The gas in solution at submergence pressure can be determined as

$$\text{solution gas} = (R_s \times \text{BOPD}) / 1{,}000 = \text{Mcf} . \ \text{....................................} \quad (13.22)$$

The free gas equals the total gas minus the solution gas. The volume of oil (V_o) at the pump intake is equal to stock-tank barrels multiplied by B_o, the formation volume factor. The volume of gas (V_g) at the pump intake is equal to the amount of free gas multiplied by B_g, the gas volume factor. The volume of water (V_w) in the formation is approximately the same as stock tank barrels. Total fluid volume (V_t) can now be determined.

$$V_t = V_o + V_g + V_w . \ \text{..} \quad (13.23)$$

The percentage of free gas to total volume of fluids can now be calculated as

$$\text{vol \% free gas} = V_g / V_t . \ \text{...} \quad (13.24)$$

13.4.4 Step Four: Total Dynamic Head. The next step is to determine the TDH required to pump the desired capacity. The total pump head refers to feet (meters) of liquid being pumped and is calculated to be the sum of: net well lift, H_L; well-tubing friction loss, F_t; and wellhead pressure head, H_{wh}. The simplified equation is written as

$$\text{TDH} = H_L + F_t + H_{wh} . \ \text{...} \quad (13.25)$$

13.4.5 Step Five: Pump Type. Refer to the manufacturer's catalog for pump types, ranges, and pump-performance curves (60 Hz and 50 Hz). On the basis of expected fluid production rate and casing size, select the pump type that will, at the expected producing rate, be operating within the pump's operating range and near to the pump's peak efficiency.

Where two or more pump types have similar efficiencies at the desired volume, certain conditions determine the pump choice:

• Pump prices and corresponding motor sizes and prices may differ somewhat. Normally, the larger-diameter pump and motor are less expensive and operate at higher efficiencies.

• When the well's capacity is not known, or cannot be closely estimated, a pump with a "steep" characteristic curve should be chosen. If the desired volume falls at a point where two pump types have approximately equal efficiency, choose the pump type that requires the greatest number of stages. Such a pump will produce a capacity nearest the desired volume even if the well lift is substantially more or less than expected.

• If gas is present in the produced fluid, a gas separator may be required to achieve efficient operation. Note that the free gas is vented up the casing annulus. Refer to Step 3 to determine the effect of gas on the produced volume. The adjusted volume affects pump selection and the size of the other system components.

• In wells where the fluid is quite viscous and/or tends to emulsify, or in other extraordinary circumstances, some pump corrections may be necessary to ensure a more efficient operation. In such cases, contact the manufacturer for engineering recommendations.

The Variable-Speed Submersible Pumping (VSSP) System and Pump Selection. Under the previous or other pumping conditions, also consider the VSSP system. Such systems must be justified. For instance, in item two in the previous section, if the production rate is not accurately known, a VSSP system may be applicable. A VSC effectively converts a single pump into a family of pumps, so a pump can be selected for an estimated range and adjusted for the desired production level, once more data are collected.

Review Step 9 when considering the VSSP system. Variable-frequency performance curves are included in most manufacturers' information. The VSSP system with the VSC may provide additional economies of capital expenditure and operating expenses and should be considered in Step 6. The VSC and transformers for the VSSP system are discussed in Steps 8 and 9.

13.4.6 Step 6: Optimum Size of Components. ESP components are built in a number of sizes and can be assembled in a variety of combinations. These combinations must be carefully determined to operate the submersible pumping system within production requirements, material strength, and temperature limits. While sizing components, refer to the manufacturer for the following information: equipment combinations in various casings, maximum loading limits, maximum diameter of units, velocity of a fluid passing a motor, shaft HP limitations at various frequencies.

Pump. Refer to the manufacturer's performance curve of the selected pump type, and determine the number of stages required to produce the anticipated capacity against the previously calculated total dynamic head. Usually, performance curves for 60-Hz, 50-Hz, and variable-frequency operations are provided in the manufacturer's catalog. The pump characteristic curves are stage performance curves based on water with a specific gravity of 1.0. At the intersection of the desired production rate (bottom scale) and the head-capacity curve (vertical scale), read the head value on the left scale. Divide this value into the TDH to determine the number of stages: total stages = TDH/(head/stage).

Separator. Refer to the manufacturer's catalog for gas-separator information. Make the necessary adjustments in HP requirements and housing length.

Motor. To select the proper motor size for a predetermined pump size, the BHP required by the pump must be determined. The HP per stage is obtained by referring to the performance curve for the selected pump. The BHP required to drive a given pump is easily calculated by the following formula: BHP = total stages × (BHP/stage) × SG.

Refer to the manufacturer's information for motor specifications. Select a motor size that closely meets the design conditions. The maximum load conditions should not exceed 110% of rating. Minimum operating loads should not put the motor into an idle condition, otherwise protection monitoring is nullified. Manufacturers should be contacted for specific operating ranges. Typically, operators try to select a motor that operates in the range from 70 to 100% of its rating.

Seal Section. Refer to a manufacturer's catalog for selection of the proper seal section.

13.4.7 Step 7: Electric Cable. ESP electric cables are normally available in conductor sizes 1, 2, 4, and 6. These sizes are offered in both round and flat configurations. Several types of armor and insulation are available for protection against corrosive fluids and severe environments.

Cable selection involves the determination of cable size, cable type, and cable length.

Cable Size. The proper cable size is dependent on combined factors of voltage drop, amperage, and available space between tubing collars and casing.

Refer to the cable voltage drop curve (samples are shown in Fig 13.28) for voltage drop in cable. At the selected motor amperage and the given downhole temperature, the selection of a cable size that gives a voltage drop of less than 30 volts per 1,000 ft (305 m) can be used as a guideline. This curve determines the necessary surface voltage (motor voltage plus voltage drop in the cable) required to operate the motor.

Finally, check the manufacturer's information to determine if the size selected can be used with the proposed tubing and well casing sizes. The cable diameter plus tubing-collar diameter must be less than the ID of the casing. To determine the optimum cable size, consider future equipment requirements that may require the use of a larger-sized cable.

Where power cost is a major concern, kilowatt-hour loss curves can be used to justify the cable selection. Although power rates vary widely, this information is valuable in determining the economics of various cable sizes.

Cable Type. Selection of the cable type is primarily based on fluid conditions, bottomhole temperature, and space limitations within the casing annulus. Carefully select the type of cable for hostile environments. Refer to the manufacturers catalog for cable specifications. Where there is not sufficient space to run round cable, use electric cable with a flat configuration. The flat cable configuration induces a voltage imbalance. If it is significant, a transition splice may be required. Verify this with the manufacturer.

Cable Length. The total cable length should be about 100 ft (30 m) longer than the measured pump setting depth to make surface connections a safe distance from the wellhead. Check the voltage available at the motor terminal block to avoid the possibility of low voltage starts. The available motor terminal voltage is the surface supply voltage minus the cable voltage drop.

Cable Venting. In all wells, it is necessary to vent gases from the cable prior to the motor controller to avoid explosive conditions. A cable venting box is available to protect the motor controller from such gases.

13.4.8 Step 8: Accessory and Optional Equipment. *Downhole Accessory Equipment. Flat Cable (Motor Lead Extension).* Select a length at least 6 ft (1.8 m) longer than the pump intake (standard or gas separator) and seal section for the motor series chosen. Refer to the manufacturer's information for dimensions.

Flat-Cable Guard (Optional). Choose the required number for 6-ft (1.8-m) guard sections to at least equal the flat-cable length. Do not use guards for installation of a 400 series pump and seal section with 5½-in. OD and 20-lbm casing, and a 513 series pump and seal section with 6⅝-in. OD and 26-lbm casing.

Cable Bands. Use one 30-in. (76-cm) cable band every 2 ft (60 cm) for clamping flat cables to pumps. The 22-in. (56-cm) length can be used for all tubing/cable combinations through 3½-OD tubing. For 4½-in.- and 5½-in.-OD tubing, use 30-in. (76-cm) bands. One band is required for each 15 ft (5 m) of setting depth. Refer to the manufacturer's information for dimensions.

Swaged Nipple, Check Valve, and Drain Valve (Optional). Select these accessories on the basis of required ODs and type of threads.

Motor Controllers. Motor controllers are typical state-of-the-art digital controls consisting of two components.

System Unit. This unit performs all the shutdown and restart operations. It is mounted in the low-voltage compartment of the control panel.

Display Unit (Optional). This unit displays readings, set points, and alarms. It is normally mounted in the amp chart enclosure for easy access. It provides all the basic functions, such as underload, overload, phase imbalance, phase rotation, and many other parameters including password and communication protocols.

Single-Phase and Three-Phase Transformers. The type of transformer selected depends on the size of the primary power system and the required secondary voltage. Three-phase isolation stepup transformers are generally selected for increasing voltage from a low-voltage system, while a bank of three identical single-phase transformers is usually selected for reducing a high-voltage primary power source to the required surface voltage.

On existing systems, some ESP units operate without the use of an additional transformer. For new installation of units with higher voltages, it is usually less expensive to install three single-phase transformers, connected wye, to eliminate the auto-transformer.

In choosing the size of a stepup transformer or a bank of three single-phase transformers, Eq. 13.26 is used to calculate the total kilowatts/volts/amps (KVA) required.

$$KVA = (V_s \times A_m \times 1.73) / 1,000. \dots\dots\dots\dots\dots\dots\dots\dots (13.26)$$

Surface Cable. Choose the approximate length required for connecting the controller to the primary power system or transformer. Two pieces are generally required for installations using an auto-transformer. Size should equal the well cable size, except in the case of stepup or auto-transformer, where the primary and secondary currents are not the same.

Wellheads and Accessories. Select the wellhead on the basis of casing size, tubing size, maximum recommended load, surface pressure, and maximum setting depth. Electric cable passes through the wellhead where pressure fittings are not required.

Electric-feed-through (EFT) mandrels are also available. The electric cable is spliced to pigtails. The EFT wellheads seal against downhole pressure and prevent gas leaks at the surface.

Servicing Equipment. Cable Reels, Reel Supports, and Cable Guides. Select the size of cable reel required to handle the previously selected cable size. Select a set of cable-reel supports on the basis of cable-reel size. Cable guides are designed to handle cable sizes 1 through 6. Normally, customers retain one cable reel, one set of reel supports, and one cable guide wheel for future use.

Shipping Cases. Select the type and length of the case required accommodating the previously selected motor, pump, gas separator, and seal.

Optional Equipment. Bottomhole Sensing Device. The downhole sensor provides continuous measurement of parameters such as wellbore pressures, wellbore or ESP temperature, discharge flow rates, water contamination of the motor, or equipment vibration.

Automatic Well Monitoring. Motor controllers are available for the continuous monitoring of pump operations from a central location.

13.4.9 Step 9: Variable Speed Submersible Pumping System. The ESP system can be modified to include a variable-frequency controller so that it operates over a broader range of capacity, head, and efficiency. Most of the ESP manufacturers and several third parties have computerized pump-selection programs to assist in VSSP-system selection; what follows is a basic explanation of the principles involved.

Variable Frequency. The VSC is commonly used to generate any frequency between 30 and 90 Hz. Pump-performance curves for frequencies other than 60 Hz can be generated with the affinity laws (Eqs. 13.2 through 13.4). The output rating of the motor is also affected by the operating frequency (Eq. 13.9).

A set of curves can be developed for an arbitrary series of frequencies with these equations, as shown in the variable-frequency performance curves at the end of this step (**Fig. 13.51**). Each curve represents a series of points derived from the 60-Hz curve for flow and corresponding head points, transformed using the previously mentioned equations.

Suppose we are given the following data at a frequency of 60 Hz: rate = 1,200 B/D; head = 24.5 ft (from FC-1200 curve at 1,200 B/D); BHP = 0.34 BHP (from FC-1200 curve at 1,200

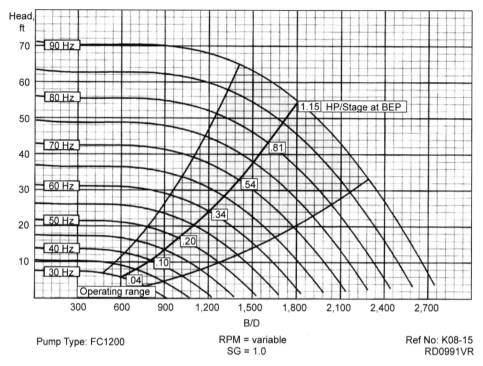

Fig. 13.51—FC-1200 stage variable-speed performance curve [after Centrilift Graphics, Claremore, Oklahoma (2003)].

B/D). If a new frequency of 50 Hz is chosen, the data will be: new rate = (50/60) × 1,200 B/D = 1,000 B/D; new head = $(50/60)^2$ × 24.5 ft = 17 ft; and new BHP = $(50/60)^3$ × 034 BHP = 0.20 BHP.

By performing these calculations at other production rates, a new curve for 50-Hz operation can be plotted. Start by locating the existing points on the one-stage 60-Hz curve:

- Q_1 rate, B/D: 0; 950; 1,200; 1550; and 1,875.
- H_1 head, ft: 32, 28.6, 24.5, 15, and 0.
- Efficiency, %: 1, 63.5, 64, 49, and 0.

Following the previous equations, calculate the corresponding values at 50 Hz:

- Q_1 rate, B/D: 0; 792; 1,000; 1,292; and 1,563.
- H_1 head, ft: 22.2, 19.9, 17, 10.4, and 0.
- Efficiency, %: 0, 63.5, 64, 49, and 0.

Plotting these coordinates gives the one-stage FC-1200 head-capacity performance curve an operation at 50 Hz. Similar calculations provide coordinates for curves at other frequencies, as shown by the FC-1200 variable-speed performance curve (Fig. 13.51). The vortex-shaped window is the recommended operating range for the pump. As long as the hydraulic requirement falls within this range, the pump is within the recommended operating range.

13.5 Design Example

13.5.1 Step 1: Basic Data. The data used for this example are given next.

Well Data. K55 casing from surface to 5,600 ft: 7 in. and 26 lbm/ft; K55 liner from 5,530 to 6,930 ft: 5 in. and 15 lbm/ft; J55 EUE API tubing: 2⅞ in. and 6.5 lbm/ft; perforations and true vertical depth (TVD): 6,750 to 6,850 ft; and pump setting TVD (just above liner top): 5,500 ft.

Production Data. Tubing pressure: 100 psi; casing pressure: 100 psi; present production rate: 850 BFPD; pump-intake pressure: 2,600 psi; static bottomhole pressure: 3,200 psi; datum point: 6,800 ft; bottomhole temperature: 160°F; minimum desired production rate: 2,300 BFPD; GOR: 300 scf/STB; and water cut: 75%.

Well Fluid Conditions. Specific gravity of water: 1.085; oil °API or SG: 32; SG of gas: 0.7; bubblepoint pressure of gas: 1,500 psi; viscosity of oil: N/A; PVT data: none.

Power Sources. Available primary voltage: 12,470 V; frequency: 60 Hz; power source capabilities: N/A.

Possible Problems. There were no reported problems.

13.5.2 Step 2: Production Capacity. Determine the well productivity at the test pressure and production rate. In this case, the maximum production rate is desired without resulting in severe gas-interference problems. The pump-intake pressure at the desired production rate can be calculated from the present production conditions.

Because the well flowing pressure (2,600 psi) is greater than bubblepoint pressure (1,500 psi), the constant-PI method will most probably give satisfactory results. First, one can determine the PI using the test data:

$$ \text{PI} = Q/(P_r - P_{wf}), \dotfill (13.27) $$

and

$$ \text{PI} = 850/(3,200 - 2,600) = 1.42 \ \text{B/D, psi} . \dotfill (13.28) $$

Next, we can determine the new well flowing pressure (P_{wf}) at the estimated production rate (Q_d).

$$ P_{wf} = P_r - (Q_d/\text{PI}), \dotfill (13.29) $$

and

$$ P_{wf} = 3,200 - (2,300/1.42) = 1,580 \ \text{psi} . \dotfill (13.30) $$

The well flowing pressure of 1,580 psi is still above the bubblepoint pressure of 1,500 psi; therefore, the PI approach should give good results. The pump-intake pressure can be determined by correcting the flowing bottomhole pressure for the difference in the pump setting depth and datum point, and by considering the friction-loss datum point and friction loss in the casing annulus. In the given example, as the pump is set 1,300 ft above the perforations, the friction loss, because of flow of fluid through the annulus from perforations to pump setting depth, is small, as compared to the flowing pressure, and can be neglected.

Because there is both water and oil in the produced fluids, it is necessary to calculate a composite SG of the produced fluids. To find the composite SG, water cut is 75%; therefore,

$$ \text{SG}_w = 0.75 \times 1.085 = 0.8138. \dotfill (13.31) $$

Oil is 25%; therefore,

$$SG_o = 0.25 \times 0.865 = 0.2163. \dots\dots\dots\dots\dots (13.32)$$

The composite SG is the sum of the weighted percentages:

$$SG_{mix} = 0.8138 + 0.2163 = 1.03. \dots\dots\dots\dots (13.33)$$

The pressure, because of the difference in perforation depth and pump setting depth (6,800 to 5,500 ft = 1,300 ft), can be determined as:

$$PSI = (head, \quad ft \times SG_{mix})/2.31 \quad ft/psi, \dots\dots\dots (13.34)$$

and

$$PSI = (1,300 \times 1.03)/2.31 = 580 \quad psi. \dots\dots\dots (13.35)$$

Therefore, the pump intake pressure is

$$1,580 \quad psi - 580 \quad psi = 1,000 \quad psi. \dots\dots\dots (13.36)$$

13.5.3 Step 3: Gas Calculations. In this third step, one must determine the total fluid mixture, inclusive of water, oil, and free gas that is ingested by the pump. Use actual PVT data if available. For this example, Standing's correlation was used.[41]

Determine the solution GOR (R_s) at the pump-intake pressure by substituting the pump-intake pressure for the bubblepoint pressure (P_b) in Standing's equation. This relationship can also be found as a monograph in many textbooks or in chapters in the General Engineering section of this *Handbook*.

$$R_s = SG_s\left[\left(P_b/18\right) \times \left(10^{0.0125 \times \text{°API}}/10^{0.0091 \times T_F}\right)\right]^{1.2048}, \dots\dots\dots (13.37)$$

and

$$R_s = 0.7\left[(1,000/18) \times \left(10^{0.0125 \times 32}/10^{0.0091 \times 160}\right)\right]^{1.2048} = 180 \quad scf/STB. \dots\dots (13.38)$$

Determine the formation volume factor (B_o) with R_s and the following Standing's equation (can also be found as a monograph).

$$B_o = 0.972 + 0.000147F^{1.175}, \dots\dots\dots\dots (13.39)$$

where

$$F = R_s(SG_g/SG_o)^{0.5} + 1.25\,T_F = 180(0.7/0.865)^{0.5} + 1.25 \times 160 = 361.9. \dots\dots (13.40)$$

Therefore,

$$B_o = 0.972 + 0.000147(361.92)^{1.175}, \dots\dots\dots\dots (13.41)$$

and

$$B_o = 1.12 \text{ actual bbl/STB at } 1{,}000\text{-psi-pump intake pressure} \quad \text{.................} \quad (13.42)$$

Determine the gas volume factor (B_g) as

$$B_g = (5.04 \, ZT_R)/P \, . \quad \text{.......................................} \quad (13.43)$$

By assuming 0.85 Z factor (use actual PVT data if available),

$$B_g = [5.04 \times 0.85 \times (460 - 160)]/1.014 = 2.62 \text{ Mcf/bbl} \, . \quad \text{........................} \quad (13.44)$$

Next, determine the total volume of fluids and the percentage of free gas released at the pump intake. Using the producing GOR and oil volume, determine the total volume of gas (V_g).

$$V_g = (\text{BOPD} \times \text{GOR})/1{,}000 = [(2{,}300 \times .25) \times 300]/1{,}000 = 172.5 \text{ Mcf} \, . \quad \text{...........} \quad (13.45)$$

Using the solution GOR (R_s) at the pump intake, determine the solution gas volume (V_{SG}).

$$V_{SG} = (\text{BOPD} \times R_s)/1{,}000 = [(2{,}300 \times .25) \times 180]/1{,}000 = 103.5 \text{ Mcf} \, . \quad \text{...........} \quad (13.46)$$

The difference represents the volume of free gas (V_{FG}) released from solution by the decrease in pressure from bubblepoint pressure of 1,500 psi to the pump-intake pressure of 1,000 psi.

$$V_{FG} = 172.5 - 103.5 = 69 \text{ Mcf} \, . \quad \text{...............................} \quad (13.47)$$

The volume of oil (V_o) at the pump intake is

$$V_o = \text{BOPD} \times 1.12 = 644 \text{ BOPD} \, . \quad \text{.............................} \quad (13.48)$$

The volume of free gas at the pump intake (V_{IG}) in barrels is

$$V_{IG} = \text{free gas} \times \text{gas volume factor } (B_g)$$
$$= 69 \text{ Mcf} \times 2.62 \text{ Mcf/bbl} = 181 \text{ BGPD} \, . \quad \text{.......................} \quad (13.49)$$

Next, is the equation for the volume of water (V_w) at the pump intake.

$$V_w = \text{total fluid volume} \times \% \text{ water}$$
$$= 2{,}300 \text{ B/D} \times 0.75 = 1{,}725 \text{ BWPD} \, . \quad \text{.......................} \quad (13.50)$$

The total volume (V_t) of oil, water, and gas at the pump intake can now be determined by

$$V_t = V_o + V_{IG} + V_w = 644 \text{ BOPD} + 181 \text{ BGPD} + 1{,}725 \text{ BWPD}$$
$$= 2{,}550 \text{ BFPD} \, . \quad \text{..} \quad (13.51)$$

The ratio or percentage of free gas present at the pump intake to the total volume of fluid is

$$\% \text{ of free gas} = V_{IG}/V_t = (181 \text{ BGPD}/2{,}550 \text{ BFPD}) \times 100 = 7 \% \, . \quad \text{..............} \quad (13.52)$$

As this value is less than 10% by volume, it has only a minor effect on the pump performance, especially if most of the free gas is vented up the annulus. Use of a gas separation component is not essential in this case.

The composite SG, including gas, is determined by first calculating the total mass of produced fluid (TMPF) from the original data given.

$$\text{TMPF} = \left[(\text{BOPD} \times \text{SG}_o) + (\text{BWPD} \times \text{SG}_w) \times 62.4 \times 5.6146\right]$$
$$+(300 \times 575 \times 0.7 \times 0.0752) = 839{,}064 \ \text{lbm}/\text{D}, \dots\dots\dots\dots\dots\dots\dots \ (13.53)$$

and

$$\text{SG}_{\text{comp}} = \text{TMPF}/(\text{BFPD} \times 5.6146 \times 62.4)$$
$$= 839{,}064/(2{,}550 \times 5.6146 \times 62.4) = 0.939. \dots\dots\dots\dots\dots\dots \ (13.54)$$

Now that the total volume of fluid entering the first pump stage is known (2,550 BFPD) and the composite SG has been determined, we can continue to the next step of designing the ESP system.

13.5.4 Step 4: Total Dynamic Head. Sufficient data are now available to determine the TDH required by the pump.

$$\text{TDH} = H_L + F_t + H_{wh}, \dots\dots\dots\dots\dots\dots\dots\dots\dots\dots\dots\dots\dots \ (13.55)$$

and

$$H_L = \text{pump depth} - (\text{PIP} \times 2.31 \ \text{ft}/\text{psi})/\text{SG}_{\text{comp}}$$
$$= 5{,}500 \ \text{ft} - (1{,}000 \times 2.31)/0.939 = 3{,}040 \ \text{ft} \ (926 \ \text{m}). \dots\dots\dots\dots \ (13.56)$$

The TDH required is based on the normal pumping conditions for the well application. If the well is killed with a heavier-gravity fluid, a higher head is required to pump the fluid out, until the well is stabilized on its normal production. More HP is also required to lift the heavier kill fluid and should be considered when selecting the motor rating for the application. F_t = tubing friction loss. Refer to **Fig. 13.52**.

Friction loss per 1,000 ft of 2⅞-in. tubing (new) is 49 ft/1,000 ft of depth at 2,440 B/D (405 m³/d) or 4.5 m/100 m. Using the desired pump setting depth,

$$F_t = (5{,}500 \times 49)/1{,}000 = 270 \ \text{ft} \ (82.3 \ \text{m}). \dots\dots\dots\dots\dots\dots\dots \ (13.57)$$

H_{wh} = desired head at wellhead (desired wellhead pressure). Using the composite SG,

$$H_{wh} = (100 \ \text{psi} \times 2.31 \ \text{ft}/\text{psi})/0.939 = 246 \ \text{ft} \ (75 \ \text{m}), \dots\dots\dots\dots \ (13.58)$$

and

$$\text{TDH} = 3{,}040 \ \text{ft} + 270 \ \text{ft} + 246 \ \text{ft} = 3{,}356 \ \text{ft, \ or}$$
$$926.6 \ \text{m} + 82.3 \ \text{m} + 75 \ \text{m} = 1084 \ \text{m}. \dots\dots\dots\dots\dots\dots\dots \ (13.59)$$

Based on Hazen - Williams Formula

Water SG = 1.0   Temperature = 100 ° F
"Old" = Schedule 40 pipe, 10 yrs old   "New" = Schedule 40 pipe

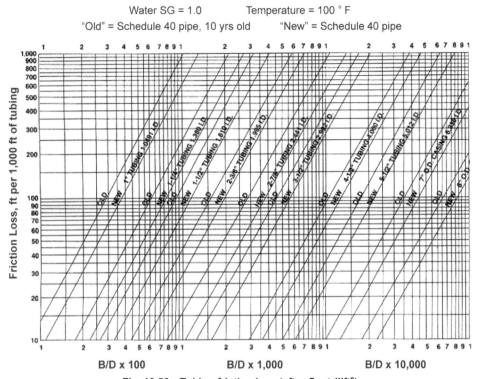

Fig. 13.52—Tubing friction loss (after Centrilift[9]).

13.5.5 Step 5: Pump-Type Selection. From the manufacturer's catalog information, select the pump type with the highest efficiency at the calculated capacity 2,440 B/D (405 m³/d) that will fit the casing. Select the 513 series GC-2200 pump (**Fig. 13.53**).

The head in feet (meters) for one stage is 2,550 B/D (405 m³/d) and is 41.8 ft (13 m). The BHP per stage is 1.16. To determine the total number of stages required, divide the TDH by the head/stage taken from the curve. The number of stages = TDH/(head/stage). The number of stages = (3,556 /41.8) = 85 stages.

Refer to the manufacturer's information for the GC-2200 pump. The housing no. 9 can house a maximum of 84 stages, 93 stages for a housing no. 10. Because the 84-stage pump is only one stage less than the calculated requirement, it should be adequate and the pump will cost less. Once the maximum number of pump stages is decided, calculate the total BHP required as

$$BHP = BHP / stage \times no.\ stages \times SG_{mix}, \quad\dots\dots\dots\dots\dots\dots\dots\dots\dots (13.60)$$

and

$$BHP = 1.16 \times 84 \times 0.939 = 91.5\ hp\ . \quad\dots\dots\dots\dots\dots\dots\dots\dots\dots (13.61)$$

13.5.6 Step 6: Optimum Size of Components. *Gas Separator.* If a gas separator was required, refer to a catalog to select the appropriate separator and determine its HP requirement. In this

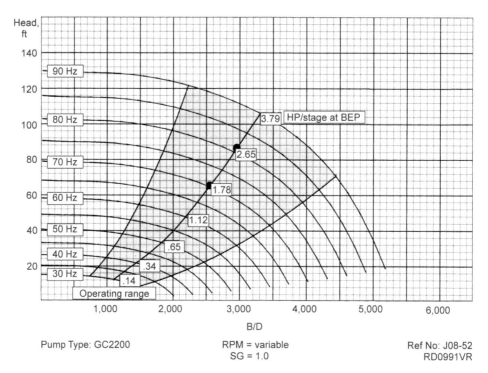

Fig. 13.53—GC-2200 stage variable-speed performance curve [after Centrilift Graphics, Claremore, Oklahoma (2003)].

example, one was not needed. If gas interference causes operating problems, a gas separator can be added on the next ESP repair.

Seal Section. Normally, the seal section series is the same as that of the pump, although there are exceptions and special adapters available to connect the units together. Here, the 513 series GSB seal section is selected.

The HP requirement for the seal depends on the TDH produced by the pump. The manufacturer's information shows a requirement of 3.0 hp for the 513 series seal operating against a TDH of 3,556 ft. Therefore, the total HP requirement for this example is 91.5 hp for the pump, plus 3.0 hp for the seal, or 94.5 hp total.

Motor. Generally, a 500 series motor should be used with the 513 series pump. When a motor is selected, consideration should be given to choose as large a diameter unit as possible for the casing to optimize the initial cost, motor efficiency, operating costs, and repair costs. In this example select the 100-hp 562 series motor from the catalog. The motor voltage can be selected on the basis of considerations discussed next.

The high-voltage, consequently low-current, motors have lower cable losses and require smaller conductor-size cables. High-voltage motors have superior starting characteristics—a feature that can be extremely important if excessive voltage losses are expected during starting. Although, the higher the motor voltage, the more expensive is the motor.

In some cases, the savings, because of smaller cable, may be offset by the difference in motor-controller cost, and it may be necessary to make an economic analysis for the various voltage motors. However, for this example, the high-voltage motor (100 hp; 2,145 V; 27 amps) is an excellent choice. Check the manufacturers catalog and equipment information to assure that all operating parameters are well within their recommended ranges (e.g., thrust bearing, shaft HP, housing burst pressure, and fluid velocity).

13.5.7 Step 7: Electric Cable. *Determine Cable Size.* The cable size is selected on the basis of its current-carrying capability. Using the motor amps (27) and the cable voltage-drop chart in the catalog, select a cable size with a voltage drop of less than 30 V/1,000 ft. All conductor sizes 1 through 6 fall in this category. The no. 6 cable has a voltage drop of $18.5 \times 1.201 = 22.2$ V/1,000 ft (305 m), and based on \$0.06/kW-hr. results in a monthly I^2R loss of \$255. A no. 4 cable has 14.1 V/1,000 ft and costs \$158/month. The operating cost savings of \$97/month is divided into the added cost of the no. 4 over the no. 6 cable to calculate a payout. A no. 6 cable size was selected for this example.

Cable Type. Because of the gassy conditions and the bottomhole temperature, the polypropylene ("poly") cable should be used. Check to be sure the cable diameter plus tubing collar diameter is smaller than the casing ID.

Cable Length. The pump setting depth is 5,500 ft (1676.4 m), with 100 ft (30.5 m) of cable for surface connections; the total cable length should be 5,600 ft (1707 m). Check to verify that the cable length is within the manufacturer's recommended maximum length,

Cable Venting. A cable vent box must be installed between the wellhead and the motor controller to prevent gas migration to the controller.

13.5.8 Step 8: Accessory and Miscellaneous Equipment. Flat Cable—Motor Lead Extension. As described in section 13.4.8, calculate the length for the MLE. Pump length = 14.8 ft (4.51 m); seal length = 6.3 ft (1.92 m); plus, 6 ft = 6.0 ft (1.83 m) = 213.1 ft (8.26 m); select 35 ft (10.7 m) of 562 series flat cable.

Flat Guards. Cable guards are available in 6-ft sections; therefore, six sections are sufficient.

Cable Bands. The pump and seal section is approximately 20 ft (6 m) long. Twenty-two-inch (56 cm) bands are required to clamp to the housing with bands spaced at 2-ft (61 cm) intervals (10 bands). On the production-tubing string above the pump, the same length cable bands can be used. The bands should be spaced at 15-ft (4.5-m) intervals. The setting depth of 5,500 ft requires 367 bands.

Downhole Accessory Equipment. Refer to the manufacturer's catalog for the accessories listed next.

Swaged Nipple. The pump outlet is 2⅞ in., per the manufacturer's information, so a swaged nipple is not required for the 2⅞-in. tubing.

Check Valve. The 2⅞-in.-EUE, 8-round, thread check valve is recommended.

Drain Valve. The 2⅞-in.-EUE, 8-round, thread drain valve should be used (in conjunction with the check valve) to eliminate pulling a wet string.

Motor Controller. The motor-controller selection is based on its voltage, amperage, and KVA rating. Therefore, before selecting the controller, one must first determine the motor controller voltage. Assume the controller voltage is the same as the surface voltage going downhole. The surface voltage (SV) is the sum of the motor voltage and the total voltage loss in the cable. (Adjust taps on the transformer to closely achieve this value.)

$$V_s = 2{,}145 \text{ V} + [(22.2 \text{ V} \times 5{,}600 \text{ ft})/1{,}000 \text{ ft}] = 2{,}269 \text{ V}. \quad\text{................} \quad (13.62)$$

The motor amperage is 27 amps; the KVA can now be calculated.

$$\text{KVA} = (V_s \times \text{motor amps} \times 1.73)/1{,}000, \quad\text{................................} \quad (13.63)$$

and

$$\text{KVA} = (2{,}269 \times 27 \times 1.73)/1{,}000 = 106. \quad\text{................................} \quad (13.64)$$

The 6H-CG motor controller suits these requirements.

Transformer. The transformer selection is based on the available primary power supply (12,470 V), the secondary voltage requirement (2,269 V) and the KVA requirement (106 KVA). Choose three 313.5 KVA single-phase transformers as shown in the manufacturer's catalog.

Surface Cable. Select 50 ft (15.2 m) of no. 1 cable for surface connection to transformers.

13.6 Example

13.6.1 Step 1: Variable-Speed Pumping System.
Use the previous example, and design a new system using a VSC. To help justify the use of a VSC, two new conditions were added. First, assume that we need to maintain a constant oil production (575 BOPD), although, reservoir data indicate we should see an increase in water cut (75 to 80%) over the next few months. Next, to satisfy our economic justification in using the VSC, we must optimize the initial cost and size of the downhole assembly.

To maintain oil production as the water cut increases, we must determine the maximum desired flow rate with 80% water.

$$\text{Maximum flow rate} = \text{BOPD}/\text{oil }\%, \quad\quad\quad (13.65)$$

and

$$\text{Maximum flow} = (575/0.20) = 2,875 \text{ B/D}. \quad\quad\quad (13.66)$$

13.6.2 Step 2: Production Capacity.
We can now calculate the pump intake pressure at the maximum rate of 2,875 B/D. First, make the assumption that even though the water cut changes, the well's PI will remain constant. Now, determine the new well flowing pressure (P_{wf}) at the maximum desired production rate (Q_d).

$$P_{wf} = P_r - (Q_d/\text{PI}), \quad\quad\quad (13.67)$$

and

$$P_{wf} = 3,200 - (2,875/1.42) = 1,175 \text{ psi}. \quad\quad\quad (13.68)$$

The new well flowing pressure of 1,175 psi is slightly below the bubblepoint pressure of 1,500 psi; therefore, the PI approach should still give good results.

The pump-intake pressure can be determined the same as before, although, a new composite specific gravity must be calculated.

$$\text{Water cut is } 80\% ; \text{SG}_w = 0.80 \times 1.085 = 0.868. \quad\quad\quad (13.69)$$

$$\text{Oil is } 25\% ; \text{SG}_{ol} = 0.20 \times 0.865 = 0.173. \quad\quad\quad (13.70)$$

The composite SG is the sum of the weighted percentages:

$$\text{SG}_{mix} = 0.868 + 0.173 = 1.04. \quad\quad\quad (13.71)$$

The pressure because of the difference in perforation depth and pump setting depth $(6,800 + 5,500 \text{ ft} = 12,300 \text{ ft})$ can be determined as

$$\text{psi} = (\text{head}, \text{ ft} \times SG_{mix})/2.31 \text{ ft}/\text{psi}, \dots\dots\dots\dots\dots\dots\dots\dots \quad (13.72)$$

and

$$\text{psi} = (1,300 \times 1.04)/2.31 = 585 \text{ psi} . \dots\dots\dots\dots\dots\dots\dots\dots \quad (13.73)$$

Therefore, the pump-intake pressure (PIP) can now be determined as

$$\text{PIP} = 1,175 \text{ psi} - 585 \text{ psi} = 590 \text{ psi} . \dots\dots\dots\dots\dots\dots\dots\dots \quad (13.74)$$

13.6.3 Step 3: Gas Calculations. Next, determine the total fluid mixture that will be ingested by the pump at the new maximum desired flow rate (2,875 B/D). Determine the solution GOR (R_s) at the pump-intake pressure or by substituting the pump-intake pressure for the bubble-point pressure (P_b) in Standing's equation.[41]

$$R_s = Y_s[(P_b/18) \times (10^{0.0125 \times \text{API}}/10^{0.0091 \times T_F})]^{1.2048}, \dots\dots\dots\dots\dots \quad (13.75)$$

and

$$R_s = 0.7[(585/18) \times (10^{0.0125 \times 32}/10^{0.0091 \times 160})]^{1.2048} = 94 \text{ scf}/\text{STB} . \dots\dots\dots \quad (13.76)$$

Determine the formation volume factor (B_o) with the R_s from Standing's monograph (see the General Engineering section of this *Handbook*) or use Standing's equation[41]

$$B_o = 0.972 + 0.000147F^{1.175}, \dots\dots\dots\dots\dots\dots\dots\dots\dots \quad (13.77)$$

where

$$F = R_s(Y_g/Y_o)^{0.5} + 1.25T_F, \dots\dots\dots\dots\dots\dots\dots\dots\dots \quad (13.78)$$

and

$$F = 94(0.7/0.865)^{0.5} + 1.25 \times 160 = 284.56. \dots\dots\dots\dots\dots\dots\dots \quad (13.79)$$

Therefore,

$$B_o = 0.972 + 0.000147(284.56)^{1.175} = 1.08 \text{ reservoir bbl}/\text{STB} . \dots\dots\dots\dots \quad (13.80)$$

Determine the gas volume factor (B_g) as

$$B_g = (5.04ZT_R)/P . \dots\dots\dots\dots\dots\dots\dots\dots\dots\dots \quad (13.81)$$

Assuming a 0.85 Z factor,

$$B_g = [5.04 \times 0.85 \times (460 - 160)]/604 = 4.40 \; \text{bbl}/\text{Mcf}. \quad\text{..............}\quad (13.82)$$

Next, determine the total volume of fluids, and the percentage of free gas released at the pump intake. Using the producing GOR and oil volume, determine the total volume of gas (T_G).

$$T_G = (\text{BOPD} \times \text{GOR})/1{,}000, \quad\text{...............................}\quad (13.83)$$

or

$$T_G = [(2{,}875 \times 0.20) \times 300]/1{,}000 = 172.5 \; \text{Mcf}. \quad\text{....................}\quad (13.84)$$

Using the solution GOR (R_s) at the pump intake, determine the solution gas volume (V_{SG}).

$$V_{SG} = (\text{BOPD} \times R_s)/1{,}000 = [(2{,}875 \times 0.20) \times 94]/1{,}000$$
$$= 54.05 \; \text{Mcf}. \quad\text{.....................}\quad (13.85)$$

The difference represents the volume of free gas (V_{FG}) released from solution by the decrease in pressure from the bubblepoint pressure of 1,500 psi to the pump intake pressure of 1,000 psi.

$$V_{FG} = 172.5 - 54.05 = 118.5 \; \text{Mcf}. \quad\text{....................}\quad (13.86)$$

The volume of oil (V_o) at the pump intake is

$$V_o = \text{BOPD} \times B_o, \quad\text{.............................}\quad (13.87)$$

and

$$V_o = 575 \; \text{BOPD} \times 1.08 = 621 \; \text{BOPD}. \quad\text{.....................}\quad (13.88)$$

The volume of free gas at the pump intake is

$$V_g = V_{FG} \times B_g, \quad\text{..............................}\quad (13.89)$$

and

$$V_g = 118.5 \; \text{Mcf} \times 4.40 \; \text{bbl}/\text{Mcf} = 521 \; \text{BGPD}. \quad\text{.................}\quad (13.90)$$

The volume of water (V_w) at the pump intake is

$$V_w = \text{total fluid volume} \times \% \; \text{water}, \quad\text{....................}\quad (13.91)$$

and

$$V_w = 2{,}875 \; \text{B}/\text{D} \times 0.80 = 2{,}300 \; \text{BWPD}. \quad\text{....................}\quad (13.92)$$

The total volume (V_t) or oil, water, and gas at the pump intake can now be determined

$$V_t = V_o + V_g + V_w, \quad \text{...} \quad (13.93)$$

$$V_t = 621 \ \text{BOPD} + 521 \ \text{BGPD} + 2,300 \ \text{BWPD}, \quad \text{...............................} \quad (13.94)$$

and

$$V_t = 3,442 \ \text{BFPD} . \quad \text{...} \quad (13.95)$$

The ratio or percentage of free gas present at the pump intake to the total volume of fluid is

$$\% \ \text{free gas} = V_g / V_t, \quad \text{..} \quad (13.96)$$

and

$$\% \ \text{free gas} = (521 \ \text{BGPD} / 3,442 \ \text{BFPD}) \times 100 = 15\% . \quad \text{........................} \quad (13.97)$$

As this value is greater than 10% by volume, there is significant free gas to affect pump performance; therefore, it is recommended that a gas separator be installed. Next, we must assume the gas separator's efficiency. At 15% free gas, a 90% efficiency of separation is used on the basis of the manufacturer's gas-separator performance information.

The percentage of gas not separated is 10%.

$$V_g = \text{volume of gas at PIP} \times \% \ \text{ingested}, \quad \text{....................................} \quad (13.98)$$

and

$$V_g = 521 \ \text{B/D} \times 0.1 = 52 \ \text{B/D} . \quad \text{..} \quad (13.99)$$

Total volume of fluid mixture ingested into the pump is

$$V_o = 621 \ \text{B/D}, \quad \text{..} \quad (13.100)$$

$$V_g = 52 \ \text{B/D}, \quad \text{..} \quad (13.101)$$

$$V_w = 2,300 \ \text{B/D}, \quad \text{..} \quad (13.102)$$

and

$$V_t = 2,973 \ \text{B/D} . \quad \text{..} \quad (13.103)$$

The amount of free gas entering the first pump stage as a percent of the total fluid mixture is

$$\% \ \text{free gas} = V_g / V_t, \quad \text{..} \quad (13.104)$$

and

$$\% \ \text{free gas} = (52 / 2,973) \times 100 = 2\%. \quad \text{.....................................} \quad (13.105)$$

As the free gas represents only 2% by volume of fluid being pumped, it has little significant effect on the well fluid composite SG and may be ignored for conservative motor sizing.

Now that the total volume of fluid entering the first pump stage is known (2,973 BFPD) and the composite SG has been determined, we can continue to the next step of designing the ESP system.

13.6.4 Step 4: Total Dynamic Head. Sufficient data are now available to determine the TDH required at the maximum desired flow rate (2,973 B/D). The TDH for the minimum desired flow rate (2,550 B/D) was previously determined to be 3,556 ft.

$$\text{TDH} = H_L + F_t + H_{wh}, \quad\quad\quad\quad\quad\quad\quad\quad\quad (13.106)$$

where H_L = the vertical distance in feet between the estimated producing fluid level and the surface, and

$$H_L = \text{pump depth} - (\text{PIP} \times 2.31) / \text{SG} = 5,500 - (590 \times 2.31) / 1.04$$

$$= 4,190 \text{ ft (1277 m)} . \quad\quad\quad\quad\quad\quad\quad (13.107)$$

From Fig. 13.52, friction loss per 1,000 ft of $2\frac{7}{8}$-in. tubing (new) is 60 ft/1,000 ft of depth at 2,973 B/D (405 m³/d), or 4.5 m/100 m. Using the desired pump setting depth,

$$F_t = (5,500 \times 60) / 1,000 = 330 \text{ ft (100.6 m)} . \quad\quad\quad\quad (13.108)$$

H_{wh} = the discharge pressure head (desired wellhead pressure). Using the composite SG,

$$H_{wh} = (100 \times 2.31) / 1.02 = 226 \text{ ft (68.9 m)}, \quad\quad\quad\quad (13.109)$$

and

$$\text{THD} = 4,190 \text{ ft} + 330 \text{ ft} + 226 \text{ ft} = 4,746 \text{ ft}, \quad\quad\quad\quad (13.110)$$

or

$$1277 \text{ m} + 100.6 \text{ m} + 68.9 \text{ m} = 1446.6 \text{ m} . \quad\quad\quad\quad (13.111)$$

13.6.5 Step 5: Pump-Type Selection. The hydraulic requirements for our variable speed pumping system have been determined. Those requirements are the minimum hydraulic requirement (flow rate 2,550 B/D; total dynamic head 3,556 ft) and maximum hydraulic requirement (flow rate 2,973 B/D; total dynamic head 4,746 ft).

In the economic justification for using the VSC, the size of the downhole unit was determined. This was done using the guidelines discussed next.

As the operating frequency increases, the number of stages required to generate the required lift decreases. The closer the operation is to the best efficiency point, the lower the power requirement and power cost.

A fixed frequency motor of a particular frame size has a maximum output torque, provided that the specified voltage is supplied to its terminals. The same torque can be achieved at other speeds by varying the voltage in proportion to the frequency. This way the magnetizing current and flux density will remain constant, and so the available torque will be a constant (at no-slip RPM). As a result, power output rating is directly proportional to speed because power rating is obtained by multiplying the rated torque with speed. Using the variable-speed performance curves, select a pump that will fit in the casing so the maximum flow rate (2,973 B/D) falls at its BEP. The GC-2200 satisfies these conditions at 81 Hz.

Next, select the head per stage from the curve. It indicates 86 ft/stage. With the maximum TDH requirement of 4,746 ft, the number of pump stages required can be determined. The number of stages = the maximum TDH /head per stage and = 4,746 /86 = 55 stages. A 55-stage GC-2200 meets our maximum hydraulic requirement. To determine if it meets our minimum hydraulic requirement, divide the minimum TDH requirement by the number of stages. The minimum head per stage = 3,556 /55 = 64.7 ft/stage. Plotting the minimum head/ stage (64.7 ft) and the minimum flow rate (2,550 B/D) on the curve indicates an operating frequency of 70 Hz. Note, the minimum hydraulic requirement is also near the pump's BEP.

Next, using the VSC curve for the GC-2200 find the BHP/stage at the 60-Hz BEP (1.12 hp). To calculate the BHP at the maximum frequency use Eqs. 13.112 and 13.113.

$$\text{BHP}/\text{stage} \times \text{no. stages} \times (\text{max. HP}/60 \text{ Hz}) \times \text{SG}, \dotfill (13.112)$$

and

$$1.12 \times 55 \times (81/60)^3 \times 1.04 = 157.6 \text{ hp}. \dotfill (13.113)$$

Because a rotary gas separator was selected (which is a centrifugal machine using HP), it will add additional load to the motor. The HP requirement also changes by the cube function. Referring to the manufacturer's information, the 513 series rotary gas separator requires 5 hp at 60 Hz.

$$\text{HP}_{separator} = 5 \times (81/60)^3 \times 1.04 = 12.8 \text{ hp}. \dotfill (13.114)$$

Total BHP for the pump and separator = 157.6 + 12.8 = 170.4 hp. With Eqs. 13.115 and 13.116, the equivalent 60-Hz BHP for both the pump and gas separator can be calculated:

$$60\text{-Hz BHP} = \text{BHP at max. Hz} \times (60 \text{ Hz}/\text{max. Hz}), \dotfill (13.115)$$

or

$$60\text{-Hz BHP} = 170.4 \times (60/81) = 126.2 \text{ hp}. \dotfill (13.116)$$

Select the appropriate model seal section and determine the HP requirement at the maximum TDH requirement. Select a motor that is capable of supplying total HP requirements of the pump, gas separator, and seal. In this example, a 562 series motor with 130 hp; 2,145 volts; and 35 amps was selected.

Using the technical data provided by the manufacturer, determine if any load limitations were exceeded (e.g., shaft loading, thrust bearing loading, housing burst pressure limitations, fluid velocity passing the motor, etc.).

Next, select the power cable and calculate the cable voltage drop. On the basis of the motor current (35 amps) and the temperature (160°F), no. 6 cable can be used. Adding 200 ft for surface connections, the cable voltage drop is written as

$$\text{cable voltage drop} = (24 \text{ V} \times 1.201 \times 5,700)/1,000 = 164 \text{ V}. \dotfill (13.117)$$

We can now calculate the required surface voltage (SV) at the maximum operating frequency as

$$SV = [\text{motor volts} \times (\text{max}. \ Hz/60 \ Hz)] + \text{voltage drop}, \quad \text{...................} \quad (13.118)$$

and

$$SV = [2{,}145 \times (81/60)] + 164 = 3{,}060 \ V. \quad \text{.....................} \quad (13.119)$$

Note that the surface voltage is greater than standard 3KV cable. Therefore, 4KV or higher cable construction should be selected. Sufficient data are available to calculate KVA.

$$KVA = (SV \times \text{motor amps} \times 1.73)/1{,}000, \quad \text{.....................} \quad (13.120)$$

and

$$KVA = (3{,}060 \times 35 \times 1.73)/1{,}000 = 185 \ KVA. \quad \text{...............} \quad (13.121)$$

Referring to the manufacturer's catalog, select the model 2200-3VT, 200 KVA, NEMA3 (outdoor enclosure) VSC. All other accessory equipment should be selected as in the previous example.

Nomenclature

A_m = motor amperage, amps

B_g = gas volume factor, scf/bbl [m^3/m^3]

B_o = oil volume factor, bbl/STBO

C = constant = 3,960, where Q is in gal/min, and TDH is in ft [= 6,750, where Q is in m^3/D, and TDH is in m]

D = diameter, in. [cm]

F = correlating function for Eq. 13.18

F_t = well-tubing friction loss

H = head, ft [m]

H_L = net well lift

H_{wh} = wellhead pressure head, ft [m]

J = slope

N = rotating speed, rev/min

P = pressure, psi [kg/cm^2]

P_b = bubblepoint pressure, psi [kg/cm^2]

$P_{\text{discharge}}$ = pump-discharge pressure, psi [kg/cm^2]

P_r = well static pressure, psi [kg/cm^2]

P_{wf} = well flowing pressure, psi [kg/cm^2]

Q = flow rate, B/D [m^3/d]

Q_d = estimated production rate

Q_o = maximum production at $P_{wf} = 0$, B/D [m^3/D]

R_s = solution gas/oil ratio, scf/bbl [m^3/m^3]

T = torque, ft-lbf

$T_{\text{conductor}}$ = wellbore temperature at the ESP setting depth

T_C = temperature, °C

T_F = temperature, °F

T_G = total volume of gas

T_K = temperature, K

T_R = temperature, °R

V = voltage, volts
V_{FG} = volume of free gas
V_g = volume of gas
V_{IG} = volume of free gas at the pump intake
V_o = volume of oil, bbl [m^3]
V_s = surface voltage, volts
V_{SG} = solution gas volume
V_t = total volume
V_w = volume of water
Z = gas-compressibility factor (typically 0.50 to 1.00)
η_m = motor efficiency
η_p = pump efficiency

Subscripts

g = gas
o = oil
t = total
w = water

References

1. Williams, J.: *A Story of People and a Company Called TRW REDA,* TRW REDA Pump Div., Bartlesville, Oklahoma (1980) 19–33.
2. Brookbank, E.B.: "Electric Submersible Pumps—The First Sixty Years," paper presented at the 1988 European ESP Workshop, London, 24 May.
3. *RP11S3, Recommended Practice for Electrical Submersible Pump Installations,* second edition, API, Washington, DC (March 1999).
4. *RP11S2, Recommended Practice for Electrical Submersible Pump Testing,* second edition, API, Washington, DC (August 1997).
5. Lund, R.: "Acceptance Tests for Mixed Flow, Axial and Centrifugal Pumps," *World Oil* (1983) **206,** 398.
6. Bearden, J. and James, M.: "ESP Seal Assembly Design and Application," paper presented at the 1988 SPE Gulf Coast ESP Workshop, Houston, 28–29 April.
7. *RP11S7, Recommended Practice for Application and Testing of Electrical Submersible Pump Seal Chamber Sections,* second edition, API, Washington, DC (March 1999).
8. Vandevier, J.: "Understanding Downhole Electric Submersible Motors—A Tutorial," paper presented at the 1992 SPE Gulf Coast ESP Workshop, Houston, 29 April–1 May.
9. *Submersible Pump Handbook,* fifth edition, Centrilift, Claremore, Oklahoma (1994).
10. Cashmore, D.: "Electrical Submersible Motor Tests," paper presented at the 1998 SPE Gulf Coast ESP Workshop, Houston, 29 April–1 May.
11. Breit, S.: "Rating of Electrical Submergible Motors," paper presented at the 1988 SPE Gulf Coast ESP Workshop, Houston, 28–29 April.
12. *RP11S5, Recommended Practice for Application of Electrical Submersible Cable Systems,* first edition, API, Washington, DC (February 1993).
13. *RP11S6, Recommended Practice for Testing of Electric Submersible Cable Systems,* first edition, API, Washington, DC (December 1995).
14. Neuroth, D.: "ESP Cable Design and Application Fundamentals—Power Cable Design to Operational Success," paper presented at the 2000 Southwestern Petroleum Short Course Conference, Lubbock, Texas, 12–13 April.
15. *Standard 1019, Recommended Practice for Specifying Electric Submersible Pump Cable— Polypropylene Insulation,* Inst. of Electrical and Electronics Engineers, New York City (1991).

16. *Standard 1018, Recommended Practice for Specifying Electric Submersible Pump Cable— Ethylene-Propylene-Rubber Insulation,* Inst. of Electrical and Electronics Engineers, New York City (1991).

17. *Standard 1017, Recommended Practice for Field Testing Electric Submersible Pump Cable,* Inst. of Electrical and Electronic Engineers, New York City (1991).

18. Leuthen, M.: "Variable Speed Drives: Definitions, Applications, and Comparisons," paper presented at the 1997 SPE Gulf Coast ESP Workshop, Houston, 30 April–May 2.

19. *Standard 519 Recommended Practice and Requirements for Harmonic Control in Electrical Power Systems,* Inst. of Electrical and Electronic Engineers, New York City (1992).

20. Lea, J.F. and Bearden, J.L.: "Effect of Gaseous Fluids on Submersible Pump Performance," *JPT* (1982) 2922.

21. Lea, J.F. and Bearden, J.L.: "Gas Separator Performance for Submersible Pump Operation," *JPT* (1982) 1327.

22. Dunbar, C.: "Determination of Proper Type of Gas Separator," paper presented at the 1989 SPE Artificial Lift Workshop, Long Beach, California, 16–17 October.

23. Wilson, B.L.: "ESPs and Gas," paper presented at the 1993 SPE Gulf Coast ESP Workshop, Houston, 28–30 April..

24. Turpin, J., Lea, J., and Bearden, J.: "Gas/Liquid Flow Through Centrifugal Pumps—Correlation of Data," paper presented at the 1980 Intl. Pump Symposium, Texas A&M U., College Station, Texas, 1 September.

25. Bearden, J. and Sheth, K.: "Free Gas and a Submersible Centrifugal Pump—Application Guideline," paper presented at the 1996 SPE Gulf Coast ESP Workshop, Houston, 1–3 May.

26. Wilson, B.L.: "The Effects of Abrasives on ESPs," paper presented at the 1988 SPE Gulf Coast ESP Workshop, Houston, 28–29 April.

27. Wilson, B.L.: "Sand Resistant ESPs," paper presented at the 1990 SPE Gulf Coast ESP Workshop, Houston, 30 April–May 2.

28. Woelflin, W.: *Drilling and Production Practices,* API, Washington, DC (1942).

29. Patterson, J., Henry, J., and Dinkins, W.: "Emulsion Viscosity Testing with ESPs," paper presented at the 2002 SPE Gulf Coast ESP Workshop, Houston, 1–3 May.

30. Adams, D.L.: "Biocorrosion of Electrical Submersible Pump Components by Sulfate Reducing Bacteria or Other Bacterium," paper presented at the 2002 SPE Gulf Coast ESP Workshop, Houston, 1–3 May.

31. *RP11S, Recommended Practice for the Operation, Maintenance, and Troubleshooting of Electric Submersible Pumps,* third edition, API, Washington, DC (November 1997).

32. *RP11S1, Recommended Practice for Electrical Submersible Pump Teardown Report,* third edition, API, Washington, DC (September 1997).

33. Baillie, A.: "Optimizing ESP Run Life—A Practical Checklist," paper presented at the 2002 European ESP Roundtable, Aberdeen, 6 February.

34. Lea, J.F. and Bearden, J.L.: "Operational Problems and Their Solutions—Electrical Submersible Pumps," paper presented at the 1992 SPE Gulf Coast ESP Workshop, Houston, 19 April–2 May.

35. Lea, J. *et al.:* "Electrical Submersible Pumps: On and Offshore Problems and Solutions," paper SPE 28694 presented at the 1994 SPE International Petroleum Conference and Exhibition, Veracruz, Mexico, 10–13 October.

36. Lea, J. and Bearden, J.: "ESP's: On and Offshore Problems and Solutions," paper SPE 52159 presented at the 1999 SPE Mid-Continent Operations Symposium, Oklahoma City, Oklahoma, 28–31 March.

37. Lea, J. and Bearden, J.: "ESP's: On and Offshore Problems and Solutions," paper presented at the 2002 Southwestern Petroleum Short Course Conference, Lubbock, Texas, 23–24 April.

38. *The Nine Step,* Centrilift, Claremore, Oklahoma (1999) 1–27.

39. Gilbert, W.E.: "Flowing and Gas Lift Well Performance," *API Drilling and Production Practice,* API, Washington, DC (1954) 143.

40. Vogel, J.V.: "Inflow Performance Relationships For Solution-Gas Drive Wells," *JPT* (January 1968) 83.

41. *Electrical Submersible Pumps and Equipment,* Centrilift, Claremore, Oklahoma (2001) 11.

SI Metric Conversion Factors

bbl ×	1.589 873	E – 01	= m^3
cp ×	1.0*	E – 03	= Pa·s
ft ×	3.048*	E – 01	= m
°F	(°F – 32)/1.8		= °C
gal ×	3.785 412	E – 03	= m^3
hp ×	7.460 43	E – 01	= kW
in. ×	2.54*	E + 00	= cm
lbf ×	4.448 222	E + 00	= N
lbm ×	4.535 924	E – 01	= kg
psi ×	6.894 757	E + 00	= kPa

*Conversion factor is exact.

Chapter 14
Hydraulic Pumping in Oil Wells
James Fretwell, Weatherford Artificial Lift Systems

14.1 Introduction

Hydraulic pumping is a proven artificial-lift method that has been used since the early 1930s. It offers several different systems for handling a variety of well conditions. Successful applications have included setting depths ranging from 500 to 19,000 ft and production rates varying from less than 100 to 20,000 B/D. Surface packages are available using multiplex pumps ranging from 15 to 625 hp. The systems are flexible because the downhole-pumping rate can be regulated over a wide range with fluid controls on the surface. Chemicals to control corrosion, paraffin, and emulsions can be injected downhole with the power fluid, while fresh water can also be injected to dissolve salt deposits. When pumping heavy crudes, the power fluid can serve as an effective diluent to reduce the viscosity of the produced fluids. The power fluid also can be heated for handling heavy or low-pour-point crudes. Hydraulic pumping systems are suitable for wells with deviated or crooked holes that can cause problems for other types of artificial lift. The surface facilities can have a low profile and may be clustered into a central battery to service numerous wells. This can be advantageous in urban sites, offshore locations, areas requiring watering systems (sprinkle systems), and environmentally sensitive areas.

Hydraulic pumping systems transmit power downhole by means of pressurized power fluid that flows in wellbore tubulars. Hydraulic transmission of power downhole can be accomplished with reasonably good efficiency using a reciprocating piston pump. With 30°API oil at 2,500 psi in 2⅞-in. tubing, 100 surface hydraulic horsepower can be transmitted to a depth of 8,000 ft with a flow rate of 2,350 B/D and a frictional pressure drop of less than 200 psi. Even higher efficiencies can be achieved with water as the hydraulic medium because of its lower viscosity.

The downhole pump acts a transformer to convert the energy into pressure in the produced fluids. A common form of a hydraulic downhole pump consists of a set of coupled reciprocating pistons, one driven by the power fluid and the other pumping the well fluids. Another form of a hydraulic downhole pump that has become more popular is the jet pump, which converts the pressurized power fluid to a high-velocity jet that mixes directly with the well fluids.[1,2] In the turbulent mixing, momentum and energy from the power fluid are added to the produced fluids.[3,4] The operating pressures in hydraulic pumping systems usually range from 2,000 to 4,000 psi. The most common pump used to generate this pressure on the surface is a multiplex positive displacement pump driven by an electric motor or multicylinder gas or diesel engine.

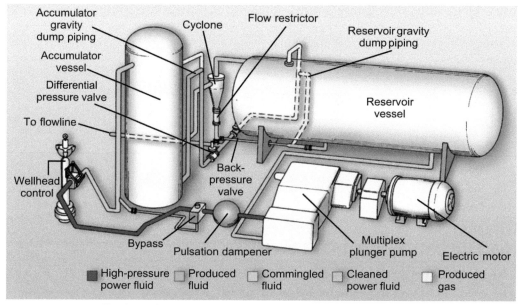

Fig. 14.1—Schematic of a single-well hydraulic pumping system.

Multistage centrifugal pumps[5] and horizontal electrical submersible pumps (ESPs) have been used,[6] and some systems have been operated with the excess capacity in water-injection systems.[7] The hydraulic fluid usually comes from the well and can be either produced oil or water. A fluid reservoir at the surface provides surge capacity and is usually part of the cleaning system used to condition the well fluids for use as power fluid. Appropriate control valves and piping complete the system. A schematic of a typical hydraulic pumping system is shown in **Fig. 14.1**.

14.2 Downhole Pumps

14.2.1 Types of Installations. The two basic types of installations are the "fixed"-pump and the "free"-pump design. In the fixed installation, the downhole pump is attached to the end of a tubing string and run into the well. Free-pump installations are designed to allow the downhole pump to be circulated into and out of the well inside the power-fluid string, or it can also be installed and retrieved by wireline operations.

14.2.2 Fixed-Pump Installations (Conventional Installations). In the fixed-insert (or tubing-conveyed) design, the pump typically lands on a seating-shoe in the larger tubing. Power fluid is normally directed down the inner tubing string, and the produced fluids and return power fluid flow to the surface inside the annulus between the two tubing strings, as shown in Part A of **Fig. 14.2**. These systems provide a passage for free gas in the annular space between the outer tubing string and the inside of the well casing, but to take full advantage of this gas-venting passage, the pump should be set below the perforations. The power-fluid string is usually ¾-in., 1-in., or 1¼-in. nominal tubing or 1-in., 1¼-in. or 1½-in. coiled tubing. The fixed-pump system is used mainly to fit a large-diameter downhole pump into restricted casing sizes and still retain the gas-vent feature. It also can be used to lift one or both zones of a dual well with parallel strings.

In the fixed-casing design, the tubing with the pump attached to its lower end is seated on a packer, as shown in Part B of Fig.14.2. With this configuration, the power fluid is directed

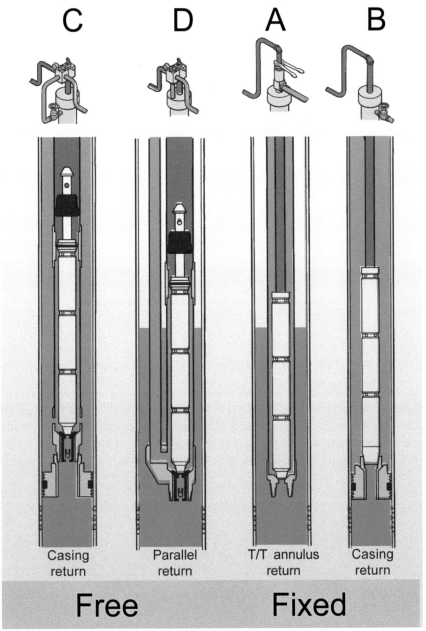

Fig. 14.2—Free and fixed hydraulic downhole pumping installations.

down the tubing string, and the mixed power fluid and the produced well fluids return to the surface in the tubing/casing annulus. Because the well fluids enter the pump from below a packer, the pump must handle all the free gas. This type of installation is normally used with large-diameter high-capacity pumps in wells with little free gas, and if space permits, a gas-vent string can be run from below the packer to the surface. As with the fixed-insert design, this installation is no longer common, and both have been largely supplanted by the various free-

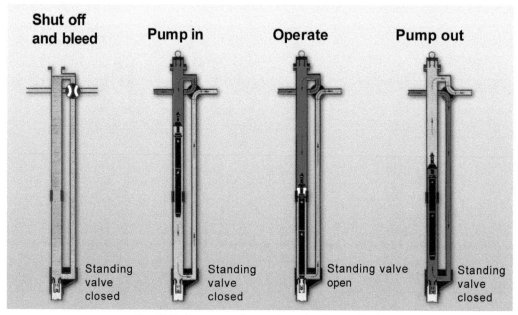

Fig. 14.3—Free pump (pump in-and-out operation).

pump installations. Note that in both of the fixed-type installations, when using a reciprocating piston pump, the power fluid mixes with the produced fluid after passing through the pump.

14.2.3 Free-Pump Installations. The free-pump feature is one of the most significant advantages of hydraulic pumping systems. Free-pump installations permit circulating the pump to the bottom, producing the well, and circulating the pump back to the surface for repair or size change. **Fig. 14.3** shows pump in-and-out operations for a typical free-pump installation. They require that a bottomhole assembly (BHA) be run in on the tubing string. The BHA consists of a seating shoe and one or more sealbores above it and serves as a receptacle for the pump itself. BHAs are of robust construction and use corrosion-resistant sealing bores to ensure a long life in the downhole environmental conditions. The extensions needed on the BHA also can be adapted with different metallurgy to accommodate a changing environment. Once run in on the tubing string, the BHA normally remains in place for years, even though the downhole pump may be circulated in and out numerous times for repair or resizing. As shown in **Fig. 14.4**, a wireline-retrievable standing valve is landed in the seating shoe below the pump. The pump is run in the hole by placing it in the power-fluid string and pumping fluid down the tubing. When the pump reaches bottom, it enters the sealbores, begins stroking or jetting, and opens the standing valve. During normal pumping, this valve is held open by well fluid drawn into the pump suction. During pump-out, the normal flow of fluids is reversed at the surface with appropriate valving and pressure applied to the discharge flow path of the pump. This reversal of flow closes the standing valve and permits the pump to be circulated to the surface —a process that normally takes 30 minutes to 2 hours, depending on depth, tubing size, and the circulating flow rate.

The benefits of being able to circulate the downhole pump in and out of the well include reduced downtime and the ability to operate without a pulling unit for tubing, cable, or rod removal. Another significant advantage is that pressure and temperature recorders can be mounted on the pump to monitor downhole conditions with different pumping rates. At the conclusion of the test, circulating the pump to the surface also retrieves the recorder. Substituting a

2¹/₂-in. Standing Valve

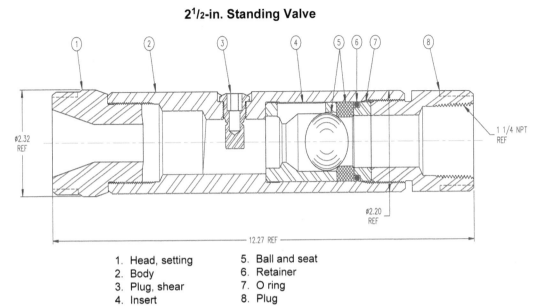

1. Head, setting
2. Body
3. Plug, shear
4. Insert

5. Ball and seat
6. Retainer
7. O ring
8. Plug

Fig. 14.4—Hydraulic wireline retrievable standing valve assembly.

dummy pump for the normal production unit can be used to check for leakage of tubing pressure. Steaming, acidizing, or chemical treatment of the formation can be done if the pump is circulated out and the standing valve retrieved on wireline. A flow-through blanking tool may be run instead of the pump for such treatment if isolation of the power fluid and discharge flow paths is desired.

The casing-free installation, shown in Part C of Fig. 14.2, is attractive from an initial cost standpoint because it uses only one string of tubing. At first glance, it seems to be the same as the fixed-casing design, but the crucial difference is that instead of being attached to the end of the power-fluid string, the pump fits inside it to allow circulation into and out of the well. For a given diameter pump, this requires a larger-diameter string that reduces the annular flow path for the discharge fluids, but in most cases, a more than adequate flow area remains. Nominal tubing as small as 1½ in. can be run in systems with 2⅞-in.-outside-diameter (OD) tubing used as casing, and coiled tubing as small as 1¼ in. can be run in systems with 2⅜-in.-OD tubing used as casing. In the 1½-in. and 1¼-in. nominal-size tubing, only the jet pump can be used, while in 2⅜-in.-OD or larger tubing, either jet or reciprocating pumps are suitable. Usually, 2⅜-in.-OD power-fluid tubing is used in 4½-in.-OD or larger casing, 2⅞-in.-OD tubing in 5½-in.-OD casing or larger, and 3½-in.-OD tubing in 6⅝-in.-OD casing or larger. Because the BHA sits on a packer, the pump must handle all the gas from the well in addition to the liquids, even though a gas-vent string can be run if gas interference limits pump performance. In both the vented and unvented systems, the power fluid mixes with the produced fluids and returns to the surface. In wells where the produced fluid should be kept off the casing wall or where gas venting is desired, the parallel-free installation should be considered. This installation, which requires two parallel tubing strings, normally does not require a packer. As shown in Part D of Fig. 14.2, the BHA is suspended on the power-fluid string, and the return is either screwed into the BHA or is run separately with a landing spear that enters a bowl above the BHA. The tubing/casing annulus serves as a gas vent passage, and to take full advantage of this, the unit should be set below the perforations. In wells with corrosive gas and/or liquid, it may be undesirable to use the casing for return of gas or to have the liquid in the casing annulus. In such cases, a packer can be installed; however, the pump must handle all the gas and produced liquids.

14.2.4 Open and Closed Power-Fluid Systems. All installations discussed so far are open power-fluid (OPF) types, which means that all the power fluid and the produced fluid are mixed together after leaving the downhole pump and return to the surface together in a common flow passage. Jet pumps are inherently OPF pumps because the energy transfer depends on mixing the power fluid with the produced fluid. All reciprocating piston pumps (not jets) keep the power and produced fluids separate during the energy transfer process because there is a separate piston for each fluid. If the BHA has appropriate sealbores and passages to keep the two fluids separated, the power fluid can return to the surface in a separate tubing string, thus creating a closed power-fluid system.

14.2.5 Reverse-Flow Systems. Considerations for a reverse-flow system for a jet-pump installation are the need to keep produced fluid off the casing, help minimize fluid friction losses, and aid in drillstem testing or unloading of wells. A reverse-flow installation is shown in **Fig. 14.5**. It uses the tubing/casing annulus for power fluid and the tubing string, which contains the pump, and is used for the combined power fluid and production. This protects the casing with inhibited power fluid and is most useful when severe corrosion is anticipated. In permanent installations, heavy wall casing should be a consideration to avoid casing burst conditions when power-fluid pressure is applied. In reverse-flow installations, the pump is run and retrieved on wireline in most cases but can be pumped in and out with a pusher-type locomotive.

14.2.6 Dual Wells. Hydraulic pumps lend themselves to solution of the complex problem of the production of two separate zones or reservoirs in a single wellbore. To meet the artificial-lift requirements of the two distinct zones, two downhole pumps are usually required. It would be highly unusual if the same power-fluid pressure and rate were required for each zone; consequently, a separate power-fluid line for each pump is usually required. A number of completion configurations are possible, but small casing sizes and high gas/liquid ratios may severely hinder dual-well operation.

14.3 Principles of Operation

14.3.1 Reciprocating Pumps. The pump end of a hydraulic downhole pump is similar to a sucker-rod pump because it uses a rod-actuated plunger (also called the pump piston) and two or more check valves. The pump can be either single-acting or double-acting. A single-acting pump closely follows rod-pump design practices and is called single-acting because it displaces fluid on either the upstroke or downstroke (but not both). An example is shown schematically in **Fig. 14.6**. **Fig. 14.7** shows a double-acting pump that has suction and discharge valves for both sides of the plunger, which enables it to displace fluids to the surface on both the upstroke and downstroke. With either system, motion of the plunger away from a suction valve lowers the pressure that holds the valve closed; it opens as the pressure drops, and well fluids are allowed to enter the barrel or cylinder. At the end of the stroke, the plunger reverses, forcing the suction valve to close and opening the discharge valving.

In a sucker-rod installation, the rod that actuates the pump plunger extends to the surface of the well and connects to the pumping unit; however, in hydraulic pumps, the rod is quite short and extends only to the engine pistons. The engine piston is constructed similarly to the pump plunger and is exposed to the power-fluid supply that is under the control of the engine valve. The engine valve reverses the flow of the power fluid on alternate half-strokes and causes the engine piston to reciprocate back and forth. Four-way engine valves are used with engines that switch from high-pressure to low-pressure power-fluid exhaust on both sides of the engine pis-

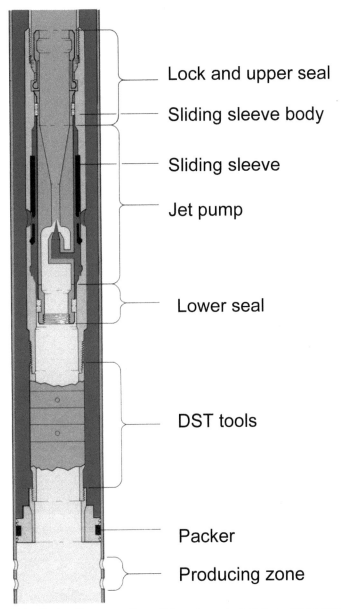

Fig. 14.5—Hydraulic reverse-flow sliding-sleeve installation with jet pump.

ton in an alternate manner. These engine (or reversing) valves are used with double-acting pump ends to give equal force on both upstroke and downstroke. Three-way engine valves are used with unequal-area engine pistons that always have high-pressure power fluid on one side and switch the power-fluid from high to low pressure on the other face of the piston. This type of reversing valve is commonly used with single-acting pumps that do not require a high force on the half-stroke because it is not displacing produced fluid to the surface. An example of this type of engine attached to a single-acting pump is illustrated in **Fig. 14.8**.

The engine or reversing valve can be activated by several methods. Commonly, ports on a rod direct pressure to control the engine valve at the extremes of the upstroke and downstroke,

Piston Pumps

Model 220

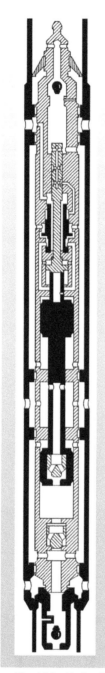

Fig. 14.6—Hydraulic piston single-acting pump (model 220).

causing the valve to shift hydraulically. The shifting of the engine valve redirects the flow of power fluid to the engine piston and causes the reversal of the rod-and-plunger system. Alternatively, the engine can be mechanically "bumped" from one position to the other by the rod and plunger system as it nears the end of the upstroke and downstroke. Combinations of mechani-

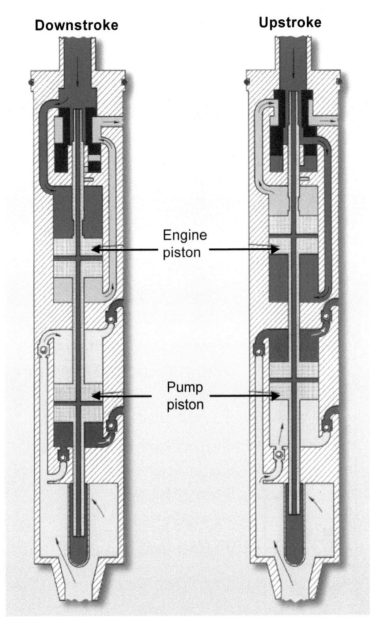

Downstroke   **Upstroke**

Engine piston

Pump piston

Fig. 14.7—Hydraulic piston double-acting pump.

cal and hydraulic shifting are possible, and the engine valve may be located above the rod-and-plunger system, in the middle of the pump, or in the engine piston.

Note that the two designs illustrated and discussed do not exhaust the design possibilities offered by the various pump manufacturers; many combinations are possible, and tandem pumps or engine sections are sometimes advantageous. Examples of combinations of these design concepts can be seen in the cross-section schematics of the various pump types that accompany the pump specifications in **Tables 14.1 through 14.3**, which show the producing abilities and other factors that should be considered in designing reciprocating pumps. In the past, many tables were used in choosing the correct pump for the application, but today, the

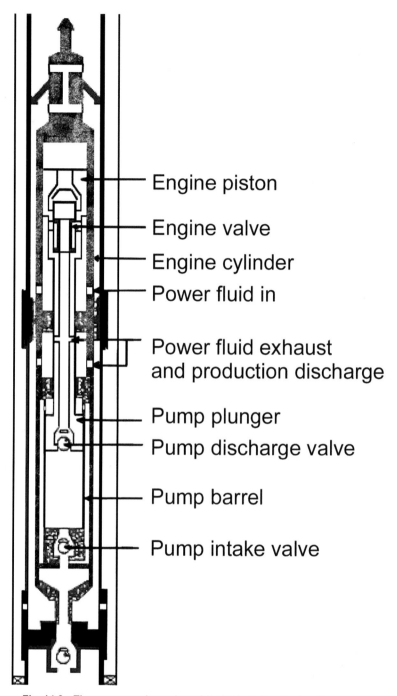

Engine piston

Engine valve

Engine cylinder

Power fluid in

Power fluid exhaust
and production discharge

Pump plunger

Pump discharge valve

Pump barrel

Pump intake valve

Fig. 14.8—Three-way engine valve with single-acting hydraulic pump.

use of computers eliminates the errors inherent in reading charts and tables, making the process much simpler. Common to all designs, however, is the concept of a reversing valve that causes an engine piston (or pistons) to reciprocate back and forth, stroking the pump plunger (or plungers) that lifts fluid from the well.

TABLE 14.1—PRODUCTION UNIT DATA, MANUFACTURER A								
					Displacement, B/D			
Unit Model Number, Free Pumps	Pressure Ratio, Pump/ Engine Ratio (P/E)	Balance Pressure, psi/1,000 ft	Stroke Length, in.	Rated Speed, strokes/min	Per SPM (Displacement Factor)		Rated Speed	
					Engine	Pump	Engine	Pump
Balanced Units								
2³/₈-in. tubing OD:								
F201311	.71	305	22	68	4.2	3.0	286	204
F201313	1.00	433	22	68	4.2	4.2	286	286
F201611	.47	203	22	68	6.4	3.0	435	204
F201613	.66	286	22	68	6.4	4.2	435	286
FEB201613	.66	286	32	55	9.4	6.2	517	340
2⁷/₈-in. tubing OD:								
F251611	.47	203	24	65	7.0	3.3	455	214
F251613	.66	286	24	65	7.0	4.6	455	299
F251616	1.00	433	24	65	7.0	7.0	455	455
FE251613	.66	286	34	53	10.0	6.6	530	350
FE251616	1.00	433	34	53	10.0	10.0	530	530
FE252011	.30	130	36	51	16.5	4.95	843	250
FE252013	.43	186	36	51	16.5	7.0	843	355
FE252016	.64	277	36	51	16.5	10.6	843	540
200 Series								
2⁷/₈-in. tubing OD:								
548-252019	.93	403	48	72	22.35	20.17	1609	1452
548-252017	.78	338	48	72	22.35	20.17	1609	1232
348-252015	.57	247	48	72	22.35	20.17	1609	905
348-252012	.40	173	48	72	22.35	20.17	1609	629
2³/₈-in. tubing OD:								
330-201615	.89	385	30	100	8.94	7.86	894	786
330-201612	.63	273	30	100	8.94	5.46	894	546
330-201611	.49	212	30	100	8.49	4.22	894	422
3¹/₂-in. tubing OD:								
548-302422	.643	279	48	72	32.2	20.2	2321	1455
548-302422	.914	396	48	72	32.2	29.7	2321	2067
548-302423	.961	402	54	72	37.4	35.0	2693	2520

Because the engine and pump are closely coupled into one unit, the stroke length can be controlled accurately; thus, the unswept area or clearance volume at each end of the stroke can be kept very small, leading to high compression ratios. This is very important when gas is present, and it generally prevents gas locking in hydraulic pumps. The engine valves and their switching mechanisms usually include controls to provide a smooth reversal and to limit the plunger speed under unloaded conditions. The unloaded plunger speed control is often called "governing" and minimizes fluid pound when the pump is not fully loaded with liquid. In this way, shock loads in the pump, as well as water hammer in the tubing strings, are softened, which reduces stress and increases life. (Caution: high pump speeds, at or above the rating, may significantly shorten piston pump run lives.)

14.3.2 Jet Pumps. Jet pumps are a type of downhole pump that can be used in hydraulic pumping systems instead of the reciprocating piston pumps previously discussed. They can be adapted to fit interchangeably into the BHAs designed for the stroking pumps. In addition, special BHAs have been designed for jet pumps to take advantage of their short length and their high-volume characteristics. Because of their unique characteristics under different pumping conditions, jet pumps should be considered as an alternative to the conventional stroking pumps.

TABLE 14.2—RECIPROCATION PUMP SPECIFICATIONS, MANUFACTURER B DISPLACEMENT

Pump Type A	B/D per strokes/min		Rated Speed, B/D			P/E	Maximum Rated Speed, strokes/min
	Pump	Engine	Pump	Engine	Total		
$2^3/_8$-in. tubing:							
$2 \times 1 \times {}^{13}/_{16}$	1.15	2.15	139	260	399	.545	121
$2 \times 1 \times 1$	2.10	2.15	255	260	515	1.000	121
$2 \times 1 \times 1^{13}/_{16}$	3.25	2.15	393	260	653	1.545	121
$2 \times 1^3/_{16} \times {}^{13}/_{16}$	210	3.30	255	399	654	.647	121
$2 \times 1^3/_{16} \times 1$	2.10	3.30	393	399	792	1.00	121
$2 \times 1^3/_{16} \times 1^3/_{16}$	3.25	3.30	508	399	907	1290	121
$2^7/_8$-in. tubing:							
$2^1/_2 \times 1^1/_4 \times 1$	2.56	5.02	256	502	758	.520	100
$2^1/_2 \times 1^1/_4 \times 1^1/_8$	3.67	5.02	367	502	868	.746	100
$2^1/_2 \times 1^1/_4 \times 1^1/_4$	4.92	5.02	492	502	994	1.00	100
$2^1/_2 \times 1^1/_4 \times 1^7/_{16}$	7.03	5.02	703	502	1205	1.431	100
$2^1/_2 \times 1^7/_{16} \times 1^1/_4$	4.92	7.13	492	713	1205	.700	100
$2^1/_2 \times 1^7/_{16} \times 1^7/_{16}$	7.03	7.13	703	713	1416	1.00	100
$2^1/_2 \times 1^5/_8 \times 1^7/_{16}$	7.03	9.27	703	927	1630	.770	100
$2^1/_2 \times 1^5/_8 \times 1^1/_2$	7.45	9.27	745	927	1672	.820	100
$2^1/_2 \times 1^5/_8 \times 1^5/_8$	9.09	9.27	909	927	1836	1.00	100
$3^1/_2$-in. tubing:							
$3 \times 1^1/_2 \times 1^1/_4$	5.59	9.61	486	836	1322	.592	87
$3 \times {}^1/_2 \times 1^3/_8$	7.43	9.61	646	836	1482	.787	87
$3 \times {}^1/_2 \times {}^1/_2$	9.44	9.61	821	836	1657	1.00	87
$3 \times 1^3/_4 \times {}^1/_2$	.944	14.17	821	1233	2054	.676	87
$3 \times 1^3/_4 \times 1^3/_4$	14.00	14.17	1218	`133	2451	1.00	87

Note: sample of models offered by manufacturer B.

Although technical references to jet pumps can be found as far back as 1852,[8] it was not until 1933[9] that a consistent mathematical representation was published that included suggestions for pumping oil wells.[10] Angier and Crocker[11] applied for a patent on an oilwell jet pump in 1864 that looked very much like those currently marketed. Jacuzzi[12] received a patent in 1930 for jet pumps that were subsequently used in shallow water wells successfully. McMahon[13] also received the first of six patents on oilwell jet pumps in 1930. Apparently McMahon built and marketed pumps in California in the late 1930s, but they did not achieve widespread use. Hardware improvements and the advent of computer models for correct applications sizing in oil wells led to the successful marketing of jet pumps in 1970, and the use of jet pumps has grown steadily since then. More recent publications on hydraulic pumping that describe the use of jet pumps in oil wells include those by Wilson, Bell and Spisak, Christ and Zublin, Nelson,[14] Brown,[15] Clark,[16] Bleakley,[17] and Petrie et al.[18] Much of the following discussion derives from Refs. 15, 18, and 19.

An example of the simplest downhole jet free-pump completion, the single-seal style, is shown in **Fig. 14.9**. The most significant feature of this device is that it has no moving parts; the pumping action is achieved through energy transfer between two moving streams of fluid. The high-pressure power fluid, supplied from the surface, passes through the nozzle, where its potential energy (pressure) is converted to kinetic energy in the form of a very-high-velocity jet of fluid. Well fluids surround the power-fluid jet at the tip of the nozzle, which is spaced back from the entrance of the mixing tube. The mixing tube, usually called the throat, is a straight, cylindrical bore about seven diameters long with a smoothed radius at the entrance. The diameter of the throat is always larger than the diameter of the nozzle exit, allowing the

TABLE 14.3—DISPLACEMENT DATA, MANUFACTURER C

| Pump | Displacement | | | | | | Maximum Rated Speed, strokes/min |
| | B/D per stroke/min | | Rated Speed, B/D | | | | |
	Pump	Engine	Pump	Engine	Total	P/E	
Powerlift I							
$2^3/_8$-in. tubing:							
$2 \times 1^5/_8 \times 1^1/_{16}$	6.45	15.08	225	528	753	0.52	35
$2 \times 1^5/_8 \times 1^1/_4$	8.92	15.08	312	528	840	0.72	35
$2 \times 1^5/_8 \times 1^1/_2$	11.96	14.03	478	561	1,039	1.16	40
$2 \times 1^5/_8 \times 1^5/_8$	14.03	14.03	561	561	1,122	1.36	40
$2^7/_8$-in. tubing:							
$2^1/_2 \times 2 \times 1^1/_4$	12.02	30.80	264	678	942	0.44	22
$2^1/_2 \times 2 \times 1^1/_2$	17.30	30.80	467	832	1,299	0.68	27
$2^1/_2 \times 2 \times 1^5/_8$	20.30	30.80	574	832	1,379	0.80	27
$2^1/_2 \times 2 \times 1^3/_4$	23.60	30.80	826	1,078	1,904	1.06	35
$2^1/_2 \times 2 \times 2$	30.80	30.80	1,078	1,078	2,156	1.38	35
$2^1/_2 \times 1^5/_8 \times 1^1/_{16}$	6.45	15.08	225	528	753	0.52	35
$2^1/_2 \times 1^5/_8 \times 1^1/_4$	8.92	15.08	312	528	840	0.72	35
$2^1/_2 \times 1^5/_8 \times 1^1/_2$	12.85	15.08	450	528	978	1.03	35
$2^1/_2 \times 1^5/_8 \times 1^5/_8$	15.08	15.08	528	528	1,056	1.21	35
$2^1/_2 \times 1^5/_8 \times 1^1/_{16}$	8.69	20.30	234	5.48	782	0.52	27
$2^1/_2 \times 1^5/_8 \times 1^1/_4$	12.02	20.30	325	5.48	873	0.72	27
$2^1/_2 \times 1^5/_8 \times 1^1/_2$	17.03	20.30	467	5.48	1,015	1.03	27
$2^1/_2 \times 1^5/_8 \times 1^5/_8$	20.30	20.30	547	5.48	1,095	1.21	27
$3^1/_2$-in. tubing:							
$3^1/_2 \times 2^1/_2 \times 2^1/_2$	43.71	43.71	1,311	1,311	2,622	1.21	30
$3^1/_2 \times 2^1/_2 \times 2^1/_4$	35.41	43.71	1,062	1,311	2,373	0.98	30
$3^1/_2 \times 2^1/_2 \times 2$	27.98	43.71	840	1,311	2,151	0.77	30
$3^1/_2 \times 2^1/_2 \times 1^3/_4$	21.42	43.71	643	1,311	1,954	0.59	30
Powerlift II							
$2^3/_8$-in. tubing:							
$2 \times 1^1/_{16}$	5.53	12.10	597	1,307	1,904	0.524	108
$2 \times 1^1/_4$	7.65	12.10	826	1,307	2,133	0.725	108
$2 \times 1^3/_{16}$	30.00	26.35	1,560	1,370	2,930	1.147	52
$2^7/_8$-in. tubing:							
$2^1/_2 \times 1^1/_2$	12.59	17.69	1,322	1,857	3,179	0.725	105
$2^1/_2 \times 1^1/_4$	8.74	17.69	918	1,857	2,775	0.503	105
$2^1/_2 \times 1^7/_8$	50.00	43.97	2,500	2,199	4,699	1.146	50

well fluids to flow around the power-fluid jet and be entrained by it into the throat. In the throat, the power fluid and produced fluid mix, and momentum is transferred from the power fluid to the produced fluid, causing its energy to rise. By the end of the throat, the two fluids are intimately mixed, but they are still at a high velocity, and the mixture contains significant kinetic energy. The mixed fluid enters an expanding area diffuser that converts the remaining kinetic energy to static pressure by slowing down the fluid velocity. The pressure in the fluid is now sufficiently high to flow it to the surface from the downhole pump.

With no moving parts, jet pumps are rugged and tolerant of corrosive and abrasive well fluids. The nozzle and throat are usually constructed of tungsten carbide or ceramic materials for long life. Successful jet-pump adaptations have also been made for sliding side doors in both the normal and reverse-flow configurations. These are normally run in on wireline or as a fixed or conventional installation on continuous coiled tubing and have been successful in off-shore drillstem testing (DST) of heavy-crude reservoirs. Other applications include the dewatering of gas wells.[20]

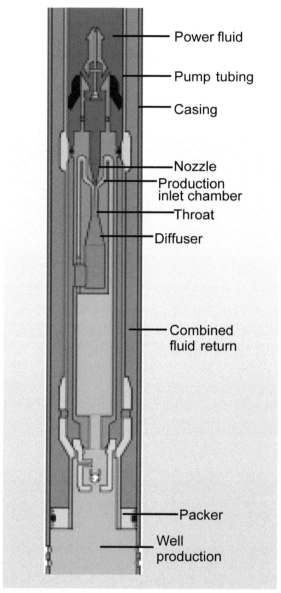

- Power fluid
- Pump tubing
- Casing
- Nozzle
- Production inlet chamber
- Throat
- Diffuser
- Combined fluid return
- Packer
- Well production

Fig. 14.9—Downhole single-seal-style jet free-pump.

With different sizes of nozzles and throats, jet pumps can produce wells at less than 50 B/D or in excess of 15,000 B/D. To achieve high rates, a special BHA is required as the BHA itself is used as a crossover for the production, allowing for larger passages for the produced fluid to travel to the jet nozzle as shown in **Fig. 14.10.** As with all hydraulic pumping systems, a considerable range of production is possible from a particular downhole pump by controlling the power-fluid supply at the surface, but for any given size of tubing, the maximum achievable rates are usually much higher than those possible with stroking pumps. Significant free-gas volumes can be handled without the problems of pounding or excessive wear associated with positive-displacement pumps, or the inlet choking encountered in centrifugal pumps. The

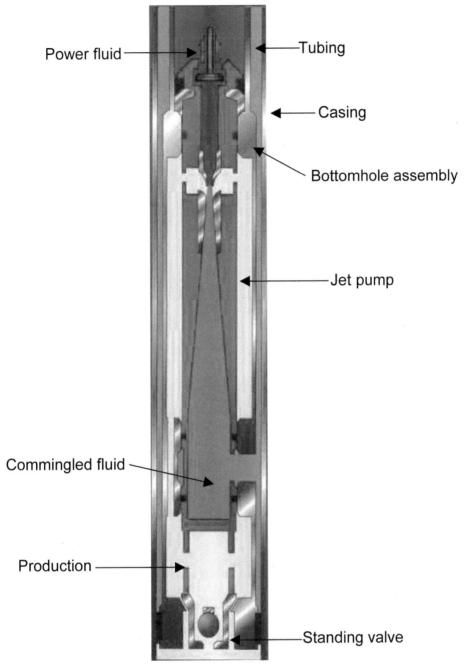

Fig. 14.10—High-volume jet pump.

lack of vibration and the free-pump feature make them ideal for use with pumpdown pressure recorders to monitor BHPs at different flow rates.

Because they are high-velocity mixing devices, there is significant turbulence and friction within the pump, leading to lower horsepower efficiencies than achieved with positive-displacement pumps. This often leads to higher surface horsepower requirements, although some gassy wells may actually require less pressure. Jet pumps are prone to cavitation at the entrance of

Jet Pump Nomenclature

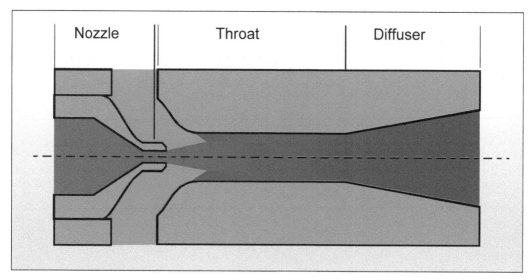

Red—high pressure
Blue—production
Purple—mixed power fluid and production

Fig. 14.11—How the jet pump works.

the throat at low pump intake pressures, and this must be considered in design calculations. Also, because of the nature of their performance curves, the calculations used for installation design are complex and iterative in nature and are best handled by computers. Their overall energy efficiencies are low, which may lead to high energy costs; despite these limitations, their reliability, low maintenance costs, and volume capability make them attractive in many wells, and their use has increased since commercial introduction in the early 1970s.

14.3.3 Performance Characteristics. Intuitively, larger-diameter nozzles and throats would seem to have higher flow capacities, and this is normally the case. The ratio of the nozzle area to the throat area is an important variable because it determines the trade-off between produced head and flow rate. **Fig. 14.11** shows a schematic of the working section of a jet pump. If, for a given nozzle, a throat is selected such that the area of the nozzle, A_n, is 60% of the area of the throat, A_t, a relatively high-head, low-flow pump will result. There is a comparatively small area, A_s, around the jet for well fluids to enter. This leads to low production rates compared to the power-fluid rate, and because the energy of the nozzle is transferred to a small amount of production, high heads develop. Such a pump is suited for deep wells with high lifts, and substantial production rates can be achieved if the pump is physically large, but the production rate will always be less than the power-fluid rate.

If a throat is selected such that the area of the nozzle is only 20% of the area of the throat, much more flow area around the jet is available for the production. However, because the nozzle energy is transferred to a large amount of production compared to the power-fluid rate, lower heads will be developed. Shallow wells with low lifts are candidates for such a pump.

Any number of such area combinations is possible to match different flow and lift requirements. Attempting to produce small amounts of production compared to the power-fluid rate with nozzle/throat-area ratio of 20% will be inefficient because of high-turbulent mixing losses between the high-velocity jet and the slow-moving production. Conversely, attempting to produce high production rates compared to the power-fluid rate with a nozzle/throat-area ratio of 60% will be inefficient because of high friction losses as the produced fluid moves rapidly through the relatively small throat. Optimal ratio selection involves a trade-off between these mixing and friction losses.

As a type of dynamic pump, the jet pump has characteristic performance curves similar to those of an ESP. A family of performance curves is possible, depending on the nozzle pressure supplied to the pump from the surface. Different sizes of throats used in conjunction with a given nozzle size give different performance curves. The curves are generally fairly flat, especially with the larger throats, which makes the jet pump sensitive to changes in intake or discharge pressure. Because variable fluid mixture densities, gas/liquid ratios, and viscosity affect the pressures encountered by the pump, the calculations to simulate performance are complex and iterative in nature and lend themselves to a computer solution.

14.3.4 Cavitation in Jet Pumps. Because the production must accelerate to a fairly high velocity (200 to 300 ft/sec) to enter the throat, cavitation is a potential problem. The throat and nozzle flow areas define an annular flow passage at the entrance of the throat. The smaller this area is, the higher the velocity is of a given amount of produced fluid passing through it. The static pressure of the fluid drops as the square of the velocity increases, declining to the vapor pressure of the fluid at high velocities. This low pressure causes vapor cavities to form, a process called cavitation. This results in choked flow into the throat, and production increases are not possible at that pump-intake pressure, even if the power-fluid rate and pressure are increased. Subsequent collapse of the vapor cavities, as pressure is built up in the pump, may cause erosion known as cavitation damage. Thus, for a given production flow rate and pump intake pressure, there is a minimum annular flow area required to keep the velocity low enough to avoid cavitation. This phenomenon has been the subject of numerous investigations—the most notable being that of Cunningham and Brown,[21] who used actual oilwell pump designs at the high pressures used in deep wells.

The description of the cavitation phenomenon suggests that if the production flow rate approaches zero, the potential for cavitation will disappear because the fluid velocities are very low. Under these conditions, however, the velocity difference between the power-fluid jet and the slow-moving production is at a maximum, which creates an intense shear zone on the boundary between them, generating vortices, the cores of which are at a reduced pressure. Vapor cavities may form in the vortex cores, leading to erosion of the throat walls as the bubbles collapse because of vortex decay and pressure rises in the pump. Although no theoretical treatments of this phenomenon have been published, it has been the subject of experimental work, which has led to the inclusion, by suppliers, of potential damage zones on their published performance prediction plots. This experimental correlation predicts cavitation damage at low flow rates and low pump-intake pressures before the choked flow condition occurs. Field experience has shown, however, that in most real oil wells, the erosion rate in this operating region is very low, probably because of produced gas cushioning the system by reducing the propagation velocity of the bubble-collapse shock waves. It is generally agreed that this phenomenon is of concern only in very-high-water-cut wells with virtually no gas present. Under these conditions, cavitation erosion has been observed even at very low production rates; however, if a jet pump is operated near its best efficiency point, the shear vortices are a distinctly second-order effect in the cavitation process.

14.3.5 Nozzle and Throat Sizes. Each manufacturer has different sizes and combinations of nozzles and throats. Manufacturers A and B increase the areas of nozzles and throats in a geometric progression (i.e., the flow area of any nozzle or throat is a constant multiple of the area

TABLE 14.4—NOZZLE AND THROAT SIZES			
Nozzle	Area	Throat No.	Area
Manufacturer A:			
1	0.0024	1	0.0064
2	0.0031	2	0.0081
3	0.0039	3	0.0104
4	0.0050	4	0.0131
5	0.0064	5	0.0167
6	0.0081	6	0.0212
7	0.0103	7	0.0271
8	0.0131	8	0.0346
9	0.0167	9	0.0441
10	0.0212	10	0.0562
11	0.0774	11	0.0715
12	0.0346	12	0.0910
13	0.0441	13	0.1159
14	0.0562	14	0.1476
15	0.0715	15	0.1879
16	0.0910	16	0.2392
17	0.1159	17	0.03046
18	0.1476	18	0.3878
19	0.1879	19	0.4938
20	0.2392	20	0.6287
Manufacturer B:			
1	0.0024	1	0.0060
2	0.0031	2	0.0077
3	0.0040	3	0.0100
4	0.0052	4	0.0125
5	0.0067	5	0.0167
6	0.0086	6	0.0215
7	0.0111	7	0.0278
8	0.0144	8	0.0359
9	0.0186	9	0.0464
10	0.0240	10	0.0599
11	0.0310	11	0.0744
12	0.0400	12	0.1000
13	0.0517	13	0.1292
14	0.0668	14	0.1669
15	0.0863	15	0.2154
16	0.1114	16	0.2783
17	0.1439	17	0.3594
18	0.1858	18	0.4642
19	0.2400	19	0.5995
20	0.3100	20	0.7743

of the next smaller size). Manufacturer B's factor is 1.29155, and Manufacturer A's factor is $4/\pi = 1.27324$. The system of sizes offered by Manufacturer C uses a similar geometric progression concept but does not use the same factor over the total range. In the smaller sizes, where the change in horsepower per size is small, the rate of increase in area is more rapid than in the systems of Manufacturers A and B. In the larger, higher-horsepower sizes, the percent increase in size is less rapid than in the other systems to limit the incremental increase in horsepower. The sizes offered by Manufacturer C cover a slightly larger range than those of Manufacturers A and B. The sizes from these manufacturers are listed in **Table 14.4**. The maximum sizes of nozzles and throats that are practical in pumps for a given tubing size depend on the fluid passages of the particular pump, BHA, swab nose, and standing valve. Single-seal pumps cannot use nozzles as large as those practical in higher-flow, multiple-seal pumps. In general, nozzles larger than 0.035 in.² in flow area are used only in pumps for 2½- and 3½-in. tubing.

TABLE 14.4—NOZZLE AND THROAT SIZES (Continued)			
Nozzle	Area	Throat No.	Area
Manufacturer C:			
DD	0.0016	000	0.0044
CC	0.0028	00	0.0071
BB	0.0038	0	0.0104
A	0.0055	1	0.0143
B	0.0095	2	0.0189
C	0.0123	3	0.0241
D	0.0177	4	0.0314
E	0.0241	5	0.0380
F	0.0314	6	0.0452
G	0.0452	7	0.0531
H	0.0661	8	0.0661
I	0.0855	9	0.0804
J	0.1257	10	0.0962
K	0.1590	11	0.1195
L	0.1963	12	0.1452
M	0.2463	13	0.1772
N	0.3117	14	0.2165
P	0.3848	15	0.2606
		16	0.3127
		17	0.3750
		18	0.4513
		19	0.5424
		20	0.6518

The strict progression used by Manufacturers A and B establishes fixed area ratios between the nozzles and different throats. A given nozzle matched with the same number throat always gives the same area ratio: 0.380 in Manufactures A's system and 0.400 in Manufacturer B's system (Table 14.4). This is called the A ratio. Successively larger throats matched with a given nozzle give the B, C, D, and E ratios. In the systems of Manufacturers A and B, the nozzle size and ratio designate the size of a pump. Examples are 11-B, which is a No. 11 nozzle and a No. 12 throat, and 6-A, which is a No. 6 nozzle and a No. 6 throat.

Because the size progression for the nozzles and throats in Manufacturer C's system is not constant over the whole range, the nozzle/throat combinations do not yield fixed ratios. However, the ratios that result cover the same basic range as the other two systems. The actual ratios are listed in **Table 14.5**. In Manufacturer C's system, the nozzle and mixing tube (throat) sizes designate the size of a pump. An example is C-5, which are the size C nozzle and the No. 5 throat. This combination has an area ratio of 0.32. The annular flow areas of Manufacturer C's jet pumps used in cavitation calculations are also included in **Table 14.6.** The annular areas for Manufacturers A and B's jet pumps are listed in **Tables 14.6 and 14.7.**

The most commonly used area ratios fall between 0.235 and 0.400. Area ratios greater than 0.400 are sometimes used in very deep wells with high lifts or when only very low surface operating pressures are available and a high head regain is necessary. Area ratios less than 0.235 are used in shallow wells or when very low BHPs require a large annular flow passage to avoid cavitation. The smaller area ratios develop less head but may produce more fluid than is used for power fluid ($F_{mfD} > 1.0$). Where the curves for different area ratios cross, the ratios have equal production and efficiency; however, different annular flow areas (A_s) may give them different cavitation characteristics.

14.3.6 Jet-Pump Application Sizing. The widespread current use of jet pumps can be credited to the advent of computer programs capable of making the iterative calculations necessary

TABLE 14.5—MANUFACTURER C RATIOS AND THROAT ANNULUS AREAS, IN.^{2}

Nozzle									
DD	Throats	000	00						
	R	0.36	0.22						
	A_s	0.0028	0.0056						
CC	Throats	000	00	0	1				
	R	0.64	0.40	0.27	0.20				
	A_s	0.0016	0.0043	0.0076	0.0115				
BB	Throats	00	0	1	2				
	R	0.37	0.37	0.27	0.20				
	A_s	0.0032	0.0065	0.0105	0.0150				
A	Throats	0	1	2	3				
	R	0.53	0.39	0.29	0.23				
	A_s	0.0048	0.0088	0.0133	0.0185				
B	Throats	0	1	2	3	4	5	6	
	R	0.92	0.66	0.50	0.40	0.30	0.25	0.21	
	A_s	0.0009	0.0048	0.0094	0.0145	0.0219	0.0285	0.0357	
C	Throats	1	2	3	4	5	6	7	
	R	0.86	0.65	0.51	0.39	0.32	0.27	0.23	
	A_s	0.0020	0.0086	0.0116	0.0191	0.0257	0.0330	0.0406	
D	Throats	3	4	5	6	7	8	9	
	R	0.74	0.56	0.46	0.39	0.33	0.27	0.22	
	A_s	0.0054	0.0137	0.0203	0.0276	0.0354	0.0464	0.0628	
E	Throats	4	5	6	7	8	9	10	11
	R	0.77	0.63	0.53	0.45	0.36	0.30	0.25	0.20
	A_s	0.0074	0.0140	0.0212	0.0290	0.0420	0.0564	0.0722	0.0954
F	Throats	6	7	8	9	10	11	12	
	R	0.69	0.59	0.46	0.39	0.33	0.26	0.22	
	A_s	0.0138	0.0217	0.346	0.0490	0.848	0.0860	0.1138	
G	Throats	8	9	10	11	12	13	14	
	R	0.68	0.56	0.47	0.38	0.31	0.26	0.21	
	A_s	0.0206	0.0352	0.0510	0.0742	0.1000	0.1320	0.1712	
H	Throats	10	11	12	13	14	15	16	
	R	0.69	0.55	0.45	0.37	0.30	0.25	0.21	
	A_s	0.0302	0.0643	0.0792	0.1112	0.1504	0.1945	0.2467	
I	Throats	11	12	13	14	15	16	17	
	R	0.72	0.59	0.46	0.40	0.33	0.27	0.23	
	A_s	0.0339	0.0597	0.0917	0.1309	0.1750	0.2272	0.2895	
J	Throats	13	14	15	16	17	18	19	
	R	0.71	0.56	0.48	0.40	0.34	0.28	0.23	
	A_s	0.0515	0.0908	0.1349	0.1671	0.2493	0.3256	0.4167	
K	Throats	15	16	17	18	19	20		
	R	0.61	0.51	0.42	0.35	0.29	0.24		
	A_s	0.1015	0.1537	0.2150	0.2922	0.3833	0.4928		
L	Throat	16	17	18	19	20			
	R	0.63	0.52	0.44	0.36	0.30			
	A_s	0.1164	0.1787	0.2549	0.3460	0.4556			
M	Throats	17	18	19	20				
	R	0.66	0.55	0.45	0.38				
	A_s	0.1164	0.2050	0.2961	0.4055				
N	Throat	18	19	20					
	R	0.69	0.57	0.48					
	A_s	0.1395	0.2305	0.3401					
P	Throat	19	20						
	R	0.71	0.59						
	A_s	0.1575	0.2670						

for application design. Jet-pump performance depends largely on the pump discharge pressure, which in turn is strongly influenced by the gas/liquid ratio, F_{gL}; in the return column to the surface, higher values of F_{gL} lead to reduced pump discharge pressure. Because the jet pump is

TABLE 14.6—THROAT ANNULUS AREAS FOR MANUFACTURER A

Nozzle	A-	A	B	C	D	E
1		0.0040	0.0057	0.0080	0.0108	0.0144
2	0.0033	0.0050	0.0073	0.0101	0.0137	0.0163
3	0.0042	0.0065	0.0093	0.0129	0.0175	0.0233
4	0.0054	0.0082	0.0118	0.0164	0.0222	0.0296
5	0.0088	0.0104	0.0150	0.0208	0.0282	0.0377
6	0.0087	0.0133	0.0191	0.0265	0.0360	0.0481
7	0.0111	0.0169	0.0243	0.0339	0.0459	0.0812
8	0.0141	0.0215	0.0310	0.0431	0.0594	0.0779
9	0.0179	0.0274	0.0395	0.0548	0.0743	0.0992
10	0.0229	0.0350	0.0503	0.0698	0.0947	0.1264
11	0.0291	0.0444	0.0639	0.0888	0.1205	0.1608
12	0.0369	0.0564	0.0813	0.1130	0.1533	0.2046
13	0.0469	0.0716	0.1035	0.1438	0.1951	0.2605
14	0.0597	0.0914	0.1317	0.1830	0.2484	0.3316
15	0.0761	0.1154	0.1677	0.2331	0.3163	0.4223
16	0.0969	0.1482	0.2136	0.2968	0.4028	0.5377
17	0.1234	0.1858	0.2720	0.3779	0.5128	
18	0.1571	0.2403	0.3469	0.4812		
19	0.2000	0.3060	0.4409			
20	0.2546	0.3896				

TABLE 14.7— THROAT ANNULUS AREAS FOR MANUFACTURER B

Nozzle	A-	A	B	C	D	E
1		0.0036	0.0053	0.0076	0.0105	0.0143
2	0.0029	0.0046	0.0089	0.0098	0.0136	0.0184
3	0.0037	0.0060	0.0089	0.0127	0.0175	0.0231
4	0.0048	0.0077	0.0115	0.0164	0.0227	0.0306
5	0.0062	0.0100	0.0149	0.0211	0.0293	0.0397
6	0.0080	0.0129	0.0192	0.0273	0.0378	0.0513
7	0.0104	0.0167	0.0246	0.0353	0.0468	0.0663
8	0.0134	0.0216	0.0320	0.0456	0.0631	0.0856
9	0.0174	0.0278	0.0414	0.0569	0.0614	0.1106
10	0.0224	0.0360	0.0634	0.0760	0.1051	0.1428
11	0.0289	0.0484	0.0690	0.0981	0.1356	0.1840
12	0.0374	0.0509	0.0891	0.1298	0.1749	0.2382
13	0.0483	0.0774	0.1151	0.1633	0.2255	0.3076
14	0.0624	0.1001	0.1482	0.2115	0.2926	0.3974
15	0.0806	0.1287	0.1920	0.2731	0.3780	0.5133
16	0.1036	0.1666	0.2479	0.3528	0.4881	0.6829
17	0.1344	0.2155	0.3205	0.4557	0.8304	0.6562
18	0.1735	0.2784	0.4137	0.5855	0.8142	1.1058
19	0.2242	0.3595	0.6343	0.7600	1.0616	1.4282
20	0.2895	0.4643	0.6901	0.9817	1.3883	1.8444

inherently an OPF device, F_{gL} depends on the formation gas/oil ratio (GOR) and on the amount of power-fluid mixed with the production, which in turn depends on the size of the nozzle and the operating pressure. As the power-fluid pressure is increased, the lift capability of the pump increases, but the additional power-fluid rate decreases F_{gL}, thereby increasing the effective lift. Finding a match between the power-fluid rate, the pump performance curve and the pump discharge pressure, $p,$ is an iterative procedure involving successive refined guesses.

The various suppliers of jet pumps also have developed in-house computer programs for application design that are faster than the past calculator routines and incorporate more correlation for fluid properties and the pump discharge pressure. The object of the calculation

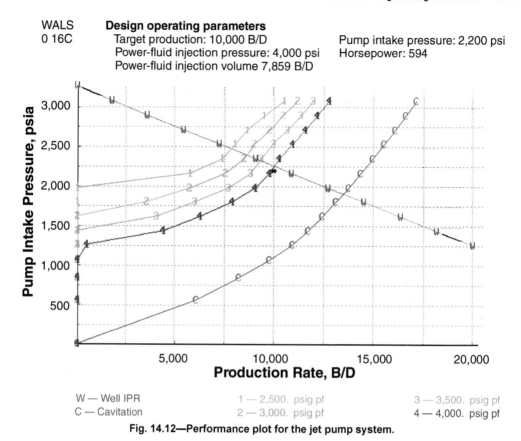

Fig. 14.12—Performance plot for the jet pump system.

sequence is to superimpose a jet-pump performance curve on the inflow performance relationship (IPR) curve of the well and to note the intersections that represent the pump performance in that particular well. Therefore, a plot of the best estimate of the IPR or productivity index (PI) curve of the well is the starting point. An example of a completed performance plot in this format is shown in **Fig. 14.12**.

14.3.7 Calculation Sequence and Supplemental Equations. Fig. 14.13 shows a typical jet-pump installation with the appropriate pressures that determine pump operation. Although a parallel installation is shown for clarity of nomenclature, the same relationships hold for the casing-type installation.

14.4 Downhole Pump Accessories

14.4.1 Swab Cups. A number of accessories are available for downhole pumping systems. Free-pump systems require swab cups and a standing valve to accomplish the pump-in and pump-out operations. The swab cups are carried on a mandrel, extending above the pump, which may contain a check valve to limit the amount of fluid by passing the pump as it is circulated to the surface. If the pump does not enter a lubricator on the wellhead, the check valve may include a valve bypass that is actuated when the pump enters the wellhead catcher to prevent excessive pressure buildup. Two examples of swab cup assemblies are shown in **Fig. 14.14**. Jet pumps usually use the simpler system.

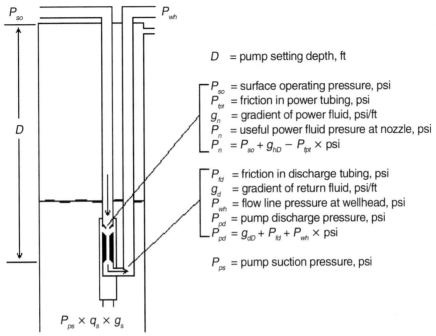

Fig. 14.13—Schematic for jet pumping.

14.4.2 Standing Valves. Standing valves are necessary in free-pump systems to create a "U" tube and prevent the circulating fluid from flowing back into the reservoir. During pumping operations, the standing valve is opened by flow from the formation to the pump suction; whenever the pump is shut down, the standing valve closes. In some cases, the standing-valve ball is held open by a small magnet to prevent it from cycling during reciprocating pump-stroking reversals. When the downhole pump is unseated, fluids attempting to flow back into the formation wash the ball off the magnet and onto the seat. The standing valve is wireline-retrievable and includes a provision for draining the tubing before attempting to pull it. In most cases, the standing valve forms the no-go and bottom seal for the pump. Some jet-pump installations, however, use high-flow designs that do not serve as a pump seat. An example of each type is shown in **Fig. 14.15.**

14.4.3 Pressure Recorders. To obtain producing BHPs at several different withdrawal rates, downhole pressure recorders are often run in conjunction with hydraulic pumps, hung below the standing valve. While this arrangement provides not only pressure drawdown but also pressure-buildup data, it has the disadvantage of requiring wireline operations to run and retrieve the recorder. Some reciprocating pumps can be run with a pressure recorder attached, which eliminates the wireline operations but does not permit observation of pressure buildup because the recorder is above the standing valve. Virtually all jet pumps can be run with recorders attached, and very smooth recordings are obtained.

14.4.4 Dummy Pumps. Dummy pumps are sometimes run to blank off one or more tubing strings so that they may be checked for leaks. If the dummy pump has a fluid passage in it, the terms "flow-through dummy" or "blanking tool" are often used. These tools are useful for acidizing or steaming.

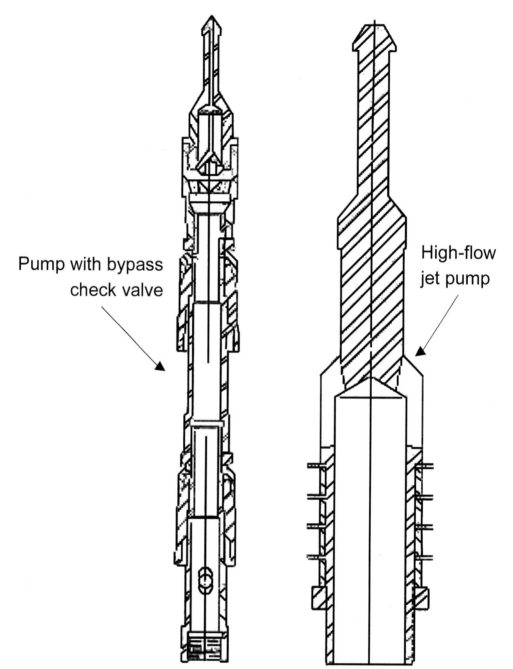

Fig. 14.14—Hydraulic pump swab cup assemblies.

14.4.5 Screens and Filters. To protect the downhole pump from trash in the well, various types of screens and filters are sometimes run. Because circulating pumps in and out of a well may dislodge scale and corrosion products in the tubing, a starting filter can be attached to the swab-cup assembly to filter the power fluid. Because this must be a relatively small filter, it will eventually plug up, and an automatic bypass arrangement is provided. This system collects foreign material during the crucial startup phase with a newly installed pump. For long-term

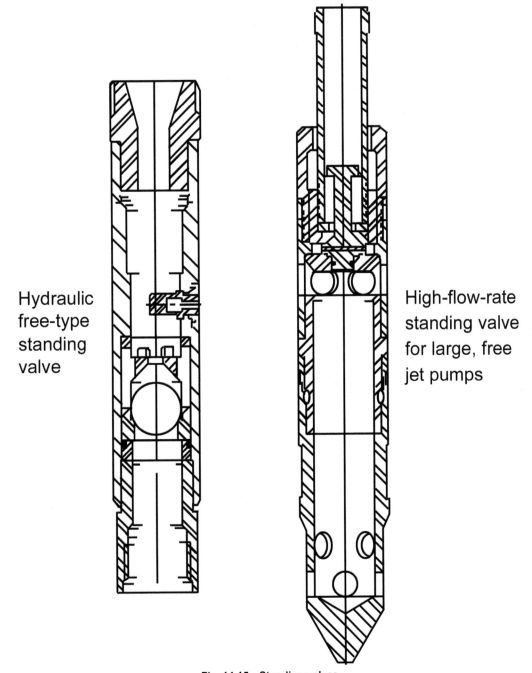

Fig. 14.15—Standing valves.

operation, power-fluid and pump intake screens or strainers are used, which exclude large-diameter objects that could damage or plug the pump.

14.4.6 Safety Valves. In some areas, subsurface safety valves are required. When a packer is set and the BHA is above it, a wireline-retrievable safety valve can be installed between the standing valve and the packer to isolate the formation. The safety valve is normally closed unless the pump supplies high-pressure fluid to it by way of a control line run from the main power-fluid tubing just above. The pump discharge pressure provides the reference pressure to the safety valve. When the pump is on bottom and power-fluid pressure is applied to it, the safety valve opens to allow well fluid to enter the pump. Most safety valves will not hold pressure from above, so the standing valve is still necessary for circulating the pump in and out of the well. **Fig. 14.16** illustrates this type of installation.

14.5 Surface Equipment

14.5.1 Surface Pumps. Hydraulic pumping systems have evolved toward the use of relatively high pressures and low flow rates to reduce friction losses and to increase the lift capability and efficiency of the system. Surface operating pressures are generally between 2,000 and 4,000 psi, with the higher pressures used in deeper wells, and power-fluid rates may range from a few hundred to more than 3,000 B/D. While some surface multistage centrifugal pumps are rated to this pressure range, they are generally quite inefficient at the modest flow rates associated with single-well applications. Multistage centrifugals can be used effectively when multiple wells are pumped from a central location. The surface pump for a single well or for just a few wells must be a high-head and low-specific-speed pump. Wide experience in the overall pumping industry has led to the use of positive-displacement pumps for this type of application, and triplex or quintuplex pumps, driven by gas engines or electric motors, power the vast majority of hydraulic pump installations. See **Fig. 14.17.**

Multiplex pumps consist of a power end and a fluid end. The power end houses a crankshaft in a crankcase. The connecting rods are similar to those in internal combustion engines, but connect to crossheads instead of pistons. The fluid end houses individual plungers, each with intake and discharge check valves usually spring loaded, and is attached to the power end by the spacer block, which houses the intermediate rods and provides a working space for access to the plunger system. Most units being installed in the oil field are of the horizontal configuration, which minimizes contamination of the crankcase oil with leakage from the fluid end. Vertical installations are still found, however, particularly with oil as the pumped fluid or when space is at a premium, as in townsite leases.

Multiplex pumps applied to hydraulic pumping usually have stroke lengths from 2 to 7 in. and plunger diameters between 1 and 2½ in. The larger plungers provide higher flow rates but are generally rated at lower maximum pressure because of crankshaft loading limitations. The larger plungers provide higher flow rates, but are generally rated at lower maximum pressure because of crankshaft loading limitations. The normal maximum rating of multiplexes for continuous duty in hydraulic pumping applications is 5,000 psi, with lower ratings for the larger plungers, but applications above 4,000 psi are uncommon. Multiplex pumps are run at low speed to minimize vibration and wear and to avoid dynamic problems with the spring-loaded intake and discharge valves. Most applications fall between 200 and 450 rev/min, and because this is below the speeds of gas engines or electric motors, some form of speed reduction is usually required. Belt drives are found on some units, although gear reduction is more common while gear-reduction units are integral to some multiplexes and separate on others. A variety of reduction ratios are offered for each series of pumps. Because a positive-displacement pump has an essentially constant discharge flow rate for a given prime-mover speed, bypass of excess fluid normally is used to match a particular pressure and flow demand. Another option that has been used successfully is to drive the multiplex pump through a four-speed transmission, which greatly enhances the flexibility of the system. This allows much closer tailoring of the triplex output to the demand, thereby pumping at reduced speed when needed, which also tends to increase the life of such components as the packing and valving.

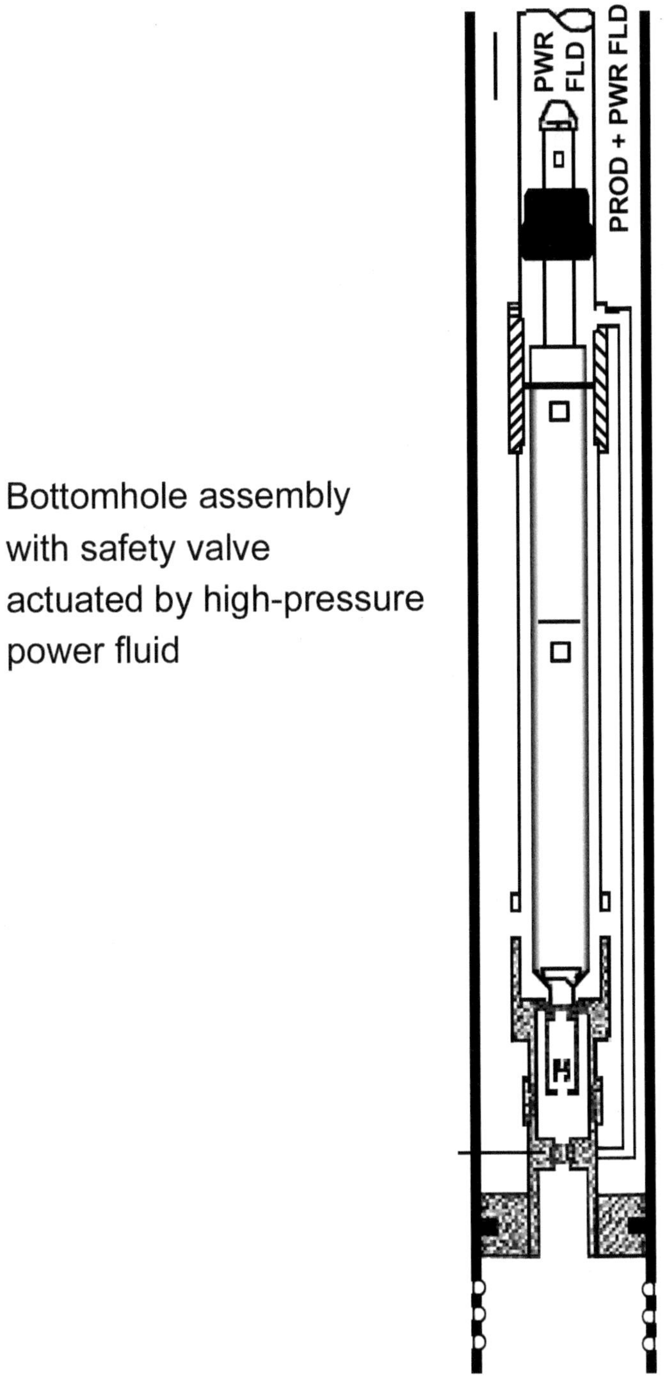
Bottomhole assembly with safety valve actuated by high-pressure power fluid
PWR FLD
PROD + PWR FLD

Fig. 14.16—Safety valve.

Each plunger pumps individually from a common intake manifold into a common discharge, and because discharge occurs only on the upstroke, there is some pulsation, for which pulsation dampers are commonly used.

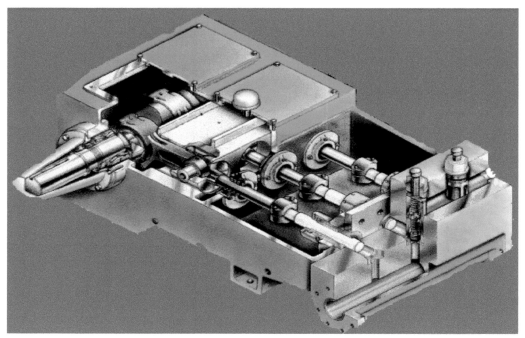

Fig. 14.17—Horizontal plunger pumps.

Two types of plunger systems are in common use. For oil service, a simple and effective plunger-and-liner system is used that consists of a closely fitted metallic plunger inside a metallic liner. Sprayed metal coatings or other hard-facing means are often used to extend the life of the plunger and liner. When pumping water, the metal-to-metal system is not practical because the fit would have to be extremely close to keep leakage to an acceptable level. Galling and scoring are problems with close fits and the low lubricity of water, and to solve this problem, spring-loaded packing systems are used that do not require adjusting. The advent of high-strength aramid fibers for packing, in conjunction with other compounds to improve the friction characteristics, has resulted in a pronounced improvement in the ability of the pump to handle high-pressure water for extended periods of time. Water still presents a more severe challenge than oil, however, and water systems show much better life if operated at or below 3,500 psi.

Suction conditions are important to multiplex operation. Friction losses in piping, fluid end porting, and across the suction valving reduce the pressure available to fill the pumping chamber on the plunger downstroke, and if these losses are sufficiently great, cavitation may result. When pumping oil with dissolved gas, the reduction in pressure liberates free gas and causes knocking, so it is necessary to have a positive head on the suction side to overcome the friction losses. In addition, another phenomenon known as "acceleration head" must be considered. The flow in the suction piping must accelerate and decelerate a number of times for each crankshaft revolution. For the fluid (which has inertia) to follow the acceleration, energy must be supplied, which is then returned to the fluid on deceleration. The energy supplied during acceleration comes from a reduction in the pressure in the fluid, and if this drops too low, cavitation or gas liberation will result. The minimum suction head for the multiplex pump is then the sum of the friction losses and the acceleration head. Although the pump can draw a vacuum, this will flash gas and may tend to suck air across the valve or plunger packing. Manufacturers of multiplex pumps recommend appropriate suction charging pressures for their products, but it is worth noting that long, small-diameter suction lines increase the acceleration head loss and friction loss. It is therefore recommended for suction lines to be short and of large diameter, with no high spots to trap air or gas. Suction stabilizers or pulsation dampeners that tend to absorb the pulsations from the pump also reduce acceleration head, and users are encouraged to follow good piping practices in the installation of surface pumps.

In many cases, sufficient hydrostatic head is not available to provide the necessary suction pressure, and charge pumps are used to overcome this problem. Positive displacement pumps of the vane or crescent-gear type driven from the triplex have been used extensively, but they require a pressure-control valve to bypass excess fluid and match the multiplex displacement. Where electric power is available, centrifugal charge pumps have given excellent service. Centrifugal pumps generally need to run at speeds considerably above the multiplex speed, and so driving them from the multiplex presents problems, particularly with a gas engine drive where prime-mover speed variations cause significant variations in the charge-pump output pressure.

While good charging pressures are necessary to ensure proper loading and smooth operation, there are problems associated with very high charge pressures. These add to the crankshaft loading, and for charge pressures above about 250 psi, it is advisable to derate the maximum discharge pressure by one third of the charge pressure. High charge pressures also can adversely affect the lubrication of bearings, particularly in the crosshead wristpin. In addition, the mechanical efficiency of multiplex pumps is some 3 to 5% lower on the suction side compared to the discharge side.[22] Consequently, the combination of a charge pump and multiplex pump is most efficient with low charging pressures and a high boost by the multiplex pump. The charging pressure should therefore be limited to that necessary to give complete filling of the multiplex pump with a moderate safety allowance for variations in the system parameters.

In some cases, it is desirable to inject corrosion inhibitors or lubricants into the multiplex suction, and fresh water is sometimes injected to dissolve high salt concentrations. In severe pumping applications with low-lubricity fluids, lubricating oil is sometimes injected or dripped onto the plungers in the spacer block area to improve plunger life. Injection pumps are often driven from the multiplex drive for these applications. A troubleshooting guide for multiplex pumps is given in **Table 14.8**.

14.5.2 Fluid Controls. Various types of valves are used to regulate and to distribute the power-fluid supply to one or more wellheads. Common to all free-pump systems is a four-way valve or wellhead control valve, which is mounted at the wellhead, as shown in **Fig. 14.18**. Its function is to provide for different modes of operation by shifting it to different positions. To circulate the pump into the hole, as shown in Fig. 14.15, power fluid is directed down the main tubing string. The power fluid begins to operate the pump once it is on bottom and seated on the standing valve. In the pump-out mode, power fluid is directed down the return tubing or casing annulus to unseat the pump and to circulate it to the surface. When the pump is on the surface, putting the valve in the bypass and bleed position permits the well to be bled down and the pump to be removed and replaced.

Most systems include a constant-pressure controller, as shown in **Fig. 14.19**, which maintains a discharge-pressure load on the multiplex pump by continuously bypassing the excess discharge fluid. It generally operates on the principle of an adjustable spring force on a piston-and-valve assembly that is pressure compensated. If the pressure rises on the high-pressure side, which is being controlled because of changing system loads, the pressure forces on the various areas within the valve will cause the valve to open and to bypass more fluid, restoring the high-pressure side to the preset condition. Jet pumps frequently are operated with a constant-pressure valve as the only surface control valve. The constant-pressure controller can be used to regulate the pressure on a manifold assembly serving multiple wells.

Reciprocating downhole pumps are usually regulated with a constant-flow control valve. The downhole unit can be maintained at a constant stroking rate if a constant volume of power

TABLE 14.8— POWER FLUID PLUNGER PUMPS TROUBLESHOOTING GUIDE

Possible Cause	Correction
Knocking or Pounding in Fluid End and Piping	
Suction line restricted by	
(a) Trash, scale buildup, etc.	Locate and remove.
(b) Partially closed valve in suction line.	Locate and correct.
(c) Meters, filters, check valves, nonfull opening, cutoff valves, or other restrictions.	Rework suction line to eliminate.
(d) Sharp 90° or 90° blind tees.	Rework suction line to eliminate.
Air entering suction line through valve stem packing.	Tighten or repack valve-stem packing.
Air entering suction line through loose connection or faulty pipe.	Locate and correct.
Air or vapor trapped in suction.	Locate rise or trap and correct by straightening line, providing enough slope to permit escape and prevent buildup.
Low fluid level.	Increase supply and install automatic low-level shutdown switch.
Suction damper not operating.	Inspect and repair as required.
Worn pump valves or broken spring.	Inspect and repair as required.
Entrained gas or air in fluid.	Provide gas boot or scrubber for fluid.
Inadequate size of suction line.	Replace with individual suction line or next size larger than inlet or pump.
Leaking pressure relief valve that has been piped back into pump suction.	Repair valve and rework piping to return to supply tank—not suction line.
Bypass piped back to suction.	Rework to return bypassed fluid back to supply tank—not supply line.
Broken plunger.	Inspect when rotating pump by hand and replace as required.
Worn crosshead pin or connecting rod.	Locate and replace as required.
Knock in Power End	
Worn crosshead pin or connecting rod.	Locate and replace as required. Check oil quality and level.
Worn main bearings.	Replace as required. Check oil quality and level.
Loose plunger (intermediate rod) crosshead connection.	Inspect for damage—replace as required and tighten.
Rapid Valve Wear or Failure	
Cavitation.	Predominant cause of short valve life and always a result of poor suction conditions. This situation can be corrected by following appropriate recommendations as listed under No. 1.
Corrosion.	Treat fluid as required.
Abrasives in fluid.	Treat to remove harmful solids.
Fluid Seal Plunger Wear, Leakage, or Failure	
Solids in power oil.	This is likely to cause greatest amount of wear. Power oil should be analyzed for amount and type of solids content. Proper treating to remove solids should be instigated.
Improper installation.	Follow written instructions and use proper tools. Remember plunger and liner are matched sets. Ensure proper lubrication at startup. (Be sure air is bled out of fluid end before starting up.)
Reduced Volume or Pressure	
Bypassing fluid.	Locate and correct.
Air in fluid end of triplex.	Bleed off.
Inaccurate meter or pressure gauge.	Check and correct.
Pump suction cavitation due to improper hook-up, suction restriction, or entrained gas.	Locate and correct.
Valves worn or broken.	Replace.
Plungers and liners worn.	Replace.
Reduced prime mover speed because of increased load, fuel, or other conditions.	Determine cause and correct. (There may be increased pressure caused by paraffin, temperature change, etc.)

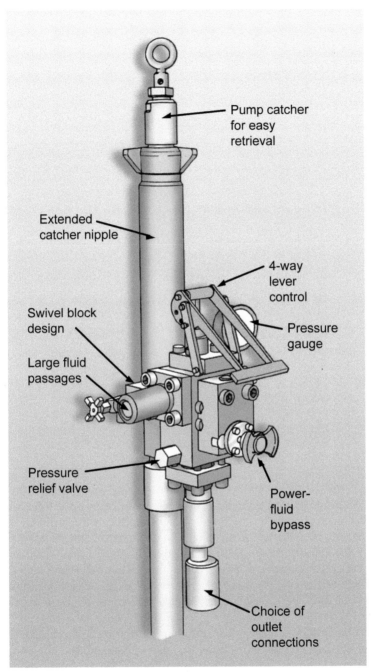

Fig. 14.18—Wellhead control valve.

fluid is supplied to it, and the constant-flow control valve is designed to provide a preset flow rate even if the downhole operating pressure fluctuated because of changing well conditions. Because this valve does not bypass fluid, it must be used with a constant-pressure controller on the higher-pressure or inlet side.

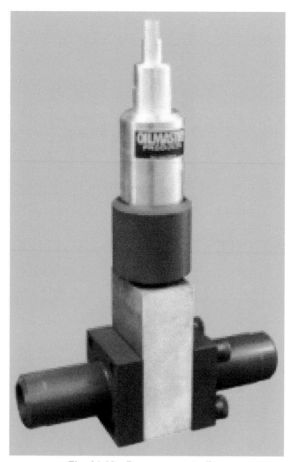

Fig. 14.19—Pressure controller.

14.5.3 Control Manifolds. Where a number of wells are to be pumped from a central battery, a control manifold is used to direct the flows to and from the individual wells. Control manifolds are designed to be built up in modular fashion to match the number of wells being pumped and are generally rated for 5,000 psi working pressure. A constant pressure control valve regulates the pressure on the common power fluid side of the manifold. This pressure is generally a few hundred pounds per square inch greater than the highest pressure demanded by any well to allow proper operation of the individual well-control valves. Individual constant-flow control valves regulate the amount of power fluid going to each well. The use of a constant pressure valve allows excess fluid to bypass at the highest pressure. Meter loops or individual meters for each station can be integrated into the manifold.

14.5.4 Lubricator. Some wells flow or "kick back" when the operator is attempting to re-move or insert a pump into the wellhead. Also, the presence of water may make it inadvisable to open up the entire tubing string for pump insertion and removal. The use of a lubricator allows the master valve below the wellhead to be closed, and the entire lubricator with the pump in it to be removed from the wellhead. The lubricator is essentially an extended piece of the tubing with a sideline to allow fluid flow when the pump is circulating in or out of the hole.

14.5.5 Power-Fluid Systems. The function of the surface treating systems is to provide a con-stant supply of suitable power fluid to be used to operate the subsurface production units. The successful and economical operation of any hydraulic pumping system is to a large extent dependent on the effectiveness of the treating system in supplying high-quality power fluid. The presence of gas, solids, or abrasive materials in the power fluid adversely affects the operation and wears both the surface and downhole units. Therefore, the primary objective in treating crude oil or water for use as power fluid is to make it as free of gas and solids as possible. In addition, chemical treatment of the power fluid may be beneficial to the life of the downhole unit. In tests, it has been found that for best operation of the unit, a maximum total solids of 20 ppm, maximum salt content of 12 lbm/1,000 bbl oil, and a maximum particle size of 15 μm should be maintained. (These norms were established using oil in 30 to 40°API gravity range). It has been observed, however, that acceptable performance has been achieved in many cases where these values were exceeded, especially with the use of jet pumps and larger nozzles and throats. When using piston hydraulic pumps in heavy crude, these limitations have been exceeded and satisfactory results achieved, probably because the resulting wear does not increase leakage to the same degree. The periodic analysis of power fluid indicates steps to be taken for improved operation. For example, if the power-fluid analysis shows that iron sulfide or sulfate compounds make up the bulk of the solids, then a corrosion or scale problem exists that would require the use of chemical inhibitors to correct the problem. Water is the primary power fluid being used for jet pumping on offshore platforms and in applications where the majority of produced fluid being made is water. Water requires that a lubricant be added for use with reciprocating pumps. Other considerations in the choice of water or oil as a power fluid include:

• Maintenance on surface pumps is usually less with the use of oil. The lower bulk modulus of oil also contributes to reduced pressure pulsations and vibrations that can affect all the surface equipment.

• Well testing for oil production is simpler with water as the power fluid because all the oil coming back is produced oil. With oil power fluid, the power rate must be closely metered and subtracted from the total oil returning to surface. This can be a source of considerable error in high-water-cut wells where the power oil rate is large compared to the net production.

• In high-friction systems, as sometime occurs with jet pumps in restricted tubulars, the lower viscosity of water can increase efficiency. With no moving parts, the jet pump is not adversely affected by the poor lubrication properties of water.

• In deep casing-type installations, particularly with a jet pump, water when used as the power fluid can load up in the casing annulus return, negating any beneficial gas lifting effects for the produced gas.

It has been found that, in most cases, an upward velocity of 1ft/hr is low enough to provide sufficient gravity separation of entrained particles to clean power fluid to requirements, provided that there is no free gas in the fluids or large thermal effects.

14.5.6 Open Power-Fluid System. A typical power-oil treating system that has proved adequate for most OPF systems, when stock-tank-quality oil is supplied, is shown in **Fig. 14.20**. This system has the general characteristic that all return fluids from the well, both production and power fluid, must pass through the surface treating facility. The power-oil settling tank in this system is usually a 24-ft-high, three-ring, bolted steel tank. A tank of this height generally provides adequate head for gravity flow of oil from the tank to the multiplex pump suction. If more than one multiplex pump is required for the system, individual power-oil tanks can be set up for each pump, or a single large tank can be used, whichever is more economical and best meets the operating requirements. If a single large tank supplies the suction for several pumps, individual suction lines are preferable.

The gas boot is essentially a part of the power-oil tank; its purpose is to provide final gas/ oil separation so that the oil will be stable at near-atmospheric pressure. If the gas is not sufficiently separated from the oil, entrained free gas can enter the power-oil tank and destroy the

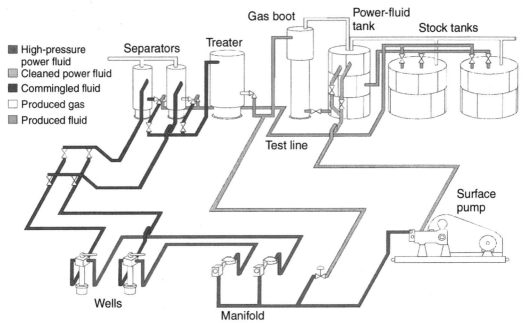

Fig. 14.20—Central OPF hydraulic power-oil treating system.

settling process by causing the fluid in the tank to roll. The following piping specifications for the gas boot are necessary to ensure undisturbed settling:

• The gas-boot inlet height should be 4 ft above the top of the power-oil tank to allow the incoming fluid to fall, so that the agitation will encourage gas/oil separation.

• The top section of the gas boot should be at least 3 ft in diameter and 8 ft higher than the top of the power-oil tank. These two factors will provide a reservoir that should absorb the volume of the surges.

• The gas line out of the top of the boot should be tied into the power-oil tank and stock-tank vent line with a riser on the top of the power-oil tank. In the event the gas boot does become overloaded and kicks fluid over through the gas line, this arrangement will prevent the raw or unsettled fluid from being dumped in the top of the power-oil tank, where it may contaminate the oil drawn off to the multiplex. A minimum diameter of 3 in. is recommended for the gas line.

• The line connecting the gas boot to the power-oil tank should be at least 4 in. in diameter. This is necessary to minimize restrictions to low during surge loading of the boot.

Oil entering a large tank (at the bottom and rising to be drawn off the top) tends to channel from the tank inlet to the outlet; thus, an inlet spreader is used. The purpose of the spreader is to reduce the velocity of the incoming fluid by distributing the incoming volume over a large area, thus allowing the fluid to rise upward at a more uniform rate. The recommended spreader consists of a round, flat plate with a diameter approximately half that of the tank with a 4-in. skirt that has 60° triangular, saw-tooth slots cut in it. The slots provide automatic opening adjustment for varying amounts of flow. It is essential that they be cut to uniform depth to obtain an even distribution of flow. This type of spreader must be installed with the tops of all the slots in a level plane to prevent fluid from "bumping out" under a high side, and it should be mounted about 2 ft above the bottom rim of the tank.

The location of the stock-tank take-off and level control is important because it establishes the effective settling interval of the power-oil tank and controls the fluid level. All fluid coming from the spreader rises to the stock take-off level, where stock-tank oil is drawn off. Fluid rising above this level is only that amount required to replace the fluid withdrawn by the multiplex pump, and it is in this region that the power-oil settling process takes place. The light solids settled out are carried with the production through the stock-tank take-off, and the heavier particles settle to the bottom, where they must be removed periodically. The location of the stock take-off point should be within 6 ft of the spreader. The height to which the stock oil must rise in the piping, to overflow into the stock tank, determines the fluid level in the power-oil tank. The diameter of the piping used should be sufficient to provide negligible resistance to the volume of flow required (4-in. minimum diameter recommended). The extension at the top of the level control is connected to the gas line to provide a vent that keeps oil in the power-oil tank from being siphoned down to the level of the top of the stock tank.

The power-oil outlet should be located on the opposite side of the power-oil tank from the stock take-off outlet to balance the flow distribution within the tank. Because the fluid level in the tank is maintained approximately 18 in. from the top of the tank, the location of the upper outlet, for use in starting up or filling tubing strings, depends on estimated emergency requirements and the capacity per foot of the tank. A distance of 7 ft from the top of the tank is usually sufficient. This lower outlet line contains a shutoff valve that is kept closed during normal operations so that the full settling interval is used.

14.5.7 Closed Power-Fluid Systems. In the closed power-fluid system, the power fluid returns to the surface in a separate conduit and need not go through the surface production treating facilities. The consequent reduction in surface treating facilities can tend to offset the additional downhole cost of the system. Virtually all closed power-fluid systems are in California because of the large number of townsite leases and offshore platforms, and water is usually the power fluid. Gravity settling separation in the power-fluid tank ensures that the power fluid remains clean despite the addition of solids from power-fluid makeup, corrosion products, and contamination during pump-in and pump-out operations. The power-fluid makeup is required to replace the small amount of fluid lost through fits and seals in the downhole pump and wellhead control valve. A certain amount of power fluid is also lost during circulating operations as well.

14.5.8 Single-Well Systems. The central battery systems previously discussed have been used successfully for years and provide a number of benefits. The use of lease fluid treating facilities as part of the of the hydraulic system ensures good, low-pressure separation of the gas, oil, water, and solids phases present in any system. Good triplex charging of clean, gas-free oil and consistently clean power fluid supplied to the downhole pump are desirable features of this system. The lease treating facilities, however, must have sufficient capacity to process both the well production and the return power fluid. When the wells are closely spaced, the clustering of power generation, fluid treating, and control functions in one location (but sufficiently spread out) is very efficient and allows good use of the installed horsepower. Because the system is not limited by production variations on any one well, an adequate supply of the desired power fluid is ensured by the size of the system. A further benefit associated with the use of the lease separation facilities is the option of a closed power-fluid system. When well spacing is large, however, long, high-pressure power-fluid lines must be run. Also, individual well testing is complicated by the need to meter the power-fluid rate for each well, which can introduce measurement errors. As a final consideration, only a few wells in a field may be best suited to artificial lift by hydraulic pumping, so the installation of a central system is difficult to justify.

To address the limitations of the central battery system, single-well systems have been designed,[23,24] many of the requirements of which are the same as for a central battery. The oil, water, gas, and solids phases must be separated to provide a consistent source of power fluid to run the system. A choice of water or oil power fluid should be possible, and the fluid used as power fluid must be sufficiently clean to ensure reliable operation and that it is gas-free at the multiplex suction to prevent cavitation and partial fluid end loading. An adequate reservoir of fluid must be present to allow continuous operation and the various circulating functions associated with the free-pump procedures. Finally, a means of disposing of and measuring the well production to the lease treating and storage facilities must be provided.

To achieve these objectives, several of the manufacturers of hydraulic pumping units offer packaged single-well systems that include all the control, metering, and pumping equipment necessary. All components are skid mounted on one or two skids to facilitate installation at the well and to make the systems easily portable if the unit is to be moved to a different well. Usually, the only plumbing required at the wellsite is the power fluid and return-line hookup at the wellhead and the connection of the vessel outlet to the flowline.

An example of a typical single-well power unit is illustrated in Fig. 14.1. All units of this type share certain design concepts, with small variations depending on the manufacturer. Either one or two pressure vessels are located at the wellsite. The size of the main reservoir vessel depends on the nature of the well and the tubular completion. The reservoir vessel should ensure that, if the wellhead partially empties the return conduit to the flowline, adequate capacity remains to operate the downhole unit until production returns re-enter the vessel. Even if the well does not head, extra capacity is needed. When the unit is shut down for maintenance or pump changes, that portion of the return conduit occupied by gas needs to be filled from the vessel to unseat the pump and to circulate it to the surface. The vessel sizes normally used range from 42 × 120 in. to 60 × 240 in. In some wells, even the largest vessel may not be able to compensate fully for heading, in which case it is common to use backpressure to stabilize the heading. The vessels themselves are normally in the 175- to 240-psi working pressure range, with higher ratings available for special applications. Coal-tar-epoxy internal coatings are common, with special coatings for extreme cases.

The return power fluid and production for the well enter the vessel system where basic separation of water, oil, and gas phases takes place. Free gas at the vessel pressure is discharged to the flowline with a vent system that ensures a gas cap in the vessel at all times, while the oil and water separate in the vessel, and the desired fluid is withdrawn for use as power fluid. The power fluid passes through one or more cyclone desanders to remove solids before entering the multiplex suction, where it is pressurized for reinjection down the power-fluid tubing. Any excess multiplex output that is bypassed for downhole pump control is returned to the vessel. The underflow from the bottom of the cyclone desanders contains a high-solids concentration and is discharged either into the flowline or back into the vessel system. Once the system is stabilized on the selected power fluid, the well production of oil, water, and gas is discharged into the flowline from the vessel, which is maintained at a pressure above the flowline. Because the flowline is carrying only what the well makes, additional treating and separating facilities are not needed, as they are in the central battery system that handles mixed well production and power fluid. This feature also facilitates individual well testing.

Overall, simple gravity dump piping, which consists of a riser on the outside of the vessel, controls the fluid level in the vessel system. To prevent siphoning of the vessel, the gas-vent line is tied in the top of the riser as a siphon breaker. The choice of oil or water power fluid is made by selection of the appropriate take-off points on the vessel so that the production goes to the flowline and the power fluid goes to the multiplex pump. If the multiplex suction is low in the vessel and the flowline is high in the vessel, water will tend to accumulate in the vessel and will be the power fluid. If the multiplex suction is high in the vessel and the flowline is low, oil will tend to accumulate in the vessel and will be the power fluid. Opening and closing appropriate valves sets the system up for the chosen power fluid. The multiplex suction outlets are positioned with respect to the overall fluid level in the vessel to avoid drawing power fluid

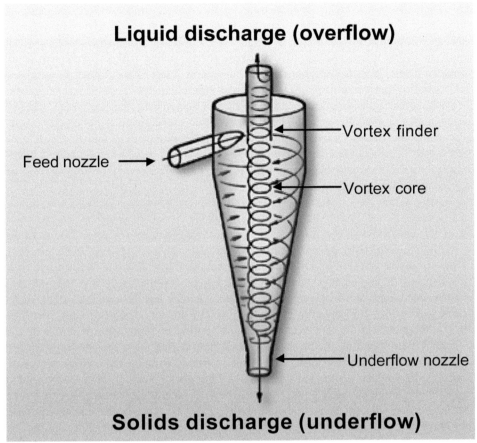

Liquid discharge (overflow)

Vortex finder

Feed nozzle →

Vortex core

Underflow nozzle

Solids discharge (underflow)

Fig. 14.21—Hydrocyclone.

from the emulsion layer between the oil and water because this layer generally contains a significantly higher concentration of solids and is not easily cleaned in the cyclones.

The power-fluid cleaning is accomplished with cyclone desanders that require a pressure differential across them. In the two-vessel system, a differential pressure valve between the two vessels that stages the pressure drop from the wellhead accomplishes this. The energy to maintain this staged pressure is supplied by the multiplex pump through the downhole pump.

The flow path through a cyclone cleaner is shown in **Fig. 14.21**. Fluid enters the top of the cone tangentially through the feed nozzle and spirals downward toward the apex of the cone. Conservation of angular momentum dictates that the rotational speed of the fluid increases as the radius of curvature decreases, and it is the high rotational speed that cleans the fluid by centrifugal force. The clean fluid, called the overflow, spirals back upward through the vortex core to the vortex finder, while the dirty fluid exits downward at the apex through the underflow nozzle. The cones are usually constructed of cast iron with an elastomer interior. Different feed-nozzle and vortex-finder sizes and shapes are available to alter the performance characteristics of the cyclone. Different sizes of cyclones are available, with the smaller sizes having lower flow-rate capacities but somewhat higher cleaning efficiencies.

Maintaining the proper flow through the cyclone to ensure good cleaning depends on correctly adjusting the pressures at the feed nozzle, overflow, and underflow. At the design flow rates, a 30- to 50-psi drop normally occurs from the feed nozzle to the overflow. In the single-vessel system, a charged pump supplies the pressure, while in a dual-vessel system, the pressure is supplied by a higher backpressure on the returns from the well. Because of the centrifugal head, the cyclone overflow pressure is generally 5 to 15 psi higher than the underflow pressure. An underflow restrictor is commonly used to adjust the amount of underflow to between 5 and 10% of the overflow. This ensures good cleaning without circulation of excessive fluid volumes. It should be noted that the volume flow rates through a cyclone vary inversely with the specific gravity of the fluid, and that within the range of normal power fluids, increased viscosity leads to increased flow rates. The viscosity that suppresses the internal vortex action causes this latter effect. Therefore, proper cyclone sizing to match the charge and multiplex pump characteristics must be done carefully and with detailed knowledge of the fluid to be processed. The manufacturers of the packaged systems supply appropriate cyclones for the installation, but it should be noted that moving the portable unit to another well might require resizing of the cyclone system.

The routing of the dirty underflow varies with different systems, and may be an adjustable option in some systems. Two basic choices are available: return of underflow to the vessel or routing of the underflow to the flowline. In a dual-vessel system, the underflow must be returned to the flowline downstream of the backpressure valve to provide sufficient pressure differential to ensure underflow. Discharging the solids to the flowline is attractive because they are disposed of immediately and are excluded from possible entry into the power fluid. Under some conditions, however, continuous operation may not be possible. If the net well production is less than the underflow from the cyclone for any length of time, the level of fluid in the vessel will drop, and over an extended period of time, this can result in a shutdown of the system. Shutting off the cyclone underflow during these periods stops the loss of fluid, but apex plugging occurs during the shutoff period. Returning the underflow to the vessel eliminates the problem of running the vessel dry but does potentially reintroduce solids into the power fluid. In single-vessel units, the underflow is generally plumbed back to the vessel in a baffled section adjacent to the flowline outlet. This provides for the maximum conservation but requires a differential pressure valve, between the cyclone underflow and the vessel, which is normally set at about 20 psi to ensure a positive pressure to the underflow fluid.

As mentioned previously, the vessel pressure is held above the flowline pressure to ensure flow into the flowline and a backpressure control valve is sometimes used for this purpose. This keeps the vessel pressure, which is backpressure on the well, at a minimum for any flowline pressure that may occur during normal field operation. When water is the power fluid, "riding" the flowline in this manner is acceptable. However, when oil is the power fluid, changing vessel pressure causes flashing of gas in the power oil and adversely affects the multiplex suction. When oil is used as power fluid, it is recommended that a pressure control valve be used to keep the vessel at a steady pressure some 10 to 15 psi above the highest expected flowline pressure.

Although, the single-vessel system was developed for applications involving widely spaced wells, two or three well installations have been successfully operated from a single-well system. This installation is very attractive on offshore platforms. With a large number of highly deviated wells, offshore production is well suited to hydraulic pumping with free pumps, but the extra fluid treating facilities with an open power-fluid system is a drawback when severe weight and space limitations exist. The closed power-fluid system answers this problem, but the extra tubulars in deviated holes create their own set of problems and expense. Furthermore, the use of jet pumps, which is quite attractive offshore, is not possible with the closed power-fluid system. For safety and environmental reasons, water is almost always the power fluid of choice offshore. A large single-well system can receive the returns from all the wells and separate the power water necessary for reinjection to power downhole units. Full 100% separation of the oil from the power water is not necessary, and, in fact, some minor oil carryover will contribute to the power-fluid lubricity. The platform separation facilities then have to handle

TABLE 14.9—JET PUMP DESIGN EXAMPLE

Customer: ABC Oil Co.
Field and Well: Well 2
Location: Anywhere
1. Perforation depth, ft: 5,400
2. Pump vertical depth, ft: 5,231
3. Pump Installation (1) parallel free
              (2) casing free: 2
4. Casing ID, in.: 6.094
5. Upstring ID, in.: N/A
6. Downstring tubing ID, in.: 2.441
7. Downstring tubing OD, in.: 2.875
8. Tubing length, ft: 5,400
9. Pipe condition (1) new, (2) average, (3) old: 2
10. Oil gravity, °API: 37
11. Water cut, %: 79
12. Water specific gravity (SG): 1.050
13. Producing GOR, scf/STB: 215
14. Gas SG (air = 1): 0.8
15. Separator press, psig: 30
16. Well static BHP, psig: 2,122
17. Well flowing BHP, psig: 1,422
18. Well test flow rage, B/D: 700
19. Wellhead temperature, °F: 100
20. Bottomhole temperature, °F: 148
21. (1) vented, (2) unvented: 2
22. Power fluid (1) oil, (2) water: 1
23. Power fluid API/SG: 37
24. Bubblepoint pressure, psia: 796
25. Wellhead pressure, psig: 100

Oilmaster 10 bbl Jet Pump Performance Summary For User-Specified Target With a Production Rate of 1,200 B/D at 850 psig Pump Intake Pressure

PIP, psi	Well	Cavitation	Power Fluid (PF) = 2,500 psi		PF = 3,000 psi		PF = 3,500 psi		PF = 0 psi	
			q_s	q_n	q_s	q_n	q_s	q_n	q_s	q_n
2,051	0	2,342	2,426	1,431	2,710	1,577	2,965	1,709	0	0
1,936	114	2,276	2,318	1,467	2,614	1,610	2,881	1,740	0	0
1,822	228	2,208	2,199	1,501	2,511	1,641	2,785	1,769	0	0
1,708	342	2,138	2,064	1,534	2,397	1,671	2,685	1,797	0	0
1,594	456	2,065	1,920	1,567	2,270	1,701	2,576	1,825	0	0
1,480	570	1,990	1,762	1,599	2,139	1,730	2,459	1,852	0	0
1,366	685	1,912	1,592	1,630	1,995	1,759	2,335	1,879	0	0
1,252	799	1,830	1,415	1,660	1,841	1,787	2,201	1,905	0	0
1,138	913	1,745	1,237	1,690	1,681	1,815	2,063	1,931	0	0
1,024	1,027	1,655	1,063	1,720	1,518	1,843	1,914	1,957	0	0
910	1,141	1,560	893	1,749	1,349	1,870	1,766	1,983	0	0
795	1,255	1,452	735	1,778	1,183	1,896	1,600	2,008	0	0
675	1,369	1,321	575	1,807	1,003	1,924	1,417	2,034	0	0
533	1,483	1,156	405	1,842	811	1,957	1,211	2,064	0	0
349	1,597	907	207	1,885	564	1,998	928	2,103	0	0
0	1,707	0	0	1,960	0	2,074	0	2,175	0	0
Maximum power required:			96 hp		122 hp		149 hp		0 hp	

only the actual production from the wells. A compact bank of cyclone cleaners completes the power-fluid separation and cleaning unit.

In summary, the hydraulic system normally is used in areas where other types of artificial lift have failed or, because of well conditions, have been eliminated because of their shortcomings. Hydraulic pumping systems have been labeled expensive, where, in truth, the use of other artificial lift methods may not be feasible. These include, but are not limited to, the following:

• Using hydraulic free pumps in remote areas where the rig costs are unusually high or the availability of workover rigs is limited.

• Crooked or deviated wells

• Use of hydraulic systems in relatively deep, hot, high-volume wells. (Note: Hydraulic pumps can go through tubing with as much as a 24° buildup per 100 ft.)

• The use of jet pumps in sandy corrosive wells.

• The use of reciprocating pumps in deep wells with low bottomhole producing pressure.

• Wells with rapidly changing producing volumes.

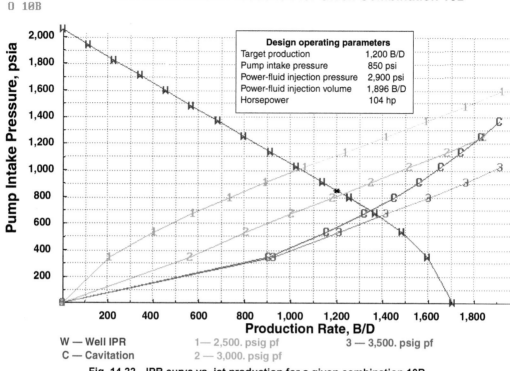

Fig. 14.22—IPR curve vs. jet production for a given combination 10B.

• The use of jet pumping systems in wells producing with gas/liquid ratios less than 750:1 but producing under a packer where free gas must be pumped.
• Using hydraulic free pumps in wells with high-paraffin contents.
• Using hydraulic OPF systems in low-API-gravity wells.

14.5.9 Jet Pumping System Design Example. The following is an example of a design for a well using a jet pumping system. The design data must be carefully collected and is shown in **Table 14.9.** Because there are numerous possible combinations, and a design typically requires many iterations, current design methods utilize computer software programs.

A jet pumping system was chosen because of the remote location, the advantage of the free-pump system to reduce pump pulling costs, and the advantages and flexibility of a central system to produce several wells drilled in the same field. There are no gas-sales lines, and the produced gas is used to provide the necessary energy to drive the prime movers. The wells are 5,400 ft in depth and have a static reservoir pressure of 2,050 psia. The jet hydraulic pumping system has been operating successfully for 5 years with low operating expenses.

One well was producing only 150 B/D, and a pressure buildup survey and production test indicated a skin of 50. Following a successful reperforating and stimulation treatment, the well is capable of producing significantly higher rates. By running the original jet combination and matching the power fluid, injection pressure, and total production, a new pump intake was calculated, and a new IPR curve was determined.

A design was made to find what could be produced with the existing horsepower and also what might be achieved if excess horsepower from a second well was used. A throat and nozzle (10B) with an annulus of 0.0503 was determined to be a good fit for both cases. See Table 14.6. The selected jet has an ability to produce 1,063 B/D using 1,720 B/D of power fluid at

TABLE 14.10—RECIPROCATING HYDRAULIC PUMP DESIGN EXAMPLE

Design Data for a Reciprocating Hydraulic Pump System

1. SG of the produce gas: .8
2. Produced oil API gravity: 33
3. Water cut of the produced fluids: 15%
4. SG of the produced water (fresh water = 1,0) : 1.05
5. GOR at the test separator conditions: 175 scf/STB
6. Total fluid production rate at test separator conditions: 110 B/D
7. Operating pressure of the test or metering separator: 30 psig
8. Operating temperature of the test or metering separator: 80°F
9. Flowing bottomhole pressure at the pressure datum of the perforation interval: 60 psig
10. Static bottomhole pressure (reservoir pressure): 1,200 psig
11. Bottomhole temperature at the perforations: 195°F
12. Wellhead backpressure of the oil + water + gas + power fluid in the casing/tubing annulus: 60 psig
13. Wellhead temperature of the oil + water + gas + power fluid in the casing /tubing annulus: 100°F
14. Bubblepoint pressure of the oil: 843.67

Well Completion and Pump Installation Data Summary

1. Vertical depth to the fluid intake of the pump: 12,000 ft
2. Vertical depth to the pressure datum of the perforation interval(s): 12,100 ft
3. Vertical depth at which the well fluids enter the end of the tubing or bottomhole assembly below the fluid intake of the pump: 12,100 ft
4. Power fluid type: (1) oil or (2) water: 1
5. Power fluid SG (input API gravity for oil, SG for water): 33
6. Operating pressure of the power fluid reservoir vessel or the power fluid settling (wash) tank: 25 psig
7. Operating temperature of the power fluid reservoir vessel or the power fluid settling (wash) tank: 80°F
8. Casing string diameter: 4.892 in.
9. Power fluid supply ID: 2.441 in.
10. Power fluid supply tubing diameter: 2.875 in.
11. Casing string ID pipe conditions: (1) new, (2) average, or (3) old = 2 (.0018 in. roughness)
12. Power fluid supply tubing length: ft = 12,400
13. Power fluid tubing ID and OD pipe conditions: (1) new, (2) average, or (3) old = 2 (.0018 in. roughness)

Pump Performance Summary

System type: standard casing free pump, open power fluid
Hydraulic production unit type: Oilmaster Model 220
Power fluid type: oil
Hydraulic production unit model number: 252017
Total fluid production rate: 350 B/D
Stroke rate of pump: 33.4 strokes/min
Percent of the rated speed for the pump: 46.3%
Volumetric efficiency of the produced fluids at the pump suction conditions for the pressure and temperature: 65.8%
Calculated pump end efficiency: 61.2%
Engine end mechanical efficiency: 95%
Pump end mechanical efficiency: 92%
Power fluid rate required: 741 STB/D
Power fluid pressure required at the surface: 3,211.8 psig
Required surface horsepower (90% efficiency): 44.9 hp
Suction pressure of the pump at 12,000 ft: 469.8 psig
Vertical multiphase flow pump discharge pressure: 4,376 psig

2,500 psi injection or 81 hp. See Table 14.9. If the power-fluid injection pressure is increased to 3,000 psi, the power-fluid volume is increased to 1,896 B/D, and the pump intake pressure is reduced to 850 psig, then 1,200 B/D of production is feasible, which will take 108 hp.

The predicted performance of the jet pump system for this well is shown in **Fig. 14.22**. Line 1 on the graph represents 2,500 psi injection and 81 hp. Line 2 represents 3,000 psi and 108 hp. If pressure is increased to 3,500 psi, the pump will go into cavitation, and damage might occur to the jet nozzle throat.

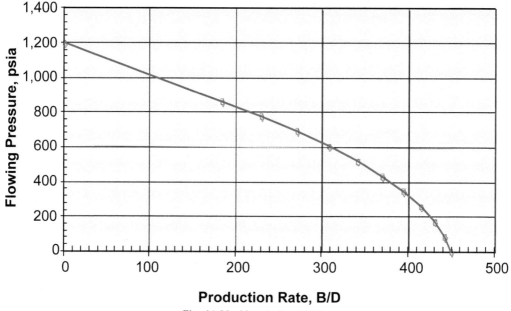

Fig. 14.23—Vogel oilwell IPR.

14.5.10 Design Example for a Reciprocating Hydraulic Pump System. Currently a 12,000-ft well is equipped with a sucker rod beam pumping system with the pump set at only 9,000 ft. The design data, plus the well completion and pump installation data summary and a pump performance summary, are shown in **Table 14.10**. The well is deviated with a severe dogleg at 9,100 ft and produces only 100 B/D with a pump intake pressure (PIP) of about 1,000 psi. Workover rig cost is high, and a free-pump installation is desirable to reduce maintenance costs. Furthermore, a production increase is essential for this remotely located well. A review of the IPR data shown in **Fig. 14.23** indicates that production can easily be increased from 100 B/D to 350 B/D, if the well can be pumped with a P_{wf} of 500 psi without significant gas interference. Pressure maintenance operations have begun in the field, and further decrease in the reservoir pressure is not expected. An economic analysis indicates a payout from changing to the hydraulic system in less than 3 years.

The 5½-in. casing has a significant effect on the proposed design. Considering the casing size, depth, production requirements, and reservoir conditions, a casing free-pump system was selected. Power oil is pumped down the tubing and returned up the casing-tubing annulus with the oil, water, and gas production. The 2⅞-in. [2.441-in. inside diameter (ID)] N-80 tubing now in the well has ample tension, burst, and collapse strengths and will be used. The pump is set at the lowest possible depth (12,000 ft) in order to achieve an operating pressure of 500 psi at the perforations. At design conditions, a pump displacement of about 580 B/D is required to produce the oil and water liquids, plus the free gas. In order to decrease the number of pump failures, the strokes per minute are limited to 33.4. Pump model 252017 was chosen to stay within this range. See Table 14.1.

The selected pump is designed to run at 46.3% of rated speed, requiring a power-fluid volume of 741 B/D and an injection pressure of 3,211.8 psi. Horsepower required for this well is 44.9 hp, and a 60-hp system is selected to provide more flexibility and compensate for wear and possible higher gas volumes.

Nomenclature

A_n = cross-sectional area of nozzle, in.^{2}
A_s = cross-sectional area of annulus between throat and jet, in.^{2}
A_t = cross-sectional area of throat, in.^{2}
D = pump setting depth, ft
F_{gL} = gas/liquid ratio, scf/bbl
F_{mfD} = dimensionless mass flow ratio
g_d = gradient of return fluid, psi/ft
g_n = gradient of power fluid, psi/ft
p = pressure, psi
P_{fd} = friction in discharge tubing, psi
P_{fpt} = friction in power tubing, psi
P_n = useful power fluid pressure at nozzle, psi
P_{so} = surface operating pressure, psi
P_{pd} = pump discharge pressure, psi
P_{ps} = pump suction pressure, psi
P_{wf} = bottomhole flowing pressure psi
P_{wh} = flowline pressure at wellhead, psi
q_n = nozzle flow rate, B/D
q_s = production (suction) fluid rate, B/D
R = gas/oil ratio

Acknowledgments

Figs. 14.1 through 14.11 and 14.13 through 14.21 are reprinted with permission from Weatherford. Copyright © 2004 by Weatherford U.S., L.P. All rights reserved. Weatherford U.S., L.P. disclaims all responsibility for the consequences of any errors or omissions in the materials.

References

1. Wilson, P.M.: "Jet Free Pump, A Progress Report on Two Years of Field Performance," paper presented at the 1973 Southwestern Petroleum Short Course, Texas Tech U., Lubbock, Texas, 26–27 April.
2. Bell, C.A. and Spisak, C.D.: "Unique Artificial Lift System," paper SPE 4539 presented at the 1973 SPE Annual Meeting, Las Vegas, 30 September–3 October.
3. Grant, A.A. and Sheil, A.G.: "Development, Field Experience, and Application of New High Reliability Hydraulically Powered Downhole Pumping System," paper SPE 11694 presented at the 1993 SPE Regional Meeting, Ventura, California, March 23–24.
4. Petrie, H. and Erickson, J.W.: "Field Testing the Turbo-Lift System," paper SPE 8245 presented at the 1979 SPE Annual Technical Conference and Exhibition, Las Vegas, 23–26 September.
5. Boone, D.M. and Eaton, J.R.: "The Use of Multistage Centrifugal Pumps in Hydraulic-Lift Power Oil Systems," paper SPE 7408 presented at the 1978 SPE Annual Technical Conference and Exhibition, Houston, 1–3 August.
6. Grubb, Bill: "Horizontal Pumping System and Jet Pump," *Weatherford W. Magazine* (March 2001) **3**, No. 1, 18.
7. Christ, F.C. and Zublin, J.A.: "The Application of High-Volume Jet Pumps in North Slope Water Source Wells," paper SPE 11748 presented at the 1983 SPE Regional Meeting, Ventura, California, 23–25 March.
8. Thompson, J.: *1852 Report British Association.*
9. Gosline, J.E. and O'Brien, M.P.: *The Water Jet Pump,* U. of California Publication in Eng. (1933).

10. Gosline, J.E. and O'Brien, M.P.: *Application of the Jet Pump to Oil Well Pumping,* U. of California Publication in Eng. (1933).
11. Angier, J.D. and Crocker, F.: "Improvement in Ejectors for Oil Wells," U.S. Patent No. 44,587 (1864).
12. Jacuzzi, R.: "Pumping System," U.S. Patent No. 1,758,400 (1930).
13. McMahon, W.F.: "Oil Well Pump," U.S. Patent No. 1,779,483 (1930).
14. Nelson, C.C.: "The Jet Free Pump—Proper Application Through Computer Calculated Operating Charts," paper presented at the 1975 Southwestern Petroleum Short Course, Texas Tech. U., Lubbock, Texas, 17–18 April.
15. Brown, K.: "Overview of Artificial-Lift System," *JPT* (October 1982) 2384.
16. Clark, K.M.: "Hydraulic Lift Systems for Low-Pressure Wells." *Pet. Eng. Intl.*
17. Bleakley, W.B.: "Design Considerations in Choosing a Hydraulic Pumping System Surface Equipment for Hydraulic Pumping Systems." *Pet. Eng. Intl.* (July/August 1978).
18. Petrie, H., Wilson, P., and Smart, E.E.: "The Theory, Hardware, and Application of the Current Generation of Oil Well Jet Pumps," paper presented at the 1983 Southwestern Petroleum Short Course, Texas Tech. U., Lubbock, Texas, 27–28 April.
19. Petrie, H., Wilson, P., and Smart, E.E.: "Jet Pumping Oil Wells," *World Oil* (November–December 1983; January 1984).
20. Kempton, E.A.: "Jet Pump Dewatering, What it is and How it Works," *World Oil* (November 1980).
21. Cunningham, R.G. and Brown, F.B.: "Oil Jet Pump Cavitation," paper presented at the 1970 ASME Cavitation Forum, Joint ASME Fluids Engineering, Heat Transfer, and Lubrication Conference, Detroit, Michigan, 24–27 May.
22. *Hydraulic Institute Standards,* 13th edition, Hydraulic Inst., Cleveland, Ohio (1975).
23. Palmour, H.H.: "Produced Water Power Fluid Conditioning Unit," paper presented at the 1971 Southwestern Petroleum Short Course, Texas Tech. U., Lubbock, Texas, 15–16 April.
24. Feldman, H.W. and Kelley, H.L.: "A Unitized, One-Well Hydraulic Pumping System," paper presented at the 1972 Southwestern Petroleum Short Course, Texas Tech. U., Lubbock, Texas, 20–21 April.

SI Metric Conversion Factors

°API	$141.5/(131.5 + °API)$		$= g/cm^3$
bbl $\times$	1.589 873	E – 01	$= m^3$
ft $\times$	3.048*	E – 01	$= m$
hp $\times$	7.460 43	E – 01	$= kW$
in. $\times$	2.54*	E + 00	$= cm$
in.^{2} $\times$	6.451 6*	E + 00	$= cm^2$
lbm $\times$	4.535 924	E – 01	$= kg$
psi $\times$	6.894 757	E + 00	$= kPa$

*Conversion factor is exact.

Chapter 15
Progressing Cavity Pumping Systems

Cam M. Matthews, SPE, **Todd A. Zahacy**, SPE, **Francisco J.S. Alhanati**, SPE, **Paul Skoczylas**, SPE, C-FER Technologies, and **Lonnie J. Dunn**, SPE, Weatherford Artificial Lift Systems

Introduction

Progressing cavity pumping (PCP) systems derive their name from the unique, positive displacement pump that evolved from the helical gear pump concept first developed by Rene Moineau in the late 1920s.[1-3] Although these pumps are now most commonly referred to as progressing cavity (PC) pumps, they also are called screw pumps or Moineau pumps. PC pumps initially were used extensively as fluid transfer pumps in a wide range of industrial and manufacturing applications, with some attempts made to use them for the surface transfer of oilfield fluids. However, it was not until after the development of synthetic elastomers and adhesives in the late 1940s that PC pumps could be applied effectively in applications involving petroleum-based fluids. Except for several limited field trials, it was not until the late 1970s that a concerted effort was made to use PC pumps as a method of artificial lift for the petroleum industry. Over the past two decades, with the technical contributions and persistence of many individuals and companies, PCP systems have experienced a gradual emergence as a common form of artificial lift.[4-7] Although precise numbers are difficult to obtain, it is estimated that more than 50,000 wells worldwide currently are being produced with these systems.

This chapter serves as a guideline for the design and operation of the various PCP systems currently being used in various downhole applications worldwide. The chapter is broken into five major parts as follows: Part 1—PCP Lift System Equipment, Part 2—PCP System Design, Part 3—Specific Application Considerations, Part 4—PCP System Installation, Automation, Troubleshooting and Failure, and Part 5—Design Example.

Readers are encouraged to refer to the numerous references at the end of this chapter for additional details on PC pumps and PCP systems.

The two key features that differentiate PCP systems from other forms of artificial lift are the downhole PC pump and the associated surface drive systems. Although other major components, such as the production tubing and sucker rod strings, are found in other downhole lift systems, the design and operational requirements typically differ for PCP applications. Also, many additional equipment components may be used in conjunction with PCP systems to contend with specific application conditions.

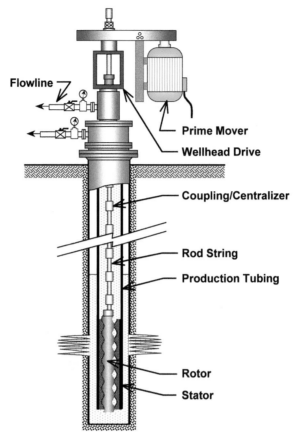

Flowline

Prime Mover

Wellhead Drive

Coupling/Centralizer

Rod String

Production Tubing

Rotor

Stator

Fig. 15.1—Configuration of a typical progressing cavity pumping (PCP) system.

The basic surface-driven PCP system configuration illustrated in **Fig 15.1** is the most common, although electric and hydraulic downhole drive systems and various other hybrid PCP systems are also available (see Alternative PCP System Configurations). The downhole PC pump is a positive displacement pump that consists of two parts: a helical steel "rotor" and a "stator" comprised of a steel tubular housing with a bonded elastomeric sleeve formed with a multiple internal helix matched suitably to the rotor configuration. The stator is typically run into the well on the bottom of the production tubing, while the rotor is connected to the bottom of the sucker rod string. Rotation of the rod string by means of a surface drive system causes the rotor to spin within the fixed stator, creating the pumping action necessary to produce fluids to surface.

PCP systems have several unique design features and operating characteristics that favor their selection for many applications[8–10]:

• High overall system energy efficiency, typically in the 55 to 75% range.
• Ability to produce high concentrations of sand or other produced solids.
• Ability to tolerate high percentages of free gas.
• No valves or reciprocating parts to clog, gas lock, or wear.
• Good resistance to abrasion.
• Low internal shear rates (limits fluid emulsification through agitation).
• Relatively low power costs and continuous power demand (prime mover capacity fully utilized).

- Relatively simple installation and operation.
- Generally low maintenance.
- Low profile surface equipment.
- Low surface noise levels.

PCP systems, however, also have some limitations and special considerations:

- Limited production rates (maximum of 800 m^3/d [5,040 B/D] in large-diameter pumps, much lower in small-diameter pumps).
- Limited lift capacity (maximum of 3000 m [9,840 ft]). Note that the lift capacity of larger displacement PC pumps is typically much lower.
- Limited temperature capability (routine use to 100°C [212°F], potential use to 180°C [350°F] with special elastomers).
- Sensitivity to fluid environment (stator elastomer may swell or deteriorate on exposure to certain fluids, including well treatment fluids).
- Subject to low volumetric efficiency in wells producing substantial quantities of gas.
- Sucker rod strings may be susceptible to fatigue failures.
- Pump stator may sustain permanent damage if pumped dry for even short periods.
- Rod-string and tubing wear can be problematic in directional and horizontal wells.
- Most systems require the tubing to be pulled to replace the pump.
- Vibration problems may occur in high-speed applications (mitigation may require the use of tubing anchors and stabilization of the rod string).
- Paraffin control can be an issue in waxy crude applications (rotation as opposed to reciprocation of the rod string precludes use of scrapers for effective wax removal).
- Lack of experience with system design, installation, and operation, especially in some areas.

Many of these limitations continue to change or be alleviated over time with the development of new products and improvements in materials and equipment design. If configured and operated properly in appropriate applications, PCP systems currently provide a highly efficient and economical means of artificial lift.

15.1 PCP Lift System Equipment

The basic system components include the downhole pump, sucker rod and production tubing strings, and surface drive equipment, which must include a stuffing box. However, a PCP installation may also include different accessory equipment, such as gas separators, rod centralizers, tubing-string rotator systems, and surface equipment control devices. The following sections describe the various components of a PCP installation in further detail.

15.1.1 Downhole PC Pump.
PC pumps are classified as single-rotor, internal-helical-gear pumps within the overall category of positive displacement pumps.[11,12] The rotor comprises the "internal gear" and the stator forms the "external gear" of the pump. The stator always has one more "tooth" or "lobe" than the rotor. The PC pump products currently on the market fall into two different categories based on their geometric design: single lobe or multilobe. Currently, the vast majority (i.e., estimated at > 97%) of PC pumps in use downhole are of the single-lobe design and thus are the primary focus of this chapter. Other variations of these basic configurations include semi-elliptical rotor/stator geometries and uniform-thickness elastomer pumps.

The geometric design of a single-lobe PC pump is illustrated in **Fig. 15.2**. The longitudinal cross-section in Fig. 15.2 shows the single external helical shape of the rotor and the corresponding double internal helical geometry of the stator. Note that the stator pitch length (L_s) is exactly double the rotor pitch length in single-lobe pumps. With the mating of the rotor and stator in a single-lobe PC pump, two parallel, helical cavities are formed (180° apart and one rotor pitch out of phase) that spiral around the outside of the rotor along the pump length, with each cavity having a length equal to the stator pitch length. Note that the parallel cavities are

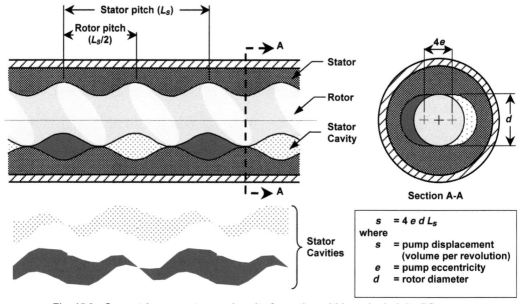

Fig. 15.2—Geometric parameters and cavity formation within a single-lobe PC pump.

offset lengthwise, with the end of a cavity on one side of the rotor corresponding to the maximum cavity cross-section on the opposite side. In a single-lobe pump, the rotor is circular in cross section (with a minor diameter, d), whereas the cavity within the stator has a semi-elliptical geometry. Another important geometric parameter is the pump eccentricity (e), which is equal to the distance between the centerlines of the major and minor diameters of the rotor. The distance between the stator axis and rotor major diameter axis is also equal to the eccentricity value. The rotor creates an interference fit seal with the stator elastomer on both sides of the semi-elliptical opening and a seal over the semicircular end of the stator opening at the positions corresponding to the ends of the longitudinal fluid cavities. The fluid-filled cavities are formed by the open areas left between the rotor and stator at each cross section. **Fig. 15.3** shows a section view of a single-lobe PC pump and the different rotor and stator geometries of several different pump models.

During production operations, the rotor translates back and forth across the stator opening as it is rotated within the fixed stator. This occurs because of a combination of two motions: rotation of the rotor around its own centroidal axis in the clockwise direction and eccentric reverse rotation (i.e., nutation) of the rotor about the centroidal axis of the stator. **Fig. 15.4** illustrates the rotor movement within the stator opening at a given longitudinal position through one full revolution. The rotor movement causes the series of parallel fluid cavities formed by the rotor and stator to move axially from the pump suction to discharge on a continuous basis. The nutation of the rotor about the stator centerline is also shown in Fig. 15.4.

Typically, rotors are precision machined from high-strength carbon steel (e.g., ASTM 1045 or 4140) into an external helix, although some manufacturers have recently developed techniques that allow rotors to be fabricated through a metal forming process. In most cases, the rotors are coated with a thin layer of wear-resistant material, usually chrome, to resist abrasion and then are polished to a smooth finish to reduce rotor/stator friction. Rotors are also fabricated from various stainless steels for service in corrosive or acidic environments because these materials are less susceptible to corrosive fluid attack. These rotors, however, tend to be far more susceptible to abrasion wear than chrome-coated rotors. For most applications, the chrome plating thickness is typically 0.254 mm (0.01 in.) on the rotor major diameter. Howev-

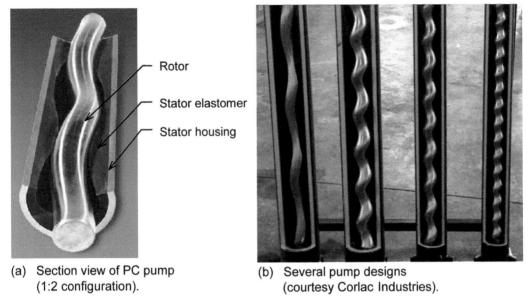

(a) Section view of PC pump
(1:2 configuration).

(b) Several pump designs
(courtesy Corlac Industries).

Fig. 15.3—Rotor/stator sections from different PC pump models.

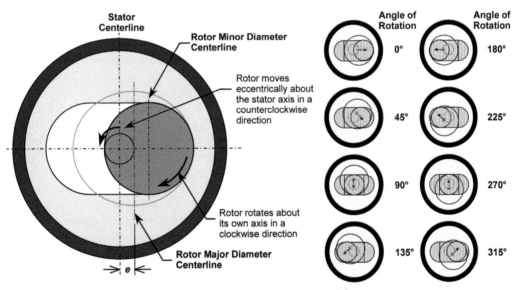

Fig. 15.4—Rotor motion in a single-lobe PC pump.

er, for severe wear applications, vendors typically offer rotors with a "double" chrome thickness to prolong service life. Other processes used by vendors to fabricate rotors with more abrasion-resistant coatings include boronizing, nitriding, and also thermal spray methods which are used to apply carbide-based coatings materials.

Stators typically are fabricated by placing a machined core (i.e., with the shape of the helical stator opening) inside a steel tubular and then injecting and subsequently curing an elastomer material within the annular space. Achieving a good bond between the elastomer sleeve and the steel tubular is essential. Depending on the chemical composition and the curing

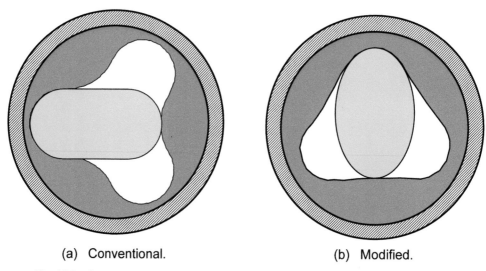

(a) Conventional.   (b) Modified.

Fig. 15.5—Cross sections of conventional and modified 2:3 multilobe PC pumps.

process of the elastomer, the chemical and mechanical properties of the material can vary considerably, as discussed in detail later.

Multilobe PC Pumps. In response to increasing demand for higher displacement PC pumps, several manufacturers have developed various models of multilobe PC pumps. Although the basic operating principles are the same, multilobe designs can be differentiated from single-lobe pumps by the presence of three or more parallel cavities within the stator and by rotor geometries with two or more lobes. The stator must always have one more lobe than the matching rotor; thus, the multilobe pump geometries are often referenced according to their rotor/stator lobe ratio (e.g., 2:3 and 3:4 pumps). Although it is possible to manufacture pumps with higher ratios, the multilobe pump models currently available have a 2:3 lobe ratio configuration. The cross-sectional shapes of the rotors and stators can also be varied somewhat from the original Moineau geometry, which has round (i.e., circular) lobes. All the major pump manufacturers have adopted semi-elliptical rotor and matching stator geometries for their multilobe pump products. This decision was based primarily on fabrication considerations, because it is possible to machine the rotors in the same manner as single-lobe rotors, which is substantially less costly than cutting rotors with a milling machine. **Fig. 15.5** presents cross-sectional diagrams of the two pump designs to illustrate the differences in the rotor and stator shapes. Note that the interference fit that develops between the rotor and stator is also affected by the different component geometries, and this can affect the pressure integrity of the seals between the pump cavities, which in turn can influence pump performance and life.

The primary advantage that multilobe pumps have over single-lobe designs is their ability to achieve higher volumetric and lift capacity with shorter pumps of the same diameter. The increased displacement can be attributed to a larger stator cavity area and the fact that each stator cavity is swept multiple times during a single revolution of the rotor (i.e., twice in a 2:3 lobe geometry), as opposed to only once for a single-lobe pump. As a result, the fluid is advanced multiple stator pitch lengths per revolution. Because the cavities also tend to overlap more along the pump length than in single-lobe designs, a shorter pump is typically required to achieve the same pressure capacity. The shorter lengths also help to reduce product costs.

Multilobe pumps also have some disadvantages: (1) higher flow velocities through the pump, which can lead to increased fluid shear rates and flow losses and greater potential for erosion of the elastomer; (2) higher frequency of stator flexing, which increases hysteretic heat

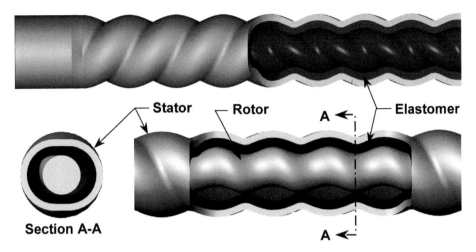

Fig. 15.6—PC pump design with uniform thickness elastomer (courtesy Weatherford).

generation and may impact pump life; (3) greater potential for inflow problems to develop when high-viscosity fluids are pumped; (4) more prone to cause vibration problems because of the larger rotor mass and increased nutation speeds; and (5) increased torque requirements corresponding to the typically larger pump displacements. In general, the potential problems associated with these various disadvantages can be avoided through proper system design and operation.

Uniform-Thickness PC Pumps. An example of another type of hybrid PC pump product, the "uniform-thickness" pump, is illustrated in **Fig. 15.6**. These products were first introduced in the mid-1990s as one approach to overcome non-uniform distortion of the stator cavity caused by swelling or thermal expansion of the elastomer. A variety of manufacturing techniques have since been developed to fabricate stators with an elastomer sleeve of uniform thickness around the entire stator opening. Note that only the stator component differs and that conventional rotors are typically used with these pump models. Because the potential for stator distortion is minimized, these pumps should perform better in light-oil or high-temperature applications. Note, however, that because of the relatively thin elastomer sleeve, proper pump sizing is critical for these pump models if reasonable run lives are to be achieved.

15.1.2 Pump Models and Specifications. A wide variety of PC pump models are available from many different manufacturers. It is important to note that currently no industry standards (e.g., API) govern PC pump designs and that pump geometries and materials vary considerably between vendors. In addition, although it is typical among vendors to specify pump models according to their volumetric displacement and pressure differential capabilities, the rating criteria may vary (i.e., particularly with respect to pressure ratings) and should be understood for proper pump selection. **Fig. 15.7** shows the wide range of displacement and pressure capabilities associated with currently available PC pumps categorized according to the minimum casing size in which they can be installed with reasonable clearances.

Pump Displacement. The displacement of a PC pump is defined as the volume of fluid produced for each turn of the rotor. When the rotor completes a full revolution, the series of cavities within the pump have advanced one full stator pitch length, thus discharging a corresponding fluid volume to the production tubing. Because the cavity area between the rotor and stator remains constant at all cross sections along the pump length, a PC pump delivers a uniform nonpulsating flow at a rate directly proportional to pump speed.

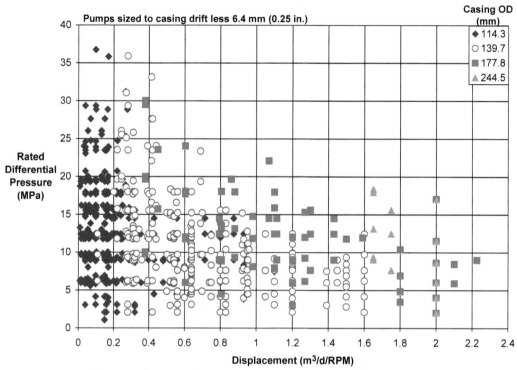

Fig. 15.7—Current PC pump displacement and pressure capabilities.

The volumetric displacement of a single-lobe PC pump (s) is a function of the pump eccentricity (e), rotor minor diameter (d), and stator pitch length (L_s) and can be calculated as follows:

$$s = 4 \ e \ d \ L_s . \dots\dots\dots\dots\dots\dots\dots\dots\dots\dots\dots\dots\dots\dots\dots\dots\dots (15.1)$$

For convenience, most pump manufacturers specify pump displacement in terms of volume per day at a certain pump speed, typically 1, 100, or 500 rpm. Although product selection varies among manufacturers, PC pump displacements generally range from 0.02 m³/d/rpm [0.13 B/D/rpm] to > 2.0 m³/d/rpm [12.6 B/D/rpm]. This requires using an appropriate conversion factor with Eq. 15.1.

It is apparent from Eq. 15.1 that different combinations of the parameters e, d, and L_s can be used to obtain equivalent pump displacements. The performance and serviceability of a PCP system can be influenced strongly by these geometrical variations under certain completion and production conditions. Unfortunately, the potential impacts associated with using different pump geometries are usually difficult to assess because these geometric specifications are typically considered proprietary and thus are not published by pump manufacturers.

The theoretical flow rate of a PC pump is directly proportional to its displacement and rotational speed and can be determined by

$$q_{th} = s \ \omega, \dots\dots\dots\dots\dots\dots\dots\dots\dots\dots\dots\dots\dots\dots\dots\dots\dots\dots (15.2)$$

where q_{th} = theoretical flow rate (m³/d [B/D]), s = pump displacement (m³/d/rpm [B/D/rpm]), and ω = rotational speed (rpm).

However, as the differential pressure across the pump increases, some fluid slips backward through the seal lines between the rotor and the stator, reducing the discharge flow rate and volumetric efficiency of the pump. As a result, the actual flow rate of a PC pump is the difference between its theoretical flow rate and the slippage rate:

$$q_a = q_{th} - q_s, \quad\quad\quad\quad\quad\quad\quad\quad\quad\quad\quad\quad\quad\quad (15.3)$$

where q_a = actual flow rate (m³/d [B/D]), q_{th} = theoretical flow rate (m³/d [B/D]), and q_s = slippage rate (m³/d [B/D]).

The slippage rate is dependent on rotor/stator fit, elastomer properties, fluid viscosity, and pump differential pressure capacity. Note that the actual displacement of a PC pump may vary from the manufacturer's published values even without consideration for slippage in cases when the stator cavity volume is reduced because of expansion or swelling of the elastomer under downhole conditions. In some cases, the displacement reduction can exceed 10% of the published value.

Pressure Ratings. The overall pressure capacity of a PC pump is controlled by the maximum pressure that can be developed within individual cavities and the number of cavities (i.e., full stator pitches) along the pump. The maximum pressure capacity of each cavity is a function of the seal integrity between the rotor and stator and the properties of the produced fluid. In general, the differential pressure capacity of the seal lines increases with tighter rotor/stator interference fits and higher-viscosity fluids. However, the pump geometric parameters and the properties of the stator elastomer can significantly influence seal capacity. For example, long pitch pumps tend to have more effective seals (i.e., all other variables being equal) as a result of minimal cavity distortion or elastomer deformation in the axial direction of the pump during operation. The rotor diameter and eccentricity also affect the nature of the rotor/stator interaction, which can affect sealability during pump operation. The elasticity and stiffness of the elastomer also govern sealability. For metal-elastomer interference fits, the pressure differential per cavity typically ranges from 410 to 620 kPa [60 to 90 psi]. Determination of appropriate pressure ratings for multilobe and uniform-thickness PC pumps must also consider the different leak paths and/or seal behavior compared with single-lobe pumps. Pressure ratings for both single-lobe and multilobe PC pumps are generally considered to be insensitive to pump speed.

Historically, PC pump pressure ratings were often referenced to the number of pump "stages" or cavities, which led to substantial confusion given that different vendors used different stage definitions. As a result, most manufacturers now specify pump pressure capabilities in terms of maximum differential pressure (or equivalent head of water). Fig. 15.7 shows the range of pressure ratings for most of the currently available PC pumps. Currently, no industry standards govern the setting of pressure ratings by individual PC pump manufacturers.

Operating a PC pump at excessive differential pressures leads to high fluid slippage rates across the rotor/stator seal lines, which causes excessive stator deformation. Sustained operation under such conditions will lead to accelerated deterioration of the elastomer material properties and will likely result in the premature failure of the stator.

15.1.3 Elastomer Types, Properties, and Selection Methods.
In downhole applications, most PC pump failures involve the stator elastomer and often result from chemical or physical elastomer breakdown induced by the wellbore environment. The environment can vary considerably between different reservoirs and individual operations. The bottomhole temperature may range from 15 to 200°C [60 to 360°F]; the well may be pumped off or have a high bottomhole pressure; and the produced fluids may contain solids (e.g., sand, coal fines), gases (e.g., CH_4, CO_2, H_2S), and a wide range of other constituents, including water, paraffins, naphthenes, asphaltenes, and aromatics. Additionally, the methods and fluids used to drill, treat, and stimulate

TABLE 15.1—KEY ELASTOMER PROPERTIES AND STANDARD TEST REFERENCES		
Parameter	Test	Typical Range of Values
Hardness (Shore A)	ASTM D2240, DIN 53505	55 to 75 Shore A
Tensile strength	ASTM D412, DIN 53504	1,800 to 3,200 psi
Elongation at break	ASTM D412, DIN 53504	200 to 700%
100% modulus	ASTM D412, DIN 53504	300 to 900 psi
Tear strength	ASTM D624 (Die T)	20 to 200 lbf/in.
Abrasion resistance (drum)	ASTM D5963, DIN 53516	100 to 300 mm^3
Dynamic properties (Tan D)	No Standard	0.15 to 0.4 (x% strain/15 Hz)
Resilience	ASTM D2632, D1054	5 to 25%
Compression set (70 hours at 100°C)	ASTM D395	20 to 60%

wells introduce a variety of other chemicals into the wellbore, such as drilling muds, completion fluids (heavy salt solutions), treatment fluids (e.g., diluents, hot oil, strong acids), corrosion inhibitors (e.g., amines), and flooding materials (e.g., CO_2).

Successful use of PC pumps, particularly in the more severe downhole environments, requires proper elastomer selection and appropriate pump sizing and operation. PC pump manufacturers continue to develop and test new elastomers; over time, these efforts have resulted in performance improvements and an expanded range of practical applications. Despite this success, the elastomer component still continues to impose severe restrictions on PC pump use, especially in applications with lighter oils or higher temperatures.

Mechanical and Chemical Properties. The performance of an elastomer in a PCP application depends heavily on its mechanical and chemical properties.[13,14] Although many different mechanical properties can be quantified for elastomers, only a few are highly relevant to PC pump performance. One important property is hardness because it characterizes the relationship between the rotor/stator interference fit and the resulting sealing force. Tear strength is also important because it provides a measure of an elastomer's resistance to tearing and indicates its fatigue and abrasion resistance. Although abrasion resistance is a critical parameter in many applications, the ASTM abrasion tests (drum, tabor, pico) do not represent the PC pump wear mode and should be interpreted with caution. Dynamic properties, which characterize the hysteretic heat buildup behavior, are not overly critical in PC pumps because the flexing frequencies of the single-lobe geometries are generally not high enough to result in significant temperature rise, except when the fit is very tight or heat removal is minimal. Although tensile strength and elongation are commonly referenced properties, they have little practical relevance to PC pumps other than their relationship to other mechanical properties because the elastomer is strained to only a fraction of its capacity. **Table 15.1** summarizes the most commonly referenced mechanical properties, along with any corresponding ASTM and DIN test references. The range of values typical of commercially available PC pump elastomers is included to show the variations that exist in these properties.

Chemical resistance is normally evaluated through compatibility testing with the fluids in question. Elastomer samples are exposed to the fluid in an autoclave environment for a predetermined period of time (typically 72 or 168 hours); then, the volume and mass change are measured. To be representative, these tests should also assess the change in mechanical properties through measurements of hardness and, if possible, tensile strength and elongation. Because these tests are performed on small samples (which seldom come from actual pumps) for a limited period of time, they are most useful for ranking elastomers as opposed to determining the actual swell level within a stator.

The chemical and mechanical properties of an elastomer are very sensitive to temperature, and the nature of changes in these properties can vary dramatically between elastomers. Although testing is normally done at room temperature, in most cases the mechanical properties will deteriorate significantly with increasing temperature. The rate of fluid swell will also increase at higher temperatures, although in most cases the ultimate level of swell will remain the same. Whenever possible, any testing to evaluate elastomers should be done as close to the anticipated downhole conditions as practical.

PC Pump Elastomers. Most PC pump manufacturers have stator products available with several different elastomer types. Because the formulations of these elastomers are considered proprietary, there is no standard naming convention. Certain generic names are common to the different manufacturers, but elastomer properties may vary significantly.

Although there is a wide range of different elastomer types, almost all PC pumps use some variation of a synthetic nitrile elastomer. Within the class of nitrile elastomers, there is a virtually unlimited number of different formulations possible with an associated wide range of mechanical and chemical properties. A discussion of the more common types of elastomers used in PC pumps follows.

Nitrile (NBR). Most elastomers in PC pumps can be classified as conventional nitrile (NBR).[14] The base polymers for these elastomers are manufactured by emulsion copolymerization of butadiene with acrylonitrile (ACN). ACN contents in nitrile elastomers typically vary from 30 to 50%, with the cost of the elastomer increasing marginally with increasing ACN level. Most manufacturers distinguish between a medium nitrile (sometimes called Buna, which typically has an ACN content < 40%) and a high nitrile (> 40% ACN). Increasing ACN levels produce increasing polarity, which improves the elastomer's resistance to nonpolar oils and solvents. However, higher ACN levels result in increased swell in the presence of such polar media as esters, ketones, or other polar solvents and leads to a decline in certain mechanical properties. It is important to note that aromatics such as benzene, toluene, and xylene swell NBR elastomers considerably, regardless of ACN level.

NBR elastomers are normally sulfur cured, and the combination of sulfur with the natural unsaturation of the elastomer can result in additional cross-linking and associated hardening in the presence of heat. As a result, NBR elastomers are not recommended for continuous use at temperatures that exceed 100°C [212°F]. For a similar reason, NBR elastomers also are not recommended for applications that contain high levels of H_2S because the sour gas contributes additional sulfur, which leads to post-vulcanization and surface hardening. These changes result in a loss of resilience and elasticity, typically causing premature stator failure.

Historically, the hardness of NBR elastomers has been between 65 and 75 Shore A. More recently, manufacturers have introduced soft medium NBRs (55 to 60 Shore A) for abrasive, heavy oil applications. The rationale was that they would be more forgiving to the gravel and iron pyrite solids that are produced occasionally and have a tendency to tear the stator material. The soft elastomer requires the use of a higher degree of rotor/stator interference fit, which has the advantage of maintaining some sealing even after extensive wear of the rotor or stator.

Hydrogenated NBR (HNBR). Conventional NBR elastomers, especially when sulfur cured, often contain a large degree of unsaturation in the form of double and triple carbon-carbon bonds in the base polymer. Relative to a more stable single bond, these unsaturated hydrocarbon groups are susceptible to chemical attack or additional cross-linking. This is the primary reason why NBRs experience problems upon exposure to high temperatures, H_2S, and aggressive chemicals.

Through a hydrogenation process, it is possible to increase the saturation (i.e., decrease the number of double and triple carbon-carbon bonds) of the NBR polymer, thus stabilizing the associated elastomer. The degree of saturation can vary, but typically it is > 90% and can be as high as 99.9%. If the saturation is very high, then a sulfur cure system is no longer effective, and a peroxide cure must be used. These compounds are typically referred to as highly saturated nitriles (HSN) or hydrogenated nitriles (HNBR).[15–17] For an equivalent volume, the cost of an HNBR elastomer is typically four times that of a conventional NBR, making the stators made from such elastomers considerably more expensive.

The primary advantage of an HNBR is increased heat resistance. Sulfur-cured HNBRs can ideally be used up to 125°C [257°F], whereas higher-saturation peroxide-cured compounds can potentially be used in applications with temperatures up to 150°C [300°F]. Other advantages, especially if the elastomer is peroxide cured, include improved chemical resistance and H_2S tolerance. The mechanical properties of HNBR elastomers usually are similar to those of NBR elastomers.

Most PC pump manufacturers offer HNBR stators, but the limited number of applications that warrant the higher cost have kept their use to relatively low levels. Historically, the HNBR polymers have been highly viscous and difficult to inject into stators, increasing manufacturing costs substantially. However, within the last few years, the polymer manufacturers have introduced lower-viscosity, high-ACN HNBR elastomers. As a result, pump manufacturers have taken a renewed interest in these elastomers, which may lead to more use of HNBR compounds in stator products in the future.

Fluoroelastomers (FKMs). FKMs have been expanding in availability and use over the last decade. Although a number of different varieties of FKMs are available, common to all is the presence of high levels of fluorine that saturate the carbon chain. The carbon-fluorine bonds in FKMs are extremely strong, giving this formulation heat and chemical resistance superior to that of most other elastomers.

FKMs are, to a large extent, made up of the fluoro-polymer and thus contain a low level of fillers and additives. As a result, the mechanical properties of FKMs tend to be inferior to those of NBR and HNBR elastomers. In terms of chemical stability, they have excellent resistance to heat, although their mechanical properties tend to deteriorate further at high temperatures from already relatively low initial levels. A variety of cure systems are used for FKM elastomers, including peroxide, but they require an extended post-curing session to optimize their properties, adding considerably to manufacturing process costs. As a result, the cost for an equivalent volume of FKM elastomer may range from 20 to several hundred times that of a conventional NBR. This makes all but the lower-cost grades of FKMs uneconomical for PC pump stators, and even those that are viable carry a high cost premium.

The primary advantage of an FKM elastomer is the increased heat and chemical resistance. FKM elastomers have the potential to be used up to 200°C [400°F] as long as they are not subject to excessive mechanical loading (proper sizing of PC pumps is critical). In terms of fluid resistance, they have minimal swell with most oilfield fluids, including aromatics.

General use of FKM elastomers in PC pump applications is relatively recent, with several PC pump manufacturers now offering these products. Some success has notably been encountered in lighter-oil applications in which NBR stators swell, necessitating multiple rotor changes. Despite being expensive, FKM stator products appear to be viable in certain applications, especially if the pumps are sized properly and extended run times are achieved.

Elastomer Selection. Elastomer selection for a particular application involves deciding on a particular formulation or type (i.e., medium or high NBR, HNBR, or FKM) and a specific stator supplier because the basic formulations differ between manufacturers. For the most part, elastomer selection is based on the downhole conditions and required fluid resistance. Although mechanical properties are also important, sufficient detailed information is not routinely available from the PC pump manufacturers to make this a consideration in elastomer selection.

Most manufacturers publish guidelines for elastomer selection that are based on anticipated downhole conditions, including fluid type, gases, solids, and operating temperature. Historically, API fluid gravity has been used as the primary measure of fluid aggressiveness in terms of elastomer swell and associated property deterioration. Although a strong trend does exist directionally, problems can arise when API gravity is used as the main selection criterion (i.e., especially at the higher end), given that fluids of the same gravity can have vastly different compositions of the aromatic components that cause swell. There are exceptions to this rule, such as the heavy oil fields in Venezuela, where the gravity is low but the quantity of aromatics is relatively high and can lead to problems with fluid swell. Although the exact value varies somewhat between manufacturers, the crossover point for medium to high NBR use is typically about 25°API. Most manufacturers do not recommend the use of a conventional NBR beyond 35 to 40°API. At the higher API gravities, the only options are FKM or perhaps HNBR formulations, although these elastomers are available only from certain manufacturers and their use is usually restricted to a narrow range of applications.

When a question exists as to the best elastomer to use, it is common practice to perform compatibility tests with the wellbore fluid and selected elastomer samples. These tests generally provide an effective means to rank the suitability of different elastomers (i.e., especially of the same type from different manufacturers) and can be helpful in establishing appropriate rotor sizing. Results almost always consist of volume, mass, and hardness change and, in some cases, may include changes in mechanical properties. From previous testing experience and tracking of pump performance, most pump suppliers have established limits for the maximum volume and hardness change for which they recommend use of their products.

Although compatibility testing provides a more scientific way to select elastomers, it is not practical in many cases because it is difficult to get the well fluids, representative elastomer samples, and a laboratory that does the specialized testing all in the same location. Nevertheless, there are a number of techniques based solely on fluid analyses that may be used to assist in elastomer selection. Hydrocarbon analysis through chromatographic techniques has been the most widely used method, but for it to be helpful in assessing elastomer compatibility, the analysis must include detection of the hexanes plus. This results in a breakdown (mole, mass, and volume percent) by component up to C30+, so the test is often referred to by this name (i.e., C30+). Results are normally divided into paraffin, aromatic, and naphthene groups, with breakdowns of specific components within each group. The most useful information includes the total percent aromatics and levels of individual aromatic components. Most PC pump manufacturers are familiar with this testing method and have guidelines on the maximum percent aromatics recommended for each of their elastomers. A less expensive, more readily available method for fluid analysis is an aniline point test (ASTM D611). Aromatic hydrocarbons exhibit the lowest aniline point (e.g., 60°C [140°F] for diesel), whereas oils with low aromatics typically have values that are > 100°C [212°F]. This test has been used extensively to assess elastomer compatibility in the drilling industry, but its use for PC pumps is new, so relationships between aniline point and recommended elastomers are still being compiled.

The limitations to the elastomer selection "rules" associated with API gravity or hydrocarbon analysis are usually the result of temperature or H_2S. Conventional NBR elastomers are normally not recommended for temperatures > 100°C [212°F] or with H_2S concentrations > 2% because of the elastomer hardening that occurs over time, frequently leading to cracking and fatigue. In these cases, HNBR or FKM elastomers are more appropriate choices. However, caution must be exercised when these elastomers are considered because the fluid resistance of the HNBR elastomers varies significantly by manufacturer and mechanical loading considerations must be addressed with FKM elastomers.

Fig. 15.8—Examples of spin-through centralizers, coated centralizers, and rod guides.

Despite all these selection methods, it is important to point out that operators are typically faced with using a "trial-and-error" approach to determine optimal elastomer selection and pump sizing when applying PCP systems in new areas.

Rod Strings and Production Tubing. Surface-driven PCP systems require a sucker-rod string to transfer the torsional and axial loads from the surface drive system down to the bottomhole PC pump. Although conventional sucker rods[18] continue to be used in many PCP applications, some rod manufacturers have developed products designed especially for PCP applications: (1) larger-diameter rods (e.g., 25.4 mm [1.0 in.] and 37.5 mm [1.5 in.]) to handle the high loads associated with large-displacement PCPs; (2) hollow rods designed to handle high loads and to facilitate downhole injection of diluents or treatment fluids; (3) rods with different connection designs that minimize the coupling diameter to reduce flow losses (typically, the pin diameter is reduced one size relative to standard rods, e.g., 25.4 mm [1 in.] rods fabricated with 22.2 mm (⅞ in.) pin connections, which allows the use of smaller-diameter couplings); and (4) relatively large-diameter (e.g., up to 29.2 mm [1.15 in.]) round continuous rod.

Several different rod-string configurations are commonly used in PCP applications. These include continuous rods, standard rods with couplings (including hollow rods), standard rods with centralizers, and standard rods with bonded/molded rod guides. Within these categories are numerous additional variations resulting from differences in centralizer and rod guide design. The centralizers can be divided into two groups based on functionality. The first group consists of "coated" centralizers that have a urethane, plastic, or elastomer sleeve bonded to either a coupling or the rod body. The second group consists of "spin-thru" centralizers that have an outer stabilizer that is free to rotate on either an inner core or the rod body. With the spin-thru design, the rod string rotates inside the stabilizer, which remains stationary against the tubing. **Fig. 15.8** shows several different types of centralizers and rod guides. Continuous-rod products are not currently available in all countries but are used extensively in Canada, Venezuela, and selected regions of the U.S.

The production tubing strings used in most PCP applications are typical of those used in most other oil and gas production operations. The tubulars conform to API product standards,[19] with EUE and NU connections and Grade 55 pipe used in most cases. In some situations, large-diameter tubing strings are warranted to contend with high flow losses or to facilitate the use of an alternative PC pumping system (see below), and small-diameter casing products are used

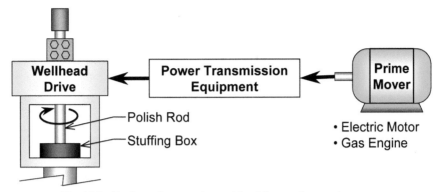

Fig. 15.9—Basic surface equipment for PC pumping systems.

instead. Some special internally coated tubing-string products, including boron-coated tubing and tubing with polyethylene liners, are available for use in applications in which wear and/or corrosion problems may occur.

Surface Drive Systems. The surface equipment used in a conventional surface-driven PCP system must perform the following functions: suspend the rod string and carry the axial loads; deliver the torque required at the polished rod; safely rotate the polished rod at the required speed; provide for safe release of the stored energy during shutdowns; and prevent produced fluid from escaping the system. To facilitate these requirements, all surface equipment systems include a wellhead drive unit (drive head), a stuffing box, power transmission equipment, and a prime mover, as illustrated in **Fig. 15.9**. In addition, the surface equipment may also include safety shutdown devices, torque limiters, recoil control devices, and electronic speed control (ESC) and monitoring systems.

Wellhead Drive Units. The wellhead drive unit consists of a wellhead frame, thrust bearing, a polished-rod braking system (in most cases), and sometimes a fixed gear or belt and sheave system. **Fig. 15.10** shows two types of drive heads. In many cases, the wellhead frame threads directly onto the tubing head. However, there is a growing trend toward the use of flanged connections, especially for applications involving drive systems that are 60 hp or larger. These systems facilitate proper alignment of the drive on the wellhead to help prevent stuffing box leakage and provide sufficient strength to carry the much heavier drive heads and motors used today. The drive heads typically mount onto composite pumping tees, which in turn mount onto the casing head. Note that the wellhead frame usually incorporates the stuffing box assembly and that some units are fabricated to allow mounting of either electric prime movers or hydraulic motors.

One important function of the drive head is to support the axial rod-string load. The thrust bearing, contained in the wellhead frame, supports this load while allowing the rod string to rotate with minimal friction. Most wellhead frames are available with a variety of thrust bearings to suit different loading applications. The expected life of the thrust bearing is usually quantified by an L_{10} rating. Within a large sample, the median bearing life is typically between four and five times the L_{10} life.

Most drive heads have either a hollow shaft or an integral shaft design that facilitates the connection of the drive to the polished rod. With the most common hollow shaft design, the polished rod passes through the entire wellhead and is suspended by a polished-rod clamp that seats into a drive slot on top of the wellhead frame. In a modification of this design, a hexagonal rod substitutes for the polished rod, and the drive unit has a mating hollow shaft through which torque is applied to the rod. Polished rod and stuffing box exposure depends on whether the particular design incorporates an open (Fig. 15.10a) or closed (see Fig. 15.10b) frame. The

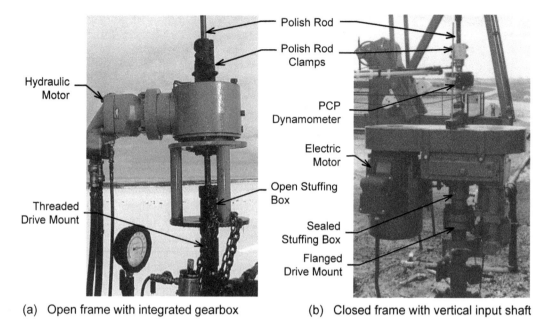

(a) Open frame with integrated gearbox   (b) Closed frame with vertical input shaft

Fig. 15.10—Hollow shaft wellhead drive units.

hollow shaft design allows some repositioning of the rod string without removal of the well-head. This is done by loosening the polished rod clamp, raising or lowering the polished rod as required, and then tightening the clamp. This flexibility to reposition the rod string simplifies rod space-out procedures, flush-bys, and the repositioning of the rod string to prevent wear-related failures. In drives with an integral shaft design, the polished rod threads directly into the drive mechanism as opposed to passing through it. As a result, the only way to reposition the rod string is to add pony rods of different lengths to change the string length. Initial space-out procedures and flush-bys are not easily accommodated with the integrated shaft design.

Drive heads also incorporate a stuffing box that seals on the rotating polished rod to con-trol fluid leakage from the production string and wellhead. The two basic types of stuffing boxes available are conventional and specialty (i.e., rotating) systems. The conventional stuff-ing boxes function similar to those used with beam-pump systems. They use a special packing material compressed against the polished rod to effect a seal; (i.e., the rod rotates directly against the packing material, so the compressive loading imposed by tightening the stuffing box must balance the resultant friction forces against fluid seal integrity). These stuffing boxes require regular inspection and maintenance (i.e., greasing and tightening). Rotating stuffing box-es are designed to seal differently, typically incorporating an inner sleeve that seals against the polished rod and rotates with it during operation. Additional seals designed to operate in a clean fluid environment provide a seal between the rotating sleeve and the fixed outer housing of the stuffing box. A clean lubricating oil environment is ideally maintained in this interstitial region during operation. One key consideration for stuffing box selection is access for packing material or seal replacement, and another is tightening of the packing as required. To minimize stuffing box leakage and maintenance requirements, it is also important to ensure that the pol-ished rod has not been bent. Some new stuffing box designs rely on injectable packing materials (viscous materials that require an injection pressure of approximately 7 MPa [1,000 psi] that readily facilitate repacking of a stuffing box).

Normally, drive heads are connected to the power transmission equipment by a vertical shaft (Fig. 15.10b). However, horizontal connections can be facilitated by incorporating right-

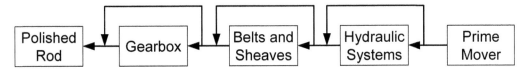

Fig. 15.11—Alternative configurations of power transmission equipment.

angle gearboxes directly into the drive head (Fig. 15.10a). These gearboxes typically enclose gears that provide a reduction ratio of up to 4:1. To prevent gearbox failure, operators should adhere to manufacturer guidelines for maximum gearbox speed and torque.

Power Transmission Equipment. Power transmission equipment is used to transmit power (torque and speed) from the prime mover to the polished rod. This equipment almost always incorporates some type of speed reduction/torque transfer system that permits the prime mover to operate at a higher speed and lower torque than the polished rod. In some cases, power transmission components, such as gearboxes and fixed speed belts and sheaves, are integrated into the drive head.

Power transmission equipment can be arranged in a variety of different configurations as is illustrated in **Fig. 15.11**. The various configurations can include almost any combination of hydraulic equipment, belts and sheaves, and gearboxes to provide the desired operating speed and torque characteristics. Note that power transmission equipment is usually classified as either direct drive or hydraulic on the basis of whether or not it incorporates hydraulic system components.

Hydraulic power transmission systems incorporate a hydraulic system between the prime mover and the input shaft of either a gearbox or fixed speed belt and sheave system that is integrated into the drive head. The hydraulic system itself consists of a hydraulic pump connected to the output shaft of the prime mover, various intermediate valves and plumbing, and a hydraulic motor attached to the input shaft of the drive head (**Fig. 15.12a**). Note that variable displacement hydraulic pumps and motors are typically used. Additional required components include a hydraulic fluid reservoir and fluid filtration system. All hydraulic equipment, except the hydraulic motor and connecting hoses, is usually mounted on a skid (Fig. 15.12b). The torque delivered by the hydraulic motor to the drive head is proportional to the hydraulic system pressure and a function corresponding to the hydraulic motor design. The hydraulic system flow rate may be controlled with either prime-mover speed control systems or, more commonly, pump displacement adjustments (i.e., through changes in the swash plate position in variable-displacement pumps) to set the rotational speed of the hydraulic motor. The relationship between prime-mover speed and hydraulic motor speed is a function of the relative displacements of the hydraulic pump and motor. As an alternative, some vendors also sell in-line hydraulic drive units that use high-torque, low-speed hydraulic motors to drive the polish rod directly without any gear or belt and sheave reduction. These units tend to be relatively compact and quiet compared with the more standard systems.

Direct-drive power transmission systems can be categorized as mechanical fixed speed, mechanical variable speed, or electronic. Mechanical fixed speed refers to a direct-drive system with a fixed gear ratio powered by a prime mover that can operate at a single speed (i.e., typically an AC electric motor). Mechanical variable-speed systems have either internal combustion prime movers that can operate at variable speeds or a belt and sheave system that accommodates a variety of sheave sizes. To vary pump speed in the latter case, the well must be shut down to permit changing of the sheaves. Electronic systems consist of an electric motor with an ESC system. **Fig. 15.13** shows different types of direct-drive systems.

The features of the different types of power transmission systems are compared in **Table 15.2**. Although hydraulic systems are typically less efficient than direct electric drives, they

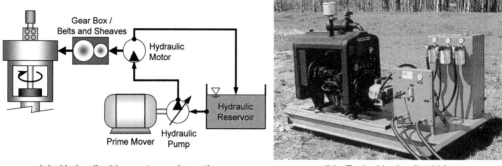

(a) Hydraulic drive system schematic.   (b) Typical hydraulic skid.

Fig. 15.12—Hydraulic drive system equipment.

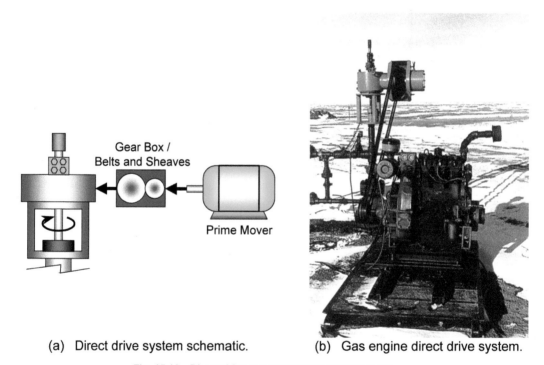

(a) Direct drive system schematic.   (b) Gas engine direct drive system.

Fig. 15.13—Direct drive power transmission systems.

generally require little field infrastructure and have a high variable-speed turndown rate, which makes them popular for low-rate, high-viscosity applications in which prime-mover speeds are much higher than pump speeds and flexible speed control is desirable. The simplicity of mechanical fixed- and variable-speed systems makes them practical for applications in which fluid rates are relatively stable and speed adjustment requirements are limited. The direct-electric-drive systems typically have better energy efficiency than hydraulic drives, although they typically are more expensive and can be more difficult to repair. Field electrification is usually required for effective use of electric-drive systems.

TABLE 15.2—POWER TRANSMISSION SYSTEM FEATURE COMPARISON

Feature	Prime Mover				
	Electric			Internal Combustion Engine	
Speed control	Hydraulics	VFD	None	Hydraulics	None
Speed turndown	High	Moderate	None	High	None
Relative cost	$$	$$$$	$	$$	$
Maintenance requirements	Moderate	Low	Low	High	Moderate

Prime Movers. The prime mover provides the energy to drive the surface equipment and ultimately the rod string and downhole pump. The amount of power that the prime mover must deliver depends on the power demand at the polished rod and the efficiency of the power transmission system. Typical prime-mover power ratings range from 4 to 75 kW [5 to 100 hp], although higher capacity wellhead units designed to accommodate twin electric motors providing power up to 225 kW [300 hp] have recently been introduced by several vendors in conjunction with new large displacement PC pumps.

The two types of prime movers commonly used to drive PCP systems are internal combustion engines and electric motors. Internal combustion engines (Fig. 15.13b) have the advantages of a simple setup with minimum capital investment and variable-speed capability. They are often used on wells in remote areas where electricity is not available. In some situations, depending on gas production and composition, it is possible to fuel the engine with produced gas. Nevertheless, electric motors are the most common form of prime mover used for PCP systems because of low maintenance requirements, high efficiency, low energy costs, easy operation, and low noise levels. The major disadvantage of using electric motors for the prime mover is that the cost of powering the motor can be prohibitively high unless the well site is electrified. Another drawback is that speed adjustment is possible only through sheave changes, motor rewiring, or the use of ESC systems.

Most electric motors used as prime movers in PCP applications are three-phase, squirrel-cage induction motors. The operating characteristics of an induction motor are illustrated in the speed-vs.-torque curve in **Fig. 15.14**. During motor startup, the difference between the developed torque and load torque determines the rate at which the motor will accelerate up to speed. If sustained, the large current draw during startup would cause permanent motor stator damage. Therefore, the startup torque capabilities of the system must be well above (e.g., 1.25–1.5×) that required by the system operating load. Note that in PCP applications, the static friction within the pump, combined with initial system inertial loads, can, in some cases, cause the torque required at startup to be substantially higher than the normal operating torque. In particular, the startup or breakaway torque of the pump can be affected by excessive compression set or swelling of the elastomer. Fig. 15.14 shows that the normal operating range for motors is the linear region below the full-load torque (i.e., torque required to produce rated power at rated speed). Continuous operation at torques above the full-load torque may result in excessive heat generation, which will cause permanent motor damage.

High-efficiency motors designed to NEMA B standards[20] (see Chap. 8 in the Facilities and Construction Engineering section of the *Handbook*) are typically used in PCP applications. They characteristically have startup torques of between 125 and 150% of full load (i.e., for motors with synchronous speeds of 1,200 rpm), breakdown torques of 200% of full load, and a slip of < 5%. In addition, because the motors are unsheltered in most PCP installations, totally enclosed fan-cooled motor enclosures are typically used for these applications. The fans are considered critical for providing adequate cooling to prevent damage to the motor under warm-

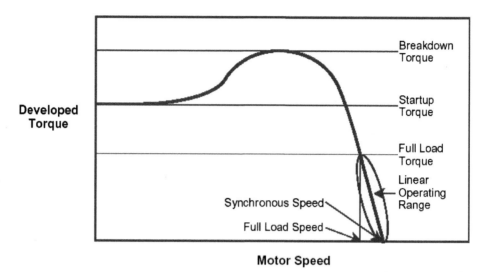

Fig. 15.14—Speed vs. torque characteristics for a squirrel-cage induction motor.

climate operating conditions. Most PCP drive systems use six pole motors that operate at slightly < 1,200 rpm with supply power of 460 V and 50 to 60 Hz.

Nominal power factors are sometimes quoted by manufacturers based on operation at full load under the rated voltage, current, and frequency conditions. For the induction motors used in PCP applications, nominal power factors typically range from 0.80 to 0.90. However, motors are designed to operate with a maximum power factor when loaded to full capacity, and this is often not the case in the field. Actual power factors can be measured during motor operation with specialized equipment.

Nominal overall energy conversion efficiency values for electric motors are often quoted by manufacturers based on operation at full load under the rated voltage, current, and frequency conditions. In the range of motor sizes used in PCP applications, nominal efficiencies range between approximately 90 and 95%. However, as for the power factor, motors are designed to operate at maximum efficiency when loaded to full capacity. Operation above or below full capacity or deviations from rated conditions will result in lower efficiencies.

Motor power factors and efficiency values may decrease when a motor is used in less-than-ideal operating environments (e.g., high ambient temperatures) or with increased motor age. Thus, differences between summer and winter operating conditions should be taken into consideration with respect to motor performance and efficiency.

Safety Shutdown Devices. Surface equipment components, such as the hydraulic system or the prime mover, may be at risk of sustaining costly damage if allowed to operate continuously under certain conditions. As a result, surface drive systems usually incorporate devices that automatically shut the system down when adverse conditions exist. For example, hydraulic systems often have a switch to shut the system down if the hydraulic fluid level drops too low; internal combustion engines usually have high-engine-temperature and low-oil-pressure shutdown switches; and many electronic systems are equipped with high-current shutdown switches.

Torque Limiters. Bottomhole pump seizures resulting from sanding or elastomer swelling, parted tubing, and blocked flowlines can all result in a sudden escalation in rod-string torque. If uninterrupted, the power transmission equipment will continue to increase the applied torque until the rod string or some other component fails. To prevent such failures, torque limiters are installed on the surface equipment to ensure that polished-rod torque cannot exceed some pre-

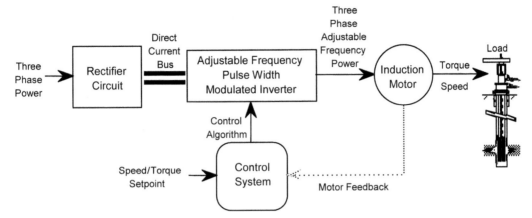

Fig. 15.15—Block diagram for an electronic speed-control setup.

set limit. Hydraulic systems, for example, typically use a pressure control valve that allows some hydraulic fluid to bypass the hydraulic motor when the system pressure becomes too high. This reduces rod-string speed while allowing the prime mover to keep operating at a safe torque level. Electronic drives either receive torque feedback from a mechanical device on the drive head or determine torque directly with special algorithms. When this operating torque exceeds the preset limit, the electronic drive will reduce the rod-string speed in an attempt to lower torque. If that fails, the drive will eventually shut the prime mover off.

ESC Systems. ESC systems are used to vary the speed of direct-drive systems. ESC systems incorporate an inverter operating from a three-phase power source, a control system that directs and excites the inverter, and an induction motor. Currently, several variations of ESC systems are being used in PCP applications. The primary difference between these systems is in the control system strategy and types of inverters used. Motor speed is controlled by adjusting the frequency of the input power signals generated by the inverter on the basis of the control system algorithms.

Most ESC systems typically operate the electric motor at a speed setpoint, although more advanced systems also allow torque-based control. Three-phase AC power is fed into a rectifier circuit that produces a DC bus. The pulse-width-modulated inverter draws energy from this bus and creates three-phase AC power at the frequency commanded by the control system. Although basic speed control is typically open loop, the more elaborate systems often use closed-loop speed control capabilities. The control modules of more advanced ESC systems may incorporate sophisticated motor algorithms, microprocessors, and digital signal processors to perform a multitude of motor current, magnetic flux, rotor slip, winding resistance, temperature correction, and magnetizing reactance calculations using several different feedback signals from the motor. The system then uses this information to achieve the desired motor operating condition. **Fig. 15.15** shows a block diagram illustrating the typical configuration for these systems.

Most ESC systems allow programming of such basic control options as torque limits, speed ramping, and regenerative braking. More advanced systems include features like automatic restart after fault trips and delays, frequency skipping to avoid resonance, and power-loss ride-through. Many ESC systems also have an optional serial communications interface that enables digital links to programmable logic controllers or computers for remote access to monitoring, adjustment, and control functions.

Rod-String Backspin Control Devices. When a surface-driven PCP system is in operation, a significant quantity of energy is stored in the torsional strain of the rods and within the fluid column above the pump within the tubing string. The development and use of larger-displace-

TABLE 15.3—TYPES OF RECOIL CONTROL DEVICES USED IN PCP SYSTEMS	
Type	Description
Hydraulic constriction	• Hydraulic pump is engaged on backspin, which pushes fluid through an orifice. • Can either be integral with hydraulic drive system or a standalone device.
Torque converter	• Vanes are forced to rotate within a viscous fluid. • Some converters sit on top of the wellhead drive system.
Mechanical friction	• Activates brake mechanically or with a hydraulic pump powered from the rod string. • Some models do not engage until a minimum speed is reached.
Regenerative	• Electric motor is loaded during backspin, causing it to act like a generator.

ment and higher-pressure-capacity PC pumps have led to a substantial increase in the magnitude of the torsional strain and fluid energy that become stored in the production system during normal pumping operations. The stored energy is released with backspin of the pump and/or rod string whenever the PCP system is shut down through routine operator intervention or automatic power cutoff in high-torque-overload cases. When the power supply to the drive is lost or interrupted, the potential energy that remains in the system will cause the surface equipment and drive string to accelerate in the direction opposite its normal operating mode. Uncontrolled backspin can lead to surface equipment damage and backed-off rod strings or tubing. These conditions also pose a significant hazard to field personnel working on or near the surface equipment. Thus, it is essential that brakes be used to control the release of rod-string torque and restrict rod recoil to a safe speed. In many applications, if unrestrained by the surface drive/brake equipment, backspin speeds can increase to the point at which the drive-head sheaves or motor fans fragment and "explode" radially outward because of the high centrifugal forces generated.

Typically, two different types of backspin events may occur: the seized pump scenario, in which the pump rotor seizes within the stator, and the normal shutdown scenario that occurs during routine shutdowns of the pumping system. Upon shutdown in the seized pump case, the pump has stopped turning and the torsional strain energy (i.e., twists) stored in the rod string causes the surface system to start spinning in the reverse direction until all the energy is dissipated. The response period is generally short, and little or no fluid drains from the production tubing because of the seized-pump condition. In the normal shutdown case, fluid remaining in the production tubing drains back to the well through the pump, causing both the pump and the drive system to accelerate backward. This continues until the fluid energy in the tubing (i.e., fluid level) is balanced by the fluid column in the annulus and the pump friction, which can take anywhere from several minutes to hours, depending on the circumstances.

Several incidents have occurred in which uncontrolled backspin of a PCP system drive head has led to explosive sheave fragmentation. In a few cases, personnel were struck by sheave fragments and seriously injured. This has led to a heightened awareness by equipment manufacturers and operators of the need to ensure that surface equipment (i.e., particularly the braking system) is properly sized for each application and to implement operating and workover procedures that enhance worker safety.

Most drive heads are equipped with some type of brake system to limit backspin speeds to the allowable speed ratings of the drive-head and sheave components. **Table 15.3** summarizes the major types of recoil control devices used in PCP systems.

In hydraulic systems, when the rods backspin, the hydraulic motor becomes a pump, causing the hydraulic fluid to flow in the reverse direction through the system. Braking is usually accomplished by forcing the fluid to pass through a flow restriction. Standalone hydraulic constriction devices use a hydraulic pump driven by rod backspin to force fluid through a flow restriction. Torque converters provide braking by forcing vanes to rotate within a viscous fluid. Another basic type of recoil control device uses brake pads activated either mechanically or through the use of a hydraulic pump driven by rod backspin. Regenerative braking has been incorporated into some of the newer ESC systems. With this type of braking, the electric motor is loaded during the backspin, causing it to act as a generator and convert recoil energy into electrical energy. However, the utility of these systems relies on the integrity of the drive-system components (e.g., belts and sheaves) that link the polished rod and electric motor, which poses additional risk of failure.

It is important for operators to ensure that the brake specifications of the drive equipment installed are adequate for their specific application conditions under both backspin scenarios described above. Apart from physical compatibility with the drive system being used, it is important to consider the speed at which the braking device engages, the torque that it can resist, and the energy that it can dissipate safely. If the recoil control device does not engage until the rods reach a relatively high speed or if it cannot handle the amount of torque applied by the rods, it may prove ineffective in preventing excessive backspin speeds.

15.1.4 Auxiliary Equipment. This section outlines some auxiliary equipment commonly used with PCP systems. a brief description of the design and application features of each product is provided.

Tag Bar Assemblies and Tail Joints. A tag bar or "rotor stop" is normally required to facilitate installation and spaceout of the rod string. Several different tag bar designs are available, but they usually consist simply of a steel rod or bar (approximately 25 mm [1 in.] in diameter) fastened widthwise across the middle of a short (e.g., 0.6 m [2 ft]) perforated tubing pup joint that is threaded to the pump intake. In some designs, the rod is replaced with a steel plate with holes to permit fluid flow. The number and shape of the perforations in the pup joint vary among manufacturers. A large perforated area is particularly important in highly viscous fluid applications to minimize flow losses and to facilitate sand flow to the pump intake. The pump vendor usually supplies a tag bar joint with the PC pump.

Although the tag bar pup is usually the bottom component of the tubing string in a PC pump completion, an additional length of tubing is sometimes run below the tag bar as a tail joint to lower the pump intake. For example, in horizontal wells, the pump may be seated in the vertical section to alleviate wear problems while a tail joint is installed to allow fluid to be drawn from the curved or horizontal sections of the wellbore. This technique can also be used effectively to increase the fluid flow velocity below the pump, which can be important for maintaining solids in suspension. In some cases, tail joints can be used to reduce the gas-to-liquid ratio at the pump intake, although the pressure losses through the tail joint may lead to additional solution gas breakout, resulting in little or no improvement in volumetric pump efficiency. If tail joints are used, they should not be centralized and the string should be landed at a position where the intake is on the low side of the wellbore to minimize the amount of free gas that enters the pumping system.

Tubing Anchors. Most PCP systems operate in the clockwise direction, so the resistive (i.e., friction) torque in the system tends to unthread the production tubing connections. As a result, tubing anchors are often run below or above the PC pump so that the resistive torque loading is transferred directly to the casing. They also alleviate the need to over-torque the tubing connections during makeup, which can substantially increase the number of makeups possible before thread damage occurs. Tubing anchors should be run with large-volume pumps and in high-speed applications in which the high resistive torques and system vibrations increase the potential for tubing backoff problems. Although several vendors supply conventional tubing anchors that can be used in this application, several manufacturers sell products specifically designed for PC pumping systems that differ from conventional anchors in that they resist torque while providing minimal axial load resistance. This facilitates removal of the tubing string from a well that has sanded in.

Tubing Rotators. When tubing wear is a major issue, such as in slant and horizontal wells, tubing rotator systems can be used to substantially improve the service life of the tubing string. Rotating tubing hangers that allow the tubing to be rotated while the pump is in operation have been designed. The tubing is suspended by a thrust bearing, and a rotator mechanism that can be ratcheted manually or can be equipped to rotate the tubing continuously is provided. Rotating tubing hanger products are available from several different vendors.

Tubing Drain. Tubing drains provide an alternative means to drain produced fluid from the production tubing string in PCP applications when the rotor cannot be pulled from the stator. These devices are commonly run in wells that are prone to experiencing seized rotors because of a buildup of produced sand above the pump or excessive elastomer swell. The drains are run with the production tubing string and are typically located a few tubing joints above the pump. To activate the drain, the production tubing is pressurized from surface to the point at which the drain "blows" (i.e., a plate ruptures or shear pins fail), allowing the fluid column in the tubing string to drain back to the casing annulus. The existing tubing drain products cannot be reset (i.e., closed) from surface; therefore, the tubing string must be tripped to replace them once they have been activated.

Tubing Centralizers. PCP systems can experience severe vibration problems in some wells, particularly those operating at high speeds. Tubing centralizers can be run in conjunction with the production tubing to help stabilize the string and reduce the vibration amplitudes, which helps to mitigate tubing failures caused by backoff and/or fatigue.

Downhole Gas Separators. Downhole gas separators are used routinely in the oil industry to separate free gas from the production fluid before it enters the pump. Eliminating free gas from the produced fluid reduces its compressibility and therefore increases the volumetric efficiency of the downhole pump (which is determined based on liquid volume only). The gas separators used in PCP applications are normally passive devices that simply create a flow path that encourages the free gas to flow up the casing annulus. As a result, the completion details (e.g., casing size, pump seating location, and use of torque anchors) can have a significant influence on the effectiveness of these devices. Flow losses within the separator may also affect the amount of free gas entering the pump. A gas separator device designed specifically for directional- and horizontal-well applications uses a weighted cam and swivel system to ensure that the intake remains on the low side of the wellbore.

Monitoring and Control Systems. Since the early 1990s, operators have begun to incorporate field instrumentation and logic functions into process control systems for PCP systems.[21] These systems monitor a variety of production-related parameters, make decisions that are based on their values, and then automatically implement these decisions. For example, some pumpoff control systems measure fluid levels or bottomhole pressures, compare the measured values with preset upper and lower limits, and then adjust the pump speed to maintain the fluid level within the desired range. These systems hold considerable promise for reducing manual monitoring time, decreasing downtime, and increasing productivity.

Pressure and Flow Switches. Pressure switches are used to shut down the PCP system in the event of either excessive or low flowline pressures to prevent damage to or failure of the surface or downhole equipment. Flow switches are used to control flow rates within prescribed upper and lower limits and to shut down the system if the rates move outside the desired operating range (i.e., usually low-flow conditions).

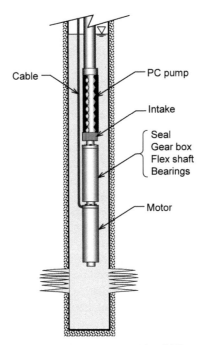

Fig. 15.16—Schematic of a downhole drive PCP system.

15.1.5 Alternative PCP System Configurations. Several nonstandard PCP systems have been developed by various companies to improve pumping capacity, performance, and serviceability for certain applications. These include a number of different downhole drive systems that inherently eliminate tubing wear problems and reduce fluid flow losses. Rod-insert PC pump designs are available that preclude the need to pull the tubing string for pump replacement. Charge pumps and fluidizer pumps are currently being used to increase the gas- and solids-handling capabilities of PCP systems. The following sections provide a brief description of the rationale for developing each hybrid system and a description of the basic operating principles of the product where applicable.

Electric Downhole Drive PCP Systems. The use of PC pumps driven by conventional electric submersible pump (ESP) motors was first attempted by a Canadian operator in a heavy oil well in 1966, unfortunately with little success, and then to a much greater extent by Russian operators in the 1970s. However, only within the last decade have these downhole drive (DHD) PCP systems been more fully developed and successfully deployed on a commercial basis.[22] Several major ESP vendors now market motors, gear boxes, and other equipment for DHD PCP systems; as a result, these systems have begun to see wider use. The entire surface unit drive system and rod string required in a conventional PCP system are replaced with a DHD unit that typically consists of an ESP motor (either a 2- or 4-pole design that has synchronous speeds of 3,600 and 1,800 rpm, respectively), a gearbox and flex-shaft assembly, and a pump intake unit. **Fig. 15.16** shows a schematic of a generic DHD system.

A key feature of the DHD systems is the gearbox/seal/flex-shaft assembly. Although various vendors use different designs and configurations for these components, the overall functions are typically the same: (1) to isolate the motor oil from the well fluids; (2) to provide a speed reduction between the motor and the pump; (3) to isolate the motor and gearbox from the pump's eccentric motion; (4) to support the thrust load generated by the pump; and (5) to provide a path for the produced fluid to flow from the wellbore past the motor (i.e., for cooling) to the pump inlet. The speed reduction is necessary because 2- and 4-pole ESP motors normally rotate at 3,600 and 1,800 rpm, respectively (i.e., synchronous speed at 60 Hz), which is much higher than the ideal operating speed for PC pumps. The eccentric motion of the pump is typically absorbed by a specially designed flex-shaft or knuckle-joint assembly positioned between the pump and the gear box.

DHD systems offer certain advantages in applications in which neither an ESP nor a rod-driven PCP can be used optimally. For example, PC pumps generally perform better than conventional ESPs in viscous-oil, high-sand-cut, or high-GOR applications. In deviated or horizontal wells, the rod strings required in surface-driven PCP systems create potential for severe wear or fatigue problems, particularly if there is a large differential pressure on the pump. In such cases, a DHD system may offer a better overall solution by combining the pumping capabilities of a PC pump with the benefits of a rodless drive system. Eliminating sucker rods also results in lower flow losses, which may, in some cases, allow less expensive, smaller-diameter production tubing to be used. In addition, there are no backspin safety issues because the rotating parts are all run downhole. A DHD system also eliminates the need for a stuffing box at surface, thereby reducing the potential for leaks. Drawbacks of the DHD systems include the additional capital and servicing costs associated with the power cable for the downhole motor, some size restrictions, and in most cases, additional coordination between the ESP and PCP vendors for equipment design, supply, installation, and service. In practice, these systems are normally used only in higher-rate applications because their use in low-productivity wells generally is not economical.

It is imperative to design a DHD system properly because changing equipment once the system has been installed in a well is costly. Once installed, speed control can be achieved only with a variable-frequency drive. It is important to ensure that the cable and seal systems chosen are compatible with the well fluids to prevent premature system failure. Also, the pump is not normally "sumped" because there must be liquid flow past the motor at all times during operation to ensure that the motor is adequately cooled.[23] Manufacturers recommend a 0.3 m/s [1 ft/s] minimum liquid flow velocity past the motor, but this recommendation is based on high-water-cut ESP system designs in which the flow is turbulent. With viscous oil, it is possible that the flow will be laminar, even at 0.3 m/s [1 ft/s], which may result in insufficient motor cooling and thus increased potential for motor failure. Shrouded systems may be used when seating the pump below the perforations is desirable or when the flow velocity past the motor is expected to be too low for adequate cooling. Note, however, there may be additional flow losses through the shroud that should be taken into consideration. During installation of DHD systems, the susceptibility of the power cable to damage is a concern; thus, particularly in directional- and horizontal-well applications, the use of cable protectors is recommended.

Wireline-Retrievable DHD PCP Systems. Recently, DHD PCP systems have been developed in which the motor, drive assembly (i.e., seals and gearbox) are run into the well on the tubing string, and the pump (both rotor and stator) are run in and latched to the drive system by wireline.[24] This allows relatively fast and inexpensive pump replacement when necessary, which is attractive in regions where rig costs are high or when frequent pump replacement is required. These systems typically require large casing (e.g., typically 177 mm [7 in.]) and tubing string sizes (e.g., 114 mm [4.5 in.] and larger) to accommodate the use of PC pumps with adequate displacement capacities.

Hydraulic DHD PCP Systems. There are two types of hydraulic DHD systems for PC pumps that are either commercially available or are under development by different manufacturers. These include a closed-loop hydraulic system with a downhole hydraulic motor driving a PC pump and a closed- or open-loop fluid-driven PC motor coupled to a PC pump. Both of these hydraulic drive systems require a surface pump and a fluid handling system to provide power fluid to the downhole hydraulic motor. In an open-loop system, the power fluid is commingled with the produced fluid for return to surface; in a closed-loop system, a separate flowline is required for the return stream. In the closed-loop systems, hydraulic oil is typically used as the power fluid, whereas water is normally used in open-loop systems. The systems in which a second PC pump is used as a motor to drive the production pump are typically open-loop designs, and the two pumps are sized relative to one another so that the power fluid used to drive the motor pump is produced with the formation fluid back to surface by the production pump. In viscous-fluid applications, this arrangement can provide the advantage of viscosity reduction and lower flow losses.

The major advantages of these systems are the elimination of the backspin hazard, stuffing-box leaks, and wear and failure problems associated with rod strings. Drawbacks include the added complexity of the surface facilities and downhole completion, higher workover costs, and limited production rate capacity. The availability and use of these systems have been quite limited.

Rod-Insert PCPs. Rod-insert PCP systems are configured the same as the conventional surface-driven systems, with the exception that both the rotor and stator are run on the rod string. This design allows the stator to be pulled without removal of the tubing string. The obvious benefit to this design is savings in service rig time. The major drawback is the limitations imposed by standard tubing-string diameters on the size (i.e., displacement) of the PC pump that can be deployed. Problems with latching and release of the downhole assembly can also be an issue in some cases (e.g., sand buildup above the pump). Note that some of these systems rely on the use of conventional pump hold-down subs designed for beam pump systems.

Tubing-Driven PCP Systems. This type of system, currently at the prototype development stage, is another hybrid of the conventional surface-driven PCP system in which the tubing string is used to drive the downhole pump and to provide a conduit for fluid production to surface. The surface-drive system must support, rotate, and seal the tubing string, and the downhole completion must be modified to include an anchoring system for the stator, a swivel fixture to facilitate rotation of the rotor within the stator, and tubing centralizers to prevent casing wear. They are capable of delivering much higher torque to the pump than the conventional rod-driven systems. The tubing strings should also be equipped with centralizers designed to alleviate casing wear concerns.

Charge Pump Systems. For many years, Canadian operators have successfully used PCP systems specially configured with two pumps run in series with common rod and tubing strings.[25] These so-called charge pump systems consist of a higher-displacement, low-lift pump run below a lower-displacement, normal-lift pump, as illustrated in **Fig. 15.17**. The two pumps are separated by one or more joints of tubing to facilitate the different rotor eccentricities and the "timing" of the two rotor/stator pairs. Charge pumps are used to raise volumetric pumping efficiency in gassy wells by using the larger-volume pump to compress the produced fluid substantially before it enters the second pump (on which the efficiency is based). This can allow increased drawdown under gassy conditions and helps to ensure adequate fluid cooling of the main PC pump, which facilitates longer run life. The drawbacks of charge pump systems include their increased capital cost, increased energy consumption because of the higher mechanical friction of the system, and increased pump length, which makes them more difficult to handle and install. A number of vendors supply these pumps on a special-order basis.

Fluidizer Pumps. Fluidizer or recirculating pumps are simply a variation of the charge pump configuration. The basic difference between the two systems is that the tubing segment separating the two pumps is perforated in a fluidizer pump configuration. This design allows some of the fluid produced by the larger pump to be recirculated back into the casing annulus while still helping to improve the efficiency of the second pump. Fluidizer pumps are typically used to help prevent sand bridging and settlement as a means to decrease the workover frequency in wells producing sand-laden fluids.[26]

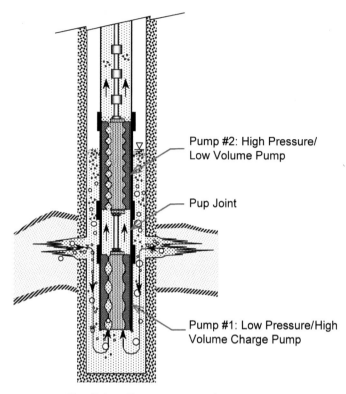

Fig. 15.17—Charge pump configuration.

Water Reinjection Systems. In addition to common use in dewatering coalbed methane wells, PCPs have been used to dewater gas wells. They have also seen use in conjunction with downhole water injection systems[27] and in various configurations of downhole oil/water separation systems.[28] In a gas-well dewatering system with downhole injection, a packer and sealbore assembly are used to isolate the producing zone from the lower water-disposal zone and a bypass sub is run below the PC pump (typically a rod-insert pump design which latches into the bypass sub assembly). The PCP system operates in a normal manner, pumping the water, which separates by gravity from the gas and collects above the packer, into the production tubing above the pump, while the gas flows to surface in the casing/tubing annulus. The water builds up sufficient head in the tubing string to create flow down past the PC pump through the bypass sub into the disposal zone. The PCP downhole oil/water separation systems tend to be more complex in terms of the downhole equipment configuration given the added requirement of performing effective oil/water separation and downhole water reinjection. These systems represent an emerging technology with relatively few field trials completed to date.

15.1.6 Industry Standards. As mentioned, despite the large number of installations worldwide, PC pumps and drive systems do not, in general, conform to any industry standards or common specifications. As a result, there is significant variation in the products available from different vendors, which generally precludes interchangeability of equipment components. The nomenclature (e.g., naming conventions, ratings) used in conjunction with both pumps and drive units also varies considerably, which can make it difficult for users to easily compare and select products from different suppliers. Nevertheless, there have been some recent efforts to develop industry standards for PCP systems.

In the late 1990s, the International Organization for Standardization (ISO) commissioned the development of a standard for downhole PC pumping systems. This effort led to the issuance of *ISO Standard 15136-1, Part 1: Pumps*[29] in 2001, with further work currently being undertaken to develop a Part 2 dealing with drive units. The published standard provides guidelines related to PC pump manufacturing, design, and bench testing; therefore, it is useful from an informational perspective. However, the provisions of the standard tend to be very general, and it does not attempt to preclude individual vendors from continuing to offer a unique line of pump products with different elastomers. Although many provisions are consistent with the current practices of major suppliers of PC pump products, the standard as a whole does not appear to have been widely adopted by the industry at this time, in part because of some of the nomenclature requirements.

In response to a number of drive/sheave failures in the mid- to late-1990s, a group of surface-drive manufacturers in Canada initiated the development of an industry standard for surface drives that encompassed braking systems.[30] The standard provides guidelines for the design, specification, and use of PCP surface-drive units in an effort to support safe operation of this equipment.

15.2 PCP System Design

PCP systems are, in general, highly flexible in terms of their ability to function effectively in a diverse range of applications. As with other artificial-lift systems, the basic objective in the design of a PCP system is to select system components and operating parameters (e.g., pump speed) that can achieve the desired fluid production rates while not exceeding the mechanical performance capabilities of the equipment components to facilitate optimal service life and system value. When a PCP system is designed for a particular application, both the system components and operating environment must be considered to ensure that a suitable system design is achieved.

15.2.1 Overview of the Design Process. Fig. 15.18 presents a "design process" flow chart that outlines the many factors and considerations that should be addressed in the selection of an effective overall system configuration and operating strategy. At each step, the designer selects certain operating parameters or specific equipment components and must then assess the impacts of these decisions on system performance. For example, selection of a particular tubing size is based on such design considerations as flow losses and casing size. Some considerations apply to more than one decision, as is the case with flow losses that affect pump, tubing, and rod-string selection. Other design considerations may produce conflicting results, which complicates the decision-making process. For example, the use of rod-string centralizers may minimize wear but may also increase flow losses. As with other artificial-lift systems, the design process is generally iterative, and individual parameters are often adjusted to achieve an optimal design for a particular application. As Fig. 15.18 shows, the primary design considerations for a PCP system are pump selection and sizing, fluid flow effects, rod loading and fatigue, rod and tubing wear, and power transmission selection.

The first step in the design process is to gather information for the application of interest. Past experience, fluid properties, production, well records, and reservoir data are all useful sources of relevant information. Next, it is necessary to determine the anticipated fluid rates. These can be estimated from historical data or by setting a dynamic fluid level and calculating production rates based on reservoir data and an inflow performance relationship.[31] Initial values must then be set for the wellbore geometry, pump-seating location, dynamic fluid level, tubing size, and rod-string configuration. If the design is for an existing well, some of these parameters may already be constrained.

Once these equipment and operating parameters are established, flow losses can be calculated. If the estimated flow losses are unacceptably high, they can be reduced by increasing the

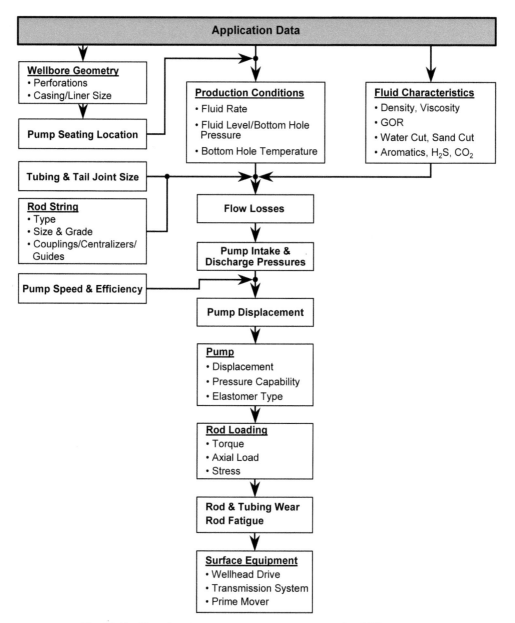

Fig. 15.18—Flowchart illustrating the design process for PCP systems.

tubing size, reducing the rod-string induced flow restrictions, or decreasing the fluid rate. Next, initial values for pump intake and discharge pressures, net lift, pump speed, and pump displacement can be set. This allows the designer to select a range of pump models capable of satisfying the desired pump displacement and lift requirements. However, if there are no pumps available that meet both requirements, then the prescribed pump displacement and lift specifications must be relaxed by decreasing the fluid rate expectations, increasing pump speed, reducing discharge pressure requirements, increasing pump intake pressure, or by implementing some combination of these changes. The individual pumps that satisfy the requirements are then evaluated on the basis of geometric design and fluid considerations to select the most appropriate pump model.

Once a specific pump model has been selected, rod loading, rod-string/tubing wear, and surface equipment requirements can be evaluated. If the calculated rod stresses exceed the allowable value, then either the rod-string strength must be increased through the use of a larger rod or higher-strength material, or the loading must be decreased through a reduction in the net lift requirements or the use of a smaller-displacement pump. Similarly, if the predicted rod-string/tubing wear rates are unacceptable, then steps must be taken to reduce axial loads (e.g., use of a smaller pump), or the rod string must be reconfigured so that it is less prone to wear. After the rod loading and wear considerations are satisfied, the final step in the design process is the selection of surface equipment. If the available surface equipment cannot meet the polished-rod power requirements, then the design process must be repeated to configure a downhole system or operating parameters that result in reduced system loads. For example, reduced power requirements can be achieved by lowering the pump speed (which will also likely lead to a lower differential pump pressure) or by selecting another pump with a smaller displacement. Once a final system design has been established, any areas of potential concern should be reevaluated to confirm that the design satisfies the functional requirements of the application within acceptable operating guidelines.

It is quite apparent that the interdependency between the numerous equipment selection and well completion options, variations in operating conditions, and complex fluid flow and mechanical interactions that affect system loading and performance can make the assessment and design of PCP systems difficult and time consuming. In new applications, numerous iterations may be required just to establish a workable system. Because design optimization based on manual calculations is usually impractical, computer programs have been developed to help designers work faster and more effectively. The following sections provide further details on specific design parameters.

15.2.2 Pump Selection. Fig. **15.19** summarizes the key technical considerations and decisions involved in selecting a PC pump for a particular application (note that other considerations, such as local vendor choice and economics, can also affect pump selection). As illustrated, the selection criteria include pump displacement, pressure capability, geometric design, elastomer type, and rotor coating characteristics.

Pump Displacement and Pressure Capability. When selecting a PC pump, the two most critical requirements are adequate displacement capacity and pressure capability to ensure that the pump can deliver the required fluid rate and net lift for the intended application.

It is typical to select pumps with a design (i.e., theoretical) flow rate that is somewhat higher than the expected fluid rate to reflect pump inefficiencies during production operations. Fluid slippage, inflow problems, and gas interference all contribute to reduced pump volumetric efficiency. Together, the design fluid rate and prescribed pump rotational speed define the minimum required pump displacement as

$$s_{\text{min}} = \frac{q_a}{\omega E}, \quad\text{...(15.4)}$$

where s_{min} = minimum required pump displacement (m³/d/rpm [B/D/rpm]), q_a = required fluid rate (m³/d [B/D]), ω = pump rotational speed (rpm), and E = volumetric pumping efficiency in service.

Initially, an optimal pump speed should be assumed on the basis of the intended application conditions, with the primary considerations being the viscosity of the produced fluids and tubing-wear potential. **Table 15.4** lists typical pump speeds recommended for the production of fluids

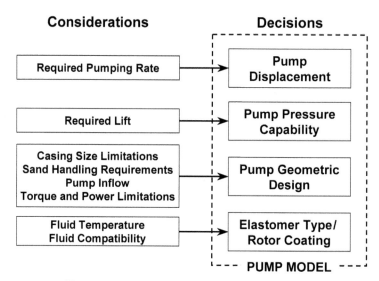

Fig. 15.19—Flow chart for pumping considerations.

TABLE 15.4—RECOMMENDED PUMP SPEED RANGES FOR VARIOUS OPERATING CONDITIONS	
Viscosity, cp	Optimal Speed Range, rpm
<500	200 to 400
500 to 5,000	150 to 300
>5,000	100 to 250

in different viscosity ranges. Higher speeds may be considered if these suggested values do not deliver the required production rates or if a pump with the preferred displacement cannot be sourced. In most cases, it is preferable to pump at the lowest speed practical to increase the life of the pump, rod string, tubing, and surface equipment. However, consideration should also be given to the impact that the selection of larger-displacement pumps will have on the sizing of the rod string and surface drive.

In general, there has been a trend recently toward higher speeds because new pump models and better sizing practices have been developed that have led to improved pump lives. For example, pump speeds of 300 to 400 rpm remain typical for high-water-cut applications, but some operators now routinely pump at 500 rpm and higher in such applications. Higher speeds may also be practical in some high-viscosity applications in which sand production and tubing-wear problems are not an issue and reasonable pump efficiencies can be maintained. For example, the new large-capacity PC pumps used to produce the prolific heavy oil wells in several eastern Venezuela fields are being run successfully at speeds of 400 to 500 rpm.

The net pump lift requirement determines the minimum required pressure capability of the pump. In determining the net lift value for pump selection, the full service life conditions should be considered. Net lift is defined as the difference between discharge and intake pressures of the PC pump under the expected operating conditions and is estimated as follows:

$$p_{\text{lift}} = p_d - p_i, \quad\quad\quad\quad\quad\quad\quad\quad\quad\quad\quad (15.5)$$

where p_{lift} = net lift required (kPa [psi]), p_d = pump discharge pressure (kPa [psi]), and p_i = pump intake pressure (kPa [psi]).

Pump intake pressure is normally a function of the casing-head pressure plus the pressure caused by the gas and liquid column above the pump intake in the casing/tubing annulus. However, in systems in which tail joints or gas separators are used, the pressure drop that results from flow through these components must also be subtracted from the intake pressure. An estimate of the pump intake pressure can be calculated as follows:

$$p_i = p_{ch} + p_g + p_L - p_{tail}, \dotfill (15.6)$$

where p_i = pump intake pressure (kPa [psi]), p_{ch} = casing-head pressure (kPa [psi]), p_g = annular gas-column pressure (kPa [psi]), p_L = annular liquid-column pressure (kPa [psi]), and p_{tail} = pressure loss associated with auxiliary components (kPa [psi]).

The pump discharge pressure can be calculated as the sum of the tubing head pressure, the liquid column pressure in the production tubing and the flow losses that occur in the tubing as follows:

$$p_d = p_{th} + p_L + p_{losses}, \dotfill (15.7)$$

where p_{th} = tubing-head pressure (kPa [psi]) p_L = tubing liquid-column pressure (kPa [psi]), and p_{losses} = tubing flow losses (kPa [psi]).

For most existing applications, an accurate estimate of the tubing-head pressure will be available from previous measurements, but some additional calculations may be required to establish an appropriate value for the surface piping and related facilities in new installations. When the producing wells flow directly to a central gathering facility, consideration needs to be given to the fact that production from individual wells may be diverted to a test separator system that, in some cases, may impose above-normal backpressures on the pumping system.

Although the determination of static liquid- and gas-column pressures is routine, accurate calculation of flow losses and fluid densities can be much more difficult, especially in multiphase flow situations. As such, the use of analytical or empirical models is often necessary to determine these values.

Once the minimum pump displacement and net lift requirements are established, these values can be used to determine the range of pump models that will satisfy the requirements of a particular application. The main sources for obtaining pump specification information are product brochures and Websites of the various PC pump manufacturers and distributors, as well as design program databases. As noted, if there are no pumps that satisfy a particular set of requirements, then the system design or operating conditions must be changed. The relative cost and availability of particular pump models should also be taken into consideration during the pump selection process.

Torque Requirements. Rotation of the rotor within the stator forces fluid to move up the pump from cavity to cavity. A series of dynamic interference seals separate the cavities and provide a differential pressure capacity. The energy required to turn the rotor and move the fluid against this pressure gradient is provided in the form of torque. Pump torque is composed of hydraulic, viscous, and friction components. Hydraulic torque, the component used to overcome differential pressure, is directly proportional to pump displacement and differential pressure and can be calculated from

$$T_h = C \ s \ p_{lift}, \dotfill (15.8)$$

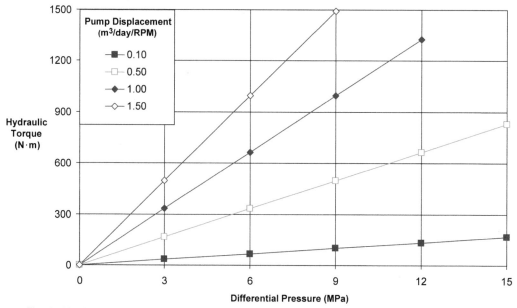

Fig. 15.20—Variation in hydraulic torque with pump displacement and differential pressure.

where T_h = hydraulic pump torque (N·m [ft·lbf]), s = pump displacement (m³/d/rpm [B/D/rpm]), p_{lift} = differential pump pressure (kPa [psi]), and C = constant (0.111 [8.97 × 10⁻²]).

Fig. 15.20 shows the variation in hydraulic torque as a function of differential pressure for a number of different pump displacement values.

"Friction torque" must be applied to overcome the mechanical friction associated with the interaction between the rotor and stator. The magnitude of the friction torque depends on the interference fit of the rotor and stator, the type of rotor coating and stator elastomer, the lubricating properties of the fluid, and the pump length. Because friction torque reduces the mechanical efficiency of a PC pump, use of rotor/stator pairs with excessive values should be avoided. Understanding the magnitude of the friction torque in a downhole application can be difficult because the torque value can only be established empirically from bench test results (see the Pump Sizing Practices section).

In wells producing highly viscous oil, PC pumps require some magnitude of additional input torque to overcome flow losses that occur within the pump itself. The magnitude of this torque requirement depends on the fluid properties (viscosity vs. shear rate), pump geometry, pump speed, and fluid rate. The additional torque requirements are typically quite small (i.e., can be ignored) in most low-rate wells (e.g., < 20 m³/d) but can be quite significant in heavy oil wells producing at high rates (e.g., > 150 m³/d). Unfortunately, little published information is available at this time to provide guidance or models to estimate these loads accurately. However, some proprietary empirical determinations have been made with data from several instrumented, high-rate, heavy oil wells in Venezuela and full-scale pump tests conducted with viscous oils.[32]

The total pump torque is thus equal to

$$T_t = T_h + T_f + T_v, \quad\quad\quad\quad\quad\quad\quad (15.9)$$

where T_t = total pump torque (N·m [ft·lbs]), T_f = pump friction torque (N·m [ft·lbf]), T_v = viscous pump torque (N·m [ft·lbf]).

In the pump selection process, it is essential to make a proper allowance for the torque requirements associated with pump friction and viscous pump torque (i.e., especially in the case of highly viscous fluids) to ensure that the power limitations and load capacities of the surface-drive system and rod string are not exceeded. In some cases, the available torque or power may affect pump selection by limiting the maximum pump displacement. Also, note that the friction torque at startup can be considerably higher than the nominal operating torque due to swell or compression set of the stator elastomer or settling of produced sand above the pump after a shutdown.

Pump Geometric Design. In most cases, several different pumps will satisfy the minimum fluid rate and lift requirements. However, depending on the application, some pumps will likely be more suitable than others. As discussed, pumps with similar displacements can differ significantly in terms of design. These geometric variations cause pumps to perform differently under certain conditions. When selecting a specific pump, it is important to evaluate the nature of the application, the geometric design of the pump, and the compatibility between the performance characteristics inherent to the pump design and the anticipated operating conditions.

The first consideration is whether the casing size will impose a restriction on the pump diameter. Pump diameters currently range between 48 and 170 mm [1.89 and 6.75 in.], typically increasing with pump displacement, as illustrated in Fig. 15.7. Most vendors have pumps available in both standard diameters and slimhole configurations; i.e., the stator housing of many pump models can be machined down to facilitate use in smaller casing sizes. Reasonable clearances (e.g., > 6 mm [0.25 in.] diametrical clearance on casing drift) should be maintained to limit the annular fluid flow velocities to facilitate annular gas separation and to help prevent sand bridging. In the pump selection process, once the maximum allowable stator diameter has been determined, pumps that do not satisfy this requirement can be eliminated. Note also that the rotor major diameter for the selected pump model must be less than the drift diameter of the production tubing string.

For applications producing significant quantities of sand (i.e., > 2% sand by volume), the respective capabilities of different PC pump models to effectively transport the sand becomes an important selection criterion (see also High-Sand-Cut Wells). The sand-handling capabilities of a PC pump are strongly influenced by its geometric design, with shorter-pitch-length, wider-cavity pumps generally offering better performance than pumps with long, narrow cavities.

In applications producing high-viscosity fluids, pump inflow should be considered in the pump selection process. The rate at which fluids can flow into and along the narrow pump cavities is limited. The inflow rate declines with increasing fluid viscosity (because of viscous restrictions) and decreasing pump intake pressure (because of reduced driving force). Some vendors refer to a minimum net positive suction head. If the pumping rate exceeds the inflow rate, incomplete cavity filling occurs, resulting in a pressure drop at the pump inlet, possible cavitation, and reduced pump efficiency (see also High-Viscosity Oil Wells).

Suppliers should be consulted for assistance when choosing between different pump models to contend with sand or highly viscous fluid production.

Pump Elastomer Type and Rotor Coating. In many cases, the most important pump selection consideration is fluid compatibility. Even if the optimal pump geometry has been selected, reasonable pump service life can be achieved only if the stator elastomer is properly matched to the produced fluid conditions. Refer to the Elastomer Types, Properties, and Selection section for guidance on elastomer selection criteria.

Fluid properties should also be considered when it comes to rotor selection. In most cases, the standard chrome-plated rotor is the most suitable. However, if pumping corrosive or acidic fluids, a stainless steel rotor will be less susceptible to corrosion damage. Because the rotor is often the first component to wear when pumping abrasive solids,[33,34] the use of better wear-resistant coating materials should be considered. Most pump suppliers offer rotors with special coatings for improved wear resistance.

15.2.3 Pump Sizing Practices. To contend with the wide range of application conditions, PC pump manufacturers typically fabricate rotors in a range of minor diameters for each pump model. The different rotor sizes are often categorized by standard (i.e., nominal), single or double oversized or undersized designations or by different temperature ratings. The minor rotor diameter typically changes by 0.25 mm [0.010 in.] per size increment. This allows individual pump models to be provided with various degrees of interference fit between the rotor and the stator. The task of selecting a "fit" that will result in optimal pump functionality under downhole conditions is often referred to as "pump sizing."

Through experience, operators and pump suppliers have developed sizing guidelines for many different field applications. These applications are usually classified in terms of fluid viscosity, temperature, and fluid composition (i.e., sand and water cut, aromatic and H_2S content) at downhole conditions. Sizing guidelines take into account anticipated elastomer expansion and swell, clearances for abrasives, fluid slippage rates, and volumetric efficiency. For a given application, there is generally a relatively narrow range of acceptable volumetric efficiencies for the pump at rated pressure, as measured on a test bench under certain standard conditions. In some cases, the sizing guidelines may also contain limitations on maximum allowable friction torque.

When a new pump is sized, an initial pump bench test is completed with a particular rotor and stator. Depending on the results of this test, it may be necessary to conduct additional tests with different rotor sizes until a rotor/stator combination is found that meets the predetermined sizing criteria. It is essential to bench test a PC pump to establish its performance characteristics quantitatively given the numerous design, material, and fabrication parameters that can affect the results. The following section describes bench testing equipment, practices, and results in further detail.

Pump Testing Procedures. In a typical PC pump test, the pump is installed horizontally on a test bench (**Fig. 15.21**). Rotation and power are provided to the rotor through either a direct or hydraulic drive system. Fluid is pumped through a closed-loop system consisting of the pump, discharge lines, fluid reservoir, filtering system, and intake lines. In almost all cases, water with a small amount of oil added for lubrication is used as the test fluid. A choke on the discharge line is used to regulate the pump differential pressure. The test process normally consists of varying the discharge pressure while operating the pump at a constant speed. Various test parameters are monitored and recorded. The discharge pressure is usually set at zero at the start of the test and is then sequentially increased to the maximum test pressure that, in most cases, matches or exceeds the rated pressure of the pump. Depending on the manufacturer, this procedure is repeated at up to four different speeds. Some manufacturers also determine the maximum pressure that a pump can withstand. This is done by completely restricting the pump discharge and measuring the pressure under that condition.

Pump test reports usually contain such information as test speeds, pump discharge pressures, temperatures, actual fluid rates, volumetric efficiencies, hydraulic pressures, and torques. These reports should also include information on the pump components, including model number, unique rotor and stator serial numbers, dimensions, elastomer type, and threaded connections. In terms of the data reported for a pump test, the only parameters actually measured during the test are speed, discharge pressure, temperature, fluid rate, and torque. Speed is directly measured with any one of several mechanical, magnetic, or optical techniques, all of which generally provide quite accurate measurements. Discharge pressure is monitored with either a pressure gauge or pressure transducer. Depending on the type of instrument, the accuracy and resolution of the pressure measurements can vary substantially. Several different methods are commonly used to measure fluid rates. These include measuring the time required to fill a spe-

Fig. 15.21—Typical test equipment for PC pump bench tests.

cific volume in a tank, use of a flowmeter or measuring mass changes in the discharge reservoir with time. Except for properly sized flowmeters, the reliability of measurements made with these techniques increases with sample size (volume or mass). Pump torques are determined either directly with the use of a load cell installed on the drive rod or indirectly by monitoring hydraulic pressure in a hydraulic drive system or by monitoring prime-mover current in an electric drive system. In general, the further removed the measurement point is from the pump rotor, the more the torque values will be influenced by frictional losses within the drive equipment.

In addition to differences in test equipment, there are currently no accepted industry standards for conducting bench tests, so test procedures differ among pump suppliers. This is particularly true for fluid additives and the lubrication of pump specimens. Although all suppliers typically use water for the test fluid, various amounts of oil are usually added to the water or applied directly to the pump rotor to provide lubrication. Differences in the type and quantity of oil in the test fluid can result in a large variation in fluid lubricity, which strongly affects the mechanical friction of the pump and thus the measured torque values.

Fluid temperature is also an important parameter that can have a large impact on the results of a pump test. Some manufacturers use temperature control systems to ensure that the test fluid temperature remains relatively close to the specified value throughout a pump test. The target fluid temperatures typically range between 15 and 50°C [59 and 122°F] among vendors. In other cases, no temperature control is used, and the test fluid is subject to temperature changes during individual tests (due to heat produced by the pump) or from one test to another, depending on the test setup and conditions (i.e., ambient temperature, duration, and frequency of tests). Whether regulated or not, a rise in temperature will generally cause the stator elastomer to expand, which can change the rotor/stator fit and pump performance. The duration of a pump test also varies between suppliers, depending on the equipment and procedures used, which also can lead to different test results.

In most pump test reports, the speed, pressure, fluid rate, and torque data are presented in a format similar to that shown in **Fig. 15.22**. Depending on the particular test, there may be data

PCP BENCH TEST REPORT

Tested At:	Bench 123		Date:	5/17/1997
Tested By:	Pump Tester		Test Time:	12:34:14

Specifications:

Customer:	Company ABC	
Pump Model:	94-800	
Pump Displacement	94	m³/D/100 RPM
Pump Lift:	800	m
Rotor Material:	4140	
Stator Material:	Nitrile	

Dimensions

		Rotor	Stator	
Overall Length:		4.50	5.20	m
Major Diameter:		54.5	n/a	mm
Minor Diameter:		37.6	n/a	mm
Top Thread Size:		25.4 mm	88.9 mm (3½") EUE	
Bottom Thread Size:		n/a	88.9 mm (3½") EUE	

Nominal Displacement:	94.0	m³/D/100 RPM	Actual Displacement:	89.4	m³/D/100 RPM

Test Data:

Pump Speed (RPM)	Differential Pressure (m)	Fluid Rate (m³/D)	Total Torque (N·m)	Nominal Volumetric Efficiency (%)	Actual Volumetric Efficiency (%)	Hydraulic Torque (N·m)	Friction Torque (N·m)	Actual Power (kW)	Total Efficiency (%)
100	0	89.4	180	95.1	100.0	0.0	180.5	2.58	0
100	200	87.6	414	93.2	98.0	194.7	219.2	5.92	33.6
100	300	86.0	478	91.5	96.2	292.0	185.6	6.83	42.9
100	400	85.5	558	91.0	95.7	389.4	168.3	7.98	48.7
100	500	78.7	659	83.7	88.0	486.7	172.7	9.43	47.4
100	600	74.4	794	79.1	83.2	584.1	209.7	11.35	44.6
100	700	64.3	893	68.4	71.9	681.4	211.4	12.77	40.0
100	750	57.4	980	61.1	64.2	730.1	249.6	14.01	34.9
100	800	51.7	1019	55.0	57.8	778.7	240.3	14.57	32.2
100	850	46.1	1072	49.0	51.5	827.4	244.5	15.33	29.0

Performance

Fluid Rate at Rated Lift:	51.7	m³/D	Volumetric Efficiency at Rated Lift:	57.8	%
Total Torque at Rated Lift:	1019	N·m	Total Efficiency at Rated Lift:	32.2	%

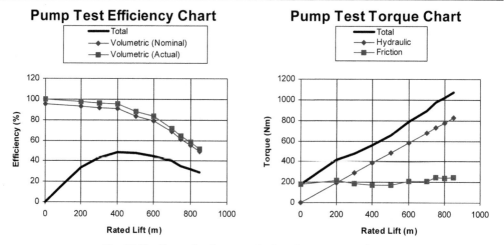

Fig. 15.22—Example of a pump test performance graph.

for more than one speed, or the test results may encompass a different pressure range. Nevertheless, the volumetric efficiency and torque-vs.-pressure curves contain the information used to evaluate characteristics of the pump that was tested.

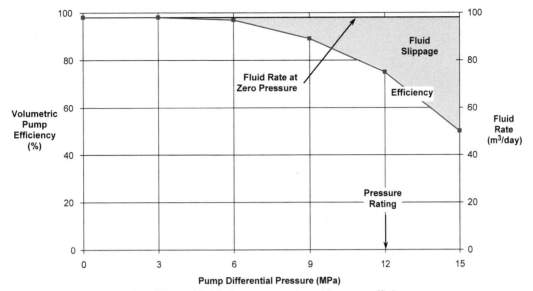

Fig. 15.23—Effect of fluid slippage on volumetric pump efficiency.

Volumetric Efficiency. Volumetric efficiency is calculated as the ratio of the measured flu-id rate to the theoretical fluid rate for the pump being tested. Theoretical fluid rates are determined based on the test speed and nominal displacement of the pump. At zero differential pressure, however, it is expected that a PC pump would operate at a volumetric efficiency of 100%. Invariably, because of manufacturing and sizing differences between pumps of a given model or variations in the bench test conditions and procedures, the actual efficiency of a PC pump at zero differential pressure can vary significantly from 100%.

In general, volumetric efficiency decreases with increasing differential pressure (**Fig. 15.23**). This decrease is caused by fluid slippage, or the leakage of fluid across the rotor/stator seal line from higher- to lower-pressure cavities. Accordingly, it is evident that higher pressure differentials cause the slippage rate to increase further once the pump efficiency drops below 100%.

In addition to being a function of differential pump pressure, volumetric efficiency and slip-page also depend on the pump pressure capability, fluid viscosity, and interference fit. In **Fig. 15.24**, efficiency-vs.-pressure curves are shown for four pumps with the same displacement but different pressure ratings. At a particular pressure differential, the slippage rates decrease and efficiency values increase as the pressure capability of the pump increases. This trend can be attributed to the higher number of cavities and seal lines in the pumps with higher pressure ratings. For the same total differential pressure, the pumps with more cavities have a lower differential pressure across each cavity; as a result, they experience lower slippage rates.

Higher fluid viscosities may also contribute to decreased slippage rates and increased volu-metric efficiencies. Although fluid viscosity variation is not typically an issue in pump testing because bench tests are usually conducted with water, it is an important consideration in the sizing of new pumps or in evaluating the potential reuse of used pumps in different heavy-oil applications.

At a given differential pump pressure, the slippage rate and volumetric efficiency depend primarily on the "interference fit" between the rotor and stator. The tighter the fit, the more difficult it is for fluid to leak across the seal lines and hence the lower the slippage rate and the higher the pump efficiency. These effects are illustrated in the pump test results in **Fig. 15.25** for three similar pumps with loose (undersized), normal, and tight (oversized) fits.

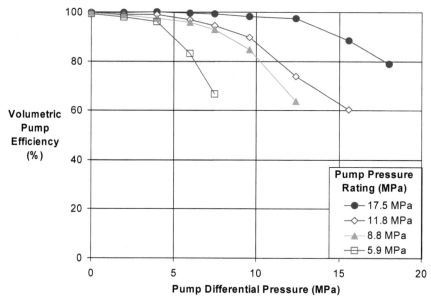

Fig. 15.24—Example of the effect of pressure rating on volumetric pump efficiency.

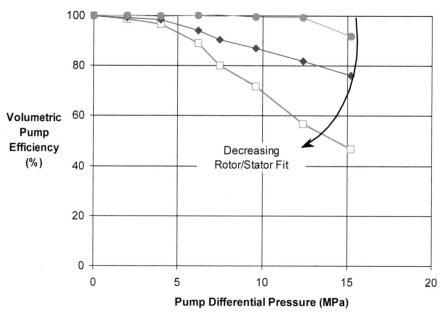

Fig. 15.25—Example of the effect of rotor/stator fit on pump volumetric efficiency.

Pump speed variations have a large effect on volumetric efficiency but generally are considered to have little effect on slippage rates. **Fig. 15.26** shows efficiency-vs.-pressure data for a single pump tested at three different speeds. The notable improvement in pump efficiency with increased speed can be attributed to the fact that the fluid rate increases in direct proportion to speed, while slippage rates tend to vary predominantly as a function of pressure (see slippage rate curves in Fig. 15.26).

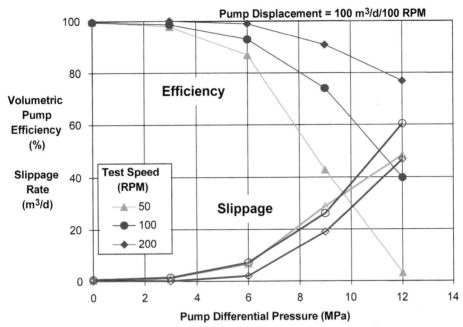

Fig. 15.26—Example of the effect of pump test speed on volumetric efficiency.

Under specific test conditions (speed, fluid, and temperature), bench test results provide the best indicator of the interference fit of a pump. However, when quantifying pump performance, most suppliers specify only the volumetric efficiency of a pump at its rated pressure and one speed. Although this parameter is commonly used for pump sizing and reuse criteria, the previous discussions illustrate the importance of paying close attention to other test parameters (e.g., test fluid temperature and test speed) that may have influenced the bench test results. This is especially important when pump sizing practices of different suppliers are compared.

Pump Torque. The torque values measured during pump tests can be used to diagnose certain pump characteristics. As discussed previously, pump torque consists of a combination of hydraulic, friction, and viscous components (viscous pump torque will be negligible for tests conducted with water). Hydraulic torque can be estimated accurately from pump displacement and differential pressure. Therefore, friction torque can be estimated by subtracting hydraulic torque from the measured pump torque. For example, **Fig. 15.27** shows this breakdown for a typical pump test. In general, for a particular pump, friction torque remains relatively constant with changes in both differential pressure and speed.

Friction torque can vary substantially between different pumps and with variations in the factors that contribute to pump friction. Tighter rotor/stator fits are usually accompanied by larger elastomer displacements (and hence increased hysteretic heating) and higher energy losses, which lead to a corresponding increase in pump friction. Poor meshing or alignment between the rotor and stator also leads to increased friction torque. This "meshing" between the rotor and stator is closely related to the quality control on pitch specifications imposed during the manufacturing process. Material properties, surface finish, and test fluid lubricity control the magnitude of the friction developed because of the rolling/sliding surface interaction between the rotor and stator. The size and shape of the rotor and stator (i.e., the pump model design and fit) influence the seal surface geometry and have a direct influence on the friction torque values. Pump friction tends to increase as the number and length of the seal

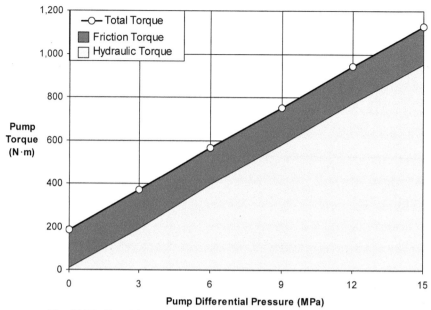

Fig. 15.27—Breakdown of torque components from a pump test.

lines are increased. As a result, multilobe and higher-pressure-rated pumps tend to have higher friction torque magnitudes.

The input energy consumed by pump friction is largely converted into heat within the pump. Excessive heat generated as a result of pump friction and elastomer hysteresis can lead to thermal expansion and cracking of the rotor coating and to progressive damage to the stator elastomer.

It is important to recognize the friction torque values from pump test reports for a given pump model tend to correspond closely to the rotor/stator fit; therefore, they tend to be low for loose-fit pumps and quite high for normal-fit pumps. However, what matters in a system design is the friction torque that develops under the downhole operating conditions. Most pumps sized loosely on the basis of bench results will either swell up because of the fluid environment or expand because of increased temperature downhole, so their friction torque values will increase substantially relative to the bench test. In general, the friction torque of a properly fitted pump will range from 30 to 40% of its hydraulic torque at rated lift for smaller models (e.g., < 0.3 m³/d/rpm) to as low as 10 to 15% for the larger models (e.g., > 0.8 m³/d/rpm). If the geometric tolerances of a rotor/stator pair match poorly or the interference is overly tight, then the friction torque values can become much higher and may exceed the hydraulic torque.

15.2.4 Fluid Flow Considerations. In a PCP system, produced fluid flows from the pump to surface through the annular area between the rod string and tubing. High fluid viscosities, elevated flow rates, or restricted flow paths can result in large shear stresses developing in the fluid, which cause large frictional forces to act on the rod string. These effects can have the following implications on system loading:

• Fluid shear stresses produce flow losses along the tubing and across couplings, centralizers, and rod guides that contribute to increased pump pressure loading.

• Rotational frictional forces acting on the surfaces of the sucker rods, couplings, centralizers, and rod guides produce resistive rod string torque.

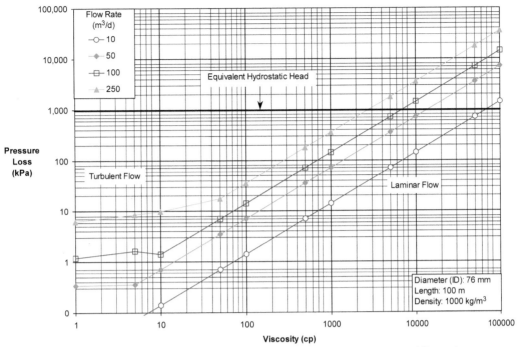

Fig. 15.28—Variation in pressure losses through tubing with viscosity and flow rate.

• Axial frictional forces acting on the rod-string body, couplings, centralizers, and rod guides and flow losses across couplings, centralizers, and rod guides produce upward forces that reduce rod-string tension.

Fluid-flow effects can range from having a minor to a dominant influence on PCP system design. This is illustrated in **Fig. 15.28**, which shows pressure losses for a range of flow rates and viscosities through a 100 m [328 ft] length of 76 mm [3.0 in.] ID tubing (typical of 89 mm [3.5 in.] tubing) without sucker rods present. Note that the pressure-drop values range from nearly zero to values that exceed the corresponding hydrostatic pressure. The change in slope in the curve of pressure loss vs. viscosity is a result of the transition from laminar to turbulent flow.

Unfortunately, depending on conditions, accurately quantifying fluid-flow effects can be extremely challenging. Difficulties arise when the calculations involve non-Newtonian fluid behavior, multiphase flow, or complicated flow patterns around couplings and rod guides. Designers typically resort to an appropriate computer model to perform these calculations. It is beyond the scope of this chapter to describe in detail the methods or formulations typically used to quantify the fluid-flow parameters (e.g., pressure-loss profile along tubing, fluid-column density profile) used in the design of a PCP system. However, the following sections briefly overview the general approach used and outline some special considerations required in these assessments.

Single-Phase Flow. When single-phase flow effects are assessed, the first step is to establish the type of flow regime. Normally, single-phase flow conditions can be classified as either laminar or turbulent. Laminar flow is smooth and steady and governed primarily by viscous forces (viscosity, velocity). Turbulent flow is fluctuating and agitated and depends mostly on inertial forces (density, velocity). The type of flow regime is determined by calculating the Reynolds number for the flow conditions in question.[35] Usually, the transition Reynolds number for annular pipe flow is assumed to be 2,100 for Newtonian fluids. Flow conditions with

Reynolds numbers < 2,100 are considered laminar; conditions that have numbers > 2,100 are considered turbulent. The Reynolds number decreases as fluid viscosity increases or flow rate decreases. Thus, flow tends to be laminar in most heavy-oil applications.

Once the flow regime has been determined, appropriate annular pipe flow equations are used to evaluate the flow (pressure) losses within a surface-driven PCP system. These equations take into consideration the fluid properties, flow rate, and respective rod-string and tubing dimensions. In the case of standard rod strings, the reduced annular space associated with couplings, centralizers, and rod guides can lead to significant additional pressure losses, which should also be taken into consideration. In addition, the common flow-loss equations are typically based on a Newtonian fluid model in which the applied shear stress is proportional to the shear strain rate and the viscosity is the constant of proportionality (shear stress = viscosity × shear rate). However, most high-viscosity petroleum fluids (> 100 cp [100 mPa·s]) tend to be non-Newtonian, exhibiting pseudoplastic (shear thinning) behavior, which implies that the fluid effective viscosity decreases with increasing shear rate.[36,37] Fluid viscosities typically are strongly influenced by temperature and variations in fluid composition (water cut, solution gas content). Therefore, it is very important to obtain representative fluid-property information for the application in question and to pay attention to the temperature and shear rates associated with fluid viscosity tests.

Most annular flow correlations assume that the flow is through two concentric pipes.[35] In a rod-string and tubing system, however, wellbore curvature and gravity will position the rod string against one side of the tubing in most situations. As a result, the flow pattern that develops may deviate from the concentric case. The effect of offsetting the rod string is to create a larger, unrestricted area for flow, thus reducing the magnitude of the fluid shear rates and pressure losses.[38] The magnitude of this reduction depends on the amount that the rod string is offset from center (i.e., eccentricity) and the relative diameters of the tubing, rods, and couplings. Conservative reductions for laminar flow are 40% for coupling, centralizer, and rod-guide losses and 25% for rod-body losses. For turbulent flow, reductions of 10% for coupling, centralizer, and rod-guide losses and 5% for rod-body losses are reasonable.

The significance that flow losses have on system design depends on the application. In many instances, such as wells producing light oil or high-water-cut fluids at moderate rates, the flow losses are generally small, so they often are neglected in system design. However, in wells producing high-viscosity fluids, excessive flow losses may occur with certain rod-string and tubing combinations (i.e., large rods in small-diameter tubing). In such cases, flow losses are an extremely important consideration in system design that must be addressed through appropriate sizing of the rod-string and tubing components. For example, consider flow of a 2,500 cp [2500 mPa·s] fluid through a 760 m [2,493 ft] length of tubing with 25.4 mm [1 in.] rods and slimhole standard couplings. The corresponding flow losses are shown as a function of flow rate in **Fig. 15.29** for 73 mm [2.875 in.] tubing (Case 1) and 88.9 mm [3.5 in.] tubing (Case 2). These flow losses have been "corrected" to account for non-concentric flow. The results show that excessive flow losses would render it impractical to use 73 mm [2.875 in.] tubing unless operating at very low flow rates (i.e., < 20 m³/d [126 B/D]). In contrast, use of 88.9 mm [3.5 in.] tubing leads to much lower flow losses because of the increased flow area. Fig. 15.29 also illustrates the effect that flow restrictions have on the magnitude of flow losses. With the 73 mm [2.875 in.] tubing, flow losses associated with the couplings comprised approximately 25% of the total losses even though the coupling flow length was a very small portion of the total rod length (10 of 760 m [33.3 of 2,493 ft]).

Multiphase Flow. Multiphase flow can be defined as the simultaneous flow of two or more phases of fluid, normally liquid and gas. In an oil well producing gas-saturated liquids, when the pressure drops below the bubblepoint, gas will evolve, resulting in multiphase gas/liquid flow. As this gas/liquid mixture flows through the production system, the two phases may com-

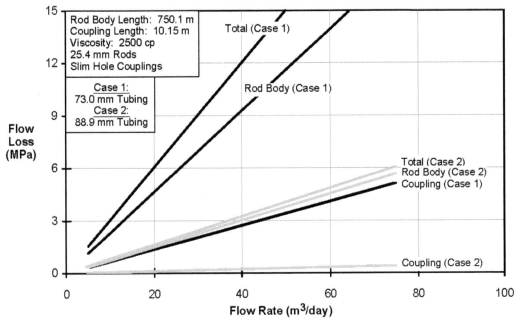

Fig. 15.29—Example of flow losses in a well producing high-viscosity fluid.

mingle in a variety of flow patterns.[39] The particular pattern or "flow regime" that occurs has a significant effect on multiphase-flow behavior and pressure loss.[40] Flow-regime maps facilitate the determination of flow patterns from gas and liquid flow rates, fluid properties, and well-bore inclinations. Fluid properties are usually obtained from empirical correlations. Depending on the particular flow regime, different multiphase-flow algorithms are used to calculate the hydrostatic and frictional pressure gradients. The hydrostatic gradient is determined from both gas and liquid densities and takes into account the different velocities of the different phases. The frictional gradient is calculated from friction factors based on two-phase fluid properties. **Fig. 15.30** illustrates the procedure used for multiphase-flow calculations, which generally are too complex to perform manually.

Most common empirical correlations for fluid properties have been developed for lighter oils,[41] and they may not apply to heavier crudes. In general, caution must be exercised when these empirical correlations are extrapolated out of the range for which they were developed. In addition, correlations developed for heavy oils from a particular field can differ considerably for heavy oils of the same API gravity in another region.

15.2.5 Rod Loading. In a PCP system, the rod string must be capable of carrying axial load and transmitting torque between the bottomhole pump and the surface drive. Therefore, rod-string design encompasses an evaluation of the axial tension and torque loading conditions for the full range of anticipated operating conditions. An appropriate size and grade of rod string can then be selected on the basis of appropriate design criteria, such as ensuring that the maximum calculated combined stress does not exceed the yield capacity or manufacturer's recommended values. Fatigue-loading considerations must also be addressed in certain applications.

Axial Load and Torque. The axial load and torque at any location along a rod string is made up of several different components (**Fig. 15.31**). Several major load components (pump hydraulic torque and pump axial load) are applied to the rod string at the pump; others (resistive torque and rod weight) are developed in a distributed manner along the length of the rod

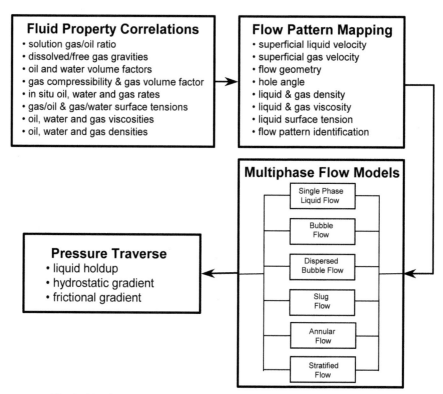

Fig. 15.30—Outline of multiphase fluid flow calculation procedure.

string. In almost all cases, the rod-string axial load and torque are maximum at the polished-rod connection at surface. Rod-string axial load at any location is equal to

$$F_r = F_p + \sum F_w - \sum F_u, \qquad (15.10)$$

where F_r = rod-string axial load (N [lbf]), F_p = pump pressure load (N [lbf]), $\sum F_w$ = sum of rod-string weight below location (N [lbf]), and $\sum F_u$= sum of uplift forces below location (N [lbf]).

Rod-string weight is a *function* of the unit weight and vertical length of the rod string. The uplift forces result from fluid flow effects, as discussed previously. The pump pressure load results from the differential pressure across the pump acting on the pump rotor and is analogous to the plunger load in a beam pump. There has been some controversy over how this load develops on the rotor, and several different formulations have been published. One correlation that provides a reasonable approximation of the pump pressure load is as follows[42]:

$$F_p = C[(p_d - p_i) \times 0.6 \times (2d^2 + 13ed + 16e^2) - p_d d_r^2], \qquad (15.11)$$

where F_p = pump pressure load (N [lbf]), p_d = pump discharge pressure (kPa [psi]), p_i = pump intake pressure (kPa [psi]), d = nominal rotor diameter (mm [in.]), e = pump eccentricity (mm [in.]), d_r = rod-string diameter (mm [in.]), and C = constant (7.9 × 10⁻⁴ [0.79]).

At any rod-string location, the torque is equal to

$$T_r = T_h + T_f + \sum T_R + T_v, \qquad (15.12)$$

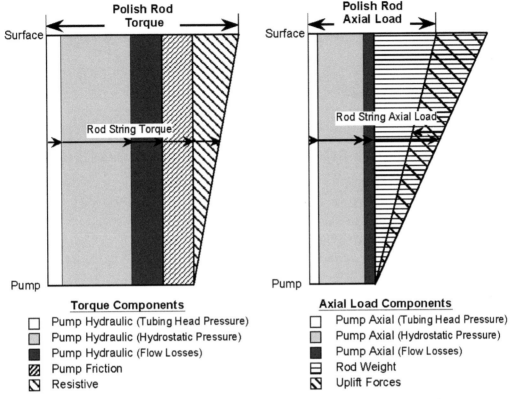

Fig. 15.31—Components that contribute to rod string torque and axial load.

where T_r = rod-string torque (N·m [ft·lbf]), T_h = pump hydraulic torque (N·m [ft·lbf]), T_f = pump friction torque (N·m [ft·lbf]), T_v = viscous pump torque (N·m [ft·lbf]), and ΣT_R = sum of rod-string resistive torque below location (N·m [ft·lbf]).

The pump torque components were discussed above. Resistive torque is usually smaller than the other two components but should be considered in high-fluid-viscosity applications.[43]

Rod-string axial loads increase with increases in well depth, rod-string diameter, and pump displacement. In applications with high fluid viscosities, changes in axial load with flow rate depend on the offsetting effects of the flow losses and rod-string uplift forces. Rod-string torque increases with increases in pump differential pressure, pump displacement, and pump friction. In applications with high fluid viscosities, torque will increase with both flow rate (because of higher flow losses that increase the pump discharge pressure) and rotational speed (because of an increase in resistive torque).

Combined Stress. The combined loading of a rod string (i.e., rod body) as a result of axial load and torque can be represented by the effective (Von Mises) stress calculated as follows:

$$\sigma_e = \sqrt{\frac{C_1 F_r^2}{\pi^2 d_r^4} + \frac{C_2 T_r^2}{\pi^2 d_r^6}}, \quad\quad\quad\quad\quad\text{.. (15.13)}$$

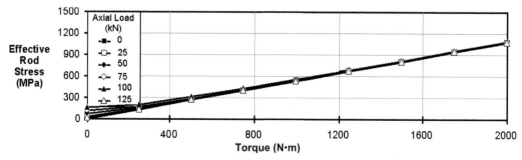

Fig. 15.32—Effective rod stress of 25.4 mm rod under combined tension and torque loading.

where σ_e = effective stress (MPa [ksi]), F_r = rod-string axial load (N [lbf]), T_r = rod-string torque (N·m [ft·lbf]), d_r = rod-string diameter (mm [in.]), C_1 = constant (16.0 or [1.6 × 10⁻⁵]), and C_2 = constant (7.680 × 10⁸ or [0.1106]).

Because the connections (couplings) used in standard rods are usually designed to have greater strength than the rod body, only the effective stresses of the rods typically need to be checked. However, proper makeup during installation is essential to ensure that the connections will function as designed by the manufacturers and provide the specified minimum load capacity. Some vendors offer sucker rods with reduced connection sizes (e.g., 25.4 mm [1 in.] rods fabricated with 22.2 mm [⅞ in.] pin connections); connection capacity can be the limiting factor in such cases. **Fig. 15.32** shows the magnitude of the maximum effective stress that develops in a 25.4 mm [1 in.] rod string for a wide range of axial load and torque conditions. These results clearly show that effective stress is primarily a function of torque and that the impact of tension on the stress magnitude at lower torque values is normally of little consequence. From these results, it becomes quite evident that there is little advantage to using tapered rod strings in PCP applications.

In contrast to the inherent cyclic rod stress that occurs in beam pumping, the rod stresses in PCP applications tend to be relatively constant. As a result, the effective rod stresses may approach the yield stress of the rod material without causing failures in PCP applications, although fatigue induced by bending is an issue in directional and horizontal wells (see below). The minimum yield stress for Grade D sucker rods is 690 MPa [100 ksi], although several manufacturers also offer higher-strength grades with yield strengths up to 860 MPa [125 ksi]. For continuous-rod products, the minimum yield stress typically ranges from 586 MPa [85 ksi] at the low end to 790 MPa [115 ksi] for the higher-strength materials. The most common continuous-rod size is 25.4 mm [1.0 in.].

In PCP system design, rod loading should be evaluated for the full range of anticipated operating conditions to ensure that the selected rod string will have adequate capacity. It is advisable to use at least a 20% safety factor in rod sizing. This will allow for unanticipated torque increases that might be brought about by such factors as sand slugs, stator swelling, or startup friction. In addition, it will provide a margin of safety in the case of rod-strength reductions caused by rod-body wear or corrosion damage. Note that a 20% decrease in rod diameter can produce a 100% increase in rod stress and a 50% reduction in the load capacity of the rod.

Rod String Fatigue. It is well established that mechanical components subjected to alternating loads are susceptible to metal fatigue, even if the peak stress level in the material is well below the yield strength. The fatigue life of a component is affected by the average (mean) stress it experiences, the magnitude of fluctuations in the applied stress, and the frequency of the stress fluctuations. Load fluctuations, coupled with a high mean stress, result in a more severe fatigue situation than in a load case with fluctuations of a similar magnitude but negligible mean stress. This is important in the context of PCP applications, which usually will involve a high mean stress in the rod string. Most steels exhibit an endurance limit, which corresponds to the maximum alternating stress that will result in an "infinite" fatigue life (i.e., for polished materials without any corrosion). Designing rod strings for alternating stress levels below the endurance limit is an excellent design criterion.[44,45]

The operating conditions in many PCP applications expose rod strings to severe load fluctuations. Variations in pump discharge pressure caused by gas in the production tubing or increases in pump friction as a result of sand or fluid slugs can cause significant fluctuations in pump torque and axial load. However, the use of PCP systems in directional wells typically presents a more critical fatigue situation, because the rods are subjected to cyclic bending stresses at a frequency matching the rotational speed of the pump. Given the typical operating speeds of PCPs, the number of loading cycles can reach several million in a relatively short time (weeks or months); therefore, fatigue analyses should be considered when these loading conditions are expected. In calculations of fatigue life, both the high frequency (i.e., bending effects in deviated wells) and low frequency (e.g., gas slugging effects) should be considered, given the different impacts they may have on stress levels.

15.2.6 Rod-String/Tubing Wear. Rod-string and tubing wear is an important consideration in the design of surface-driven PCP systems for directional, slant, and horizontal wells. The rod-string configuration, magnitude of the contact loads that develop between the rod string and tubing, produced-fluid conditions, and rotational speed of the rod string all interact to determine the wear mechanisms that will predominate and the corresponding component wear rates that will occur in different circumstances. From a design perspective, the goal is to assess the potential for wear problems and then to select a PCP system configuration that will maximize the service life of the installation.

For standard rod strings, contact between the rod string and tubing tends to be concentrated at the couplings or rod guides, although rod-body contact can also develop under certain loading conditions. In contrast, continuous sucker rods tend to contact the tubing uniformly along the wellbore. As a result, the contact load magnitudes differ considerably between these two rod configurations for the same wellbore geometry and rod-tension conditions. Particularly for standard rods, contact loads can be quite high in moderate- to high-curvature well segments, such as the angle-build sections of directional and horizontal wells. Also, well shapes that allow the tension/curvature contact loading to act in tandem with the gravity loads acting on the rod string (common in slant wells) can be particularly prone to wear problems. **Figs. 15.33 and 15.34** present charts that can be used to estimate contact loads for standard and continuous rod strings, respectively, as a function of the well-curvature and rod-tension conditions.

Field experience[6] has shown that tubing wear rates correlate most strongly with sand cut, followed in decreasing order by contact load, centralizer type, rotational speed, and water cut. In general, tubing wear rates increase exponentially with increasing sand cut (to a limit) and linearly with increasing contact load. Because of reduced lubrication, wear rates may increase significantly in situations in which the water cut increases substantially. Coated centralizers exhibit lower wear rates than standard couplings, with the degree of reduction being a function of the coating material. Note that field experience has shown some coating materials to be prone to the embedding of sand, which resulted in accelerated instead of reduced tubing wear rates. Spin-thru centralizers eliminate tubing wear very effectively as long as they remain functional. Because of the much lower uniform contact loads, tubing wear rates associated with continuous rod tend to be substantially (e.g., 5 to 20 times) lower than standard rod strings with metal couplings (material hardness and size factors play a role in the reduction). In applications using high-volume PC pumps and large-diameter standard rods, the increased surface

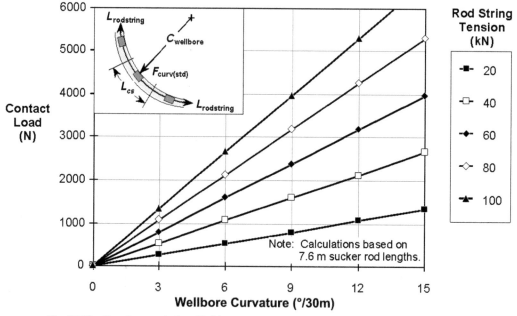

Fig. 15.33—Development of rod/tubing contact loads with standard sucker rod strings.

velocity of the couplings may contribute to a form of hydrodynamic lubrication that tends to reduce wear rates relative to the expected rates based on the load conditions involved.

Although failures resulting from rod-string/tubing wear usually occur infrequently in vertical-well applications, failures are not uncommon within weeks or even days in directional or slant wells producing sandy fluids. Although there are costs associated with wear prevention (centralizers, continuous-rod or tubing rotator systems), they are often justified by the increased workover and equipment replacement costs (e.g., couplings/centralizer and tubing) that would otherwise be incurred in such cases. In many cases, repeated failures occur because of the operating practices used and the lack of data collected during workovers to characterize the source and locations of the wear problem properly. Operators must develop an understanding of wear processes and become familiar with the workover histories and operating characteristics of a variety of wells that have experienced wear failures to become effective at designing, equipping, and operating wells to prevent wear failures.

One of the most common locations for severe rod/tubing wear is the first couple of joints above the pump. In many instances, failures have occurred in this section of the well despite the well curvature and rod tensions being higher at various uphole locations. The increased wear rates directly above the pump can be attributed to the eccentric motion of the rotor, which may cause the rod string directly above the pump to develop an impacting/rotating interaction with the tubing. This interaction results in a more severe wear mechanism. The use of robust rod centralizers as opposed to standard couplings is recommended for at least the first two or three rod connections above the pump. Ensuring that a full-length standard rod (7.6 m [25 ft]), as opposed to a short pony rod, is attached directly to the pump rotor is important. The pony rod may restrict the required orbital motion of the rotor head, causing damage to the pump stator or failure of the rotor pin.

15.2.7 Power Transmission Equipment Design. The various surface-drive system components will generally have specified maximum load and speed limits. For example, drive-head manu-

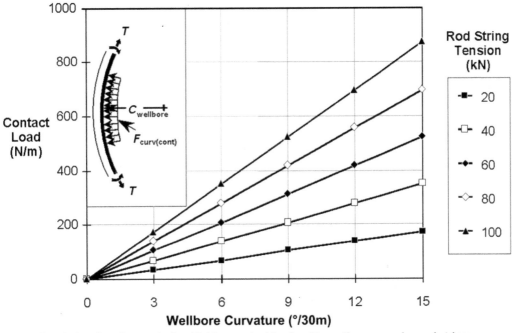

Fig. 15.34—Development of rod/tubing contact loads with continuous sucker rod strings.

facturers' catalogs will typically specify a maximum torque, polished-rod speed, and power as well as give a thrust bearing rating for their equipment. Some may also provide a maximum axial load value for their drives. The maximum torque limits typically are set for structural purposes, whereas the power limits reflect the safe operating capacity of the power transmission system (belts and sheaves or gear set). There are also torque limits related to the braking system capacity, and in many cases, only the lower of the two is published. The structural load capacity of a drive head is typically specified from an allowable overhanging motor size or weight. Motor size specifications are also important with respect to functionality of the frame, doors, and other components. Hydraulic systems have maximum and minimum speeds and a maximum hydraulic pressure indicated by the manufacturer.

Note that the maximum axial load specification of a drive head is typically not the same as the thrust bearing load rating (i.e., the Ca-90 thrust bearing rating is the loading at which 90% of bearings will survive 90 million revolutions). At a speed of 200 rpm, this number of revolutions equates to only 312 days of life, so the actual axial load on the drive head should be kept significantly lower than the thrust bearing rating to ensure long service life. It is reasonable to expect the bearing life to increase by about 10 times if the load is reduced by half.

The prime mover should be able to provide sufficient power to the system without being overloaded. The prime-mover power can be calculated as follows:

$$ P_{pmo} = \frac{CT_{pr}\omega}{E_{pt}}, \quad\dots\dots\dots\dots\dots\dots\dots\dots\dots\dots\dots\dots\dots\dots (15.14) $$

where P_{pmo} = required prime-mover power output (kW [hp]), T_{pr} = polished-rod torque (N·m [ft·lbf]), ω = polished-rod rotational speed (rpm), E_{pt} = power transmission system efficiency (%), and C = constant (1.047×10^{-2} [1.904×10^{-2}]).

In calculating the prime mover power requirement, the efficiencies of all the power transmission equipment must be considered. Belts, gears, bearings, and hydraulic systems all have associated energy losses. When selecting an electric motor, it is important to ensure that the motor will be loaded reasonably close to its rating to facilitate efficient operation. The system torque capacity should be sufficient to handle the worst-case operating conditions in the application, including startup.

Drive-head manufacturers' catalogs list maximum and minimum sheave sizes for the two sheaves required (for drive heads that use sheaves). The maximum sizes are usually determined by size restrictions; the minimum size of the motor sheave will typically be based on a belt curvature limitation and/or torque transfer performance. The sheave sizes and hydraulic equipment displacements will determine the speed at which the system operates, in conjunction with the gear reduction ratio in the drive head (if the drive head has a gearbox). They should be selected so that the prime mover operates as close as possible to its nameplate speed, even in systems in which it is possible to adjust the prime-mover speed (e.g., use of an ESC with an electric motor). When electric motors are operated at lower speeds, they are subject to reduced efficiency and overheating.

In most applications, a backspin brake is required to ensure safe operation of a PCP system. The brake system should have sufficient capacity to ensure that the maximum rated speed of the equipment is not exceeded during a worst-case backspin scenario. Again, both stuck pump and normal shutdown cases should be taken into consideration.

15.3 Specific Application Considerations
Different PCP system applications have unique operational issues and challenges. Appropriate equipment configurations, installation procedures, sizing standards, and operating practices may be required, depending on the application characteristics.

This section discusses some specific application considerations, including (1) high-viscosity oil wells; (2) high-sand-cut wells; (3) low-productivity wells; (4) gassy wells; (5) directional- and horizontal-well applications; (6) hostile fluid conditions; (7) high-speed operations; (8) coalbed-methane and water-source wells; and (9) elevated-temperature applications.

15.3.1 High-Viscosity Oil Production.
Over the past decade, PCP systems have become a very popular artificial-lift method for producing heavy oil (API gravity < 18°) wells throughout the world.[46,47] Fluid viscosity under downhole conditions can range from a few hundred centipoise to > 100,000 cp in these applications, and the production rates also vary significantly although low rates are far more typical. In Canada, for example, the low-GOR, heavy oil wells generally have low productivities (< 10 m³/d [63 B/D]), whereas recent heavy oil field developments in eastern Venezuela using horizontal wells have demonstrated very high productivities (> 500 m³/d [2,000 B/D]). These latter applications have prompted revolutionary developments in large-volume PCP systems.

Production of high-viscosity fluids can result in significant flow losses through the production tubing and surface piping. In some instances, the pressure requirements generated because of flow losses can exceed the hydrostatic head on a well. As discussed previously, pressure losses in the system accumulate and are reacted at the pump, where they cause additional pump pressure loading, leading directly to increased rod-string axial loads and system torque. It is critical that system design account for the "worst-case" flow losses, particularly the selection of the pump (pressure rating), rod string (torque capacity), and prime mover (power output).

Fig. 15.35 shows a good example of the effects that viscous flow losses and water slugging can have on pump loads in a heavy oil well. The axial and torsional loads on the well were monitored in real time with a purpose-built PCP system dynamometer unit.[48] The data show that the axial load and torque values remained relatively constant at about 45 kN and 1100 N·m [10,050 lbf and 800 ft·lbf], respectively, over the first hour of the monitoring period. Over

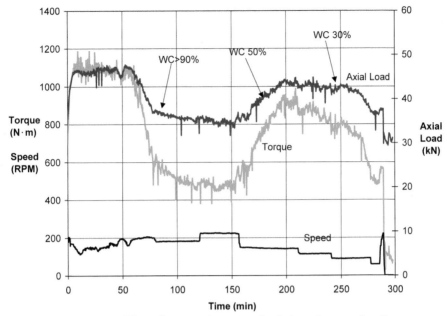

Fig. 15.35—Effect of water cut on pump loads in a viscous oil well.

the next 2 hours, both loads declined significantly, with the torque dropping to less than one-half the initial value. The loads subsequently increased again but remained somewhat below the initial load levels. Fluid samples taken regularly during the monitoring period confirmed that the well had gone from initially producing heavy oil at a very low water cut to producing a large slug of water with relatively little oil during the period. Representative water-cut values are shown at different times in Fig. 15.35. Because the only significant difference during the operating period was the viscosity of the fluid being produced, these results clearly demonstrate the pronounced effect that flow losses can have on PCP system loads.

Several alternative methods are available to minimize flow losses. Because most of the pressure drop usually occurs in the production tubing, it is important to ensure that the rod/tubing annular flow area is not overly constricted. This is most easily accomplished through the use of large-diameter tubing. However, tubing sizing must also take into account casing limitations, economics, and sand transport considerations that favor small-diameter tubing. Streamlining of the rod string is another effective way to minimize tubing flow restrictions. Large-diameter centralizers and/or a number of sucker-rod guides can contribute to significant incremental flow losses and should be avoided when flow losses are an issue. Continuous rod provides the lowest-pressure-drop alternative.

Surface piping flow losses should also be considered. Use of small-diameter flowlines and 90° elbows and tees should be avoided. Because of the logarithmic effect that temperature typically has on viscosity, surface flow losses are usually quite temperature sensitive, so insulated systems or buried flowlines are a necessity in cold climates. These alternatives should also be considered in hot climates to preserve heat and to avoid daily temperature variations in long flowlines.

In certain situations, changing the equipment configuration is not an option; other methods must be implemented to reduce flow losses. This can be accomplished by reducing the viscosity of the produced fluid, typically by injecting diluent (light petroleum products or water) down the annulus (to reduce pressure losses in the tubing) or into the flowline near the wellhead (to reduce flowline losses). Note that if viscosity-reducing additives are injected down the annulus, special caution must be taken to ensure that they will not damage the stator elastomer.

Elastomer selection and pump sizing are important in heavy oil applications to achieve optimal performance and pump run lives. It is normally preferred to start with medium-NBR elastomers in these applications because of the superior mechanical properties of these materials. However, in heavy oil applications in which the pumps are prone to swelling (e.g., eastern Venezuela), consideration should be given to the use of high nitrile elastomers. Several vendors have recently introduced soft elastomers (i.e., < 65 shore A hardness) for heavy oil service to facilitate effective sealing while allowing high concentrations of sand to pass through the pump without causing damage. Because slippage rates decrease and pump efficiencies increase with higher fluid viscosities, PC pumps can typically be sized with bench-test efficiencies of 70 to 80% at speeds of 100 to 150 rpm (i.e., at rated pressure without consideration for swell or thermal expansion) without negatively affecting performance. In new applications, optimal sizing criteria can be determined only on a trial-and-error basis by varying pump sizing and subsequently tracking both short-term and long-term performance. There is a tradeoff between sizing pumps more tightly to permit a larger degree of wear to be tolerated before a significant loss in efficiency is incurred and relaxing the fit to reduce the elastomer stresses and prevent elastomer fatigue failures. As a result, it is preferable to start by sizing pumps in the middle and adjusting the sizing criteria based on the types of failures that occur.

Production from heavy oil wells can also be highly variable in nature. To respond to the changing operating conditions, it is important to have a flexible power transmission system. Hydraulic systems are quite common because they provide variable speed capability with a high turndown ratio that is often necessary to facilitate the low pump speeds typically required. Electronic systems (electric motors with speed control systems) can also be effective as long as they have the ability to operate within the lower speed ranges.

15.3.2 High-Sand-Cut Wells. Sand production is frequently a byproduct of oil production, especially in some primary heavy oil operations (e.g., Canada) where it is an important part of the recovery process. In such operations, sand influx is usually most severe during the initial stage of production when the volumetric sand cuts can exceed 40%. Subsequently, the sand cuts often stabilize at ≤ 3%. In high-rate applications (e.g., Venezuela), even low sand cuts can equate to significant volumes of produced sand over time. Sand and other solids production can cause problems in PCP systems by accelerating equipment wear, increasing rod torque and power demand, or causing a flow restriction by accumulating around the pump intake, within the pump cavities, or above the pump in the tubing. Also, given its specific gravity of ≈ 2.7, even moderate volumes of sand can substantially increase the pressure gradient of the fluid column in the production tubing.

With proper system design and operation, PCP systems can effectively handle produced fluids with significant sand cuts under reasonably steady-state conditions. Severe operational problems (equipment failures, shutdowns requiring workovers) generally develop due to short periods of rapid sand influx (slugging). Although some slugging occurs naturally, sudden sand influx can also be initiated by operating practices that cause fairly rapid changes in bottomhole pressure. The pressure variations affect inflow rates and can disturb stable sand bridges that develop around perforations, causing the bridges to collapse and sand to flow into the wellbore. For example, experience has shown that large changes in pump speed can precipitate sand slugging. Therefore, large adjustments in pump speed should be made gradually over a few days to allow the well time to stabilize. If possible, other practices that produce sudden variations in bottomhole pressure, such as well loading or casing gas blowdown, should also be avoided. Workover operations that cause swabbing of a well (e.g., rapid pulling of the production tubing string within the perforated interval) are often followed by periods of high sand production. Changes in the produced-fluid conditions can also precipitate sand influx. For example, a sudden increase in water production or a slug of higher-viscosity fluid can lead to a breakdown of stable sand arches, causing a slug of sand to enter the wellbore.

Sand accumulation inside the tubing just above the pump is a common problem. It leads to increased pump discharge pressures, reduced fluid rates, and in severe cases, increased potential for sudden pump failure. Sand buildup occurs when the produced-fluid stream cannot carry all the sand up the tubing to surface. Therefore, it is very important to assess the sand-handling capabilities of a PCP system design for applications in which sand production is expected. Sand settling and fluid transport velocities (in vertical pipes) can be assessed by comparing the fluid drag forces calculated using well-established methods[49] with the weight of the sand particles or particle conglomerates as appropriate.

Sand buildup in the pump intake area causes decreased production rates and, in severe cases, pump failure due to complete blockage of the intake. One effective way to minimize sand accumulation around the intake is to provide a sump below the pump where excess sand can settle. Deeper sumps provide a larger buffer, and therefore it will take longer before sand accumulates to the pump level. Certain pump intake designs also contribute to sanding problems. Restricted intakes tend to produce stagnant flow regions where the sand will settle out. For sandy applications, the pump intake should be configured so that fluids can readily flow (i.e., limited bends, channels) from the wellbore into the pump intake.

Operational problems associated with sand settlement and bridging, both above and below the pump, occur most commonly in directional and horizontal wells. The ability of the produced fluid to transport sand improves with increasing fluid viscosity and flow velocity. Initial system design should consider whether the lowest anticipated production rate will be capable of moving the sand up the tubing, and allowances should be made for slugs of sand entering the system. Decreasing the tubing size and increasing the flow rate are the easiest ways to improve sand transport capability. However, the use of smaller-diameter tubing must be evaluated in terms of its effect on flow losses. Injecting a fluid down the annulus and pumping at higher rates or introducing fluid into the tubing above the pump (recirculation system) are two possible ways to increase tubing flow rates. Because water has a low viscosity, it is often more effective (but more costly) to inject produced or blend oil.

Another recommended practice for operations prone to sand production is to build excess capacity into the equipment design to allow for the associated peak loading condition. If a system normally operates at full capacity in terms of torque, power, etc., any incremental loading will cause either a reduction in speed or a complete system shutdown, which may allow sand to settle out above the pump and necessitate a workover if the rotor cannot be freed.

Produced sands tend to be highly abrasive, causing accelerated wear of the pump, rod string, and tubing. Because abrasive wear is directly proportional to the number of revolutions, the use of larger-displacement pumps operated at lower speeds can help to extend equipment life. However, large-displacement pumps may not handle the sand as effectively as small-displacement pumps. Stator wear can be minimized by choosing an elastomer with good abrasion resistance. Although the standard chrome coating used on most rotors generally provides good wear resistance, double-thickness chrome coatings are commonly specified for abrasive applications; alternatively, special coatings designed to withstand abrasive wear are also available and have shown superior performance in service.[33] Note that chrome-coated rotors with visible wear can be repaired by replating as long as the underlying base metal has not been worn.

15.3.3 Low-Productivity or Pumped-Off Wells. Low-productivity wells by definition deliver relatively low fluid rates; as a result, operators usually attempt to maximize recovery rates by producing them at low bottomhole pressures. If produced aggressively, the fluid column can be drawn down to very low levels even in some relatively high-productivity wells. These pumped-off conditions can cause pump inflow and gas interference problems that prevent the pump

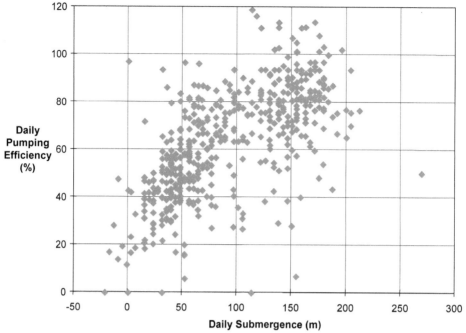

Fig. 15.36—Effect of submergence on pump efficiency.

cavities from filling completely with liquid. This results in low volumetric pump efficiency, as illustrated by the field data in **Fig. 15.36.**

Pump inflow problems are common in wells producing viscous fluids under low submergence conditions. With highly viscous fluids, difficulties occur when the pump is operated at a speed that exceeds the rate at which the fluid can flow into and up the narrow pump cavities (cavity flow velocity of the PC pump). **Fig. 15.37** shows, for example, a dramatic decline in pump operating efficiency with higher speed in a heavy oil well application. Although the trend evident in the data can be attributed in part to increased gas interference and reduced well inflow over time, the lower bottomhole pressures and pump inflow constraints definitely contributed to the large decline in efficiency.

Operating a PC pump at low volumetric efficiencies results in reduced heat removal rates, higher elastomer temperatures, and increased fluid slippage, which can substantially escalate wear rates (especially if sand is produced). As a result, continued operation at low volumetric efficiency (< 30%) can lead to significantly reduced pump life. Pump selection is a key consideration in low-productivity wells, given the potential for inflow problems to be mitigated to some degree through the use of a larger-displacement pump run at lower speed (i.e., the resultant higher torque requirements need to be considered). Pump intake designs with minimal flow restrictions are also desirable. In horizontal wells, pump submergence should be maximized by seating the pump intake as low as practical within the well.

The sensitivity of the dynamic fluid level to changes in the produced-fluid rate varies considerably between wells. Extra attention must be paid when implementing speed changes on low-productivity wells that can be pumped off rapidly to avoid damaging the pump. Caution should also be used when basing decisions on fluid-shot data in heavy oil and bitumen applications because it is common for a layer of foamy oil to exist in the annulus, which makes the acoustically measured fluid levels misleading.

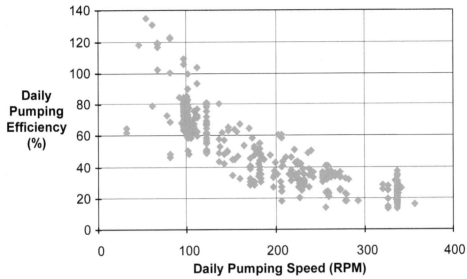

Fig. 15.37—Effect of pump speed on efficiency in well producing highly viscous fluid.

15.3.4 Gassy Well Production. In most operations, dissolved gas begins to evolve as free gas when the pressure drops as the fluid moves toward and then enters the well. Depending on the fluid properties and gas volumes, the free gas may coalesce and flow as a separate phase, or, as in the case of many heavy oil wells, it may remain trapped as discrete bubbles within the liquid phase (foamy oil). Gas entering the pump causes an apparent decrease in pump efficiency because the gas occupying a portion of the pump cavities is normally not accounted for in the fluid volume calculations. The pump must then compress the gas until it either becomes solution gas again or it reaches the required pump discharge pressure.

The best way to reduce gas interference is to keep any free gas from entering the pump intake. When possible, the intake should be located below the perforations to facilitate natural gas separation. Even if the pump can be sumped below the perforations, small casing/tubing annuli can lead to high flow velocities that can "trap" free gas and carry it to the pump intake, thereby reducing the effectiveness of the natural gravity-based separation. Thus, seating of the stator, which typically has a larger diameter than the tubing, either within or above the perforation interval should be avoided if possible. Another option is the use of slimhole PC pumps in such circumstances.

In gassy wells in which the pump must be seated above the perforations, passive gas separators that divert free gas up the casing/tubing annulus can be effective. In such cases, assemblies that centralize the pump intake in the center of the casing should be avoided because free-gas bypass tends to be more efficient in a skewed annular space.[50] In directional or horizontal wells, it is best to have the pump intake positioned on the low side of the wellbore away from any free-gas flow, which naturally tends to be along the high side of the casing. With the gravity assistance available in such wells, a short tail joint can be used to locate the pipe intake on the low side of the well casing. Special intake devices are also available that incorporate a swivel assembly to ensure that the fluid intake port remains on the low side of the wellbore. Small-diameter or long tail joints should be avoided since flow losses within the tail joint can result in increased gas volumes entering the pump.

Gas production through the pump can lead to substantial fluctuations in rod-string loading, as illustrated by the field data shown in **Fig. 15.38**. Loading variations can be attributed to discharge pressure fluctuations associated with changes in the fluid-column density and to the

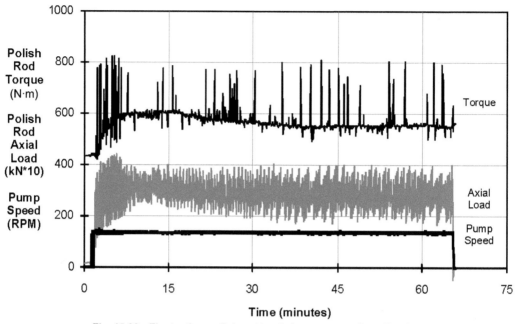

Fig. 15.38—Fluctuating polish rod loads in a gassy well application.

lifting effects of the gas produced up the tubing. Pump friction may also vary because of changes in fluid lubricity. The load fluctuations can be significant, particularly when substantial percentages or slugs of gas enter the pump. Large, continuous changes in load may accelerate rod fatigue problems or damage surface power transmission equipment.

When attempts are made to maximize fluid rates in gassy wells, the pump speed should be increased in relatively small increments, with subsequent monitoring of the resulting effects on production rates in order to identify the onset of gas interference problems.

15.3.5 Directional- and Horizontal-Well Applications. Because of the inherent curvature (angle build sections) and angled bottomhole segment of directional and horizontal wells, optimization of a PCP system design for such applications begins with the drilling program. The proposed well geometry, or directional plan, should take into consideration the design and operation attributes of a PCP system, including equipment selection, to contend with potential rod/ tubing-wear and rod-string fatigue problems, the preferred pump seating location for achieving optimal production rates throughout the well life, and possible issues related to gas and solids production.

The first line of defense against rod/tubing-wear and sucker-rod fatigue problems in deviated and horizontal wells is a good wellbore profile (see previous sections on rod-string/tubing wear and rod loading). Ideally, the planned angle build rates should be kept as low as practical, and additional monitoring is typically required during drilling to ensure that the well closely follows the prescribed path. Note that slant wells (wells spud at an angle on surface), which typically have no planned curvature, often provide a good alternative to deviated wells for shallow reservoir developments as a means to avoid rod/tubing-wear problems. With slant wells, it is important to ensure that the well profile remains straight and does not "drop down" into the target bottomhole location. If it is not possible to avoid high wellbore curvature (> 5°/30 m [5°/100 ft]) in directional or horizontal wells, it becomes even more important to obtain the smoothest wellbore profile possible. Fluctuations in wellbore curvature and curvature reversals usually lead to severe wear. Therefore, drilling programs should include clauses that

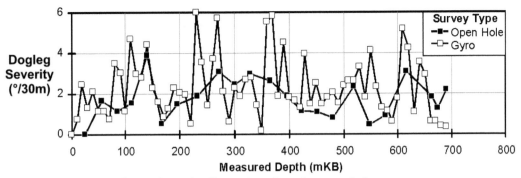

Fig. 15.39—Comparison of well curvatures based on open hole vs. gyro surveys.

specify both maximum curvatures (i.e., dogleg severity) and allowable rates of change in curvature.

Experience[6] has clearly demonstrated that closely spaced surveys (< 20 m [65 ft]) help to prevent large local curvature fluctuations and can typically be justified from an overall capital- and operating-cost perspective. Closely stationed directional surveys are also helpful in determining rod centralization requirements at a later stage. Caution should be exercised when specifying rod strings for directional and horizontal wells (i.e., where the pump is seated in the build section) based on directional surveys with long survey intervals (> 30 m [100 ft]) because the survey data may not reveal high-curvature segments that exist in the actual wellbore. This is illustrated in **Fig. 15.39**, which compares the dogleg severity established along a directional well based on the widely stationed openhole survey data recorded during drilling and a subsequent closely stationed gyro survey run in the cased wellbore. The gyro survey depicts significant variations and much higher curvatures. Therefore, if unexpected wear problems occur repeatedly at one or more locations along a directional or slant well, the survey may have provided a poor representation of the actual well curvature, and appropriate wear mitigation strategies must be taken to prevent additional failures.

In general, PCP installations that operate within the curved portions of directional or horizontal wells must be equipped to deal with potential wear and fatigue problems. To protect against rod and tubing-wear failures, options include the use of coated centralizers or rod guides with standard rod strings, use of continuous-rod strings, and use of coated and/or surface-hardened tubing joints. Use of tubing rotator systems has also grown considerably over the past decade because they have proved to be an effective preventive measure for severe wear problems in such applications. For example, a horizontal well that had experienced tubing failures monthly was subsequently on production for > 5 months without a failure after installation of a tubing rotator. From a rod-string fatigue perspective, slimhole coupling or centralizer designs offer the best performance because the inherent curvature localization adjacent to the connection is minimized. Keeping the stresses in the rod string at reasonable levels under all operating conditions is crucial, and undertaking detailed loading/fatigue analyses is highly recommended at the system design stage to facilitate proper equipment selection for the specific well conditions. Downhole-drive PCP systems, which remove any concerns about wear or fatigue problems, are another option.

Fortunately, PC pumps can operate effectively at high well angles, even beyond horizontal. However, attention is required when the pump seating interval is selected to avoid potential wear, pump inflow, and gas interference problems. This is illustrated by **Fig. 15.40**, which presents a vertical section plot of a horizontal well that was inadvertently drilled with a "trap" at the base of the build section. Because the severe sand plugging and gas slugging problems that occurred with the pump initially seated within the angle build section led to several

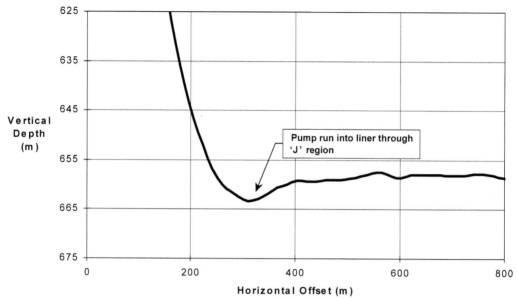

Fig. 15.40—Example of undesirable horizontal well geometry.

workovers, the operator was forced to try seating the pump in the horizontal section beyond the trap at the location shown. Although the equipment options were quite limited and wear problems were still a concern for this well, it was successfully pumped in this configuration through the use of a continuous-rod string and a larger pump that could be run at low speeds.

Ideally, the pump should be seated as low as possible in directional and horizontal wells to maximize intake pressures. As mentioned, use of long, small-diameter tail joints should be avoided as a means to lower the intake position because of the inherent pressure losses. Depending on casing size, reducing the wellbore curvature over the planned pump seating interval may be important to prevent the pump from having to operate in a bent configuration. This condition would negatively affect pump life and increase the potential for wear and rod-string fatigue failures directly above the pump. Operating a PC pump while bent may also introduce the possibility for fatigue failures of the rotor within the stator. Close attention to the wellbore inclination and curvature is also important in the selection of an optimal pump intake location to ensure that the intake will not be positioned against the high side of the casing, thus increasing the potential for gas interference problems. This is especially crucial in horizontal wells, which are more prone to gas-slugging conditions as a result of elevation variations along the horizontal section. Sand production should also be taken into consideration in establishing the pump intake position. Given that sand transport capabilities are reduced in the casing relative to the smaller-diameter production tubing, seating the pump at nearly horizontal will reduce the potential for problems resulting from sand buildup.

Achieving proper rotor space out (i.e., positioning of the rotor within the stator) is also more difficult in directional and horizontal wells because rod weight is normally a key parameter used during rod-string installation to determine when the rotor enters the stator downhole. Because of friction and the non-vertical-well profile, the weight of the rod string is partially supported by the tubing in such wells. Experience and close attention to other details, such as recording accurate measurements of tubing/rod-string component lengths and monitoring for rotation, become more important in these applications.

15.3.6 Hostile Fluid Conditions. In many applications, the constituents of the produced fluids pose the greatest difficulty in the successful use of PC pumps.[51] In fact, the current use of PCP systems in many medium- and light-oil wells can be attributed to the recent development of new elastomers that can withstand the produced-fluid chemistry, allowing reasonable pump run lives to be achieved. However, further developments and improvements are required because there are still relatively few PCPs used in fields producing light oils with gravities > 40°API. The presence of different quantities of carbon dioxide, methane and hydrogen sulfide gases, aromatics, and paraffins in the produced fluids, as well as different downhole temperature conditions, requires that special consideration be given to elastomer selection, pump sizing, and well operation. Aromatics such as benzene and toluene typically induce swelling of the stator elastomer, which makes pump sizing more difficult, whereas H_2S can cause extended vulcanization, which results in hardening and eventual breakdown of the elastomer material. Diffusion of a significant quantity of gas (in particular, CO_2) into the stator elastomer can lead to blistering or fracturing of the rubber because of rapid decompression of the pump during shutdowns.

Pump selection should be based on geometry considerations and stator elastomer properties to minimize the swell potential, although some swelling of the elastomer is inevitable in most cases. Depending on the type of elastomer and the downhole conditions, total elastomer swelling can exceed 3 to 4 vol% in extreme cases, although much lower percentages are usually required for a pump to operate effectively and have a reasonable run life. Performing swell tests is highly recommended to assist in pump selection and sizing when fluid compatibility is expected to be an issue. Experience has shown that the swelling process can be quite gradual, with it sometimes taking up to 6 months for the stator to reach the maximum swell condition. To compensate for the substantial swelling expected in some challenging well applications, pumps may be sized so loosely that they cannot generate any flow at pressures below their rated capacity in a standard bench test. In such cases, the sizing process is usually a delicate balance because, if pumps are fit too loosely, they will not be able to generate sufficient head to produce fluid to surface for a long period of time. One approach used to avoid low initial pumping efficiency because of loose sizing requirements is to complete the initial pump installation with a tighter-fit rotor and then occasionally to replace the rotor with progressively smaller sizes as the stator swells. However, this approach obviously requires additional workovers, which must be justified by the economics of the operation and comparison to other practical options.

Given the many parameters that can influence pump life, it is highly recommended that operators maintain a detailed database of all pump testing and field performance records to establish optimal pump selection and sizing criteria. This information is also crucial in terms of monitoring failure causes and effectively guiding pump replacement decisions as well conditions change.

The most common problem associated with gas diffusion into a stator is the damage caused by expansion of the gas trapped within the elastomer as a result of the rapid decompression that may occur under shutdown conditions. Elastomer selection is obviously important under such conditions because some materials are much less prone to damage than others. Although the options available to prevent rapid decompression and potential damage to the pump are limited, use of drive systems with brakes that prevent rapid drainage of the tubing during shutdown events is highly recommended in these situations. There was also a unique check valve product available previously that prevented the fluid column in the tubing from draining through the pump in the event of a shutdown. Caution should be exercised when attempting to restart such wells immediately after a shutdown to avoid a high-torque-overload condition and potential pump damage. It is also very important to avoid multiple restart attempts in rapid succession because this may lead to reduced brake effectiveness, rod-string failures, or severe pump damage. If a high-torque condition can be attributed to stator swelling/expansion, the options are to load the tubing string to surface before attempting a restart or simply leaving the well shut down for several hours (perhaps a full day) to give the elastomer time to relax.

The fluids produced in light-oil applications often contain substantial quantities of paraffin. As fluid temperature declines through the production system, the waxes precipitate and accumulate on the inside of the tubing and flowlines. If the buildup becomes large enough to severely restrict flow, additional flow losses are generated that increase the operating torque and power requirements of the drive system. Because of the rotational nature of PCP systems, scrapers are not effective at cleaning wax from the tubing. Although chemical and hot-oil treatments are available to remove wax, operators must ensure these treatments will not damage the stator elastomer.

The combination of CO_2 and high water cuts may accelerate corrosion of the rod and tubing strings, leading to failures of these components. The rotary interaction of the rod string against the tubing, even in "vertical" wells, results in a corrosion/erosion process whereby the material that would otherwise provide a protective film is constantly removed, leaving a fresh surface exposed for further corrosion attack. Given the mechanisms involved, in many cases the problems cannot be resolved by use of conventional rod guides or continuous-rod strings, although operators have successfully used standard rod strings equipped with spin-thru centralizers or rod guides to prevent additional failures in some wells. It is also important to instruct field personnel to handle and install the rod strings carefully in such wells because any surface damage will increase the potential for corrosion and corrosion/fatigue failures to occur. The use of rod strings made with special materials may help to mitigate these corrosion problems, but they are usually costlier. Some recently developed tubular products with liners or coatings have also proven to be successful in reducing corrosion-related failures. Corrosion inhibitors can also be used, but they must be compatible with the stator elastomer.

Different well stimulation treatments are commonly used by operators to improve production. When contemplating treatment of a well produced with a PCP system, particular attention must be paid to the chemistry of any fluids that may come into contact with the pump. For example, the fluids commonly used in acidizing jobs will remove the chrome from standard rotors. Other chemicals may be incompatible with the elastomer and cause stator failure.

15.3.7 High-Speed Operations. As the equipment has improved and operators have gained familiarity with PCP systems, pump operating speeds have increased substantially. Although the initial heavy oil well installations were typically run at speeds between 30 and 100 rpm, speeds in the 300 to 500 rpm range are now common, and some operators have been known to produce high-water-cut wells at speeds up to 1,000 rpm. Generally, speeds exceeding 500 rpm are not recommended because they typically lead to reduced pump and surface equipment life, increased potential for sucker-rod fatigue failures, and vibration problems.

Rod strings commonly experience excessive vibrations within certain speed ranges because of the resonant frequencies of the system. The potentially harmful vibrations can usually be minimized by adjusting the speed slightly up or down. Some speed control systems even allow the locking out of frequencies that cause harmonic problems. However, it is important to recognize that the resonant frequencies of the system will likely change over time with variations in the load and fluid flow conditions. Harmonics are an especially important consideration for the portion of the rod string directly above the pump that naturally experiences a "whipping" action because of the orbital motion of the rotor. The various factors influencing the severity of the whipping motion include the mass and eccentricity of the rotor, the extent to which the rotor sticks out above the stator, the well configuration, operating speed, anchored vs. unanchored tubing, and rod-string configuration. At higher speeds, this whipping action can lead to accelerated rod and tubing wear and fatigue failures of the sucker rod. In wells that experience repeated problems, additional rod centralization or different types of centralizers should be used.

Ensuring that PCP installations are equipped with effective braking systems and tubing-string torque anchors becomes very important for high-speed operations, particularly in deeper wells. These devices help to prevent failures associated with parted rod or tubing strings and surface equipment damage during shutdowns.

Tubing-string failure is another problem that has been encountered in some higher-speed PCP applications. The failures were characterized by a parting of one or more tubing joints at the last thread on the pin adjacent to a coupling. The failures occurred at many different locations in the wells, including near surface, midstring, and above the pump, and attempts to solve the problem with tubing anchors and tubing centralizers simply led to a subsequent failure at another location in some cases. The failures occurred after only a few weeks in some wells and after many months in others. Available anecdotal information suggests that the problems were more prevalent in wells with large-volume pumps, high speeds, and improper rotor space-out (i.e., substantial rotor stickup above the stator). The evidence points to tubing fatigue failure induced by vibration; therefore, consideration should be given to possible corrosion-enhanced fatigue. Possible remedies may include changes in pump speed or pump seating depth.

15.3.8 Coalbed-Methane and Water-Source Well Applications. PCPs have become one of the most common types of lift methods for dewatering coalbed-methane wells. Water rates are typically high during initial production and may exceed 400 m^3/d [2,500 B/D] in some cases but normally decline to $\approx$ 25% of their original level after a few months. The produced water often contains high concentrations of suspended sand from hydraulic fracturing, coal particles, and dissolved solids. To facilitate maximum gas production, the wells are usually maintained in close to a pumped-off condition. This tends to exacerbate the problems associated with the handling of produced gas. Because coalbed-methane wells typically have quite modest gas flow rates, capital outlays and operating expenses must consequently be minimized for these operations to be economically viable.

Stator elastomer selection and pump sizing are critical in coalbed-methane applications. The many substances contained in the produced water, either naturally or as additives, can have a very detrimental effect on the performance of certain elastomers. Elastomer erosion characteristics are also important, given the typical presence of significant quantities of frac sand and coal particles in the produced water. In general, the best choice of elastomer for such abrasive pumping conditions is a medium NBR because it generally has the best mechanical properties and, with the inherently low ACN content (i.e., most nonpolar), can be expected to swell the least amount when producing water that is polar. However, one must use caution because some NBR compounds are prone to high water swell. This is not the result of the polymer itself but rather the presence of certain fillers or additives that have a tendency to draw in water. Since there is no oil in the fluid to provide lubrication in these applications, it is very important to ensure minimal elastomer swell because the tightening of the rotor/stator fit leads to high levels of friction, which in turn can cause operational problems and dramatically reduce pump life. As a result, some vendors offer elastomer products specifically formulated for water-production applications.

Solids production is usually most severe the first few weeks after a coalbed-methane well is brought on production. PC pumping systems usually can effectively handle the sand and coal particles contained in the produced water. However, some coal particles can reach diameters of up to 20 mm [0.8 in.]. Difficulties arise when these larger coal particles become lodged in the pump, resulting in a sharp escalation in operating torque, severe tearing of the stator, or complete pump seizure. To prevent these problems, slotted pump intake or tailpipe assemblies should be installed that are sized to prevent the entry of large coal particles but to allow passage of coal fines, sand, and water. Buildup of sand and coal particles around the pump intake can decrease production rates and may cause pump failure as a result of complete blockage of the pump intake. To minimize solids accumulation around the intake, it is common for the wells to have sumps that extend up to 50 m [160 ft] below the pump. When the tubing is pulled for a workover, the well must be flushed out to ensure that the maximum volume is available for solids deposition. To prevent solids from settling out in the tubing above the pump, the transport velocity of the water must exceed the settling velocity of the solids. Because the flow losses associated with water production are normally insignificant, relatively small-diameter tubing can be used to create high flow velocities and thus enhanced solids transport capability.

By nature, coalbed methane operations produce substantial quantities of gas. Ideally, the produced gas flows up the casing/tubing annulus to the gathering facilities. In practice, however, some gas usually enters the pump, causing a corresponding reduction in efficiency (see Gassy-Well Applications section). Maintaining reasonably high pump efficiencies is especially important in coalbed-dewatering and water-source well applications because more heat is generated by pump friction than in an oil well where the produced fluids provide more lubrication. This is reflected by the fact that burnt pumps are a most common mode of pump failure in dewatering applications. As a result, it is important to keep gas away from the pump intake and to carefully monitor for pumped-off conditions. The pump intake should always be located below the perforations or near the bottom of openhole well completions to encourage natural gas separation. It is not uncommon for pumps to be seated up to 100 m [325 ft] below the perforations in coalbed-methane wells. In some coalbed-methane operations, the produced gas may contain a fairly high percentage of CO_2, which, as noted, can cause elastomer swelling and rapid decompression problems. In such cases, it becomes even more important to limit gas flow through the pump, although the elastomer selection and pump sizing should take potential swelling into consideration.

To achieve economic gas rates in most coalbed operations, the pressure (i.e., fluid level) at the coal seam must be maintained at a very low level. It is not uncommon for pressures to be as low as 140 kPa [20 psi], which equates to a fluid column above the perforations of only 14 m [45 ft]. The low fluid level requirements, combined with the natural fluctuations in water flow rates from the coalbed, make it critical to use some form of pumpoff control to prevent premature pump failures. The sophistication of these systems depends on the application and can vary from basic manual to fully automated control. Typically, more elaborate systems are required for wells that either have low water flow rates or need the fluid level to be maintained near the pump intake. The most basic pumpoff control systems use some form of apparatus that senses whether water is flowing at surface. Commonly used devices include differential pressure switches and hot-wire anemometers mounted in the flowline near the wellhead. Once a low-flow condition is detected, the control system will usually shut down the pumping system. Some systems will subsequently have to be manually restarted; other more sophisticated systems will automatically restart the well after a certain time delay.

15.3.9 Elevated-Temperature Applications. Elevated-temperature applications can be divided into medium- and high-temperature categories. The medium-temperature category covers deeper-well applications with natural, higher-temperature reservoir conditions ranging from 40°C [104°F] to ≈ 100°C [212°F]. Field experience has proved that PC pumps can be used successfully in wells producing fluids within this temperature range if the fluid temperatures remain relatively constant. However, to achieve reasonable run lives in such wells, additional attention must be given to elastomer and pump model selection, pump sizing practices, and system operation. The importance of these considerations rises substantially as temperatures increase toward the higher end of this range. In such applications, some additional investigations should be undertaken to assess the effects that elevated temperatures may have on the compatibility of the selected elastomer and the produced fluids. Stator elastomer debonding problems may be encountered in wells producing high-water-cut fluids at bottomhole temperatures exceeding ≈ 85°C [185°F].

Applications that fall into the high-temperature category (temperatures > 100°C [212°F]) include many geothermal wells and most thermal recovery operations. Thermal operations include mature steamfloods in which the temperatures are also relatively constant but may be as high as 200°C [400°F]; cyclic steam operations in which the temperatures can be even higher and typically change substantially; and steam-assisted gravity-drainage wells, which may operate over a wide range of high-temperature and -pressure conditions. Currently, such high-temperature applications pose significant challenges to routine PCP system use, and most of the relevant experience to date has been acquired through various experimental projects. Although the results from high-temperature tests conducted recently by various PC pump manufacturers under controlled laboratory conditions have shown considerable improvement and promise, caution is warranted in translating such results to a field application because other factors besides temperature may affect performance under the downhole operating conditions. Nevertheless, given the potential market, both equipment manufacturers and operators continue to actively pursue alternative pump design and elastomer developments to effectively extend the service temperature range of PC pumps for such applications.

Although the tolerance that elastomers have for high temperatures varies significantly with formulation, the different elastomers used in PC pumps will all begin to experience permanent chemical and physical changes with continued exposure to temperatures above their respective limits. These changes may cause the elastomer to become hard, brittle, and cracked and in some cases to shrink, which typically results in rapid deterioration in pump performance. In addition, the susceptibility of elastomers to damaging chemical attack always increases with higher temperatures. A general assessment of the values in the product literature from several different PC pump vendors indicates that the temperature limit for NBR elastomers is typically 100°C [212°F]; the limits for HNBR elastomers are 125°C [265°F] (sulfur cured) and 150°C [318°F] (peroxide cured); and for FKM elastomers, 200°C [425°F]. High temperature resistance typically comes at the expense of other desirable attributes, such as good mechanical properties (e.g., abrasion resistance), and these requirements often limit elastomer selection.

Severe problems with the sizing and performance of PC pumps are most common when the producing temperatures in a well fluctuate substantially. Although different-sized rotors may be interchanged to compensate for gradual temperature changes over several months, installation of PC pumps in wells in which the bottomhole temperature varies regularly by > 15°C [27°F] is usually not recommended.

The thermal expansion coefficient of elastomers is approximately an order of magnitude higher than that of steel; therefore, temperature changes cause stator elastomers to expand and contract far more than the steel tube housing or the mating steel rotor. The stator housings are also much stiffer than the elastomeric sleeve, so the thermal expansion of the elastomer leads to inward deformation and distortion of the pump cavity. The magnitude of the distortion is proportional to the elastomer thickness at any given point on the pump cross section. **Fig. 15.41** shows the change in stator cavity geometry with increasing thermal expansion of the elastomer. It is important to understand that thermal expansion changes are independent of any fluid-induced swell effects, which can exacerbate pump sizing problems. As a result, some vendors now offer high-temperature bench-testing capabilities as a means to eliminate elastomer thermal expansion as a parameter to be addressed indirectly in the sizing of PC pumps. Because pump performance and fit are highly dependent on temperature, caution should be exercised when bench-test results from different vendors are compared to ensure consistency among test parameters.

In certain situations, rod space-out procedures must take thermal expansion into consideration. If the tubing is anchored, temperature changes will cause the rod string to lengthen

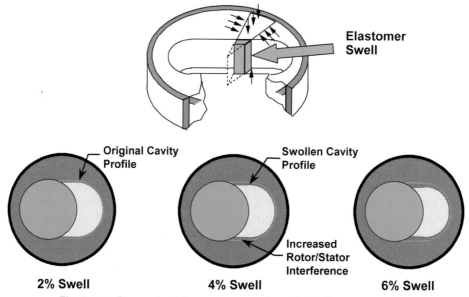

Fig. 15.41—Change in stator cavity geometry with elastomer expansion.

relative to the constrained tubing. For example, an average temperature rise of 50°C [106°F] will cause a 1000-m [3,280-ft] rod string to increase in length by > 0.5 m [1.6 ft]. However, temperature variations do not affect spaceout in wells with unanchored tubing because the resultant lengthening of the rod string and tubing is equal.

15.4 PCP System Installation, Automation, Troubleshooting, and Failure Diagnosis
Adherence to proper installation procedures for both downhole and surface equipment is key to the successful operation and performance of a PCP system. Given the many different types of equipment available and the number of system configuration alternatives, it is advisable to review the product manuals provided by PCP equipment vendors to obtain detailed installation instructions and system operating information for specific installations. The well-servicing guide books available from some service companies also provide useful information. Although the following list highlights a few key system installation and startup considerations, it is not intended to be comprehensive, and the appropriate equipment manuals should be consulted in all cases:

• Confirm that the equipment at the wellsite is configured properly for making the following connections: stator to tubing, tubing to drive head, rotor to sucker rods, and sucker rods to drive shaft or polished rod. Ensure that the stator OD is sufficiently under the casing drift diameter and that the rotor major diameter is less than the tubing-string drift diameter. Also, check to ensure that the size of any rod guides or centralizers is appropriate for the selected tubing size and weight.

• Visually inspect the various equipment components, new or used, for any signs of physical or chemical damage.

• Ensure that proper handling procedures are followed for all equipment components.

• Ensure that the tubing string is made up properly to API 5C1 specifications (i.e., makeup torque levels) to prevent backoff problems. This is especially important if a tubing anchor is not used. If the production tubing is of a smaller diameter than the pump stator, run at least one joint of larger-diameter tubing above the pump to allow for the eccentric motion of the rod string above the pump, and then swage down.

• Ensure that the rod-string connections are cleaned, undamaged, and made up to the proper API torque specifications (power tongs will likely be required for larger rod string sizes).[18] Proper makeup is essential to prevent failures during production operations, so it is recommended that every connection be validated by use of a makeup calibration card available from the rod manufacturers. Installation of at least two rod centralizers directly above the pump is recommended for directional-well applications. Record the type and position of all centralizers used.

• In hollow-shaft-drive installations, ensure proper spaceout of the rod string so that polished-rod stickup above the polished-rod clamp is minimal ($\approx$ 30 cm [1 ft] maximum). Adequate spaceout allowance is also required for thermal expansion of the rod string in higher-temperature applications in which a tubing anchor is used.

• Give special attention to wellhead alignment, especially in cases in which hammer union connections are used. The use of flanged wellhead equipment is recommended.

• If possible, start the pump slowly and increase speed gradually after a minimum of 5 minutes. Note that after startup it is normal to hear some noise generated by the rods if rod guides are not used. The noise should subside once the produced fluid reaches surface. Continue to monitor the system operation until it is clear that the unit is functioning properly.

• If possible, record torque and speed with time during startup to obtain breakaway torque information.

15.4.1 PCP System Monitoring and Automation. Well monitoring typically refers to the periodic or continuous measurement of production parameters and evaluation of the pumping system operating conditions. Reasons for well monitoring include production optimization, failure detection, and production accounting. Production parameters include fluid rates, gas rates, water cuts, sand cuts, and fluid levels. Operating parameters include tubing-head pressure, casing-head pressure, rotational speed, hydraulic pressure, motor current, and polished-rod loads. Additional production performance parameters, such as pump efficiency, can be calculated from measured values of the production and operating parameters and installed equipment specifications.

Depending on equipment type and application, a variety of methods are available to obtain measurements of the production and operating parameters. The accuracy or frequency of the measurements required for production optimization varies considerably, depending on the parameter and application. The cost and accuracy of the various methods available to measure the individual parameters can also vary considerably.

Automated Monitoring and Control Systems. Relatively few PCP systems are operated with any sort of fully automated control system, although the use of ESC systems has grown considerably. In most cases, measurements of such key parameters as fluid level and polished-rod torque are taken infrequently. These data are generally used by the operator to make decisions regarding changing the pump speed on a particular well. In many cases, there may be periods between these assessments where either the pump runs too fast and the well becomes pumped off, which increases the potential for pump damage, or the pump runs too slow and the system does not produce fluid at the maximum rate possible. Therefore, from both workover and production perspectives, there is considerable incentive to optimize the production process by automating the measurement of a few key production and operation parameters and implementing a system that uses the data to control the pumping system. Potential benefits of implementing such a system include the following:

• Provide accurate, timely data for use in analysis of individual well production performance.

• Provide operators with a means to visually assess current well conditions and performance from remote locations.

• Provide immediate identification of existing or potential problems that could lead to downtime.

• Provide access to historical data for use with production optimization software tools.

• Increase the time available to operators and engineers for identifying and implementing production optimization programs.

The first and probably most beneficial step toward fully automated well monitoring and control is implementing a pumpoff control system. Most operators base their operating strategies on the bottomhole pressure they wish to maintain. The common practice is to try to pump the well at the rate which maintains the bottomhole pressure at the lowest level possible without running the pump dry or causing it to produce large quantities of gas. Usually, this strategy is implemented by periodically checking the annular fluid level and adjusting the pump speed according to the interpreted results. However, this approach suffers from inaccuracies in the methods used to measure fluid levels and the relatively long periods that are typical between actual measurements.

The preferred approach is to measure bottomhole pressure directly with a downhole pressure gauge or an automatically actuated acoustic device. The gauge can be suspended on wireline, strapped to the tubing string, or permanently installed on the well casing. The output from the downhole gauge can be displayed at surface for manual reading, or better yet, it can be processed and stored by a data logging system at a given time interval. The data acquired can be interpreted and used by the operator to adjust the pump speed. A more effective use of the data is in conjunction with a variable-speed controller and a feedback control system. The operating speed of the downhole pump can be adjusted automatically by a feedback control system, thereby ensuring that the bottomhole pressure in the well is maintained at the desired level. Other available systems measure pump temperature, fluid rate, or axial loads as a means to control pumpoff.[52-54]

Providing fluid rate, polished-rod torque, polished-rod axial load, and various other parameters as additional feedback to a control system is conceivable. Certain consistent decisions can be made automatically by software algorithms, and accurate data can be made available to the operator so that more complex optimization and diagnosis decisions can be made.

Often, motor line current is measured and used to estimate rod-string torque. However, the relationship between current and torque depends on the efficiency and power factor of the motor. When speed remains constant, the current draw will often vary linearly with changes in torque demand. This indicates that the motor efficiency–power factor product remains relatively constant over what is usually a small torque range. However, when an ESC system is introduced, speeds and loads usually change significantly over time. These changes can result in large variations in motor efficiency and power factor. This is illustrated in **Fig. 15.42**, which shows, for a single well, the variation in polished-rod torque, motor efficiency-power factor product, and motor output power with line current. At high currents, with the motor loaded near its rated power of 30 kW [40 hp], the motor efficiency-power factor product is ≈ 70%. This corresponds to a motor efficiency of 90% and a power factor of 0.8, which are close to nominal for full-load conditions. Unfortunately, as the current draw decreases, the motor efficiency-power factor product declines to ≈ 30%. Thus, when the motor was operating at low-load conditions, the efficiency and power factor were also very low. Consequently, torque values determined from nominal motor efficiencies and power factors may be artificially high. Depending on the conditions, this might result in a well operating at a lower speed than necessary on the basis of prescribed torque limits. Therefore, caution is required when polished-rod torque is determined from motor line current.

15.4.2 Troubleshooting. Most PCP equipment vendors provide information describing troubleshooting procedures and suggestions for solving problems that may be encountered with their equipment. To assist in the diagnosis and correction of operational problems that may be encountered in PCP system installations, **Table 15.5** outlines several problematic operating scenarios and provides some possible explanations and corresponding actions or strategies that may be taken to solve the problems. In some cases, the source of a particular operational prob-

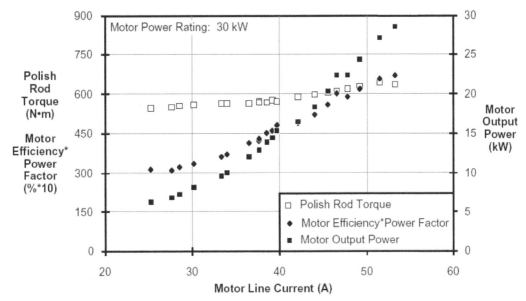

Fig. 15.42—Variation in polish rod torque, motor efficiency/power factor product with line current.

lem may be easily addressed; in other situations, the problem may be quite difficult to diagnose and expensive to resolve, especially if a workover is required. It is important to consider all the information available because further problems can be caused if the diagnosis is incorrect and the wrong mitigation strategy is taken. Specific troubleshooting actions may be taken to determine the actual source of a problem if the system remains operational. For example, some additional backpressure can be applied to the system by partially closing the flowline valve to test the pressure integrity of the pump (e.g., if a worn or damaged pump condition is suspected). In such a case, the pump is likely okay if the flow rate remains constant and the system torque increases proportionally. Another technique is to implement speed changes to diagnose problems associated with well inflow or gas interference conditions.

15.4.3 Pump Failure Analyses. When a PC pump is pulled during a workover, it should be sent to a pump shop for a thorough examination and pump test. Usually, the pump components are first cleaned and visually inspected. Inspection of the rotor involves examining the condition of the threads and pin, assessing the amount and location of any wear, and identifying the presence of any heat checking. Although equipment is available to perform a full examination of the internals of a stator (e.g., bore-scope camera), not all vendors have these systems, and stator inspections are often limited to the visual checking of the long stator cavity for signs of damage or deterioration from the two ends. The elastomer surface typically is examined as carefully as possible to locate any areas of worn, hardened, cracked, torn, swollen, or missing rubber. If the rotor and stator components show no evidence of failure, the pump will subsequently be bench tested. If the test results show that the pump is within the accepted performance guidelines for the particular application, it will usually be sent back to the field for redeployment. Pumps that are tested but do not meet the guidelines may be retested with a new rotor if the stator appears to be in good condition. The stator will be scrapped if further testing provides evidence that it has sustained permanent damage (e.g., severe wear or loss of rubber).

| TABLE 15.5— TROUBLESHOOTING CONSIDERATIONS FOR PCP INSTALLATIONS | | | | | | | | | | | |
| Symptom | | | | | | | | Possible Problem | | Possible Root Cause | Possible Remedial Action(s) |
Low torque	Normal torque	High torque	High apparent volumetric efficiency	Normal apparent volumetric efficiency	Low apparent volumetric efficiency	Unstable torque	Unstable volumetric efficiency	Component	Descriptor		
	x				x			Pump	Low efficiency	Lower reservoir inflow	Reduce pump speed
	x				x	x	x	Pump	Low efficiency	High gas fraction at pump intake	Increase pump depth, install tail joint
	x				x	x	x	Pump	Plugged intake	Excessive sand production	Perform workover flush-by
	x				x			Pump	Worn stator/rotor	Normal wear	Replace pump, size tighter
x		x	x					Pump	Stator swell	Improper pump sizing improper elastomer selection	
	x				x	x	x	Pump	Rotor stuck by sand	Improper sand production management	Perform workover/ flush-by
x	x				x			Pump	Rotor positioning in stator	Improper installation	Reposition rotor
	x		x		x			Pump	Rotor touching tag bar	Improper installation	Reposition rotor
x					x			Rods	Parted	Improper system design	Follow recommended design guidelines for load limits
x					x			Rods	Parted	Improper connection makeup	Follow recommended makeup procedures
x					x			Rods	Parted	Improper setting of drivehead torque limiter	Set torque limiter according to rod torque capacity
x	x				x			Tubing	Leak	Tubing wear because of improper system design	Install rod centralizers, use continuous rod
		x		x				Tubing	High pressure drop	Improper system design	Check for flow restrictions caused by centralizers
						x	x	Surface drive system	Belts slipping	Improper system installation	Repair surface drive system

Observations made during failed-pump inspections typically provide information that is crucial to the accurate determination of the root cause of failures. This knowledge is usually essential for establishing appropriate remedial actions to achieve improved pump run lives. The failure attributes provide clear indications of the physical mechanisms that resulted in damage to either the rotor or stator. The following sections provide descriptions of the unique damage characteristics associated with different types of pump failure mechanisms.

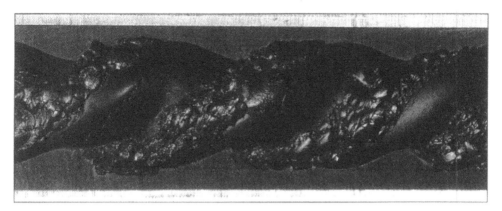

Fig. 15.43—Example of fatigue failure.

Stator Fatigue Failure. Fatigue failures are characterized by missing rubber primarily along the rotor/stator seal lines. The regions of torn or missing rubber are typically shiny and irregular (**Fig. 15.43**). Fatigue failures can be attributed to excessive cyclic deformation of the elastomer. As the material properties degrade, shear stresses can more readily generate cracks in the elastomer that subsequently propagate and eventually cause pieces of the rubber to separate from the pump. Excessive hysteretic heat buildup can accelerate material damage and associated crack growth. The loss of material along the rotor/stator seal lines leads to increased slip and a rapid decline in pump performance. Stators that have missing rubber as a result of fatigue damage are not suitable for reuse and must be scrapped.

Stator Wear. Stator wear usually can be attributed to the forced movement of abrasive solids along the stator cavities, although some wear can also occur because of the normal interaction of the rotor and stator during pump operation. Worn stators are characterized by the presence of roughened worn surfaces, usually along the minor diameter. The rate of abrasive wear is related most strongly to the quantity and abrasiveness (i.e., size, shape, and hardness) of the solid particles contained in the produced fluid. Wear rates are also influenced by elastomer type; soft stator materials are more likely to deform instead of tearing as solids pass through the pump. Stator wear is also proportional, but not necessarily linear, to the amount of interaction that occurs between the rotor and stator; consequently, stators tend to wear out more quickly at higher rotational speeds. Stator wear produces a gradual decline with time in volumetric efficiency and fluid rate. This effect is most pronounced when producing low-viscosity (< 100 cp [100 mPa·s]) fluids. Stators damaged by significant wear cannot be repaired and should be scrapped.

Rotor Wear. Rotor wear results from normal pumping action. Depending on the downhole conditions and exposure time, the severity of the wear rates can vary dramatically. Normal abrasive wear can be identified by the presence of erosion marks in the chrome plating along the major diameter of the rotor. Extreme abrasive wear is characterized by material loss through the surface coating and into the underlying base metal of the rotor. Examples of coating wear and severe base metal wear are shown in **Fig. 15.44**. Worn rotors can be rechromed and reused as long as the wear has not progressed through the chrome surface. Rotors that have sustained base-metal wear usually must be scrapped.

In some cases, base-metal wear is observed only on the top section of a rotor. This usually indicates contact between the upper portion of the rotor and the production tubing and can be attributed to the rotor being landed too high above the tag bar.

Stator Fluid Incompatibility. Fluid incompatibility and gas permeation can pose serious problems for stator elastomers. Signs of damage caused by fluid incompatibility include

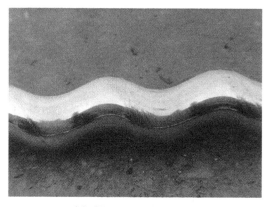 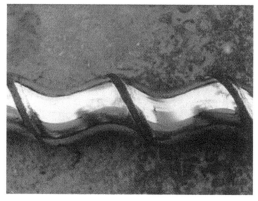

(a) Normal coating wear.   (b) Severe base metal wear.

Fig. 15.44—Abrasive rotor wear.

swelling, softening, or surface blistering of the stator elastomer. Visible swelling is the most common, occurring to some extent in many different applications. The compatibility between the elastomer and produced fluid determines the degree of swelling and the rate of any subsequent deterioration in mechanical properties. Badly swollen stators will often fail pump tests as a result of excessive torque or poor performance and must be scrapped. Stators that are only slightly swollen may be paired with a smaller-diameter rotor and reused.

Gas Permeation and Rapid Decompression. In gassy wells, stators are prone to severe damage under rapid decompression conditions (e.g., shutdown events) that facilitate the expansion of any gas that has diffused into the elastomer. The damage is caused when the force exerted by the pressurized gas trapped within the elastomer exceeds the tear strength, which leads to subsurface tearing of the material. These failures are characterized by a number of very soft, typically raised bubble areas or blisters on the stator cavity surface.

Rotor Fluid Incompatibility. Fluid incompatibility also occurs with rotors, but to a much lesser extent than with stators. Incompatibility can be identified by discoloration of the rotor and, in some cases, pitting of the base metal. It usually results from corrosive or acidic fluids attacking the chrome coating. Removing the outer chrome coating makes the rotor more susceptible to abrasive wear and may produce a noticeable increase in friction torque because of the loss of the smooth surface finish. Unless the rotor has extensive pitting, it usually can be rechromed and reused.

High-Temperature Stator Damage. Stators that have failed because of exposure to high temperatures typically exhibit elastomer surfaces that are hard, brittle, and extensively cracked. **Fig. 15.45** shows an example of a stator damaged by high-temperature operation. Causes of excessive heat include running the pump dry, high produced-fluid temperatures, and heat generation within the pump. Heat damage usually produces a rapid decline in the pump's volumetric efficiency. Stators that have failed because of high-temperature damage cannot be repaired and must be scrapped.

Rotor Heat-Cracking Damage. Heat cracking can be identified by fine cracks in the chrome plating of the rotor, primarily along the major diameter, although cracking may extend over the entire surface. Heat cracking is the result of differential expansion of the chrome and base metal in response to temperature changes. These cracks are considered normal, and minor heat cracking does not appear to affect PC pump performance negatively, although the slightly roughened surface may affect pump life. Most operators reuse rotors that have sustained minor heat cracking.

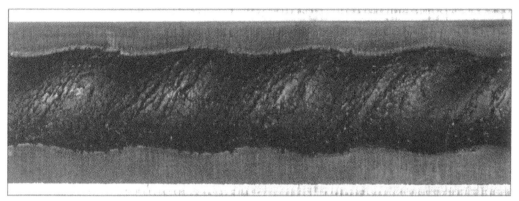

Fig. 15.45—High-temperature stator damage.

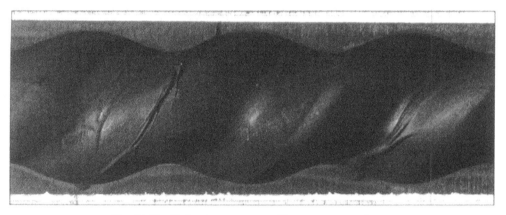

Fig. 15.46—Stator damage caused by pressure wash.

Stator Debris Damage. Occasionally, stators will exhibit damage in the form of large gouges or tears in the elastomer. This type of damage can be attributed to large foreign particles, such as pebbles, perforation plugs, or metallic debris, passing through the pump. In many cases, debris damage may go undetected unless an internal camera is used or caliper inspection is performed. Depending on the degree of damage, the pump may or may not be suitable for reuse.

Stator High-Pressure Wash. High-pressure wash or channeling is a common stator damage mechanism characterized by worm-like holes or groves cut in the elastomer (**Fig. 15.46**). These channels develop during production when a large sand particle or other debris becomes embedded in the elastomer material, creating a small orifice across the rotor/stator seal through which fluid passes at high velocity, eroding and cutting away the stator rubber. Because the channeling damages the pressure integrity of the pump, stators with extensive pressure-wash damage are not recommended for reuse.

System-Failure Analysis. A thorough analysis should be conducted after each downhole equipment failure incident to identify the circumstances during design, manufacturing, installation, and operation that likely resulted in the failure. Over time, this will lead to a valuable database of information that can be used to optimize PCP system design and operation for a particular well or field.

15.5 Design Example

15.5.1 Problem Statement. A vertical well is expected to produce 100 m³/d [629 B/D] of 12°API oil and no water, gas, or sand. The well is cased with 177.8 mm [7 in.] OD casing perforated at 1000 m [3,281 ft] from surface. At the desired flow rate, the fluid level is expected to be 600 m [1,968 ft] from surface. The casing is vented to atmosphere, while the flowline pressure is 1500 kPa [218 psi]. The oil viscosity is 1,000 cp [1000 mPa·s].

Design a PCP system to produce this well with the following constraints. The pump should be set below the perforations at 1010 m [3,312 ft]; its speed should not exceed 350 rpm; and the pump should not be loaded above its rated pressure. The rod stress should be < 80% of yield (assume API Grade D rods).

The following pumps are available. Assume that any of these pumps will operate at 85% volumetric efficiency under downhole conditions and that the friction torque will be 20% of the hydraulic torque at the pump's rated pressure.

	Pump A	Pump B	Pump C	Pump D	Pump E
Displacement, $m^3/d/rpm$	0.15	0.30	0.45	0.70	1.00
Pressure rating, kPa	12,000	12,000	18,000	15,000	12,000
Major diameter, mm	50	54	52	58	74
Minor diameter, mm	38	41	35	44	51
OD, mm	88.9	95	108	114.3	114.3
Length, m	4.0	4.5	8.0	12.0	10.0

Solution. Using Eq. 15.4, we can determine the minimum displacement required to achieve the desired flow rate without exceeding the specified maximum pump speed:

$$s_{min} = \frac{100 q_a}{\omega E} = \frac{100 \times 100 \text{ m}^3/\text{d}}{85\% \times 350 \text{ rpm}} = 0.336 \text{ m}^3/\text{d}/\text{rpm} .$$

The pump displacement must be > 0.336 m³/d/rpm. This eliminates Pumps A and B from further consideration.

The next step is to determine the differential pressure on the pump using Eqs. 15.5 through 15.7. The pump intake pressure is:

$$p_i = p_{ch} + p_g + p_L .$$

Casing-head pressure was defined in the problem statement to be atmospheric pressure, or 0 kPa (gauge pressure). The gas and liquid hydrostatic pressures can be calculated from the gas and liquid densities and the column heights. The pump intake is 1010 m from surface, and the fluid level is 600 m from surface. This means that there is 600 m of gas column and 410 m of liquid column. An average gas density can be estimated from the pressure at surface: 0.8 kg/m³.

$$p_g = \rho_g \times g \times h_{gas} = 0.8 \text{ kg/m}^3 \times 9.81 \text{ m/s}^2 \times 600 \text{ m} = 4700 \text{ Pa} \approx 5 \text{ kPa} .$$

This gives a gas column hydrostatic pressure of 5 kPa. (Note that this method is an approximation; the actual gas density will change as the pressure increases, but because the value is so small relative to the other pressures in the system, the error introduced by this approxima-tion is small.) The density of 12°API oil is 984 kg/m³, so the liquid hydrostatic pressure is 3958 kPa:

$$p_L = \rho_L \times g \times h_L = 984 \text{ kg/m}^3 \times 9.81 \text{ m/s}^2 \times 410 \text{ m} = 3\ 958\ 000 \text{ Pa} \approx 3958 \text{ kPa} .$$

$$\text{The pump intake pressure is } p_i = 0 + 5 + 3958 = 3963 \text{ kPa} .$$

In this case, the produced oil must flow from the perforations past the pump to reach the intake. Any flow losses here must also be considered in calculating the pump intake pressure. However, because the distance is small and there is a large clearance between the pump and casing, these losses are small and can be neglected. Note that if 139.7 mm OD casing had been used instead, there would be a very small annulus between the casing and the pump, and the flow losses between the perforations and the intake could be quite significant.

The pump discharge pressure is calculated from:

$$p_d = p_{th} + p_L + p_{losses} .$$

The tubing-head pressure is given as 1500 kPa. The liquid hydrostatic head will depend on the location of the top of the pump. The pump is seated at 1010 m (intake depth), but the three pump alternatives have different lengths, so the top will be at a different location in each case. Also, the flow loss will depend on the selection of tubing and rods. The solution process will be iterative; it is necessary to calculate these values for one set of equipment and then redo the calculation if it appears that the selected equipment may not be the best choice. If the pump length is 8 m, the top of the pump will be at 1002 m, and the hydrostatic head of the liquid in the tubing is 9673 kPa:

$$p_g = \rho_g \times g \times h_g = 984 \text{ kg/m}^3 \times 9.81 \text{ m/s}^2 \times 1002 \text{ m} = 9\ 673\ 000 \text{ Pa} \approx 9673 \text{ kPa} .$$

The calculation of flow losses was not described in detail in this chapter, but many differ-ent formulations are available in the literature, including this *Handbook*. For now, we will consider the use of 88.9 mm × 13.8 kg/m tubing, with 25.4 mm rods, 7.62 m in length, with standard couplings (55.6 mm diameter, 101.6 mm length). For the specified well depth, 131 couplings are needed, for a total length of 13.3 m; the remaining 988.7 m (assuming that the top of the pump is at 1002 m) is covered by rod segments. We can calculate the flow losses past 988.7 m of rod and 13.3 m of coupling separately and then add the two results together to obtain the total flow loss. This approximation neglects the flow effects at the ends of the cou-plings, but it should still provide adequate results. The ID of 88.9 mm × 13.8 kg/m tubing is 76.0 mm, and the drift diameter is 72.82 mm. For flow calculations, it is recommended that the ID instead of drift diameter be used. Assuming that the rods and couplings are concentric, the flow losses can be calculated (using one method) to be 5223 kPa past the rod body and 841 kPa past the couplings for a total of 6064 kPa. If, as normally expected, the rods and couplings are not concentric within the tubing, the flow losses would be somewhat reduced, but such a reduction will not be considered here, so the results are conservative.

We can now calculate the pump discharge pressure,

$$p_d = p_{th} + p_L + p_{losses} = 1500 + 9672 + 6064 \text{ kPa},$$

and the pump differential pressure,

$$p_{lift} = p_d - p_i = 17\ 237 - 3963 = 13\ 274\ \ kPa\ .$$

The pump is required to work against a differential pressure of 13 274 kPa. Only Pumps C and D have a pressure rating exceeding this value. Also, note that Pump E cannot be used with this tubing because the major rotor diameter is larger than the drift diameter of the tubing. However, if a larger tubing size that would accommodate the large rotor diameter were used, the flow losses would be reduced, possibly to the point that the pressure rating of Pump E would not be exceeded. Therefore, Pump E will continue to be considered a potential candidate. All of the pumps have an OD that is less than the drift diameter of even the heaviest-wall 177.8 mm casing. Therefore, none of these pumps must be eliminated due to casing size.

The next task is to estimate the torque in the rods. The torque on the pump is given by:

$$T_t = T_h + T_f .$$

The friction torque was estimated in the problem statement to be 20% of the hydraulic torque at the pump's rated pressure. Hydraulic torque is calculated from Eq 15.8:

$$T_h = 0.111\ \ s\ \ p_{lift}\ .$$

From this, we can estimate the friction torque for each pump. For example, for Pump C,

$$T_f = 0.111 \times 0.45\ \ m^3/d/rpm \times (20\% \times 18000\ \ kPa) = 180\ \ N \cdot m\ .$$

Accordingly, the values are: Pump C - 180 N·m; Pump D - 233 N·m; and Pump E - 266 N·m.

Next, the hydraulic torque for a differential pressure of 13 274 kPa is calculated for each of these pumps as

$$T_h = 0.111 \times 0.45\ \ m^3/d/rpm \times 13274\ \ kPa = 663\ \ N \cdot m\ \ (for\ \ Pump\ \ C)\ .$$

Thus, the hydraulic torque values are as follows: Pump C - 663 N·m; Pump D - 1026 N·m; and Pump E - 1470 N·m.

The torque on the rod string includes the pump torque plus torsional loading of the rod string resulting from mechanical interaction (friction) with the tubing and the resistance to rotation caused by the fluid viscosity. In a vertical well, the tubing friction loads can usually be considered negligible. The resistive torques for each of these pumps can be calculated at the speed at which they would run to produce the required amount of oil[42]: Pump C - 69.4 N·m; Pump D - 44.4 N·m; and Pump E - 31.2 N·m. The total rod torque is then the sum of the respective pump friction, hydraulic torque and rod resistive torque values: Pump C - 912 N·m; Pump D - 1304 N·m; and Pump E - 1768 N·m.

When considering rod loading, we must calculate the axial load in the rods and the torque. Axial load can be found from Eq. 15.10:

$$F_r = F_p + \sum F_w - \sum F_u\ .$$

Calculation of the uplift forces will be neglected for this example, providing a slightly conservative result. The rod weight is easily calculated from the specific weight of steel and the rod volume, neglecting the additional weight from the couplings and upsets. For a 25.4 mm rod that is 1002 m long (Pump C) with a steel specific weight of 77 kN/m³, the rod weight is

$$F_w = V \times 77 \text{ kN/m}^3 = 1002 \ m \times \frac{\pi}{4} \times (0.0254 \text{ m})^2 \times 77 \text{ kN/m}^3 = 39.1 \text{ kN} \ .$$

For pumps D and E, with their respective rod lengths, the rod weights are 38.9 kN and 39.0 kN. Pump load is given by Eq. 15.11 as

$$F_p = C[(p_d - p_i) \times 0.6 \times (2d^2 + 13ed + 16e^2) - p_d d_r^2],$$

where $C = 7.9 \times 10^{-4}$ when p is in Newtons, d and e are in millimeters, and pressures are in kPa.

To get the eccentricity values for the pumps for use in this equation, we must recognize that the major diameter is equal to the minor diameter plus twice the eccentricity. Therefore, the eccentricities for Pumps C, D, and E are 8.5, 7.0, and 11.5 mm, respectively. At a discharge pressure of 17 238 kPa and intake pressure of 3963 kPa, the axial load at the pump is as follows: Pump C - 38.2 kN; Pump D - 45.5 kN; and Pump E - 85.0 kN. So, neglecting the uplift forces, the total axial rod loads corresponding to the three pumps are: Pump C - 77.3 kN; Pump D - 84.4 kN; and Pump E - 124.1 kN.

The total stress of the rods can now be determined using Eq. 5.13. For Pump C, this gives:

$$\sigma_e = \sqrt{\frac{16 \cdot 77300^2}{\pi^2 25.4^4} + \frac{7.68 \times 10^8 \times 912^2}{\pi^2 25.4^6}}$$
$$= \sqrt{23723 + 241018}$$
$$= 514 \text{ MPa} \ .$$

The maximum stress is 514 MPa, which is 88% of the minimum yield for Grade D rods [586 MPa]. Note that the rod stresses exceed the yield capacity if the other two pumps are used. This condition would be in violation of the 80% loading criterion included in the problem statement.

To redesign the system to produce the well within the specified parameters, it appears that two viable options would be to decrease the differential pressure on the pump, or to increase the strength of the rods. There is nothing that can be done to reduce the hydrostatic head on the system while maintaining the same flow rate. However, a decrease in flow rate would reduce flow losses and would cause the fluid level in the casing to rise, thus increasing the pump intake pressure and decreasing the pump differential pressure. The tubing-head pressure can typically be reduced significantly only through changes in the gathering system to reduce the flowline pressure, through the addition of a transfer pump, or through the use of viscosity-reducing chemicals at surface.

Another way to decrease the pressure on the pump is to reduce the flow losses, which accounted for almost half the differential pump pressure. This can be achieved either through diluent injection or by increasing the flow area in the production tubing by using a larger-diameter pipe or a smaller-diameter rod string. Although using smaller rods would reduce flow losses, the load capacity would also be reduced (assuming the same material), so this does not appear to be a viable option, although the use of higher-strength rods may be an option in some cases. However, the use of a larger tubing string seems quite practical in this case.

The flow losses with 114.3 mm tubing with 25.4 mm rods would be $\approx$ 1338 kPa. This reduces the differential pressure to 8548 kPa, producing a corresponding reduction in the pump hydraulic torque values. The resistive torque is also reduced slightly. The total torque on the rod string for the three pump candidates can be recalculated to give the following values:

Pump C - 671 N·m; Pump D - 935 N·m; and Pump E - 1241 N·m. The total axial load on the rod string can be recalculated as follows: Pump C - 63.0 kN; Pump D - 67.5 kN; and Pump E - 93.0 kN. With the lower torque and axial loads, the peak rod stress in the three cases is as follows: Pump C - 382 MPa (65%); Pump D - 520 MPa (89%), and Pump E - 693 MPa (118%). Pump C now gives a rod stress that is below 80% of yield, the criterion in the problem statement; the other two pumps will still cause the rod stress to exceed the specified criterion. Note that Pump C will operate at 261 rpm to produce 100 m^3/d/rpm at a volumetric efficiency of 85%.

At this point in a typical system design, the pump, tubing, and rods have all been selected. The surface-drive system must now be established. The rod-string axial load at the surface is 63 kN, the torque is 671 N·m, and the operating speed of the polished rod is 261 rpm. A suitable drive can be selected from any manufacturer's catalog by comparing these values to the published load and speed limits. The type of drive head (right angle or vertical, solid or hollow shaft, direct electric or hydraulic, etc.) normally is based on user preferences and field characteristics. For example, if electricity is not available, then an internal combustion engine must be used, which normally leads to the selection of a hydraulic system because otherwise the belts would typically have to be very long. If electricity is available but electronic speed control systems are not available or used in the area, hydraulic systems are often still preferred if regular speed adjustments are anticipated; otherwise, direct electric drives with a fixed selection of belts/sheaves or gears are typically used.

This example problem did not address wear and fatigue considerations because a vertical well was specified. In directional wells, however, wear- and fatigue-related problems can be significant. Estimating fatigue life and wear rates is quite difficult and is beyond the scope of this chapter. The example problem also did not consider the many issues that can arise when wells produce gas. The presence of gas affects both the frictional pressure losses and the hydrostatic gradient, and the corresponding calculations are much more complex. Pump efficiency is also significantly affected by any free gas that enters the pump intake. Most pump vendors have access to software tools that can be used to complete a system design evaluation for these more complex applications.

Nomenclature

d = rotor minor diameter, mm [in.]

d_r = rod-string diameter, mm [in.]

e = rotor eccentricity, mm [in.]

E = volumetric pumping efficiency in service

E_{pt} = power transmission system efficiency

F_p = axial load resulting from pump differential pressure, N [lbf]

F_r = rod-string axial load, N [lbf]

F_u = uplift forces on rods, N [lbf]

F_w = sum of rod-string weight below location, N [lbf]

L_s = stator pitch length, mm [in.]

p_{ch} = casing-head pressure, kPa [psi]

p_d = pump discharge pressure, kPa [psi]

p_g = gas-column pressure, kPa [psi]

p_i = pump intake pressure, kPa [psi]

p_L = liquid-column pressure, kPa [psi]

p_{lift} = differential pump pressure, kPa [psi]

p_{losses} = tubing flow losses, kPa [psi]

P_{pmo} = required prime-mover power output, kW [hp]

p_{th} = tubing-head pressure, kPa [psi]

p_{tail} = pressure losses resulting from auxiliary components, kPa [psi]

q_a = actual pump flow rate, m³/d [B/D]

q_s = slippage rate, m³/d [B/D]

q_{th} = theoretical pump flow rate, m³/d [B/D]

s = pump volumetric displacement, m³/d/rpm [B/D/rpm]

s_{min} = minimum required pump displacement, m³/d/rpm [B/D/rpm]

T_f = pump friction torque, N·m [ft·lbf]

T_h = hydraulic pump torque, N·m [ft·lbf]

T_{pr} = polished-rod torque, N·m [ft·lbf]

T_r = rod-string torque, N·m [ft·lbf]

T_R = rod-string resistive torque, N·m [ft·lbf]

T_t = total pump torque, N·m [ft·lbf]

T_v = viscous pump torque, N·m [ft·lbf]

ρ_g = liquid density, kg/m³

ρ_L = liquid density, kg/m³

σ_e = Von Mises effective stress, MPa [ksi]

ω = pump rotational speed, rpm

References

1. Moineau, R.J.L.: "Gear Mechanism," U.S. Patent No. 1,892,217 (1932).
2. Moineau, R.J.L.: "Gear Mechanism," U.S. Patent No. 2,085,115 (1937).
3. Cholet, H.: *Progressing Cavity Pumps,* Inst. Francais du Petrole, Paris (1997).
4. Lea, J.F., Anderson, P.D., and Anderson, D.G.: "Optimization of Progressive Cavity Pump Systems in the Development of the Clearwater Heavy Oil Reservoir," paper 87-38-03 presented at the 1987 Annual Technical Meeting of the Petroleum Soc. of CIM, Calgary, 7–10 June.
5. Gaymard, B., Chanton, E., and Puyo, P.: "The Progressing Cavity Pump in Europe: Results and New Developments," paper OSEA 88136 presented at the 1988 Offshore South East Asia Conference, Singapore, 2–5 February.
6. Matthews, C.M. and Dunn, L.J.: "Drilling and Production Practices to Mitigate Sucker Rod/Tubing-Wear-Related Failures in Directional Wells," *SPEPF* (November 1993) 251.
7. Wright, D. and Adair, R.: "Progressive Cavity Pumps Prove More Efficient in Mature Waterflood Tests," *Oil & Gas J.* (August 1993) 43.
8. Clegg, J.D., Bucaram, S.M., and Hein, N.W. Jr.: "Recommendations and Comparisons for Selecting Artificial-Lift Methods," *JPT* (December 1993) 1128.
9. Saveth, K.J., Klein, S.T., and Fisher, K.B.: "A Comparative Analysis of Efficiency and Horsepower Between Progressing Cavity Pumps and Plunger Pumps," paper SPE 16194 presented at the 1987 SPE Production Operations Symposium, Oklahoma City, 8–10 March.
10. Eson, R.: "Optimizing Mature Oil Fields Through the Utilization of Alternative Artificial Lift Systems," paper SPE 38336 presented at the 1997 SPE Western Regional Meeting, Long Beach, California, 25–27 June.
11. Karassik, I.J., Krutzsch, W.C., Fraser, W.H. *et al.: Pump Handbook,* second edition, McGraw-Hill Book Co. Inc., New York City.
12. Saveth, K.J. and Klein, S.T.: "The Progressing Cavity Pump: Principle and Capabilities," paper SPE 18873 presented at the 1989 SPE Production Operations Symposium, Oklahoma City, 13–14 March.
13. Gent, A.N.: *Engineering With Rubber,* Rubber Div. of the American Chemical Soc., Oxford University Press, New York City (1992).
14. Morton, M.: *Rubber Technology,* third edition, Chapman and Hall, London (1995).

15. Morrell, S.H.: *Recent Developments in Nitrile Rubber,* Elsevier Applied Science Publishers, London, Vol. 46, Section 2, 43–84.
16. Campomizzi, E.C.: "Engineering Properties of Hydrogenated Nitrile Rubber," paper presented at the 1985 Energy Rubber Group Education Symposium, Arlington, Texas, 17–18 September.
17. Hashimoto, K., Noboru W., and Akira Y.: "Highly Saturated Nitrile Elastomer: A New High Temperature, Chemical Resistant Elastomer," paper presented at the 1983 Meeting of the Rubber Division of the ACS, Houston, 25–28 October.
18. *Spec. 11B, Specification for Sucker Rods,* API, Washington, DC (1990).
19. *Spec. 5CT, Specification for Casing and Tubing,* API, Washington, DC (1990).
20. Lange, J. and Strawn, J.: "Prime Movers," *Petroleum Engineering Handbook,* SPE, Richardson, Texas (2006) Chapter 8.
21. Klein, S.T., Thrasher, W.B., Mena, L. *et al.:* "Well Optimization Package for Progressive Cavity Pumping Systems," paper SPE 52162 presented at the SPE Mid-Continent Operations Symposium, Oklahoma City, 28–31 March.
22. Delpassand, M.S.: "High Volume Down-Hole Progressing Cavity Pumps in Viscous Applications with Electric Submersible Motors," paper 18 presented at the 1998 Gulf Coast Section ESP Workshop, Houston, April.
23. Skoczylas, P. and Alhanati, F.J.S.: "Flow Regime Effects on Downhole Motor Cooling," paper presented at the 1998 SPE Gulf Coast Section ESP Workshop, Houston, April.
24. Dinkins, W. *et al.:* "Thru-Tubing Conveyed Progressive Cavity Pump ESP Operational Issues: A Short Story," paper presented at the SPE Electric Submersible Pump Workshop, Houston, May 2002.
25. Dunn, L.J., Matthews, C.M., and Brown, D.: "Field Experience With Instrumented PC Charge Pump Systems," paper presented at the 1996 Progressing Cavity Pump Workshop, Tulsa, 19 November.
26. Campbell, B.: "Recirculation Systems for Heavy Oil Primary Production in the Lindbergh Oil Sands," paper presented at the 1992 Challenges and Innovations Heavy Oil and Oil Sands Technical Symposium, Lloydminster, Alberta, 11 March.
27. Klein, S.T., Thompson, S.: "Field Study: Utilizing a Progressing Cavity Pump for a Closed-Loop Downhole Injection System," paper SPE 24795 presented at the 1992 SPE Annual Technical Conference and Exhibition, Washington, DC, 4–7 October.
28. Peachey, B.R. *et al.:* "Downhole Oil/Water Separation Moves Into High Gear," paper CIM 97-91 presented at the 1997 Annual Technical Meeting of the CIM, Calgary, 8–11 June.
29. *ISO Standard 15136-1, Downhole Equipment for Petroleum and Natural Gas Industries: Progressing Cavity Pump Systems for Artificial Lift, Part 1: Pumps,* first edition (July 15, 2001).
30. Wagg, B.T.: "Development of a Standard for PCP System Surface Drives," paper 2002-091 presented at the 2002 Intl. Petroleum Conference of the CIM, Calgary, 11–13 June.
31. Vogel, J.V.: Inflow Performance Relationships for Solution-Gas Drive Wells," *JPT* (1968) 83.
32. Weir, B.: "PC Pumps for High Volume Heavy Oil Production," paper presented at the 2001 SPE Applied Technology Workshop— Progressing Cavity Pumps, Puerto La Cruz, Venezuela, January.
33. Delpassand, M.S.: "Progressing Cavity (PC) Pump Design Optimization for Abrasive Applications," paper SPE 37455 presented at the 1997 SPE Production Operations Symposium, Oklahoma City, 9–11 March.
34. Vetter, G., Kiebling, R., and Wirth, W.: "Abrasive Wear in Pumps: A Tribometric Approach to Improve Pump Life," *Proc.,* 13th Intl. Pump Users Symposium.
35. White, F.M.: *Fluid Mechanics,* McGraw-Hill Inc., New York City (1986)
36. Metzner, A.B. and Reed, J.C.: "Flow of Non-Newtonian Fluids: Correlation of the Laminar, Transition, and Turbulent-Flow Regions," *AIChE J.* (1 December, 1995) 434.
37. Dodge, D.W. and Metzner, A.B.: "Turbulent Flow of Non-Newtonian Systems," *AIChE J.* (June 1959) **5,** No. 2, 189.
38. Haciislamoglu, M., and Cartalos, U.: "Fluid Flow in a Skewed Annulus," *Drilling Technology* (1994) **56,** 31.
39. Brill, J.P. and Mukherjee, H.: *Multiphase Flow in Wells,* Monograph Series, SPE, Richardson, Texas (1999) **17.**

40. Barnea, D.: "A Unified Model for Predicting Flow-Pattern Transitions for the Whole Range of Pipe Inclinations," *Int. J. Multiphase Flow* (1987) **13**, No. 1, 1–12.
41. McCain, W.D. Jr.: *The Properties of Petroleum Fluids,* PennWell Publishing Co., Tulsa (1989).
42. Matthews, C.M., Skoczylas, P., and Zahacy, T.A.: *Progressing Cavity Pumping Systems: Design, Operation and Performance Optimization: Short Course Notes,* CFER Technologies (2001).
43. Blanco, L.B. and Ribeiro, P.R.: "Finite Element Modeling of Heavy Oil Production Using PCP," paper SPE 53961 presented at the 1999 SPE Latin American and Caribbean Petroleum Engineering Conference, Caracas, Venezuela, 21–23 April.
44. Shigley, J.E.: *Mechanical Engineering Design,* McGraw-Hill Book Co. Inc., New York City (1986) 227–281.
45. Bannantine, J.A. *et al.: Fundamentals of Metal Fatigue Analysis,* Prentice Hall, New York City (1990).
46. Dunn, L.J., Matthews, C.M., and Zahacy, T.A.: "Progressing Cavity Pumping System Applications in Heavy Oil Production," paper SPE 30271 presented at the 1995 SPE International Heavy Oil Symposium, Calgary, 19–21 June.
47. Wild, A.G.: "Pumping Viscous Fluids With Progressing Cavity Pumps," paper presented at the 1991 Intl. Pump Conference: Meeting the Pump Users' Needs, Regents Park, London, 17–19 April.
48. Matthews, C.M., Dunn, L.J., and Zahacy, T.A.: "Real Time Monitoring of Fluid Rates, Fluid Viscosity and Polished Rod Loads in Progressing Cavity Pump Installations," paper presented at the 1993 CIM/CHOA Heavy Oil and Oil Sands Symposium, Calgary, 9 March.
49. Govier, G.W. and Aziz, K.: *The Flow of Complex Mixtures in Pipes,* Krieger Publishing Co., Florida (1995).
50. Podio, A.L. and Wood, M.D.: "Decentralized, Continuous-Flow Gas Anchor," paper SPE 29537 presented at the 1995 SPE Production Operations Symposium, Oklahoma City, 2–4 April.
51. Matthews, C.M., Alhanati, F.J.S, and Dall'Acqua, D.: "PC Pumping System Design Considerations for Light Oil Applications," paper presented at the 1997 Progressing Cavity Pump Workshop, Tulsa, 19 November.
52. Quijada, E., Brunings, C., and Mena, L.: "Automated Diagnostic of Progressive Cavity Pumps," UNITAR. paper 1998.067 (1998).
53. Carvalho, P.G., Morooka, C., and Bordalo, S.: "CONTROL: PCP—An Intelligent System for Progressing Cavity Pumps," paper SPE 63048 presented at the 2000 SPE Annual Technical Conference and Exhibition, Dallas, 1–4 October.
54. Mena, L. and Klein, S.: "Surface Axial Load Based Progressive Cavity Pump Optimization System," paper SPE 53962 presented at the 1999 SPE Latin American and Caribbean Petroleum Engineering Conference, Caracas, Venezuela, 21–23 April.

SI Metric Conversion Factors

°API	141.5/(131.5 + °API)		= g/cm³
bbl ×	1.5897 873	E–01	= m³
cp ×	1.0*	E–03	= Pa·s
°F	(°F – 32)/1.8		= °C
ft·lbf ×	1.355 818	E+00	= N·m
hp ×	0.7460*	E+00	= kW
in. ×	25.4*	E+00	= mm
lbf ×	4.448 222	E+00	= N
ft ×	0.3048	E+00	= m
psi ×	6.895 757	E+00	= kPa
scf/STB ×	0.178	E+00	= m³/m³

*Conversion factor is exact.

Chapter 16
Plunger Lift
Scott D. Listiak, SPE, EOG Resources Inc. and **Daniel H. Phillips,** SPE, ConocoPhillips Co.

16.1 Introduction

Plunger lift has become a widely accepted and economical artificial-lift alternative, especially in high-gas/liquid-ratio (GLR) gas and oil wells (**Fig. 16.1**). Plunger lift uses a free piston that travels up and down in the well's tubing string. It minimizes liquid fallback and uses the well's energy more efficiently than does slug or bubble flow. As with other artificial-lift methods, the purpose of plunger lift is to remove liquids from the wellbore so that the well can be produced at the lowest bottomhole pressures. [CD edition includes video clips—*Basic Plunger Animation* and *Plunger Lift System.*]

Whether in a gas well, oil well, or gas lift well, the mechanics of a plunger-lift system are the same. The plunger, a length of steel, is dropped through the tubing to the bottom of the well and allowed to travel back to the surface. It provides a piston-like interface between liquids and gas in the wellbore and prevents liquid fallback—a part of the liquid load that effectively is lost because it is left behind. Because the plunger provides a "seal" between the liquid and the gas, a well's own energy can be used to lift liquids out of the wellbore efficiently.

A plunger changes the rules for liquid removal. In a well without a plunger, gas velocity must be high to remove liquids,[1] but with a plunger, gas velocity can be very low.[2-4] Thus, the plunger system is economical because it needs minimal equipment and uses the well's gas pressure as the energy source.[5-7] Used with low line pressures or compression, plunger lift can produce many types of wells to depletion.[3,5,8]

In recent years, the advent of microprocessors and electronic controllers,[9-12] the studies detailing the importance of plunger seal and velocity,[13] and an increased focus on gas production have led to a much wider use and broader application of plunger lift. Microprocessors and electronic controllers have increased the reliability of plunger lift.[9,10,12] Earlier controllers were on/off timers or pressure switches that needed frequent adjustment to deal with operating-condition changes such as line pressures, plunger wear, variable production rates, and system upsets. This frustrated many operators and caused failures, and thus limited plunger use. New controllers contain computers that can sense plunger problems and make immediate adjustments. Techniques with telemetry, electronic data collection, and troubleshooting software continue to improve plunger-lift performance and ease of use.[12]

Fig. 16.1—Plunger installed in Canada. (Courtesy of Ferguson Beauregard.)

Traditionally, plunger lift was used on oil wells—as the wells started to load or as a means of gas lift assist—and many early articles discussed optimization of liquid production.[8,14–16] Plunger lift lately has become more common on gas wells, and papers from the 1980s onward have focused on this aspect.[2–7,9,17]

In the 1980s, several studies were conducted in the field and on test wells to verify 1950s and 1960s models and to better understand plunger operation. Morrow and Rogers,[9] Mower et al.,[13] Lea,[18] and Rosina[19] (among others) presented papers that verified and modified earlier models presented by Beeson et al.[14] and Foss and Gaul.[16] Importantly, for example, these studies clarified the relationship between plunger seal and velocity, indicating that a plunger that more completely seals against the tubing and travels at the proper ascent velocity minimizes gas slippage around the plunger. Reducing gas slippage allows the well to operate more efficiently at lower bottomhole pressures, which in turn increases production. The studies also found that efficient ascent velocities for various plungers range from 500 to 1,000 ft/min. These velocity data have been used successfully to improve methods for controlling and optimizing plunger-lift cycles and to produce highly efficient plungers.

These improvements have enabled plunger lift to be used for a broader range of well types and conditions, allowing its application even in extremely low-pressure wells (< 100 psia), wells with high liquid production (> 100 B/D), deep wells (16,000+ ft), slimhole wells (2⅞- to 3½-in. casing), and wells with packers. Operators have successfully used plunger lift in paraffin-, scale-, sand-, and hydrate-production environments.

Success in plunger lift systems depends on proper candidate identification, proper well installation, and the effectiveness of the operator. Candidate identification primarily consists of choosing a well with the proper GLR and adequate well-buildup pressure; however, makeup gas or compression can be used to amend unmet GLR and buildup-pressure requirements.

Proper well installation is important. A plunger must travel freely from the bottom of the well to the top and back to the bottom, carry well liquids, and produce gas with minimal restriction. Problems with tubing, the wellhead, or well configuration can cause failure.

The well operator must be able to understand the system. Plunger lift can be a difficult process to visualize because it comprises liquid and gas movement downhole during flowing and shut-in periods. Operators must understand the mechanism for oil- and (especially) gas-well loading, have a basic understanding of inflow performance, and be able to troubleshoot

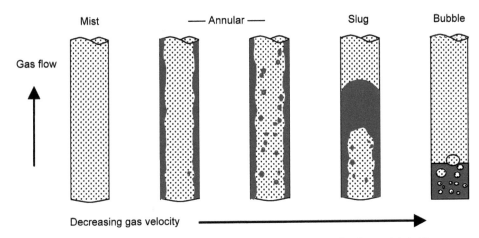

Fig. 16.2—Gas-well loading flow regimes. (Modified from Govier and Aziz.[20])

wells on the basis of tubing and casing pressures and flow performance. Even with electronic controllers, operators are necessary for finding initial plunger-lift operating ranges, choosing appropriate plunger types, and performing basic maintenance and troubleshooting. An operator without these skills will have trouble even with the best plunger-lift candidates.

16.2 Basics/Operation

16.2.1 Purpose of Plunger Lift. Early in the life of a liquid-producing gas well or high-GLR oil well, rates and velocities usually are high enough to keep the wellbore clear of liquids (**Fig. 16.2**). At this point, liquids typically are produced as a mist entrained in the gas stream. The high turbulence and velocity of these gas rates provides an efficient lifting mechanism for the liquids and the well produces at steady flow rates.

As reservoir pressures decline and flow rates/velocities decrease, the lifting mechanism changes.[20] Liquids no longer are entrained in mist and begin to coalesce on the walls of the production tubing. The liquids still might move up and out of the well, but somewhat less-efficiently than in mist form.

As gas rates and velocities continue to drop, the effect of gravity on the liquids becomes more apparent. Liquids on the tubing walls that were moving upward begin to stall, and gas slips through the center of the liquid. When enough liquids stall, liquid "slugs" are formed that inhibit gas flow. The well begins a cyclic process of unloading liquids that commonly is referred to as "heading" or "slugging." Liquid collects on the tubing walls, increases hydrostatic backpressure, restricts gas flow, and further decreases gas velocity.

In a short period of time, the reservoir might build sufficient gas pressure under the liquid slugs to overcome the hydrostatic pressure and force the slug back up the tubing. This gas expands, partially carrying liquid, partially slipping through the liquid. Much of the liquid is carried out of the wellbore, and the well flows at higher rates because of a decrease in hydrostatic pressures. Eventually, the liquid left behind in the tubing and the new liquid from reservoir form slugs, and the process repeats (**Fig. 16.3**).

Whereas mist flow is an efficient method of removing wellbore liquids, severe heading is not. The reason for this inefficiency is that gas tends to flow through liquids rather than to push them up and out of the wellbore, especially at low velocities. In intermittent gas lift, a rule of thumb is that 5 to 7% of the liquid load is left behind for every 1,000 ft of depth. In a

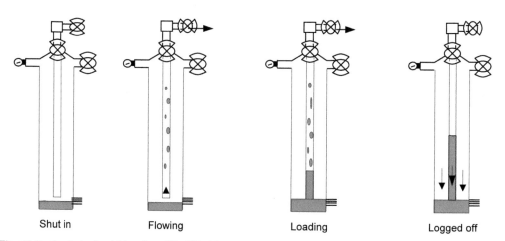

Fig. 16.3—Cycle to liquid loading. (Modified from Phillips and Listiak.[10]) This cycle can occur over hours or days in wells that have stabilized flow rates below the critical unloading rate. Such is the behavior of many wells that are temporarily shut in or blown to atmosphere to unload liquids.

10,000-ft well, that can be 70% of the liquid load! This fallback exerts hydrostatic backpressure on the reservoir, restricting gas production.

Left alone, heading can occur for weeks or possibly several months, depending on reservoir permeability, reservoir pressure, and liquid inflow. Eventually, a well will cease heading and stop producing liquids (or most liquids) altogether. The well sometimes will continue to produce at low flow rates, or it might stop flowing completely (known as "loaded," "logged-off," or "dead"). At this point, the liquids are not moving out of the well, and any production gas merely is bubbling through a static liquid column.

According to the Turner et al.[1] critical-flow-rate correlation (Fig. 16.4), a well that produces gas and water in 2⅜-in. [1.995-in. inner diameter (ID)] tubing to a 100-psia surface pressure requires approximately a 320 Mscf/D flow rate to prevent fallback and unload liquids. Below this rate, liquid fallback will occur and liquids will not be removed adequately. The same well with a reservoir pressure of 500 psia only requires a water column of 800 to 1,000 ft to shut off flow completely. That hydrostatic pressure is equivalent to < 4 bbl of water in 2⅜-in. tubing! So, below critical flow rates, a very small amount of liquid can limit production severely.

When using plunger lift, however, unloading relies less on critical flow rates and much more on the well's ability to store sufficient gas pressure to lift the plunger and a liquid slug to surface. The piston-like interface the plunger provides between liquid and the gas acts as a seal between the two, preventing fallback and allowing the well's energy to build up sufficiently to lift liquids out of the wellbore. Thus, liquids can be removed efficiently, even when gas velocity is very low.

16.2.2 Plunger-Lift Operation and Cycles. In its simplest form, plunger operation consists of shut-in and flow periods. The flow periods are divided into periods of unloading and flow after plunger arrival. The lengths of these periods vary with application, producing capability of the well, and pressures. In specialized cases that use plungers that can fall against flow, there might not be a shut-in period; however, most wells require some shut-in, which is the basis of the discussion below.

A plunger cycle starts with the shut-in period that allows the plunger to drop from the surface to the bottom of the well (**Fig. 16.5**). At the same time, the well builds gas pressure that

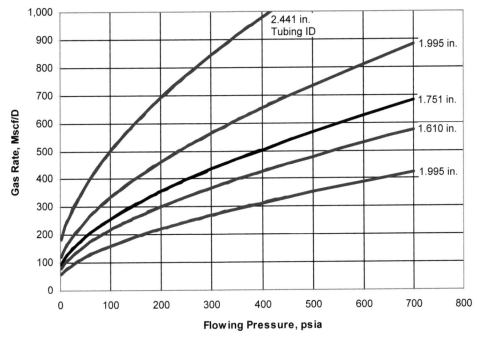

Fig. 16.4—Unloading rates for various tubing sizes. (From Turner et al.[1]).

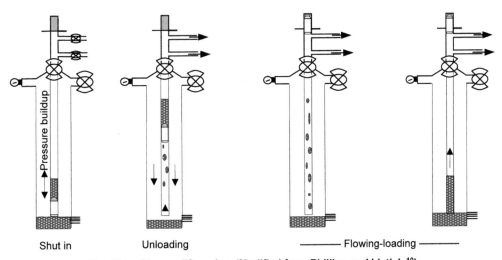

Shut in   Unloading   ——— Flowing-loading ———

Fig. 16.5—Plunger-lift cycles. (Modified from Phillips and Listiak.[10])

is stored in either the casing, the fracture, or the near-wellbore region of the reservoir. The well must be shut in long enough to build sufficient reservoir pressure to provide energy to lift both the plunger and liquid slug to the surface against line pressure and friction. When this pressure has been reached, the flow period is started and unloading begins.

In the initial stages of the flow period, the plunger and liquid slug begin traveling to the surface. Gas above the plunger quickly flows from the tubing into the flowline, and the plunger and liquid slug follow up the hole. The plunger arrives at the surface, unloading the

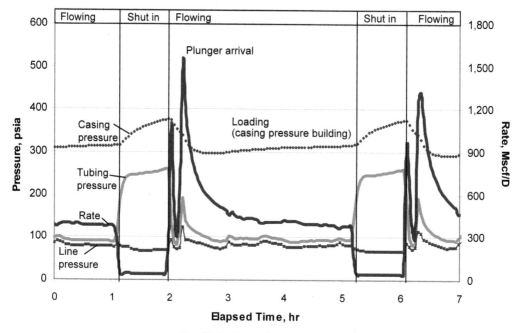

Fig. 16.6—Typical plunger cycle.

liquid. Initially, high rates prevail (often three to four times the average daily rate) while the stored pressure is blown down. The well now can produce free of liquids, while the plunger is held at the surface by the well's pressure and flow. As rates drop, so do velocities. Eventually, velocities drop below the critical rate, and liquids begin to accumulate in the tubing. The well is shut in, and the plunger falls back to bottom to repeat the cycle.

There are many common names for these periods. Shut-in also is known as a "closed," "off," or "buildup" period. The time during which the plunger travels up the hole also is called an "open," "on," "unloading," or "flow" period. The flow period after the plunger reaches the surface is known variously as an "open," "on," "flow," "afterflow," "blowdown," or "sales" period.

16.2.3 Pressure Response During Plunger Cycles.
The pressure response of a well on plunger lift helps explain the plunger lift cycles. **Figs. 16.6 and 16.7** and the discussion below describe a typical pressure response for a well with tubing and no packer and for which surface tubing and casing pressures can be measured. Fig. 16.6 shows three pressures—casing, tubing, and line—and the instantaneous flow rate of a well during a plunger cycle. Fig. 16.7 shows the same pressures and rate over a period of several days.

By the end of the shut-in period, the well has built up to the maximum casing pressure, and to a tubing pressure that is lower than the casing pressure. The difference between these is equivalent to the hydrostatic pressure of the liquid in the tubing.

When the well is opened, the tubing pressure quickly drops to line pressure while the casing pressure slowly decreases until the plunger reaches the surface. As the plunger nears the surface, the liquid on top of the plunger might surge through the system, causing spikes in line pressure and flow rate. This continues until the plunger reaches the surface. After the plunger surfaces, a large increase in flow rate will produce higher tubing pressures and an increase in flowline pressure. Tubing pressure then will drop to very near line pressure. Casing pressure

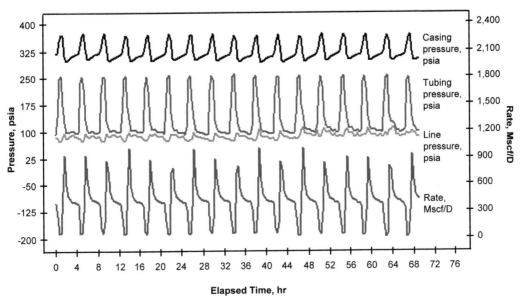

Fig. 16.7—Typical plunger production chart. (Courtesy of Ferguson Beauregard.)

will reach its minimum either upon plunger arrival, or afterward while the casing blows down and the well produces with minimal liquids in the tubing. If the well stays above the critical unloading rate, casing pressure will remain fairly constant or might decrease further. As the gas rate drops, liquids become held up in the tubing and casing pressure increases.

Upon shut-in, the casing pressure builds more rapidly. How quickly depends on the inflow performance and reservoir pressure of the well. As the flowing gas friction ceases, the tubing pressure will increase quickly from line pressure and eventually will track casing pressure (minus the liquid slug). Casing pressure will continue to increase toward maximum pressure until the well is opened again.

16.2.4 Obtaining Maximum Production on Plunger Lift. In a well with plunger lift, as with most wells, maximum production occurs when the well produces against the lowest possible bottomhole pressure. On plunger lift, the lowest average bottomhole pressure almost always is obtained by shutting in the well for the minimum time.[8–10] However, practical experience and plunger-lift models show that lifting large liquid slugs requires higher average bottomhole pressure, however, so the goal of plunger lift should be to shut in the well for the minimum time period and to produce only as much liquids as can be lifted at this minimum buildup pressure (**Fig. 16.8**).

The absolute minimum shut-in time, regardless of other operating conditions, is the time it takes the plunger to reach bottom. (The exception to this rule is specialized plungers that fall while the well is flowing.) Plungers typically fall 200 to 1,000 ft/min in dry gas, and 20 to 250 ft/min in liquids.[13,16,23] Total fall time depends on plunger type, amount of liquid in the tubing, the condition of the tubing (e.g., crimped, corkscrewed, corroded), and the deviation of the tubing or wellbore.

The length of the flow period during and after plunger arrival is used to control liquid loads. In general, a short flow period brings in a smaller liquid load, and a long flow period brings in a larger liquid load, so that the well can be flowed until the desired liquid load has entered the tubing. A well with a high GLR might be capable of long flow periods without

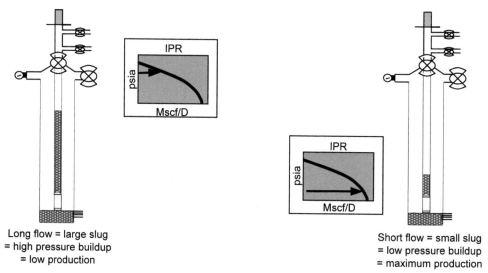

Long flow = large slug
= high pressure buildup
= low production

Short flow = small slug
= low pressure buildup
= maximum production

Fig. 16.8—Effect of liquid-load sizes on plunger-lift production rates. (IPR = inflow performance relationship. After Vogel[21] and Mishra and Caudle.[22])

requiring more than minimum shut-in times. In such case, the plunger could operate as few as one or two cycles per day. Conversely, a well with a low GLR might never be able to flow after plunger arrival, and might require 25 or more cycles per day. In practice, if the well is shutting in for only the minimum amount of time, it can be flowed as long as possible to maintain target plunger rise velocities. If the well is shutting in for longer than the minimum time, there should be little or no flow after the plunger arrives at the surface.

16.3 Applications

Plungers currently are being used in many countries. Applications include wells with depths of 1,000 to 16,000 ft, producing bottomhole pressures of 50 to > 1,500 psia, and liquid rates of 1 to > 100 B/D. These are common ranges of application, but not necessarily limits of operation.[2,3,8,17,24]

The most common plunger-lift applications are for liquid removal in gas wells, but plungers also are used successfully for oil production in high-GLR oil wells, in conjunction with intermittent gas lift operations,[24-27] and to control paraffin and hydrates. In fact, plungers have been installed on wells for the sole purpose of preventing paraffin or hydrate buildup, thereby reducing paraffin scraping or methanol injection.[2,3,17]

For this use, when plunger lift is installed, paraffin, hydrates, and salt should be removed so that the plunger will travel freely up and down the tubing. Given initially clean tubing, a plunger excels at preventing formation of such deposits because of the scraping action of the plunger against the walls of the tubing, along with slugs of warm reservoir fluids.

Wellbore configurations for plunger lift include wells with an open annulus (most desirable), wells with packers, slimhole wells (2.875-in. and 3.5-in. casing), deviated wells, wells with coiled tubing, and wells with no tubing (casing plungers). Also, plunger lift is used in conjunction with intermittent gas lift, external gas supplies/injection, wellhead compression, vent options to tanks or low-pressure systems, some sand production, tubing/casing flow control (three-valve controllers), and carbon dioxide (CO_2) floods.[17,25-27]

16.3.1 Typical Plunger Installation: Tubing With Open Annulus. Most commonly, plunger lift is applied in a gas or oil well with sufficient pressure and GLR to operate the system without additional supply gas. It is desirable to have tubing with no packer in the well. The annular space provides a storage area (volume chamber) for the gas under pressure and allows this gas to work freely on the plunger and liquid slug. Gas can flow from the casing to the tubing and provide lift with little restriction, and inflow from the reservoir is not relied on as the plunger moves up the hole. Because the stored-gas pressure provides the means to lift the plunger and liquid slug, adequate GLR and well pressures are critical.

16.3.2 Packers and Slimhole Completions. Some success has been experienced with plunger lift in gas wells with packers and slimhole completions. These installations are more difficult than those in a well with tubing and an adequate open annulus and will require higher bottom-hole pressure and GLR. Because an annular volume is not available, gas must be stored in the near-wellbore region or in a natural or hydraulic fracture. The near-wellbore region must be large enough to store the volume necessary to operate the plunger and must be able to deliver that volume with minimal restriction or loss of energy through the reservoir and perforations. In addition, plunger-controller options that use the casing pressure cannot be used.

In some instances, production in wells with packers can be improved by shooting several holes in the tubing and allowing communication between the tubing and casing. In this manner, the casing annulus can be used, but because packers may be set high above the producing interval, wells may see increased hydrostatic backpressure in the loaded portion of the casing below the packer. In addition, scale and debris might easily plug the perforated holes. It is important to shoot enough holes to provide adequate flow area from the casing to the tubing.

Some slimhole wells have been equipped with small tubing in an attempt to gain annular volume. This may or may not provide improved plunger performance, depending on the annular volume obtained and the reduced hydraulic efficiency of plunger lifting in smaller tubing.

16.3.3 Deviated Wells. Theoretically, plunger lift can be run successfully in wellbores up to a 60° deviation. Several installations exist in 20° deviations. Because the plunger is small, it can handle some dogleg severity, but in this type of installation, be especially aware of plunger fall times. The greater the deviation, the more slowly the plunger falls and the longer it takes to get to the bottom. Fall times in deviated wells can be measured with slickline, by acoustic measurement, or by examining well production characteristics with various minimum shut-in times. Excessive fall times can reduce or prevent plunger-lift production.

16.3.4 Coiled Tubing. Nontapered coiled tubing can be plunger lifted. Larger coiled-tubing strings are very applicable to plunger lift, especially when the flash is removed. Flash on coiled tubing is a byproduct of welding during the manufacturing process. It is a thin bead of material that runs the inside length of the coiled tubing at the weld seam and upsets the smooth, continuous ID of the tubing. Plungers cannot seal against flash (except for some special brush plungers). The flash can be removed during manufacturing, but this must be specified.

Special plungers have been made for coiled tubing.[28] A flexible brush plunger has been designed to help curve around potential bends in coiled tubing at the bottom of the well; however, small coiled tubing (as with any small tubing) has tubing hydraulic problems that make plunger lift difficult. Smaller tubing requires much more pressure to lift the same volume of liquids, has larger pressure losses because of gas friction, and creates more backpressure on the formation. In addition, small-plunger equipment is less durable and might fail frequently.

16.3.5 Casing Plungers. Casing plungers act more like true pistons. The casing plunger has a synthetic sealing element that forms a seal against the walls of the casing and eliminates gas or liquid slippage. The well must only overcome the weight of the plunger, the liquid slug, and friction of the seal against the casing. Because large casing diameters are used (mostly 4.5-in. or greater), wellbore hydrostatics work in favor of this method. Larger slugs can be lifted with a lower pressure requirement. When the casing plunger reaches the surface, an internal bypass is opened to allow the plunger to fall against flow. This method has been used successfully in some areas of the U.S.A. (e.g., Ohio and Pennsylvania). Plunger sticking might occur in casing with varying weights and IDs, with poor casing integrity or condition, and with the reaction of some sealing elements to produced fluids (e.g., CO_2, condensate).

16.3.6 Intermittent Gas Lift. Plungers work well with intermittent gas lift by reducing liquid fallback. The same amount of liquid then can be lifted with less gas volume and pressure, and wells can be lifted from greater depths. Long plungers with seals at both ends might be required to maintain plunger seal across gas lift mandrels.[24–27]

16.3.7 External Gas Supplies. Using makeup gas with plunger lift will increase the range of operation. A compressor or gas lift system can be used to supply external gas pressure and volume. This allows plungers to work at much lower pressures and GLRs. Injection-gas systems have been installed successfully to convert pumping fields to plunger lift with gas assist. Operators have used this technique to reduce costs caused by pumping failures and difficulty in pumping high-GLR oil wells.[24–27]

16.3.8 Wellhead Compression. It is not always possible to install centralized compression, and a single wellhead compressor might be necessary for production. Even with a compressor, wells still might experience liquid loading. To alleviate this problem, a plunger system can be installed in conjunction with wellhead compression. When using an electric compressor, the plunger controller can be used to control the compressor. During the shut-in period, the compressor is turned off. During the unloading and flow periods, the compressor is turned on.[29]

For a gas-engine-driven compressor, the installation is somewhat more difficult. A gas compressor cannot easily be automated to start and stop, so it is desirable to keep the gas engine running during both the flowing and shut-in periods. When flowing, the compressor simply sends gas to the sales pipeline. For shut-in periods, a bypass can be installed on the compressor that allows gas to circulate. The controller that operates the motor valve can be used to control an additional sales/bypass valve. To avoid potential problems with this setup, such as overheating of the circulating gas or insufficient supply gas to keep the compressor running, shut in the well for the minimum amount of time necessary to operate the plunger. Other possible solutions are to use a plunger with a bypass that can travel to bottom while the well is flowing, which reduces or eliminates shut-in; to provide an outside source of supply gas; and to improve the cooling capacity of the compressor.

16.3.9 Vent Options to Tanks or Low-Pressure Systems. Lower-pressure wells that do not meet plunger-lift pressure requirements at current line pressures might be able to operate if temporary vent or low-pressure cycles are used. Such a well can be set up to flow to a lower pressure while the plunger is ascending with the liquid load. Once unloaded, the well can be switched into the sales line until loading begins again.

Venting also is effective where gathering systems have large swings in line pressures. When line pressures increase erratically, the well can vent automatically to keep the plunger operating and to keep the well from loading and dying. If a well is vented correctly, only a small portion of the gas above the plunger will be lost to the atmosphere.

Before considering venting, however, take a few important precautions. First, use an automated controller that continually attempts to minimize and eliminate venting. Second, evaluate where the vented gas will flow. Venting to the atmosphere is the simplest option, albeit the least desirable one because it involves environmental-impact, government regulatory, and safety considerations. For example, if the surface equipment malfunctions, will liquids be discharged? If poisonous gases such as hydrogen sulfide (H_2S) are present, venting directly to atmosphere can create additional safety hazards. Open atmospheric discharges might not be allowed in certain areas.

Vent tanks can be used to ensure that system upsets do not cause liquid spills. A combination high-/low-pressure separator is an option that will catch fluids and reduce venting pressures before sending vented gases to a tank; however, using vent tanks has drawbacks. For example, if downcomers or downspouts are used, rapid gas entry might cause liquid to be blown out of the tank hatch. Also, a vent line that is improperly piped into the tank can generate static electricity. Furthermore, if the thief hatch is blown open, oxygen might enter the tank, increasing the chances of reaching explosive mixtures in the tank.

The best venting option is to use a lower-pressure gathering system, or possibly a vapor-recovery system with a vent tank; however, if a low-pressure system is available and has sufficient capacity, producing to that system would be preferable over venting to it.

Plungers installed in marginal applications require more venting by design. When this is the case, consider alternate applications or artificial-lift methods. Possible alternatives to venting are to assist the plunger with injected gas down the casing or down a parallel tubing string.[25,26]

16.3.10 Some Sand Production. Wells that produce some sand can operate with plunger lift. Selecting a plunger with a brush-type seal, or a loose-fitting plunger with a poorer seal will allow sand production and help prevent the plunger from sticking in the tubing. An effective technique is to use a brush plunger that has a standard bristle outer diameter and smaller (downturned) metal ends. Installing sand traps at the surface or using sand-friendly seats on motor valves can prevent sand damage to seats and trims that would prevent the motor valve from closing. With sand, plungers also are prone to getting stuck in the lubricator and require cleaning at the surface. Some wells might require periodic downhole cleanouts.

Good plunger operation can reduce sand production relative to poor plunger operation. Short shut-in periods reduce pressure buildups, which leads to more consistent production and less-intense production surges. In some wells, sand production decreases with time; in others, continued sand production might make plunger lift impossible or uneconomical.

16.3.11 Tubing and Casing Flow. In some plunger-lift applications, casing-annulus flow improves production. If pressures and flow rates are such that the gas friction in the tubing chokes the well, casing flow might be beneficial.[30] This is the case for many low-pressure, high-permeability gas wells. The cycle is like a standard plunger-lift cycle (**Fig. 16.9**), but with two additional periods. After the shut-in and unloading periods, the casing annulus is opened to flow. Before shutting in the well again, the casing annulus is closed and the tubing left open to allow accumulated liquids in the casing to be transferred to the tubing.

Take care that the casing flow does not cause the tubing to cease flowing. Place a pressure-differential device or other type of choke on the casing outlet to keep sufficient flow up the tubing. If the tubing stops flowing, the plunger will drop, but probably will not reach the plunger stop by the time the casing purge cycle begins. Even if it does reach the stop, there might not be enough energy for the plunger to lift any liquid to the surface. Either way, the well eventually will load up.

This type of system is more difficult to operate than standard plunger installations. Their operation will benefit from knowledgeable operators and automatically adjusting plunger controllers.

16.3.12 CO$_2$ Floods. Any gas can be used as the motivating force in plunger operations, even CO$_2$. When CO$_2$ breakthrough occurs in a CO$_2$ flood, GLRs might increase substantially, which leads to pumping problems and possible well-control problems. When the GLR meets the minimum requirement, plunger lifting wells might alleviate some of these problems and help reduce field pumping costs.[17]

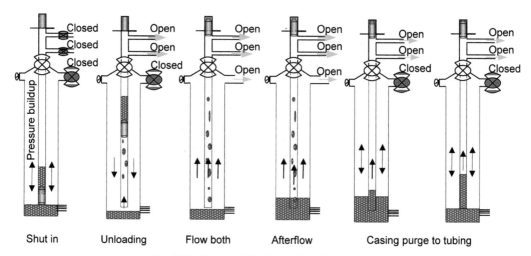

Fig. 16.9—Plunger lift with casing-flow control.

16.3.13 Other Methods. Development and testing of new and improved plunger-lift methods is ongoing. Variations of the applications discussed above, as well as combinations of these plunger-lift techniques with other concepts and methods of artificial lift, continue to transform plunger-lift capabilities and to expand the limits and applications for this technology.

16.4 Design and Models
Plunger-lift systems can be evaluated using rules of thumb in conjunction with historic well production, or with a mathematical plunger model. Because plunger-lift systems typically are inexpensive and easy to install and test, most are evaluated by rules of thumb.

16.4.1 GLR and Buildup Pressure Requirements. The two minimum requirements for plunger-lift operation are minimum GLR and well buildup pressure. Plunger-lift operation requires available gas to provide the lifting force, in sufficient quantity per barrel of liquid for a given well depth. The minimum GLR requirement is approximately 400 scf/bbl per 1,000 ft of well depth and is based on the energy stored in a compressed volume of 400 scf of gas expanding under the hydrostatic head of 1 bbl of liquid.[3] One drawback to this rule of thumb is that it does not consider line pressures. Excessively high line pressures relative to buildup pressure might increase the requirement. The rule of thumb also assumes that the gas expansion can be applied from a large open annulus without restriction, but slimhole wells and wells with packers that require gas to travel through the reservoir or through small perforations in the tubing will cause a greater restriction and energy loss, which increase the minimum GLR requirement to as much as 800 to 1,200 scf/bbl per 1,000 ft.

Well buildup pressure is the bottomhole pressure just before the plunger begins its ascent (equivalent to surface casing pressure in a well with an open annulus). In practice, the minimum shut-in pressure requirement for plunger lift is equivalent to one and a half times the maximum sales-line pressure, although the actual requirement might be higher. This rule of thumb works well in intermediate-depth wells (2,000 to 8,000 ft) with slug sizes of 0.1 to 0.5 bbl/cycle. It does not apply reliably, however, to higher liquid volumes, deeper wells (because of increasing friction), and excessive pressure restrictions at the surface or in the wellbore.

An improved rule of thumb for minimum pressure is that a well can lift a slug of liquid when the slug hydrostatic pressure (p_{hs}) equals 50 to 60% of the difference between shut-in casing pressure (p_{cs}) and maximum sales-line pressure:

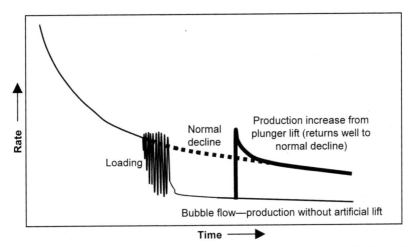

Fig. 16.10—Effects of plunger lift on a typical gas-well production decline. (Modified from Ferguson and Beauregard.[3])

$$p_{hs} = \left[p_{cs} - (p_l)_{max} \right](0.5 \text{ to } 0.6), \quad\text{.. (16.1a)}$$

or

$$p_{cs} = \frac{p_{hs}}{(0.5 \text{ to } 0.6)} + (p_l)_{max} \quad \text{.. (16.1b)}$$

This rule of thumb accounts for liquid production, can be used for wells with higher liquid production that require slug sizes of more than 1 to 2 bbl/cycle, and is regarded as a conservative estimate of minimum pressure requirements. To use Eqs. 16.1a and 16.1b, first estimate the total liquid production on plunger lift and number of cycles possible per day. Then, determine the amount of liquid that can be lifted per cycle. Use the well tubing size to convert that volume of liquid per cycle into the slug hydrostatic pressure, and use the equations to estimate required casing pressure to operate the system (see example below).

A well that does not meet minimum GLR and pressure requirements still could be plunger lifted with the addition of an external gas source. At this point, design becomes more a matter of the economics of providing the added gas to the well at desired pressures. Several papers in the literature discuss adding makeup gas to a plunger installation through existing gas lift operations, installing a field gas supply system, or using wellhead compression.[11,14,16,24–27,29]

16.4.2 Estimating Production Rates With Plunger Lift. The simplest and sometimes most accurate method of determining production increases from plunger lift is decline-curve analysis[3] (**Fig. 16.10**). Gas and oil reservoirs typically have predictable declines, either exponential or hyperbolic. Initial production rates usually are high enough to produce the well above critical rates (unloaded) and establish a decline curve. When liquid loading occurs, a marked decrease and deviation from normal decline can be seen. Unloading the well with plunger lift can re-establish a normal decline. Production increases from plunger lift will be somewhere between the rates of the well when it started loading and the rate of an extended decline curve to the present time. Ideally, decline curves would be used with critical-velocity curves to predetermine when plunger lift should be installed. This would enable plunger lift to maintain production on a steady decline and to never allow the well to begin loading.

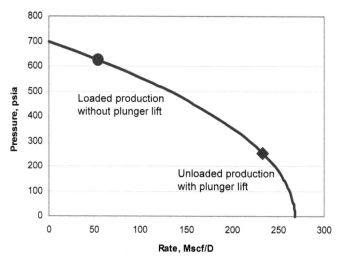

Fig. 16.11—Inflow-performance-relationship analysis for estimating plunger-lift performance. Chart shows production increase resulting from reducing liquid hydrostatic pressure with a plunger-lift system. (IPR after Vogel[21] and Mishra and Caudle.[22])

Another method for estimating production is to build an inflow performance (IP) curve on the basis of the backpressure equation (**Fig. 16.11**).[4,10,21,22] This is especially helpful if the well has an open annulus and is flowing up the tubing, and if the casing pressure is known. The casing pressure closely approximates bottomhole pressure. Build the IP curve on the basis of estimated reservoir pressure, casing pressure, and current flow rate. Because the job of the plunger lift is to lower the bottomhole pressure by removing liquids, estimate the bottomhole pressure with no liquids. Use this new pressure to estimate a production rate with lower bottomhole pressures.

16.4.3 Models. Plunger-lift models are based on the sum of forces acting on the plunger while it lifts a liquid slug up the tubing (**Fig. 16.12**). These forces at any given point in the tubing are:
• Stored casing pressure freely acting on the cross section of the plunger.
• Stored reservoir pressure acting on the cross section of the plunger, based on inflow performance.
  • The weight of the fluid.
  • The weight of the plunger.
  • The friction of the fluid with the tubing.
  • The friction of the plunger with the tubing.
  • Gas friction in the tubing.
  • Gas slippage upward past the plunger.
  • Liquid slippage downward past the plunger.
  • Surface pressure (line pressure and restrictions) acting against the plunger travel.
Several publications have dealt with this approach. Beeson *et al.*[14] first presented equations for high-GLR wells in 1955, on the basis of an empirically derived analysis. Foss and Gaul[16] derived a force-balance equation for use on oil wells in the Ventura Avenue field in 1965. Lea[18] presented a dynamic analysis of plunger lift that added gas slippage and reservoir inflow, and mathematically described the entire cycle (not just plunger ascent) for tight-gas/very high-GLR wells.

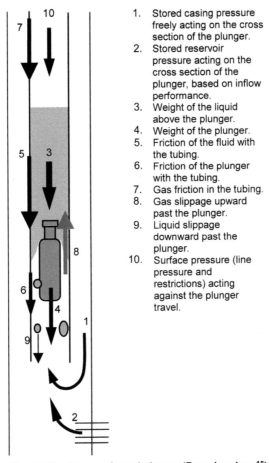

1. Stored casing pressure freely acting on the cross section of the plunger.
2. Stored reservoir pressure acting on the cross section of the plunger, based on inflow performance.
3. Weight of the liquid above the plunger.
4. Weight of the plunger.
5. Friction of the fluid with the tubing.
6. Friction of the plunger with the tubing.
7. Gas friction in the tubing.
8. Gas slippage upward past the plunger.
9. Liquid slippage downward past the plunger.
10. Surface pressure (line pressure and restrictions) acting against the plunger travel.

Fig. 16.12—Plunger force balance. (Based on Lea.[18])

Foss and Gaul's methodology[16] was to calculate $(p_c)_{min}$, the casing pressure required to move the plunger and liquid slug just before it reaches the surface. Because $(p_c)_{min}$ is at the end of the plunger cycle, the energy of the expanding gas from the casing to the tubing is at its minimum. Adjusting $(p_c)_{min}$ for gas expansion from the casing to the tubing during the full plunger cycle yields $(p_c)_{max}$, the pressure required to start the plunger at the beginning of the plunger cycle. The pressure must build to $(p_c)_{max}$ to operate successfully.

The average casing pressure $\overline{p}_c$, maximum cycles C_{max}, and gas required per cycle (V_g) can be calculated from $(p_c)_{min}$ and $(p_c)_{max}$. The equations below are essentially those presented by Foss and Gaul[16] but are summarized here as presented by Mower et $al.$[13] The Foss and Gaul model is not rigorous—it assumes constant friction associated with plunger rise velocities of 1,000 ft/min; does not calculate reservoir inflow; assumes a value for gas slippage past the plunger; assumes an open, unrestricted annulus; and assumes that the user can determine unloaded gas and liquid rates independently of the model. Also, because this model originally was designed for oilwell operation that assumed the well would be shut in upon plunger arrival, $\overline{p}_c$ is only an average during plunger travel. The net result of these assumptions is an overprediction of required casing pressure. If a well meets the Foss and Gaul criteria, it is almost certainly a candidate for plunger lift. For a full description of the Foss and Gaul model and for a description of improved models, see the references.[4,13,16,19,31]

TABLE 16.1—APPROXIMATIONS OF K, p_{lh}, AND p_{lf} FOR VARIOUS TUBING SIZES (AFTER FOSS AND GAUL[16])		
Tubing size, in.	K/bbl	$(p_{lh}+p_{lf})$/bbl
1.995	33,500	165
2.441	45,000	102
2.992	57,600	63

16.5 Basic Foss and Gaul[16] Equations (Modified by Mower et al.[13] and Lea[18])

16.5.1 Required Pressures.

$$(p_c)_{min} = \left[p_p + p_t + (p_{lh} + p_{lf})S \right] \left(1 + \frac{D}{K} \right), \quad \text{.................................. (16.2)}$$

$$(p_c)_{max} = (p_c)_{min}(R_a), \quad \text{.................................. (16.3)}$$

and

$$\bar{p}_c = (p_c)_{min} \left(1 + \frac{A_t}{2A_a} \right), \quad \text{.................................. (16.4)}$$

where

$$p_{lh} = \gamma_l L, \quad \text{.................................. (16.5)}$$

$$p_{lf} = \frac{\gamma_l f_l L v^2}{\frac{d}{12}(2.0)(32.2)}, \quad \text{.................................. (16.6)}$$

$$\frac{1}{K} = \frac{f_g v^2 g_g}{\frac{d}{12}(2.0)(32.2)(\bar{T}_g + 460)ZR}, \quad \text{.................................. (16.7)}$$

and

$$R_a = \frac{A_a + A_t}{A_a}. \quad \text{.................................. (16.8)}$$

Foss and Gaul suggested an approximation where K and $p_{lh} + p_{lf}$ are constant for a given tubing size and a plunger velocity of 1,000 ft/min (**Table 16.1**).

<table>
<tr><th colspan="2" align="center">TABLE 16.2—WELL DATA</th></tr>
<tr><td>Gas rate (q_g)</td><td>200 Mscf/D expected when unloaded</td></tr>
<tr><td>Liquid rate (q_l)</td><td>10 B/D expected when unloaded</td></tr>
<tr><td>Liquid gradient (γ_l)</td><td>0.45 psi/ft</td></tr>
<tr><td>Tubing, ID (d_{ti})</td><td>1.995 in.</td></tr>
<tr><td>Tubing, outer diameter (OD) (d_{to})</td><td>2.375 in.</td></tr>
<tr><td>Casing, ID (d_{ci})</td><td>4.56 in.</td></tr>
<tr><td>Depth to plunger (D)</td><td>7,000 ft</td></tr>
<tr><td>Maximum line pressure ($p_l)_{max}$</td><td>100 psia</td></tr>
<tr><td>Available casing pressure (p_c)</td><td>800 psia</td></tr>
<tr><td>Reservoir pressure (p_R)</td><td>1,200 psia</td></tr>
<tr><td>Gas factor (Z)</td><td>0.99</td></tr>
<tr><td>Average gas temperature ($\overline{T}_g$)</td><td>140°F</td></tr>
<tr><td>Plunger weight (W_p)</td><td>10 lbm</td></tr>
<tr><td>Average plunger fall velocity in gas ($\overline{V}_{fg}$)</td><td>750 ft/min</td></tr>
<tr><td>Average plunger fall velocity in liquid ($\overline{V}_{fl}$)</td><td>150 ft/min</td></tr>
<tr><td>Average plunger rise velocity ($\overline{v}_r$)</td><td>1,000 ft/min</td></tr>
</table>

16.5.2 Gas (Mscf) Required per Cycle.

$$V_g = F_{gs}\overline{p}_c\left(\frac{V_t}{14.7}\right)\left(\frac{520}{\overline{T}_g + 460}\right)\left(\frac{1}{Z}\right), \dotfill (16.9)$$

where

$$V_t = \frac{A_t(D - SL)}{1,000} . \dotfill (16.10)$$

16.5.3 Maximum Cycles.

$$C_{max} = \frac{1,440}{\dfrac{D - SL}{\overline{v}_{fg}} + \dfrac{D}{\overline{v}_r} + \dfrac{SL}{\overline{v}_{fl}}} . \dotfill (16.11)$$

16.5.4 Examples of Rules of Thumb and Foss and Gaul Calculations. The examples of rules of thumb and of Foss and Gaul calculations in this section use the well data in given in **Table 16.2**.

Example of Rule-of-Thumb GLR Calculation. The minimum GLR (R_{gl}) = 400 scf/bbl per 1,000 ft of well depth. The well's GLR is:

$$R_{gl} = \frac{q_g / q_l}{D / 1,000} \dots\dots\dots\dots\dots\dots\dots\dots\dots\dots\dots\dots\dots\dots (16.12)$$

$$R_{gl} = \frac{200,000 / 10}{7,000 / 1,000} = 2,857,$$

where q_g is given in scf. The well GLR is >400 scf/bbl per 1,000 ft and is adequate for plunger lift.

Example of Rule of Thumb for Casing Pressure Requirement to Plunger Lift (Simple). The rule of thumb for calculating the minimum shut-in casing pressure for plunger lift, in psia, is:

$$p_{cs} = 1.5 \left(p_l \right)_{max} \dots\dots\dots\dots\dots\dots\dots\dots\dots\dots\dots\dots\dots\dots (16.13)$$

$$p_{cs} = 1.5(100) = 150.$$

With 800 psia of available casing pressure, the well meets the pressure requirements for plunger lift; however, this is the absolute minimum pressure required for low liquid volumes, intermediate well depths, and low line pressures.

Example of Rule of Thumb for Casing Pressure Requirement (Improved). For this case, assume 10 cycles/day, equivalent to a plunger trip every 2.4 hours. Any reasonable number of cycles can be assumed to calculate pressures.

At 10 cycles/day and 10 bbl of liquid, the plunger will lift 1 bbl/cycle. The slug hydrostatic pressure (p_{hs}) of 1 bbl of liquid in 2⅜-in. tubing with a 0.45-psi/ft liquid gradient is approximately 120 psia. Using Eq. 16.1b, the required casing pressure, in psia, is calculated as:

$$p_{cs} = \frac{p_{hs}}{(0.5 \text{ to } 0.6)} + \left(p_l \right)_{max}, \dots\dots\dots\dots\dots\dots\dots\dots\dots\dots (16.1b)$$

$$p_{cs} = \frac{120}{(0.5 \text{ to } 0.6)} + 100 = 300 \text{ to } 340 .$$

With 800 psia of available casing pressure, the well meets the pressure requirements for plunger lift.

Example of Foss and Gaul Type of Method to Determine Plunger-Lift Operating Range. In determining plunger-lift operating range, use Foss and Gaul K and $p_{lh} + p_{lf}$ values for 2⅜-in. tubing and average rise velocities of 1,000 ft/min. Calculate new friction factors if velocities are more or less than 1,000 ft/min.

Calculate the constants A_t, p_p, A_a, R_a, F_{gs}, L, and V_t:
Area of tubing, ft²:

$$A_t = \left(\frac{d_{ti}}{12} \right)^2 \left(\frac{\pi}{4} \right), \dots\dots\dots\dots\dots\dots\dots\dots\dots\dots\dots\dots (16.14)$$

$$A_t = \left(\frac{1.995}{12}\right)^2\left(\frac{\pi}{4}\right) = 0.0217.$$

Differential pressure required to lift plunger, psi:

$$p_p = \frac{W_p}{A_t}, \dotfill (16.15)$$

where A_t is given as in.^{2}. Therefore:

$$p_p = \frac{10}{1.995^2\frac{\pi}{4}} = 3.2.$$

Area of annulus, ft^2:

$$A_a = \left[\left(\frac{d_{ci}}{12}\right)^2 - \left(\frac{d_{to}}{12}\right)^2\right]\left(\frac{\pi}{4}\right), \dotfill (16.16)$$

$$A_a = \left[\left(\frac{4.56}{12}\right)^2 - \left(\frac{2.375}{12}\right)^2\right]\left(\frac{\pi}{4}\right) = 0.0826.$$

Ratio of total area to tubing area (Eq. 16.8):

$$R_a = \frac{A_t + A_a}{A_a},$$

$$R_a = \frac{0.0217 + 0.0826}{0.0826} = 1.26.$$

Lea[18]-modified Foss and Gaul[16] slippage factor [Foss and Gaul used a 15% factor (1.15) that could be translated to approximately 2% per 1,000 ft[18]]:

$$F_{gs} = 1.0 + 0.02\left(\frac{D}{1,000}\right), \dotfill (16.17)$$

$$F_{gs} = 1.0 + 0.02\left(\frac{7,000}{1,000}\right) = 1.14.$$

Length of 1 bbl of fluid in the tubing, ft/bbl (5.615 = scf in 1 bbl):

$$L = \frac{5.615}{A_t}, \dotfill (16.18)$$

								Maximum	
						Required		liquid	Liquid
S	$(p_c)_{min}$	$(p_c)_{max}$	$\bar{p}_c$	V_t	V_g	GLR		production	production
bbl	psia	psia	psia	Mscf	Mscf	Mscf/bbl	C_{max}/day	bbl	of well
									= 10 B/D
0.01	145	182	164	0.152	1.770	177.0	88	1	
0.05	153	193	173	0.152	1.865	37.3	88	4	
0.10	162	205	184	0.151	1.984	19.8	87	9	
0.20	182	230	206	0.151	2.219	11.1	87	17	
0.50	242	306	274	0.149	2.914	5.8	85	42	
1.00	342	432	387	0.146	4.036	4.0	81	81	
1.50	442	558	500	0.144	5.113	3.4	78	117	
2.00	541	684	613	0.141	6.145	3.1	75	151	
2.50	641	810	725	0.138	7.132	2.9	73	182	
3.00	741	936	838	0.135	8.074	2.7	70	211	
5.00	1,140	1,439	1,290	0.124	11.388	2.3	62	310	
10.00	2,137	2,699	2,418	0.096	16.513	1.7	48	478	

TABLE 16.3—PLUNGER-LIFT OPERATING RANGE METHOD SIMILAR TO FOSS AND GAUL[16]

Operating Range

Available casing-pressure buildup of well = 800 psi

$$L = \frac{5.615}{0.0217} = 259.$$

Volume of tubing above the slug (use for various slug sizes) (Eq. 16.10, but here in Mscf):

$$V_t = \frac{A_t[D - (SL)]}{1,000},$$

$$V_t = \frac{0.0217[7,000 - S(259)]}{1,000}.$$

Assume some values for S (bbl) and construct **Table 16.3**. (Table 16.3 in the CD version of this chapter is an interactive electronic spreadsheet.)

It was given that the estimated production when unloaded is 200 Mscf/D with 10 B/D of liquid (GLR = 200/10 = 20 Mscf/bbl), and that the available casing pressure (or the pressure to which the casing will build between plunger cycles) is 800 psia. The available casing pressure, p_c, is equivalent to the calculated $(p_c)_{max}$—or the pressure required to lift the assumed slug sizes. The well GLR is equivalent to the calculated required GLR. The maximum liquid production is a product of the slug size (S) and the maximum cycles per day (C_{max}). Importantly, C_{max} is not a required number of plunger trips, but rather the maximum possible on the basis of plunger velocities. In reality, most wells operate below C_{max} because well shut-in time is required to build any casing pressure. In Table 16.3, note that the casing pressure $(p_c)_{max}$ of 810 psia, the GLR of 20 Mscf/bbl, and the production rate of 10 B/D occur at slug sizes between 0.1 and 2.5 bbl. The well will operate on plunger lift.

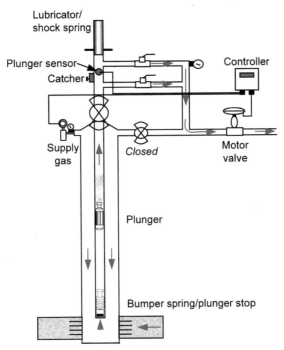

Fig. 16.13—Plunger-lift system.

16.6 Equipment Installation and Maintenance

A plunger lift candidate must meet GLR and pressure requirements, but the method of installation and the mechanical setup of the well also are extremely important. Installation is a frequent cause of system failure.[10] The following are key elements in the proper installation of a plunger system:

- Equipment quality and metallurgy.
- Evaluation of current and possible wellbore configurations.
- Tubing and wellbore preparation.
- Evaluation and installation of the downhole plunger equipment.
- Evaluation and installation of wellhead and plunger surface equipment.
- Design considerations and selection of a plunger.
- Evaluation of control methods.
- Evaluation and modification of production facilities.

For reference, **Fig. 16.13** is a full wellbore schematic of major plunger-lift components, and **Fig. 16.14** is a plunger-lift troubleshooting guide.

16.6.1 Equipment Quality and Metallurgy. There are many plunger-lift manufacturers and equipment options, so quality and design vary. Neither American Petroleum Inst. (API) standards nor those of similar agencies govern plunger-equipment specifications at this time. Purchasers have the ultimate responsibility for investigating the manufacturing process. Manufacturers who use International Organization for Standardization (ISO) 9000/9001 standards or equivalents help to ensure that customers will receive a quality product.

Evaluate material used in equipment manufacturing on the basis of the operating environment of each specific application. Carbon/carbon steel can be used in most installations; however, an appropriate grade of stainless steel might be necessary for some or all of the components in corrosive environments (e.g., H_2S or CO_2). Bottomhole temperature is another factor

Plunger-Lift Troubleshooting Guide	Check/change plunger	Optimize program settings	Increase of time	Increase afterflow	Reduce off time	Reduce afterflow	Inspect tubing or restrictions	Check wellhead design	Clean sensor/inspect wiring	Check controller fuse	Adjust sensor sensitivity	Check/change supply-gas filter	Check/adjust supply-gas pressure	Clean controller bleed ports	Change/clean/repair latch valve	Check/change battery	Check solar panel	Repair motor valve trim	Eliminate flow restrictions	Inspect catcher	Inspect controller module	Inspect motor valve diaphragm	Inspect plunger	Check to see if control is in "swab mode" if so equipped
No plunger arrival	6	3	2		1				5		4							8	9				7	
Slow plunger arrival	4	3	2			1	8	7										5	6					
Fast plunger arrival		3		1	2		6													4			5	
Fast plunger arrival at all settings, or plunger will not fall		1					4				2									2				
Slow plunger arrival at all settings, or plunger will not come to surface	4	3	2		1	7	6												5					
Short lubricator spring life		4		2	3		5																	
Short plunger life		3		4	5		2	1																
Sensor errors									3	4	2										1	5		
Sales valve will not open or close		1							5	10		4	3	6	7	2	8	9				11	12	
Vent valve will not open or close		1							5	10		4	3	6	7	2	8	9				11	12	
Latch valve will not switch												4	3	5	6	1	2							
Motor valves will not close, or close slowly												4	3	1	2	5	6	7				8		
Short battery life																1	2					3		
Controller will not allow flow time		3							2													4		1

Fig. 16.14—Plunger-lift troubleshooting guide. (Taken from Phillips and Listiak.[10]) Numbers represent rank in order of most likely solution.

to consider. The minor ID expansion of tubing in a deeper, hotter well might affect the choice of material, as well as type of equipment. Some fiber and plastic materials used in brush and pad plungers have a maximum operating temperature.

16.6.2 Evaluation of Current and Possible Wellbore Configurations. The two typical installation scenarios are those in which existing wellbore configurations are used and those in which the wellbore is reconfigured to take full advantage of the plunger-lift system. Setting the tubing at the proper depth and with an open annulus offers the greatest chance of success. Other installations can work, but require sacrifices in production rates and longevity. One of the biggest factors affecting plunger-lift success is the forcing of applications into unfavorable configurations, such as wells with packers (with or without holes shot in tubing for communica-

Fig. 16.15—Cutaway of a gauge ring. (Courtesy of Ferguson Beauregard.)

tion), highly deviated wells (> 20 to 60°), slimhole wells (2⅞-in. and 3½-in. casing), and small tubing (jointed pipe or coiled tubing smaller than 1¾-in. ID).

Keeping plunger lift in mind when originally completing a well is ideal. If a plunger is considered to be a potential lift method, then proper tubing, wellhead, and surface piping can be installed initially, making plunger lift inexpensive and effective.

16.6.3 Tubing and Wellbore Preparation. Often, plunger-lift installation is attempted in unacceptable tubing. Problems can arise from use of tubing that is degraded or worn (trash/fill, holes, crimps, scale, tight spots, pitting, and/or rod cut), has ID variations (out of place nipples, oversized or undersized blast joints, and/or mixed strings), is set at the wrong depth (too high or too low), or is undersized. Review well records to determine whether an acceptable tubing configuration is in place.

16.6.4 Slickline Tubing-Integrity Checks. Perform a slickline inspection even if records indicate that the wellbore has an acceptable tubing configuration for plunger installation. Tagging for fill and gauging the tubing are the minimum requirements for this inspection.

To tag for fill, run a small-OD tool (e.g., a sinker bar or sample basket) out of the end of the tubing. This ensures that the perforations are not covered and that the end of tubing is not plugged. At the same time, an end-of-tubing locator can be run to verify tubing depth. This is more important when well records do not clearly indicate the tubing depth.

Next, inspect the tubing ID with a gauge ring (**Fig. 16.15**). There are many varieties of gauge rings. Typically, gauge rings do a good job of finding the smallest ID of the tubing; however, they do a poor job of drifting the tubing because they usually are shorter than the plunger. Longer gauge rings can be built that mirror plunger sizes. Another option is to use the plunger selected for the specific well to drift the tubing. An even better option is to machine a hollow gauge ring with the same length and OD dimensions as the chosen plunger. The hollow gauge ring allows for quicker slickline trips in and out of the hole than does a solid plunger or solid gauge ring.

If the tubing gauges to the proper ID, plunger-lift equipment can be installed. If not, run a broach and/or swage to try to clean the tubing of obstructions or to bend the tubing walls out to the proper ID. A broach is a hardened piece of round steel with grooves, much like a round file. Broaches often are built in the shape of a swage. They are most effective on light scale buildup or similar light deposits. Smooth swages often are used when crimped tubing is suspect-

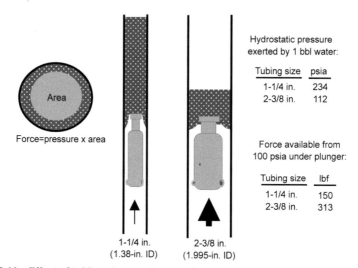

Fig. 16.16—Effect of tubing size on plunger lift. (Taken from Phillips and Listiak.[10])

ed. The risk in running broaches and swages is the possibility of their getting stuck. A broach is more likely than the smooth swage to become stuck in crimped tubing. It might be less risky to use coiled tubing with a bit or scraper for slimhole or permanent-packer installations, where a stuck broach might become a permanent obstruction.

16.6.5 Considerations for Changing or Reconfiguring Tubing. If the current wellbore configuration is unacceptable, tubing may be reconfigured or a new string of tubing may be run. Decisions on the tubing size, where to land the end of tubing, and whether to reuse tubing should be weighed.

Used Tubing. Reusing tubing might be possible if the tubing has good integrity. Tubing that is pitted, rod-cut, or has weak pins is not recommended because it might fail prematurely, inhibit plunger rise and fall, and/or prevent an effective plunger seal. One solution is to line the tubing with an insert lining. Lined tubing is an uncommon application, but has very good sealing and friction characteristics and has been used successfully. Choose a durable lining that holds up against plunger wear and is designed for well temperatures and fluids.

Tubing Size. A common misconception is that tubing with larger diameters is more difficult to operate on plunger lift than tubing with smaller diameters (**Fig. 16.16**). The larger tubing actually is easier to operate because of the increased cross-sectional area, which has better hydraulics. A larger plunger, like a larger hydraulic cylinder, requires less pressure to move. Large tubing also holds more liquid per foot of height, thereby unloading larger volumes with a lower pressure requirement. The smaller tubing requires higher pressures to lift the same amount of liquids. Friction also can be more of a problem with smaller tubing.

Plunger-lift systems can be operated in practically any size tubing, with 2-1/16-in. OD (1-3/4-in. ID) or larger being more desirable. There is also a benefit in using "standard" equipment. Because of their abundance, 2-3/8-in. and 2-7/8-in. external-upset-end (EUE) tubing usually are the sizes of choice.

Tubing Depth. Evaluate each well for correct placement of the tubing. Place the end of the tubing very near a gas productive interval, typically in the middle to top perforations. Single pay zones with narrow perforated intervals are the easiest to correctly place tubing. Multiple commingled zones and/or large perforated intervals (> 500 ft) require additional analysis because bottomhole pressure and pressure differentials between zones come into play. Use reservoir analysis, examination of well logs, and production logs to estimate reservoir quality

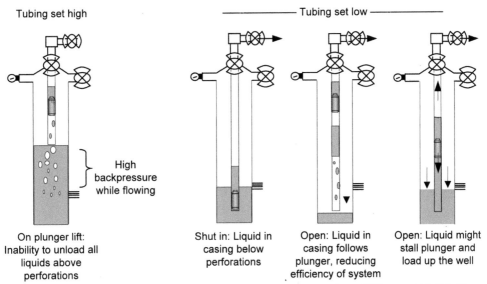

Fig. 16.17—Effect of tubing depth on plunger-lift production. (Taken from Phillips and Listiak.[10])

and to help determine the best spot to land the end of tubing. Often, trial and error ultimately decide the best tubing depths, and may take a few attempts to get right, especially on wells with large perforated intervals and wells with low bottomhole pressures.

The most common setting mistake is to set the tubing too deep (**Fig. 16.17**). In this case, gas and liquid must flow below the perforations before entering the tubing. On shut-in, liquids end up above the plunger in the tubing, and between the plunger and perforations in the casing. When the well is opened, the plunger rises with liquids above, but the liquid in the casing enters the tubing behind the plunger. This additional liquid places increased backpressure on the well, is lifted inefficiently, might prevent the plunger from surfacing, and might load up the well. Even if the plunger operates, the well might still produce at much lower than expected flow rates. Tubing that is set too deep can either be raised or perforated higher to remedy the problem. Use slickline or electric line to shoot holes in the tubing at a shallower depth. If perforated, move the plunger stop to above the holes.

Setting the tubing high above the perforations is another common mistake[10] (Fig. 16.17). The large-ID casing will load more easily, leading to a permanent gas-cut liquid column between the end of tubing and the perforations. Higher backpressure and lower flow rates from these zones are the result.

Tools Run on the End of Tubing. Downhole plunger equipment can be maintained with slickline, so a re-entry guide might be desirable. Re-entry guides facilitate smooth return of slickline tools back into the tubing string. Re-entry tools can be as simple as a plain tubing collar, a mule shoe (standard collar cut at a 45° angle), or a specially designed guide shoe. Installing notched collars on the end of the tubing is discouraged because notches often are bent inward when tubing is run into the well. Slickline tools run in this situation are more likely to become stuck.

Drifting Tubing in the Hole. Ideally, to eliminate the possibility of crimps and other imperfections, the new or used tubing would be drifted as it is run in the well. Machine the drift to the same length and OD as the plunger that will be used. Build a standard fishing neck with a horizontal hole in the neck, to which a length of cotton rope can be attached. The rope should be longer than the average length of the stands of tubing being run in the well. As each stand of tubing is run in the wellbore, the drift can be safely lowered from the rig floor down the

Without standing valve

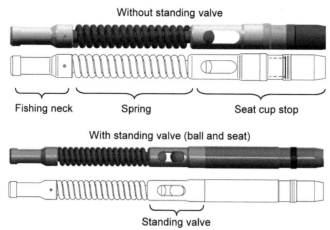

Fishing neck   Spring   Seat cup stop

With standing valve (ball and seat)

Standing valve

Fig. 16.18—Seat-cup/bumper-spring plunger stops. (Courtesy of Ferguson Beauregard.)

tubing. If tubing is overtightened or was crimped by tongs as it was made up, the drift will not fall, indicating that the stand of tubing being inspected should be pulled and replaced. Running the tubing with the plunger bottomhole assembly in place keeps the drift from being run out of the tubing or lost. Using cotton rope makes fishing easier, should the rope break.

Often, the mistake is made of drifting on the rig sand line after running the entire tubing string. The results of this are misleading because the weight of the sand line can force the drift through spots that are too small for smooth plunger travel.

16.7 Evaluation and Installation of Downhole Plunger Equipment

The bottomhole assembly may contain one or a combination of a plunger stop, bumper spring, standing valve, and strainer nipple. If tubing has not yet been run in the well, the bottomhole assembly can be run in place from the surface. If the tubing is in place, slickline can be used, or the stop can be dropped from the surface.

16.7.1 Plunger Stop. A plunger stop is placed inside the bottom of the tubing string to keep the plunger from falling through the tubing into the wellbore. Plunger stops can be set in a profile nipple, directly in the tubing walls with a slip assembly, or in the collar recesses of a tubing string.

Seat-Cup Stop Assembly. The seat-cup stop assembly has cups and a no-go similar to an insert sucker-rod pump and is installed in a profile nipple (**Figs 16.18 and 16.19**). Cup sizes can be changed to accommodate profile nipples with different IDs. It is very common for these stops to be built with a standing valve and/or bumper spring integrated into the assembly. These are the most common stops run because of ease of installation and retrieval.

A seat-cup stop is the only stop that can be dropped from the surface; however, it might still be desirable to run the stop on slickline to verify the setting force and depth, especially when a standing valve is integrated into the stop. Proper setting is necessary to ensure that the standing valve functions as desired.

Tubing Stop. A tubing stop has slips that bite directly into the tubing, without need of a profile to hold it in place (**Figs. 16.19 and 16.20**). It is useful when profile nipples are not run in a tubing string, or where the stop will be set some distance above the seating nipple (such as when tubing is too deeply set and will be perforated more shallowly). This stop can be set with slickline, with no need to pull tubing or install a profile nipple.

Collar Stop. A collar stop uses a type of slip that can be set only in a collar recess (Figs. 16.19 and 16.20). It can be set in most types of tubing that have space between the tubing

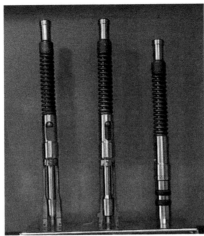

Fig. 16.19—Bumper-spring assemblies (left to right): tubing stop, collar stop, seat-cup assembly. (Courtesy of Ferguson Beauregard.)

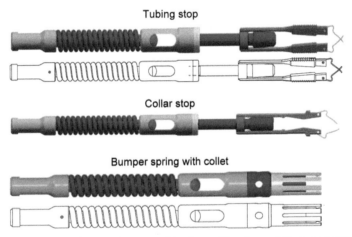

Fig. 16.20—Bumper-spring/plunger-stops combinations. (Courtesy of Ferguson Beauregard.)

collars. The collar stop is like the tubing stop, except that setting depths are limited to even tubing lengths. The collar stop actually is the easiest stop to unseat, and it can be unseated by high gas-flow velocities. Poor-quality stops might unseat more easily.

Pin Collar. The pin-collar type of stop is a collar with a pin welded inside it. It is screwed to the bottom of the tubing string, and its pin acts as a permanent stop. These are more common in smaller-ID tubing strings used as siphon or velocity strings. The benefits of using a pin collar include lower cost, minimum pressure drops, and simplicity. Because the pin collar is permanent, however, slickline cannot be run to tag the bottom of the well, clean out fill from the bottom of the well, or run tools out the end of the tubing. Also, the pin collar cannot be replaced without pulling tubing.

16.7.2 Bottomhole Bumper Spring (Optional Equipment; Not Found in All Installations). (See Figs. 16.18 through 16.20.) A spring installed on the plunger stop prevents damage to the plunger, stop, or tubing, if the plunger descends in completely "dry" tubing (tubing without liquid). Damage is more likely with poorly sealing plungers (e.g., bar stock or wobble washer plungers), which fall at much higher velocities. The bumper spring absorbs the plunger impact in these cases.

16.7.3 Standing Valve (Optional Equipment; Not Found in All Installations). For plunger lift to be effective, produced liquids need to stay in the tubing when the well is shut in. Installing standing valves between the plunger stop and bumper spring (Fig. 16.18) will keep liquid accumulations in the tubing. Standing valves are more common in wells with low bottom-hole pressures, where liquids may easily and quickly flow back into the formation because of gravity segregation of the gas and liquid.

A disadvantage of standing valves is that they eliminate the ability to equalize the tubing and casing, should the well load with liquids because of a system upset. Some valves have notched seats to allow some liquid slippage past the valve and to allow long-term equalization. Other problems with standing valves include increased pressure drops across the valve and sand or scale deposition that can plug the valve or prevent it from closing.

16.7.4 Strainer Nipple (Optional Equipment; Not Found in All Installations). Running a strainer nipple on the bottom of the tubing will prevent sand, scale, and other debris from entering the tubing. It might also plug, inhibiting plunger operation.

16.8 Evaluation and Installation of Wellhead and Plunger Surface Equipment

16.8.1 Wellhead. The wellhead should have the same or very close to the same continuous ID from the tubing through the wellhead. It is common to have variations in wellhead IDs, especially around tubing hangers, backpressure threads, or blast joints set just below the surface (**Fig. 16.21**). When wellhead IDs are significantly larger IDs than that of the tubing, the plunger can stall, which prevents unloading or keeps automated controllers from sensing the plunger arrival. Some tubing adapters have areas large enough for shorter plungers to turn and hang in the wellhead. Smaller-ID restrictions can cause impact damage to the wellhead and plunger. ID changes can be solved by changing wellheads, installing sleeves in tubing hangers (especially in the backpressure-valve threads), and minimizing wellhead height by reducing the number of master valves, flow tees, and swab valves.

It is better to flange, rather than thread, master-valve adapters and master valves because threaded adapters are more prone to breaking with system upsets. If a plunger ascends without a liquid slug, it can reach speeds that can cause damage to the surface equipment. It is more desirable to keep this damage above the master valve, especially because this valve is the last isolation valve between the well and the atmosphere. A slip-type wellhead with the master valve screwed directly to the tubing string is a possible exception. The strength and durability of 8-round threads for EUE tubing is much greater than that of normal line-pipe threads; however, in any application, flanged master valves are preferable.

In some installations with no packer, it is desirable to connect the casing to the tubing and flowline. During normal operation, the casing remains shut-in, but, if the system is upset and the well loads and dies, the tubing and casing can be equalized. Equalizing allows liquid to reach a common level in the tubing and casing, reducing hydrostatic head in the tubing. Gas that migrates into the casing during shut-in then can more easily and quickly displace liquids back into the formation. Equalizing can be used to bring a plunger installation back on line more quickly, or to prevent swabbing to unload the well.

16.8.2 Lubricator/Catcher Assembly. A lubricator/catcher assembly (**Fig. 16.22**) is used to receive the plunger at the surface. It is built with a shock spring, catcher mechanism, and flow ports. The lubricator is built with O-ring seals, and usually is made to seal when hand-tight-

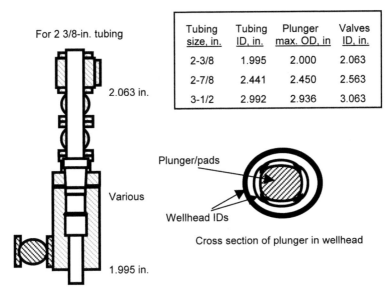

For 2 3/8-in. tubing

2.063 in.

Various

1.995 in.

Tubing size, in.	Tubing ID, in.	Plunger max. OD, in	Valves ID, in.
2-3/8	1.995	2.000	2.063
2-7/8	2.441	2.450	2.563
3-1/2	2.992	2.936	3.063

Plunger/pads

Wellhead IDs

Cross section of plunger in wellhead

Fig. 16.21—Effect of wellhead ID on plunger lift. Large changes in wellhead ID might cause the plunger to get caught in the wellhead or to stall. Sample dimensions show the difference between one type of pad plunger's ODs and tubular/valve IDs.

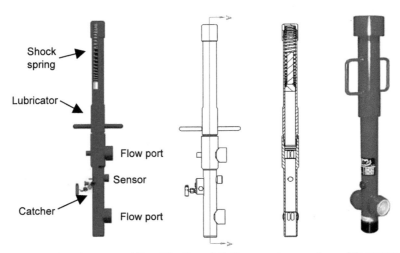

Shock spring

Lubricator

Flow port

Sensor

Catcher

Flow port

Fig. 16.22—Lubricator/catcher assemblies. (The three left diagrams are courtesy of Ferguson Beauregard; far-right diagram is courtesy of Multi Products Co.)

ened (which facilitates plunger inspection). The lubricator/catcher size should match the tubing and wellhead ID, and its installation should be plumb. If the lubricator is not plumb, the ascending force of the plunger will try to straighten the assembly, causing metal fatigue and failure.

Shock Spring. The shock spring (Fig. 16.22) absorbs the impact of the plunger at the surface, especially in the event of a dry ascent. The shock spring should be easily accessible and replaceable, because a good shock spring will extend plunger life. Premature spring wear might indicate very high plunger velocities and incorrect controller settings.

Catcher Mechanism. The catcher mechanism (Fig. 16.22) can be manually or automatically set to catch the plunger at the surface. This facilitates periodic plunger inspections and proper shut-in of plunger-lifted wells.

Flow Ports. Flow ports tie the lubricator/catcher assembly into the flowline piping (Fig. 16.22). Dual flow ports are preferred over single flow ports. Because the plunger is held in the wellhead by well flow, it tends to ride just above or across from the single flow port. This tends to create flow restrictions and the possibility of hydrate formation in the wellhead in colder climates.

Catcher Extension (Optional Equipment; Not Found in All Installations). Attaching an extension to the catcher improves cushioning at plunger arrival. The extension consists of additional tubing placed between the top flow port and the shock spring. When the plunger passes the flow ports and enters the extension, the loss of the driving force of the gas and the compression of gas above the plunger slows it down. The extra length allows the plunger to stop with less impact on the shock spring. The longer the extension, the greater this benefit. Extensions are more prevalent with plungers in small tubing, where the small equipment increases possibility of plunger damage. Extensions also may be used where a long plunger, such as the side-pocket-mandrel plunger, is used.

16.8.3 Plunger Sensors. Plunger sensors (Fig. 16.22) are placed on the lubricator/catcher to sense when the plunger has reached the surface. Simple controllers use the sensor strictly to count the number of times the plunger has reached the surface. More-sophisticated controllers make cycle adjustments on the basis of sensor data for plunger arrival and ascent velocity.

Different types of sensors are available, but most are either acoustic or magnetic. Sensor dependability is imperative when controllers use plunger speed as a criterion for adjusting cycle times. In many cases, sensor failure causes well shut-in by the controller, or well loading and dying.

Sensors are susceptible to stray electrical currents, such as those produced by cathodic protection. Such currents may cause erratic sensing of plunger arrivals. Insulating the lubricator and sensor from stray currents caused by cathodic protection or installing capacitance to level current fluctuations can improve performance.

16.8.4 Motor Valves. Pneumatically actuated motor valves (Fig. 16.13) commonly are used to shut in and flow a plunger-lifted well, but electric motors, pneumatic diaphragms, and hydraulic operation can be used. Maintain the seat and trim on these motor valves in good condition. If the valves leak even a small amount, the well might load and die. Consider the seat and trim size when selecting and installing a motor valve. If sized too small, the seat and trim can act as a choke to the well and prevent plunger arrival.

16.9 Design Considerations and Plunger Selection
Desirable features in a plunger include efficient sealing, reliability, durability, and the ability to descend quickly.[8,13] Rarely does a plunger exhibit all these characteristics, though. Usually a plunger that excels at one aspect sacrifices others. A wide variety of plungers is available to accommodate differences in well performance and operating conditions.

16.9.1 Plunger Seal and Velocity. The plunger seal is the interface between the tubing and the outside of the plunger, and probably is the most important plunger design element. Most plungers do not have a perfect seal; indeed, turbulence from a small amount of gas slippage around the plunger is necessary to keep liquids above and gas below the plunger. A more efficient seal limits slippage and allows the plunger to travel more slowly, which reduces the energy and pressure required to lift the plunger and liquid load. Less efficient seals allow excessive slippage, and so increase the energy and pressure required to operate the plunger.[13]

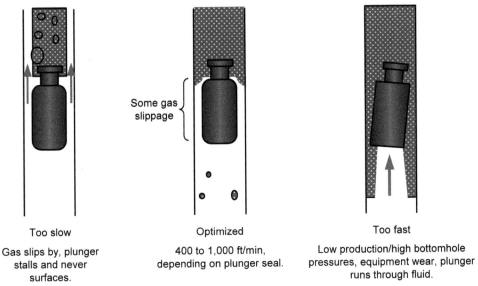

Too slow	Optimized	Too fast
Gas slips by, plunger stalls and never surfaces.	400 to 1,000 ft/min, depending on plunger seal.	Low production/high bottomhole pressures, equipment wear, plunger runs through fluid.

Fig. 16.23—The importance of plunger velocity. (Taken from Phillips and Listiak.[10])

The velocity at which the plunger travels up the tubing also affects plunger efficiency[9,10,13] (**Fig. 16.23**). Very low velocities increase gas slippage and lead to inefficient operation and possible plunger stall. High velocities tend to push the plunger through the liquids. High velocities waste well pressure, cause equipment wear, and increase well backpressure. Target velocities allow just enough slippage to provide a good seal.

Target velocities have been be determined for various plunger types on the basis of each plunger's sealing ability.[13] Better-sealing plungers operate efficiently at low velocities of 400 to 800 ft/min, whereas poor-sealing plungers must travel at 800 to 1,200 ft/min to maintain an adequate seal. Brush and/or pad plungers have the best seal, and bar stock plungers have the worst.

16.9.2 Reliability and Durability. Reliability refers to the ability of the plunger to repeat performance over time or in adverse environments. Many plungers have internal moving components (e.g., pads, seals, valve rods, and bypasses) that might fail in the presence of sand or corrosive environments. Other plungers (e.g., brush or bar stock plungers) have no internal moving components and generally are more reliable.

Durability is a plunger's ability to operate over many cycles with minimal wear and breakage. Typically, metal sealing plungers such as pad plungers are longer wearing, whereas brush plungers with fiber sealing elements wear quickly. Small-diameter plungers (for 1¼-in. or 1½-in.-OD tubing) tend to break more easily than larger-diameter plungers (those for 2⅜-in. or 2⅞-in.-OD tubing).

Plunger wear reduces the sealing efficiency of plungers over time. Inspect plungers periodically, typically every 1 to 3 months, depending on operating conditions and plunger type. Inspect new installations monthly until normal wear is determined. On the basis of such inspection results, plunger replacement can be documented and predicted.

16.9.3 Rapid Plunger Descent. Rapid plunger descent is a desirable plunger characteristic for wells that build pressure quickly. These wells typically are ready to operate as soon as the plunger reaches bottom. A plunger that falls more quickly can help to reduce shut-in times and

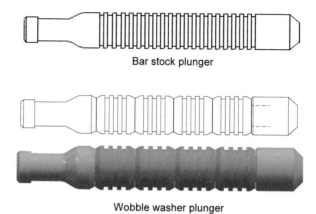

Bar stock plunger

Wobble washer plunger

Fig. 16.24—Turbulent seal plungers. (Courtesy of Ferguson Beauregard.)

buildup pressures, yielding lower average bottomhole pressures. In wells that require additional buildup after the plunger is on bottom, rapid plunger descent is not beneficial.

Typical plunger fall velocities range from 500 to 1,000 ft/min in tubing that contains only dry gas, but have been reported as low as 200 ft/min and as high as 2,000 ft/min, depending on such conditions as the type of plunger, condition of the tubing, and deviation of the well. In liquid, fall times typically are 150 to 250 ft/min, but have been reported as low as 25 to 50 ft/min.[10,13,23,32]

Plungers that seal poorly or that have built-in bypasses have the highest fall velocities. Better-sealing plungers fall more slowly. An internal bypass can be built into most plungers to increase fall velocity.

16.9.4 Other Plunger Characteristics. Plungers are built with either an internal or external fishing neck to enable slickline retrieval. Plungers might need to be retrieved when stuck, when the well loads because of equipment malfunction, or when a plunger wears out and will not surface.

There are many misconceptions regarding plunger design and choice. Weight sometimes is incorrectly perceived to be the most important consideration in plunger design.[10] This misconception stems from the incorrect belief that 1 psia is equivalent to 1 lbm, such that a 10-lbm plunger would require 10 psia, for example, or a 50-lbm plunger would require 50 psia. Actually, a 10-lbm plunger requires just over 3 psia to move in 2⅜-in. tubing (ignoring friction). Although the weight of the plunger does affect the pressure requirements, the seal and liquid-slug size play a more important role in determining efficient plunger operation and required buildup pressure.

16.9.5 Plunger Types. Of the many plunger types that are available, the most common ones are bar stock, wobble washer, sealed pad, retractable pad, brush, internal bypass, and side-pocket mandrel. Plungers can be manufactured in a combination of these types. Lengths and diameters also can be adjusted to meet installation requirements.

Bar Stock. A bar stock plunger (**Fig. 16.24**) is a piece of metal (solid or hollow) whose surface is machined with grooves, spirals, or other shapes to create turbulence and thus the seal, between it and the tubing wall. The bar-stock-plunger seal is one of the least efficient available.

Wobble Washer. A wobble washer plunger (Fig. 16.24) is similar to a length of bolt that is full of loose-fitting washers. Its sealing characteristics are comparable to those of a bar stock

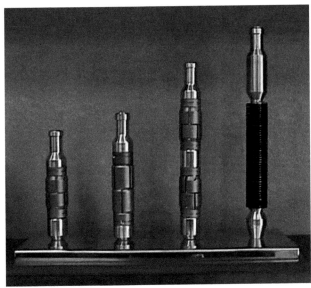

Fig. 16.25—Pad and brush plungers (left to right): single flexible pad, dual flexible pads, dual-pad plunger, brush plunger. (Courtesy of Ferguson Beauregard.)

plunger, but the side-to-side movement of its loose washers sometimes allows it to travel through tubing anomalies that would stick a bar stock plunger. The wobble washer plunger can be less durable than a bar stock or brush plunger, and should it fail in the well, retrieving all its washers can be difficult.

Pad. Pad plungers are popular because of their durability and efficient seal. A pad plunger (**Figs. 16.25 and 16.26**) incorporates spring-loaded metal pads that are fitted on a mandrel that expands to maintain contact with the tubing walls. The pads improve the sealing ability of the plunger by providing less bypass area for gas slippage, but because of this the pad plunger falls more slowly than other plungers. Pad plungers are available with one set or multiple sets of pads. In general, the more sets of pads, the better the seal, but the fit of the pad against the tubing wall also can improve the seal.

Sand can create problems for most pad plungers because the sand has a tendency to deposit behind the pads. When this happens, the pads are unable to retract and the plunger might become stuck.

Sealed Pad. A sealed pad plunger (**Fig. 16.27**) is an improved version of the pad plunger. In a normal pad plunger, gas can slip behind the pads, making the seal less efficient. The improved plunger has seals behind the pads, eliminating gas slippage. The seals may be made up of metal, rubber, polymer, or a tortuous path that creates turbulence behind the pads. Take care that the sealing material is compatible with well fluids.

Retractable Pad. A retractable-pad plunger seals well when unloading liquid, and falls very quickly. This type of pad plunger is built with a shift rod that enables the pads to retract and expand. The pads retract when the plunger reaches the surface and contacts a strike plate in the catcher. The plunger then has a much smaller than normal OD, which helps it to descend quickly. It might even be able to fall against flow. When the plunger drops to the bottom of the well, the shift rod strikes the plunger stop and causes the pads to expand, readying the plunger to lift the next liquid load. Because of its internal moving parts, the retractable-pad plunger is less durable and can become stuck if the pads fail to expand when the plunger reaches the bottom of the well.

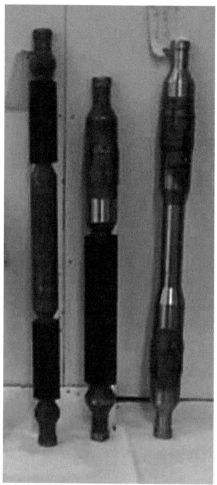

Fig. 16.26—Pad/brush combination plungers (left to right): brush/brush, brush/pad, pad/pad configurations. (Courtesy of Ferguson Beauregard.)

Brush. A brush plunger seals very well and falls rapidly, but its bristles may wear quickly. A brush plunger (Figs. 16.25 and 16.26) is similar to a pipe cleaner. Bristles made of a fiber appropriate for well conditions are attached to a central mandrel. The OD of the bristles can be adjusted for varying tubing diameters and can be specified to be larger or smaller than the tubing diameter. In most cases, new brush plungers have bristle diameters slightly larger than the tubing so that the bristles maintain constant contact with the tubing. This, coupled with the high turbulence created when gas flows through the bristles, gives the plunger excellent sealing characteristics.

Brush-fiber material and stiffness affect plunger durability and influence what diameter is chosen. A stiff bristle will wear longer, but can be cut so large that it prevents the plunger from falling. A softer bristle can be built with an oversized brush diameter for increased seal, but tends to wear out more quickly. Material selection is important in wells with high temperatures because some nylon-fiber material melts at higher temperatures.

Internal Bypass. An internal bypass can be built into any type of plunger (**Figs. 16.28 and 16.29**). As with the retractable-pad plunger, in an internal-bypass plunger there is a shift rod that causes the bypass to open at the surface and close at the plunger stop. There are variations

Fig. 16.27—The tortuous flow path behind the pads in the sealed pad plunger helps to prevent gas slippage behind the pads. (Courtesy of Opti-Flow LLC.)

of the shift-rod mechanism that require a special lubricator with a permanent rod built into the shock-spring strike plate. An even newer variation is a two-piece plunger, which includes a ball and cylinder that fall separately but rise as a single unit. The bypass also allows the plunger to fall more quickly. These types of plungers sometimes are used without any surface control because of their ability to freely cycle while the well is flowing.

Side-Pocket-Mandrel. The side-pocket-mandrel plunger (**Fig. 16.30**) is designed for use with gas lift side-pocket mandrels. It is longer than other plungers (5 to 20 ft), with seals on both ends, and is used to bridge large ID increases across gas lift mandrels. Such ID increases can cause excess gas slippage or plunger stall on shorter plungers, preventing operation. The side-pocket-mandrel plunger always keeps either the top or bottom seals in contact with normal tubing ID, allowing a continuous seal in the tubing as the plunger passes through the large ID. This specialty plunger also can be used when a packer, blast joints, subs, or other equipment is installed with an ID that is larger than the tubing ID.

16.10 Evaluation of Control Methods

16.10.1 Plunger Controller. A plunger controller controls the shut-in, unloading, and flow periods of a plunger system. It does this by operating one or more surface control valves to shut in and flow the well. Different controllers use various set points and well data to determine the lengths of these periods. Controllers can be either manually set devices, such as timers or differential-pressure controls, or self-adjusting systems, such as electronic "smart" controllers that operate on the basis of time, pressure, and/or plunger velocity.

16.10.2 Manual On/Off Timer. A manual on/off timer controls the plunger system according to preset shut-in and flow times. Originally, manual timers were wind-up pinwheel models that actuated a pneumatic valve. Newer versions use electronic clocks and a solenoid to actuate the valve. The operator programs them with appropriate predetermined on and off times. Frequently these times are determined through a long trial-and-error process, during which operators must make small changes each day to optimize the well. If operating conditions are static, the on/off timers may provide efficient plunger operation, but when conditions change (e.g., if line pressure increases), the operator must make changes to the settings. To keep the plunger running in all conditions requires a program that assumes the worst-case conditions, such as the highest line pressures experienced during normal operations. Such conservative programming of the manual on/off timer minimizes the chances of well loading, but causes higher average bottomhole pressures and, therefore, lower production rates.

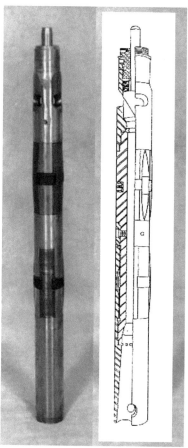

Fig. 16.28—The internal-bypass (freewheeling) plunger is capable of falling in gas flow. (Courtesy of Plunger Lift Systems Inc.)

16.10.3 Pressure-Differential Controller. Pressure-differential controllers monitor tubing, casing, and line pressures to determine shut-in and flow periods. Early versions of a pressure controller simply monitored casing pressure. When a high casing pressure was reached, the well opened. When the well blew down to a low casing pressure, it was shut in again. If operating conditions varied, the control set points had to be reset.

Newer controllers use tubing, casing, and line pressure, as well as the design criteria presented earlier in this chapter (and below) to calculate when sufficient casing pressure has been reached to open the well. Eq. 16.1b calculates required casing pressure:

$$p_{cs} = \frac{p_{hs}}{(0.5 \ \text{to} \ 0.6)} + \left(p_l\right)_{\text{max}},$$

where

$$p_{hs} = p_c - p_t \cdot \ .... \ (16.19)$$

Fig. 16.29—Ball and cylinder plungers. (Courtesy of Pacemaker Plunger Co.)

The well is opened when it meets this calculated required casing pressure. Once the plunger has reached the surface, tubing and casing pressures are used to calculate a differential pressure that gives an estimate of slug size. When a preset differential pressure is reached, it is assumed that an adequate liquid load is in the tubing, and the well is shut in.

Automation and remote monitoring have helped make this type of controller more dependable. The ability of some pressure-differential controllers to make adjustments on the basis of changing operating conditions improves well performance. Without this capability, a program that assumes the worst-case operating conditions must be used.

16.10.4 Automated On/Off Timer Based on Plunger Velocity. Adding microprocessors and plunger-velocity tracking to on/off timers was a major advance in controller technology (**Fig. 16.31**). These automated controllers monitor plunger velocity to continually optimize the well, eliminating the time-consuming trial-and-error process.[9]

The importance of plunger velocity and efficient velocities for various plunger types has been discussed already. In essence, a plunger must travel at the correct velocity to lift liquids efficiently. If the plunger ascends faster than the target velocity, then more energy was available than was required to lift the plunger, either because the liquid load was too small or because pressure buildup was too great for operating conditions. In such a situation, the automated controller would decrease the shut-in time (to decrease pressure buildup) and increase the flow time (to increase the liquid load).

Conversely, if the plunger ascends more slowly than the target velocity, then too little energy was available to lift the plunger efficiently, either because the liquid load was too large or there was not enough casing pressure available. The automated controller then would increase the shut-in time (to increase pressure buildup) and decrease the flow time (to reduce the liquid load).

The controller increases and decreases shut-in and flow times on the basis of user-set time increments. For example, an operator might set the controller to decrease the shut-in time by three minutes and increase flow time by two minutes every time the plunger ascends too fast. In this manner, the controller slowly adjusts until the well is optimized. This slow adjustment will optimize the well, but it also can be an issue in that it takes the controller many cycles to

Fig. 16.30—Side-pocket-mandrel plunger. This plunger is designed to maintain contact with the tubing when passing through gas-lift mandrels or packers. (Courtesy of Ferguson Beauregard.)

react to changing conditions. The problem can be partially remedied by using a controller that allows for proportional adjustments. In proportional adjustments, if the target plunger velocity is missed by a small amount, the changes to shut-in and flow times also might be small. If the target velocity is missed by a larger amount, the changes might be larger. This allows a well to react quickly to fast or slow plunger velocities.

A drawback with time-based plunger-velocity controllers is that a target velocity can be reached with either large slugs and long shut-in periods, or small slugs and short shut-in periods. As discussed earlier, production will be higher with short shut-in periods, but the controller might assume that the well is optimized with large slugs and long shut-ins. Good initial controller setup can help to prevent this problem, but it is important for the operator to check the controller periodically to make sure it is operating with the minimum amount of shut-in time, and to make a manual adjustment, if necessary.

16.10.5 Combination Automated On/Off and Pressure Monitoring. One of the most efficient controllers currently available monitors flow rates, pressure differential, and plunger speed. It is efficient because it reacts quickly to changing well conditions. To determine flow time, this combination controller compares the flow rate of the well to a calculated critical or unloading rate. The well is allowed to flow a specific length of time in relation to this flow

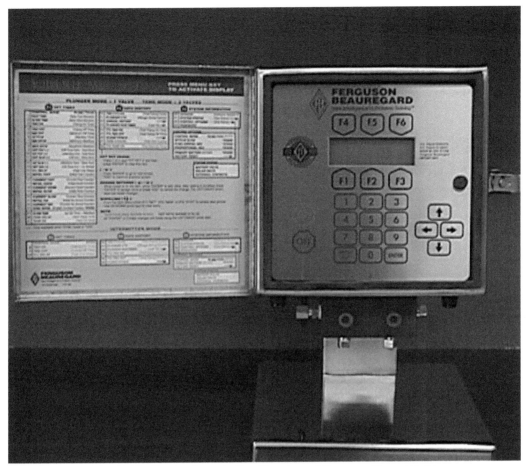

Fig. 16.31—Electronic controller. (Courtesy of Ferguson Beauregard.)

rate and then is shut in. While the well is flowing, the controller constantly recalculates the critical rate on the basis of actual tubing pressure, which allows quick reaction to changing flowing conditions.

To determine shut-in time, the casing, tubing, and line pressures are monitored. Like an advanced pressure-differential controller, the combination controller uses plunger design equations to determine when the casing pressure has reached the minimum needed to open the well and operate the plunger. Thus, the controller allows the plunger to operate as soon as the well is ready.

Using these parameters alone is an efficient means to control plunger lift, but it can be further optimized by using plunger velocity with flow and shut-in multipliers. The flow multiplier is an adjustment to the critical flow rate. A flow multiplier of 1.0 flows the well until it reaches critical flow rate. A flow multiplier of 0.9 flows the well until it falls to 90% of the critical flow rate (resulting in a longer flow time). A flow multiplier of 1.1 flows the well until it is at 110% the critical flow rate (shorter flow time). If the plunger ascends too quickly, the controller lowers the flow multiplier. If the plunger ascends too slowly, the flow multiplier is increased. The shut-in time is changed similarly with a casing-pressure multiplier.

16.10.6 Venting (Optional; Not Found in All Installations). All the plunger controllers discussed here can be used with a venting option. With a venting system, the controllers typically will switch to venting if the plunger does not reach the surface in a specified period of time. The manual controller requires an operator to determine when the controller vents. An automated controller uses flowing conditions to determine when and how long the well should vent and, over time, attempts to eliminate venting by making changes to shut-in and flow times. For automated controls, venting is a preventative measure to keep the plunger operating during short periods of high line pressures. Venting is discussed in more detail in the Applications section of this chapter.

16.10.7 High-Line-Pressure Delay (Optional; Not Found in All Installations). High-line-pressure delay prevents the plunger from operating against abnormally high line pressures, which cause the plunger to load and die. Although optional, this delay feature is recommended with all applications. With high-line-pressure delay, a pressure transducer or switch gauge monitors surface pressures and shuts in the well when pressures are too high for the plunger to operate. Automated controllers incorporate a delay that requires the high pressure to continue for a period of time (usually 5 to 15 minutes) before shutting in the well. Once line pressure drops, the controller typically will return the well to the start of the shut-in cycle.

This option is very useful in gathering systems that use a single compressor. When the compressor stops running for any reason, high-line-pressure delays at individual wells override control of the plunger control valve and shut in the well, then automatically reset the well, making compressor downtime easier for the operator to handle.

16.10.8 Acoustic Fluid-Level/Plunger-Descent Tracking (Optional; Not Found in All Installations). Acoustic fluid-level devices can be used to track plunger descent and liquid-load sizes.[23,32] Analysis equipment is being developed that will automatically track plunger descent, using acoustic signals sent from the wellhead or by listening to the impact the plunger has with each tubing collar, and will use this measurement to determine the exact minimum shut-in time required for each cycle. This is useful for operating the well with the least amount of shut-in time, for making sure the plunger is on bottom before attempting to flow the well, and for troubleshooting plunger problems.

This equipment also may be used with tubing/casing-flow plunger lift. The casing purge cycle can be managed more efficiently by determining exactly when the fluid has been transferred from the casing annulus to the tubing.

16.10.9 Remote Control/Telemetry (Optional; Not Found in All Installations). Adding the ability to monitor and make adjustments remotely will improve any plunger-lift controller. Several manufacturers have incorporated electronic flow measurement, pressure monitoring, computer software, and either phone, radio, or Internet communications into their plunger systems (**Figs. 16.32 through 16.34**). Case studies have shown that adding remote control increases production, even on wells that previously had been equipped with self-adjusting electronic controllers.[12] One advantage is the ability to view production and pressure data on a very small time scale, such as 1-min increments. This makes diagnostic work very easy because all stages of the plunger cycle can be analyzed for pressure or flow anomalies. Also, viewing the data remotely enables quick diagnostics on many wells, as well as the ability to use experts who cannot be on site. Remote control allows immediate adjustments to the system when troubleshooting. As with all artificial-lift equipment, better accessibility leads to quicker response time and an increased understanding of the operations taking place.

16.10.10 Missed-Trip Protection (Optional; Not Found in All Installations). Some controllers have missed-trip protection, a feature that can save operator time and prevent equipment damage by shutting in the well in situations involving repeated plunger nonarrival and/or slow arrival. If the plunger fails to surface a preset number of times, usually five or fewer, the

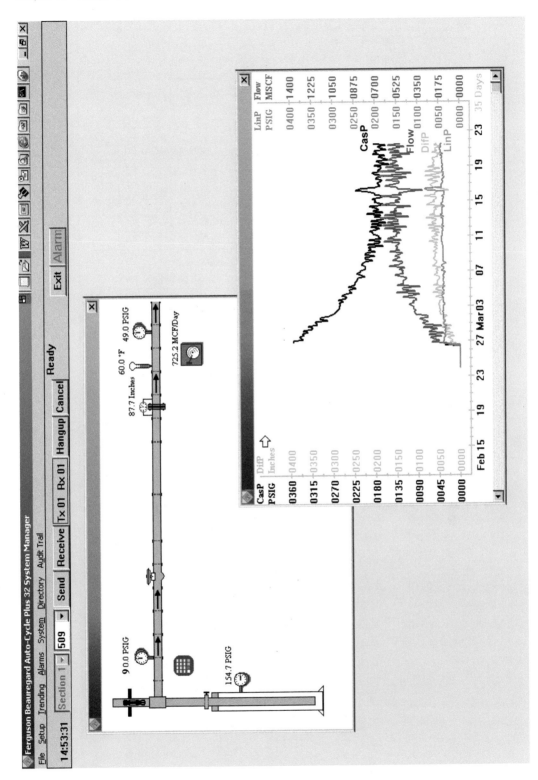

Fig. 16.32—Sample computer screens from computer software for controlling and analyzing plunger-lift systems. (Courtesy of Ferguson Beauregard.)

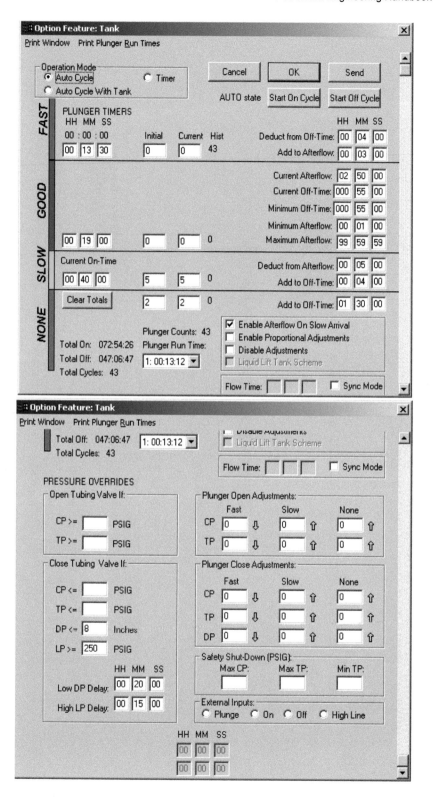

Fig. 16.33—Sample computer screens from remote plunger-lift control software. Such software can be used to control the system on site or remotely by radio, telephone, or the Internet. (Courtesy of Ferguson Beauregard.)

Fig. 16.34—Plunger-lift controller that incorporates electronic gas measurement and telemetry. (Courtesy of Ferguson Beauregard.)

system can be automatically suspended and the well shut in, which keeps the well from loading and dying and gives it time to build pressure. The operator then can restart the plunger system immediately upon arriving at the well, whereas if the well is not automatically shut in, the operator might have to make additional trips back to the well.

Missed-trip protection also prevents dry plunger trips when there is damage to the plunger sensor or sensor line. If the sensor or sensor line is damaged, the controller will not recognize plunger arrivals. On the basis of this perception, automated controllers will try to make the plunger surface by making adjustments (flowing less and shutting in longer), leading to very fast plunger arrivals. In such situations, if the controller is allowed to continue to adjust, the plunger velocity can become so high that the plunger and the lubricator/catcher will be damaged.

Controllers with this capability also can shut in the well when the plunger arrivals repeatedly have been at a slower than targeted velocity. This is usually not as useful. If the plunger velocity is slower than ideal, an automated controller should be able to adjust to bring the plunger back to the target velocity. If a system problem is causing the slower trips, then the plunger eventually will fail to arrive. The missed-trip protection would then shut in the well.

16.10.11 Swab Mode (Optional; Not Found in All Installations). Some controllers incorporate a swab mode, which is used primarily in wells that have been worked over with completion fluids or chemically treated, such that it might be necessary to remove the additional liquids before starting normal plunger operation. In swab mode, the well is shut in immediately upon plunger arrival at the surface. This tends to conserve well pressure and produce many small liquid loads. In this manner, the additional fluids are "swabbed" with the plunger.

Controllers operate in swab mode by requiring the plunger to make a preset number of consecutive arrivals at or above the target velocity before flow time is allowed. Shut-in time adjustments usually continue, while flow time adjustments are suspended. When the plunger arrival criterion has been met, the additional well liquids are assumed to be unloaded, and the controller resumes normal operation.

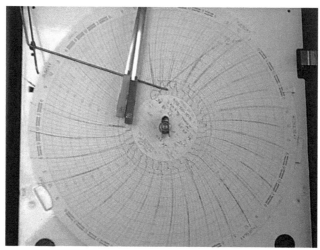

Fig. 16.35—Circular paper-chart recorder. Large, cyclical production swings make measurement more difficult with this type of chart. (Courtesy of Ferguson Beauregard.)

16.11 Evaluation and Modification of Production Facilities

16.11.1 Surface Production Facilities and Equipment. Surface equipment (e.g., separators, heater treaters, and compressors) should be sized to handle the high instantaneous flow rates that accompany cyclical plunger-lift flow. Proper plunger-system operation can minimize these fluctuations (by operating at the minimum shut-in period), but flow rates still will vary.

Monitor pressures from the wellhead through all surface equipment to the sales point and beyond, and use these pressure nodes to identify and eliminate restrictions and leaks. Piping, connections, valves, check valves, and even chokes sometimes are already in place, and are overlooked when plunger lift is installed. Every restriction increases the pressure necessary to operate the plunger lift and potentially reduces well production. Eliminate leaks upstream of the control valve to enable effective static-pressure buildup. Leaking equipment can allow liquid entry into the wellbore during the shut-in cycle, loading the well or preventing efficient plunger operation.

Dehydration can be very difficult in single-well applications. If initial rates are too high, glycol could be forced out of the dehydrator and lost. Minimize the loss of dehydration fluid by installing pressure-differential controllers or bypasses or by using desiccant-type dehydrators.

16.11.2 Measurement. Electronic flow measurement (Fig. 16.34) is very beneficial for plunger-lifted wells. Electronic measurement more accurately records cyclical production rates, increasing the profitability of plunger-lift applications. Dry-flow paper-chart recorders (**Fig. 16.35**) are difficult to integrate if production has a wide sweep on the chart or overranges the recorder, or if the chart time cycle is too long.

Larger-range springs and orifice plates help to keep differentials within a measurable range. The orifice plate should be capable of measuring the peaks and valleys of the plunger flow. Install as large an orifice plate as possible; as with the motor valve and other surface equipment, an orifice plate that is too small can act as a choke. Small plates also can become bowed or damaged if subjected to high differentials at the beginning of a cycle.

16.11.3 Pressure-Differential Controls. A pressure-differential control (PDC) limits the maximum flow rate through production equipment of a plunger-lifted well. The PDC uses an orifice to measure differential pressure and flow rates, and throttles the plunger control valve. Using a

PDC can prevent overranging of measurement equipment, solve dehydration problems, and even remedy surface-equipment sizing problems.

The drawback to using a PDC is that it effectively is a choke, and so increases the pressure required to operate the system; however, it chokes the well only when a specific flow rate is exceeded, and the temporary loss in flow rate might be less costly than replacing surface equipment.

16.11.4 High-Low-Pressure Control Pilots. High-low-pressure control pilots also can be incorporated with plunger-lift control valves. Although they do not control flow rates, they are effective at limiting maximum surface flowing pressures. If well flowing pressures exceed the surface-equipment allowable operating pressures, the high/low pilot will protect the equipment by shutting in the well.

Nomenclature

a = variable equaling approximately 50 to 60% of the difference between shut-in casing pressure and maximum sales-line pressure

A_a = cross-sectional area of annulus, ft²

A_t = cross-sectional area of tubing, ft² or in.²

C_{max} = maximum number of plunger round trips possible per day

d = tubing diameter, in.

d_{ci} = casing inner diameter, in.

d_{ti} = tubing, inner diameter, in.

d_{to} = tubing, outer diameter, in.

D = deepest point of plunger travel (well depth), ft

f_g = Darcy-Weisbach friction factor for gas flow through the tubing

F_{gs} = Foss and Gaul slippage factor of gas lost past plunger on rise cycle [approximately 2% per 1,000-ft depth ($= 1+ D/1,000 \times 0.02$); Foss and Gaul used 1.15 factor on 8,000-ft wells.]

f_l = Darcy-Weisbach friction factor for the liquid slug

g_g = gas specific gravity

K = gas friction in tubing

L = the length of one barrel of liquid in the tubing, ft/bbl

p_c = casing pressure, psia

$\overline{p}_c$ = average casing pressure during operation, psia

$(p_c)_{max}$ = the pressure required to start the plunger at the beginning of the plunger cycle, psia

$(p_c)_{min}$ = the casing pressure required to move the plunger and liquid slug just before it reaches the surface, psia

p_{cs} = casing pressure at shut-in, psia

p_{hs} = slug differential hydrostatic pressure, psi

p_l = line pressure, psia

p_{lf} = differential pressure required to overcome liquid friction per barrel, psi/bbl

p_{lh} = differential pressure required to lift liquid weight per barrel, psi/bbl

= maximum line pressure during plunger ascent, psia

p_p = differential pressure required to lift plunger weight, psi

p_R = reservoir pressure, psia

p_t = tubing pressure, psia

q_g = gas flow rate, Mscf/D

q_l = liquid flow rate, B/D

R = specific gas constant (air), 53.3 lbf-ft/(°R-lbm)

R_a = ratio of annulus + tubing cross-sectional area to the annulus cross-sectional area

R_{gl} = gas/liquid ratio, scf/bbl

S = volume of load (slug) above plunger, bbl

$\bar{T}_g$ = average gas temperature in the well during plunger ascent, °F

v = velocity, ft/sec

$\bar{v}_{fg}$ = average velocity of plunger falling through gas, ft/min (typically 200 to 1,200 ft/min)

$\bar{v}_{fl}$ = average velocity of plunger falling through liquid, ft/min (typically 50 to 250 ft/min)

$\bar{v}_r$ = average rise velocity of plunger, ft/min (typically 400 to 1,200 ft/min)

V_g = volume of gas required per cycle, Mscf

V_t = volume of the tubing above the liquid load, Mscf

W_p = plunger weight, lbm

Z = gas factor

γ_l = liquid gradient, psi/ft

Acknowledgments

The authors wish to express their appreciation to ConocoPhillips and EOG Resources for supporting the publication of this chapter, and to Gary Thomas, James Lea, Norm Hein, Bill Myers, Jack Rogers, Bill Elmer, Daniel Sanchez, Larry Vinson, and Scott Williams for their support and help in preparing the presentation materials. Thanks to Ferguson Beauregard; Gulf Publishing; Multi Products Co.; Opti-Flow LLC; Pacemaker Plunger Co.; Plunger Lift Systems Inc.; The Southwestern Petroleum Short Course; Van Nostrand Reinhardt; and Weatherford International Ltd. for providing pictures, diagrams, and consultation, and to Jay Simmons of Sugar Mountain Design Co. for figure animation in CD version.

References

1. Turner, R.G., Hubbard, M.G., and Dukler, A.E.: "Analysis and Prediction of Minimum Flow Rate for the Continuous Removal of Liquids from Gas Wells," *JPT* (November 1969) 1475.

2. Beauregard, E. and Ferguson, P.L.: "Introduction to Plunger Lift: Applications, Advantages and Limitations," paper SPE 10882 presented at the 1982 SPE/AIME Rocky Mountain Regional Meeting, Billings, Montana, 19–21 May.

3. Ferguson, P.L. and Beauregard, E.: "Will Plunger Lift Work In My Well?," *Proc.,* Thirtieth Annual Southwestern Petroleum Short Course, Lubbock, Texas (1983) 301–311.

4. Lea, J.F. Jr. and Tighe, R.E.: "Gas Well Operation With Liquid Production," paper SPE 11583 presented at the 1983 SPE of AIME Production Operation Symposium, Oklahoma City, Oklahoma, 27 February–1 March.

5. Ferguson, P.L. and Beauregard, E.: "Extending Economic Limits and Reducing Lifting Costs: Plungers Prove To Be Long Term Solutions," *Proc.,* Thirty-Fifth Annual Southwestern Petroleum Short Course, Lubbock, Texas (1988) 233–241.

6. Sanchez, D. and Ary, B.: "Case Study of Plunger Lift Installation in the San Juan Basin," *Proc.,* Forty-Third Annual Southwestern Petroleum Short Course, Lubbock, Texas (1996) 8–13.

7. Brady, C.L. and Morrow, S.J.: "An Economic Assessment of Artificial Lift in Low-Pressure, Tight Gas Sands in Ochiltree County, Texas," paper SPE 27932 presented at the 1994 SPE Mid-Continent Gas Symposium, Amarillo, Texas, 22–24 May.

8. Hacksma, J.D.: "User's Guide to Predicting Plunger Lift Performance," *Proc.,* Nineteenth Annual Southwestern Petroleum Short Course, Lubbock, Texas (1972) 109–118.

9. Morrow, S.J. Jr., and Rogers, J.R. Jr.: "Increasing Production Using Microprocessors and Tracking Plunger-Lift Velocity," paper SPE 24296 presented at the 1992 SPE Mid-Continent Gas Symposium, Amarillo, Texas, 13–14 April.

10. Phillips, D.H. and Listiak, S.D.: "How to Optimize Production from Plunger Lift Systems," *World Oil* (May 1998) 110.

11. Christian, J., Lea, J.F., and Bishop, R.: "Plunger Lift Comes of Age," *World Oil* (November 1995) 43.

12. Lusk, S. and Morrow, S.J. Jr.: "Plunger Lift: Automated Control Via Telemetry," *Proc.,* Forty-Seventh Annual Southwestern Petroleum Short Course, Lubbock, Texas (2000) 73.

13. Mower, L.N. *et al.:* "Defining the Characteristics and Performance of Gas-Lift Plungers," paper SPE 14344 presented at the 1985 SPE Annual Technical Conference and Exhibition, Las Vegas, Nevada, 22–25 September.

14. Beeson, C.M., Knox, D.G., and Stoddard, J.H.: "Plunger Lift Correlation Equations and Nomographs," paper AIME 501-G presented at the 1955 AIME Petroleum Branch Annual Meeting, New Orleans, 2–5 October.

15. Lebeaux, J.M. and Sudduth, L.F.: "Theoretical and Practical Aspects of Free Piston Operation," *JPT* (September 1955) 33.

16. Foss, D.L. and Gaul, R.B.: "Plunger Lift Performance Criteria with Operating Experience— Ventura Avenue Field," *Drilling and Production Practices,* API, Dallas (1965) 124–140.

17. Beauregard, E. and Morrow, S.: "New and Unusual Applications for Plunger Lift System," paper SPE 18868 presented at the 1989 SPE Production Operations Symposium, Oklahoma City, Oklahoma, 13–14 March.

18. Lea, J.F.: "Dynamic Analysis of Plunger Lift Operations," paper SPE 10253 presented at the 1981 SPE Annual Technical Conference and Exhibition, San Antonio, Texas, 5–7 October.

19. Rosina, L.: "A Study of Plunger Lift Dynamics," MS Thesis, U. of Tulsa, Tulsa (1983).

20. Govier, G.W. and Aziz, K.: *The Flow of Complex Mixtures in Pipes,* Van Nostrand Reinhold Company, New York (1972).

21. Vogel, J.V.: "Inflow Performance Relationships for Solution-Gas Drive Wells," *JPT* (January 1968) 83.

22. Mishra, S. and Caudle, B.H.: "A Simplified Procedure for Gas Deliverability Calculations Using Dimensionless IPR Curves," paper SPE 13231 presented at the 1984 SPE Annual Technical Conference and Exhibition, Houston, 16–19 September.

23. McCoy, J.N. *et al.:* "Plunger Lift Optimization By Monitoring And Analyzing Wellbore Acoustic Signals And Tubing And Casing Pressures," *Proc.,* Forty-Eighth Annual Southwestern Petroleum Short Course, Lubbock, Texas (2001) 80–87.

24. Abercrombie, B.: "Plunger Lift," *The Technology of Artificial Lift Methods,* Vol. 2b, K.E. Brown (ed.), PennWell Publishing Co., Tulsa (1980) 483–518.

25. Hall, J.C. and Bell, B.: "Plunger Lift By Side String Injection," *Proc.,* Forty-Eighth Annual Southwestern Petroleum Short Course, Lubbock, Texas (2001) 17–18.

26. Morrow, S.J. Jr. and Aversante, O.L.: "Plunger Lift: Gas Assisted," *Proc.,* Forty-Second Annual Southwestern Petroleum Short Course, Lubbock, Texas (1995) 195–201.

27. White, G.W.: "Combine Gas Lift, Plungers to Increase Production Rate," *World Oil* (November 1982) 69.

28. O'Connell, T., Sinner, P., and Guice, W.R.: "Flexible Plungers Resolve CT, Slim Hole Problems," *Amer. Oil & Gas Reporter* (January 1997) **40, 82**.

29. Phillips, D.H. and Listiak, S.D.: "Plunger Lift With Wellhead Compression Boosts Gas Well Production," *World Oil* (October 1996) 96.

30. Schneider, T.S. and Mackey, V. Jr.: "Plunger Lift Benefits Bottom Line for a Southeast New Mexico Operator," paper SPE 59705 presented at the 2000 SPE Permian Basin Oil and Gas Recovery Conference, Midland, Texas, 21–23 March.

31. Lea, J.F.: "Plunger Lift vs. Velocity Strings," paper presented at the 1999 Energy Sources Technology Conference & Exhibition, Houston, 1–2 February.

32. Rowlan, O.L. *et al.:* "Optimizing Plunger Lifted Wells By Acoustically Tracing the Plunger Fall," *Proc.,* Forty-Eighth Annual Southwestern Petroleum Short Course, Lubbock, Texas (2001) 104– 114.

SI Metric Conversion Factors

bbl $\times$	1.589 873	E – 01	= m^3
cp $\times$	1.0*	E – 03	= Pa·s
ft $\times$	3.048*	E – 01	= m
ft^2 $\times$	9.290 304*	E – 02	= m^2
ft^3 $\times$	2.831 685	E – 02	= m^3
°F	(°F – 32)/1.8		= °C
°F	°F + 459.67		= °R
in. $\times$	2.54*	E + 00	= cm
in.^{2} $\times$	6.451 6*	E + 00	= cm^2
in.^{3} $\times$	1.638 706	E + 01	= cm^3
lbf $\times$	4.448 222	E + 00	= N
lbm $\times$	4.535 924	E – 01	= kg
mL $\times$	1.0*	E + 00	= cm^3
psi $\times$	6.894 757	E + 00	= kPa
U.S. gal $\times$	3.785 412	E – 03	= m^3

*Conversion factor is exact.

AUTHOR INDEX

SUBJECT INDEX